GENETICS

GENETICS

IRWIN H. HERSKOWITZ

*Hunter College,
The City University of New York*

Second Edition

LITTLE, BROWN AND COMPANY
Boston and Toronto

FIRST PRINTING

Published simultaneously in Canada
by Little, Brown & Company (Canada) Limited

PRINTED IN THE UNITED STATES OF AMERICA

PREFACE

SINCE the beginning of this century the science of genetics has had a spectacular growth. The discovery of basic principles and the application of these principles are occurring at an ever-increasing rate. It is generally agreed that a knowledge of genetics is essential for an understanding of present and future biology. The impact of genetics is not restricted, however, to professional teachers and research workers in pure and applied biology, nor to physicians and dentists. More and more students whose major interest is in psychology, biochemistry, chemistry, biophysics, physics, or mathematics find that the study of genetics offers new and challenging opportunities in these various fields.

How can a text for an introductory course in genetics be best organized to serve students with such varied interests? An introductory text must provide the reader with an understanding of the nature of the genetic material, for this knowledge is a prerequisite for a fruitful genetic approach to the solution of problems in biology and all the other fields mentioned. Accordingly, insofar as possible, the subject matter of this book is arranged so that principles dealing with the nature of the genetic material are separated from the applications of these principles. The nature of the genetic material is studied through the use of the operations or methods of recombination, mutation, chemistry and physics, replication, and function. The presentation is designed to encourage the reader to use his powers of inductive reasoning to arrive at the primary generalizations of genetics on the basis of experimental evidence. Whenever feasible, genetic principles are derived scientifically—by recognizing and stating a problem, designing appropriate experiments to test hypotheses, analyzing the experimental results, and drawing conclusions. The aim is to present genetics as a rational, organized body of knowledge.

Because of its importance the introductory genetics course is being offered more frequently in the earlier rather than the later years of college study. Since such a course is elected more and more frequently by students who do not wish to specialize in biology, simple biological examples and terminology are used whenever possible, and certain biological phenomena generally understood by students specializing in biology are explained in some detail. Because many students in a first course in genetics may not have an adequate background, certain aspects of chemistry and physics important for understanding genetics are described in greater detail than in other texts.

No single text can include the ways each principle of genetics apply to every plant and animal studied, or give examples of the application of each of these principles to all the different kinds of organisms. Accordingly, only one or a few experimentally favorable or historically important organisms are usually employed in this text to establish a principle or to illustrate an application. Additional proofs, applications, or examples are left to the instructor who, depending upon his students' training and interest, can supply other illustrations by means of lectures and laboratory sessions or by means of assignments to detailed accounts in other texts and in the original literature.

It is hoped that the text will stimulate readers to utilize the books and journals in their libraries. The reading of genetic works in the original after studying appropriate sections of the text can be a very rewarding experience. Accordingly, references requiring different degrees of sophistication are given at the ends of chapters. Since the later chapters deal with recent advances in genetics, whose discussion may be absent from already published textbooks, more references are given to particular workers in the later than in the earlier chapters.

Part of a letter by G. Mendel and the Nobel Prize Lectures presented by geneticists are included in the book as supplements. These supplements should be completely understandable, or nearly so, if appropriate chapters have been read beforehand, and can serve as a review and overview of genetic principles and their applications. The citations to the literature included in the Nobel Prize talks should prove especially valuable to those who wish to do additional reading on key topics. The supplements can also function to bridge the gap between the textbook and the research worker, giving the reader some idea of the history of the subject and the personalities of the people involved.

The Second Edition

The subject matter is presented in forty-two chapters, each ending, as before, with a summary, questions for discussion, and references. An appendix, "Elementary Biometrical Inferences," has been added, and the supplements now include three additional Nobel Prize lectures. A description of representative life cycles and genetic maps of several higher organisms have also been added. Recent advances—for example, in human, corn, and Drosophila genetics and in

our understanding of the genetic code and the regulation of gene synthesis and gene action—have required that several chapters be combined or rearranged in sequence and that new chapters be written. Additional figures, photographs, problems, and references are also included.

Suggestions for Use of the Book

The text contains more information than is usually covered in a one-semester, introductory course for undergraduates. The chapters or chapter sections that are marked by an asterisk do not contain principles or terminology needed to understand unmarked parts and are, therefore, optional.

A *one-semester* lecture course (meeting about 30 to 45 periods) can be based upon (1) thirty chapters—those whose chapter numbers are unstarred, or (2) twenty-eight chapters—numbers 1 through 4 and 19 through 42.

A *two-semester* lecture course (meeting a total of about 60 to 90 periods) can be based upon (1) the first eighteen chapters for the first semester and the last twenty-four chapters for the second semester, or (2) all thirty unstarred chapters for the first semester and all starred chapters and sections for the second semester.

Acknowledgments

I wish to thank my wife, Reida Postrel Herskowitz, for preparing the typescript, and my sons, Ira and Joel, and my present and former students for numerous suggestions.

CONTENTS

1 Genetic Material and Mitosis *1*

2 Meiosis and Chromosomal Segregation *15*

3 Segregation of Alleles *31*

4 Independent Recombination by Nonalleles *42*

5 Multiple Alleles; Multigenic Traits *57*

*6 Phenotypic Effects of Gene Action *69*

7 Sex Chromosomes and Sex-Linked Genes *90*

*8 Sex Determination *102*

9 Linkage and Crossing Over Between Genes *116*

10 Gene Arrangement; Crossover Maps *131*

11 Changes Involving Unbroken Chromosomes *149*

12 Structural Changes in Chromosomes *164*

*13 Radiation-Induced Structural Chromosome Changes *179*

*14 Point Mutations *189*

15 The Gene Pool; Equilibrium Factors *201*

*16 Genetic Loads and Their Population Effects *216*

*17 Chromosomal Rearrangements in Nature *228*

*18 Races and the Origin of Species *241*

19 Chemical Nature of Genes *252*

20 Organization and Replication of DNA *in Vivo* *265*

21 Replication of DNA *in Vitro* *279*

22 Clones; Transformation; Strand Recombination *in Vitro* *292*

23 Bacterial Mutation and Conjugation *306*

24 The Episome F *317*

25 Transduction *330*

26 Bacteriophage: Recombination and Genetic Maps *339*

27 Bacterial Episomes and Genetic Recombination *355*

28 RNA as Genetic Material *363*

vii

*29   Extranuclear Genes   *369*

30   The Genetic Control of Mutation   *383*

31   The Molecular Basis of Mutation   *391*

32√   Gene Action and Polypeptides   *404*

offprints

33 √ Polypeptide Synthesis and RNA   *423*

34 √ Genetic Amino Acid Coding   *436*

35   Regulation of Gene Synthesis   *449*

36 √ Regulation of Gene Action—Operons   *457*

*37   Regulation of Gene Action—Gene Control Systems in Maize   *465*

*38   Regulation of Gene Action—Position Effect in Drosophila   *473*

*39   Regulation of Gene Action—Dosage Compensation   *484*

40√   Regulation of Gene Action—Its Molecular Basis in Higher Organisms   *492*

*41   Regulation of Gene Action—Growth, Differentiation, and Development   *501*

42   The Origin and Evolution of Genetic Material   *509*

Appendix—Elementary Biometrical Inferences   *519*

Supplements   *s-1*

I   Part of a Letter (1867) from Gregor Mendel to C. Nägeli   *s-9*

II   Nobel Prize Lecture (1934) of Thomas Hunt Morgan   *s-15*

III   Nobel Prize Lecture (1946) of Hermann Joseph Muller   *s-19*

IV   Nobel Prize Lecture (1962) of Maurice H. F. Wilkins   *s-31*

V   Nobel Prize Lecture (1959) of Arthur Kornberg   *s-60*

VI   Nobel Prize Lecture (1958) of George Wells Beadle   *s-75*

VII   Nobel Prize Lecture (1958) of Edward Lawrie Tatum   *s-88*

VIII   Nobel Prize Lecture (1958) of Joshua Lederberg   *s-98*

IX   Nobel Prize Lecture (1962) of James Dewey Watson   *s-111*

X   Nobel Prize Lecture (1962) of Francis H. C. Crick   *s-135*

Author Index   *541*

Subject Index   *546*

The essential feature of the operational viewpoint is that an object or phenomenon under experimental investigation cannot usefully be defined in terms of assumed properties beyond experimental determination but rather must be defined in terms of the actual operations that may be applied in dealing with it. . . .

What is a gene in operational terms?

L. J. STADLER, "The Gene,"
Science, 120:811–819, 1954

Must we geneticists become bacteriologists, physiological chemists and physicists, simultaneously with being zoologists and botanists? Let us hope so.

H. J. MULLER, "Variation Due to Change in the Individual Gene,"
American Naturalist, 56:32–50, 1922

GENETICS

Chapter 1

GENETIC MATERIAL
AND MITOSIS

SURELY each of us has observed that we are the same kind of creatures as our parents. They gave rise to us, other humans—not to a plant, or a fish, or a bird. Let us start, therefore, by assuming the existence of some intrinsic factor which determines that humans shall beget humans, and let us call this inborn factor for the genesis of like from like the *genetic factor.* Since each plant and animal produces offspring of its own kind, or species, we can generalize and hypothesize that every species of organism has such a built-in genetic factor. But it must also be admitted that the genetic factors for dog, for apple tree, and for man all differ in some way in order to produce such different organisms as end products.

In addition to basic likenesses within the species, each person is similar to and different from his parents in respect to certain details. What is the basis for this? If parents and offspring have similar caloric intakes, all will weigh more nearly alike at a comparable age than if their caloric intakes were different. Apparently, then, environment in which parents and children live can sometimes be the cause of their similarities and differences. But are all similarities and differences among human beings produced by environment, or does the genetic factor presumed responsible for like begetting like play a role in their production?

In trying to formulate the answer to this question, it may be helpful to consider the results of certain studies with bean plants.[1] The particular kind of bean plant concerned reproduces sexually, a single plant performing the functions both of male and female parent. For the present, *assume that the genetic factor is transmitted from the parent to the offspring, and that the transmitted factor must be the same as that of the parent.* Assume also that the genetic factor has a natural rather than a supernatural or spiritual basis. If the genetic factor has a natural basis then it ought to have a material basis and have chemical and/or physical properties, as have other material things. One is led, therefore, to postulate the existence of *genetic material.*

Genetic Material

Consider a particular bean. When the plant grown from this seed produces offspring beans (Figure 1–1A), these are found to vary in size, some being very small, some small, and some medium. According to the assumptions made, these beans all have the same type of genetic material or genetic constitution—or *genotype.* The simplest explanation one can offer for the size differences is that they were caused by environmental differences occurring during seed formation. This view can be tested by growing each of the beans and scoring the size of seeds each produces. When this is done, each bean is also found to produce offspring beans of very small, small, and medium sizes, regardless of the size of the parent seed itself. This test can be repeated generation after generation with the same result. Such a line of descent, whose members carry the same genotype, can be called a *pure line.* The manifestation of the genotype in traits or characteristics (size, in our example) is

[1] Based upon W. Johannsen's experiments. See reference on p. 12.

1

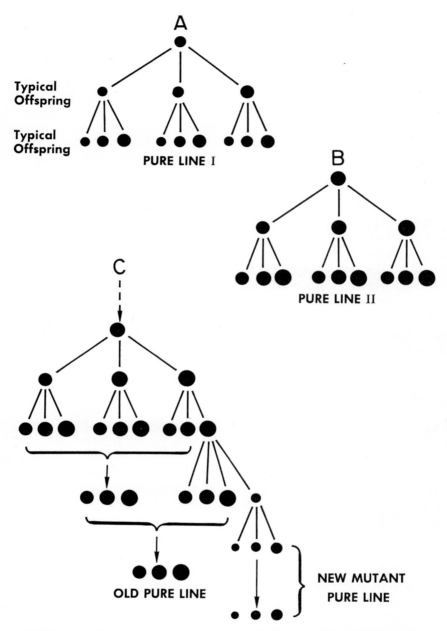

Typical
Offspring

Typical
Offspring

FIGURE 1–1.   *Relative sizes of seeds obtained from self-fertilized bean plants.*

called the *phenotype*. Environmental differences can cause the same genotype to produce a variety of phenotypes, and one can conclude that the differences between the beans of a pure line are environmentally produced and are not due to differences in genotype.

Now consider another bean, of the same species, which gives rise to offspring beans (Figure 1–1B) that are very large, large, and medium sized. Since each of these produces offspring beans which again show the same range of phenotypes, another and different pure line is clearly involved, within which phenotypic variability is attributable to environmental fluctuation.

How can one explain the differences between these two different pure lines, one producing some very small and small beans and the other producing some very large and large ones? Since all the beans are grown under the same environmental conditions, these phenotypic differences cannot be due to environmental differences; instead they must be due to genotypic differences. It must be concluded, then, that the genetic material in these two pure lines is different. How can one explain that some of the seeds in both of these genotypically different pure lines are similar—medium sized? Apparently, different genotypes have produced the same phenotype due to the influence of the environment.

As already mentioned, under similar environmental conditions the average size of the beans produced within a pure line remains the same regardless of the size of the specific beans planted. That is, in the pure line first described the offspring beans have the same average size whether the very small or the medium seed is used as parent. Similarly, the average size of seed produced in the second pure line is the same whether the medium or the very large seed is the parent. In other words, selection within pure lines

is futile, as expected in view of the hypothesis that all members of a pure line are genetically identical.

Throughout the bean experiments described, every effort was made to keep the environment the same. This does not mean that the environment did not vary, but that it varied approximately in the same ways and to the same extent for all the groups in the study. In this particular work it happens that phenotypic variability due to the fluctuations of environment is not so great as to mask completely the phenotypic effect of a genetic difference. In any randomly chosen case, however, one cannot predict offhand to what degree any particular phenotype will be influenced by the genotype and by the environment. Hypothetically, then, two individuals of the same species can have both phenotypic similarities and phenotypic differences resulting from each of the following four combinations, as the examples indicate:

1. IDENTICAL GENOTYPES
   IN NEAR-IDENTICAL ENVIRONMENTS
   Phenotypic difference—one small and one medium sized bean from the same pure line.
   Phenotypic similarity—two small sized beans from the same pure line.

2. DIFFERENT GENOTYPES
   IN NEAR-IDENTICAL ENVIRONMENTS
   Phenotypic difference—one small and one large bean from genetically different pure lines.
   Phenotypic similarity—two medium sized beans from genetically different pure lines.

3. IDENTICAL GENOTYPES
   IN DIFFERENT ENVIRONMENTS
   Phenotypic difference—one bean plant grown in the light is green, while another grown in the dark is white, though both are from the same pure line.

FIGURE 1–2. *Male Siamese cat, grown under temperate conditions, showing the same pigmentation pattern as the Himalayan rabbit. (After C. E. Keeler and V. Cobb.)*

Phenotypic similarity—two rabbits from a certain pure line (genetically black rabbits) both have black coats even though one individual grew at high temperatures and the other grew at low temperatures.

4. DIFFERENT GENOTYPES
   IN DIFFERENT ENVIRONMENTS
   Phenotypic difference—a rabbit from a genetically black line, grown in a cold climate, has black fur, while a rabbit from a Himalayan line, grown under temperate conditions, is Himalayan, i.e., white except for the extremities (paws, tail, snout, and ears), which are black (see Figure 1–2).
   Phenotypic similarity—a rabbit from a genetically black line grown at a moderate temperature and a rabbit from a genetically Himalayan line grown at a cold temperature both have black fur.

The final example illustrates that genotypically different individuals which are phenotypically different in one environment may become phenotypically similar when placed in different environments. The all-black Himalayan rabbit is termed a *phenocopy* of the genetically black rabbit. Persons who are genetically diabetic and take insulin are phenocopies of genetically normal persons who do not take insulin. Genetically normal embryos whose mothers are exposed to the drug thalidomide develop into phenocopies of genetically abnormal, phocomelic persons lacking most or all of the four limbs. So both normal and abnormal phenotypes can be phenocopied.

The case of coat color in rabbits is instructive in another respect. The rabbit that is genetically black will always produce a black coat no matter what the temperature is, provided the temperature is not lethal. In the case of this genotype there seems to be no range of phenotypic expression with respect to temperature variations. In the Himalayan strain, however, the situation is different, as already described in part. If grown at very high temperatures such rabbits have entirely white coats. In this case the *phenotypic range of reaction, or norm of reaction, of the genotype* is relatively great, varying with increasing temperature from completely black through the Himalayan pattern to completely white.

We are now in a position to answer the question concerned with the basis of similarities and differences among offspring or between them and their parents. Extending the principles just described for beans and rabbits to all other kinds of organisms, including man, it is concluded that not only is the genetic material different in different species of organisms, but that it can also differ from one organism to another in the same species. Phenotypic similarities between individuals may occur when they are carrying the same or different genotypes, and phenotypic differences between individuals may or may not be accompanied by genotypic differences.

Having agreed that *genetic variation exists within as well as between species,* one may now ask: How does genetic variation arise? If a pure line of large beans is bred for many generations, one finds, on rare occasions, a very small bean which gives rise to offspring beans ranging from tiny to small, and which clearly make up a new, different, pure line (Figure 1–1C). What has apparently happened is that the genetic material in the pure line of large beans somehow changed to another transmissible form which henceforth caused the production of beans which are, on the average, very small. Such a change in the genotype that is transmitted to progeny may be attributed to a process called *mutation.* The result of mutation is a *mutant,* a term which is applicable to either or both the genotype and the phenotype of the new kind of individual.

Just as it is easy to ascribe differences between dogs and cats to genetic differences, so it is often simple to tell that certain differences between lines of the same species have a genetic basis. There are many strains or breeds of pigeons, dogs, cattle, and of other domesticated animals, each of which differs from the other in phenotype. That many of these differences are due to genetic differences is proved by finding that the phenotypic differences are retained even after the different breeds are raised together generation after generation in essentially identical environments. Revealed in this way, the genotypes within a species are of immense variety. This already-present genetic variation should be kept in mind in seeking to learn more about the nature of the genetic material.

In order to learn more about the genetic material, the material things comprising organisms can be examined more closely, particularly those substances transmitted from parent to offspring. Most types of organisms are composed of (usually microscopic) building blocks, or *cells,* plus substances that have been manufactured by cells. Such an organism begins life either as a single cell, or by the fusion of two cells into one, or as a group of nonfusing cells derived from the parents. The cell serves as the link or bridge between generations. In those cases where the new individual begins life as one cell or as a group of nonfusing cells derived from a single parent, reproduction is *asexual,* whereas in cases where two parents contribute cells, reproduction is *sexual.* In sexual reproduction two mature sex cells, or *gametes,* fuse in the process of fertilization into one new cell, the *zygote,* which is the start of a new individual. In higher animals the gametes are called *egg* (female) and *sperm* (male), and the zygote the *fertilized egg.* In the bean plant, as already mentioned, male and female gametes are produced in the same individual and self-fertilization normally occurs; in human beings the two kinds of sex cells are produced in separate individuals of different *sex,* so that cross-fertilization always occurs.

When might the hypothesized genetic material be transferred from parent to offspring? Consider certain organisms, composed of only a single cell, which reproduce asexually by dividing into two cells. In this process the parent becomes extinct, so to speak, its individuality being replaced by two daughter cells of the same kind. Once formed, the two daughters often separate, never to meet again. In such a case, the genetic material must have been transmitted before the completion of cell division. Accordingly, the cell and this process of cell division should be studied in some detail for clues concerning the physical basis and transmissive characteristics of the genetic factors.

Mitosis

Attention has already been called to the cellular bridge between generations. It is only via this bridge that genetic transmission may take place, at least in single-celled organisms for which cell division is equivalent to reproduction. All cellular organisms are remarkably similar in the way they accomplish cell division. Accordingly, let us examine briefly certain general features of cell structure and the appearance, under the microscope, of cells undergoing division, in initiating our search for the material basis of the genotype.

There are two major parts of the cell (Figure 1–3): a peripheral portion comprising the *cytosome,* containing substances making up *cytoplasm,* and a more central portion called the *nucleus,* containing *nucleoplasm.* In the final stages of cell division in higher plants, the cytoplasm is divided by a cell plate, whose growth starts internally and proceeds toward the periphery until the separation into two daughter cells is complete. In the case of animal cells, a furrow starts at the periphery of the cell and deepens until the parent cell is cleaved into two. The degree to which the two daughter cells are identical with respect to cytoplasmic components depends upon the position of the cell plate or furrow in the parent cell. In some cases these occur in the middle of the cell, but in many other cases they are located off-center, producing daughter cells which contain very different amounts of cytoplasm. Although the cytoplasmic components of a parent cell are often distributed unequally between daughter cells, this is not true for the nuclear contents. Ordinarily, nuclear division directly precedes cytosomal division. But the nucleus does not simply separate into two parts by the formation of a furrow or cell plate. Instead, the nucleus undergoes a remarkable series of activities in order to divide; this whole process of indirect nuclear division is called *mitosis.*

During the time that a nucleus shows no visible evidence of mitosis, it is nevertheless very active biochemically. In appearance (Figure 1–4A), it is bounded by a *nuclear membrane* and is filled by a more or less homogeneous-appearing ground substance or matrix in which are located one or more small bodies, called *nucleoli.*

The first indication that the nucleus is preparing to divide is the appearance in its ground substance of a mass of separate fibers (Figure 1–4B), some of which seem to be associated with the nucleoli. These fibers are called *chromosomes,* and their appearance marks the start of the first phase of mitosis, or *prophase.* Careful cytological observation reveals that each chromosome is in turn composed of two major delicate threads irregularly coiled about each other. Each of the paired threads within each chromosome is called a *chromatid.* As prophase continues, the chromatids within each chromosome become shorter and thicker and untwist from each other (Figure 1–4C). Some of the material incorporated to thicken the chromatids may be derived from the nucleoli, which are seen to become smaller. By the end of prophase (Figure 1–4D), the nucleoli and nuclear membrane have disappeared and the chromatids have formed thick rods which begin to move actively for the first time. Active motility is not the property of the entire chromosome, however, but is restricted to a particular region of it called the *centromere* or *kinetochore* (see p. 379).

The centromeres move in a particular direction relative to a fibrillar structure called the *spindle* which has been forming throughout prophase. The completed spindle has a shape similar to what is produced when one extends and separates the fingers and touches corresponding fingertips together. The wrists represent the poles of the spindle and the fingers, the spindle fibers. The chromosomes migrate from whatever position in the spindle region they may have, until each centromere comes to lie in a single plane perpendicular to the axis between the poles, that is, at the *equatorial plane* or *equator*

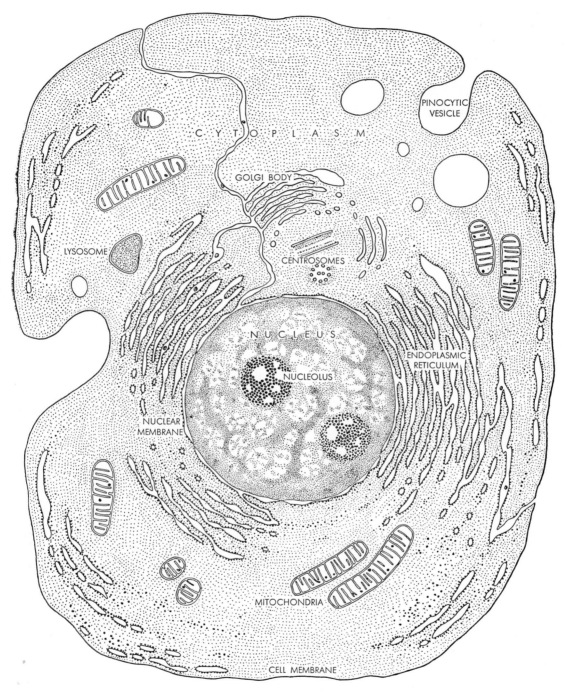

FIGURE 1–3. *Diagrammatic cross-section of a cell. (Reprinted with permission. Copyright © 1961 by Scientific American, Inc. All rights reserved.)*

of the spindle, which is represented by the plane formed where the fingertips touch. The rest of each chromosome, being passive, can be in any position in the spindle. When all the centromeres have arrived at the equatorial plane of the spindle, mitosis has reached the middle phase, or *metaphase* (Figure 1–4E).

Until this point the chromatids of a chromosome are still attached to each other at or near the centromere, although elsewhere they are largely free. Next they also separate at the centromere and the two daughter centromeres suddenly move apart, one going toward one pole of the spindle, the other toward the other pole, with the rest of each chromatid, which is now recognized as a chromosome, being passively dragged along. This stage, in which the chromatids separate, move toward, and arrive at the poles as chromosomes, is called *anaphase* (Figure 1–4F).

When the chromosomes have reached the poles, the last stage, or *telophase,* occurs (Figure 1–4G), in which the events appear to be the reverse of those that happened in prophase. Specifically, the spindle disintegrates, a new nuclear membrane is formed around the chromosomes, and nucleoli reappear. The chromosomes become thinner and longer and then can be seen to consist of two delicate threads (chromatids) wound one about the other. Finally, as the chromosomes lose their visible identity, the nucleus enters the *interphase, intermitotic,* or *metabolic stage* (see again Figure 1–4A).

The impression may have been gained that, in one respect, the preceding generalized account of the mitotic phases was either incomplete or misleading. It was stated that the prophase chromosome is composed of two chromatids or threads, that metaphase puts these into position for separation at anaphase, and that after separation their newly attained individuality is recognized by calling them chromosomes. But chromosomes were defined as containing two visible threads! The question rightly asked is: does the anaphase chromosome contain the two threads that are later seen at telophase? This would be true if each chromatid somehow visibly reproduced itself between the time it was seen relatively uncoiled at prophase and the next time it was seen relatively uncoiled, at telophase. Remember that we have been discussing the replication of chromatids as detected by microscopic observation. Chromosome and chromatid replication can also be studied by other means. Let us consider some evidence regarding chromosome replication at the chemical level, which may help us understand its replication at the visible level.

Chromosomes ("colored bodies") are unique since they are the only objects in the cell that are made purple by the Feulgen staining technique. It is possible to measure the amount of chromosomal material by the amount of purple stain held by the chromosomes. The amount of *chromatin*—Feulgen-stainable chromosomal material—does not change between prophase and telophase, but doubles over a period of hours during the intermitotic stage. By the beginning of prophase, therefore, each chromosome, as revealed by its stainability, has already replicated chemically. At the visible level, however, this is not yet apparent, so that each of the two visible chromatids in a chromosome also contains the chemical materials for an identical chromatid which is still not resolved as a separate thread under the microscope. This new material is unresolved either because it has not yet assumed a proper chromatid form or has done so but is so tightly paired with its sister chromatid that together they appear as one strand. Before the next occasion when unwound threads can be seen— that is, at the telophase of the same mitosis —this replication at the visible level has al-

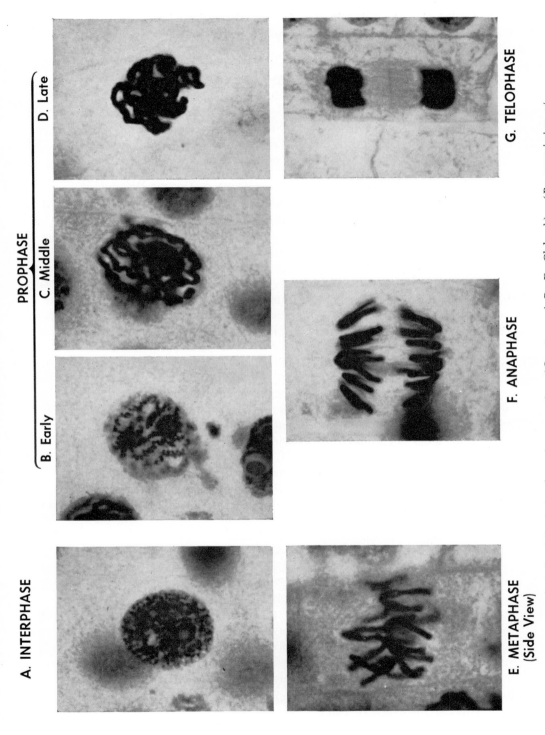

FIGURE 1–4. *Mitosis in the onion root tip. (Courtesy of R. E. Cleland.) (By permission of McGraw-Hill Book Co., Inc., from Study Guide and Workbook for Genetics, by I. H. Herskowitz, copyright 1960.)*

ready been accomplished. Thus, the chemical replication that takes place in a given interphase is not visible in chromatid form until the succeeding telophase.

What are the consequences of mitosis? Speaking in terms of visible structures, the chromosomal content of the parent nucleus has become repeated in each daughter nucleus, so that the subsequent division of the cytoplasm produces daughter cells whose chromosomal composition is identical to each other's and to that of the parent cell from which they were derived. Mitosis merely provides the cellular machinery for the exact partitioning of previously replicated chromosomal material. The cells of different species are different in that they have different numbers of chromosomes per nucleus, or the chromosomes differ in appearance, or both. One chromosome may differ from another in size, in stainability with various dyes, and in the position of the centromere. Most chromosomes have a single centromere which is not located terminally, i.e., at an end, and therefore separates the two *arms* of a chromosome; all chromosomes and chromatids are unbranched fibers.

Examination of the kinds of chromosomes present at metaphase in sexually reproducing organisms typically reveals that for each chromosome which arrives at the equatorial plane, there is another chromosome very similar or identical in appearance which also takes a position independently in this plane. Chromosomes thus occur as pairs; the members of a pair are called *homologous chromosomes,* or *homologs,* whereas chromosomes of different pairs are *nonhomologous,* or *nonhomologs.* It should be repeated that the members of a pair of homologs take their positions at mitotic metaphase independently of each other.

The number of chromosomes seen in typical mitosis of the garden pea is 7 pairs; in Indian corn (maize) there are 10 pairs,

in the domesticated silkworm 28, and in human beings 23; thus the chromosomes of a species are characteristic in number [2] as well as in form. Whatever the number of chromosomes present in the zygote, then, other things being equal, the same number of chromosomes will be found in every cell of a multicellular organism descended from the zygote by cell divisions in which mitosis has occurred.

Chromosomes as Genetic Material

The chromosomes are one of the characteristic components transmitted by all cells to daughter cells. Chromosomes reproduce themselves and are transmitted in mitosis equally to the daughter cells so that these are identical, in this respect, to each other and to their parent cell. Let us make the additional reasonable assumptions that *genetic material arises only by the replication of pre-existing genetic material,* and also that *different genotypes arise only from each other by mutation,* that is, by a genotype's changing to an alternative mutant form which in turn is involved in reproducing the alternative form until it undergoes mutation. A chromosome may occasionally become visibly altered in certain ways; in these cases all chromosomes ordinarily derived from such a modified chromosome via mitosis have exactly the same alteration. Therefore, both genetic material and chromosomes are considered capable of mutation and are subsequently involved in replicating their new form. On this basis, then, *we can hypothesize that the chromosome is, or carries, the genetic material.*

It has been implied that the genetic material routinely retains its individuality or integrity regardless of the nature of the environment. One indirect piece of evidence has already been cited for believing this is

[2] See S. Makino (1951) and C. D. Darlington and E. K. Janaki-Ammal (1945).

true for the chromosomes—namely the independence with which each chromosome arrives at metaphase. It might be thought, when the chromosomes "disappear" during interphase, that their individuality is lost and even that their contents are dispersed. That the nuclear material is not dispersed into the cytoplasm between successive mitoses is indicated by the retention of the full amount of chromosomal material within the nucleus during interphase, insofar as revealed by the Feulgen staining technique. Even so, it is still possible that those components of chromosomes which remain in the nucleus become scrambled during interphase and later resynthesize their proper form during the next prophase. Four lines of evidence bearing on this matter can be mentioned. The first three come from studying the appearance of successive mitoses. It is possible to observe the relative positions of the chromosomes at late anaphase or telophase and also their relative positions as they enter the next prophase. When this is done, the chromosomes are found to have held the same relative positions, as expected had they retained their integrity during the intervening interphase. Second, since the nucleolus does not fragment during interphase, those parts of the chromosomes, called *nucleolus organizers,* with which the nucleolus is associated probably remain associated during that interval.[3] Third, it sometimes happens that two originally identical homologs are modified by mutation so that each is changed in a different respect. The finding, mitosis after mitosis, that both homologs retain their separate differences is evidence that each homolog has retained its individuality cell generation after cell generation. Finally, more direct evidence on the retention of chromosomal individuality during interphase is available from cells of

larval salivary glands of certain flies. These giant cells have interphase nuclei that contain giant chromosomes which, though relatively uncoiled, are clearly equivalent to the more contracted chromosomes seen during mitosis.

The number of points of similarity between genetic material and chromosomes is already impressive. However, if all nuclei divide by mitosis, a gamete should contain the same number of chromosomes as the other cells derived from the original zygote; and since the zygote of any generation combines two gametes, the number of chromosomes should increase in the zygotes of successive generations. One would therefore expect an increase in the amount of genetic material in successive sexual generations. This expectation is not realized, however, since one finds that all individuals of a species have a characteristic, typically stable, chromosomal content. In fact, as expected, human gametes do not contain the paired, *diploid,* chromosome number, that is, 23 pairs of nonhomologous chromosomes. Instead each usually contains 23 chromosomes, one of each nonhomologous type, comprising a complete, unpaired, *haploid* or *monoploid,* set of chromosomes. The zygote, therefore, has the diploid chromosome constitution restored because each gamete furnishes a haploid set of chromosomes, one set contributed by the sperm from the father, and another set by the egg from the mother. In this way chromosomes remain as pairs, sexual generation after sexual generation, and the number of chromosomes in zygotes remains unchanged. Clearly, then, the cell divisions preceding gamete formation cannot be invariably mitotic, but must involve at some point a special mechanism for reducing the number of chromosomes from diploid to haploid. The nature of this special kind of nuclear behavior is considered in the next chapter.

[3] See also F. H. Ruddle (1962).

SUMMARY AND CONCLUSIONS

Organisms are assumed to contain an intrinsic genetic factor which is responsible for like reproducing like. This genetic factor is presumed to have a physical basis in genetic material.

The genetic material must be different in different species of organisms, and may be different in different lines or breeds of the same species. Variations in phenotype may be due to genetic or environmental differences, or both. The contribution made to phenotypic variability by one of these two factors may be evaluated by holding the other factor as constant as possible.

Genotypic differences arise by the process of mutation. The genetic material is presumably transmitted from parents to offspring by means of the cellular bridge between generations, and is assumed to be self-replicating and to arise only from pre-existing genetic material.

Studies of cell division in which nuclei divide mitotically reveal that, of all cellular components, the chromosome is the structure most likely to serve as the genetic material or as its carrier. This hypothesis receives support from several of the properties of chromosomes which parallel established or assumed properties of genetic material. Chromosomes come only from pre-existing chromosomes; different species have different chromosomal compositions; the chromosome content is identical both quantitatively and qualitatively in each cell of a line produced by asexual reproduction; each chromosome retains its individuality, mitotic cell generation after mitotic cell generation, regardless of the nature of the other chromosomes present; chromosomes can occasionally mutate, the mutant chromosome then replicating the mutant form.

REFERENCES

Darlington, C. D., and Janaki-Ammal, E. K., *Chromosome Atlas of Cultivated Plants,* London: Allen and Unwin, 1945.

Flemming, W., 1879. "Contributions to the Knowledge of the Cell and its Life Phenomena," as abridged and translated in *Great Experiments in Biology,* Gabriel, M. L., and Fogel, S. (Eds.), Englewood Cliffs, N.J.: Prentice-Hall, 1955, pp. 240–245.

Johannsen, W., 1909. *Elemente der exakten Erblichkeitslehre.* Jena. See also a translation of the summary and conclusions of his 1903 paper, "Heredity in Populations and Pure Lines," in *Classic Papers in Genetics,* Peters, J. A. (Ed.), Englewood Cliffs, N.J.: Prentice-Hall, 1959, pp. 20–26.

Makino, S., *An Atlas of Chromosome Numbers in Animals,* Ames, Iowa: Iowa State College Press, 1951.

Mazia, D., "Mitosis and the Physiology of Cell Division," in *The Cell,* Vol. 3, *Meiosis and Mitosis,* pp. 77–412, Brachet, J., and Mirsky, A. E. (Eds.), New York: Academic Press, 1961.

Ruddle, F. H., "Nuclear Bleb: A Stable Interphase Marker in Established Lines of Cells *in Vitro,*" J. Nat. Cancer Inst., 28:1247–1251, 1962.

Schrader, F., *Mitosis: the Movement of Chromosomes in Cell Division,* New York: Columbia University Press, 1953.

Scientific American, Sept. 1961, Vol. 205, No. 3, "The Living Cell," articles by J. Brachet and D. Mazia.

Wilhelm Ludwig Johannsen
(1861–1926). *(From Genetics,
vol. 8, p. 1, 1923.)*

Spector, W. S. (Ed.), "Chromosome Numbers," in *Handbook of Biological Data,* Philadelphia: Saunders, 1956, pp. 92–96.

Swanson, C. P., *Cytology and Cytogenetics,* Englewood Cliffs, N.J.: Prentice-Hall, 1957.

Swanson, C. P., *The Cell,* 2nd Ed., Englewood Cliffs, N.J.: Prentice-Hall, 1964.

QUESTIONS FOR DISCUSSION

1.1. Does the phenotype of one generation have any effect upon the genotype of the next? Explain.

1.2. Evaluate the thesis that the genotype is more important to organisms than is the environment.

1.3. Is the environment for two organisms ever identical? Explain.

1.4. What is meant by an operational definition?

1.5. Define the genetic factor. Have you given an operational or a nonoperational definition? Explain.

1.6. When the same similarities or differences in phenotype can be produced by either the environment or the genotype, can one ever be sure which is the determining factor? Explain.

1.7. What evidence can you give to support the view that genetic material is transmitted from parent to offspring? Do you think this evidence constitutes conclusive proof of transmission? Explain.

1.8. What conclusions can you reach regarding the genetic factor in Himalayan rabbits and in Siamese cats?

1.9. Assume the genetic factor has a supernatural basis. Could we learn anything about it by the scientific method of investigation? Explain.

1.10. Do you think human beings provide good material for the study of the genetic factor? Explain.

1.11. What size limitations can you give to the genetic material?

1.12. Is the existence of genetic material presumed or proved? Explain.

1.13. What do the bean experiments reveal about genetic material?

1.14. August Weismann (1834–1914) cut off the tails of mice for a series of generations and found that tail length remained normal each new generation. Why are these experiments significant?

1.15. What are the consequences of mitosis?

1.16. For each of the properties of chromosomes listed in the Summary and Conclusions, state the corresponding property of the genetic material and identify it as one that is either proved or assumed.

1.17. If the chromosomes serve as the genetic material, each cell of the body derived by mitosis should carry the same genotype. Describe how you would test this idea, using a multicellular plant.

1.18. What are the advantages or disadvantages of chromosome coiling?

1.19. Can you imagine a spindle which is too small for normal cell division? Explain.

1.20. Suppose certain nuclei normally do not divide with the aid of a spindle. How would this affect your ideas about genetic material?

1.21. Discuss the statement that all cell divisions are normally mitotic.

1.22. Differentiate between replication of chromatids and of chromosomal material.

1.23. List the events that presumably take place before a given telophase chromosome can give rise to a chromosome made entirely of chromosomal material not yet synthesized.

1.24. Why should the peas in a pod be similar? Different?

1.25. What do each of the following observations mean with regard to the origin and/or integrity of chromosomal material?

    (a) Nonhomologous chromosomes retain their characteristic morphological differences mitosis after mitosis.

    (b) A loss or gain of one entire chromosome occurs occasionally, with all mitotic descendants having the same aberration.

    (c) T. Boveri noted in Ascaris cleavage that sister cells entering the next mitosis often have a mirror-image arrangement of their chromosomes.

1.26. What conclusions can you draw from the fact that there are three genotypically different kinds of Indian corn: one always has red kernels, one always has yellow kernels, and one has kernels which are yellow but become red if exposed to sunlight?

Chapter 2

MEIOSIS AND
CHROMOSOMAL SEGREGATION

How do both male and female gametes come to contain only one set of chromosomes, composed of one member of each pair of chromosomes found in the nucleus of an ordinary body, or *somatic,* cell? If gametes were produced by regular mitotic division, they would be diploid. The reduction from two sets to one is brought about by another type of indirect nuclear process, called *meiosis,* which actually requires two successive nuclear divisions to accomplish its result.

Meiosis

To render the cytological description of the meiotic process more meaningful, several assumptions will be made. Suppose that the processes directing the division of the nucleus act especially early in the case of meiosis, before the chromosomes have attained the degree of coiling first seen in mitotic prophase. Suppose further that a relatively more uncoiled state of the chromosome is, under these conditions, associated with an especially strong attraction between homologs of like chromosome parts for like parts and that this attractive force extends over considerable, though still microscopic, distances. Then, with one additional novelty yet to be described, the meiotic process will occur in the following predictable way when the chromosomes, without further replica-

15

tion, undergo two successive mitotic divisions.

In prophase of the first meiotic division, just as in mitotic prophase, each chromosome contains two chromatids plus an equal amount of chromosomal material not yet visible as chromatids (see p. 8). But now, because of the early onset of nuclear division, homologous chromosomes pair point for corresponding point (making a bundle of four chromatids plus an equal amount of future chromatid material). Accordingly, the chromosomes proceed as pairs to the equator of the spindle for the metaphase. (Recall that in mitosis, on the other hand, each chromosome of the two sets present goes to the equator of the spindle independently of its homologous chromosome.) At anaphase the members of a pair separate and go to opposite poles, each anaphase chromosome still containing two chromatids plus an equivalent amount of future chromatid material. In the interphase after the first telophase, no synthesis of future chromatid material takes place since what was made in the previous interphase had not been used to make visible chromatids in the first meiotic division. The second meiotic division may start at any time and proceed as a typical mitosis. In the second meiotic prophase each chromosome contains two chromatids and the material for two future chromatids. Each chromosome proceeds to metaphase independently; at anaphase the two chromatids separate and go to opposite poles of the spindle (after separation the chromatids may be called chromosomes). By telophase the future chromatid becomes visible; thus each telophase chromosome contains two chromatids.

Although mitosis always involves chromosome duplication and separation alternately, one duplication is followed by two separations in meiosis. The result is the maintenance of the diploid chromosome condition in mitosis, but a reduction from the diploid to the haploid condition upon the completion of meiosis.

Let us examine in some detail the actual meiotic process as seen under the microscope (Figure 2–1). Prophase of the first meiotic division (*prophase I*) is of long duration, as compared to mitotic prophase, and is divided into several substages, each with its own distinguishing characteristics.

1. As they emerge from the interdivision phase the chromosomes are long and thin, more so than in the earliest prophase of mitosis. This is the *leptonema* (thin thread) stage of prophase I.

2. Next the thin threads pair with each other in a process called *synapsis*. This pairing is very exact, being not merely between homologous chromosomes, but between exactly corresponding individual points of the homologs.[1] Synapsis proceeds zipperwise until the two homologs are completely apposed. This is the *zygonema* (joining thread) stage.

3. The apposition of homologs becomes so tight that it is difficult to identify two separate chromosomes in the *pachynema* (thick thread) stage (Figure 2–2A).

4. Next, the tight pairing of the pachynema is relaxed, whereupon it can be clearly seen in the *diplonema* (double thread) stage that each pair of synapsed chromosomes contains four threads, two visible chromatids for each chromosome (Figure 2–2B, C). A pair of synapsed chromosomes is called a *bivalent* (composed of two *univalents*) when referring to chromosomes, but is called a *tetrad* (composed of two *dyads* or four *monads*) when referring to cytologically detectable chromatids.

Although the chromatids in a tetrad separate from each other in pairs here and there, they are all still in close contact with each other elsewhere. Each place where the four

[1] See H. Jehle (1963) for a discussion of the physical basis for the attraction of like for like.

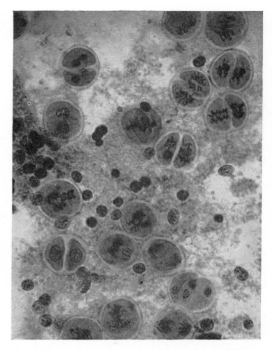

FIGURE 2–1. *Meiosis in the lily—general view.* (*Courtesy of R. E. Cleland.*)

chromatids are still held together is called a *chiasma* (Greek, cross; plural, *chiasmata*) (Figure 2–3A). In a chiasma the two chromatids that synapse to make a pair on one side of the point of contact, separate at that point and synapse with other partners on the other side of the contact point; i.e., the partners making up two synapsed pairs of chromatids are different on the two sides of the place of contact (Figure 2–3B). A tetrad typically has at least one chiasma. The occurrence of a chiasma assures that the univalents are held together. When several chiasmata occur per bivalent, loops are

FIGURE 2–2 (*opposite*). *Meiosis in the lily. The leptonema and zygonema stages of prophase I have been omitted.* (*Courtesy of R. E. Cleland.*) (*By permission of McGraw-Hill Book Co., Inc., from* Study Guide and Workbook for Genetics, *by I. H. Herskowitz, copyright 1960.*)

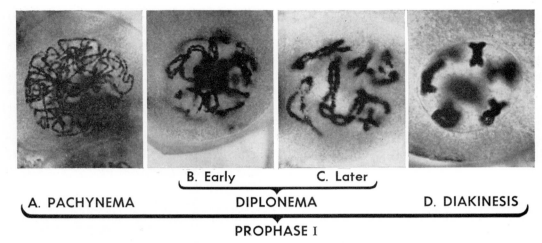

B. Early   C. Later

A. PACHYNEMA   DIPLONEMA   D. DIAKINESIS

PROPHASE I

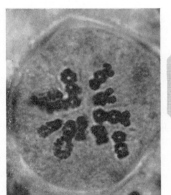

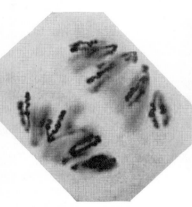

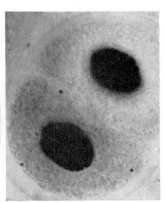

E. METAPHASE I
(Equatorial View)

F. ANAPHASE I
(Side View)

G. INTERPHASE I

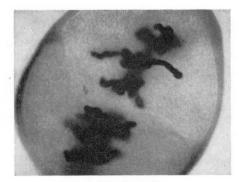

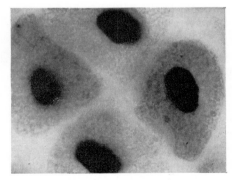

H. METAPHASE II
(Side View)

I. TELOPHASE II

formed, adjacent ones at right angles to each other.

As *diplonema* continues, the chromosomes become shorter and thicker, more compacted than they ever become in mitosis.

5. In some animals, during the formation of female gametes especially, a *diffuse* or *growth* stage follows diplonema, in which the chromosomes and nucleus revert to the appearance found in a nondividing cell. During this stage a great amount of cytoplasmic growth takes place. In human beings this stage may last for decades, after which the rest of meiosis occurs and mature eggs ready for ovulation are produced.

6. *Diakinesis* (Figure 2–2D) is characterized by the maximal contraction of diplonema chromosomes, or by maximal recontraction of the chromosomes which had entered a diffuse stage. By the end of this stage nucleoli and nuclear membrane have disappeared, the spindle has formed, and prophase I is completed.

Metaphase I (Figure 2–2E) is attained by the movement of chromosomes to the midspindle, as in mitosis, except that they move as bivalents, made up of a tetrad of chromatids still held together by chiasmata. Between diplonema and metaphase I the chiasmata move toward the end of the chromosome arms, that is, away from the centromere, especially if the bivalent is short. As a consequence of this *chiasma terminalization* the number of chiasmata present at metaphase I may be less than it was at diplonema.

During *anaphase I* (Figure 2–2F) the univalents in each bivalent separate from each other at the region of the centromere and proceed to opposite poles of the spindle. This movement completely terminalizes all remaining chiasmata. The dyad nature of each univalent is readily seen in the figure. In *telophase I* the two daughter nuclei are formed, and *interphase I* (Figure 2–2G)

follows. The length of interphase I varies in different organisms.

Each daughter nucleus undergoes the second meiotic division, which proceeds as expected from mitosis. In *prophase II*, each univalent (equivalent to a chromosome with its two visible chromatids) contracts; at *metaphase II* (Figure 2–2H) each lines up at the equator of the spindle independently; at *anaphase II* the members of a dyad separate and go to opposite poles as *monads* (each equivalent to a single chromosome, since now each contains two visible chromatids). Because two nuclei undergo this second division, four nuclei are formed at *telophase II* (Figure 2–2I). Photographs of the meiotic process in corn can be seen in Figure 2–4 (pp. 20–21).

Chromosomal Segregation

Consider next the consequences of meiosis. The organism undergoing meiosis starts its existence as a zygote produced by fertilization involving the union of two haploid sets of chromosomes, one maternal and one paternal. When meiosis is completed the diploid, paired, chromosome number is reduced to the haploid, unpaired, chromosome number. Since any postmeiotic nucleus normally contains only one representative of any given pair of chromosomes present in a premeiotic nucleus, *chromosome segregation* has occurred. Two questions come to mind at this point. First, is the haploid set of chromosomes, or *genome,* in a gamete composed of replicas of all the chromosomes contributed by the female parent or of all those contributed by the male parent?

For typical meiosis, the answer depends upon two events. The first of these is the manner in which the centromeres of the bivalents arrange themselves at the equator of the spindle at metaphase I. Relative to the poles of the spindle, each bivalent arranges itself at the equator independently of other bivalents, so that it is purely a matter of chance whether the copy of the maternally-derived chromosome will go to one specified pole and the copy of the paternally-derived chromosome to the other, or vice versa. Consider the distribution of two bivalents, for example. Since there are many cells undergoing meiosis in any sex organ, or *gonad,* at metaphase I, approximately half of these will have the two paternal univalents going to one pole and the two maternal univalents going to the other pole at anaphase I, and approximately half will have one maternal and one paternal going to one pole and one paternal and one maternal to the other. As a result, the chromosomal content of a pool of all the haploid nuclei present at the completion of meiosis will be 25% paternal + paternal; 25% maternal + maternal; 25% paternal + maternal; 25% maternal + paternal. Because the centromeres of each bivalent line up at metaphase I in one direction with a frequency equal to that in the other and because each bivalent does so independently of all other bivalents, we see that the *segregation* which follows *occurs independently for different pairs of chromosomes.*[2] Note also, from the fate of two bivalents, that 50% of haploid products have the same combinations of nonhomologous chromosomes as entered the individual in the parental gametes, therefore retaining the *old or parental combinations,* whereas 50% of haploid products carry *new, nonparental combinations or recombinations.*

Let us defer considering the genetic implications of these conclusions until we have considered the second question, which also bears upon the maternal-paternal chromosome content of gametes: our answer may modify the conclusions just reached. Is a chromosome in a gamete, in fact, a completely uniparental replica, or has it a bi-

[2] As shown by E. E. Carothers (1921).

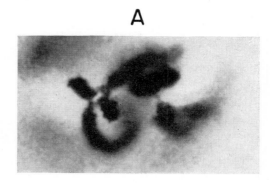

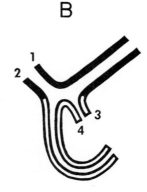

FIGURE 2–3. *Lily diplonema showing chromatids (1–4) with different synaptic partners on different sides of a chiasma. (Courtesy of R. E. Cleland.)*

parental derivation? The latter situation would obtain if one segment of a gametic chromosome were a copy of a portion of one homolog and another segment a copy of a portion of the other homolog.

Considerable evidence exists that some time between the onset of meiosis and diplonema a cytologically undetected event occurs which results in two of the four chromatids in a tetrad having segments which are biparental copies, exactly reciprocal in content. Thus, if one biparental segment of a chromatid has a linear sequence that is maternal-paternal, the other is paternal-maternal in composition. The other two chro-

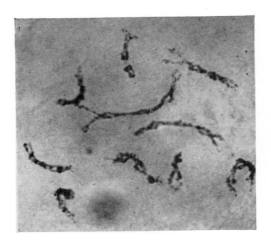

DIPLONEMA

ANAPHASE I (Middle)

PACHYNEMA

METAPHASE I

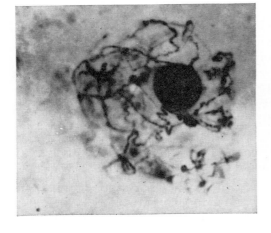

LEPTONEMA

DIAKINESIS

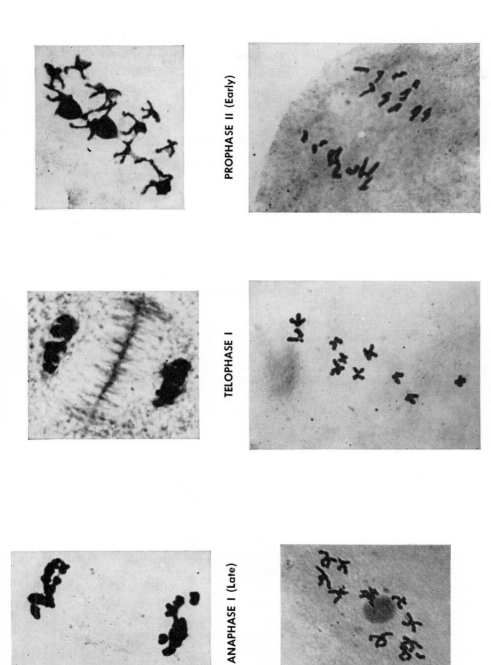

PROPHASE II (Early)

ANAPHASE II

TELOPHASE I

METAPHASE II

ANAPHASE I (Late)

PROPHASE II (Late)

FIGURE 2–4. *Meiosis in corn. The zygonema stage is omitted. Anaphase I (Middle) shows one bivalent whose univalents are delayed in separation because they are still held together by a chiasma. Prophase II and later stages show the events taking place in one of the two nuclei produced by the first meiotic division. (Courtesy of M. M. Rhoades.)*

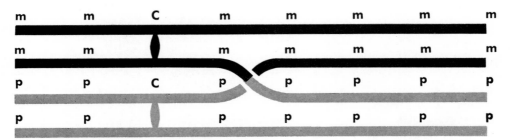

FIGURE 2–5. *Chiasma showing paternal (p) and maternal (m) composition of strands. Compare with Figure 2–3B.*

matids, then, are uniparental replicas for this region, one all-maternal and the other all-paternal. The recombinational event that produces the two biparental segments can be called an *exchange,* although this should not be taken to mean that what occurred was a cross-union following breakage of a paternal and a maternal chromatid at exactly corresponding positions. It is likely that synapsis at any level is strongest between strands having the same parental derivation. Accordingly, during diplonema of prophase I, when the chromatids separate in pairs, they should switch pairing partners at the point where the two biparental chromatids change their parental derivation. This switching would produce the chiasma configuration. Note in Figure 2–3B, where chromatid material of one parental derivation is shown filled in whereas that of the other is not, that it is necessary for chromatids to change pairing partners in order to maintain in synapsis all the corresponding paternally-derived (and also all the corresponding maternally-derived) portions of the strands. Some of the exchanges may fail to produce a visible chiasma later; this could happen if the pairing were uniparental on one side and biparental on the other side of a point of exchange. On the other hand, every chiasma can be taken to represent cytological evidence of a prior intratetrad exchange. It should be noted, however, that because of

chiasma terminalization, the position of a chiasma may be distal to the point where the two biparental chromatids changed their parental type. We will henceforth assume that chiasma terminalization is absent during diplonema, thereby making it possible to equate the position of a chiasma with the point of exchange. Accordingly, a tetrad containing one chiasma would have the paternal (p) and maternal (m) linear constitution shown in Figure 2–5, where the centromere is represented by C. The figure shows that, after one exchange, one chromatid remains entirely maternal and one entirely paternal, but the other two are biparental in origin. Note again that only two of the four chromatids are involved in a single exchange. However, a tetrad normally contains several chiasmata; this means that earlier each of the four chromatids had probably exchanged at one place or another with a chromatid derived from the other parent and consequently has a biparental composition.

We can now return to the questions regarding the maternal-paternal chromosome content of the haploid products of meiosis. The centromeres in a bivalent separate at anaphase I; thus segregation of maternal from paternal centromeres occurs at the first meiotic division. Then, as revealed by the location and number of chiasmata at diplonema, the monads having the maternal centromeres will contain different paternal segments along their lengths, and the monads with the paternal centromeres will have the complementary maternal sections along their lengths. Accordingly, segregation of maternally-derived chromatid material from paternally-derived chromatid material occurs for centromeric and some other regions of the chromatids at anaphase I and is accomplished for the remaining regions of the chromatids at anaphase II. Since bivalents line up at metaphase I independently, meiosis will normally result in the *segregation of homologous chromosomal regions* and *independent segregation of chromosomal segments located on nonhomologous chromosomes*.

Life Cycles of Multicellular Organisms

Since the diploid number of chromosomes is maintained generation after generation in sexually reproducing forms, it is not surprising that meiosis always occurs at some time in the life cycle of each sexually reproducing individual. In most animals meiosis comprises the last two nuclear divisions before the mature sperm or egg is produced. Meiosis occurs at different times in the life history of different plants, but rarely just before the formation of gametes. Different species show minor variations in the details with which meiosis is carried out. Let us consider the life cycles of certain multicellular organisms which have proven to be especially interesting both for cytological and genetic investigations—that is, in *cytogenetics*.

1. *Drosophila melanogaster* [3]

The adult stage of *D. melanogaster,* commonly called the fruit, banana, or vinegar fly, is shown in Figure 2–6. Although size depends upon nutritional and other environ-

---

[3] See the Appendix to this chapter, on p. 29, for references dealing with this and other species of Drosophila.

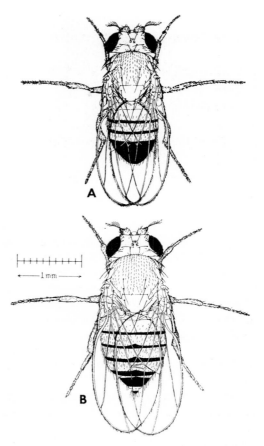

FIGURE 2–6. *Normal (wild-type)* Drosophila melanogaster *male (A) and female (B). (Drawn by E. M. Wallace.)*

mental factors, the adult is usually 2–3 mm. long, and females are larger than males raised under comparable conditions. As found in nature, the *wild-type* fly has a grey body color and dull-red compound eyes. Males are readily distinguished from females by having sex combs on the anterior pair of legs and an abdomen which terminates dorsally in a single broad black band (instead of a series of bands) and which ends ventrally in a penis and claspers (instead of an ovipositor).

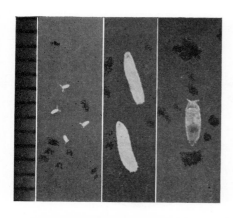

FIGURE 2–7. *Egg, mature larva, and pupa of* Drosophila melanogaster. *Each unit of scale equals 1 mm.* (*Courtesy of E. R. Balboni.*)

The adult male is diploid and has a pair of testes in which *spermatogonia* are produced by mitosis. When one of these spermatogonial cells enters meiosis it is called a *primary spermatocyte.* The first meiotic division produces two *secondary spermatocytes;* the second meiotic division, four haploid *spermatids.* Each spermatid differentiates without further division into a *spermatozoan,* or sperm cell. Note that for each diploid primary spermatocyte entering meiosis, four functional haploid sperm are produced at the completion of *spermatogenesis.* This is also true of males of many higher animals, including the frog, mouse, and man. Sperm are stored in the Drosophila male until they are ejaculated into the vagina of the female, where they proceed to swim into the female's sperm storage organs (a pair of *spermathecae* and a coiled *ventral receptacle*).

The adult female has a pair of ovaries each of which is composed of a series of egg tubes, or *ovarioles.* At one end of the ovariole are diploid *oogonia.* By four synchronous mitotic divisions each oogonium produces a nest of 16 cells, one of which enters meiosis as a *primary oocyte* while those remaining serve as *nurse cells* for the maturing oocyte. As the oocyte grows it passes down the ovariole, into the oviduct and then the uterus. At the time it reaches the uterus, the egg (Figure 2–7) is usually no further advanced than metaphase of the first meiotic division. The sperm held in the female are released to fertilize the egg in the uterus, after which the first meiotic division continues. The two *secondary oocyte* nuclei produce four haploid nuclei, three of which are *polar nuclei* and degenerate, the remaining one serving as the haploid egg nucleus. Note here, as in females of the frog, mouse, and man, that a single primary oocyte produces only one mature haploid egg at the completion of *oogenesis.* (In man, also, meiosis is completed after fertilization, the egg remaining at metaphase II until sperm entry.) Since the female Drosophila stores hundreds of sperm and uses them sparingly (only one sperm usually enters the egg), a single mating can yield hundreds of progeny.

At about 25° C embryonic development proceeds for about a day, when the *larva* hatches from the egg. After four more days and two moltings, the mature larva becomes a *pupa* (Figure 2–7). After about four days the young adult, or *imago,* ecloses (hatches) from the pupa case. Thus, the Drosophila undergoes a complete metamorphosis during its life cycle. Although mating usually occurs during the first 24 hours of adult life, oviposition usually starts during the second day, so that the generation time is about 10

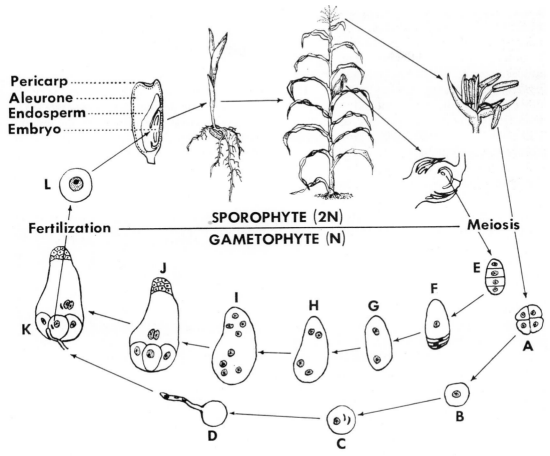

Pericarp
Aleurone
Endosperm
Embryo

L

Fertilization ——— **SPOROPHYTE (2N)** ——— **Meiosis**

GAMETOPHYTE (N)

E

J
K
I
H
G
F
A
B
C
D

FIGURE 2–8. *Life cycle of corn,* Zea mays. *See text for description.*

days. Adults can live as long as 10 weeks, during which a female can lay several thousand eggs.

2. *Zea mays* [4]

Corn or maize, like the bean and the garden pea, usually produces both male and female sex organs on the same plant and is therefore *monoecious* ("one house"). Since

[4] See the Appendix to this chapter, on p. 29, for references to corn experiments and literature.

the diploid corn plant produces male and female spores, *microspores* and *megaspores* respectively, it represents the *sporophyte stage* of the life cycle (Figure 2–8). The microspores are produced in tassels at the end of the stem. Here diploid microspore mother cells, or *microsporocytes,* each undergo meiosis to produce four haploid microspores (A), each of which develops into a pollen grain (B).

Since the haploid microspores give rise to the haploid gametes, these two points in the life cycle comprise the beginning and end of the male *gametophyte stage*. The haploid microspore nucleus divides mitotically once, to produce two haploid nuclei. One of these nuclei does not divide again and becomes the *pollen tube* or *vegetative nucleus*. The other nucleus divides mitotically once, so that the gametophyte contains three haploid nuclei (C); the two last formed function as *sperm nuclei* (D, K).

Near the base of the upper branches of the corn plant are clusters of pistils, each containing one diploid megaspore mother cell, or *megasporocyte*. (The styles of the pistils later become the silks.) The megasporocyte undergoes meiosis to produce four haploid nuclei (E), three of which degenerate (F). The remaining megaspore nucleus divides mitotically (G), as do its daughter and granddaughter nuclei (H), so that eight haploid nuclei result (I). In the *embryo sac* (J), three of the eight nuclei cluster at the apex and divide to form *antipodal nuclei,* two move to the center (*polar nuclei*), and three (composed of two *synergid nuclei* and one *egg nucleus*) move to the base of the embryo sac. The pollen tube grows down the style to the embryo sac, where one sperm nucleus fertilizes the egg nucleus (K, L), producing a diploid (2N) nucleus, and the other sperm nucleus fuses with the two polar nuclei to produce a triploid (3N) nucleus. With the occurrence of this *double fertilization* the sporophyte stage is initiated. Mitotic division of the diploid nucleus (L) produces the *embryo,* while the triploid nucleus develops into the *endosperm*. The surface cells of the endosperm comprise the *aleurone,* containing aleurone grains and oil; the remaining endosperm cells contain starch. The endosperm is gradually digested to nourish the embryo and seedling. The outer surface of the kernel is the *pericarp,* diploid tissue derived from the maternal sporophyte. In other words, a corn kernel has its pericarp produced by one sporophyte and its remaining tissue by the sporophyte of the next generation. Development from embryo sac to mature kernel requires about eight weeks (during which the antipodal and synergid nuclei or their descendents degenerate); development from the kernel to the mature sporophyte occurs in about four months (during which the first leaf completes the digestion of the endosperm).

3. *Neurospora crassa* [5]

Neurospora ("nerve spore") is a bread mold whose haploid vegetative stage is composed of threads or *hyphae* which interweave to form a mass, the *mycelium*. The hyphae branch and fuse. Since the cell walls which partition the hypha into cells are incomplete, the cytoplasm of the filament is continuous. Each hyphal cell is multinucleate.

Cultures can be propagated asexually by transplanting pieces of mycelium, or by spores (*conidia*) which contain one or several haploid nuclei. Sexual reproduction (Figure 2–9) requires the participation of molds of different mating type which produce *fruiting bodies*. A haploid nucleus from one mating type enters and divides mitotically a number of times in the fruiting body of the opposite mating type. These haploid nuclei pair with haploid nuclei of the fruiting body and fuse to produce diploid zygotic nuclei. Each zygotic nucleus then undergoes two meiotic divisions to produce four haploid nuclei; each of these divides once mitotically to form a total of eight haploid nuclei. The cytoplasm is then partitioned to form eight ovoid haploid *ascospores* which are contained in a thin-walled sac, the *ascus*. The mature fruiting body may contain 300 asci, from which the ascospores are released and carried in the air. Upon

[5] See Appendix on p. 29, for references to experimental methods, results, and literature.

germination the haploid ascospore divides mitotically and grows to produce the mycelium. Sometimes the hyphae of two different strains of the same or different mating type will fuse to form a *heterocaryon,* hyphal cells containing the nuclei of both strains.

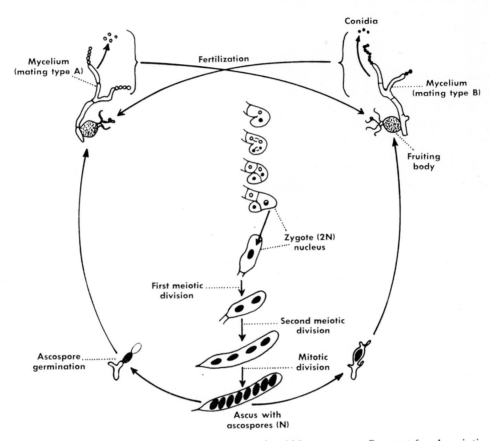

FIGURE 2–9. *Life cycle of* Neurospora. See text for description.

SUMMARY AND CONCLUSIONS

Meiosis involves two successive, essentially mitotic divisions modified by the occurrence of synapsis and of chiasmata formation during prophase I, and the nonoccurrence of chromosomal replication during interphase I. Any particular chromosome in a genome of a gamete has an equal chance of having a replica of a maternally- or a paternally-derived centromere (because of the random manner in which different bivalents align themselves on the spindle at metaphase I) and usually contains replicas of segments originally derived from the other parent (as revealed by chiasmata). As a consequence of meiosis the original pair of genomes becomes single in the gametes. Not only do homologous chromosomal segments segregate, but chromosomal segments of nonhomologs segregate independently.

EDMUND B. WILSON (*1856–1939*), *American cytologist.* (*From Genetics, vol. 34, p. 1, 1949.*)

REFERENCES

Carothers, E. E., "Genetical Behavior of Heteromorphic Homologous Chromosomes of Circotettix (Orthoptera)," J. Morphology, 35:457–483, 1921.

Darlington, C. D., and Bradshaw, A. D. (Eds.), *Teaching Genetics in School and University,* Edinburgh: Oliver & Boyd, 1963.

De Robertis, E. D. P., Nowinski, W. W., and Saez, F. A., *General Cytology,* 3rd Ed., Philadelphia: Saunders, 1960.

Jehle, H., "Intermolecular Forces and Biological Specificity," Proc. Nat. Acad. Sci., U.S., 50:516–524, 1963.

Lewis, K. R., and John, B., *Chromosome Marker,* London: J. and A. Churchill Ltd., 1963.

McLeisch, J., and Snoad, B., *Looking at Chromosomes,* New York: St. Martin's Press, 1958.

Rhoades, M. M., "Meiosis," pp. 1–75, in *The Cell,* Vol. 3, *Meiosis and Mitosis,* Brachet, J., and Mirsky, A. E. (Eds.), New York: Academic Press, 1961.

Sutton, W. S., 1903. "The Chromosomes in Heredity," Biol. Bull., 4:231–251. Reprinted in *Great Experiments in Biology,* Gabriel, M. L., and Fogel, S. (Eds.), Englewood Cliffs, N.J.: Prentice-Hall, 1955, pp. 248–254; also in *Classic Papers in Genetics,* Peters, J. A. (Ed.), Englewood Cliffs, N.J.: Prentice-Hall, 1959, pp. 27–41.

Swanson, C. P., *Cytology and Cytogenetics,* Englewood Cliffs, N.J.: Prentice-Hall, 1957.

Van Beneden, E., 1883. "Researches on the Maturation of the Egg and Fertilization," translated in *Great Experiments in Biology,* Gabriel, M. L., and Fogel, S. (Eds.), Englewood Cliffs, N.J.: Prentice-Hall, 1955, pp. 245–248.

Wilson, E. B., *The Cell in Development and Heredity,* 3rd Ed., New York: Macmillan, 1937.

APPENDIX

DROSOPHILA

Bibliographies on most, if not all, investigations with all species of Drosophila through 1962 are found in source 1 (which includes subject indexes), and the more recent work in 5. The life cycle, culture, cytological and genetic experiments for the classroom are given in 3, 4, 6, 8. All aspects of Drosophila biology are treated in detail in 3. Mutants found until about 1942 are described in 2. Many mutants found since then are described in 5, or referred to in 1. A new and complete compilation is in preparation (7). Stock lists of various Drosophila species maintained in different laboratories, addresses of Drosophila workers, research and teaching notes are given international presentation in the more or less annual bulletin of 5.

1. *Bibliography on the Genetics of Drosophila: Part I* by H. J. Muller (Edinburgh: Oliver and Boyd, 1939, 132 pp.). *Parts II, III,* and *IV* by I. H. Herskowitz (Oxford: Alden Press, 1953, 212 pp.; Bloomington: Indiana University Press, 1958, 296 pp.; and New York: McGraw-Hill, 1963, 344 pp., respectively).

2. Bridges, C. B., *The Mutants of Drosophila melanogaster* (completed and edited by Brehme, K. S.), Washington, D.C.: Carnegie Institution of Washington, Publ. 552, 257 pp., 1944.

3. Demerec, M. (Ed.), *The Biology of Drosophila,* New York: J. Wiley & Sons, 632 pp., 1950. Xerographed by University Microfilms, Inc., 313 N. 1st Street, Ann Arbor, Michigan.

4. Demerec, M., and Kaufmann, B. P., *Drosophila Guide,* 7th Ed. Washington, D.C.: Carnegie Institution of Washington, 47 pp., 1961.

5. *Drosophila Information Service* (E. Novitski, Editor, Dept. of Biology, University of Oregon, Eugene, Ore.).

6. Haskell, G., *Practical Heredity with Drosophila,* Edinburgh and London: Oliver and Boyd, 124 pp., 1961.

7. Lindsley, D. L., and Grell, E. H., *The Mutants of Drosophila,* Washington, D.C.: Carnegie Institution of Washington, 1965.

8. Strickberger, M. W., *Experiments in Genetics with Drosophila,* New York: J. Wiley & Sons, 144 pp., 1962.

ZEA

1. Kiesselbach, T. A., "The Structure and Reproduction of Corn," Univ. Nebraska Coll. Agric., Agric. Exp. Sta. Res. Bull., No. 161, 1949.

2. Maize News Letter (M. M. Rhoades, Ed., Dept. of Botany, Indiana University, Bloomington, Ind.).

3. Sprague, G. F., *Corn and Corn Improvement,* New York: Academic Press, 1955.

4. Weijer, J., "A Catalogue of Genetic Maize Types Together with a Maize Bibliography," Bibliographica Genetica, 14:189–425, 1952.

NEUROSPORA

1. Bachmann, B., and Strickland, W. N., *Neurospora Bibliography and Index,* New Haven: Yale University Press, 1965.

2. Fincham, J. R. S., and Day, P. R., *Fungal Genetics,* Oxford: Blackwell Scientific Publications, 1963.

3. Ryan, F. J., "Selected Methods of Neurospora Genetics," Methods in Medical Research, 3:51–75, 1950.

4. Wagner, R. P., and Mitchell, H. K., *Genetics and Metabolism,* 2nd Ed., New York: J. Wiley & Sons, 1964.

QUESTIONS FOR DISCUSSION

2.1. Can sexually reproducing organisms reproduce asexually? Is the reverse true? Explain.

2.2. What are the similarities and differences between mitosis and meiosis?

2.3. Suppose the meiotic process had never evolved. What do you think would have been the consequence?

2.4. Certain unusual chromosomes are rings rather than rods. Could a ring chromosome, during meiosis, have any difficulty that a rod chromosome would not have? Explain.

2.5. How many bivalents are present at metaphase I in man? Corn? The garden pea?

2.6. Discuss the statement: During meiosis, each segment of a chromosome segregates independently of its homologous segment and of all other chromosome segments.

2.7. Argue against the hypothesis that the physical basis of genetic material lies in the chromosomes.

2.8. What do you suppose happens during meiosis in individuals possessing an odd number of chromosomes?

2.9. Suppose an animal has a diploid chromosome number of six. What proportion of all its gametes would receive replicas of all the centromeres originally derived from the father? From the mother? From either the father or mother? From both the father and mother?

2.10. What do you suppose is meant by the expression "first division segregation"? "Second division segregation"? If exchanges giving rise to chiasmata can occur at a variety of positions along the chromosome, under what circumstances can a given chromosomal segment undergo first division segregation? Second division segregation?

2.11. If you saw a single cell at metaphase, how could you tell whether the cell was undergoing mitosis, metaphase I, or metaphase II at the time it was fixed and stained?

2.12. What advantages do the following organisms offer for the study of cytology and/or of the genetic material: Drosophila? Corn? Neurospora?

2.13. What are the major differences between spermatogenesis and oogenesis in Drosophila?

2.14. Suppose a pair of originally identical homologous chromosomes having arms of equal length was changed permanently so that one gained a large knob at one end and the other a small knob at the opposite end. Draw the appearance of these new homologs (a) at mitotic prophase and (b) at diplonema. Draw the appearance of all the monads in part b as seen at telophase II.

2.15. Is the female sex cell of man or Drosophila ever haploid? Explain.

2.16. How does a monad at diplonema differ from the same monad at telophase II?

2.17. Can you suggest any functions which the polar nuclei in Drosophila oogenesis may serve?

2.18. Is mitosis in triploid endosperm expected to be normal? Why?

Chapter 3

SEGREGATION OF ALLELES

THE similarities and the differences in phenotypes, both among offspring and between them and their parents, have led us to postulate the existence of genetic material. Since this material is supposedly transmitted from generation to generation, we may be able to learn more about the transmissive properties of the genetic material by studying the traits that recur in lines of descent. This area may be called "transmission genetics."

We could investigate the genetic material either in lines reproducing asexually or in lines (like the beans already discussed) that reproduce sexually by self-fertilization. However, instead of taking either of these paths of investigation, both of which deal with pure lines, let us study the transmission genetics of organisms reproducing sexually by cross-fertilization. In the experimental work described henceforth, it can be assumed, *unless stated to the contrary,* that appropriate precautions have been taken to assure that the *phenotypic similarities and differences described are genotypic in origin* and are not due to variations in environmental conditions.

Different strains of a cross-fertilizing animal or plant often show phenotypic differences with respect to a given trait. For example, with respect to height, one line might be short and the other, tall; or with respect to color, one line might be red and the other, white. The question to be raised now is what will happen phenotypically in the offspring when two lines showing dif-

ferent alternatives for the same trait are crossed? Will such results tell us anything about the genetic material?

Consider some specific experiments that can be performed with the garden pea,[1] first with respect to what should be done and why it should be done. Then we can examine the results obtained and discuss what they reveal regarding the genetic material.

The garden pea is well suited for this work because it is simple and inexpensive to raise and has a generation length short enough to permit the study of a number of successive generations. Although garden peas are normally self-fertilizing, they can also be cross-fertilized; in fact, the experimenter can control all mating by simple and appropriate techniques. Moreover, there are numerous strains which differ phenotypically with regard to different traits. It is first necessary, of course, to self-fertilize each strain for several generations and check the phenotypes, to be sure that pure lines are being used.

Which pure lines should one cross together? Since we do not know what to expect in the offspring, we should avoid using lines whose traits, for environmental reasons, are so variable that a phenotype in one line also occurs in the other (which was the situation in the bean strains studied in Chapter 1). Such phenotypic overlaps could prevent us from deciding from the phenotypes what genotypes were present. Consequently, we should select for study only those strains showing a sharp, nonoverlapping, easily detected difference. For simplicity, we should use only strains having a single major difference. We should study only lines that can be successfully cross-fertilized in both directions; that is, the male gamete should be furnished sometimes by the one line and other times by the other line. Such *re-*

[1] Based upon the experiments of G. Mendel (see p. s-9).

ciprocal matings are desirable in order to determine whether it makes any phenotypic difference to the progeny upon which parental line the offspring start developing (note that pea seeds form on the maternal parent).

All crosses should also be fully fertile; that is, the parental lines should be hardy plants that grow vigorously and produce full sets of seed capable of growing to maturity, not only when self-fertilized but when crossed to each other reciprocally. If this precaution is not taken insufficient numbers of offspring may be obtained or, more important, the offspring observed may comprise a biased sample of those starting development. Deaths that occur between the time of fertilization and the time the phenotypic observations regarding the offspring are made may not occur at random. Differential viability for different genotypes could cause one to miss, or underestimate the frequency of, certain phenotypes; this would give misleading results with regard to genotypes, especially on our present view that the genetic material is transmitted at the time the new organism starts its existence, i.e., at the time of fertilization. Of course, accurate records of lineage and of parental and offspring phenotypes must be kept.

Two strains of garden pea, one producing colored flowers and the other colorless flowers, satisfy the prerequisites discussed. Cross-fertilizations are made reciprocally between pure-line colored flowers and pure-line colorless flowers, these individuals serving as the *parents of the first generation* (P_1). The offspring seeds are planted and the color of the flowers produced is scored. All the offspring, which comprise what may be called the *first filial generation* (F_1), are phenotypically uniform, having colored flowers just like one of the P_1. The F_1 results are the same for the reciprocal matings. In the discussion that follows in this and subsequent chapters it will be correct to assume that *all crosses were made reciprocally and produced identical results, unless a statement to the contrary is made*.

What can one conclude about the genetic material from these results? Let us use symbols as a shorthand method of representing the genetic material—C for the genetic material whose action produces colored flowers, present in all members of the colored-flowered pure line, and c for the genetic material producing colorless flowers, present in all the colorless-flowered pure-line individuals. All F_1 individuals must contain C since they produce colored flowers. What has happened to c? Has it failed to be transmitted?

More may be learned by permitting the F_1 plants with colored flowers to serve as P_2 (parents of the second generation) and reproduce by self-fertilization to yield F_2 progeny. When this is done, and sufficient numbers of F_2 are obtained from each P_2 plant, one finds among the offspring of every P_2 that some are colored and some are white. In terms of genetic material, these F_2 must carry, respectively, C or c. It is no surprise that some F_2 contain C, but where did the c come from? In these cases, one could at first suppose either that c arose spontaneously from some non-genetic origin or that C mutated to c. The first explanation can be bypassed in view of the previous assumptions (p. 10) that genetic material can arise only from pre-existing genetic material, and that this material is self-reproducing (self-replicating). The second explanation can be eliminated by the observation for the pure line containing C that mutations to c are thousands of times rarer than the occurrence of c among the F_2. If the $P_2(F_1)$ are genotypically like pure-line C individuals, as assumed, mutation cannot be the explanation for the difference in breeding behavior between P_1C and P_2C.

The results of the bean experiments in Chapter 1 are consistent with the view that the genetic material in any individual is a single indivisible unit. In the absence of a simpler explanation for the present findings with peas, it seems necessary to postulate that the *genetic material is not always composed of a single indivisible unit.* The appearance of c in F_2 can be explained by making the more complex assumption that each $P_2(F_1)$ individual contains not only C but c as well; in other words, that in some individuals the genetic material contains two units. Let us use the word *gene* to refer to *a unit or restricted portion of the genetic material.* But, if it is assumed that there is a pair of genes in each P_2, then all other individuals in our experiment must be assumed to have a pair of genes, too. For, in science, we adhere to *the law of parsimony (Occam's rule)*, which states that one must use the minimal number of hypotheses or assumptions to explain a given set of observations. Instead of having some individuals with paired genes and others without pairs, then, all are assumed to have a pair of genes in their genetic material. Accordingly, the two pure lines and the P_1 must have been CC and cc, and all F_1 must have been Cc. Those F_2 which are colorless must be cc.

Attention is called to the individuals in F_2 that are cc. These have colorless flowers phenotypically identical with those of the original colorless pure line used in the P_1. In fact, crosses of F_2 colorless individuals either with themselves or with any other colorless individual (F_2, or pure line) produce all colorless progeny. In other words, F_2 cc individuals are genotypically just as pure with respect to the trait under consideration as are pure-line individuals. This is true despite the fact that both c's in the F_2 had been carried in F_1 individuals in which C was the other member of the pair of genes. We conclude, therefore, that when c is transmitted to the F_2, it is uncontaminated, or untainted, by having been in the presence of C in the F_1, even though c had not been expressed in any noticeable way in

the phenotype of the F_1 individuals. We can generalize this conclusion and state that *the nature and transmission of any gene is uninfluenced by whatever its partner gene may be.* The members of a gene pair are said to be *alleles* (partner genes), a term also applied to alternative forms of a given gene.

Since each P_2 produced colored and colorless F_2 offspring, each P_2 had the genotype Cc composed necessarily of C from the CC P_1 and c from the cc P_1. This specifies that one and only one member of a pair of genes in a parent is transmitted to each offspring, so that *in the transmission process the members of a parental pair of genes must become separated, or segregated, from each other.* The paired, or diploid, status of the genes becomes unpaired, or haploid, during transmission; but diploidy is restored in the offspring because a haploid genotype is contributed to it by each parent.

Accepting the hypothesis that paired genes are segregated by the time they are transmitted to progeny, are the two alleles in a parent equally likely to be transmitted to offspring? The F_2 produced by self-fertilization of F_1 Cc demonstrate that both genes of a given individual are transmissible. Let us test the hypothesis that both members of this pair of alleles are equally transmissible. If so, the F_1 male parent (or part) would contribute C one half the time and c the other half; similarly the F_1 female parent (or part) would contribute C half the time and c the other half. Finally, assume diploidy is restored at random; that is, the haploid gene contributed to the offspring by one parent is uninfluenced by the haploid gene contributed by the other parent. Accordingly, an offspring that receives C from the male (50% of offspring) will have an equal chance of receiving C or c from the female, so that of all offspring 25% will be CC and 25% Cc. Those offspring receiving c from the male (50% of offspring) will

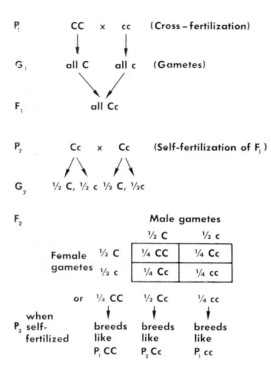

P_1 CC × cc   (Cross–fertilization)

G_1 all C   all c   (Gametes)

F_1 all Cc

P_2 Cc × Cc   (Self-fertilization of F_1)

G_2 ½ C, ½ c   ½ C, ½c

F_2 Male gametes

		½ C	½ c
Female gametes	½ C	¼ CC	¼ Cc
	½ c	¼ Cc	¼ cc

or   ¼ CC   ½ Cc   ¼ cc

when
P_3 self-
fertilized
            breeds   breeds   breeds
            like   like   like
            P_1 CC P_2 Cc P_1 cc

FIGURE 3–1. *Genotypic model proposed to explain the phenotypic results of certain crosses involving colored and colorless flowers in pea plants.*

also have an equal chance of receiving *C* or *c* from the female, so that the contribution to all the offspring genotypes will be 25% *Cc* and 25% *cc* from this source. On this basis the F_2 would be predicted to contain 25% of individuals that are *CC*, 50% that are *Cc*, and 25% *cc*. This expectation can be expressed as relative frequencies in several ways: ¼ *CC* : ½ *Cc* : ¼ *cc*, or 1 *CC* : 2 *Cc* : 1 *cc,* or .25 *CC* : .50 *Cc* : .25 *cc.* As already reasoned *CC* and *Cc* are phenotypically indistinguishable, having colored flowers, so that phenotypically 75% of the F_2 would be colored and 25% would be colorless. What is their relative frequency in the F_2 actually observed?

Although a penny has in theory a 50% chance of falling head up and a 50% chance of falling tail up, obviously a sufficiently large number of tosses is required to obtain approximately 50% heads, 50% tails. Similarly, an accurate test of the theoretical expectation of 75% colored and 25% colorless will be obtained only if a sufficiently large sample of offspring is scored. Instead of scoring the offspring of just one P_2, then, the results for the offspring of all P_2 should be totalled. When this is done, the actual F_2 results (among 929 plants, 75.9% are colored and 24.1% colorless) are very close to the expectation.

It should be emphasized that the concept of paired, untaintable, segregating genes has not depended upon obtaining any particular phenotypic ratio for the F_2. Granting these characteristics of the genetic material, obtaining or not obtaining the phenotypic ratio ¾ colored to ¼ colorless merely tests the suppositions (1) that there is an equal chance for offspring to receive either haploid product of gene segregation from a parent, and (2) that the haploid products from different parents come together at random to restore the diploid condition.

If all the assumptions so far made about genetic material are correct, the 75% of F_2 that are colored should have one of two genotypes: ⅓ of them should be *CC*, breeding like pure-line *CC* individuals, and ⅔ should be *Cc*, breeding like the F_1 *Cc* individuals. Accordingly, each F_2 colored plant is permitted to self-fertilize and, in fact, very nearly ⅓ produce only colored F_3, whereas ⅔ produce F_3 of both colored and colorless types. The theoretical genotypic ratio expected in the F_2, ¼ *CC* : ½ *Cc* : ¼ *cc*, is, in this way, fully confirmed in experience. The gene model proposed to explain these phenotypic results is summarized in Figure 3–1. It is convenient to introduce two additional terms at this time. A *homozygote* is an individual that is pure with respect to the paired genes in question, like *CC* or *cc*, whereas a *heterozygote,* or *hybrid,* is impure in this respect, like *Cc.*

An independent test of all the genetic hypotheses presented so far can be made in the following way. F_1 colored plants are crossed with colorless plants, this cross being symbolized genetically: $F_1 Cc \times cc$. As the result of segregation half of the offspring should receive *C* and half *c* from the *Cc* parent, and all should receive *c* from the *cc* parent. The genotypes of the offspring from this cross should be, theoretically, *Cc* 50% of the time and *cc* 50% of the time, and the expected phenotypic ratio should be, therefore, $\frac{1}{2}$ colored : $\frac{1}{2}$ colorless. This expectation is fulfilled experimentally (85 colored : 81 colorless).

Are the principles just established generally applicable? Thus far they apply strictly only to the genetic determination of flower color in garden peas. All these ideas can be tested six additional times, using six other traits in garden peas, each of which occurs in two clearcut alternatives and fulfills the prerequisites for suitability already described. In each case, when two appropriate pure lines are crossed, the F_1 hybrids produced are phenotypically uniform, as before. Moreover, self-fertilization of the F_1 produces F_2 in approximately the expected $1:2:1$ genotypic ratio.

Recall that the *Cc* phenotype is indistinguishable from *CC*. In *Cc* individuals the phenotypic expression of *c* is masked by the expression of *C*. The ability of a gene to express itself phenotypically in the presence of a different allele is described in terms of *dominance*. In the case of flower color, *C* produces a *dominant* effect when present with *c*, whose effect is, accordingly, *recessive*. It should be emphasized that our concept of the gene does not depend upon the occurrence or nonoccurrence of dominance. Indeed, testing our genetic postulates has been made more complicated by the fact that the

effect of *C* is, for all intents and purposes, completely dominant to that of *c*. The F_1 *Cc* expressed only *C*, and the presence of *c* was detected only by breeding F_1 individuals, and observing *cc* progeny. Only by breeding the colored F_2 were we able to determine that $\frac{1}{3}$ were *CC* and $\frac{2}{3}$ *Cc*. Dominance, then, refers to the phenotypic expression of genes in heterozygous condition and has no relation to their integrity, replication, or mechanism of transmission. For convenience, *dominant* and *recessive* will be used hereafter to refer to genes, but the precise meaning of these terms should always be kept in mind.

As mentioned, six other traits have been used to test the general applicability of the gene concept. In each case it happened that one allele was dominant to the alternative one in the hybrid. It is tempting to conclude that dominance is a universal phenomenon since it was found to hold for each of seven different traits based on genes in the garden pea. Before making this decision, however, examine the results with regard to feather color of breeding certain chickens. Here black $\times$ white produces blue-gray F_1. Mating two blue-gray F_1 produces in F_2 $\frac{1}{4}$ black, $\frac{1}{2}$ blue-gray, and $\frac{1}{4}$ white. In this case complete dominance does not occur, so that complete dominance is not a rule for the phenotypic expression of alleles in heterozygotes. Whenever dominance is incomplete or absent, genotypes can be stated with certainty from a knowledge of phenotypes.

Cross-fertilization made it possible to show that genes occur as pairs, which become unpaired after segregation, then recombine to form pairs in the offspring. In other words, the view that the genetic material contains separable paired units is based upon the recombination which these units undergo in cross-fertilizing species. The meaning of the term *genetic recombination* ought to be considered at this point. The genetic units themselves are not required to undergo novel changes (mutations) when undergoing recombination. That is, the types of genes present in a genetically recombinant individual existed before recombination. Given an individual whose gene pair is *AA'*, segregation followed by self-fertilization may produce *AA'* again. This genotype is not considered to be a genetic recombination, but rather a *reconstitution* of the original arrangement of the units. The self-fertilization under discussion may also produce *AA* or *A'A'*. These represent two new genetic combinations relative to the parental combination, and are considered to be genetic recombinations. Accordingly, when events lead to the production of "old" combinations and "new" combinations of genes, only the latter type of grouping is called genetic recombination. This usage is reasonable in view of the importance that new combinations have for our understanding of genetic material (it was possible to derive the principle of gene segregation only because new combinations of genes were produced via sexual reproduction). Ac-

cordingly, genetic recombination should be identified with any reassortment or regrouping of genes which results in a new arrangement of them. Any process, like segregation or fertilization, that has the potential of producing new arrangements of genetic units is, therefore, a mechanism for genetic recombination.

The phenotypic results of the experiments discussed in Chapter 1 led us to hypothesize the existence of genetic material which is self-replicating, mutable, and transmissible. The pea plant experiments reveal that the genetic material can be divided into a pair of units by means of the operation or technique of genetic recombination. Techniques or operations other than recombination can be employed to study the nature of the genetic material. Should other operations also divide the total genetic material into units, this would not necessarily mean that the units revealed by different operations are equivalent. Thus, to use a nongenetic analogy, a book (equivalent to the total genetic material) can be described operationally in terms of words, letters, numbers, pages, illustrations, and so forth. Each operation reveals something about the book, but the different units by which it is described are necessarily neither identical nor mutually inclusive.

What bearing has the discovery of segregating alleles upon the hypothesis that the chromosomes represent genetic material? Both genes and genomes are unpaired in gametes and paired in zygotes. Can a genome be the physical basis of a gene? Though the gametes contain a single genome, this is usually constituted (ignoring the exchanges leading to chiasmata, for the moment) of replicas of some maternal and some paternal chromosomes. Since segregated genes are uncontaminated by their former alleles, being just as pure in the gametes as they were when they entered the organism at fertilization, one can reject the

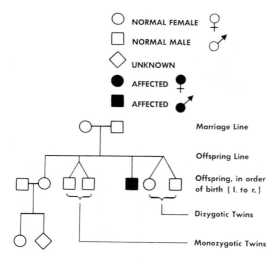

FIGURE 3–2. *Symbols used in human pedigrees.*

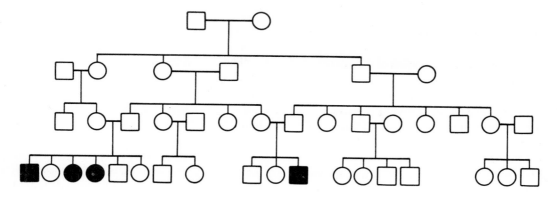

FIGURE 3–3.   *A pedigree of albinism in man.*

hypothesis that a genome is the material equivalent of a gene.   Nor can an entire chromosome be identified with a gene, since any given gametic chromosome is typically constituted of some maternally-derived and some paternally-derived parts, as a consequence of the exchanges leading to chiasmata.   However, the possibility still remains that the gene is associated with a particular segment of a chromosome which is so short that it cannot undergo an exchange leading to a chiasma with a corresponding segment on a homologous chromosome.   Such a segment would always retain its pure maternal or pure paternal constitution after meiosis.   Accordingly, the maximal size of such an uncontaminable segment would equal the maximal size of the gene.

* Segregation of Alleles in Man

The genetic principles discovered in garden peas should also hold equally well for any other sexually reproducing species, including man.   Because we naturally have great interest in ourselves, let us consider some human traits which may be based upon the action of a single pair of genes.   The study of human genetics is complicated by the fact that, unlike other species of plants and ani-

* Throughout this book, the asterisk indicates an optional chapter or section.

mals, our species is not bred experimentally.   Because of this scientific difficulty special methods of investigation have to be employed.   These include the *pedigree, family, population,* and *twin* methods.   The present discussion deals primarily with the first two of these methods.

The pedigree method uses phenotypic records of families (family trees or genealogies) extending over several generations.   In recording pedigrees certain symbols are used by convention (Figure 3–2).   In a pedigree chart a square or ♂ represents a male, a circle or ♀ represents a female; filled-in symbols represent persons affected by the anomaly under discussion.   In contrast, the family method utilizes the phenotypes only of parents and their offspring; that is, it uses data that span only one generation.

Albinism, or lack of melanin pigment, is a rare disease which occurs approximately once per 20,000 births.   Studies of families, and of pedigrees like the one in Figure 3–3, yield the following facts, each of which is discussed relative to the hypothesis that albinism occurs in homozygotes for a recessive gene, *a*.   Alternative hypotheses that albinism is due to a completely or a partially dominant gene soon prove untenable:

1. Both of the parents of albinos may be

nonalbino, i.e., normally pigmented. This may be explained by the occurrence of a homozygous albino child (aa) from the marriage of two nonalbino heterozygotes ($Aa \times Aa$).

2. The trait appears most frequently in progeny sharing a common ancestor. In Sweden and Japan, although the percentage of all marriages between cousins is less than 5% in the general population, it is 20 to 50% among the parents of albino children. Since albinos are rare, so is the a gene. Accordingly, the chance of obtaining homozygous, aa, individuals is relatively slight if the parents are unrelated, because even when the first parent is Aa or aa, the second parent is most likely to be AA. On the other hand, if once again the first parent is Aa or aa, marriage with a related individual makes it much more likely that the second parent carries an a received from the ancestor held in common with the first parent.

3. What relative frequencies of nonalbino and albino children are expected when one tallies all the children in two-child families in which albinism appears in the progeny even though both parents are nonalbino? Based on the hypothesis under consideration, the parents must be $Aa \times Aa$. From such a marriage, the chance that a given child is nonalbino is ¾ and that it is albino ¼. Each child produced from such a marriage has these same chances for nonalbinism and albinism, chances which are independent of the genotypes (or phenotypes) of the children preceding or following it in the family. Accordingly, of all two-child families whose parents are Aa, ¾ have the first child nonalbino, and of these ¾ also have the second child nonalbino. Thus, $\frac{9}{16}$ of all two-child families from heterozygous parents are excluded from our sample, since both children are normally pigmented. Our sample includes the following, however: families whose first child is normal (¾) and second child is albino (¼), making up $\frac{3}{16}$ (¼ of

¾) of all two-child families; families where the reverse is true (¾ of ¼), comprising another $\frac{3}{16}$ of all two-child families; and families in which both children are albino (¼ of ¼), which make up $\frac{1}{16}$ of all two-child families. On the average, then, every seven albino-containing families scored should contain six normal children (three from each of the two kinds of families containing one albino) and eight albinos (three from each of the two kinds of families containing one albino, and two from each family containing two albinos), so that the ratio expected is 3:4 as nonalbino:albino. The ratio actually observed closely approximates the expected one.

The observed proportions of nonalbino and albino children in families of three, or of four, or of more children from normal parents also fit the expected proportions calculated in a similar manner.

4. Marriages between two albinos produce only albino children, as expected genetically from $aa \times aa$.

5. Twins arising from the same zygote (*monozygotic* or *identical* twins) are either both albino or nonalbino. Since ordinarily such twins are genetically identical, both are expected to be normal, AA or Aa, or albino, aa. Twins arising from different zygotes (*dizygotic, nonidentical,* or *fraternal* twins) are no more likely to be the same with respect to albinism than any two children of the same parents.

These evidences offer clear proof that an albino person is usually homozygous recessive for a single pair of segregating genes.

The anomaly of *woolly hair* is a rare trait in Norwegians. After studying pedigrees, woolly hair can be attributed to the presence of a rare dominant gene, represented by W. When woolly-haired individuals (Ww) marry normal-haired individuals (ww), it is expected and found that approximately 50% of children have woolly hair and 50% have normal hair. Note that the affected parent is represented as a heterozygote. Because the trait is so rare, and because, barring mutation, both parents of a homozygous *WW* child would have to have woolly hair, *WW* probably does not occur.

Finally, consider the genetic basis for certain kinds of anemia. Two special kinds occur among native or emigrated Italians. One type, severe and usually fatal in childhood, is called *thalassemia major* or *Cooley's anemia*; the other type, a more moderate anemia, is called *thalassemia minor* or *microcytemia*. Pedigree and family studies show that both parents of t. major children have t. minor, and all the data support the hypothesis that individuals with t. major are homozygotes (*tt*) for a pair of genes, and that persons with t. minor are heterozygotes (*Tt*) for this gene. More than 100,000 people in Italy have been classified as *TT*, *Tt*, or *tt*.

Notice that in the case of thalassemia neither *T* nor *t* is completely dominant (nor completely recessive).

Although with respect to phenotypic expression the relation between the alleles in the heterozygote may involve complete, partial, or no dominance, it should be recalled that gene action ordinarily has no effect upon either the integrity of the genes or their segregation and recombination.

One can study a large number of other human traits by the pedigree and family methods and apply the principles known about genes to explain the data genetically, using the simplest suitable explanations in much the same way as was illustrated here for albinism and other traits. Sometimes, unfortunately, the data are insufficient and the investigator is left with several equally probable genetic explanations.

SUMMARY AND CONCLUSIONS

The gene is a unit or restricted portion of the total genetic material as discovered via any operational procedure. The genes discovered in the present chapter were revealed by recombination.

Genes occur in pairs. When they are transmitted in sexual reproduction the members of a pair segregate so that any offspring receives only one member of a pair from each parent. The gene is uncontaminated by the type of gene that is its partner prior to segregation, and enters the new individual uninfluenced by the allele being contributed from the other parent. The hypothesis that the chromosomes comprise or carry the genetic material can be made more specific—a recombinationally detected gene may be represented by a short chromosome segment within which an exchange leading to a chiasma cannot occur.

Data furnished in pedigree and family studies provide evidence that a number of human traits are based upon the action of a pair of segregating genes.

REFERENCES

Gates, R. R., *Human Genetics,* 2 Vols., New York: Macmillan, 1946.

Mendel, G., 1866. "Experiments in Plant Hybridization," translated in Sinnott, E. W., Dunn, L. C., and Dobzhansky, Th., *Principles of Genetics,* 5th Ed., New York: McGraw-Hill, 1958, pp. 419–443; also in Dodson, E. O., *Genetics, the Modern Science of Heredity,* Philadelphia: Saunders, 1956, pp. 285–311; also in *Classic Papers in Genetics,* Peters, J. A. (Ed.), Englewood Cliffs, N.J.: Prentice-Hall, 1959, pp. 1–20.

Mohr, O. L., "Woolly Hair a Dominant Mutant Character in Man," J. Hered., 23:345–352, 1932.

Neel, J. V., and Schull, W. J., *Human Heredity,* University of Chicago Press, 1954, pp. 83–86, 89–91, 240–241.

Stern, C., *Principles of Human Genetics,* 2nd Ed., San Francisco: Freeman, 1960.

QUESTIONS FOR DISCUSSION

3.1. How would you recognize a line of garden peas that had become genotypically pure for a given trait?

3.2. Criticize the assumption that genes come only from pre-existing genes and do not arise *de novo.*

3.3. Differentiate between phenocopies and phenotypic overlaps.

3.4. Does a parent lose its own genetic material when it is transmitted to progeny? Defend your answer.

3.5. Is it necessary to assume that genes are able to reproduce themselves? Explain.

3.6. List all the assumptions required to explain a 3:1 ratio in F_2 on a genetic basis.

3.7. A mating of a black-coated with a white-coated guinea pig produces all black offspring. Two such offspring when mated produce mostly black but some white progeny. Explain these results genetically.

3.8. A cross of two pink-flowered plants produces offspring whose flowers are red, pink, or white. Defining your genetic symbols, give all the different kinds of genotypes involved and the phenotypes they represent.

3.9. What operation was employed in studying the gene in the present chapter? Define a gene in terms of size.

3.10. Discuss the role of dominance in the study of genes.

3.11. Do organisms that reproduce asexually have genes? Explain your answer.

3.12. What relation has a gene to the phenotypic effect with which it is associated?

3.13. Do you agree with the statement on p. 33 that a cross between two colorless pea plants results in "all colorless progeny"? Why?

3.14. Throughout this book the use of the word "heredity" and its derivatives has been avoided. Why do you think this is, or is not, justified?

3.15. What is the difference between the pedigree and family methods of investigation?

3.16. What evidence is there that pigmentation (albinism vs. nonalbinism) is due to genes that are segregating?

3.17. Two nonalbinos marry and have an albino child. What is the chance that the next child is albino? Nonalbino? That of the next two children, both are albinos? Nonalbinos? One albino and one nonalbino?

3.18. What proportion of three-child families, whose parents are both heterozygous for albinism, have no albino children? All albino children? At least one albino child?

3.19. Would you conclude that the gene for woolly hair is completely dominant to nonwoolly hair? Explain.

3.20. What are the similarities and differences regarding the segregation of genes and of chromosomes?

3.21. If the genetic material is in the chromosome, is it necessary to assume that the members of a gene pair occupy exactly corresponding positions in the two homologs? Why?

3.22. If a mitotic chromosome normally contains two identical chromatids, can we decide whether each chromosome contains one gene or an identical pair of genes? Justify your answer.

3.23. In what respect do you suppose that a sample of two-child families may be biased? How would you attempt to avoid this error?

3.24. The electron microscope shows that the sperm heads of some organisms contain a mass of uniformly thin threads. Do such cases offer evidence against the retention of the integrity of chromosomes or of genes? Why?

3.25. Differentiate between the genetic recombinations that occur at the time of fertilization and at the time of meiosis.

3.26. What is the difference between the study of genetics at the cellular and at the organismal levels?

3.27. Describe the environment of a single gene.

3.28. A lack of neuromuscular coordination, *ataxia,* occurs in the pedigrees of certain families in Sweden. How can you explain that one form of this rare anomaly occurs in certain families where the parents are apparently unrelated, and another form occurs in other families where the parents are first cousins?

3.29. What bearing have the following facts relative to the generality of the phenomenon of dominance?

When pure lines of smooth-seeded plants and shrunken-seeded plants are crossed, the F_1 seeds are all smooth. Microscopic examination reveals that the margins of the starch granules in the seeds are smooth in the smooth P_1, highly serrated or nicked in the shrunken P_1, and slightly serrated in all the F_1.

Chapter 4

INDEPENDENT RECOMBINATION BY NONALLELES

IN THE preceding chapter we discussed the transmission genetics of alternatives for a single trait and found that a single pair of genes could explain the data in each case. But what is the genetic unit of transmission when two or more different traits are followed simultaneously in breeding experiments? The answer may be found in the results of some additional experiments performed with the garden pea.[1] Other studies show that seed shape and seed color, like the flower color trait described in Chapter 3, are each due to a single pair of genes. That is, a P_1 of pure-line round × pure-line wrinkled seeds gives round F_1, round being dominant. Self-fertilizing the F_1 round produces F_2 in the proportion of 3 round:1 wrinkled. Similarly, a P_1 of pure-line yellow × pure-line green seeds gives yellow F_1, yellow being dominant, and self-fertilization of the yellow F_1 gives 3 yellow:1 green in F_2.

What actually happens in a crossing of individuals that differ simultaneously with regard to both seed shape and seed color? A round yellow strain is crossed with a wrinkled green strain, these strains being available as pure lines. In F_1 only round yellow seeds are obtained (Figure 4–1). This result is what we would expect had we been studying shape and color of seeds separately. In this case, there is no phenotypic

[1] Based upon experiments of G. Mendel.

42

effect of the dominance of one trait upon the phenotypic expression of the other trait.

Self-fertilization of the round yellow F_1 gives offspring which, when counted in sufficiently large numbers, occur approximately in the relative frequencies of 9 round yellow:3 round green:3 wrinkled yellow:1 wrinkled green. Notice that segregation and recombination are involved for each trait, as revealed in F_2 by approximately 12 round:4 wrinkled and by about 12 yellow:4 green. In this generation also there is no effect of one trait upon the recombinational behavior of the genetic material for a different trait.

From these results, what else can we decide regarding the gene? Until now, we have been able to explain all the experimental data on the basis of only a single pair of genes, as if the total genetic material of a diploid cell is divisible into only two genes, any one gene having numerous different alleles, each one having effects on many different traits. To continue to consider that each P_1 individual in the present

P_1	Round Yellow	x	Wrinkled Green
F_1		ALL Round Yellow	
P_2	F_1 Round Yellow	x	F_1 Round Yellow

F_2			
PHENOTYPE	**NUMBER**	**RATIO**	
Round Yellow	315	9.06	
Round Green	101	2.9	
Wrinkled Yellow	108	3.1	
Wrinkled Green	32	0.9	

FIGURE 4–1. *Phenotypic results from studying two traits simultaneously.*

case carries but a single pair of genes, each gene must have two simultaneous effects, one on seed shape and the other on seed color. The results obtained are consistent with this requirement in the following respect: the F_1 are round yellow, and the F_2 give a 3:1 ratio for yellow vs. green and also for round vs. wrinkled. According to this hypothesis, the F_2 should be of only two types—3 round yellow:1 wrinkled green. But in F_2 not only are these grandparental (P_1) combinations found, but two new, recombinational classes of offspring appear, namely, round green and wrinkled yellow! Apparently, then, *what is genetically transmitted is not composed of a single pair of indivisible units, but is composed of pairs of units, or genes, with each gene pair capable of undergoing segregation separately.*

Let us assume, therefore, that each sexually reproducing organism contains more than one pair of genes. In the present case, let R (round) and r (wrinkled) be the alleles of one pair of genes and Y (yellow) and y (green) be the alleles of the second pair. The P_1, then, would be *RR YY* (round yel-

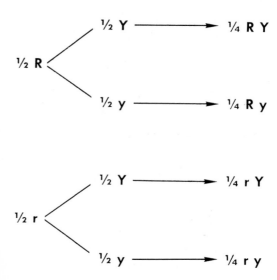

FIGURE 4–3. *Genotypes of gametes formed by a dihybrid, Rr Yy, undergoing independent segregation.*

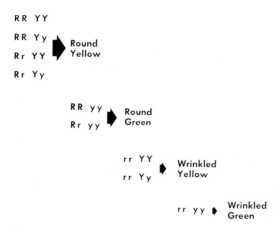

FIGURE 4–2. *Expected genotypes and phenotypes in F_2 following segregation.*

low) and *rr yy* (wrinkled green). Each pair of genes would undergo segregation so that a gamete would contain only one member of each pair. In this manner the former parent would produce only *RY* gametes and the latter only *ry*, and all F_1 would be *Rr Yy* (round yellow), as observed.

Based on the current hypothesis, the gametes formed by the F_1 would contain either R or r, and, moreover, would contain either Y or y. Since the F_2 show that R and Y do not always go together into a gamete, nor do r and y, there must be four genotypes possible in gametes, *RY, Ry, rY, ry*. Since these possible haploid genotypes will be found both in male and in female gametes, it is expected that the F_2 would contain the diploid genotypes and their corresponding phenotypes indicated in Figure 4–2. Note that nine different genotypes are possible in F_2, four giving the round yellow phenotype, two giving round green, two wrinkled yellow,

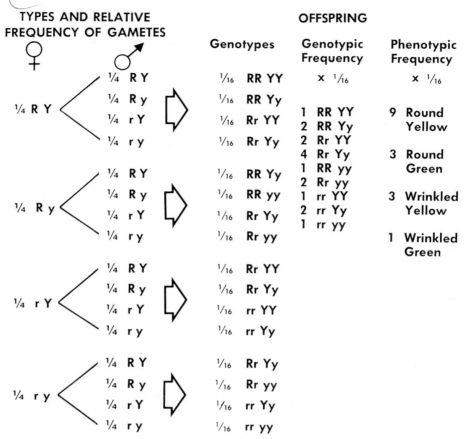

TYPES AND RELATIVE FREQUENCY OF GAMETES			**OFFSPRING**			
♀	♂		Genotypes	Genotypic Frequency	Phenotypic Frequency	

FIGURE 4–4. *Independent segregation and random fertilization in a cross between identical dihybrids.*

and one wrinkled green. This is consistent with the four phenotypes found in F₂, substantiating our hypothesis that the genetic material transmitted in a gamete is composed of subunits, each of which has the properties of a nonallelic gene.

How can we account for the observation that the F₂ phenotypes occurred in the relative proportions of 9:3:3:1, respectively? This question can be answered by making the additional assumption that the *segregation of the members of one pair of genes occurs independently of the segregation of* *the members of another pair of genes.* According to this assumption (see Figure 4–3) half of all gametes of *Rr Yy* receive *R*, of which half will carry *Y* and half *y*; the other half of all gametes receive *r*, of which half will carry *Y* and half *y*. Thus, the male gamete population in the P₂ will be 25% each *RY*, *Ry*, *rY*, and *ry*. The P₂ also produce female gametes of the same four genotypes in the same relative frequencies. Since fertilization has already been assumed to occur at random, the F₂ expected are as shown in Figure 4–4.

The branching track in Figure 4–4 can be read from the top: ¼ of female gametes are *RY* and are fertilized ¼ of the time by *RY* male gametes (producing $\frac{1}{16}$ of all offspring as *RR YY*); ¼ of the time fertilization is by *Ry* male gametes (so that $\frac{1}{16}$ of all offspring are *RR Yy* from this origin), etc. Summing up like classes, the kinds and relative numbers of genotypes and of phenotypes are obtained as shown in the figure. The observed ratio (Figure 4–1) is in excellent agreement with the expected one.

The branching track may be used to obtain the 9:3:3:1 phenotypic ratio more simply. We know that crossing together two identical *monohybrids* (heterozygotes for only one of all the gene pairs under consideration) yields a 3:1 phenotypic ratio of dominant:recessive trait. If the recombinational activity of two pairs of genes is independent, both pairs being heterozygous and showing dominance, then the two independently produced 3:1 ratios may be combined in the progeny as shown in Figure 4–5. This may be read: among the offspring, the ¾ which are round (because of segregation, random fertilization, and the dominance of *R* in the cross *Rr × Rr*) will also be yellow ¾ of the time and green ¼ of the time (because of segregation, random fertilization, and the dominance of *Y* in the cross *Yy × Yy*); so, of all progeny $\frac{9}{16}$ will be round yellow and $\frac{3}{16}$ round green, etc.

We see, then, that independent segregation by two pairs of genes results in the formation of gametes whose gene combinations, new and old, are in equal frequency. In the present case, the F_1 *dihybrid* (heterozygote for two of all the gene pairs under consideration) received both *R* and *Y* from one parent and both *r* and *y* from the other, its gametic recombinations being *Ry* and *rY*. Had the F_1 dihybrid received *Ry* from one parent and *rY* from the other, the gametic recombinations would have been *RY* and *ry*, and the old combinations *Ry* and *rY*. Regardless of how the genes enter the individual, then, the dihybrid forms four, equally frequent, genetically different gametes.

The types and frequencies of gametes formed by the *Rr Yy* dihybrid can be determined more easily after mating it with a *double recessive* individual, i.e., an individual homozygous recessive for both pairs of genes concerned. In the cross of *Rr Yy* by *rr yy*, the double recessive parent produces only *ry* gametes whereas the dihybrid is expected to produce four different and equally frequent types: *RY*, *Ry*, *rY*, *ry*. Accordingly, finding among the offspring of this cross (Figure 4–6) that very nearly 25% are round yellow (55 offspring), 25% round green (51 offspring), 25% wrinkled yellow (49 offspring), and 25% wrinkled green (52 offspring) is a direct confirmation both

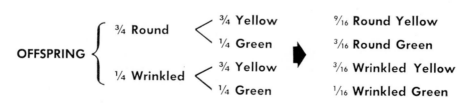

PARENTS   Rr Yy x Rr Yy

OFFSPRING
- ¾ **Round**
  - ¾ Yellow
  - ¼ Green
- ¼ **Wrinkled**
  - ¾ Yellow
  - ¼ Green

- $\frac{9}{16}$ **Round Yellow**
- $\frac{3}{16}$ **Round Green**
- $\frac{3}{16}$ **Wrinkled Yellow**
- $\frac{1}{16}$ **Wrinkled Green**

FIGURE 4–5. *Phenotypic results of a cross between identical dihybrids.*

GAMETES		GENOTYPES	PHENOTYPES
♀	♂		
¼ R Y	1 r y	¼ Rr Yy	¼ Round Yellow
¼ R y	1 r y	¼ Rr yy	¼ Round Green
¼ r Y	1 r y	¼ rr Yy	¼ Wrinkled Yellow
¼ r y	1 r y	¼ rr yy	¼ Wrinkled Green

FIGURE 4–6. *Test cross of the* F_1 *dihybrid* (Rr Yy) *with the double recessive individual* (rr yy).

of segregation by the members of a single pair of genes and of independent segregation by different pairs of genes.

Whenever one is dealing with complete dominance, a cross to an individual recessive for the pairs of genes involved will always serve to identify the genotype of the other parent, since the phenotypic types and frequencies of the offspring will correspond to the genotypic types and frequencies occurring in the gametes of the latter. This kind of cross is, therefore, called a *test cross,* or a *backcross* when one of the parents in the series of crosses is homozygous recessive for the genes under study.

We are now in a position to return to a consideration of the material basis for genes. If one gene pair is to be associated physically with the corresponding short regions in a pair of homologous chromosomes, within which an exchange leading to a chiasma cannot occur, the question is, where, in relation to one pair of genes, is a second pair located? Two possibilities occur—either both pairs are on the same chromosome pair or they are on different, nonhomologous chromosome pairs. Consider the latter assumption—that different pairs of genes are located on different pairs of chromosomes. If this is true, then there are several differ-

ent arrangements that the parts of different pairs of chromosomes may take relative to each other at metaphase I of meiosis (Figure 4–7).

It has been established that different pairs of chromosomes arrive at metaphase I independently of each other. Moreover, it is entirely reasonable that the orientation toward the poles, of the centromeres in tetrads at metaphase I and in dyads at metaphase II, is not influenced by the presence or absence of chiasmata or exchanges. If, as in Case A (Figure 4–7), no exchange occurs— and, hence, no chiasma is formed—between the centromere and gene pair *Aa* or between the centromere and gene pair *Bb*, alignments I and II, being equally frequent, will result in four different, equally frequent types of gametes at the end of meiosis. The same result is also obtained either when there is a chiasma between the centromere and the gene in question in one tetrad but not the other (Case B), or when a chiasma occurs in each of the tetrads (Case C). Both in Case CI and CII the dyads can orient to the poles at metaphase II in four equally likely arrangements, with the same net result, four equally frequent types of gametes. Therefore, independent segregation of different pairs of chromosomes can serve as

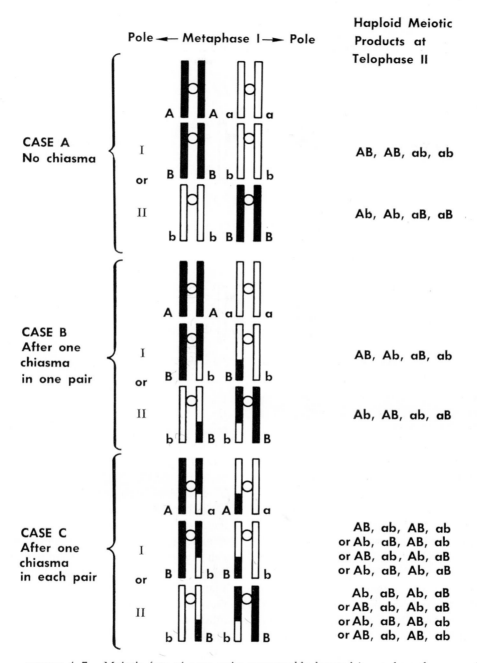

FIGURE 4–7. *Meiotic fate of gene pairs presumably located in nonhomologous pairs of chromosomes. Note that when all alternatives in Case CI (and II) are considered AB = ab = Ab = aB.*

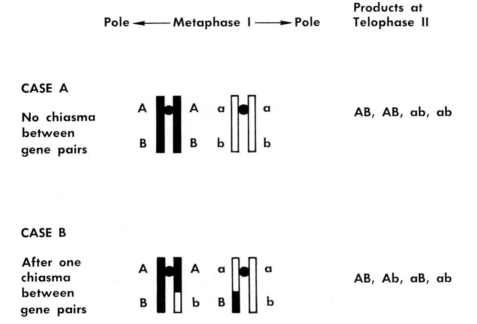

FIGURE 4–8. *Meiotic fate of gene pairs presumably located in the same pair of chromosomes.*

the physical basis for independent segregation of different pairs of genes, regardless of chiasma formation.

Let us examine next the consequences of assuming that *A* and *B* are on the same chromosome, and *a* and *b* are on the homologous chromosome of the pair (Figure 4–8). When no chiasma occurs between the two different pairs of genes, Case A, only the old (maternal and paternal) combinations are found in the gametes. When such a chiasma occurs, Case B, four gametic classes are produced with equal frequency (two old and two new combinational types). But, unless every tetrad has a chiasma in the region between the nonalleles, the number of old gene combinations found among the gametes will exceed the new combinations. Although a tetrad usually contains one or several chiasmata, there are numerous points along the chromosome where an exchange leading to a chiasma might occur. An additional hypothesis would be needed if each tetrad were required to form a chiasma within a given interval, such as between *A* and *B*. Moreover, we have no knowledge as to the *genic interval,* or the distance between nonalleles presumed to be in the same chromosome. Accordingly, we shall neglect, for the time being, the possibility that nonalleles in the same chromosome pair can form old and new combinations with equal frequency—that is, we shall assume that two pairs of genes which do so, and are therefore segregating independently of each other, are located in different pairs of chromosomes. Evidence consistent with this assumption is obtained from studies with garden peas. From the breeding behavior of hybrids for two or more gene pairs, it is possible to establish the existence of seven different pairs of genes (each happening to

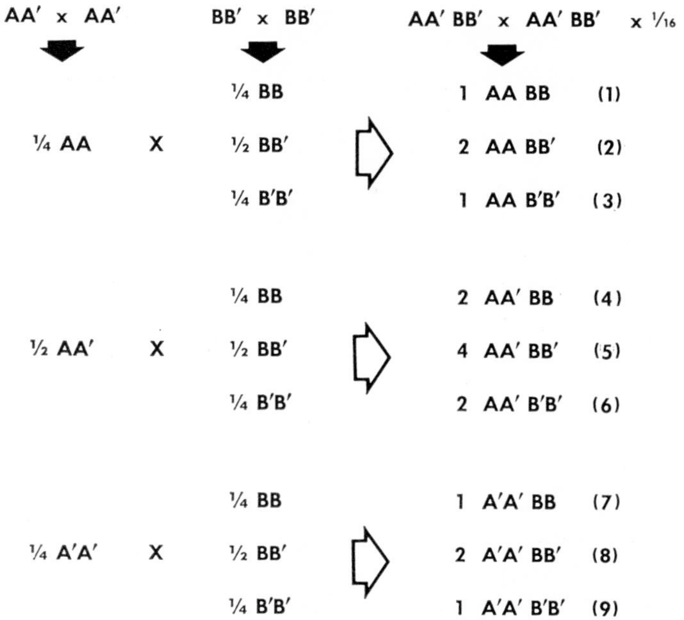

AA' × AA'		BB' × BB'		AA' BB' × AA' BB' × 1/16	
		¼ BB		1 AA BB	(1)
¼ AA	X	½ BB'	⟹	2 AA BB'	(2)
		¼ B'B'		1 AA B'B'	(3)
		¼ BB		2 AA' BB	(4)
½ AA'	X	½ BB'	⟹	4 AA' BB'	(5)
		¼ B'B'		2 AA' B'B'	(6)
		¼ BB		1 A'A' BB	(7)
¼ A'A'	X	½ BB'	⟹	2 A'A' BB'	(8)
		¼ B'B'		1 A'A' B'B'	(9)

FIGURE 4–9. *Genotypic recombination frequencies.*

show dominance in the hybrid condition), each pair seeming to segregate independently of all the others. Since the garden pea possesses a diploid number of seven pairs of chromosomes, there are enough chromosome pairs for each pair of genes to be located on a different pair of chromosomes.

* Different Phenotypic Ratios [2]

A monohybrid may show the phenotypic effects of only one allele, some of the effects of both alleles, or the complete effects of both alleles. These phenotypic consequences have already been designated as complete, partial, and no dominance, respectively. In the garden pea experiments already discussed, complete dominance produced the 3:1 phenotypic ratio obtained from a cross between identical monohybrids. This necessitated breeding the offspring with the dominant phenotype in order to identify the 1:2:1 genotypic ratio predicted from such crosses. Had no dominance or partial

[2] See W. Bateson (1909).

dominance occurred, the phenotypic and genotypic ratios would have been identical. Nevertheless, in all cases the recombining genes retained their individuality, and the specific ratios observed depended only upon the *dominance relation* within the gene pair —that is, the relation between the expression of one allele and that of its partner.

Complete dominance also has no influence upon the individuality or segregation of nonallelic pairs of genes. Although the genotypic ratio expected from crossing two particular dihybrids has already been derived (Figure 4–4), let us rederive this ratio, employing more general symbols for the genes, using the branching-track method in a slightly different way. Let A and A' be one pair of alleles and B and B' another. Mating $AA'BB'$ by $AA'BB'$ gives the genotypic ratio seen in Figure 4–9.

Notice here that among every 16 offspring, on the average, there would be 9 different genotypes in the ratio of 1:2:1:2: 4:2:1:2:1. How did this genotypic ratio give rise to the 9:3:3:1 phenotypic ratio in crosses between identically dihybrid garden peas? Two factors were responsible. One was the occurrence of dominance for each pair of alleles; this converted the 1:2:1 genotypic ratio for each gene pair to a 3:1 phenotypic ratio. The other factor was that the action of the two gene pairs was independent and resulted in detectable effects on different traits. This permitted both 3:1 ratios to be recognized separately even when these ratios were distributed at random in the progeny (Figure 4–5). It becomes apparent, therefore, that the *particular phenotypic ratios obtained,* following crosses involving more than one gene pair, *depend both upon the dominance relationships between alleles and the gene interaction relationships between nonalleles.*

If neither gene pair shows dominance, and if each pair acts both independently and on different traits, two 1:2:1 phenotypic ratios will be produced, and these, when distributed at random, will result in the 1:2:1:2:4:2:1:2:1 phenotypic ratio. Here, because no

genotype is masked phenotypically by any other, the phenotypic and genotypic ratios are the same. (This would also be true of the following crosses: $AA'\ BB' \times AA\ BB$, $AA'\ BB' \times A'A'\ B'B'$, $AA'\ BB \times AA\ BB'$.) This kind of result is illustrated in the progeny of parents both of whom have thalassemia minor (Tt) and MN (MM') "blood type." (MM is phenotypically M, $M'M'$ is phenotypically N, as described on p. 58.)

When, however, the aforementioned conditions are changed so that one of the two pairs of genes shows dominance, two different genotypes will produce the same phenotype, and fewer than 9 phenotypes are expected. Thus, if B is dominant to B', genotypes 1 and 2 (in Figure 4–9) are expressed as one phenotype, genotypes 4 and 5 as another, and 7 and 8 as another, so that the phenotypic ratio becomes 3:1:6:2:3:1. This is the phenotypic ratio expected in the progeny of parents both heterozygous for albinism (Aa) and having MN blood type (MM'). If both gene pairs show dominance, one phenotype is expressed by geno-

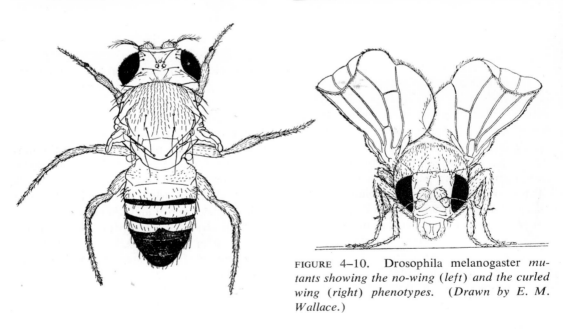

FIGURE 4–10. Drosophila melanogaster *mutants showing the no-wing (left) and the curled wing (right) phenotypes. (Drawn by E. M. Wallace.)*

types 1, 2, 4, 5, another by genotypes 3 and 6, another by 7 and 8, and another by genotype 9, producing the 9 : 3 : 3 : 1 ratio already discussed. Dominance causes a reduction in the number of phenotypic classes.

What phenotypic ratios are expected when two different, independently active, pairs of genes affect the same trait in the same manner or direction? If one or more allelic combinations for one gene pair produce the same phenotype as one or more allelic combinations for the other gene pair, the number of phenotypes will also be reduced from the maximum (9 when identical dihybrids are crossed). Of course, the number of different phenotypes detected will be further reduced if the absence of dominance in both gene pairs is changed to dominance in one gene pair, and still further reduced if both gene pairs show dominance. Thus, if A and B produce equal amounts of melanin pigment in human skin, the amount of pigment being cumulative, and A' and B' produce none, dominance being absent, a cross between identical dihybrids yields the ratio 1 "black" (type 1) : 4 "dark" (types 2, 4) : 6 "mulatto" (types 3, 5, 7) : 4 "light" (types 6, 8) : 1 "white" (type 9), instead of 9 different phenotypes. Moreover, if both A and B show complete dominance, for example either gene producing full flower color, the phenotypic ratio becomes 15 colored (types 1–8) : 1 colorless (type 9). Note that when different pairs of genes act on the same trait in the same direction or way, they have a common phenotypic background on which their effects *superpose,* and the effect of one gene pair interferes with the detection of the effect of the other pair.

Sometimes different gene pairs act independently on the same trait in different— antagonistic or cooperative—ways. For example, in Drosophila (Figure 4–10), A' is a recessive allele which reduces the wing to a stump, whereas B' is a recessive allele which causes the wing to be curled, the dominant allele A making for normal sized wings and the dominant allele B straight wings. A cross between two identical dihybrids does not produce the customary 9 : 3 : 3 : 1 ratio. In the present case, the ratio becomes 9 flies with long, straight wings : 3 with long, curled wings : 4 whose wings are mere stumps (of which one quarter would have had curled wings if the full wing had formed). Here, then, the phenotypic expression of one gene pair can prevent detection of the phenotypic expression of another gene pair.

In another case, either of two pairs of genes may prevent a given phenotype from occurring. Suppose the dominant alleles A and B each independently contribute something different but essential for the production of red pigment, whereas their corresponding recessive alleles A' and B' fail to make the respective independent contributions to red pigment production. Then crosses between two identical dihybrids will produce 9 red : 7 nonred (composed of 3 homozygotes for A' only, 3 homozygotes for B' only, and 1 homozygote for both A' and B'). Notice that if the recessive alleles are considered, we have just dealt with examples of unilateral and mutual opposition to phenotypic expression, respectively, but if the dominant alleles are considered these become cases of unilateral and mutual cooperation in phenotypic expression.

In all cases where two pairs of genes affecting the same trait interact phenotypically by superposition, antagonism or cooperation, one pair of genes has had an influence upon distinguishing the effects of the other. The general term *epistasis* may be used in these cases to describe the interference with— suppression or masking of—the phenotypic expression of one pair of genes by the members of a different pair. Genes whose detection is hampered by nonallelic genes are said to be *hypostatic,* or to exhibit *hypostasis.* As dominance implies recessiveness, so epistasis implies *hypostasis.* There need be no relationship between the dominance of a gene to its allele and the ability of the gene to be epistatic to nonalleles. In theory, then, epistatic action may depend upon the presence of *A, A',* or *AA';* moreover, hypostatic reactions may depend upon the presence of *B, B',* or *BB'.* Consequently, it should be noted that in crosses between identical dihybrids, epistasis–hypostasis can produce phenotypic ratios still different from those already described.

Consider another example of a dihybrid in which both pairs of genes show dominance but no epistasis. In Drosophila, the dull-red eye color of flies found in nature is due to the presence of both red and brown pigments. Let *A* be the allele which produces the red pigment and *A'* its recessive allele which produces no red pigment; let *B* be the nonallele producing the brown pigment whose allele *B'* makes no brown pigment. A mating between two dull-red dihybrid flies (from a cross of pure red, *AA B'B'* by pure brown, *A'A' BB*) produces offspring in the proportion 9 dull-red (containing *A— B—*):3 red (containing *A— B'B'*):3 brown (containing *A'A' B—*):1 white (*A'A' B'B'*). The last phenotypic class, resulting from the absence of both eye pigments, is new in this series of crosses. This case illustrates that the interaction of nonallelic genes

may result in *apparently novel phenotypes.* Such interactions change not the number but the kind of phenotypes obtained.

The preceding discussion suggests that any given phenotypic trait may be the result of the interaction of several gene pairs. One is even led to conclude that the total phenotype is the product of the total genotype acting together with the environment. The difference between phenotypic and genotypic ratios is often due to products of gene action—by alleles and nonalleles—which superpose, cooperate, or conflict at the physiological or biochemical level. It is also possible that there is sometimes a direct influence of one gene upon the ability of an allele or nonallele to act. Although the nature of gene interactions can be predicted partially, in a general way, from the kind of modified ratio obtained, an understanding of the mechanisms involved must ultimately be based upon a knowledge of how genes act and the nature and fate of gene products. In no case has a phenotypic ratio that differs from the expected genotypic one served to disprove either segregation or independent segregation. In fact, segregation and independent segregation were first proved despite the misleading phenotypic simplifications of genotypic ratios wrought by the occurrence of dominance; moreover, the principle of independent segregation could also have been first proved from crosses involving epistasis or apparently novel phenotypes.

SUMMARY AND CONCLUSIONS

When two different traits were studied separately, the phenotypic alternatives were found to be due to the presence of a single pair of genes in each case. Studies were then made of the distribution of phenotypes in successive generations when these two pairs of traits were followed simultaneously in the same individuals. The data obtained showed that each trait is due to the presence of a different pair of genes, proving that the genetic material is made up not of a single segregating pair of genes but of a number of segregating gene pairs. Moreover, the results are best explained by the principle that the segregation of one pair of alleles is at random with respect to the segregation of all the other nonalleles tested. The simplest hypothesis for the physical

WILLIAM BATESON (*1861–1926*).
(*From Genetics, vol. 12,
p. 1, 1927.*)

basis for the independent recombination of such nonalleles is that different pairs of genes reside in nonhomologous pairs of chromosomes.

The phenotypic expression of genes depends upon their alleles, insofar as dominance is involved, and upon nonalleles, insofar as epistasis (including superposition, cooperation, and antagonism) and the production of apparently novel phenotypes are involved. The absence both of dominance and of epistasis will always produce phenotypic ratios which directly represent genotypic ratios, whereas the occurrence of one, the other, or both reduces the number of phenotypic classes. In any case, segregation and independent segregation, being genetic properties, are totally uninfluenced by the manner whereby genes do or do not come to phenotypic expression.

REFERENCES

Bateson, W., *Mendel's Principles of Heredity,* Cambridge, England: Cambridge University Press, 1909.

Mendel, G. See reference at the end of Chapter 3.

Supplement I (at the end of this book).

QUESTIONS FOR DISCUSSION

4.1. Make genetic diagrams for the crosses and progeny discussed in the second and third paragraphs on p. 42. Be sure to define your symbols.

4.2. Is a test cross or backcross used to determine genotypes from phenotypes in cases of no dominance? Explain.

4.3. What types and frequencies of gametes are formed by the following genotypes, all gene pairs segregating independently?

    (a) *Aa Bb CC*   (c) *Aa Bb Cc*

    (b) *AA BB Cc DD*   (d) *Mm Nn Oo Pp*

4.4. How many different diploid genotypes are possible in offspring from crosses in which both parents are undergoing independent segregation for the following numbers of pairs of heterozygous genes—1, 2, 3, 4, n?

4.5. What conclusions could you reach about the parents if the offspring had phenotypes in the following proportions?

    (a) 3:1   (c) 9:3:3:1

    (b) 1:1   (d) 1:1:1:1

4.6. Would you be justified in concluding that a pair of chromosomes can contain only a single pair of genes? Explain.

4.7. Suppose a particular garden pea plant is a septahybrid. What proportion of its gametes will carry all seven recessive nonalleles? All seven dominant nonalleles? Some dominant and some recessive nonalleles?

4.8. What proportion of the offspring of the following crosses, involving independent segregation, will be completely homozygous?

    (a) *Aa Bb × Aa Bb*   (c) *Aa BB Cc × AA Bb cc*

    (b) *AA BB CC × AA bb cc*   (d) *AA' × A"A'''*

4.9. Following independent segregation, why would you expect that gametes fertilize at random with respect to their genotypes?

4.10. Discuss the particulate nature of the genetic material.

4.11. Does the discovery of independent segregation of nonalleles affect your concept of gene size? Explain.

4.12. Discuss your current understanding of the term "genetic recombination."

4.13. Discuss the factors that can modify the expected phenotypic ratio.

4.14. In snapdragons, red flowers (*R*) are incompletely dominant to white (*r*), the hybrid being pink; narrow leaves (*N*) are incompletely dominant to broad leaves (*n*), the hybrid being intermediate in width ("medium"). Assuming the gene pairs recombine independently, give the genotypic and phenotypic ratios expected among the progeny of a cross between the following:

    (a) a red medium and a pink medium plant

    (b) a pink medium and a white narrow

    (c) two identical dihybrids

4.15. Suppose an albino child also suffers from thalassemia minor. Give the most likely genotypes of the parents.

4.16. How can you explain that a certain kind of baldness, due to a single gene pair, is dominant in men and recessive in women?

4.17. Though blue-eyed couples ordinarily have only blue-eyed progeny, brown-eyed couples may also have blue-eyed children. Select and define gene symbols so you can give the complete genotypes of all individuals mentioned in each of the families listed:

    (a) One member of a pair of twin boys has brown eyes, the other has blue eyes.

    (b) A blue-eyed, woolly-haired child resembles his father in one of these respects and his mother in the other respect.

    (c) A brown-eyed, nonthalassemic child is like the grandmother but unlike the mother in both of these respects.

4.18. Differentiate between dominance and epistasis.

4.19. What is the maximum number of genotypes possible in the progeny if the parents are monohybrids?

4.20. Two green corn plants are crossed and produce offspring of which approximately $\frac{9}{16}$ are green and $\frac{7}{16}$ are white. How can you explain these results?

4.21. Does gene interaction occur only when identical monohybrids (or identical dihybrids) are crossed? Explain.

ROSE COMB   PEA COMB   WALNUT COMB   SINGLE COMB

4.22. A chicken from a pure line of "rose" combs is mated with another individual from a pure line of "pea" combs (see the accompanying illustration). All the F_1 show "walnut" combs. Crosses of two F_1 "walnut" type individuals provide F_2 in the ratio 9 "walnut":3 "rose":3 "pea":1 "single." Choose and define gene symbols to provide a genetic explanation for these results.

4.23. Three walnut-combed chickens were crossed to single-combed individuals. In one case the progeny were all walnut-combed. In another case one of the progeny was single-combed. In the third case the progeny were either walnut-combed or pea-combed. Give the genotypes of all parents and offspring mentioned.

4.24. Matings between walnut-combed and rose-combed chickens gave 4 single, 5 pea, 13 rose, and 12 walnut progeny in F_1. What are the most probable genotypes of the parents?

4.25. A mating of two walnut-combed chickens produced the following F_1 with respect to combs: 1 walnut, 1 rose, 1 single. Give the genotypes of the parents.

4.26. The hornless, or polled, condition in cattle is due to a completely dominant gene, P, normally horned cattle being pp. The gene for red color (R) shows no dominance to that for white (R'), the hybrid (RR') being roan color. Assuming independent segregation, give the genotypic and phenotypic expectations from the following matings:

(a) $Pp\,RR \times pp\,RR'$
(b) $Pp\,RR' \times pp\,R'R'$
(c) $Pp\,RR' \times Pp\,RR'$
(d) hornless roan (whose mother was horned) $\times$ horned white

4.27. When dogs from a brown pure line were mated to dogs from a white pure line all the numerous F_1 were white. When the progeny of numerous matings between F_1 whites were scored there were 118 white, 32 black, and 10 brown. How can you explain these results genetically?

4.28. Using your answer to the preceding question, give the phenotypic and genotypic expectations from a mating between the following:

(a) a black dog (one of whose parents was brown) and a brown dog
(b) a black dog (one parent was brown, the other was black) and a white dog (one parent was brown, the other was from a pure white strain)

4.29. When one crosses pure White Leghorn poultry with pure White Silkies, all the F_1 are white. In the F_2, however, large numbers of progeny occur in a ratio approaching 13 white:3 colored. Choosing and defining your own gene symbols, explain these results genetically.

4.30. (a) In the yellow daisy the flowers typically have purple centers. A yellow-centered mutant was discovered which when crossed to the purple-centered type gave all purple-centered F_1, and among the F_2 47 purple and 13 yellow. Explain these results genetically.

(b) Later, another yellow-centered mutant occurred which also gave all purple F_1 from crosses with purple-centered daisies. When these F_1 were crossed together, however, there were 97 purples and 68 yellows. Explain these results genetically.

(c) How can you explain that a cross between the two yellow-centered mutants produced all purple-centered F_1?

4.31. Give a single genetic explanation that applies to all the following facts regarding human beings:

(a) One particular deaf couple has only normal progeny.
(b) One particular deaf couple has only deaf progeny.
(c) One particular normal couple has many children, about ¾ are normal and ¼ deaf.
(d) One particular normal couple has all normal children.
(e) Normal, identical twins marry normal, identical twins and have a total of 9 normal and 9 deaf children.

4.32. How can you explain the observations with regard to lint color of cotton that brown $\times$ green gives green F_1, which when mated together produce F_2 which contain mostly brown, some greens, and a few whites?

4.33. Suppose two unrelated albinos married and had 8 children, 4 albino and 4 non-albino. How could you explain these results?

4.34. When, during the life cycle, can dominance and/or epistasis occur or not occur in maize? Neurospora?

4.35. When two plants are crossed it is found that ⁶³⁄₆₄ of the progeny are phenotypically like the parents, and ¹⁄₆₄ of the progeny are different from either parent but resemble each other. Give a genetic explanation for this.

4.36. Would you expect to find epistasis in man in marriages involving genetic alternatives for both woolly hair and baldness? Brown eyes and albinism? Baldness and brown eyes?

4.37. Assume, in man, that the difference in skin color is due primarily to two pairs of genes which segregate independently: *BB CC* is black, *bb cc* is white, any three of the genes in black produce dark skin, any two medium skin, and any one produces light skin color. Give the genotypes of parents who are:

(a) Both medium, but have one black and one white child.
(b) Both black but have an albino child.
(c) Both medium and can have only medium children.
(d) Medium and light and have a large number of children: ⅜ medium, ⅜ light, ⅛ dark, ⅛ white.

MULTIPLE ALLELES;
MULTIGENIC TRAITS

ALL the phenotypic results discussed in preceding chapters can be explained genetically by dividing the genetic material into gene pairs. Since no proof has been presented that a particular gene can occur in more than two different states, one could maintain at this point that the only alternative for a given gene (causing round seeds) is the absence of that gene (thus causing wrinkled seeds). This may be called the *presence–absence view of gene alternatives.* It is clear that it requires finding a gene with more than two alternatives to prove that not all mutations remove an entire gene, and that genes can mutate to alternative gene forms. If, as assumed, genes arise only by gene replication, one would expect to find *multiple alleles,* since each individual carries many different nonallelic genes, many of which must have been derived from a common ancestral gene in past evolution.

Multiple Alleles

1. *Human Blood Types.* Numerous family studies of blood type provide us with data regarding the number of alternatives possible for an allele. However, before discussing these studies, it is necessary to learn what is meant by a *blood type* or *blood group.*

Human blood contains red blood corpuscles (cells) carried in a fluid medium, the plasma. The corpuscles carry on their surfaces substances called *antigens,* whereas the plasma contains, or may form, substances called *antibodies.* An antibody is a very specific kind of molecule capable of reacting with and binding a specific antigen. This reaction may be visualized as a lock (antibody) which holds or binds a particular key (antigen). If a rabbit is injected with suitable antigenic material—foreign red blood cells, for example—to which it has never before been exposed, certain antibody-producing cells of the rabbit will manufacture an abundance of antibodies, which will appear in its plasma. Some of these antibodies will be used to react specifically with the antigenic component of the foreign red blood cells. If, on some later occasion, the same antigen is injected into the rabbit's bloodstream, specific antibodies will already be present to bind the antigen. The antigen–antibody complex then formed often causes the blood to clump, or agglutinate. It is simple to arrange the procedure so that this reaction may be observed in a test tube or on a glass slide.

Red blood corpuscles from different people are injected into different rabbits, with the result that the rabbits form antibodies against the antigens introduced. The isolated rabbit's blood, centrifuged free of cells, can then serve as an *antiserum,* containing antibodies that will clump any red blood cells added to it carrying the original types of antigens. It is found [1] that two very distinct antisera are formed by these rabbits, and that any person's blood cells tested with these two antisera can react in one of three ways: the red blood cells are agglutinated or clumped either in one antiserum (arbitrarily called anti-M), or in the other (called anti-N), or in both of these antisera. All people can be classified by their blood cell antigens as belonging to either M, or N, or MN blood group, respectively.

[1] Based upon work of K. Landsteiner and P. Levine.

PARENTS			CHILDREN		
			M	MN	N
1	M × M		ALL	—	—
2	N × N		—	—	ALL
3	M × N		—	ALL	—
4	MN × N		—	½	½
5	MN × M		½	½	—
6	MN × MN		¼	½	¼

FIGURE 5–1. *Distribution of MN blood group phenotypes in different human families.*

Parents and their offspring can be tested for MN blood type. The results of such family studies are summarized in Figure 5–1. Parents of type 6 produce offspring in the proportion of 1:2:1 for M:MN:N blood types. This result suggests that these blood types are due to the action of a single pair of genes. If we let M represent the gene for blood antigen M, and M', the allele which produces the N blood antigen, mating 6 must be, genetically, $MM' \times MM'$ and the offspring $1\ MM : 2\ MM' : 1\ M'M'$. Note that these alleles show no dominance, MM' individuals having both M and N blood antigens. All the other family results also are consistent with the genetic explanation proposed.

Different antisera can be prepared to test for other blood types. One of these antisera determines the presence or absence of what is called the *Rhesus* or *Rh factor*. Red blood cells from Rhesus monkeys are injected into rabbits; if a second injection of Rhesus blood is given sometime later, it will be clumped. This is explained by the presence of an antigen carried by Rhesus red blood cells against which the rabbit had manufactured antibodies before its second exposure to Rhesus blood. The antigen involved here is called Rh; the antibodies induced are anti-Rh.

When human blood is injected into a rabbit having anti-Rh antibodies in its serum, it is found that 85% of all people have blood which is clumped—these people have what is called Rhesus-positive (or Rh-positive) blood type; 15% of all people have blood which is not clumped—these people have Rhesus-negative (or Rh-negative) blood type. Accordingly, 85% of human beings have the same Rh antigen as have Rhesus monkeys, and 15% do not. A combination of family and pedigree studies shows that presence of Rh antigen in human beings is controlled by a dominant gene we can represent by R, and its absence by a recessive allele, r.

Two other antisera, called anti-A and anti-B, can be prepared.[2] Blood from different people tested with these antisera is found to be of one of four types: clumped in anti-A (blood type A), clumped in anti-B (blood type B), clumped in both (type AB), and clumped in neither type of antiserum (O).

Family studies of *ABO blood types* give the phenotypic results shown in Figure 5–2. Note that two kinds of results are obtained from A × O and also from B × O parents. In each case one kind of result (marriage types 9 and 11) can be explained if one assumes that the non-O parent is a heterozygote in which the gene for O is recessive. Let i be the gene for O blood type and I^A the allele for A blood type, the latter being dominant. Then the parents are thus: in marriages type 9, $I^A i \times ii$; in type 10, $I^A I^A \times ii$; and in 13, $ii \times ii$. In order to explain 11 and 12 we shall have to assume the presence of a gene I^B for B blood type, which is also a dominant allele of i and from which it segregates. Then mating 11 is

[2] Based upon K. Landsteiner's work.

$I^B i \times ii$ and 12 is $I^B I^B \times ii$. Note that we have made a new supposition with regard to genes. In the former case the alternative allelic form of i is I^A, whereas in the latter case it is I^B. This must mean that I^A and I^B are also alleles. The results of marriage types 7 and 8 confirm this hypothesis, the heterozygote $I^A I^B$ showing no dominance and appearing as AB blood type. All the results indicated in the table are now explained genetically. Note that I^A and I^B produce qualitatively different antigenic effects. We have, therefore, proved that the gene can exist in any one of two or more alternative genetic states, so that *a gene can have multiple—different—alleles.* Of course, any one person normally carries no more than two of all the multiple alleles possible.

2. *Blood Type Isoalleles.* It has been shown that persons with A blood type really have one of three different subtypes, resulting from slightly different allelic forms of I^A—I^{A1}, I^{A2}, I^{A3}. Three slightly different

allelic alternatives are known also for I^B, producing three subtypes within the B blood group. Thus, alleles which at first seem identical may prove to be different when tested further. Such alleles are said to be *isoalleles.* Other examples of isoalleles have been detected because different alleles show varied responses to the presence of nonallelic genes, to environmental changes such as temperature and humidity, or to agents which modify mutation rates. Of course, the number of isoalleles detected will depend upon how many different phenotypic criteria are employed to compare alleles, and how small a phenotypic difference is perceptible.

In the case of ABO blood type, it is sometimes adequate to classify individuals on the basis of alleles that produce A-type, B-type, or neither type of antigen. Therefore, only three alleles need to be considered. When one studies the genetic relationships among individuals in detail, however, it is often necessary to deal with all seven alleles.

3. *Isoalleles in Drosophila.* In different wild Drosophila populations, designated as 1, 2, and 3, the venation of the wings is complete and identical. In the hybrids produced by all possible crosses between these populations, the venation is unchanged. This result suggests that all three populations are genotypically identical in this respect. The venation in a mutant strain is incomplete, the cubitus vein being interrupted ($ci = cubitus\ interruptus$) in homozygotes (Figure 5–3). Hybrids formed by crosses between $ci\ ci$ and wild populations 1 or 2 have complete venation, so that the gene for normal venation, ci^+, in these populations is completely dominant to ci. But the hybrid between $ci\ ci$ and wild flies from population 3, $ci^{+3}\ ci$, shows the cubitus vein interrupted. Furthermore, the lack of dominance of ci^{+3} over ci can be shown to be

PARENTS		CHILDREN			
		A	AB	B	O
7	AB x AB	¼	½	¼	—
8	AB x O	½	—	½	—
9*	A x O	½	—	—	½
10*	A x O	ALL	—	—	—
11*	B x O	—	—	½	½
12*	B x O	—	—	ALL	—
13	O x O	—	—	—	ALL

FIGURE 5–2. *Distribution of ABO blood group phenotypes in different human families.*
* *In some families.*

FIGURE 5–3. *Normal (a) and cubitus inter-ruptus (b) wings of* Drosophila melanogaster. *(Courtesy of C. Stern; from Genetics, vol. 28, p. 443, 1943.)*

an effect of this gene pair rather than a modifying effect of some other gene pair. Apparently, then, the ci^+ allele in population 3 is different from that in populations 1 and 2. We are dealing, consequently, with two isoalleles in a multiple allelic series. (Note that a slightly different system of symbolizing genes was used here.)

4. *Eye Color in Drosophila.* Another series of multiple alleles in Drosophila involves eye color. In this case the different alleles can be arranged in a series that shows different grades of effect on eye color, ranging from dull-red to white: dull-red (w^+), blood (w^{bl}), coral (w^{co}), apricot (w^a), buff (w^{bf}), and white (w). The w^+ allele is dominant to the others listed and is the allele commonly found in wild-type flies. One can think of all the different alleles as producing the same kind of phenotypic effect, but less of it in proceeding from w^+ to w, the white allele being completely inefficient in this respect.

We have already described isoalleles for genes normally expressed in individuals living in the wild (wild-type isoalleles). Isoalleles for mutant genes (mutant isoalleles) also occur. For instance, it has been proved

that the gene producing white eye color in different strains of Drosophila is actually composed of a series of multiple isoalleles (w^1, w^2, w^3, etc.).

5. *Self-sterility in Nicotiana.* Among sexually reproducing plants it is not uncommon to find that self-fertilization does not occur even though the male and female gametes are produced at the same time on a given plant. The reason for this has been studied in the tobacco plant, Nicotiana, where it was found that if pollen grains fall on the stigma of the same plant, they fail to grow down the style. When this happens self-fertilization is impossible. A clue to an explanation for this phenomenon comes from the observation that different percentages of pollen from a completely self-sterile plant may grow down the style of other plants.

The results of certain crosses are shown in Figure 5–4. Genetically identical pistils are exposed to pollen from the same plant (A), from a second one (B), and from a third (C). No pollen, approximately half, and approximately all, respectively, are able to grow down the style of the host. Note, in B, that although all the pollen used came from one diploid individual, half of it can and half of it cannot grow on its host. Recall that the stigma and style are diploid tissues, whereas pollen grains are haploid. These results suggest that most important in determining whether or not a pollen grain can grow down a style is not the diploid genotype of its parent but the haploid genotype contained in itself.

Let us assume that self- or cross-sterility is due to a single pair of genes. Call *s3* the allele contained in the pollen which permits pollen to grow in case B. The pollen grains from the host plant furnishing the pistil cannot contain *s3*, or the pollen would be able to grow on their own parent; and they cannot (Case A). So, the host pistil tissue in this experiment cannot contain *s3*, and one of its alleles can be called *s1*. Then, half of the pollen from the host individual will carry *s1* (Case A); but since these fail to grow, we must assume that any pollen grain carrying an *s* allele also present in the host pistil will fail to grow. Excluding the possibility of a mutation, the other allele in the

host pistil cannot also be *s1*, since one *s1* would have had to be received from a paternal pollen grain growing down a maternal style that carried *s1* as one of its two alleles. Since the second allele in the pistils illustrated cannot be either *s1* or *s3*, let us call it *s2*. The other half of pollen from the pistil parent thus will contain *s2*, and also fail to grow in self-pollination (Case A). In B the pollen grains that fail to grow are either *s1* or *s2* (adhering to the law of parsimony); however, their precise identity cannot be determined without additional tests. In C, since all the pollen grew, one pollen allele must be a different one—call it *s4*. The other pollen allele may be *s3* or a still different one, *s5*. Here again more tests are needed to determine the precise identity.

In these cases the phenotypic alternatives for pollen are to grow or not to grow. Whenever the pollen grains from any one plant are placed on a given stigma and both alternatives occur, the phenotypes are in a 1:1 ratio. All these results and others are

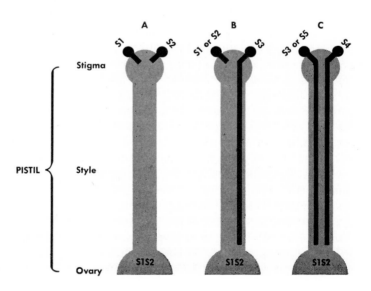

FIGURE 5–4. *Multiple alleles for cross- or self-sterility.*

consistent with the assumptions made, that self- or cross-sterility is regulated by a single pair of genes which form a multiple allelic series. Some species prove to have fifty or more multiple alleles forming a series responsible for self-sterility, group sterility, or group incompatibility.

*Multigenic Traits

Up to now, the traits chosen to study genes occur in clear-cut, qualitatively different alternatives like flower color in garden peas, or albinism vs. pigmentation, and various blood types in human beings. These are called *discontinuous* or *qualitative traits* because in each case an individual belongs clearly to one phenotypic class or another. Although the interaction of many or all genes may ultimately be involved in the appearance of a given phenotype, the phenotypic alternatives previously considered have been effected primarily by only one or a few pairs of genes. Moreover, in these cases the nongenetic environment had much less or no effect upon the phenotypic differences involved.

For practical and theoretical reasons one may also be interested in the genetic basis for certain *continuous traits* like height of corn or intelligence in man, for which there are so many grades that individuals are not separable into discrete types or classes. Such traits are also called *quantitative traits* because the continuous range of phenotypes observed requires that an individual be measured in some way in order to be classified. Are quantitative traits also determined genetically? Let us make the simplest assumption that *quantitative traits differ from qualitative ones only in degree,* the former being due to the combined effects of many gene pairs. In the case of *multigenic (polygenic) traits,* although many phenotypic classes would be made possible by the action of multiple gene pairs, the effect of any single pair would be difficult to distinguish. Consequently, since each pair of genes would contribute only slightly toward the expression of the quantitative trait, one would expect the effect of environment to be relatively larger than that of any single gene or gene pair. The large effect of fertilizer upon corn ear size and of diet upon height in human beings illustrate the importance of environment in multigenic traits.

A given trait may be determined qualitatively in certain respects and quantitatively in other respects. For example, in garden peas one pair of genes may determine whether the plant will be normal or dwarf, the actual size of a normal plant being determined by multigenic interaction with the environment playing a significant role. Similarly, a single pair of genes can determine whether a human being has a serious mental deficiency or normal mentality, though nearly all individuals have a degree of mental ability which varies in a continuous way due to environment and polygenes.

If quantitative traits are determined multigenically, it ought to be possible to derive other characteristics of them which are consistent with actual observations by considering the same trait, first as a qualitative trait (i.e., determined by one or two or three gene pairs), and then as a quantitative trait (i.e., determined by many gene pairs). Let the trait be color, and the alternatives in P_1 be black and white. Assume first that there is no dominance or epistasis (see p. 51); then, whether one, two, three, or many gene pairs are involved, the F_1 will be uniform and phenotypically intermediate (medium gray) between the two P_1. Examine, in Figure 5–5, results of matings between F_1 (by cross- or self-fertilization) in each case. As the number of gene pairs increases, the number of classes of F_2 offspring increases. As the number of classes becomes large, one would expect environmental action to cause individuals to fall out of their phenotypic class, so to speak, and into the space between classes or into an adjacent phenotypic class. And so, as gene pair number increases, classes become more numerous, then indiscrete, resulting finally in a continuum of phenotypes.

Note also that as the number of gene pairs determining the trait increases, the fraction of all F_2 resembling either P_1 becomes smaller. Thus, with one pair of genes $\frac{1}{2}$ of F_2 are black or white, with two pairs $\frac{1}{8}$, with three pairs $\frac{1}{32}$, etc. Consequently, as the number of genes increases from 10 to 20 and more, the continuous distribution of phenotypic types gives rise to an F_2 curve which becomes narrower and narrower. In other words, the chance of recovering in F_2 any phenotype a given distance off the mean decreases as gene pair number increases. Although it may be relatively easy to identify whether one, two, or three gene pairs cause a given characteristic, it is much more difficult to determine exactly how many pairs are involved whenever more than three are involved. In multigenic cases, measurement of how the population varies relative to the average phenotype can give information as to the approximate number of polygenes involved.

The variability of a trait can be measured statistically as follows: the *mean, m* (the simple arithmetic average), is found. The *variance, v* (the measure of variability from the mean), for a group of measurements is determined by finding the difference between each measurement and the mean, squaring each such difference, adding all the values obtained, and dividing the total by 1 less than the number of measurements involved. With a given sample size, all other things being equal, the greater the variance the smaller the number of gene pairs involved, as would be expected from Figure 5–5. One may find detailed statistical procedures for

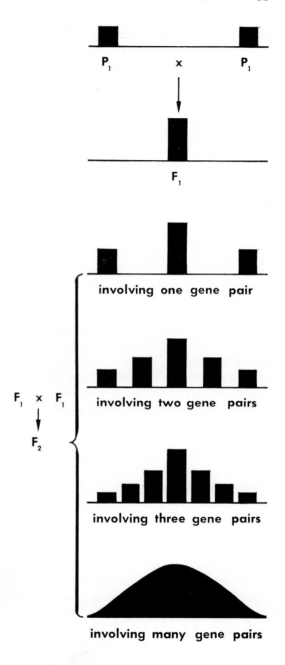

FIGURE 5–5. *Dependence of number of phenotypic classes upon number of gene pairs. Horizontal axis shows classes, vertical axis indicates relative frequencies.*

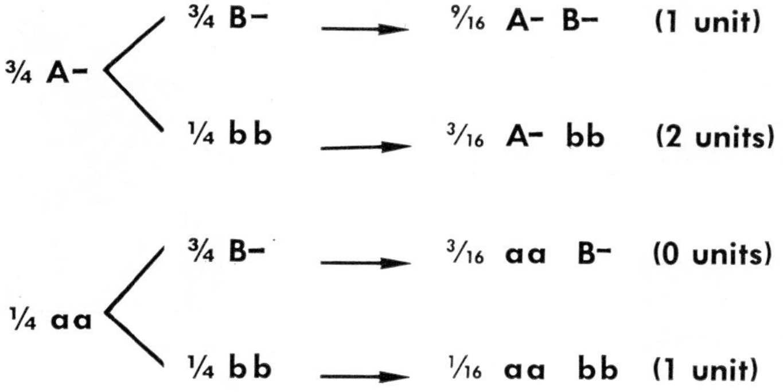

FIGURE 5–6. *Results of crossing together the dihybrids described in the text.*

using variance this way in any standard text on elementary statistical methods.

Consider next the effect of dominance upon the expression of quantitative traits. When a qualitative trait is determined by one, two, or three pairs of heterozygous genes not showing dominance, there are (as in Figure 5–5) three, five, or seven possible phenotypic classes, respectively. As a result of dominance, however, the number of classes is reduced (cf. Chapter 4, p. 51). Since the estimated number of gene pairs responsible for a phenotype is directly related to the number of phenotypic classes, the number of gene pairs involved in a quantitative trait is underestimated whenever dominance occurs. This effect is important because many genes show complete or partial dominance.

One can construct a hypothetical case in which two pairs of genes both showing dominance can give much the same phenotypic result as one pair with no dominance. Suppose gene A (as AA or Aa) adds 2 units of effect and its recessive allele a (as aa) adds only 1 unit; suppose B (as BB or Bb) subtracts 1 unit of effect and its recessive allele b (as bb) has no effect at all. Then a 2-unit individual ($AA\,bb$) mated with a 0-unit one ($aa\,BB$) will give all intermediate

1-unit F_1 ($Aa\,Bb$). The F_2 from the mating of the F_1 can be derived by a branching track as shown in Figure 5–6. The phenotypic ratio obtained in F_2 of $3:10:3$ might be, in practice, difficult to distinguish from the $1:2:1$ ratio obtained from crossing monohybrids showing no dominance.[3]

Dominance has a second effect with regard to quantitative traits; this can be illustrated by means of two crosses involving the genes just described. In the first, two 0-unit individuals are crossed, $aa\,Bb \times aa\,Bb$, yielding ¾ $aa\,B–$ (0 unit) and ¼ $aa\,bb$ (1 unit). In this case the parents, which are at one phenotypic extreme (0 unit), produce offspring which are, on the average, less extreme (0.25 unit). In the second case, two 2-unit individuals are crossed, $Aa\,bb \times Aa\,bb$, yielding ¾ $A–\,bb$ (2 units) and ¼ $aa\,bb$ (1 unit). Here the parents are at the other phenotypic extreme (2 units) but produce offspring which are, on the average, less extreme (1.75 units). These results demonstrate *regression*, the consequence of dominance which causes individuals phenotypically extreme in either direction to have progeny less extreme.

Figure 5–7 illustrates the principle of re-

[3] See J. H. Edwards (1960).

gression in polygenic situations. When no dominance occurs, the average offspring from parents at A, B, and C will be at the corresponding points A', B', C', respectively, in the offspring curve. (The environment will cause some fluctuation around these phenotypic mean points in the offspring curve.) In the case of dominance, however, the offspring of A will be, on the average, to the right of A, as shown by arrows, whereas the offspring of C will generally be to the left of C. Contrary to what one might expect, the loss of extreme individuals generation after generation will *not* make the entire population more and more homogeneous phenotypically; there will be a closely counterbalancing tendency for the average members, B, of the population to produce offspring more extreme than themselves in either direction. The result is that, as in cases of no dominance, the distribution curve for the offspring will be the same as for the parent population.

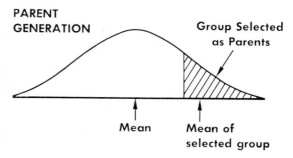

PARENT GENERATION

Group Selected as Parents

Mean   Mean of selected group

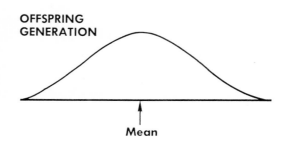

OFFSPRING GENERATION

Mean

FIGURE 5–8. *Selection for a quantitative character.*

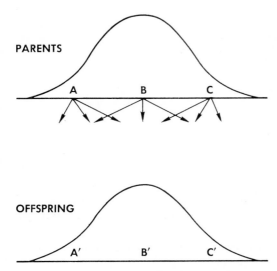

PARENTS

A   B   C

OFFSPRING

A'   B'   C'

FIGURE 5–7. *The principle of regression.*

To obtain a line of phenotypically extreme individuals from a population showing a quantitative trait, one would choose the extreme individuals as parents (Figure 5–8). If dominance were absent, the very first offspring generation would have the same mean as the group selected as parents. Some degree of dominance usually occurs, and hence regression will usually occur; and the mean size of the first generation offspring will be somewhat less extreme than that of the selected parents, but somewhat more extreme than the original mean. As one continues to select appropriately extreme individuals as parents, the offspring in successive generations will, on the average, approach more and more closely the extreme phenotype desired.

SUMMARY AND CONCLUSIONS

A gene can exist in any one of two or more genetic states. These alternatives comprise a multiple allelic (sometimes isoallelic) series.

Some alleles of a given gene may produce apparently different qualitative phenotypic effects (and therefore show no dominance when hybrid); other alleles may produce different degrees of a quantitative phenotypic effect (in which case they may or may not show dominance when hybrid).

Genes are the basis for both continuous and discontinuous traits. Continuous traits are usually determined by many gene pairs, each of which has a phenotypic effect that is small and often matched or exceeded by the action of the environment.

The variability of a quantitative trait is such that the larger the number of heterozygous polygenes determining it, the narrower is the distribution curve and the smaller the chance of recovering either of the extreme phenotypes in the offspring. When polygenes are heterozygous, dominance has the effect of reducing the number of phenotypic classes and of placing proportionally more offspring in extreme classes. Consequently, dominance usually causes one to underestimate the number of genes determining a quantitative trait. Dominance also causes regression, so that selection must be continued for a number of generations to obtain a line which approaches the desired phenotype.

REFERENCES

Crow, J. F., *Genetics Notes,* 5th Ed., Minneapolis: Burgess, 1962.

Edwards, J. H., "The Simulation of Mendelism," Acta Genet., Basel, 10:63–70, 1960.

Falconer, D. S., *Introduction to Quantitative Genetics,* New York: Ronald Press, 1961.

Race, R. R., and Sanger, R., *Blood Groups in Man,* 4th Ed., Philadelphia: F. A. Davis, 1962.

Wiener, A. S., and Wexler, I. B., *Heredity of the Blood Groups,* New York: Grune & Stratton, 1958.

QUESTIONS FOR DISCUSSION

5.1. Discuss the occurrence of dominance with respect to blood group types.

5.2. Why was it necessary to assume that a gene may have more than two allelic forms?

5.3. A baby has blood type AB. What can you tell about the genotypes of its parents? What would you predict about the blood types of children it will later produce?

5.4. If one parent is A blood type and the other is B, give their respective genotypes if they produced a large number of children whose blood types were:

   (a) All AB   (c) Half AB, half A
   (b) Half AB, half B   (d) ¼ AB, ¼ A, ¼ B, ¼ O

5.5. Give examples of complete dominance and of no dominance as found in human beings.

5.6. Is the occurrence of complete dominance helpful in determining the genetic basis of alternatives for a given trait? Explain.

5.7. A father with blood group types M and O has a child with MN and B blood types. What genotypes are possible for the mother?

5.8. Criticize the statement: "Genes can be explained on the basis of a presence-or-absence hypothesis."

5.9. A woman belonging to blood group B has a child with blood group O. Give their genotypes and those which, barring mutation, the father could not have.

5.10. What do you think of the view that all the different genes that exist can be described as being different multiples of a single basic unit which is capable of retaining its integrity and is able to self-replicate?

5.11. How many different genotypes are possible when there are four different alleles of a single gene?

5.12. Does the discussion of multiple alleles in the text imply that: (a) There is an infinite variety of isoalleles? (b) No two genes are ever identical? Explain.

5.13. Describe how you would test whether the genes for white eye color in two different populations of Drosophila were alleles, isoalleles, or nonalleles.

5.14. In rabbits the following alleles produce a gradation effect from full pigmentation to white: *agouti* (C), *chinchilla* (c^{ch}) and *albino* (c). Another allele, c^h, produces the Himalayan coat-color pattern. C is completely dominant to all these alleles, c^h is completely dominant to c, whereas c^{ch} shows no dominance to c^h or c.

    (a) How many different diploid genotypes are possible with the alleles mentioned?

    (b) A light chinchilla mated to an agouti produced an albino in F_1. Give the genotypes of parents and F_1.

    (c) An agouti mated to a light chinchilla produced in F_1 one agouti and two Himalayan. Give the genotypes possible for parents and F_1.

    (d) An agouti rabbit crossed to a chinchilla rabbit produced an agouti offspring. What genotypic and phenotypic results would you expect from crossing the F_1 agouti with an albino?

5.15. For each of the following matings involving Nicotiana give the percentage of aborted pollen tubes and the genotypes of the offspring.

	♂	♀		♂	♀
(a)	s1 s2	× s1 s3	(c)	s1 s4	× s1 s4
(b)	s1 s3	× s2 s4	(d)	s3 s4	× s2 s3

5.16. Could you prove the existence of multiple allelism in an organism that only reproduces asexually? Explain.

5.17. Do the genes for quantitative traits show epistasis? Explain.

5.18. Does the environment have a more important role in determining the phenotype in cases of quantitative than in cases of qualitative traits? Explain.

5.19. Under what circumstances are only seven phenotypes possible when three pairs of genes determine a quantitative trait?

5.20. Discuss the statement: No new principles of genetics have originated from the study of polygenic traits.

5.21. Suppose each gene represented by a capital letter causes a plant to grow an additional inch in height, *aa bb cc dd ee* plants being 12 inches tall. Assume independent segregation occurs for all gene pairs in the following mating: *Aa BB cc Dd EE* × *aa bb CC Dd Ee*.

(a) How tall are the parents?
(b) How tall will the tallest F_1 be?
(c) How tall will the shortest F_1 be?
(d) What proportion of all F_1 will be the shortest?
(e) Is dominance and/or epistasis involved in this system? Explain.

5.22. In selecting for a quantitative trait, is the desired phenotype established in a pure line more easily when dominance does or does not occur? Explain.

5.23. Measure the length of 10 lima beans to the nearest millimeter. Calculate the variance of this sample. To what can you attribute the variance?

5.24. Is it of any advantage to an organism to have a trait determined quantitatively, that is, by many gene pairs, rather than qualitatively, that is, by principally one or a few gene pairs? Why?

5.25. How would you prove that you were dealing with multiple alleles rather than multiple pairs of genes?

5.26. In cattle a cross of a solid-coat breed and a spotted-coat breed produces a solid coat in F_1. Among the individuals of the spotted breed there is considerable variation, ranging from individuals that are solid-colored except for small white patches to those that are white with small colored patches. Selection within this breed can increase or decrease the colored areas. Discuss the genetic basis for coat color in these two breeds of cattle.

5.27. Discuss the number of gene pairs involved in the following case: Golden Glow corn has 16 rows of kernels to the ear; Black Mexican has 8 rows. The F_1 is phenotypically intermediate, having an average of 12 rows. The F_2 is phenotypically variable, ranging from 8 to 18 rows, with approximately one of each 32 ears being as extreme as either P_1.

5.28. The Sebight Bantam and Golden Hamburgh are pure lines of fowl which differ in weight. Although the F_1 of crosses between these lines are fairly uniform and intermediate in weight, one in about every 150 F_2 is clearly heavier or lighter than either P_1 pure line. Suggest a genetic explanation for these results.

PHENOTYPIC EFFECTS
OF GENE ACTION

THE variations in phenotypic ratios that result from the interaction of alleles and non-alleles has been discussed (pp. 49–52). Several other phenotypic consequences of gene action are discussed in the present chapter. Let us begin with a discussion of viability effects, which also modify phenotypic ratios.

Viability Effects

In the snapdragon (Antirrhinum) one finds two kinds of full grown plants, green and a paler green called auria. Green crossed by green produces only green, but auria by auria produces seedlings of which 25% are green (AA), 50% auria (Aa), and 25% white (aa). The last type of seedling dies after exhausting the food stored in the seed, because it lacks chlorophyll. Among full grown plants, the phenotypic ratio observed is $\frac{1}{3}$ green:$\frac{2}{3}$ auria. In this case, the absence of dominance gives the $1:2:1$ ratio characteristic of a cross between monohybrids in the seedling stage which, following the death of the albino, becomes a $2:1$ ratio among the survivors.

In mice, matings between yellow-haired individuals produce F_1 in the ratio 2 yellow:1 nonyellow. It is found after this mating that $\frac{1}{4}$ of the fertilized eggs which should have completed development fail to do so and abort early in embryogenesis. Since crosses between nonyellows produce only nonyellows, the nonyellow phenotype

must be due to one type of homozygote, yellow must be a heterozygote, and the aborting individuals must be due to the other type of homozygote. The gene symbols usually employed are not satisfactory here, for we now must describe two effects for each gene—color and viability. Moreover, the allele which is dominant for the first effect is recessive for the second, and vice versa. This problem is solved by using base letters with superscripts for each gene (Figure 6–1), where the base letter refers to one trait and the superscript refers to the other trait. Let the superscript l be the recessive lethal effect of the gene dominant for yellow, Y, and the superscript L be the dominant normal viability effect of the allele recessive for nonyellow, y. Accordingly, the F_1 from crossing two yellow mice ($Y^l y^L \times Y^l y^L$) are $1\ Y^l Y^l$ (dies):$2\ Y^l y^L$ (yellow):$1\ y^L y^L$ (nonyellow).

In both the snapdragon and mouse cases described, death results from the presence of a gene in homozygous condition. Genes that kill the individual before maturity are called *lethal genes* or *lethals*—those doing so only when homozygous are *recessive lethals,* and those acting in this way when heterozygous are *dominant lethals.* Lethals may act very early or very late in develop-

P_1	yellow $Y^l\ y^L$	x	yellow $Y^l\ y^L$
G_1	$\frac{1}{2}Y^l$, $\frac{1}{2}y^L$		$\frac{1}{2}Y^l$, $\frac{1}{2}y^L$
F_1	$\left[\begin{array}{c}\frac{1}{4}Y^lY^l \\ \text{dies}\end{array}\right.$	$\frac{1}{2}Y^l y^L$ yellow	$\frac{1}{4}y^L y^L$ nonyellow

FIGURE 6–1. *Results of matings between yellow mice.*

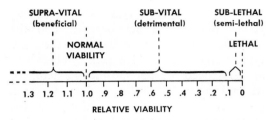

FIGURE 6–2. *Classification of effects that mutants have on viability.*

ment, or at any stage in between. Sometimes a lethal effect is produced not by one gene or a pair, but by the combined effect of several nonallelic genes. In such a case, some of the nonalleles are contributed by each parent, and the offspring dies because the nonalleles, viable when separate, are lethal when together.

Different alleles, recessive or dominant, have been shown to affect viability in different degrees. These effects cover the entire spectrum—ranging from those which are lethal, through those which are greatly or slightly detrimental, to those which are apparently neutral or even beneficial (Figure 6–2). When different combinations of alleles or nonalleles have different viabilities, the phenotypic ratios observed may differ significantly from those expected. The importance of the precautions to be taken, relative to the viability and fertility of the individuals bred in experiments designed to establish principles of transmission genetics, has already been discussed in Chapter 3.

Pleiotropism

Does each gene affect only one trait or can it have *multiple, manifold, or pleiotropic effects?*

An investigation[1] can be undertaken to answer this question, using two strains of Drosophila that are practically identical genetically (*isogenic*), except that one is pure

[1] See Th. Dobzhansky and A. M. Holtz (1943).

for the gene for dull-red eye color (w^+) and the other is pure for its allele white (w). Another trait is then chosen for examination in these two strains, one apparently unconnected with eye color. The trait selected is the shape of the spermatheca, an organ found in females which is used to store the sperm received. The ratio of the diameter to the height of this organ is determined for each of the two strains. This index of shape is found to be significantly different in the dull-red as compared to the white strain. From this result it can be concluded that the eye-color gene studied is pleiotropic. The results of other studies also show many different genes to be pleiotropic for morphological traits.

In Drosophila a recessive lethal gene called *lethal-translucida* causes pupae to be-

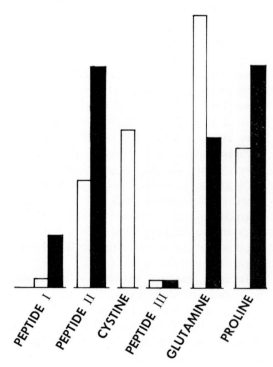

FIGURE 6–3. *Pleiotropism at the biochemical level. (After E. Hadorn.)*

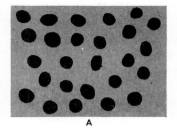
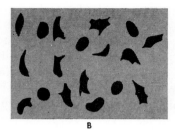
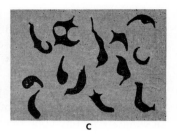

FIGURE 6–4. *Silhouettes showing various types of human red blood cells: normal, in normal homozygote (A), sickle cell trait, in mutant heterozygote (B), sickle cell disease, in mutant homozygote (C).*

come translucent and die. Using suitable techniques, one can compare the kinds and amounts of chemical substances in the blood fluid of normal larvae and pupae with those found in the recessive lethal homozygotes (Figure 6–3). Some substances are found [2] in equal amounts in both genotypes (peptide III), others are more abundant in the lethal than in the normal individual (peptide I, peptide II, and proline), still others are less abundant (glutamine) or absent (cystine) in the lethal. Thus it is clear that pleiotropism also occurs at the biochemical level.

In the case of the yellow mouse, the allele producing yellow coat color as a dominant effect also has a recessive lethal effect. On the presumption that homozygotes for this allele would have yellow body color had they survived, and on the basis that there is no obvious relation between coat color and viability, it could be concluded that this too is a case of pleiotropism.

The coat color of Himalayan rabbits ($c^h c^h$) is usually mosaic; or black at the extremities and white elsewhere (Chapter 1). Has this allele different effects on the same color trait in different parts of the coat? Because individuals with this genotype are completely black when grown under cold

temperatures, we suspect that the gene has only one effect. This hypothesis is supported by the finding that this genotype produces an enzyme, necessary for pigment formation, which is temperature sensitive, being inactivated by temperatures above about 34° C. Thus, in a cool climate, the body temperature is less than 34° C at the extremities, and pigment is produced there; on the warm parts of the body no pigment is formed because the enzyme is inactivated by heat. The Himalayan pattern is attributed, then, to a single product of gene action which, because it is subject to modification by the environment, can result in two different phenotypic alternatives of the same trait.

A genetic disease in man called *sickle-cell anemia* is due to homozygosity for a certain allele. This disease involves the following effects, either singly or in any combination: anemia, enlarged spleen, skin lesions, heart, kidney, and brain damage. As a consequence, homozygotes for the gene for sickling usually die as adolescents or young adults; this allele, therefore, almost always acts as a recessive lethal.

It is also found that the red blood cells of these homozygotes may become sickle-shaped instead of being disc-shaped (Figure 6–4). Sickle-shaped cells can clump together and clog blood vessels in various parts

[2] Based upon work of E. Hadorn.

of the body, leading to the malfunctions of all the organs already mentioned; in addition, these defective corpuscles are readily destroyed by the body, with consequent anemia.

We see, then, that the apparently unrelated phenotypic effects of the gene for sickling are merely consequences of the sickling of red blood cells. Moreover, biochemical studies show that sickling itself is the result of the presence of an abnormal type of hemoglobin (having a slightly lower oxygen-carrying capacity than normal hemoglobin) which sickle-cell homozygotes carry in their red blood cells. There is, therefore, a *pedigree of causes* for the multiple effects of the gene for sickling. The first cause is the gene, the second is the abnormal hemoglobin it produces, the third is the sickling that follows, and the fourth is the subsequent red cell clumping and destruction which produce gross organic defects and anemia.

In this case all the pleiotropic effects are attributed to a single biochemical action of a gene. This single action then affects many varied chemical reactions involved in the production of different, at first apparently unrelated, traits. In view of the Himalayan rabbit and sickle-cell anemia studies, one may even hypothesize that most, if not all, genes have a single primary phenotypic activity. The pleiotropic effects described in other cases may yet prove, upon further analysis, to be tertiary or even further removed effects in a pedigree of causes, the primary cause being genic and the single secondary cause still undetermined. Replying to the question with which this section started, the simplest hypothesis is that *most, if not all, genes have only one phenotypic activity; this gene action has a pedigree of effects which results in pleiotropism.*

Penetrance and Expressivity

Analysis of the genetic material has been greatly facilitated by the particular traits we have chosen to study. The most valuable kind of trait has been one based upon a genotype that always expresses itself in approximately the same way, despite the normal fluctuations of the environment.

Consider, however, a pedigree for *polydactyly* (Figure 6–5), a rare condition in which human beings have more than five digits on a limb. In the figure, the topmost female is affected, having five fingers on each hand and six toes on each foot. Her husband is normal in this respect. This couple has five children, three affected. This suggests that polydactyly is due to a single dominant gene, *P*, and that the mother is *Pp*, the father *pp*. Consistent with this hypothesis is the result of the marriage of one of their affected daughters to a normal man. This marriage produced two sons, one of whom is affected, and this affected son, in turn, has five children including some affected and some unaffected.

But now examine the left side of this pedigree. Note the firstborn son who is unaffected yet has an affected daughter. How may this be explained? It might be supposed that this son is genotypically *pp* and that his daughter is *Pp*, the *P* having been produced by mutation of *p*, then contributed to the daughter at conception. However, other pedigrees for polydactyly also have cases in which two normal individuals have an affected child. Since polydactyly is rare, mutations from *p* to *P* must be still more rare, so that the chance for such a mutant to appear in a sex cell of one of two normal parents is very small. It is most improbable, then, that such a rare mutation, if it occurs at random among normal individuals, would occur so often among the normals in pedigrees for polydactyly.

A different explanation is that the firstborn son is in fact *Pp*, where *P* is not expressed in any detectable way, although it is expressed in his daughter. This interpretation is supported by the kind of expression

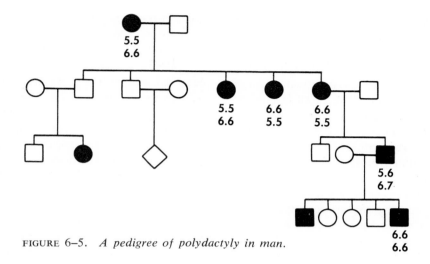

FIGURE 6–5. *A pedigree of polydactyly in man.*

that the *P* gene produces in different affected individuals in this pedigree. These may have the normal number of fingers but have extra toes, or they may have the reverse; they may have different numbers of toes on the two feet, or they may have extra fingers on one hand and the normal number on the other. The expression of polydactyly, so far as the number of extra digits is concerned, is clearly quite variable. Accordingly, since it is possible to have no expression on one limb of an individual known to be *Pp* it must also occur that, on occasion, expression fails on all four limbs of an individual with this genotype.

The ability of a given gene or gene combination to be expressed phenotypically in one way or another is called *penetrance*. The *P* gene in heterozygous condition, therefore, has a penetrance of less than 100%, sometimes failing to produce any detectable phenotypic effect when present. Although a polydactylous person is certain to carry *P*, a normal phenotype can represent either the *Pp* or *pp* genotype. Since polydactyly is rare it is usually quite safe to score as *pp* the genotype of a normal individual who marries into a line of descent containing *P*.

The expression of *P* when heterozygous is not only quite variable with respect to the number and position of extra digits, but further variability of expression is demonstrated by the different degrees of development which the extra digits show. The term *expressivity* is used to refer to the kind or degree of effect produced by a penetrant genotype. In individuals where *P* is nonpenetrant when heterozygous there is no expressivity, and when *P* is penetrant its expressivity is variable.

What factors are involved in the production of variable penetrance, or, in cases of penetrance, of variable expressivity? A study of a genetically uniform line of guinea pigs shows that polydactyly occurs more frequently in the litters from younger than from older mothers. In this case the physiological changes accompanying age modify penetrance. In another case, a genetically uniform line of Drosophila flies shows a greater percentage of penetrance of an abnormal abdomen phenotype when moisture content during development is high than when it is low. Both of these examples illustrate that variations in penetrance can be produced by variations in the environment of different individuals with essentially identical genotypes.

We are already familiar with the effect of genotypic variations upon penetrance under essentially constant environmental conditions. The penetrance of an allele may depend upon the nature of its partner allele in cases of complete or partial dominance, and the penetrance of one or a pair of alleles may be modified by its epistatic–hypostatic relations to nonallelic genes (Chapter 4). Similarly, it can be shown that variable expressivity may be the consequence of differences in either or both the environment and the genotype.

One should be careful to differentiate between penetrance and expressivity on one hand and dominance and epistasis on the other. Suppose, with respect to height, TT always produces tall, $T'T'$ always short, and TT' always medium. Although the hybrid shows incomplete, partial, or no dominance, there is 100% penetrance for each of the three genotypes. If among the mediums there was some variability in size (due to variations in environment or the rest of the genotype), we would have different expressivities for the 100% penetrant TT' genotype. If, however, for the same reasons, TT' sometimes produced a short individual, this would be a case of nonpenetrance of T in TT'.

The terms *penetrance* and *expressivity* were used to compare the phenotypic events that occur in different individuals genetically identical in one particular respect. That is, once any phenotypic expression occurred within an individual, the genotype was said to be penetrant, and all other phenotypic comparisons between penetrant individuals were considered matters of expressivity. In fact, however, one can also correctly speak about penetrance within an individual for those cases in which the particular genotype has two or more occasions to express itself. Thus, for example, the gene for polydactyly

has two apparently equal chances to be penetrant in the case of the hands, and two apparently equal chances to be penetrant in the case of the feet. The genotype may be penetrant in one hand (six fingers) and not in the other (five fingers), it may be penetrant in the feet (each foot having six toes —represented as 6.6) and not in the hands (5.5). When differences in penetrance (or expressivity) are shown by essentially duplicate parts of the same individual (one hand having seven and the other six digits, or one hand having a large and the other a small extra digit), one can be reasonably certain that these differences have an environmental and not a mutational basis. However, when different individuals are compared with respect to penetrance or expressivity, it is often impossible to attribute, with assurance, similarities or differences among them to genotype or to environment, if both of these factors can vary in uncontrolled ways (as already implied on p. 12).

Studies of Human Twins

In organisms other than man experimental conditions can be controlled so that a standard genotype exposed to different environments shows to what extent environment is responsible for phenotypic variability, whereas a standard environment to which different genotypes are exposed reveals to what extent these genotypes produce different phenotypes. Since neither the environment nor the genotypes of human beings are subject to experimental control, how can we determine to what extent a particular human trait is controlled by genotype (nature) and by environment (nurture)? Fortunately, this nature–nurture problem can be studied using the results of certain naturally occurring phenomena.

An individual contains many different parts which presumably have the identical genotype. Accordingly, as mentioned, one can attribute to nurture any phenotypic differences in expressivity or penetrance found among parts that are essentially duplicates of each other. For example, a heterozygote for polydactyly with six fingers on one hand and five on the other illustrates the extent to which environment can affect this trait. When, however, a trait involves the entire body, or only one or several different nonduplicate parts of the body, the contribution of nurture can be learned only by comparing different individuals which have identical genotypes.

Since each human individual is heterozygous for a relatively large number of genes, the chance of obtaining genetic identity in two *siblings* (children of the same parents) is very small indeed. However, two or more siblings with identical genotypes can be produced in man by asexual reproduction, which occurs in the following manner. A single fertilized egg starts development normally by undergoing a series of mitotic divisions. At some time, however, the cells produced fail to adhere to each other, as they would normally do, and separate into two or more groups, each of which may be able to develop into a complete individual. Each individual thus produced is, barring mutation, genetically identical to all others formed from the same fertilized egg. The separation referred to may occur at different stages of early development, and the number of cells in the two or more groups formed may be unequal. Separation may even occur more than once, at different times in the development of a particular zygote. The individuals produced in this asexual manner are *identical* or *monozygotic* twins, triplets, quadruplets, etc. We need consider only identical twins here, since multiple births of greater number are usually too infrequent to be useful for a general study of the nature–nurture problem.

Multiple births can also be produced directly by sexual reproduction. When twins are produced in this way, they start as two separate eggs, each fertilized by a separate sperm. Such twins are genetically different —being, in this respect, no more similar than siblings conceived at different times— and are *nonidentical* or *dizygotic* (*fraternal*) twins.

These two kinds of twins provide natural experimental material for determining the relative influence of genotype and environment upon the phenotype. Barring mutation, monozygotic twins furnish the identical genotype in two individuals, and both kinds of twins share similar environments before birth and, when raised together, after birth.

The phenotypic differences between identical twins reared together are essentially the consequence of environment alone (Figure 6–6). One can compare the average difference between such identical twins with the average difference between identical twins who, for one reason or another, were reared apart. This comparison yields information regarding the influence of greater, as compared with lesser, environmental differences upon the phenotype. Since nonidentical or identical twins reared together are exposed to environments which, on the average, vary to the same extent, a comparison of the average difference between identical twins and the average difference between nonidentical twins will give an index of the genotype's role in causing the differences observed. In order to collect valid data from twin studies, it is essential that one be able to recognize in each case whether the twins are monozygotic or dizygotic in origin.

The best way to identify nonidentical twins is to compare the siblings with reference to a large number of traits known to have a basis in those genes which are 100% penetrant and of fairly uniform expressivity —such traits as sex, eye color, ABO, MN, Rh, and other blood group types. Naturally, only traits for which at least one parent is heterozygous are of use in testing the dizygotic origin of twins. Assuming the absence of mutation, any single difference in such traits would prove the twins nonidentical. (On this basis, twins of opposite sex are classified immediately as nonidentical.) Of course, two such differences would make the decision practically infallible, since two mutations in genes governing the limited number of traits being compared in a pair of identical twins would be so rare as to be beyond any reasonable probability of occurrence.

Identification of monozygotic twins requires the same phenotypic comparisons. The larger the number of traits for which no genetic difference is demonstrated, the greater the probability that the twins are identical. When the number of traits serving to test the genotypes of twins is sufficiently large, it becomes nearly certain that they would have shown one or more differences had they been dizygotic in origin. Failure to show any such difference, then, may be attributed to identical genotypes derived from a single zygote.

Let us outline the procedure one might actually follow in using twins to study the relative roles of genotype and environment in producing specific traits. The objective is to score separately the percentage of identical and nonidentical twin pairs reared together in which one or both siblings have the trait under consideration. Suppose one wished to study the *ABO blood group* in this respect. One would determine the percentage of *concordance,* that is, the percentages of identical and of nonidentical pairs in which both members of a pair have the same phenotype. In the case of identical twins concordance for ABO blood type is found to be 100%.

In determining concordance for nonidentical twins one usually scores only pairs in which the twins are of the same sex. This convention is necessary because the post-natal environment of twins of opposite sex

FIGURE 6–6. *Identical twins, Ira and Joel, at 3½ months, at 8 years, and at 19 years of age. (Courtesy of Mrs. Reida Postrel Herskowitz, July 14, 1946.)*

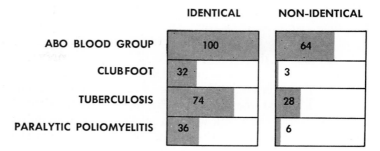

FIGURE 6–7. *Discordance (unshaded) and percentage concordance (shaded) for various physical traits in twins reared together.*

is likely to be more different than that of twins of the same sex. (If the environment differed for the two kinds of twins, one would not be able to specify whether the environment or the genotype was the cause of a phenotypic difference that is greater among nonidenticals than identicals.) Only twins of the same sex are used in the twin studies discussed here.

The concordance for ABO blood type is approximately 64% for nonidenticals. Had concordance been the same (64% or 100%) for both types of twins, we would conclude that there is no net genetic or environmental difference for ABO blood group in the two types of twins. The concordances observed do differ, however, and do so in a particular direction. Because of this difference the 100% concordance for identicals must mean that this trait is determined genetically with a penetrance of 100% despite the environmental fluctuations normally occurring between identical twins. Since an equivalent amount of environmental fluctuation caused no differences in the case of identicals, the lower percentage of concordance for nonidenticals cannot be attributed in any part to environment. This lower concordance must be attributed, therefore, to the differences in genotype which nonidenticals can have in this respect.

Of course, we could have predicted such a result from the previous knowledge that ABO blood type is genetically determined and is known to have complete penetrance. The lower concordance for nonidenticals, therefore, must be due to their receiving different genotypes from parents, one or both of whom were heterozygous for I^A or I^B.

It is theoretically possible to obtain a result in which concordance is lower for identicals than it is for nonidenticals. Such a difference in concordance could be ascribed to environmental differences being greater among the identicals than among the nonidenticals.

Consider the results of concordance studies for some physical traits in twins (Figure 6–7). Concordance for clubfoot is 32% for identicals, but only 3% for nonidenticals. The extra concordance of 29% (32% minus 3%) found among identicals must be attributed to their identical genotype. The 3% concordance found among nonidenticals might be due entirely to similarity in genotype or entirely to the environment, or to some combination of these two factors. Since we cannot decide from these data, we conclude that in twins or other individuals exposed to the same environment that twins are, the occurrence of clubfoot can be attributed to genotype approximately 29% of the time, with 32% as the approximate upper limit.

In the case of the identicals, 68% of the time the second twin failed to have clubfoot when the first twin did. The failure of concordance is called *discordance*. The 68% discordance between identicals is attributable to differences in their environment. It is concluded, then, that in twins or other individuals exposed to the same environment that twins are, the occurrence of clubfoot is the result of the environment approximately 68% of the time, with 71% as the approximate upper limit.

Concordance–discordance studies reveal only the relative contributions of genotype and environment to a particular phenotype (clubfoot, for example, as in the case just discussed). Such studies do not teach us anything about the kinds of environment involved when the genotype determines the phenotype under consideration, nor do they teach us anything about the genotypes involved when the environment decides the phenotype. The clubfoot twin studies also tell us nothing about the effect upon penetrance of clubfoot caused by environmental differences greater than those found between twins reared together. Application of the conclusions from twin studies to the general population assumes that environments for twins and nontwins are the same. Such an assumption may be invalid.

In the case of *tuberculosis,* concordance is 74% for identicals and 28% for nonidenticals. Accepting the supposition that both types of twins have the same average exposure to the tubercle bacillus, the susceptibility to this disease is determined genetically 46 to 74% of the time and environmentally 26 to 54% of the time. In support of the view that the extra concordance among identicals has a genetic basis is the finding that concordant identicals usually have the same form of this disease, affecting corresponding organs with the same severity, whereas this similarity is less frequent among concordant nonidenticals.

In earlier studies, *paralytic poliomyelitis* was 36% concordant for identicals and 6% concordant for nonidenticals. As in the case of tuberculosis, the occurrence of the disease probably did not depend upon the infective organisms because most human beings were exposed to them normally. Accordingly, the incidence of this disease depended upon the rest of the environment 64 to 70% of the time and the genotype 30 to 36% of the time. In the case of *measles,* the fact that concordance is very high among both types of twins simply means that any genetic basis for susceptibility to this disease is quite uniform throughout the population from which the twin samples were obtained.

The relative contributions of genotype and environment to personality and other mental traits can also be studied by the twin method. When a metronome is run at a series of different speeds, the tempo preferred by different persons is different. *Tempo preference* may be considered to be one aspect of the general personality. When tests are made to compare the tempo preferred by identical twins, the difference in their scores is found to be 7.8 of the units employed (Figure 6–8). This is, as might be expected, not significantly different from the difference in score of 8.7 units obtained by testing a given individual on different occasions. However, nonidenticals have a difference in score of 15, which is significantly different, being about twice that of the identicals. Since nontwin siblings have a difference in score of 14.5, they prove to be as similar in this respect as are nonidentical twins. Finally, unrelated persons show a difference in score of 19.5 units. Since the greater the genetic similarity the smaller the differ-

INDIVIDUALS	DIFFERENCE IN SCORE
Same person on different occasions	8.7
Monozygotic twins	7.8
Dizygotic twins	15.0
Siblings	14.5
Unrelated	19.5

FIGURE 6–8. *Variation in preferred tempo. (After C. Stern.)*

ence in score, there is clearly a genotypic contribution to this personality trait.

Studies of twins for the mental disease *schizophrenia* show concordance of 86% for identicals and 14% for nonidenticals. However, it is likely that the environment is not the same for both types of twins, differences in social environment causing more discordance in the case of nonidenticals than in the case of identicals. Nevertheless, in support of the view that not all the concordance for identicals is attributable to their similar environment and that some genotypic basis exists for concordance are two cases of identical twins who were separated, raised in different environments, yet were concordant at about the same age.

Different people, of course, score differently on I.Q. examinations. The differences in ability to answer questions on these examinations can be used to measure what may be called *test intelligence.* Although the scores of nonsiblings vary widely above and below 100, the difference between the scores of twins reared together is only 3.1 for identicals but 7.5 for nonidenticals. Clearly, identity in genotype makes for greater similarity in score. Identicals reared apart have scores that differ by 6. In this case the

greater difference in environment makes for a greater difference in performance of identicals, but this is still not so great a difference as is obtained between nonidenticals reared together. Therefore, both genotypic and environmental factors affect the trait, test intelligence.

In the case of ABO blood group we have already discussed the nature of the genetic factors involved. Although the twin and other methods used in this section tell whether genotypic differences are associated with the occurrence of the other phenotypes considered, they provide no information regarding the location, number, or recombinational properties of the genes involved.

Developmental Effects

Many of the mutants present at fertilization in multicellular plant and animal forms are detected by some visible change they produce in morphology. This phenotypic change is usually macroscopic and is first noted a considerable time after the organism starts its development. How does the mutant change normal development in order to produce the new morphological result? The answer to this question involves the manner in which phenotypes (of any type) come into being via gene action, and is the subject of *phenogenetics,* one aspect of which is *developmental genetics.*

Consider the genetic and phenogenetic information obtained from studying one particular case. In the chicken a novel type occurs whose legs are so short that they give the impression that the bird is creeping. This abnormal "Creeper" phenotype and the normal phenotype [3] can be seen in the roosters in Figure 6–9.

The genetic study of this phenotype gives the following results: reciprocal crosses of Creeper by normal produce a 1:1 ratio of

[3] Studied by W. Landauer, V. Hamburger, D. Rudnick, and L. C. Dunn.

FIGURE 6–9. *Normal (right) and Creeper (left) roosters.* (*Courtesy of L. C. Dunn; reprinted by permission of McGraw-Hill Book Co., Inc., from* Study Guide and Workbook for Genetics *by I. H. Herskowitz. Copyright, 1960.*)

Creeper:normal chicks; Creepers crossed with Creepers give, in the adult stage, 775:388 as Creeper:normal, a result which is considered an excellent fit to a 2:1 ratio. It is reasonable to suppose, therefore, that Creeper is heterozygous for a single pair of segregating genes, in which the Creeper gene, *Cp,* is dominant to its normal allele, +. The 2:1 ratio is taken to indicate that the mutant homozygote, *Cp Cp,* is lethal. The possibility that *Cp* acts as a recessive lethal is supported by a comparison of the survival frequency of embryos having normal parents with that of embryos having parents both of which are Creeper. It is found that about 25% more embryos die within three days of incubation in the latter than in the former case.

What is the developmental, phenogenetic basis for *Cp Cp,* which acts as a recessive lethal; *Cp +,* which produces Creeper; and + +, which produces normal? Although *Cp Cp* usually dies within three days of incubation, on rare occasions it survives 19 days, about the time of hatching from the shell. Such a rare Creeper homozygote is shown at the left of Figure 6–10 (the comparable normal individual is at the right)

and possesses the following syndrome of malformations: the eyes are split, smaller than normal, and have no eyelids; the head is misshapen, and the body is smaller; the skeleton is not ossified and—as seen on top of the black paper used as background in the figure—only the digits of the limbs are well formed.

A study of *Cp +* development shows that, at seven days of incubation, the leg buds are shorter than in normal embryos. This morphological manifestation of *Cp* action must be based upon events occurring earlier in development, for at 48 hours of incubation (Figure 6–11), a *Cp +* embryo (left) is smaller, less developed, and does not have the head flexure already present in a + + embryo (right). In fact, differences like this can be seen even twelve hours earlier, i.e., at 36 hours of incubation.

In both the homozygote and heterozygote for *Cp,* the differentiation of cartilage has been disturbed. The *Cp +* individual has the disease called *chondrodystrophy* (or *achondroplasia*) and the *Cp Cp* individual has the cartilage disease, *phocomelia* (see p. 4). Both diseases were recognized in human families more than a hundred years

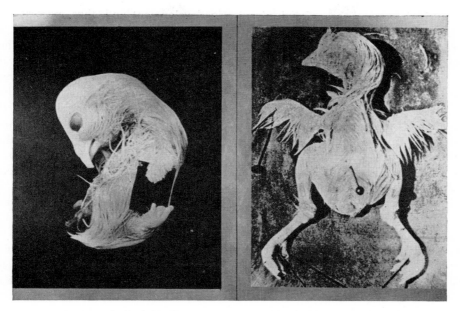

FIGURE 6–10. *Normal (right) and Creeper (left) homozygote at about 19 days of development.* (*Courtesy of L. C. Dunn; reprinted by permission of McGraw-Hill Book Co., Inc., from* Study Guide and Workbook for Genetics *by I. H. Herskowitz. Copyright, 1960.*)

FIGURE 6–11. *Normal (right) and Creeper (left) heterozygote embryos at about 48 hours of development.* (*Courtesy of L. C. Dunn; reprinted by permission of McGraw-Hill Book Co., Inc., from* Study Guide and Workbook for Genetics *by I. H. Herskowitz. Copyright, 1960.*)

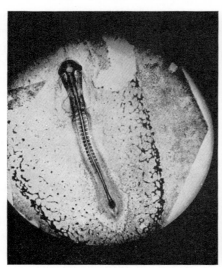
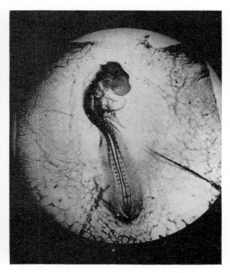

ago; when both parents are chondrodystrophic, some children are phocomelic and have severely deformed limbs. The condition observed in such individuals can be attributed to the presence of a mutant gene (like the *Cp* gene in fowl) in a double dose, that is, when homozygous.

It was already mentioned that at 36 hours of incubation, *Cp* + individuals develop more slowly than + + individuals. In normals at this stage the tissue for the hind limb buds grows very rapidly, whereas other tissues grow more slowly. If some of the effect of *Cp* in single or double dose is to cause a generalized slowing-down of growth, the structures most affected will be those growing most rapidly at the time. Such a genetically-induced slowdown in growth rate, starting at about this particular time in development, is expected, therefore, to reduce the size of the hind limbs and the long bones of fore limbs.

It should not be concluded, however, that the tissue for hind limb is completely passive to *Cp* action and that its sole response is the slowdown in growth rate. We can study the developmental fate of prospective hind-limb tissue by transplantation experiments. If such tissue from a normal chick embryo is transplanted to a more forward position in another normal chick embryo, it grows out as a normal limb. If, however, the prospective hind-limb tissue from a homozygous Creeper embryo is transplanted to a more forward position in a normal chick embryo, it grows out as a Creeper type leg. This result demonstrates that even at a very early stage, before there is any actual hind limb, prospective limb tissue from Creeper is already permanently determined by the Creeper genotype to develop as Creeper limb, that is, its *competence* to develop normally is already lost.

It also should not be assumed that all abnormal tissues found in homozygous Creepers have been determined at an early stage

in development and, thus, possess only the Creeper alternative. As mentioned, *Cp Cp* individuals have small, split eyes. The early eye *anlage* (*imaginal disc*) from a normal embryo can be transplanted to an abnormal position in a normal embryo. In this position it grows into an eye just like that of homozygous Creeper, but an eye anlage from a *Cp Cp* embryo, transplanted to the eye-forming region of a normal embryo, grows into a normal eye. We can conclude, therefore, that the abnormal Creeper eye is due, not to some change in the competence of the eye tissue, but rather to some kind of abnormality in its surroundings. It can, therefore, be supposed that in the Creeper homozygote the normally competent eye anlage probably undergoes a kind of starvation due to the poor circulation that the genotype produces. Such a hypothesis is supported by two lines of evidence: first, most prospective tissues of *Cp Cp* placed on a complete culture medium *in vitro* grow quite normally, although heart tissue does not grow as well as normal heart tissue; second, when limb rudiments from normal embryos are grown *in vitro* in a nutritionally dilute culture medium, they develop many of the characteristics of the *Cp Cp* limbs.

The study of Creeper fowl demonstrates that the multiple effects of this mutant which have been found at the completion of development are due to gene-directed changes originating much earlier in development. In fact, we can infer from the developmental fate of prospective limbs in Creeper embryos that a genotype produces changes that precede morphological changes. The Creeper gene apparently modifies the physiology of the individual in such a way that general growth is slowed down, and the prospective fate of certain tissues is fixed, so that the morphological changes later noted are a direct consequence of these changes. The gene-caused physiological changes can be attributed, in turn, to changes in the biochemical reactions involved in cellular metabolism.

The Creeper case apparently involves genetically determined metabolic changes that take place within certain cells (to produce an abnormal nutritional environment) and affect the functioning of other cells (the differentiation of eye tissue). Let us consider two groups of studies with mice to learn more about the genetic control of effects produced external to the cell in which the gene acts. One group of investigations [4] involves a comparative study of normal and dwarf mice. The dwarfs have all of their body parts proportionally reduced in size, because of an apparently completely recessive gene in homozygous condition. During early development, both dwarf and normal mice grow at equal speeds, but later, the dwarf suddenly stops growing and never reaches sexual maturity. A microscopic study of the anterior pituitary gland shows that it is considerably smaller in the dwarf than in the normal mouse. Moreover, certain large cells, normally present, are absent in dwarf pituitaries; apparently these are the cells that secrete growth hormone. That this is a case of genetically produced *pituitary dwarfism* is supported by the following type of experiment: using pairs of dwarf litter mates about 30 days old, one mouse of a pair is injected with extracts of pituitary glands from dwarf mice (Figure 6–12, B) each day for 30 days, whereas the other mouse is injected in a comparable way with extracts of pituitary glands from normal mice (Figure 6–12, A). During this period of treatment, the former mouse remains essentially dwarf, while the latter grows until it is virtually normal. Here, then, we are dealing with a chemical messenger, pituitary hormone, which regulates growth in general, and whose presence is dependent upon a single pair of genes.

[4] Based upon work of G. D. Snell, of P. E. Smith and E. C. MacDowell, and of T. Francis.

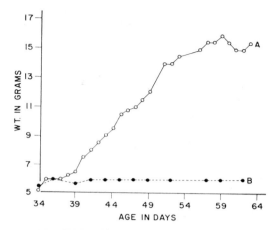

FIGURE 6–12. *Effect of injecting pituitary gland extracts into dwarf mice.* (*See text for explanation.*)

The second group of studies is concerned with mouse tails. The normal (+ +) mouse has a long tail; a particular mutant strain has a shortened tail (*Brachyury*, or *Brachy*).[5] Brachy crossed with Brachy produces ⅔ Brachy : ⅓ normal offspring, a ratio which suggests that the gene for Brachy, *T*, is dominant for short tails and recessive for lethality. Brachy mice should, therefore, be *T* +. When the embryology of offspring produced from a mating between Brachys (*T* + × *T* +) is studied, about 25% of the embryos are normal (+ +), about 50% show tail degeneration by 11 days of development (*T* +), and about 25% of the embryos (*T T*) are monsters (Figure 6–13) which have misdirected posterior limb buds, zigzag neural tubes, and no notochord. Since their whole posterior part is undeveloped, *T T* individuals cannot make a placental connection and die after about 10 or 11 days of development.

Consider further the *T T* individual, whose segments, or *somites,* in the posterior part

[5] Based upon work of L. C. Dunn, P. Chesley, and D. Bennett.

of the body are so grossly abnormal. Other embryological work shows that proper somite formation depends on the presence of presumptive notochordal tissue. When normal, presumptive notochord tissue is present, its surrounding normal mesoderm is induced to form cartilage and vertebral segments. It seems reasonable to attribute the failure of cartilage and vertebrae formation in *T T* individuals to the failure of its presumptive notochord (which has lost the ability to develop into notochord) to induce the differen-

tiation of mesoderm. This explanation is subject to test in certain experiments employing tissue culture. Using tissues from normal mice, presumptive notochordal tissue, which has mesodermal tissue from the same or another individual wrapped around it, is placed in the tissue culture medium. Development of cartilage and vertebral segments occurs under these conditions. Moreover, the mesoderm from normal embryos also develops into cartilage and vertebral segments, when surrounding presumptive

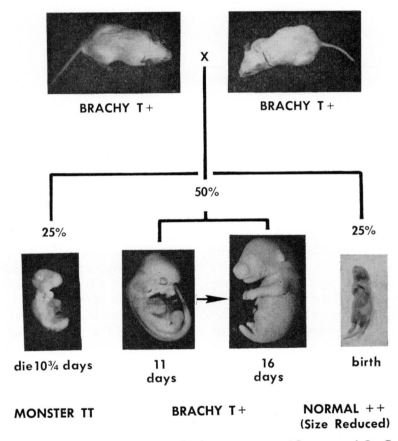

FIGURE 6–13. *Brachyury in the house mouse. (Courtesy of L. C. Dunn; reprinted by permission of McGraw-Hill Book Co., Inc., from* Study Guide and Workbook for Genetics *by I. H. Herskowitz. Copyright, 1960.)*

notochord from young *T T* embryos; under similar conditions, however, mesoderm from *T T* embryos does not form cartilage or vertebrae when it surrounds presumptive notochord from normal embryos. We must conclude—contrary to expectation—that the normal inductive relationship is disturbed in *T T* because its mesoderm is incompetent to respond to the normal inductive stimuli of presumptive notochord tissue.

The preceding discussion shows that genetic changes can influence or control development in multicellular organisms by modifying (1) the relative growth rates of parts (as in Creeper) and (2) the over-all growth rate (as in pituitary dwarfism) without affecting the competence of some or all of the tissues affected. Genetic changes can also affect differentiation by changing tissue competence (homozygous Creeper limbs). When adjacent tissues interact by induction, differentiation can be modified by gene-caused changes in competence to respond to inducing agents (nonresponsiveness of *T T* mesoderm to presumptive notochord) and, presumably, also by changes in inducing ability. It should be realized, however, that although differentiation and development in higher multicellular organisms involve intercellular interactions of all the types mentioned, some cellular traits are produced solely through the intracellular action of the genotype. Such behavior occurs, for example, in mutants induced during embryogeny which have detrimental or lethal effects in the cells containing them.

SUMMARY AND CONCLUSIONS

Different alleles may produce detectable effects upon viability at any stage in the life history of an individual and may modify the expected phenotypic ratio so that certain classes of offspring are in excess, in reduced frequency, or are absent. The last effect is produced by dominant as well as recessive lethal genes.

A gene usually produces effects upon a wide variety of morphological and biochemical traits. These pleiotropic effects are the consequence of a pedigree of causes traceable, in some cases, to a single action on the part of the gene. It is hypothesized that most, if not all, genes have only one, probably biochemical, phenotypic action.

Penetrance and expressivity depend upon both the genotype and the environment. The traits most useful for the study of transmission genetics are those whose penetrance is 100% and whose expressivity is uniform when subjected to the normal variations of environment. In human beings the occurrence of essentially duplicate parts within an individual, and of identical and nonidentical twins, offers the opportunity to test the effect of environment and of genotype upon the penetrance and expressivity of a given phenotypic alternative.

It has been shown that a considerable number of physical and mental traits are determined by the joint action of genotype and environment, sometimes one and sometimes the other having the greater influence.

The twin methods described do not study the transmissive characteristics of the genotypes involved. They do not, therefore, reveal anything regarding the location, number, or recombinational properties of genes.

Phenogenetics, the study of how genetically determined phenotypes come into being, can be investigated by using morphological traits.   Although phenogenetics often starts out as a study of the developmental genetics of morphology, the final morphological outcome—which usually is a pleiotropic one—is often found to be based upon earlier morphological changes which are, in turn, preceded by still earlier-occurring physiological changes.   Consequently, the developmental genetics of morphological features is based upon gene-caused physiological changes and leads to a study of physiological genetics.

Physiological genetics reveals that the physiological effect of the genotype is sometimes intracellular and sometimes intercellular.   The gene-based action that certain cells have on others can involve a general or localized control of growth rates and differentiation.   This action can occur nearby, via induction; or at a distance, by means of a general nutritive effect, by hormones, and probably by nerve impulses and muscular contractions.   Gene changes can modify the competence of a tissue.

Comprehension of physiological genetics must, in turn, ultimately involve a detailed understanding of how genes influence metabolism, and since metabolism involves the study of physical and chemical reactions, phenogenetics must ultimately be described in biophysical and biochemical terms.   The phenogenetic study of the gene causing sickle cell anemia proceeded from morphology to physiology to biochemistry.

REFERENCES

Dobzhansky, Th., and Holtz, A. M., "A Re-examination of Manifold Effects of Genes in *Drosophila melanogaster*," Genetics, 28:295–303, 1943.

Goldschmidt, R. B., *Theoretical Genetics*, Berkeley and Los Angeles: University of California, 1955.

Gluecksohn-Waelsch, S., "Physiological Genetics of the Mouse," Adv. in Genet., 4:2–49, 1951.

Grüneberg, H., *The Pathology of Development*, Oxford: Blackwell, 1963.

Hadorn, E., "Patterns of Development and Biochemical Pleiotropy," Cold Spring Harb. Sympos. Quant. Biol., 21:363–374, 1956.

Hadorn, E., *Developmental Genetics and Lethal Factors*, New York: J. Wiley & Sons, 1961.

Kallman, F. J., *Heredity in Health and Mental Disorder*, New York: Norton, 1953.

Landauer, W., "On the Chemical Production of Developmental Abnormalities," J. Cell Comp. Physiol., 43 (Suppl.):261–305, 1954.

Montagu, A., *Human Heredity*, Cleveland: World, 1959.

Newman, H. H., *Multiple Human Births*, New York: Doubleday, Doran, 1940.

Osborn, F., *Preface to Eugenics*, Rev. Ed., New York: Harper, 1951.

Osborn, R. H., and De George, F. V., *Genetic Basis of Morphological Variation*, Cambridge, Mass.: Harvard University Press, 1959.

Sang, J. H., "Penetrance, Expressivity and Thresholds," J. Heredity, 54:143–151, 1963.

Waddington, C. H., *New Patterns in Genetics and Development*, New York: Columbia University Press, 1962.

Wright, S., "The Physiology of the Gene," Physiol. Rev., 41:487–527, 1941.

RICHARD BENEDICT GOLDSCHMIDT (*1878–1958*). (*From Genetics, vol. 45, p. 1, 1960.*)

QUESTIONS FOR DISCUSSION

6.1. Can two genetically different individuals ever have identical viabilities? Explain.

6.2. Why can you not conclude, from the evidence presented, that the genes for MN blood type in man, or for auria phenotypes in the snapdragon, are pleiotropic?

6.3. How can genes be lethal to a genotype without producing a corpse?

6.4. Two curly-winged, stubble-bristled Drosophila are mated. Among a large number of adult progeny scored the ratio obtained is: 4 curly stubble:2 curly only:2 stubble only:1 neither curly nor stubble (therefore normal, wild-type). Explain these results genetically.

6.5. In Drosophila, a mating of ♂ A × ♀ B or of ♂ C × ♀ D produces F_1, ¼ of which turn brown and die in the egg stage. If, however, the matings are ♂ A × ♀ D or ♂ C × ♀ B, none of the F_1 eggs turn brown and die. How can you explain these results genetically?

6.6. In what respects are the terms *penetrance* and *dominance* similar and in what respects are they different?

6.7. Is it the gene for dull red eye color that is pleiotropic in Drosophila, or is it the allele for white eye color? Explain.

6.8. Most of the genes studied in Drosophila affect the exoskeleton of the fly. Do you suppose these genes also have effects on the internal organs? Why?

6.9. Would you expect to find individuals who are homozygous for polydactyly? Explain. What phenotype would you expect them to have? Why?

6.10. Why are genes whose penetrance is 100% and expressivity is uniform particularly valuable in a study of gene properties?

6.11. Two normal people marry and have a single child who is polydactylous on one hand only. How can you explain this?

6.12. A certain type of baldness is due to a gene that is dominant in men and recessive in women. A nonbald man marries a bald woman and they have a bald son. Give the genotypes of all individuals and discuss the penetrance of the genes involved.

6.13. A man has one brown eye and one blue eye. Explain.

6.14. How could you distinguish whether a given phenotype is due to a rare dominant gene with complete penetrance or a rare recessive gene of low penetrance?

6.15. In determining whether or not twins are dizygotic, why must one study traits for which one or both parents are heterozygotes?

6.16. Are mistakes ever made in classifying twins as dizygotic in origin? Why?

6.17. Can the gene P for polydactyly be considered as being partially dominant? As having pleiotropic effects? Explain.

6.18. When nonidentical twins are discordant for ABO blood type, why must one or both parents have been heterozygous for I^A or I^B?

6.19. Invent a particular situation that would result in greater discordance for identical than for nonidentical twins.

6.20. What would be the probability of twins being dizygotic in origin if both have the genotype $aa\,Bb\,CC\,Dd\,Ee\,Ff$, each pair of alleles segregating independently, if the parents are genotypically $Aa\,Bb\,CC\,DD\,Ee\,Ff$ and $Aa\,BB\,CC\,dd\,ee\,FF$?

6.21. How would you test whether, in women, there is a genetic basis for the maturation of more than one egg at a time?

6.22. In what way can you imagine that the paternal genotype could influence the frequency of twinning?

6.23. Is tuberculosis "inherited"? Explain.

6.24. What can twin studies by themselves tell you about genes? About genetic recombination?

6.25. Is it valid to apply the conclusions from twin studies to nontwin members of the population? Explain.

6.26. Does this chapter present any new information about genetic properties? Explain.

6.27. In a genetically black strain of the house mouse, W. L. Russell found a mouse with a splotchy phenotype—having white spotting on the belly and occasionally on the back. Splotchy × black gives both splotchy and black types of progeny. Splotchy × splotchy also produces the same types, but a number of embryos die *in utero* at 14 days of age and are characterized by a kinky tail and *spina bifida*. Discuss the genetic basis for and the dominance relationships involved in these results.

6.28. It has been found that mouse ovaries transplanted from embryos to adult females can develop to maturity and produce offspring. Describe how you would proceed to determine the genotype of the abnormal embryos described in 6.27.

6.29. Do you agree with J. H. Sang that penetrance (P) and expressivity (E) ". . . are descriptive terms which cloak our ignorance of the underlying reactions which determine particular values of P and E in any situation"? Explain.

6.30. In the Japanese quail (*Coturnix coturnix*) matings between normal-appearing individuals of certain strains produce some micromelic embryos, having a short broad head with bulging eyes, which die between 11 and 16 days of incubation. How would you proceed to determine whether these abnormal embryos are homozygotes for a single recessive lethal gene?

6.31. What conclusions can you draw from the data of B. Harvald and M. Hauge (J. Amer. Med. Assoc., 186:749–753, 1963) obtained from an unbiased sample of Danish twins?

	Twin pairs	One twin cancerous	Both twins cancerous	
			At same site	At different sites
Identical	1528	143	8	13
Nonidentical	2609	292	9	39

6.32. In what way does the study of genes help us understand normal embryonic development?

6.33. If most somatic cells have the same genetic content, why do different cells not differentiate in the same way?

6.34. In what ways can genes regulate embryonic development?

6.35. Do the studies of Creeper, of Brachy, or of pituitary dwarfism in mice offer any support for the view that most, if not all, genes have a single, primary effect?

6.36. What is the relationship between phenogenetics, developmental genetics, physiological genetics, and biochemical genetics?

6.37. Discuss the comparative importance of genes that act earlier, as compared with those which act later, in development.

6.38. Do you suppose that all genes act at all times in all cells of the body? Why?

6.39. "This chapter tells more about development than it does about genes." Do you agree? Why?

6.40. What can be learned about gene action if the gene studied (1) has only two alternatives, (2) has many alternatives?

Chapter 7

SEX CHROMOSOMES
AND SEX-LINKED GENES

SINCE sex has phenotypic alternatives (maleness and femaleness), the genetic basis for sex can be investigated. This basis cannot be determined by studying garden pea plants because they are bisexual; that is, both sexual alternatives occur in one individual, and no phenotypic differences will be produced by genetic recombination. The typical Drosophila individual, however, being either male or female (Figure 2–6, p. 23), can be used to study the genetic basis for sex.

When normal males and females mate together, the male:female ratio of their progeny is approximately 1:1. This suggests the simplest hypothesis—that sex in Drosophila is determined by a single gene pair, one of the sexes being a homozygote and the other a heterozygote. For the moment, however,

which sex corresponds to which genotype cannot be designated.

In accordance with the view that chromosomes contain the genes, one pair of chromosomes should be concerned with sex. Let us call the presumed homologous pair of chromosomes carried by the homozygote for the sex genes the XX pair and those carried by the heterozygote, the XY pair. Segregation and random cross fertilization then would produce equal numbers of XX and XY progeny. The X and the Y chromosomes presumed to carry the genes for sex can be called *sex chromosomes;* each of the other chromosomes which an individual carries can be called an *autosome* (A). Since *Drosophila melanogaster* has a diploid chromosome number of four pairs, each individual can be represented as either $XX + 3AA$ or $XY + 3AA$.

Sex-Linked Genes

Consider the results of certain crosses involving the recessives *cubitus interruptus* (*ci*) and *ebony body color* (*e*) and their dominant alleles ci^+ (normal wing venation) and e^+ (gray body color). One cross, $ci^+ci\ e^+e$ by *ci ci e e*—a dihybrid parent and a double recessive parent (Figure 7–1)— produces offspring in a 1:1:1:1 ratio thus

P₁ $ci^+ci\ e^+e$ x $ci\ ci\ e\ e$

G₁   ¼ci^+e^+, ¼ci^+e, ¼$ci\ e^+$, ¼$ci\ e$ $ci\ e$

F₁   ¼$ci^+ci\ e^+e$

        ¼$ci^+ci\ e\ e$

        ¼$ci\ ci\ e^+e$

        ¼$ci\ ci\ e\ e$

FIGURE 7–1. *Results of back-crossing a dihybrid.*

demonstrating that the two pairs of genes are segregating independently. The same result and conclusions hold for the cross of ci^+ci ee by ci ci e^+e. Consider, next, crosses in which the sex and wing venation traits are studied simultaneously in reciprocal matings—ci^+ci XX by ci ci XY and ci^+ci XY by ci ci XX. In both cases the result is a $1:1:1:1$ ratio of cubitus male, cubitus female, normal male, normal female. Here, then, the sex genes segregate independently of the genes for cubitus. Therefore, according to our hypothesis, the ci alleles are located autosomally.

Similarly, each of the reciprocal crosses— e^+e XX by e e XY and e^+e XY by e e XX —also gives a $1:1:1:1$ ratio, indicating that the gene for ebony is located autosomally. Since the genes for ebony and cubitus segregate independently of each other, they must be located on different pairs of autosomes.

Even though we cannot yet specify which sex is XX or XY, the last two types of crosses can be described as reciprocally made backcrosses of a monohybrid; that is, one time the hybrid parent was the male, the other time the hybrid parent was the female. In both cases the two traits appear in a $1:1$ ratio among the sons, and in a $1:1$ ratio among the daughters.

At this point, an earlier statement (p. 32)—that all crosses give the same results when made reciprocally—can be understood to mean that the observed phenotypes and their proportions are the same for sons and daughters even though the crosses were made reciprocally. So, for example, in a cross of the dihybrids ci^+ci e^+e by ci^+ci e^+e there would be a $9:3:3:1$ ratio among the sons and a $9:3:3:1$ ratio among the daughters because the parents' sex genes were located in the sex chromosomes, whereas the other gene pairs were in nonhomologous pairs of autosomes. Previously, all the crosses we dealt with involved autosomal recombination. Because autosomal genes

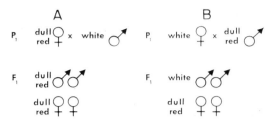

FIGURE 7–2. *Phenotypic results of reciprocal matings involving eye color.* ♂ ♂ = *males,* ♀ ♀ = *females.*

always segregate independently of the sex genes, sex did not influence the results; that is, the phenotypic results of autosomal recombination crosses are the same for sons and daughters even though reciprocal matings are made.

But consider the results of crosses involving the *dull-red* (w^+) and *white* (w) *eye color alleles*. Using pure lines, dull-red ♀ by white ♂ (Figure 7–2A) produces all dull-red sons and daughters in F_1, as expected, since w^+ is dominant. However, the reciprocal cross (Figure 7–2B), white ♀ by dull-red ♂, produces only white sons and dull-red daughters. Although the first cross gives the same result for sons as for daughters, the second (reciprocal) cross gives different results: sons resemble their mothers; daughters resemble their fathers. Because such different results are never obtained from reciprocal matings involving autosomal genes, we can conclude that w^+ and its alleles are not located autosomally.

Let us assume that the gene for white eye is located in the sex chromosomes and, therefore, is *sex-linked* and investigate the consequences of this on the gene's transmission relative to the sex phenotype.[1]

If we assume that females are XY and males XX, the first cross then is dull-red female $X^{w+}Y^{w+}$ by white male X^wX^w (Figure 7–3, A–1), and the F_1 expected are

[1] See T. H. Morgan (1910).

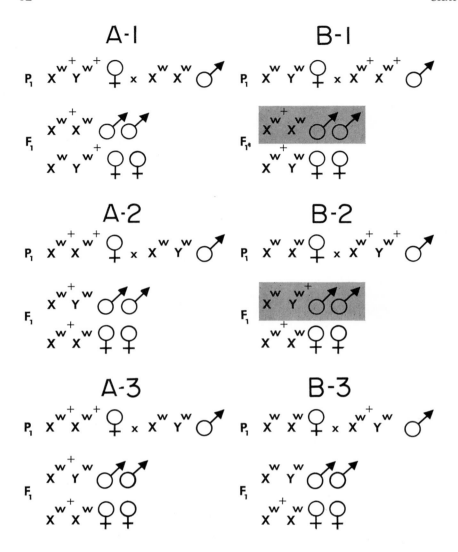

FIGURE 7–3. *Three attempts (A-1 and B-1, A-2 and B-2, A-3 and B-3) to represent matings A and B in Fig. 7–2 genotypically. Shaded genotypes must be incorrect.*

$X^{w^+}X^w$ sons and $X^wY^{w^+}$ daughters, all dull-red-eyed, as found. The reciprocal cross (Figure 7–3, B–1), therefore, is white ♀ X^wY^w by dull-red ♂ $X^{w^+}X^{w^+}$. The F_1 daughters ($X^{w^+}Y^w$) are expected to be dull-red-eyed, as found. The F_1 sons (X^wX^w), also expected to be dull-red-eyed, are, however, actually white-eyed. Therefore, we must reject this particular hypothesis for correlating sex chromosomes and eye color genes.

So let us assume the reverse situation— that females are XX and males XY. The same crosses are represented now as dull-red

♀ $X^{w+}X^{w+}$ by white ♂ X^wY^w producing $X^{w+}X^w$ (dull-red) daughters and $X^{w+}Y^w$ (dull-red) sons (Figure 7–3, A–2); reciprocally, white ♀ X^wX^w by dull-red ♂ $X^{w+}Y^{w+}$ produces $X^{w+}X^w$ (dull-red) daughters and X^wY^{w+} (dull-red) sons (Figure 7–3, B–2). Again an expected phenotype is contrary to fact—the phenotype of the F_1 sons being white, not dull-red.

Since we cannot explain these observations by identifying maleness with XX or XY alone, we must increase the number of assumptions. Let us then test two hypotheses simultaneously: (1) Assuming that Drosophila males are XY and (2) the Y chromosome carries w but no other allele, then the genotypes and results of the first cross described in the preceding paragraph remain unchanged (Figure 7–3, A–3); the reciprocal cross (Figure 7–3, B–3) becomes white ♀ X^wX^w by dull-red ♂ $X^{w+}Y^w$, producing $X^{w+}X^w$ (dull-red) daughters and X^wY^w (white) sons. Since these hypotheses fit the observations, we may accept them.

The recombination genetics of several traits in Drosophila other than sex and eye color also proves to be based upon a pair of genes in the sex chromosomes; that is, each case gives different results in F_1 when lines pure for different alternatives are crossed reciprocally. Moreover, each case can be explained by assuming that females are XX, males XY, and that the Y carries the most recessive and least effective allele known for the gene pair under test, as is w in the case of eye color. In such cases, the absence from the Y of a partially or completely dominant allele must mean that such alleles cannot be produced by mutation of the most recessive allele simply because this recessive allele does not exist on the Y. Accordingly, the Y ordinarily lacks an allele of a gene located on the X; therefore, in Figure 7–3, A–3 and B–3 a Y should be substituted for each Y^w.

Whenever the Y carries no allele of a gene on the X, sons will express phenotypically whatever allele is contained in the single X each son receives from his mother. With regard to these genes, therefore, a Drosophila female is being test crossed whenever and to whomever she mates, since her X chromosome genotype can be determined directly from the phenotypes of her sons. An otherwise diploid individual carrying one or more unpaired genes is said to be *hemizygous* in this respect. For example, a gene in the X chromosome with no allele in the Y is hemizygous in the Drosophila male; half of the zygotes he produces will receive this allele in the X he contributes, whereas the half receiving the Y will not get one. The X of a Drosophila male is obtained from his mother and transmitted to each of his daughters; the Y is transmitted from father to son.

In *poultry* a mating of a female with nonbarred feathers to a male with barred feathers produces offspring which are all barred—barred (B) being dominant to nonbarred (b) (Figure 7–4A). In the reciprocal cross (Figure 7–4), barred ♀ by nonbarred ♂, all sons are barred and all daughters nonbarred. Here also the results of reciprocal matings differ, so that we are dealing again with sex-linkage. In the reciprocal cross, note that the exceptional F_1 are nonbarred, showing the recessive trait as in the case of Drosophila. But, in poultry the sex is opposite, since the exceptional F_1 are females. (The exceptional F_1 Drosophila were white-eyed males.) To explain these results we must assume that in poultry, as in Drosophila, sex is determined by XX vs. XY, and that the X chromosome does and the Y chromosome does not contain a gene for barred or nonbarred feathers. But, contrary to Drosophila, poultry males are XX and females, XY.

The genotypes of the bird crosses are, on these hypotheses, X^bY (nonbarred ♀) by

$X^B X^B$ (barred ♂), producing $X^B Y$ (barred ♀) and $X^B X^b$ (barred ♂) in F_1; the reciprocal mating of $X^B Y$ (barred ♀) by $X^b X^b$ (nonbarred ♂) produces $X^b Y$ (nonbarred ♀) and $X^B X^b$ (barred ♂) in F_1 (Figure 7–4, A–1 and B–1).

Support for the existence of sex chromosomes may be sought from cytological observations. If the gene content of the X and Y is different as in Drosophila and poultry, the cytological appearance of the two kinds of sex chromosomes might also be different. (Note, however, that the preceding explanation of sex-linkage was made independently of any cytological expectation.)

In Drosophila it is found cytologically (Figure 7–5) that three of the four pairs of chromosomes seen at mitotic metaphase correspond in the male and the female, homologs being very similar morphologically. In the female the homologs of the fourth pair are also morphologically similar. In the male, however, only one member of this pair looks like its homologs in the female; its partner's morphology is distinctly different. Thus, the distinctive cytological appearance of this last chromosome is consistent with the genetic expectation for a Y chromosome being present once in the male and not at all in the female. The other homolog in the male is then called the X and is present twice in the female. The reverse cytological picture is observed in poultry; here the homologs are similar for each pair of chromosomes in the male, whereas the female has one *heteromorphic pair;* that is,

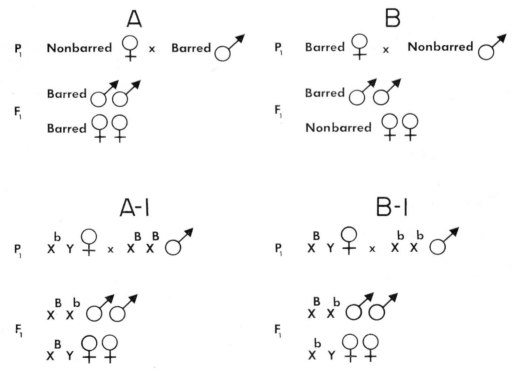

FIGURE 7–4. *Phenotypic (A and B) and genotypic (A-1 and B-1) results of reciprocal matings involving barred and nonbarred feathers in chickens.*

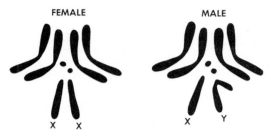

X   X   X   Y

FIGURE 7–5. *Silhouettes of chromosomes of Drosophila melanogaster as seen at mitotic metaphase.*

one pair whose members are morphologically different, one being similar to, one different from, the corresponding pair in the male.

As in birds, the male of moths, butterflies, and some amphibians and reptiles is XX and the females, XY. In human beings, genetic and cytological evidence shows XY to be male and XX to be female, just as in Drosophila. So in different species different sexes make two kinds of gametes; that is, different sexes are *heterogametic* with respect to sex chromosomes.

In man, a certain kind of *red-green color-blindness* is sex-linked due to a recessive allele, *c*, present on the X and absent on the Y. Accordingly, color-blind women (X^cX^c) who marry normal men (X^CY) have normal daughters (X^CX^c) and color-blind

FIGURE 7–6. *Pedigree showing a woman homozygous for the gene for hemophilia.*

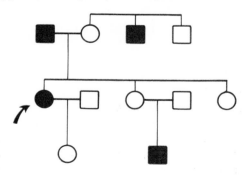

sons (X^cY). The classical bleeder's disease in human beings, *hemophilia type A*, is also due to an X-linked recessive gene, *h*, absent from the Y. This rare disease usually occurs in males. Recently, however, a few hemophilic women have been discovered in England. These homozygotes are extremely rare because, barring mutation, they must have a hemophilic father (X^hY) and a heterozygous mother (X^HX^h)—(Figure 7–6).

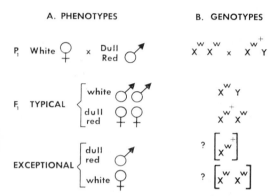

FIGURE 7–7. *Nonmutant exceptions in crosses involving eye color in Drosophila.*

Nondisjunction

Certain additional experiments have been performed with the sex-linked gene for white eye in Drosophila.[2] When white females (X^wX^w) are crossed with dull-red males $(X^{w+}Y)$ and large numbers of progeny are scored, not all F_1 are white sons (X^wY) and dull-red daughters $(X^{w+}X^w)$ as expected according to sex-linkage. One or two flies per thousand F_1 are exceptional dull-red-eyed sons or white-eyed daughters (Figure 7–7). These exceptional flies cannot be explained away as the result of careless scoring of phenotypes or contamination. Moreover, they cannot be explained as being due to mutation, since the mutation fre-

[2] Based upon work of C. B. Bridges.

quency from w^+ to w or the reverse is several orders of magnitude lower than the observed frequency of exceptional flies.

Since the exceptional F_1 females are white-eyed, each must carry $X^w X^w$ (Figure 7–7B). The only source of X's containing w is the mother. Accordingly, the father must fail to contribute his X^{w^+} chromosome to an exceptional daughter. Each exceptional dull-red-eyed son must carry X^{w^+}, which could be contributed only by the father.

In order to understand how this exceptional situation may come about, let us examine the normal consequence of meiosis in the Drosophila female as regards the sex chromosomes. Normally, the two X's synapse and form a tetrad, and due to segregation four nuclei are produced at the end of meiosis, each containing one X (Figure 7–8A). One of the four nuclei becomes the gametic (egg) nucleus; the other three are discarded (in polar bodies).

Suppose, however, segregation of the four strands in the X chromosome tetrad occasionally occurs improperly in either of two ways:

1. At anaphase I, instead of one dyad going to each pole, both dyads go to the same pole (Figure 7–8B). The daughter nucleus containing no X dyad undergoes the second meiotic division to produce two nuclei, neither one having an X. The other daughter nucleus, containing two dyads, proceeds through the second division, during which the two members of each dyad separate and go to opposite poles at anaphase II. The result is two daughter nuclei each containing two X's, one from each dyad. Therefore, at the end of meiosis, the failure of dyads to disjoin at anaphase I will result ultimately in four nuclei, two with no X and two with two X's. As a consequence the nucleus which becomes the gametic nucleus has a 50% chance of carrying no X and a 50% chance of carrying two X's.

2. Alternatively (see Figure 7–8C),

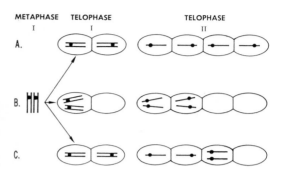

FIGURE 7–8. *Consequences of normal segregation of X chromosomes (A) and of its failure to occur (B and C).*

anaphase I is normal, and at telophase I two daughter nuclei are formed each containing one X dyad. The second meiotic division occurs normally in one of the daughter nuclei, producing two telophase II nuclei, each of which contains one X. In the other daughter nucleus, however, the members of the X dyad fail to separate at anaphase II and go instead into the same telophase II nucleus. This failure of monads to disjoin at anaphase II produces two nuclei, one containing no X and the other containing two X's. Consequently, the gametic nucleus has a 25% chance of carrying no X, a 25% chance of carrying two X's, and a 50% chance of carrying one X.

The occasional failure of normal separation of chromatids at either the first or the second meiotic division would result in the occasional production of eggs containing either no X or two X's. Such a failure of the members of a pair of chromosomes to segregate is also referred to as *nondisjunction* of chromosomes. According to the hypothesis that the X chromosome carries an allele for w, chromosomal nondisjunction can provide the mechanism by which a pair of genes fails to segregate, with the result that after meiosis, eggs are sometimes produced containing two members or no members of the gene pair. Any egg produced following nondisjunction will usually be fertilized by a sperm carrying either an X or a Y in addition to a haploid set of autosomes. (Nondisjunction can also occur during meiosis in the male. We can ignore this complication here, because it is an infrequent event and the probability that an egg produced after nondisjunction would be fertilized by a sperm produced after nondisjunction is negligible.)

If the hypothesis of chromosomal nondisjunction is valid, it should be consistent with the genetic results. After nondisjunction the exceptional eggs produced by a white ($X^w X^w$) female would be either $X^w X^w$ or 0 (zero designating the absence of the homolog normally expected to be present). The normal sperm produced by a dull-red ($X^{w+} Y$) male would carry either X^{w+} or Y. The expected genotypes of F_1 following random fertilizations between these gametes are given in Figure 7–9.

Let us momentarily ignore the sex of these exceptional offspring and classify them only for eye color. Type 1 would be dull-red-eyed, type 2 white-eyed, type 3 dull-red-eyed, and type 4's eye color undetermined. The genetic observations would be explained if types 1 and 4 were lethal; type 2, female; type 3, male. (On the hypothesis that XX is female and XY is male, it is reasonable to assume that types 1 and 4 would be neither, and therefore might be lethal.) Even more specific requirements must be fulfilled before accepting these hypotheses, namely, that each exceptional white female must prove to be XXY cytologically; that is, such females must have, in addition to the normal diploid chromosomes of a female, an extra chromosome which is Y. Moreover, each exceptional male must have, in addition to the normal autosomes, one X but no Y. When the somatic cells of exceptional females and males are examined cytologically, these chromosomal prescriptions

are found to be filled completely. It is also possible to show that Y0 zygotes are lethal, and that $X^{w+} X^w X^w$ individuals—these usually die before adulthood—are dull-red-eyed.

Although XY individuals are fertile males, X0 flies are invariably sterile males. This, therefore, implies that the Y chromosome is necessary for male fertility, the trait being attributable to a gene on the Y which has no allele on the X. Moreover, our sex chromosome formula for maleness must be modified to include XY and X0 individuals and similarly the femaleness formula also modified to include XX and XXY individuals.

Chromosomes as Genetic Material

We should now re-evaluate the hypothesis that the chromosomes serve as the material basis for genes. In preceding chapters, the following parallels were found between the properties and behavior of genes and of chromosomes: both come only from pre-existing counterparts; both are self-replicating; both occur as pairs in all cells of the diploid stage of sexually reproducing organisms except gametes; both are replicated in each mitotic division; both maintain their individuality from one mitotic division to the

EGGS	SPERM		OFFSPRING
$X^w X^w$	X^{w+}	(1)	$X^{w+} X^w X^w$
$X^w X^w$	Y	(2)	$X^w X^w Y$
0	X^{w+}	(3)	$X^{w+} 0$
0	Y	(4)	Y 0

FIGURE 7–9. *Genotypic expectation after fertilization of nondisjunctionally produced eggs by normal sperm.*

next; both are capable of mutation and subsequent replication of the new form; both segregate during gametogenesis so that they occur unpaired in the gamete; both show independent segregation for different pairs; both are combined randomly at fertilization. It was also hypothesized that the chromosome is larger than a recombinational gene (the smallest recombinational unit of the genetic material), since a gene was described as the largest distance along the length of a chromosome within which an exchange leading to a chiasma cannot form.

These parallels still might be considered merely coincidental. The present chapter provides the following additional tests of the idea that chromosomes function as the material basis for genes:

Sex-linkage, detected by the nonrandom association between sex and the genes for certain traits, was found to be an exception to the mode of transmission of the autosomal genes studied previously. This phenomenon was explained only by the assumption that certain genes have an allele in the homologous chromosome of a pair in one sex but no allele in the homologous chromosome in the other sex. Hemizygosity was a necessary assumption in the case of the Drosophila male and the poultry female. This genetic aberration was exactly paralleled by the occurrence of a pair of heteromorphic homologs in the Drosophila male and poultry female, one homologous member being present as a pair in the female Drosophila and in the male chicken.

Finally, in Drosophila, an exception to the exception of sex-linkage was found and explained genetically as resulting from the failure of the members of a single pair of sex-linked genes to segregate. This failure produces gametes containing two or no alleles of a given sex-linked gene. This *genetic nondisjunction* was shown to result from *chromosomal nondisjunction;* that is,

CALVIN BLACKMAN BRIDGES (*1889–1938*). (*From Genetics, vol. 25, p. 1, 1940.*)

the members of a pair of X chromosomes failed to segregate during meiosis. From chromosomal nondisjunction, it was predicted that the different genetically exceptional individuals would have different specific and unique sex chromosomal compositions, and further tests proved this was the case.

In the light of these results, the view that *the chromosomes are the material basis for all the genes so far studied* can no longer be considered merely a hypothesis based upon limited—therefore possibly circumstantial—evidence, but must now be accepted as a theory supported both by all the typical and all the atypical recombinational properties of genes and of chromosomes.

Ordinarily, no further comment will be made in this book about new tests that substantiate the theory. Henceforth, assume that all tests do so unless note is made to the contrary.

SUMMARY AND CONCLUSIONS

Up to now we have studied genes located in autosomes. We have found that the recombination of autosomal genes is such that reciprocal crosses between different pure lines produce F_1 which are genotypically and phenotypically uniform; that is, there is no dependency between the traits which appear and the sex of the offspring because autosomal genes segregate independently of the genetic material in sex chromosomes.

In Drosophila, sex is not the only trait directly associated with genetic material located in the sex chromosomes. Several other traits in Drosophila yield results which differ in reciprocal matings made between lines that are pure for different alternatives; the difference appearing in the phenotypes shown by one of the sexes. Genes behaving in such a sex-linked way are not located autosomally. The Y sex chromosome carries no allele of these genes, and the X does.

In human beings and Drosophila, the XY sex chromosomal constitution is male and the XX female; in birds and moths, it is the female which is heteromorphic, and, therefore, heterogametic with reference to sex chromosomes.

Occasionally, as a consequence of nondisjunction of sex chromosomes at meiosis, chromosome segregation fails, and gametes are formed containing two or, complementarily, no sex chromosomes. When this nondisjunction occurs in a Drosophila female homozygous for an X-linked recessive gene and such a female is mated to a male carrying the dominant allele, some offspring appear that are simultaneously exceptions to sex-linkage and to sex chromosome content; the exceptional feature of the one accurately predicts the exceptional feature of the other, and vice versa.

Sex-linkage and nondisjunction offer additional tests of the hypothesis that the material basis of all the genes studied thus far is in the chromosomes. This view is supported by so many and diverse lines of evidence, and contradicted by none, that it must be accepted as theory.

REFERENCES

Bridges, C. B., "Non-Disjunction as Proof of the Chromosome Theory of Heredity," *Genetics*, 1:1–52, 107–163, 1916.

Morgan, T. H., "Sex Limited Inheritance in Drosophila," *Science*, 32:120–122, 1910. Reprinted in *Classic Papers in Genetics*, Peters, J. A. (Ed.), Englewood Cliffs, N.J.: Prentice-Hall, 1959, pp. 63–66.

QUESTIONS FOR DISCUSSION

7.1. Under what circumstances would sons fail to receive a Y chromosome from their father?

7.2. In the cross $X^{w+}Y$ by X^wX^w what would you expect to be the genotypes of the zygotes produced, after sex chromosome nondisjunction during meiosis in both male and female Drosophila? What is the phenotypic outcome in each case?

7.3. If a trait is found to be due to a gene unlinked to any autosome, does this prove that the gene is linked to a sex chromosome? Explain.

7.4. A husband and wife both have normal vision, although both their fathers are red-green color-blind. What is the chance that their first child will be:
   (a) a normal son?   (c) a red-green color-blind son?
   (b) a normal daughter?   (d) a red-green color-blind daughter?

7.5. One child is hemophilic; his twin brother is not.
   (a) What is the probable sex of the hemophilic twin?
   (b) Are the twins monozygotic? Explain.
   (c) Give the genotypes of both twins and of their mother.

7.6. A hemophilic father has a hemophilic son. Give the most probable genotypes of the parents and child.

7.7. A Drosophila male with cubitus interruptus wing venation, ebony body color, and white eye color is mated to a pure wild-type female (normal wing venation, gray body color, and dull-red eyes); then the F_1 females are crossed to males like their father. Give the kinds and relative frequencies of genotypes and of phenotypes expected among the offspring of the last cross.

7.8. Are you convinced that all genes have their material basis in the chromosomes? Explain.

7.9. What reason can you give for believing that in Drosophila the Y chromosome is lacking a gene present in the X chromosome? That the X is lacking a gene present in the Y?

7.10. List evidence in support of the theory that chromosomes contain the material basis for genes.

7.11. Has any evidence been presented that a chromosome carries more than one gene? Explain.

7.12. What proportion of all genes causing hemophilia type A is found in human males? Justify your answer.

7.13. Does a gene have to be hemizygous in one sex to be sex-linked? Explain.

7.14. Two phenotypically wild-type Drosophila were mated in a vial. By accident all but one F_1 was lost. The survivor was a male with white eyes, ebony body color, and cubitus interruptus venation. Give the most probable genotypes of the parents.

7.15. Using pure stocks of Drosophila, yellow-bodied male by gray-bodied (wild-type) female produced 1241 gray-bodied daughters, 1150 gray-bodied sons, and 2 yellow-bodied sons. The reciprocal mating produced 1315 gray daughters, 924 yellow sons, and 1 yellow daughter. Give the genetic and chromosomal makeup of each type of individual mentioned. Discuss the relative viability and fertility of the different chromosomal types.

7.16. Females of Drosophila having a notch in their wing margins mated to wild-type males gave the following F_1 results: 550 wild-type ♀♀, 472 notch ♀♀, 515 wild-type ♂♂. Explain these results genetically.

7.17. A line of Drosophila pure for the sex-linked gene, coral (w^{co}) was maintained in the laboratory for many generations. To demonstrate sex-linkage to a class, a coral male was mated to a wild-type female, and all the F_1 were as expected. The reciprocal cross, between a coral female and a wild-type male, gave 62 coral females and 59 wild-type males. Present a hypothesis to explain this unusual result. How would you test your hypothesis?

7.18. The wild-type eye shape in Drosophila is ovoid. A certain mutant, X, narrows the eye. Using pure lines, and ignoring rare exceptions, mutant ♀ × wild-type ♂ produces mutant sons and daughters in F_1; wild-type ♀ × mutant ♂ produces wild-type sons and mutant daughters in F_1.

   Another mutant, Y, also narrows the eye. Using pure lines of Y and wild-type, mutant ♂ or ♀ × wild-type ♀ or ♂ produces 2 mutant ♂♂ and ♀♀ : 1 wild-type ♂♂ and ♀♀. Discuss the genetics of mutants X and Y.

7.19. Reciprocal matings using pure lines of Drosophila produce all wild-type F_1 from wild-type by vestigial wings. What are the genotypic and phenotypic expectations if the F_1 ♂ of this mating is crossed with a white-eyed vestigial-winged ♀, *w* being sex-linked?

7.20. Give two ways in which knowledge of sex-linked genes could be put to practical use.

7.21. A normal man of blood type AB marries a normal woman of O blood type whose father was hemophilic. What phenotypes should this couple expect in their children and in what relative frequencies?

7.22. The diagram below is a partial pedigree of the descendants of Queen Victoria of England (I1) which contains information regarding hemophilia only for generation IV. In this generation, the entire symbol is filled in if the person has hemophilia. A heterozygote for hemophilia would have been represented by a half filled-in symbol. Fill in the symbols of previous generations using this system.

II1 = Princess Alice	IV1 = Prince Waldemar of Prussia
II2 = Leopold, Duke of Albany	IV3 = Prince Henry of Prussia
III1 = Irene	IV8 = Tsarevitch Alexis of Russia
III2 = Alexandra	IV10 = Viscount Trematon
III3 = Alice	IV12 = Alfonso
III5 = Victoria Eugenie	IV17 = Gonzalo

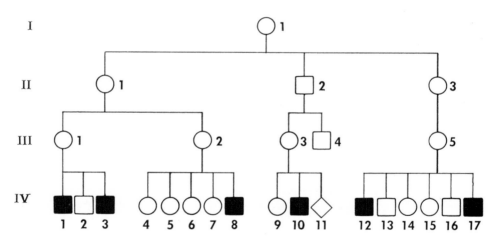

(After J. B. S. Haldane.)

Chapter *8

SEX DETERMINATION

Drosophila

In Chapter 7, it was mentioned that the ordinary *Drosophila melanogaster* female is $3AA + XX$ and the male, $3AA + X + Y$. One cannot decide the chromosomal basis for sex determination from these facts alone, however, since two variables are involved, the X's and the Y. Is the male a male because he has a Y, because he has only one X, or because he has both one X and one Y?

By knowing the sex of flies that carry—besides two sets of autosomes—either XXY (female), XXYY (female), or X0 (male), we can see that the Y is not sex determining in this organism. (As has been indicated in Chapter 7, the Y is necessary for fertility, XO males having nonmotile sperm.)

Knowing that sex in Drosophila is correlated with the chromosomal alternatives of XX versus X, one can ask: What is the detailed genetic basis for sex in terms of genes located in the X chromosome? The

data so far presented can be interpreted to mean that only a single pair of genes (in the case of XX) or a single gene (in the case of X) is the total genetic basis for sex determination. There are several implications in this interpretation. The X-linked sex gene need not have an alternative allele if the presence of one such gene produces one sex, and the presence of two, the other sex—dominance not being involved. It can also be claimed that the Y carries no allele for this sex gene. Two additional assumptions must be made, however, in Drosophila and in other species having heteromorphic sex chromosomes, to correlate the genetics with the cytology of sex.

1. That the sex gene must be located in a region of the X which distinguishes X from Y cytologically.
2. No chiasma may occur between X and Y within this cytologically different segment.

These postulates are necessary to preserve the exact correspondence between the morphology of the X and its sex gene content. Consequently, even though a chiasma occurs between the X and Y in a segment which they share (for example, both carry an allele of *bobbed*), the resultant strands that appear cytologically as X will carry the sex gene, whereas those that appear as Y will not. These requirements are reasonable

A. PHENOTYPIC RESULTS   B. GENOTYPIC EXPLANATION

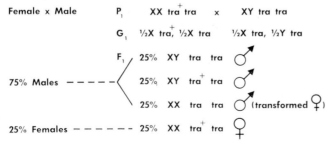

FIGURE 8–1. *Abnormal sex ratio in Drosophila.*

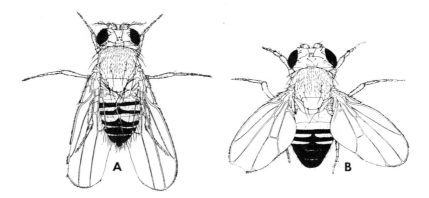

since synapsis does not occur between non-corresponding regions of homologous chromosomes, and, in the absence of pairing, exchanges leading to chiasmata cannot occur.

To further establish the cytogenetic basis for sex, we shall consider the results of crosses between certain laboratory strains of *D. melanogaster*.[1] One strain produces about 75% males and 25% females (Figure 8–1A), instead of the normal sex ratio of approximately 50% males and 50% females. Since just as many eggs become adult in this unusual strain as in a normal one, the abnormal result cannot be due to a gene that affects the viability of one sex.

In this exceptional case it can be hypothesized that an autosomal gene is affecting the determination of sex. This gene is called *transformer* and is postulated to have two alleles, *tra+*, and *tra*. Homozygotes for *tra* are presumed always to form males regardless of the X genes present (*tra tra* is epistatic and the X genes hypostatic),[2] whereas heterozygotes or homozygotes for *tra+* have their sex determined by the presence of the sex gene on the X (in this case the X sex gene is epistatic). Accordingly, XX individuals that are also *tra tra* will ap-

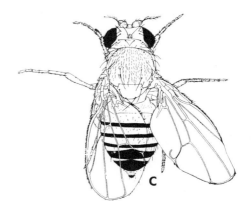

FIGURE 8–2. *Some abnormal sex types in Drosophila: A = superfemale; B = supermale; C = intersex. (Drawn by E. M. Wallace.) Compare with normal male and female in Fig. 2–6, p. 23.*

pear as males (*transformed females*), explaining the excess number of males in the progeny. Thus, a cross of XY *tra tra* (male) by XX *tra+ tra* (female) (Figure 8–1B) produces one-fourth each XY *tra tra* (males), XY *tra+ tra* (males), XX *tra tra* (males, transformed females), XX *tra+ tra* (females)—accounting for the numerical results. All these assumptions have been tested in additional crosses and are confirmed, proving that autosomal genes are also concerned with sex determination. Note, however, that the *tra* allele is very

[1] Based upon work of A. H. Sturtevant.
[2] These terms are defined in Chapter 4, pp. 51–52.

rare; almost all Drosophila found in nature are homozygous *tra+*.

So far we have described only two sex types in Drosophila. Occasionally, however, individuals occur which have, overall, an intermediate sexual appearance; that is, they are both male and female in certain respects. Such sexual intermediates, called *intersexes* (see Figure 8–2), are sterile. Intersexes are relatively frequent among the progeny of *triploid* (3N) females (whose chromosomes at mitotic metaphase are diagramed in Figure 8–3; X chromosomes are represented by filled-in blocks, autosomes by blanks, and the Y by a broken line).

Some of the gametes of triploid females are haploid and some diploid; still others contain one, two, or three nonhomologs with or without a haploid set. Whereas haploid eggs produce normal males and females when fertilized by sperm from a normal male, diploid eggs produce triploid females when fertilized by X-bearing sperm. Diploid eggs produce XXY individuals with three sets of autosomes, however, when fertilized by Y-bearing sperm. Some intersexes have this chromosomal constitution; other intersexes carry three autosomal sets and XX— one X derived from an egg containing two autosomal sets and the other from an X-bearing sperm.

Close observation reveals two additional sex types among the progeny of triploid Drosophila (Figures 8–2, 8–3). These do not appear as intersexes but as sterile "supersexes"—one type, called a *superfemale,* shows characteristic female traits even more strongly than does the normal female, the

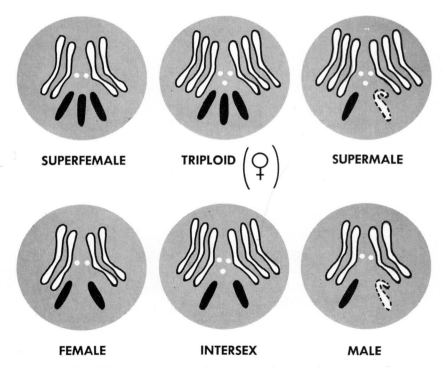

SUPERFEMALE   TRIPLOID ($\female$)   SUPERMALE

FEMALE   INTERSEX   MALE

FIGURE 8–3. *Chromosomal complements of the sexual types found among the progeny of triploid females of* D. melanogaster.

PHENOTYPES		NO. X CHROMOSOMES	NO. SETS OF AUTOSOMES (A sets)	SEX INDEX $\dfrac{\text{No. X's}}{\text{No. A sets}}$
Superfemale		3	2	1.5
Normal Female	tetraploid	4	4	1.0
	triploid	3	3	1.0
	diploid	2	2	1.0
	haploid	1	1	1.0
Intersex		2	3	0.67
Normal male		1	2	0.50
Supermale		1	3	0.33

FIGURE 8–4. *Sex index and sexual type in* D. melano-gaster.

other type, *supermale,* shows characteristic male traits even more strongly than does the normal male. Chromosomally, the superfemale contains two sets of autosomes and three X's; the X's are derived from an egg which carries one set of autosomes plus XX and is fertilized by an X-carrying sperm. The superfemale usually dies before adult-hood (see p. 97). The supermale contains three sets of autosomes plus XY; the chromosomes are derived from an egg which carries two sets of autosomes plus X and is fertilized by a Y-bearing sperm.

What conclusions can we draw about sex determination from a knowledge of the chromosomal composition of different sex types in Drosophila? [3] Since we know that genes in the X and in the autosomes are sex-determining, let us refer to Figure 8–4, which tabulates the number of X's and sets of autosomes present for each sex type and also the ratio of X's to sets of autosomes—a *numerical sex index.* This index ranges from 0.33 for supermales to 1.5 for superfemales. Note that an index of 0.50 makes for male and that adding a set of autosomes can be

interpreted as creating more maleness, producing the supermale. When the sex index is 1.0, essentially normal females are produced, indicating that the female tendency of one X overpowers the male tendency of one set of autosomes. But if the index is between 0.50 and 1.00, intersexes are produced, indicating, by the same line of reasoning, that the effect of two X's is partially overpowered by the extra autosomal set present. Finally, when the sex index is 1.5, the female tendency of the X's becomes so strong that superfemales result.

These results strongly suggest that sex determination is due to the balance of genes located in the X on the one hand, in the autosomes on the other. According to this view, only the balance of the genes involved is important, so that a sex index of 1.0 should (and does) produce a typical female, whether the individual is diploid (2X + 2 sets of A), triploid (3X + 3 sets of A), or tetraploid (4X + 4 sets of A). Individuals that contain haploid (1X + 1A set) sections have been found and, as expected from their sex index of 1.0, these parts were female. Since all known facts support the exact correspondence between chromosomal constitution and sexual types, we can accept chromo-

$2X$

$6A$

some balance as the typical basis of sex determination in Drosophila.

What is the relationship between X-autosome balance and *tra*, the sex-transforming gene? Sex is determined by X-autosome balance when the individuals carry *tra*+, which they normally do. When *tra* is homozygous, however, the balance view does not apply and 2X + 2A sets produces a male.

Gynandromorphs

On relatively rare occasions, abnormal Drosophila appear with some of their parts typically male and the remainder, typically female. Such individuals are said to be mosaic for sex traits; *sex mosaics* are also called *gynandromorphs* or *gynanders* (Figure 8–5). The male and female parts are clearly demarcated in such flies, sometimes the front and hind halves, at other times the right and left sides are of different sex. The sharp borderline between male and female parts in an insect gynander is due to the relatively small role that hormones play in insect differentiation, so that each

body part is formed according to the genotype it contains. In view of the preceding discussion, one would predict that the diploid cells in the female part of a gynander contain XX and those in the male part X, the chromosome number being otherwise normal. If this prediction is correct, then approximately half-and-half gynanders could originate as follows: the individual starts as a zygote containing 3AA + XX—that is, as a female. The first mitotic division of the zygotic nucleus is abnormal—one daughter nucleus contains 3AA + XX and is normal, the other daughter nucleus contains 3AA + X and is defective, because one of the X's failed to be included in this nucleus, degenerated, and was lost. However, subsequent nuclear divisions are normal—cells produced following mitosis of the XX nucleus and its descendants giving rise to female tissue, and cells derived from the X nucleus giving rise to male parts. In this case the gynander has about half its body male and half female. If, however, the X is lost at some later mitosis, a correspondingly smaller portion of the body will be male, explaining gynanders one quarter or less male.

We can test whether this explanation is sometimes correct by making use of an X-linked gene which produces a phenotypic effect over a large portion of the body surface; that is, a gene that affects the size and shape of the bristles and hairs. Such a gene is forked, two of its mutant alleles being f^{34b} and f. In homozygotes (females) and hemizygotes (males), f^{34b} produces bristles and hairs of normal length and shape; f causes them to be shortened, split, and gnarled. The f^{34b}/f heterozygotes have bristles and hairs slightly abnormal in these respects, showing a "weak forked" phenotype. If a cross is made to produce female offspring that are f^{34b}/f heterozygotes, the following predictions can be made regarding the phenotype of the gynanders occasionally

FIGURE 8–5. D. melanogaster *gynandromorph whose left side is female and right side is male. (Drawn by E. M. Wallace.)*

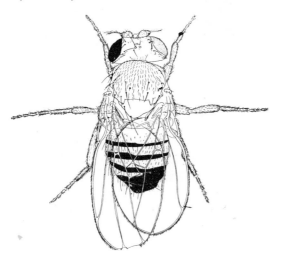

present among the siblings: All gynanders, originating as postulated, will be weakly forked in their female parts; their male parts will have either normal or strongly forked bristles and hairs, depending upon whether the lost X carried f or f^{34b}, respectively. Experimental results obtained confirm exactly these expectations.

Gynanders also occur in moths. Whereas male moths usually have large, beautifully colored wings and females, small stumps of wings, gynanders have been found with wings like the male on one side and those like the female on the other side. The explanation for these exceptions is similar to that given for Drosophila. In the case of the moth, however, the gynander usually starts as a male zygote (XX).

Although most gynanders in Drosophila and other insects in which the male has the heteromorphic sex chromosomes, can be explained in this manner, some gynanders originate another way. In extremely rare cases, an abnormal egg is produced after meiosis which contains not one but two haploid gametic nuclei. Because polyspermy sometimes occurs in insects—that is, more than the one sperm normally involved in fertilization enters an egg—one of the two haploid egg nuclei may be fertilized by an X-carrying sperm, the other by a Y-carrying one. The resultant individual is approximately a half-and-half gynander. This type of gynander can be identified if the two paternal (or the two maternal) haploid gametic nuclei are marked differently for a pair of autosomal genes.

Man and Mouse

In human beings sexual type is determined at fertilization, XY zygotes becoming males; XX zygotes, females. In early development, all sex organs or *gonads* are neutral; that is, they give no macroscopic indication whether they will later form testes or ovaries. The early gonad has two regions, an outer one, the *cortex,* and an inner one, the *medulla.* As development proceeds, the cortex degenerates in those individuals that carry a Y (male), and the medulla forms a testis; in individuals genetically determined to be females, the medulla degenerates, and the cortex forms an ovary.

Once the testis and ovary are formed, they take over the regulation of further sexual differentiation by means of the hormones they produce. The hormones direct the development or degeneration of various sexual ducts, the formation of genitalia, and other secondary sexual characteristics. Since sexual differentiation is largely controlled by the sex hormones, it is not surprising that genetically normal individuals are morphologically variable with regard to sex. Any change in the environment that can upset the production of, or tissue response to, sex hormones can produce effects which modify the sex phenotype. So, the phenotypes normally considered male and female show some variability—providing some of the spice of life. Genetically normal persons exposed to abnormal environmental conditions can differentiate phenotypes that lie between the two normal ranges of sex type, and, therefore, are intersexual in appearance. Though it is sometimes easy to classify an individual as being an intersex because the person is clearly between the two sex norms, other individuals at the extremes of normality cannot readily be labeled normal, or intersex, or supersex. Intersexual phenotypes due to environmental factors can result either from genotypic males who have developed partially in the direction of female, or from genotypic females partially differentiated in the direction of male.

Otherwise-diploid individuals are known who have various numbers of sex chromosomes. Only one type has a single sex chromosome; this is the X0 individual, who is female. The typical phenotypic effect of this condition is called *Turner's syndrome* (after its discoverer) and is characterized by the failure to mature as a woman. Turner type females usually do not develop breasts, ovulate, or menstruate. Because of variability in the genotypic details and in the environment (including medical treatment), considerable variation occurs in the phenotypic consequences of the X0 condition. In fact, one woman of this constitution is known to have given birth to a normal (XY) son. The X0 mouse is apparently less variable phenotypically since it always seems to produce a fertile female. The other single sex chromosome type, Y0, presumably lethal in man, is known to be lethal in mouse.

Otherwise-diploid individuals having three sex chromosomes are of three types: XXX is female (sometimes mentally defective); XYY is male; XXY is male. The XXY individual who is characteristically sterile, may have undersized sex organs, and may develop various secondary sexual characteristics of females, possesses *Klinefelter's syndrome* (named after its discoverer). Along with the X0 female, he is phenotypically variable; for instance, some Klinefelter males are mentally retarded, others are not; although all those presently known are sterile, some show normal sexual drive and behavior. In the mouse, XXY is a sterile male.

Otherwise-diploid persons of the following additional types are also known: XXXX (♀); XXXY (♂); XXYY (♂); XXXXX (♀); XXXXY (♂); XXXYY (♂). Contrary to the situation in Drosophila, it is clear from all these results that the Y chromosome is the primary sex-determining chromosome in man and mouse. Presence of a single Y determines the sex as male; absence of a Y produces the female. All individuals require an X in order to be viable.

The Y versus no Y sex-determining mechanism in human beings and mice implies that the Y must carry one or more genes for maleness in that portion which makes it cytologically unique, the X having no corresponding allele(s). Admitting that the presence of gene(s) for maleness on the Y makes for male, what is genetically responsible for the femaleness produced in the absence of the Y? Clearly other genetic factors are present—not limited in location to the Y chromosome—which affect sex and, therefore, femaleness. The female tendency often shown by the human XXY suggests that the X contains genes affecting normal sexual differentiation which, when present in excess, cause a shift toward femaleness. Presumably, the X also has this capacity when Y is absent.

All cases in which the entire body seems to contain an abnormal number of sex chromosomes can be explained as the result of nondisjunction leading to chromosome loss or gain which occurs either during meiosis or at an early cleavage division—probably the first—of the fertilized egg. Such nondisjunctions are correlated in human beings with the mother's advanced age at the time of pregnancy.

By following the distribution of X-linked mutants, it has been shown, however, that the nondisjunction which produces an abnormal sex-chromosome number sometimes involves the paternally contributed sex-chromosome material. This origin is exemplified by a red-green colorblind father having an X0 daughter of normal vision. Since certain aged Drosophila eggs cause the loss of paternal chromosomes after fertilization, it is important to recognize the possibility that the loss of a paternal chromosome in man can occur post- as well as pre-meiotically. Due to a premeiotic paternal nondisjunction colorblind women can, of course, have XXY Klinefelter sons of normal vision.

A considerable number of persons having different chromosomal compositions in different body parts are mosaic for sex chromosomes. These include the following mixed constitutions: XXX/X0; XX/X0; XY/X0, XXY/XX; XXXY/XY. Such cases are usually due to one or more errors in chromosome distribution among the daughter nuclei produced after fertilization. Although such individuals are sex-chromosome mosaics, and some may even have one ovary-like and one testis-like gonad, they are not gynanders in superficial characteristics because of their whole-body distribution of sex hormones. Although the XXY male is often clearly an intersex, the X0, XXX, and so on females that show incomplete maturity are best considered infra-females, being underdeveloped sexually. It should now be clear that some specific phenotypic sexual abnormalities may be based primarily either on an abnormal environment or on an abnormal chromosomal composition (recognizing also the possibility that mutants other than those involving an abnormal number of sex chromosomes can affect sex). Accordingly, chromosomal counts are often desirable in order to determine the cause—and, hence, the treatment—of sexual abnormality.

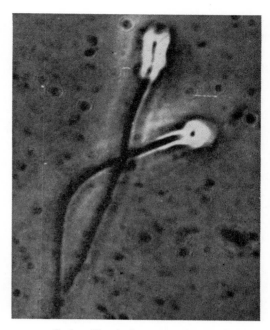

FIGURE 8–6. *Head shapes in human sperm. Round-headed sperm are reported to be smaller and more numerous than oval-headed sperm, suggesting these carry the Y and X chromosomes, respectively. (Courtesy of L. B. Shettles.)*

Human Sex Ratio

Consider how the genotype is related to the *sex ratio*, that is, to the relative numbers of males and females born. On the average, 106 boys are born for each 100 girls. This statistic might be surprising at first, since half the sperm are expected to carry X, half Y, and all eggs, an X, the ratio of boy to girl expected at conception is one to one. Even if the four meiotic products of a given cell in spermatogenesis usually carry X, X, Y, Y, there is the possibility that during or after *spermiogenesis* (conversion of the telophase II cell into a sperm) some X-bearing sperm are lost. This possibility is supported by a report [4] that human ejaculates contain sperm heads of two sizes and shapes (Figure 8–6); the smaller type sufficiently in

[4] By L. B. Shettles (1960).

excess to explain an excess of males at fertilization provided the smaller sperm contains the small Y chromosome, and the larger sperm carries the larger X chromosome. Other evidence suggests that at conception males are much more numerous than females; since more male fetuses normally abort than female, the numbers of boys and girls are more nearly equal at the time of birth than they were at conception.

A study of the sex ratio at birth shows that the ratio 1.067:1.000 is found only among young parents, and that it decreases steadily until it is about 1.036:1.000 among the children of older parents. How may this significant decrease be explained? Perhaps in older mothers there is a greater chance for chromosomally normal male babies to abort, or for chromosome loss in the earliest mitotic divisions of the fertilized egg. If the chromosome lost is an X and the zygote is XY, the loss is expected to be lethal, so that a potential boy is aborted. If the zygote losing an X is XX, a girl can still be born. Moreover, if the chromosome lost in the XY individual is a Y, a girl can be born instead of a boy. Part of the effect must be due to the increase in meiotic nondisjunction with maternal age (zygotes of XXX type form viable females, whereas zygotes of Y0 type are expected to abort).

We must include the possibility that the fathers may also contribute to this shift in sex ratio. Postmeiotic selection against Y-carrying sperm may increase with paternal age. Or, as fathers become older, the XY tetrad may be more likely to undergo nondisjunction to produce sperm containing respectively, X, X, YY, 0. The first two can produce normal daughters; the last one can produce an underdeveloped X0 daughter; and only the YY is capable of producing males. Even though the XYY individual is male, it may frequently abort. Other genetic and nongenetic explanations for the shift in sex ratio with age are also possible. This discussion merely demonstrates how the basic facts of sex determination, chromosome loss, and nondisjunction may be used to formulate various hypotheses whose validity is subject to test.

When many pedigrees are examined for sex ratio, several consecutive births of the same sex occasionally occur. This phenomenon could, of course, happen purely as a matter of chance when enough pedigrees are scored. One family, however, is reported to have only boys in 47 births and, in another well-substantiated case, out of 72 births in one family, all were girls. In both these cases the results are too improbable to be attributed to chance.

We do not know the basis for such results in man, but two different cases of almost exclusive female progeny production in Drosophila might suggest an explanation for those human pedigrees in which only one sex occurs in the progeny. In the first case, an XY male carrying a gene called *sex ratio* is responsible. Because of this gene, the X and Y fail to synapse, and the X replicates an extra time to form a tetrad; since almost all Y chromosomes degenerate during meiosis, almost all sperm carry an X. In the second case, a female transmitting a spirochaete microorganism to her offspring through the egg is responsible. Such a female mated to a normal male produces zygotes which begin development; soon thereafter the XY individuals are killed by the spirochaete, leaving almost all female survivors.

The sex ratio can be controlled if the genotypes of the zygotes formed can be controlled. Since X- and Y-bearing sperm of men apparently differ in cytological appearance (Figure 8–8), it should be possible to separate them and thereby control the sex of progeny. Using various animal forms, such experiments have been performed with some success by Russian, American, and Swedish workers, using electric currents or centrifugation. Although these experiments have been encouraging, the results are not yet consistent, and the techniques not yet suitable for practical use.

Hymenoptera

In Hymenoptera (for example, bees, ants, wasps, and saw flies) unfertilized eggs develop as males (haploids) and fertilized eggs, usually, as females (diploids). Haploid males produce haploid sperm via suitable modifications of the meiotic process, and all gametes of males and females have morphologically identical chromosomal compositions.

In the parasitic wasp, *Habrobracon juglandis,* when the parents are closely related, some of the sons are haploid, but others are diploid having ten pairs of chromosomes like their sisters. Genetic study shows that such diploid males have a biparental origin. Not only are diploid males relatively inviable, but the hatchability of sibling eggs is very poor. A study of intrastrain and interstrain breeding supports the interpretation [5] that a multiple allelic series determines sex in this form. With respect to this sex-determining locus or chromosome region, haploids are males, diploid heterozygotes are females, and diploid homozygotes are semisterile males.

Role of Genotype in Sex Determination

In certain organisms, male and female gametes are produced in the same individual. Animals of this type are said to be *hermaphroditic* (after Hermes and Aphrodite), and plants, monoecious. The hermaphrodite snail, Helix, has a gonad which produces both eggs and sperm from cells which sometimes lie very close together. In the earthworm, eggs and sperm are produced in separate gonads located in different segments of the body. In certain mosses, egg and sperm-like gametes are also produced in separate sex organs (located on the same haploid gametophyte).

In all these cases, the two types of gametes are produced by an organism that has but a single genotype; that is, one that is not genetically mosaic. Nevertheless, it might be supposed, at first, that the haploid genotype carried by eggs and by the sperm is different and causes the difference in phenotype and behavior. In the case of the gametophyte of mosses, however, the individual is haploid and so are both types of gametes it forms. Accordingly, in such organisms we cannot expect differences in gene content to be the basis either for the formation of gametes or for the different types of gametes produced.

[5] See P. W. Whiting (1943).

Gamete formation in hermaphroditic and monoecious organisms, therefore, must depend primarily upon environmental differences. Such differences must exist even between cells which lie close together, as is the case in Helix. It is reasonable to suppose that the same kinds of environmental factors which can direct one group of cells to form muscle cells and an adjacent group to form bone cells, can direct the differentiation of still other cells to make gonadal tissue in which adjacent cells can further differentiate as sperm and egg.

Note, however, that sex involves another kind of differentiation, which, at least in organisms like the mosses, is separate from the type of gamete formed. This problem (which will not be discussed in detail here) concerns the genetic and environmental factors responsible for the onset of meiosis, which is, of course, the feature most fundamental to the success of the sexual process as it presently occurs in many species.

In the examples already mentioned, the type of gamete differentiated depends upon the different positions which cells have within a single organism; consequently, they are subject to differences in internal and external environments. In the marine annelid, Ophryotrocha, the two sexes are in separate individuals, and the sex type formed is determined by the size of the organism. When the animal is small, because of youth or because it was obtained by amputation from a larger organism, it manufactures sperm; when larger, the same individual shifts to the manufacture of eggs. In this case the environment of the gonad is changed by the growth of the organism.

Finally, consider sex determination in the marine worm, Bonellia, in which the separate sexes are radically different in appearance and activity—females being walnut-sized and having a long proboscis, males being microscopic ciliated forms that live as parasites in the body of the female. Fertilized eggs, grown in the absence of adult females develop as females; they develop as males in the presence either of adult females or simply an extract of the female's proboscis. In this case, then, differentiation as a whole including sexual differentiation, is regulated by the presence or absence of a chemical messenger manufactured by females.

Nothing has been stated about the specific genetic basis for the determination or differentiation of sex in any of the examples given in this section because different sexes or gametes are determined not by genetic differences between cells, organs, or individuals, but by environmental differences acting upon a uniform genotype. The genes, nevertheless, must play a role in all these cases by making possible different sexual responses to variations in the environment.

Importance of Sexuality

Even if reproduction occurred only by asexual means, the earth would now be populated by genetically different kinds of organisms, each variant having arisen by muta-

tion in a pre-existing individual who was, in turn, produced from an unbroken line of descent. This method of direct descent is inefficient, however, since biologically fit individuals must wait for the rare occurrence of mutation to make them more fit.

The biological innovation of sexuality has a tremendous genetic advantage over asexuality by providing genetic recombination which speeds up the process of the evolution of more adaptive organisms. A more adaptive genotype may be produced in one individual by the combination of allelic and nonallelic genes originally located in two parents who, individually, may have been less well or even poorly adapted. Since genetic recombination normally occurs each generation for each gene pair, adaptive combinations of genes originate much more rapidly by recombination than by the relatively rare event of mutation. It should be clear, therefore, that sexuality, which produces a greater variety of adaptive genotypes in a given period of time than asexuality, is primarily responsible for the great variety of adapted kinds of individuals that have appeared on the Earth in recent times.

SUMMARY AND CONCLUSIONS

An understanding of the basis of sex requires the answer to two questions: What is responsible for the onset of meiosis? What is the basis for the formation of different kinds of gametes? Only the latter question is discussed in significant detail. In some cases the environment and in other cases the genotype is primarily responsible for sex determination. In the latter cases, sexual differences can often be correlated with cytogenetic differences.

Genes responsible for sex determination are located not only in the sex chromosomes but in the autosomes as well. Although sex type may be changed through the action of a single pair of genes, a given sex is usually the result of the interaction of several, and probably many, pairs of genes. Sex is, therefore, a polygenic trait (Chapter 5).

Chromosomal differences found among zygotes serve as visible manifestations of differences in the balance of genes concerned with sex. Whenever, as in female Drosophila, genic balance is unaffected by the addition or subtraction of whole sets of chromosomes, sex also is unaffected. However, changes in chromosome number which produce intermediate genic balances also produce intermediate sex types—intersexes; those which make the balance more extreme than normal produce extreme sex types—supersexes.

These principles of sex determination apply also to human beings. In man and many other organisms, a large part of sexual differentiation is controlled by sex hormones produced by the gonads. This type of control rarely, if ever, permits the occurrence of individuals who are typically male in one part and typically female in another part; it may also contribute to the formation of abnormal sex types for nongenetic reasons.

REFERENCES

Bangham, A. D., "Electrophoretic Characteristics of Ram and Rabbit Spermatozoa," Proc. Roy. Soc., Ser. B, 155:292–305, 1961.

Bridges, C. B., "Sex in Relation to Chromosomes and Genes," Amer. Nat., 59:127–137, 1925. Reprinted in *Classic Papers in Genetics*, Peters, J. A. (Ed.), Englewood Cliffs, N.J.: Prentice-Hall, 1959, pp. 117–123.

Goldschmidt, R. B., *Theoretical Genetics*, Berkeley and Los Angeles: University of California Press, 1955.

Hannah-Alava, A., "Genetic Mosaics," Scient. Amer., 202:118–130, 1960.

Lancet, No. 7075, Vol. 1, 1959, pp. 709–716.

McKusick, V. A., *Human Genetics*, Englewood Cliffs, N.J.: Prentice-Hall, Inc., 1964.

Shettles, L. B., "Nuclear Morphology of Human Spermatozoa," Nature, London, 186: 648–649, 1960.

Shettles, L. B., "Nuclear Structure of Human Spermatozoa," Nature, London, 188: 918–919, 1960.

Sturtevant, A. H., "A Gene in *Drosophila melanogaster* that Transforms Females into Males," Genetics, 30:297–299, 1945.

Whiting, P. W., "Multiple Alleles in Complementary Sex Determination in Habrobracon," Genetics, 28:365–382, 1943.

QUESTIONS FOR DISCUSSION

8.1. If sexual reproduction is as advantageous as discussed, why do so many organisms still reproduce asexually?

8.2. Does the study of sex determination offer any test of the theory that chromosomes furnish the physical basis for genes? Explain.

8.3. Is it possible to consider the factors responsible for the meiotic process separately from the factors responsible for gamete formation? Explain.

8.4. Why is meiosis the most fundamental feature in the success of sexuality?

8.5. Give the genotypes and phenotypes of the unexceptional, the nondisjunctional, and the gynandromorphic offspring expected from a mating of f^{34b}/f with f Drosophila.

8.6. Are there isoalleles for the genes determining the size and shape of the bristles and hairs of Drosophila? Explain.

8.7. Using first the autosomal alleles e and $e+$ and then the X-linked alleles y and $y+$, devise crosses by which you could identify gynanders in Drosophila resulting from two fertilizations of a single egg.

8.8. Compare the genotypes and phenotypes of sex chromosome mosaics of flies, moths, and men.

8.9. All human beings have the same number of chromosomes in each somatic cell. Discuss this statement giving evidence in support of your view.

8.10. The following types of mosaics are known in human beings:

XXX/X0   XXY/XX
XX/X0   XXXY/XY
XY/X0

Give a reasonable explanation for the probable origination of each.

8.11. In human beings, can the members of a pair of monozygotic twins ever be of different sexes? Explain.

8.12. Does a gene have to have an alternative allele before it can be discovered? Explain.

8.13. Assuming each homolog carried a different allele, a^1, a^2, a^3, of the same gene, make a schematic representation of a trivalent as it might appear during synapsis. Show diagrammatically the chromosomal and genetic content of the four meiotic products that could be obtained from your trivalent diagram.

8.14. Ignoring chiasma formation, how many chromosomally-different kinds of eggs can a triploid Drosophila female produce? How many of these eggs have more than a 5% chance of occurring?

8.15. (a) *Scurfy*, *sf*, is an X-linked recessive gene that kills male mice before they reproduce. How is a stock containing this gene maintained normally?
(b) Occasionally, the stock containing this gene produces scurfy females which also die before reproductive age. Suggest a genetic explanation for these female exceptions. Describe how you would test your hypothesis genetically by transplanting ovaries and obtaining progeny from them.

8.16. What explanations can you offer, other than those already presented, for the shift in sex ratio with age of human parents?

8.17. No Y0 human beings are known. Why is this chromosomal constitution considered to be lethal?

8.18. List the types of human zygotes formed after maternal nondisjunction of the X chromosome. What phenotypes would be expected for each of the zygotes that these, in turn, may produce?

8.19. List specific causes for the production of abnormal sex types in human beings.

8.20. How can you explain that only one X0 individual is known to have had a successful pregnancy, whereas other X0's are sterile?

8.21. Discuss the general applicability of the chromosomal balance theory of sex determination.

8.22. In Drosophila, why are gynanders not intersexes? Is this true in man also? Explain.

8.23. What chromosomal constitution can you give for a triploid human embryo that is "male"? "Female"?

8.24. A non-hemophilic man and woman have a hemophilic son with Klinefelter's syndrome. Describe the chromosomal content and genotypes of all three individuals mentioned.

8.25. A white cat reported by H. C. Thurline, had one yellow and one blue eye, a phallus and one testis, one uterine horn, and one ovary. Although the animal had 38 chromosomes (the normal diploid number), some nuclei had an XX and others, an XY content. Suggest hypotheses to explain the chromosomal content of this individual.

8.26. Give a possible chromosomal formula for human individuals who are:
(a) Triploid males
(b) Klinefelter's type of male

8.27. A 26-year-old somewhat mentally retarded man is known to be XYY but otherwise diploid. To what do you attribute the apparent rarity of this type of chromosomal constitution?

8.28. Klinefelter-type males occur who are XXXYY. Give a possible origin of this chromosomal constitution.

8.29. In the insect Protenor and certain short-horned grasshoppers, all eggs have the same number of chromosomes, and half of the sperm are different, in that they carry one less chromosome. What is the cytogenetic basis for sex determination in such cases?

8.30. In the plant genus, Melandrium, one observes individuals of the following types:

Diploid: $XX + 11 \ AA = ♀$ $XY + 11 \ AA = ♂$
Triploid: $XXX + 11 \ AAA = ♀$ $XXY + 11 \ AAA = ♂$
Tetraploid: $XXXX + 11 \ AAAA = ♀$ $XXYY + 11 \ AAAA = ♂$
                                          or
                                          $XXXY + 11 \ AAAA = ♂$

Discuss the cytogenetic basis for sex determination in Melandrium.

8.31. Discuss the sex ratio expected in the honey bee from unmated and mated females.

8.32. Does the chromosomal balance hypothesis of sex determination apply in the case of parasitic wasps? Explain.

8.33. Compare the self-sterility alleles in Nicotiana (see p. 60) with the sex-determination alleles in Habrobracon.

Chapter **9**

LINKAGE AND CROSSING OVER
BETWEEN GENES

THE alleles of a gene pair affecting the seed coat of the garden pea were symbolized in Chapter 4 as round (R) and wrinkled (r). This symbology follows the convention that uses upper and lower case of the first letter (or so) of the phenotype produced by the dominant allele—the one usually found in nature—to represent the dominant and recessive alleles, respectively.

In other conventions (see Figure 9–1), the first letter (or so) of the recessive trait (wrinkled) is used in lower case for the recessive allele (w), and the normally dominant allele (round) is given as one of the following: the same symbol in upper case (W); a + symbol as a superscript or base to the lower case symbol (w^+ or $+^w$); or + alone. Henceforth in this book we will usually ·use one form of the + system for symbolizing genes. In this system, a mutant gene—*Beadex,* for example—which is dominant to the normal wild-type allele is represented by one (or more) letters of which the first is capitalized (Bx or $+^{Bx}$) and its wild-type allele is + (or Bx^+). The hybrid $+w$ can be represented as $\dfrac{+}{w}$ or $\dfrac{+}{w}$ or $+/w$ to show that these alleles are on different members of a pair of homologous chromosomes.

Each of the first seven pairs of genes studied in the garden pea (see Chapter 4, p. 48) appeared to segregate independently. If this kind of segregation is attributed to

each gene pair being located in a different one of the seven pairs of chromosomes carried by this organism, what result will be obtained when an eighth pair of genes, showing dominance and affecting an unrelated trait, is included in such a study? When a dihybrid is made of one of the seven gene pairs and the eighth pair mentioned above, a $9:3:3:1$ phenotypic ratio is obtained when the dihybrid is self-fertilized, and a $1:1:1:1$ phenotypic ratio is obtained when the same dihybrid is test crossed to the double recessive. These two independent tests demonstrate that the two pairs of genes involved are segregating independently. The phenotypic ratios are radically different, however, when a dihybrid is made with still another of the seven gene pairs—the one affecting seed coat—

$$\frac{R}{r} \quad \frac{W}{w} \quad \frac{w^+}{w} \quad \frac{+}{w} \quad \frac{+}{w} \quad \frac{+}{w} \quad +/w$$

FIGURE 9–1. *Various ways of representing the round-wrinkled hybrid by gene symbols.*

and the same eighth. The other pair of genes involved (the eighth) determines the presence and absence of tendrils—the threadlike structures serving as a means for attachment as the plant climbs. The tendrilless allele (t) is recessive. When a double recessive pea plant—wrinkled, tendrilless ($w\,w\,t\,t$) is crossed to a pure double dominant—round, tendrils ($+ +\ + +$), all F_1 are round with tendrils ($+w\ +t$), as expected. When the F_1 are self-fertilized (dihybrid by dihybrid), the following results are obtained in F_2:

Phenotype	No. Individuals
round, tendrils	319
round, tendrilless	4
wrinkled, tendrils	3
wrinkled, tendrilless	123

Note that each gene pair shows segregation in the F_2 since the ratio of round to wrinkled is 323:126 (a 3:1 ratio), and the ratio of tendrils to no tendrils is 322:127 (a 3:1 ratio). Had these gene pairs been segregating independently, the resultant ratio would have been 9:3:3:1. Instead, the F_2 has relatively too many plants phenotypically like the P_1 parents (wrinkled, no tendrils; round, tendrils) and relatively too few new recombinational types (round, no tendrils; wrinkled, tendrils).

Examine also the phenotypic results obtained from test crossing the dihybrid in question ($+w +t$ by $w\,w\,t\,t$):

Phenotypes	No. Individuals
round, tendrils	516
round, tendrilless	9
wrinkled, tendrils	7
wrinkled, tendrilless	492

Independent segregation would have given a 1:1:1:1 ratio for each of the types. But again the dihybrids produced relatively excessive numbers of gametes containing the old (parental) combinations ($+ +$ and $w\,t$) and relatively too few new combinational or recombinational types. Based on the results of both crosses, we conclude that independent segregation does not occur in this dihybrid. The very existence of recombinational types proves—what had previously been an assumption—that we are dealing with two separate pairs of genes.

Let us assume now that the two pairs of nonalleles involved are located in the same pair of homologous chromosomes, a possibility already mentioned in Chapter 4 (p. 48). In this situation the *nonalleles in the same chromosome are linked to each other*. Recall that sex-linkage involves the linking of a single gene (such as the one for white eye in Drosophila) to a particular chromosome (the X chromosome). Our concern here is with intergenic linkage, which involves all the nonallelic genes presumed to be located in the same chromosome. We can obtain evidence for this only by studying the transmission genetics for at least two traits simultaneously. Since no genetic recombination was detected between the genetic material for sex and for a sex-independent trait (like eye color) in the X chromosome, the linkage between the two traits, sex-linkage (or, more precisely in this case, X-linkage) was complete and presented no evidence that this chromosome contained two or more separable nonalleles. Because the present experiments with peas involved two separable pairs of genes, we were able to propose the hypothesis that a chromosome contains more than one gene.

Let us reexamine the results of the two kinds of pea crosses described. In Figures 9–2 and 9–3 a horizontal line is used to represent a chromosome and to indicate the presence of one member of each pair of alleles in each chromosome. Where the genes could be either the dominant or the recessive allele, a question mark is placed in the appropriate position. Down through the genotypes of the P_2 the results in Figure 9–2 are consistent with the view that linkage is complete; that is, the chromosomes carrying $w\,t$ or $+ +$ are unchangeable (except by mutation). However, the occurrence of seven recombinational individuals in F_2 shows that linkage is not complete—that these recombinants have a chromosome which has kept one allele and received the nonallele present in the homolog. Moreover, reciprocal types of recombinants are approximately equal in frequency, suggesting that a given pair of genes switched positions in the homologs; that is, they had reciprocally crossed over. For this reason, such recombinational individuals are said to carry a *crossover* chromosome produced by a process called *crossing over*. Therefore, complete linkage between genes is prevented

P_1 Wrinkled, no tendrils   x   Round, tendrils

$$\frac{w\,t}{w\,t} \qquad\qquad \frac{+\,+}{+\,+}$$

F_1 Round, tendrils $\dfrac{+\,+}{w\,t}$

P_2 F_1 Round, tendrils (self-fertilized)

$$\frac{+\,+}{w\,t} \quad x \quad \frac{r\,+}{w\,t}$$

F_2 Round, tendrils $\dfrac{+\,+}{?\,?}$ 319

     Round, no tendrils $\dfrac{+\,t}{?\,t}$ 4

     Wrinkled, tendrils $\dfrac{w\,+}{w\,?}$ 3

     Wrinkled, no tendrils $\dfrac{w\,t}{w\,t}$ 123

             TOTAL   449

FIGURE 9–2 (*above*). *Linkage between non-allelic genes in the garden pea.*

FIGURE 9–3 (*below*). *Linkage between non-allelic genes in the garden pea. The dihybrid parent is the same as the F_1 in Fig. 9–2.*

P_2 F_1 Round, tendrils   x   Wrinkled, no tendrils

$$\frac{+\,+}{w\,t} \qquad\qquad \frac{w\,t}{w\,t}$$

F_2 Round, tendrils $\dfrac{+\,+}{w\,t}$ 516

     Round, no tendrils $\dfrac{+\,t}{w\,t}$ 9

     Wrinkled, tendrils $\dfrac{w\,+}{w\,t}$ 7

     Wrinkled, no tendrils $\dfrac{w\,t}{w\,t}$ 492

             TOTAL   1024

by a crossing-over process that produces genetic recombinations called crossovers.

What other characteristics can we establish for the crossing-over process and the crossovers it produces? Among the progeny obtained from backcrossing the dihybrid (Figure 9–3), 16 received crossovers in the gametes contributed by the dihybrid, 1008 did not. Again, the reciprocal crossover classes are about equal in frequency. So approximately one crossover was produced for each 63 noncrossovers. A simple calculation will show that the F_2 results in Figure 9–2 are consistent with this proportion.

These genes can also make a dihybrid which receives one mutant (recessive) and one normal (dominant) gene from one parent $(w +)$ and one normal and one mutant gene from the other parent $(+ t)$. When such a dihybrid is test crossed, the crossovers ($w\,t$ or $+ +$) and noncrossovers ($w +$ or $+ t$) also occur in the proportion $1:63$. Crossing over, apparently, occurs with the same frequency whether the two mutant genes enter the dihybrid from the same parent or from different parents. Crossovers, therefore, occur in the gametes of an individual with a frequency that is constant and independent of the specific combination in which the nonalleles were received. If this is the normal behavior, it must follow that even in $+ +/+ +$ and $w\,t/w\,t$ individuals, one gamete in each 64 produced is a crossover for these genes but undetected because it carries no new combination of nonalleles. Notice that the crossover progeny are fewer than the noncrossover progeny. This must mean that when two linked mutants enter a dihybrid in the same gamete, the mutants tend to be transmitted together to the gametes made by this dihybrid (*coupling*); if, on the other hand, the mutants enter the dihybrid separately, they tend to be transmitted separately to the next generation (*repulsion*).

In another species, the sweet pea, the trait purple flowers is due to a single gene ($+$) whose recessive allele (r) produces red flowers. Long pollen ($+$) is dominant to round pollen (ro). Assume two pairs of genes are involved in a cross between a pure line of purple long ($+ +/+ +$) and red round ($r ro/r ro$). The F_1 produces all purple long ($+ +/r ro$) and self-fertilization of the F_1 produces in F_2 too many P_1 phenotypes and too few new recombinational types (purple round and red long) for independent segregation. Therefore, these genes must be linked. But, as before, linkage is incomplete.

In this case, the crossovers obtained can be accounted for if the $P_2(F_1)$ dihybrid forms gametes in the relative proportions $10 + + : 10\, r\, ro : 1 + ro : 1\, r +$. This frequency of crossovers is obtained no matter how the genes enter the dihybrid. Notice, however, that the constant frequency ($1/11$) in the sweet pea differs from the frequency ($1/64$) observed previously in the garden pea.

Consider also, the following cases:

1. In Drosophila you recall, the mutant gene (w) for white eye is X-linked. So also is another (presumably nonallelic) mutant gene which produces miniature wings (m). Using pure lines, a white-eyed long-winged fly is crossed to a dull-red-eyed miniature-winged fly. The F_1 female carries two X's and is, presumably, $w +/+ m$. This female is then mated, and the sons are scored phenotypically. (Any male can be used as parent since it will usually transmit to each son a Y chromosome lacking alleles of the genes under consideration. In fact, the Y is found to lack alleles of almost all of the genes known to be present on the X except the gene for *bobbed bristles, bb.* Moreover, the Y contains several genes for male fertility that have no alleles on the X.) Since sons normally receive their single X from their mother, their phenotypes directly indicate which hemizygous X-linked alleles each has received. Among the sons of this mating, about one crossover type appears for every two that are noncrossovers.

2. In man, color-blindness (c) and hemophilia type A (h) are recessive X-linked mutant genes absent on the Y chromosome. Though rare, some women have the genotype $+ h/c +$ —with one of these mutants on each X. Available data indicate that crossover ($c\, h$ or $+ +$) and noncrossover ($+ h$ or $c +$) sons occur in the approximate ratio of 1:9.

These examples show that when linkage between nonalleles is incomplete, the percentage of progeny carrying crossovers is constant for a given case but can be quite different in different organisms.

The possibility that the strength of linkage varies in the same organism can be tested using two mutants, b (black body color) and vg (vestigial wings), of *Drosophila melanogaster.*

A P_1 cross between $vg +/vg +$ (vestigial)[1] females and $+ b/+ b$ (black) males produces all normal F_1 ($vg +/+ b$). As shown in Figure 9–4A, a test cross of the F_1 female ($vg +/+ b\,♀$ by $vg\, b/vg\, b\,♂$) produces in F_2 only 20% with recombinant chromosomes. (All F_2 carry $vg\, b$ from the father, their maternal chromosome 40% of the time is $vg +$; 40%, $+ b$; 10%, $+ +$; 10%, $vg\, b$.) Since these results are independent of sex, we conclude that b and vg are linked autosomally. Recall that the X-linked genes m and w showed 33% crossovers; therefore, the linkages between different pairs of nonalleles on different pairs of homologs can have different strengths.

When the reciprocal cross ($vg +/+ b\,♂$

---

[1] The convention used here, and usually hereafter, is to describe the phenotypes of individuals only with respect to the appearance of mutant traits, all traits not mentioned being of the normal type.

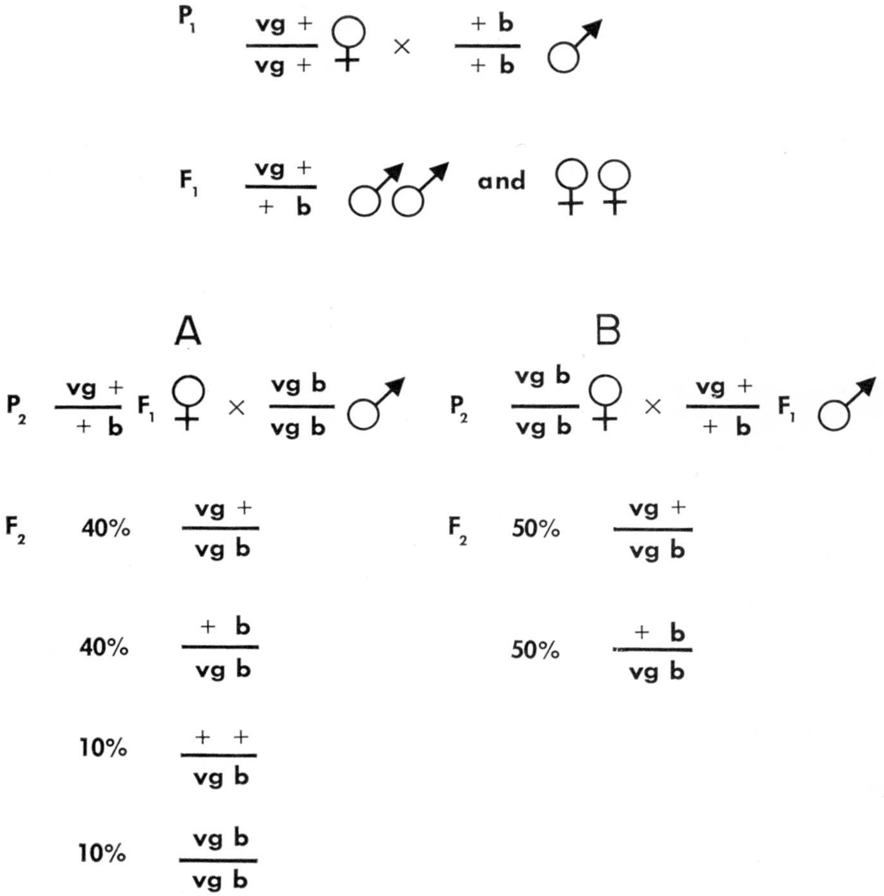

FIGURE 9–4. *Results of reciprocal crosses involving black body color* (b) *and vestigial* (vg) *wings.*

by $vg\,b/vg\,b\,♀$) is made with the F_1, 50% of offspring are $vg\,+/vg\,b$ (vestigial), and 50% are $+\,b/vg\,b$ (black) (Figure 9–4B). This cross produces no offspring with crossovers, so that linkage is complete for these genes in the male Drosophila. (Had linkage been complete in the female also, we should not have had any evidence that vg and b are separable and, therefore, two genes instead of one.) One finds, moreover, that in Drosophila any genes showing incomplete linkage in the female are completely linked in the male; the male, therefore, does not undergo the process of crossing over to produce crossovers.[2] It may be noted that in animals in general, crossing over is reduced or absent in the heterogametic sex. For example, no crossing over occurs in the females of birds.

[2] On rare occasions a special kind of "crossing over" does occur in the male Drosophila but is not of the kind that typically occurs in females.

What is the strength of linkage between a given gene and several nonalleles located in the same chromosome? This problem can be readily studied for certain X-linked genes in Drosophila. In Figure 9–5, one column shows genotypes of females; the other column shows the frequencies of crossover combinations as detected in their sons. The recombination frequencies given are those found between the gene for yellow body color (*y*) and for each of the following: white eye (*w*); crossveinless wings (*cv*); cut wings (*ct*); miniature wings (*m*); forked bristles (*f*). For example, 13 of each 100 eggs produced by the female dihybrid for *y* and *cv* carry crossovers (+ + or *y cv*). What does this value, and the other still different linkage values, mean in terms of meiosis?

So far, no commitment has been made as to where or when crossing over takes place. Since we have been concerned with complete and incomplete linkage as studied in successive generations of individuals, let us consider only crossing over that occurs in the cell line that gives rise directly to the

FEMALES	% CROSSOVER CHROMOSOMES AMONG SONS
y + / + w	1.5
y + / + cv	13
y + / + ct	20
y + / + m	34
y + / + f	48

FIGURE 9–5. *Crossover percentages between one gene and others linked to it.*

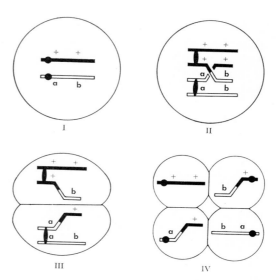

FIGURE 9–6. *The genetic consequences expected after a crossing over between linked genes.*

gametes (the *germ line*), ignoring the possibility that crossing over occurs in somatic (nongerminal) cells. Although crossing over might be premeiotic, meiotic, or postmeiotic in occurrence, we shall assume that all crossovers are produced during meiosis. The genetic consequences of an exchange (which we now call crossing over) between two pairs of linked genes during meiosis were discussed earlier (Chapter 4, p. 48) and the assumption was made (pp. 19–22) that a chiasma represents physical cytological evidence that a crossing over has occurred.

These cytogenetic events are diagrammed in Figure 9–6 in somewhat more detail than those originally shown (Figure 4–8). In stage I, one member of a pair of homologous chromosomes (hollow bar) is carrying the recessives *a* and *b* and the other (solid bar) is carrying their normal alleles. The black dots represent centromeres. The homologs synapse and form a tetrad (each univalent is now represented by two *sister strands*). After crossing over, the tetrad seems to appear at diplonema as depicted in stage II, which shows a chiasma between the *a* and *b loci* (the places in a chromosome containing the genes). Note that when the univalents are initially identical in appearance, a chiasma shows there was a physical exchange of apparently exactly equivalent segments between two nonsister strands of a tetrad, the strands being just as long after as before the exchange. Stage III shows the dyads present after the first meiotic division is completed. The upper cell or nucleus contains one + + noncrossover strand and one + *b* crossover strand, whereas the lower one contains the reciprocal crossover strand *a* + and the noncrossover strand *a b*. Stage IV shows the four haploid products (cells or nuclei) produced after the dyads form monads, and the second meiotic division is completed. According to this hypothesis, if one chiasma (representing a crossing over) occurs in any position between the loci of *a* and *b,* two of the four haploid nuclei produced contain noncrossover parental combinations, and the other two contain crossover nonparental recombinations.

Evidence that the crossovers found in gametes originate in this way is ordinarily difficult to obtain because, in females, only one of the four haploid products from each nucleus entering the meiotic divisions is usually retained as the nucleus of a functional gamete, the others being lost (as polar body nuclei or cells). Even when each of the four haploid products becomes or gives rise to a gamete, as in sperm or pollen formation, the four gametes—produced from a cell containing a given chiasma—mix with gametes produced from other meiotic cells which may or may not have had a similar chiasma. For these reasons, only one of the four meiotic products

is normally observed or identified at a time. If each chiasma results from a prior crossing over in the four-strand stage, approximately equal numbers of the two reciprocal kinds of crossovers would be expected, as seen in the crossover data already presented. However, crossing over during the two-stranded stage I is also expected to produce this result. The occurrence of noncrossover types, which are equally frequent and more numerous than the crossovers, can be explained if crossing over between the loci of *a* and *b* occurs less than 50% of the time at the two-strand stage or less than 100% of the time at the four-strand stage. The morphology of a chiasma, however, supports the view that crossing over takes place sometimes, if not always, at the four-strand stage.

Genetic evidence as to whether crossing over occurs at the two-strand or the four-strand stage might be obtained from gametes that retain not one but two or more strands of a tetrad. Finding a gamete that carries one strand which is a noncrossover and another homologous one which is a crossover, would support only the four-strand hypothesis. A suitable system for this test is found in Drosophila females whose two X's are not free to segregate since they are joined and have a single centromere. One type of such *attached-X's* is V-shaped at anaphase. During meiosis this attached-X replicates once, and the four arms synapse to form a tetrad, yielding two meiotic products each of which carries attached-X's and two products devoid of X chromosomes. Using females whose attached-X's are dihybrid and scoring their female progeny, one finds attached-X's having one arm a crossover and one that is not (Figure 9–7). Though this evidence also supports the four-strand hypothesis, it does not eliminate crossing over at the two-strand stage.

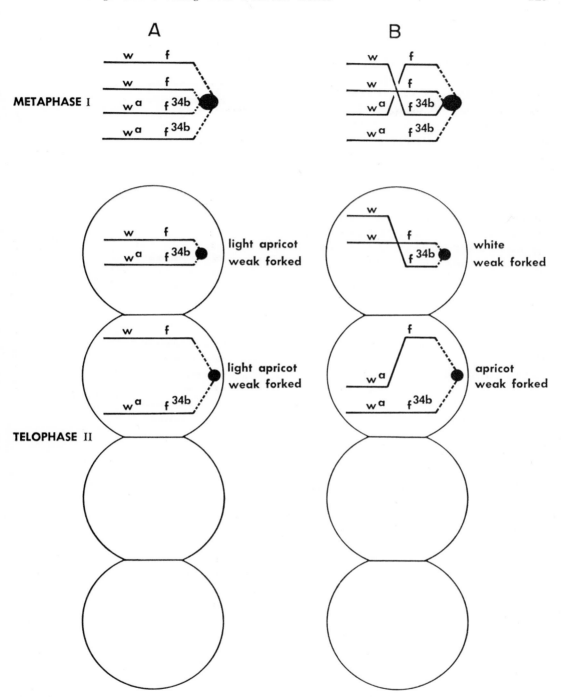

FIGURE 9–7. *Genotypic and phenotypic consequences of no crossing over (A) and of one type of crossing over (B) between marker genes in an attached-X female of Drosophila.*

The red bread mold Neurospora may provide critical evidence as to the time of crossing over. Recall that in the sexual process, so-called "fruiting" bodies are formed composed of cells containing two haploid nuclei, each of which was derived originally from a different parent (Figure 9–8). Two such haploid nuclei fuse to form a diploid nucleus containing seven pairs of chromosomes, and the cell elongates to form a sac. The diploid nucleus immediately undergoes meiosis, as shown in the figure, so that the four haploid products are arranged in tandem; that is, the two top nuclei come from one first-division nucleus, the bottom two from the other first-

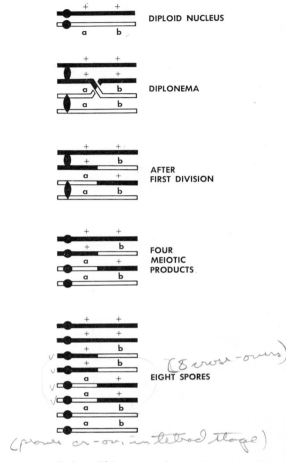

FIGURE 9–9. *Chiasma and crossing over in Neurospora.*

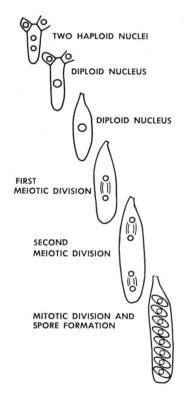

FIGURE 9–8. *Meiosis in Neurospora.*

division nucleus. Since each haploid nucleus subsequently divides mitotically once, each meiotic product is present in duplicate within the ascus. Each haploid ascospore can be removed from the ascus, grown individually, and its genotype determined directly. In this organism, then, all of the meiotic products derived from a single diploid nucleus can be obtained and identified.

Using the symbols in Figure 9–6, let us

follow in Figure 9–9 the genetic consequences of a single crossing over between the loci under study. Since only one of the seven pairs of chromosomes present is being traced, the others were omitted from the figure. As shown, a single crossing over in the four-strand stage produces two crossover and two noncrossover meiotic products. On the other hand, a crossing over in the two-strand stage (in the topmost nucleus) would produce only crossover meiotic products.

When numerous asci of a particular dihybrid for linked genes were tested, 90% had all eight spores noncrossovers for the two loci; in the remaining 10%, exactly four of their eight ascospores were crossovers. In other words, never were all eight spores from a single sac crossovers. This fact demonstrates conclusively that crossing over occurs only in the four-strand stage, as depicted in Figure 9–9 and Figure 9–10.

It has already been implied that chiasma formation is a normal part of meiosis (p. 16). The chiasma prevents the premature separation of dyads by holding them together as a tetrad until anaphase I. (Usually at least one, and as many as six chiasmata occur per tetrad.) Therefore, the crossing over that subsequently leads to the useful chiasma is also a normal part of meiosis.

Since chiasmata are found at numerous positions along a chromosome, it seems reasonable to suggest that the greater the distance between two loci, the greater will be the chance for a crossing over to occur between them, and the greater will be the frequency of crossovers for them. Conversely, the closer two loci are, the smaller will be the chance that crossing over occurs between them, and the smaller will be the frequency of crossovers for them. According to this view, *the frequency of crossovers can be used as an indication of the relative distances between loci.* (The results presented in Figure 9–5 should now have additional meaning for us.)

In the particular Neurospora test mentioned, no crossing over occurred in 90% of spore sacs in the genetically marked region (*a-b*). These sacs produced 90% of the total number of spores and carried only parental, noncrossover genotypes. From the 10% of spore sacs which did undergo

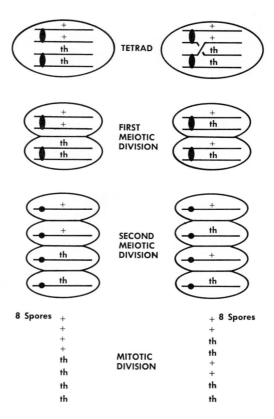

FIGURE 9–10. *Arrangement of spores in the Neurospora ascus when segregation occurs at the first meiotic division (left) and at the second meiotic division (right), as determined by the absence and presence, respectively, of a chiasma between the segregating genes and the centromere.*

crossing over, half of the spores were of the parental types and half were crossovers. So, equating the chiasma with the crossing over, a chiasma frequency of 10% resulted in 5% of all spores having crossovers. We can express the distance between the loci of *a* and *b* as being five crossover units long, *a crossover unit representing that distance between linked nonalleles which results in one crossover per hundred postmeiotic products* (spores, in the present case). Generally, when the genes are sufficiently close together (as in the present example), crossover frequency (crossover distance) is just one half the chiasma frequency, supporting our expectation of one chiasma for each preceding crossing over.

Crossover frequency can be measured in several ways in Neurospora:

1. Spores are tested from each sac (two to five per sac are sufficient) to determine whether or not the sac carries a crossover in the region under investigation. In the *a-b* example above, 10% of the sacs would have crossovers, 90% would not. Since each sac in the 10% group contains four spores that are crossovers and four that are not, crossover frequency would be 5%.

2. All the spores from many sacs are mixed, then a random sample of spores is taken and tested. This method would also give 5% recombination with *a-b* and is similar to the sampling procedure involved in determining crossover frequency in animal sperm.

3. One randomly chosen spore from each sac is tested; the others are discarded. Again, 5% crossovers are obtained. This procedure resembles the situation in many females (including Drosophila and human beings) in which one random product of meiosis normally enters the egg and the others are lost.

In the discussion above, no direct correlation was made between a genetically detected crossover and a cytologically detectable event involving a particular chromosome region. Such a connection cannot be made if both members of a pair of homologous chromosomes are identical in cytological appearance (as is assumed in Figure 9–6) because a crossover strand, having exchanged a cytologically identical segment with its homolog, appears the same as a noncrossover strand. A dihybrid for linked genes can be constructed, however, in which one homolog differs cytologically from its partner on both sides of the loci being tested. Such a genetic dihybrid is also cytologically dihybrid as specified in Figure 9–11. In this case it is possible to collect noncrossover progeny and show cytologically that they invariably retain the original chromosomal arrangement; crossovers on the other hand always show cytologically a new chromosome arrangement explained by a mutual exchange of specific chromosome regions between the homologs.[3]

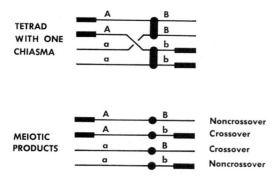

FIGURE 9–11.   *Correlation between genetical and cytological crossovers.*

[3] Using this method, genetic crossovers were correlated exactly with cytological crossovers by C. Stern (1931) using Drosophila and by H. S. Creighton and B. McClintock (1931) using maize.

Maize workers (l. to r.) at Cornell University in 1929: C. R. Burnham, M. M. Rhoades, G. W. Beadle *(crouched)*, R. A. Emerson, *and* Barbara McClintock.

SUMMARY AND CONCLUSIONS

The nonallelic genes in a given chromosome are linked and tend to be transmitted together to the next generation. Just as intergenic linkage produces an exception to independent segregation, crossing over produces an exception to linkage between nonalleles and causes linkage to be incomplete. Incomplete linkage proves that a chromosome contains more than one gene. In any given case, the degree to which linkage is incomplete—as measured by crossover frequency—is constant and independent both of the specific alleles which are present at the two different loci and of the gene combinations that enter the individual forming the gametes. Moreover, reciprocal crossover types are equally frequent. The crossover frequency in different cases is found to vary considerably.

A crossover chromosome is derived from a tetrad in which a crossing over between the linked genes showing recombination involves only two of the four strands. For closely linked genes, the crossover frequency is one half the frequency with which a chiasma or a crossing over occurs between their loci.

It is hypothesized that crossover frequency is directly related to the distance between genes in a chromosome. One unit of crossover distance between genes is defined as one crossover per one hundred postmeiotic cells (spores or gametes). Since different genes linked to the same gene show different percentages of crossing over with this gene, they are presumably different distances from it.

CURT STERN, *in the early 1930's.*

REFERENCES

Committee on Standardized Genetic Nomenclature for Mice, "A Revision of the Standardized Genetic Nomenclature for Mice," J. Heredity, 54:159–162, 1963.

Creighton, H. S., and McClintock, B., "A Correlation of Cytological and Genetical Crossing-over in Zea Mays," Proc. Nat. Acad. Sci., U.S., 17:492–497, 1931. Reprinted in *Classic Papers in Genetics,* Peters, J. A. (Ed.), Englewood Cliffs, N.J.: Prentice-Hall, 1959, pp. 155–160; also in *Great Experiments in Biology,* Gabriel, M. L., and Fogel, S. (Eds.), Englewood Cliffs, N.J.: Prentice-Hall, 1955, pp. 267–272.

Morgan, T. H., "Random Segregation Versus Coupling in Mendelian Inheritance," Science, 34:384, 1911. Reprinted in *Great Experiments in Biology,* Gabriel, M. L., and Fogel, S. (Eds.), Englewood Cliffs, N.J.: Prentice-Hall, 1955, pp. 257–259.

Stern, C., "Zytologisch-genetische Untersuchungen als Beweise für die Morgansche Theorie des Faktorenaustauschs," Biol. Zbl., 51:547–587, 1931.

QUESTIONS FOR DISCUSSION

9.1. Distinguish between sex-linkage and the linkage of nonalleles.

9.2. Does the linkage of two genes prove they are located on the same chromosome? Explain.

9.3. Discuss the advantages and disadvantages of linkage and crossing over with respect to the fitness of individuals carrying certain genotypes.

9.4. In Drosophila, *y* and *spl* are X-linked. A female genotypically $+ +/y \ spl$ produces sons. If 3% carry either $y +$ or $+ spl$, what are the genotypes and relative frequencies of gametes produced by the mother? Is the father's genotype important? Explain.

9.5. Name all the processes so far discussed which lead to genetic recombination.

9.6. Do you think that one of the main principles in this chapter is that chromosomes contain more than one gene? Explain.

9.7. In light of your present knowledge how would you proceed to state a "law of independent segregation"?

9.8. What evidence do you have that crossing over does not involve the unilateral movement of one gene from its position in one chromosome to a position in the homologous chromosme?

9.9. Does crossing over always result in genetic recombination? Explain.

9.10. In what respect do you think the development of the principles of genetics in this text would have been affected had the first two pairs of genes (Rr and Yy), simultaneously studied in crosses, been linked?

9.11. Assume that the gene for woolly hair (Chapter 3, p. 38) is located autosomally. A nonwoolly-haired, nonhemophilic man marries a woolly-haired, nonhemophilic woman. They have a woolly-haired, hemophilic son. Give the genotypes of all three individuals, and the genotypes and frequencies of the gametes usually produced by the son.

9.12. How would you defend the conclusion that the point of crossing over is located at exactly equivalent positions on the two homologs?

9.13. What are the relative frequencies of the phenotypes and genotypes expected from a mating between two Drosophila: dihybrid $vg +/+ b$?

9.14. Two dihybrids, $a +/+ b$, for autosomally linked mutants a and b in Drosophila, are crossed. If 2p equals the frequency of noncrossover eggs and 1–2p equals the frequency of crossover eggs, and if $p < 0.5$, give the relative frequencies of the phenotypes expected among the F_1 of this cross.

9.15. What result would you expect from 9.14 if the cross were between dihybrids $a b/+ +$?

9.16. A wild-type Drosophila female, whose father had crossveinless wings and mother had yellow body color, is mated to a yellow male. Give the relative frequencies of genotypes and phenotypes expected in the F_1.

9.17. A mating in Drosophila produces the results shown below. Give the genotypes of the parents, and determine which genes are linked and which are not.

Sons	*Daughters*
75 wild-type	92 wild-type
70 yellow body color, white-eyes	75 white
21 yellow, white, vestigial wings	28 vestigial
27 vestigial	20 white, vestigial
2 yellow	
1 white, vestigial	

9.18. What is the relationship in Neurospora between crossing over and first and second meiotic division segregation?

9.19. In tomatoes, the gene for tall (+) is dominant to short (s), and the gene for smooth epidermis (+) is dominant to rough (r). A cross between two plants produces 208 tall smooth, 9 tall rough, 6 short smooth, 195 short rough. Give the genotypes of the parents.

9.20. What is the percentage of crossovers for two loci, in a species in which both sexes undergo crossing over with equal frequency, if a mating between identical dihybrids (Ab/aB) gives four equally viable classes of offspring, the smallest class comprising 1% of all offspring?

9.21. How would you prove genetically that the last division in a spore sac of Neurospora is a mitotic one?

9.22. In the absence of crossing over, could you determine whether the alternatives for two different traits were due to a single pair of genes or to two pairs of linked genes? Explain.

9.23. Draw an attached-X chromosome of Drosophila heterozygous both for y and for m. Show the kinds of gametes which could be obtained after:

   (a) No chiasma
   (b) One chiasma between the nonallelic genes
   (c) One chiasma not between the genes mentioned

9.24. Suppose one member of a long pair of chromosomes in a plant has a large knob at one of its ends, and the other has a small knob at the opposite end. Suppose, moreover, that there is also a shorter pair of homologs, one member terminating with a large knob, and the other at the opposite end with a small knob. What combinations and configurations would you expect to readily find in the gametes of this individual?

9.25. What reasons can you present for believing that germ-line crossing over is based neither upon premeiotic nor upon postmeiotic events?

9.26. Calculate the number of crossover units between *black body* (b) and *dumpy wings* (dp) in the following Drosophila crosses:

   (a) P_1 pure black $\times$ pure dumpy
       P_2 F_1 ♀♀ $\times$ black dumpy ♂♂
       F_2 wild-type   272
            black   774
            dumpy   801
            black dumpy   239
   (b) P_1 black dumpy $\times$ pure wild-type
       P_2 F_1 ♀♀ $\times$ black dumpy ♂♂
       F_2 wild-type   360
            black   103
            dumpy   97
            black dumpy   314

9.27. What phenotypic results would you expect in 9.26(a) and (b) if the reciprocal mating had occurred in P_2?

9.28. Test statistically the F_2 results of 9.26(a) with those expected from independent segregation.

9.29. Test statistically whether the F_2 results in 9.26(a) and (b) differ significantly.

9.30. A trihybrid *Aa Bb Cc* is test crossed to *aa bb cc*. The F_1 show that the trihybrid produced the following gametes:

29	*ABC*	21	*abc*
235	*ABc*	215	*abC*
210	*Abc*	239	*aBC*
27	*AbC*	23	*aBc*

   (a) Which loci are linked and which are segregating independently?
   (b) Write the genotypes of both parents in view of your answer to (a).
   (c) Give the percentage of crossovers wherever applicable.

Chapter 10

GENE ARRANGEMENT;
CROSSOVER MAPS

N THE preceding chapter, the frequency of crossing over was presumed to be dependent upon the distance between genes, the interval being measured in crossover units. Different genes linked to a given gene were found to give different, essentially constant, crossover frequencies or *crossover distances*. Let us now investigate how these different genes are arranged spatially.

Crossover distances can be used to study whether linked genes are arranged in some regular three-dimensional configuration such as a sphere, cube, prism, or some two-dimensional one such as a line, circle, or triangle. To map the genes on the basis of crossover data, that is, make a *crossover (or linkage) map,* it is necessary to determine all the crossover distances for a minimum of three linked loci, since two points (such as those defined by the crossover distance between two genes) are not enough to determine a specific geometrical arrangement.

Gene Arrangement

The arrangement of linked loci can be investigated with Drosophila. Using the three X-linked genes, *y* (yellow body color), *w* (white eyes), and *spl* (split bristles), dihybrid females of the following types are obtained: *y w*/+ +; *y spl*/+ +; and *w spl*/+ +, and each type is test crossed with the appropriate double recessive male. The corresponding crossover distances are:

y to *w*, 1.5; *y* to *spl*, 3.0; and *w* to *spl*, 1.5. Since the crossover distance between *y* and *spl* equals the sum of the crossover distances from *y* to *w* and from *w* to *spl*, a linear arrangement for these three genes is described, namely, *y w spl* or *spl w y*. In other words, *the genetic map based on crossovers is linear*. If the reasonable assumption is made that crossing over is a function of physical distance between genes, the genes are also linearly arranged in the chromosomes.

When the positions of a fourth X-linked gene and all other X-linked genes are mapped relative to the three studied above, all are found to be arranged in a linear order (Figure 10–1, and page s–16). In such a crossover map, *y* is arbitrarily assigned the position, or locus, zero.

On a standard crossover map for the Drosophila X, the genes *y*, *w*, *spl*, *cv*, *ct*, *m*, and *f* line up respectively at positions 0, 1.5, 3.0, 13.7, 20, 36.1, 56.7, and one can see that *ct* and *spl* are 17 map units apart ($20 - 3$). Since one crossover *map unit* equals one crossover per hundred gametes, the dihybrid for *spl* and *ct* (Figure 10–2) should produce 17% crossovers (8.5% + + and 8.5% *spl ct*). However, such a result is obtained only under special conditions.

The crossover frequency actually observed will depend upon several factors. One of these is the number of individuals making up the sample. In small samples it is very likely that, by chance, the observed values will deviate considerably in both directions from the standard map distance. As the size of the sample increases, the observed value will more closely approach the standard one. Standard distances, therefore, are determined only after large numbers of progeny have been scored.

The relative viability (see p. 69) of different phenotypic classes is another factor influencing observed crossover frequency.

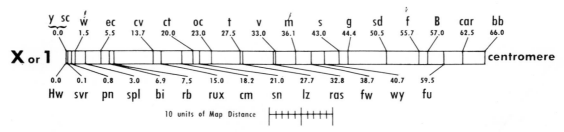

FIGURE 10–1. *Crossover map of the X chromosome of* D. melanogaster.

KEY TO SYMBOLS

SYMBOL	NAME	SYMBOL	NAME
y	yellow body color	oc	ocelliless—ocelli absent; female sterile
Hw	Hairy-wing—extra bristles on wing veins, head, and thorax	t	tan body color
sc	scute—absence of certain bristles, especially scutellars	lz	lozenge—eyes narrow and glossy
svr	silver body color	ras	raspberry eye color
pn	prune eye color	v	vermilion eye color
w	white compound eyes and ocelli	m	miniature wings
spl	split bristles	fw	furrowed eyes
ec	echinus—large and rough textured eyes	wy	wavy wings
bi	bifid—proximal fusion of longitudinal wing veins	s	sable body color
rb	ruby eye color	g	garnet eye color
cv	crossveinless—crossveins of wings absent	sd	scalloped wing margins
rux	roughex—eyes small and rough	f	forked—bristles curled and twisted
cm	carmine eye color	B	Bar—narrow eyes
ct	cut—scalloped wing edges	fu	fused longitudinal wing veins; female sterile
sn	singed—bristles and hairs curled and twisted	car	carnation eye color
		bb	bobbed—short bristles

The phenotypic expression of a + allele is usually more viable than that of its mutant forms. For example, in Figure 10–2 the phenotypically split, cut sons are not as viable as the normal (wild-type) sons; although both types are equally frequent as zygotes, the former fail to complete their development more often than the latter and, therefore, are relatively less frequent when the adults are scored. Zygotes destined to become either split or cut males are also less viable than zygotes destined to produce wild-type males. Whenever phenotypes are scored after some long developmental period, much of the error due to differential viability may be avoided by providing optimal culture conditions. Another way to avoid most of this kind of error is to delay

the scoring of crossovers for one generation. The cross is arranged in such a way that individuals with the chromosomes to be scored have a homologous chromosome containing the normal alleles of all genes under crossover test. Since the progeny of such a cross are phenotypically normal, their viability will be approximately the same, and they can be scored for chromosome type from the offspring each produces when individually test crossed. For example, the female in Figure 10–2 is crossed with wild-type males, and the F_1 daughters (all phenotypically normal) are individually mated to any male. Daughters carrying an X of one of the following types: spl +, + ct, + +, spl ct—in addition to a + + homolog obtained from the father—will produce sons of the following type respectively: some split, but none cut; some cut, but none split; all normal; some both split and cut. In this way the generation being tested for crossover frequency is largely protected from differential viability, its genotypes being scored in the next generation. For mapping and other purposes, the extra labor entailed by this method is often justified.

Variability in crossover frequency may be due also to factors—such as temperature, nutrition, age of the female, and presence of specific genes—which influence the very process of crossing over.

To better understand the relationships between crossover maps and chiasmata, consider the properties of an over-simplified model (Figure 10–3). Assume that a chromosome (ignoring the centromere) is composed of five equally long regions, the ends of each marked by a gene; that each tetrad of this type contains one, and only one, chiasma following a crossing over; and that this chiasma can occur in a random position among these segments. For the hexahybrid shown in Figure 10–3, the chance the chiasma will occur in the *a-b* region is 20%; out of each 25 tetrads (producing 100 haploid meiotic products), five or 20% will have the chiasma in the *a-b* region. These five will produce 10 crossover and 10 noncrossover strands. Adding the latter 10 and the 80 noncrossover strands from the remaining 20 tetrads, gives 90 noncrossover strands. For this region, therefore, 20% of tetrads have a chiasma and 10% of haploid meiotic products are crossovers as explained in Chapter 9. Similarly, in the *b-c* region 10% crossovers would be noted. The chiasma would occur in the *a-c* region 40% of the time, and 20% of all haploid meiotic

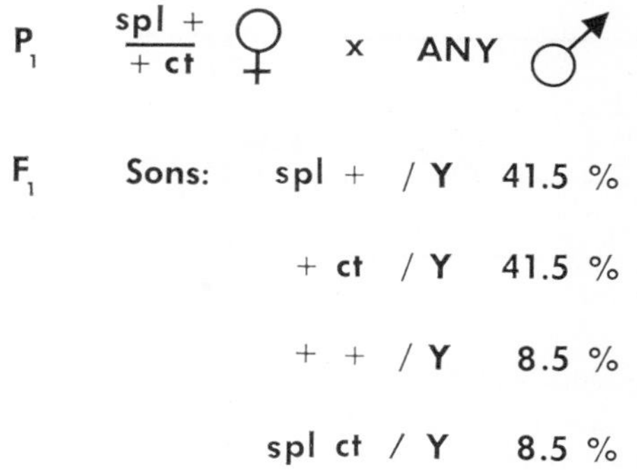

FIGURE 10–3. *Crossover consequences of a single chiasma.*

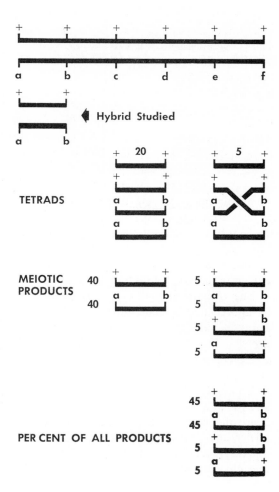

$$P_1 \quad \frac{spl +}{+ ct} \; ♀ \quad × \quad \text{ANY} \; ♂$$

F₁ Sons: spl + / Y   41.5 %

+ ct / Y   41.5 %

+ + / Y   8.5 %

spl ct / Y   8.5 %

FIGURE 10–2. *Crossover frequency for two X-linked genes in Drosophila.*

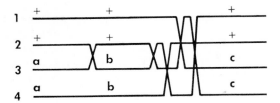

FIGURE 10–4. *Chromatid recombinations possible in a double chiasmata. (See text for details.)*

products would be crossovers relative to the markers *a* and *c*. Since the sum of the distances from *a-b* and *b-c* equals the distance between *a* and *c* measured directly, the genes of the model would be aligned linearly, just as was observed in the experiment described earlier in this chapter.

In the model proposed above, the presence of a chiasma in one region automatically excludes it from being in some other region. Consequently, the chance that a chiasma will be found in the *a-c* region is equal to the sum of the separate chances that a chiasma will be found in the *a-b* and *b-c* regions. It is a general rule that *the overall probability for the occurrence of any one of a series of mutually exclusive events is equal to the sum of their separate probabilities of occurrence.* Therefore, the chance of a chiasma occurring between *a* and *f* is $(20 + 20 + 20 + 20 + 20)\%$, or 100%. As a result, 100% of the tetrads have one crossing over (that is, one chiasma) which produces 50% crossovers, and the model chromosome has 50 map units.

The oversimplification of this model can be appreciated by remembering that a given tetrad usually contains more than one chiasma. This prompts us to ask: When a tetrad contains two or more chiasmata, which strands are involved in the exchanges?

To answer this question, let us specify the strands in a tetrad as 1, 2, 3, 4, where 1 and 2 are the sister strands carrying the normal alleles and 3 and 4 the sister strands carrying the recessive alleles (Figure 10–4). If one chiasma involves an exchange between nonsister strands 2 and 3 in the *a-b* region, a second chiasma, involving nonsister strands in the *b-c* region, can result from any one of four exchanges: 2 with 3; 2 with 4; 1 with 3; 1 with 4. The positions of these chiasmata are indicated in Figure 10–4. The four types of single chiasma in the *b-c* region together with the single chiasma in the *a-b* region form *double chiasmata* of three types:

2-strand (the same two strands exchange in both chiasmata);

3-strand (one of the two strands of the first chiasma exchanges in the second, there being two ways this double chiasmata can occur);

and *4-strand* (those strands which do not exchange in the first chiasma, exchange in the second).

Let us examine the genetic consequences of these four nonsister types of double chiasmata (shown separately at the left of Figure 10–5). The middle column shows the meiotic products of each, and the right column indicates whether these products are noncrossovers, single crossovers, or double crossovers for the *a-b-c* region. From 2-strand double chiasmata, two of the four meiotic products are genetic noncrossovers ($+ + +$ and *a b c*), and two are double crossovers ($+ b +$ and *a + c*). The double crossovers, or "doubles" as they are called, are characterized by a change in the position of the middle gene relative to the end genes. A 3-strand double chiasmata produces one double crossover, two single crossovers (in each, the position of one end gene is changed relative to the other two genes), and one noncrossover. The 4-strand double chiasmata yields four single crossover strands. Note that each type of double chiasmata produces some strands with a new genetic combination, that is, crossover strands; each of the three different types also produces a characteristic pattern of noncrossover and crossover types. Moreover, the genetic products obtained from each type of double chiasmata differ from those obtained from a single chiasma (which produces two noncrossovers and two "singles").

In view of the preceding discussion, it should be possible to learn, from the geno-

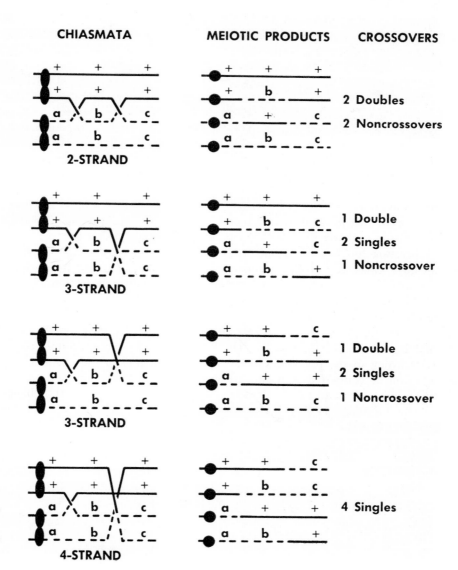

FIGURE 10–5. *Double nonsister chiasmata types and their genetic consequences.*

types of the meiotic products, the relative frequency with which the four types of double chiasmata occur. If all four types occur with equal frequency, the strands forming one chiasma would be unaffected by those which form an adjacent chiasma. Indeed, experiments with Neurospora reveal that all four types do occur—in some, the four types occur with equal frequency. For our purposes, we can accept the view that there is usually *no chromatid interference* in chiasma formation; in other words, the particular nonsister chromatids forming a chiasma are not influenced by nonsister strands which may or may not form a chiasma in an adjacent region. Thus, nonsister strands crossing over in two different regions of the same tetrad are independent.

Does the occurrence of one chiasma influence the probability that a second chiasma will occur in the same tetrad, even though when both chiasmata occur there is no chromatid interference?

Suppose that in the genetic system of Figure 10–4, each of the two regions under observation has a 20% chance of forming a single chiasma. If the occurrence of a chiasma in the *a-b* region is independent of a chiasma in the *b-c* region, then, of all tetrads, 20% of the 20% with an *a-b* chiasma will simultaneously have a *b-c* chiasma; that is, 4% will contain double chiasmata. (According to the previous discussion, this 4% will be composed of the four nonsister types in equal frequency.) It is a general rule that *the overall probability for the simultaneous or consecutive occurrence of two or more events of independent origin is equal to the product of their separate probabilities of occurrence.*

If 4% double chiasmata were actually observed in the *a-c* region, one would conclude there was *no chiasma interference* (or better still, *no crossing-over interference*); that is, the formation of one chiasma would not affect the formation of another in an adjacent region. If, on the other hand, only 2% double chiasmata were observed, this would mean that some chiasma interference had occurred.

The degree of chiasma interference can be written as

$$\frac{\text{double chiasmata observed}}{\text{double chiasmata expected}} = \frac{0.02}{0.04} = 0.50$$

This fraction, called the *coefficient of coincidence,* expresses the frequency with which the coincidence of two chiasmata is actually obtained. Consequently, a coefficient of coincidence equal to zero would mean that one chiasma completely prevented the other from occurring; whereas a value of one would mean that the one chiasma had no effect at all on the occurrence of the other.

In practice, however, because of the errors involved—particularly those stemming from chiasma terminalization (see p. 22)—one does not usually determine the frequencies and positions of double chiasmata cytologically. Can we use the frequency of genetically-detected double crossovers as an alternative for measuring chiasma or crossing-over interference?

We can be sure that each double crossover observed has resulted from multiple crossing over or chiasmata. The expected frequency of double crossovers in the *a-b-c* region of the example can be calculated in the following way: since each region (*a-b* and *b-c*) has a 0.2 chance for one crossing over, the chance for a double crossing over is 0.2 times 0.2, or 0.04. (If, as before, the coefficient of coincidence were 0.5, one would expect 0.02 tetrads to have double crossing over.) Recall that the double crossing over can occur in four ways and can involve 2, 3, or 4 strands of a tetrad. If these alternatives occur with equal frequency, only one quarter ($4/16$) of all meiotic products from double crossing over will appear as double crossovers (Figure 10–5). Since the remaining three quarters ($1\frac{2}{16}$) of the meiotic products are noncrossovers or single crossovers, they are not useful in identifying the occurrence of double crossing-over events, because they could have been produced in tetrads of other types, for example, those having single or no crossing over. Accordingly, a frequency of 0.04 double crossing over would lead us to expect a frequency of .01 double crossovers; and a frequency of only 0.005 would actually be detected were the coefficient of coincidence 0.5. In this way, the coefficient of coincidence can be determined from double crossovers observed divided by the double crossovers expected.

There is another, perhaps simpler, way to calculate the expected frequency of double crossovers. In our example above, the chance a crossing over will occur is 0.2, and the chance that a given strand will be a crossover, 0.5. The chance that both will occur once is 0.1, and that both will occur twice is 0.1 times 0.1 or 0.01. That is, the expected chance that a given strand will be a double crossover is one percent. Accordingly, the frequency of observed single crossovers in the *a-b* region multiplied by the frequency of observed single crossovers in adjacent *b-c* region equals the expected frequency of double crossovers (one in each region). In practice, therefore, one may readily determine the coefficient of coincidence from double crossovers.

Generally the coefficient of coincidence is negligible—equal to zero for all practical purposes—for short map distances and becomes larger with increased distance. This relation suggests that a tetrad in which one crossing over occurs is somehow precluded from having a second one occur close by, with this restriction diminishing as the distance to the second region increases. In Drosophila, for example, the coefficient of coincidence is zero for distances up to 10–15 map units and, consequently, no double chiasmata (or no double crossovers) occur within such distances. As the distance increases beyond 15 map units, however, the coefficient gradually increases to 1, at which point nothing interferes with the formation of double chiasmata. In two equal-armed chromosomes there does not seem to be chiasma interference across the centromere.

If each tetrad has only a single chiasma, the maximum frequency with which the end genes recombine relative to each other is 0.5. What happens to the frequency of recombination for the end genes when the chromosome has double chiasmata?

If each tetrad has two chiasmata, one might think that the end genes would form new combinations with a frequency greater than 0.5. Examination of Figure 10–5 reveals, however (each type of double chiasmata being equally probable), that on the average eight products (single crossovers) will carry a new combination with respect to one end gene, and eight products will not. Of the latter, four will be noncrossovers and four, double crossovers in which the middle gene has changed position relative to the end genes. Therefore, even if every tetrad has double chiasmata, the maximum frequency of recombination for the end genes is 0.5.

When four loci are studied and three chiasmata occur in each tetrad—one in each region—one finds that for every 64 meiotic products, 32 are recombinational for the end genes and 32 are not. For cases where four or more chiasmata lie between end genes, the frequency of meiotic products bearing odd numbers of crossover regions is easily calculated to be 0.5. In each of these cases the gene at one end is shifted relative to that at the other. However, the remaining strands contain either even numbers of crossover regions (which do not

+ + +	0.31	+ + +	0.31
a b c	0.31	a c b	0.31
+ b c	0.14	+ c b	0.14
a + +	0.14	a + +	0.14
+ + c	0.01	+ c +	0.01
a b +	0.01	a + b	0.01
+ b +	0.04	+ + b	0.04
a + c	0.04	a c +	0.04
	1.00		1.00

FIGURE 10–6. *Determination of gene order from a test crossed trihybrid.*

cause the genes at the two ends to shift relative to each other) or are noncrossovers. Accordingly, the maximum frequency of recombination of 0.5 holds for the endmost genes (and, therefore, of course, for any genes between them).

If two genes in a chromosome are sufficiently far apart, the frequency with which they undergo recombination will be near 0.5. Since a recombination frequency of 0.5 means that nonalleles are independent in their segregation, one cannot conclude from such a recombination frequency that nonalleles are on the same chromosome. Accordingly, two pairs of genes that show recombination frequencies near 0.5 can be either far apart in the same pair of homologs or located in different pairs of homologs. However, if two nonalleles segregate independently but are both linked to a third nonallele, all three are linked to one another.

Whenever the number of gene pairs investigated is considerably larger than the number of chromosome pairs, the number of groups of linked genes equals or approaches the number of chromosome pairs. The result is a *limitation in the number of linkage groups,* the maximum number equalling the haploid chromosome number. (Examination of the linkage groups of the garden pea now reveals that two of the first seven gene pairs studied [1] are in the same linkage group although a considerable distance apart. The initial recombination data were sufficiently meager for acceptance of the hypothesis that the genes were segregating independently.)

The sequence of three linked genes can be determined from the results of a single cross. Suppose the trihybrid $+ + +/a\,b\,c$ is test crossed, and the frequencies of the various phenotypes in the progeny are those shown at the left in Figure 10–6. These values, we remember, represent the frequencies of the corresponding genotypes in the gametes of the trihybrid. The middle gene in the actual sequence is the one which switches least often from the original gene combinations ($+ + +$ and $a\,b\,c$), because only the middle one requires two chiasmata for its switch. Consequently, this gene is identified as c, and the actual gene order is $a\,c\,b$ (or $b\,c\,a$). This reasoning may be easier to follow if the data are examined with the genes listed in their correct order, as shown at the right in Figure 10–6.

The frequency of observed crossovers between the a and c loci is 0.30; between c and b it is 0.10. Between a and b the frequency of single crossovers is 0.36. Crossover frequency between a and b, however, also includes double crossovers. Since each double crossover represents two single crossovers between the end genes, the frequency

[1] By G. Mendel.

of double crossovers, .02, must be doubled and added to the frequency of single crossovers to obtain the total crossover frequency between *a* and *b*. The genetic map based on crossover frequency becomes linear $(0.30 + 0.10 = 0.36 + 0.04)$, therefore, when double crossovers are taken into account. The expected frequency of double crossovers is 0.3 times 0.1 or 0.03, so that the coefficient of coincidence in this case is 0.02/0.03, or 0.66. (In the *y w spl* example discussed earlier in this chapter, the longest region, *y-spl*, was too short for double crossing over.)

Would it be satisfactory to use the data in Figure 10–6 to construct a standard linkage map for the distances between these genes, assuming that large numbers of progeny had been scored and standard experimental conditions had been used? For this purpose, the observed distance from *c* to *b* is acceptable since only a single chiasma can occur in such a short interval. The situation is otherwise for the *a-c* region, however, which is 30 map units long in the present experiment. Double chiasmata are expected to occur under these circumstances, yet the absence of genetic markers between *a* and *c* prevents their identification. Therefore, the standard map distance for *a-c* must be longer than 30 map units (and *a-b* longer than 40). Note that the identical error foreshortens the *a-c* and the *a-b* distances; therefore, for the distances observed, (*a-c*) plus (*c-b*) is equal to (*a-b*). Whether or not the chromosome is genetically marked so that all multiple crossover strands are detected, the correct order of three linked genes can always be determined, provided that two are not 50 map units away from the third.

It should now be clear why the crossover frequencies observed for large distances are less than the standard map distances, and why the standard map distances are always obtained by the summation of the short distances in which only a single chiasma can occur.

Although end genes can show at most 50% recombination, the length of the crossover map may exceed 50 units. For example, if a given pair of homologs contains an average of two chiasmata in each tetrad (see Figure 10–5), a total of 100 crossovers will occur among 100 meiotic products, and the map length will be 100 units even though the end genes will have recombined 50% of the time. In fact, it can be predicted that the length of the standard map is equal to fifty times the mean number of crossing-over events (or chiasmata) per tetrad.

Crossover Maps

Utilizing crossover frequency, genetic maps of chromosomes have been made for a number of multicellular organisms. Figures 10–7 through 10–10 give the linkage maps for a considerable number of genes in man, mouse, maize, and Neurospora.

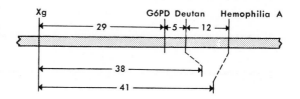

FIGURE 10–7. *Tentative linkage map of a segment of the human X chromosome. The numbers given are the values for the map distance found in five separate studies. The loci mapped are the Xg (blood group) locus, the G6PD (glucose-6-phosphate dehydrogenase) deficiency locus, the deutan (green) color-blindness locus, the classic hemophilia locus. (Courtesy of V. A. McKusick. From* Human Genetics, *1964, Prentice-Hall, Inc., Englewood Cliffs, N.J.)*

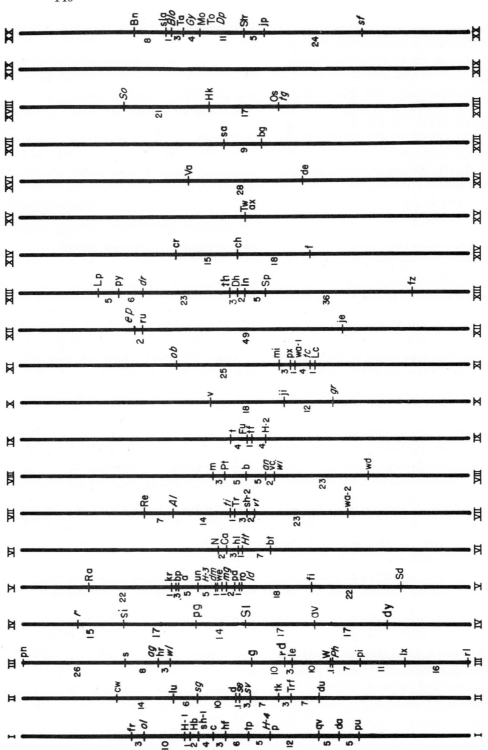

FIGURE 10–8. *Linkage groups of the mouse.* (*Courtesy of Margaret C. Green.*)

(*Margaret C. Green, 1964*)

Symbol	Name	Symbol	Name	Symbol	Name	Symbol	Name
a-series		*dy*	dystrophia muscularis	*Mo-series*		*So*	Sombre
a	nonagouti	*ep*	pale ears	*Mo*	Mottled	*Sp*	Splotch
a^e	extreme nonagouti	*f*	flexed tail	Mo^{br}	Brindled	*Str*	Striated
a^t	black and tan	*fi*	fidget	*N*	Naked	*sv*	Snell's waltzer
A^w	White-bellied agouti	*fr*	frizzy	*ob*	obese	*t-series*	
A^y	Yellow	*Fu-series*		*ol*	oligodactyly	*t*	tailless
ag	agitans	*Fu*	Fused	*Os*	Oligosyndactylism	*T*	Brachyury
av	Ames waltzer	Fu^{ki}	Kinky	*p-series*		*Ta*	Tabby
Al	Alopecia	*fz*	fuzzy	*p*	pink-eyed dilution	*tc*	truncate
an	anemia	*g*	low glucuronidase	p^d	dark pink-eye	*tf*	tufted
ax	ataxia	*gr*	grizzled	p^s	p-sterile	*tg*	tottering
b-series		*Gy*	Gyro	*pa*	pallid	*th*	tilted head
b	brown	*Hb*	Hemoglobin pattern	*pg*	pygmy	*ti*	tipsy
bc	cordovan	*hf*	hepatic fusion	*Ph*	Patch	*tk*	tail kinks
B^l	Light	*Hk*	Hook	*pi*	pirouette	*To*	Tortoise
bg	beige	*hl*	hair-loss	*pn*	pugnose	*tp*	taupe
Blo	Blotchy	*hr-series*		*Pt*	Pintail	*Tr*	Trembler
Bn	Bent	*hr*	hairless	*pu*	pudgy	*Trf*	Transferrin
bp	brachypodism	hr^{rh}	rhino	*px*	postaxial hemimelia	*Tw*	Twirler
bt	belted	*Ht*	Hightail	*py*	polydactyly	*un*	undulated
c-series		*H-1*	Histocompatibility-1	*qv*	quivering	*v*	waltzer
c	albino	*H-2*	Histocompatibility-2	*r*	rodless retina	*Va*	Varitint-waddler
c^{ch}	chinchilla	*H-3*	Histocompatibility-3	*Ra*	Ragged	*vc*	vacillans
c^e	extreme dilution	*H-4*	Histocompatibility-4	*rd*	retinal degeneration	*vt*	vestigial tail
c^h	himalayan	*je*	jerker	*Re*	Rex	*W-series*	
Ca	Caracul	*ji*	jittery	*rl*	reeler	*W*	Dominant spotting
ch	congenital hydro-cephalus	*ip*	jimpy	*ro*	rough	*Wa*	Ames dominant spotting
cr	crinkled	*kr*	kreisler	*ru*	ruby eye	*Wj*	Jay's dominant spotting
cw	curly whiskers	*Lc*	Lurcher	*s*	piebald	*Wv*	Viable dominant spotting
d-series		*le*	light ears	*sa*	satin	*wa-1*	waved-1
d	dilute	*ld*	limb deformity	*Sd*	Danforth's short tail	*wa-2*	waved-2
d^l	dilute-lethal	*ln*	leaden	*se*	short ear	*wd*	waddler
da	dark	*Lp*	Loop tail	*sf*	scurfy	*we*	wellhaarig
de	droopy-ear	*lu*	luxoid	*sg*	staggerer	*wi*	whirler
Dh	Dominant hemimelia	*lx*	luxate	*sh-1*	shaker-1	*wl*	wabbler-lethal
dm	diminutive	*m*	misty	*sh-2*	shaker-2		
Dp	Dappled	*mg*	mahogany	*si*	silver		
dr	dreher	*mi-series*		*Sl*	Steel		
du	ducky	*mi*	microphthalmia	*sla*	sex-linked anemia		
		Mi^{wh}	White				

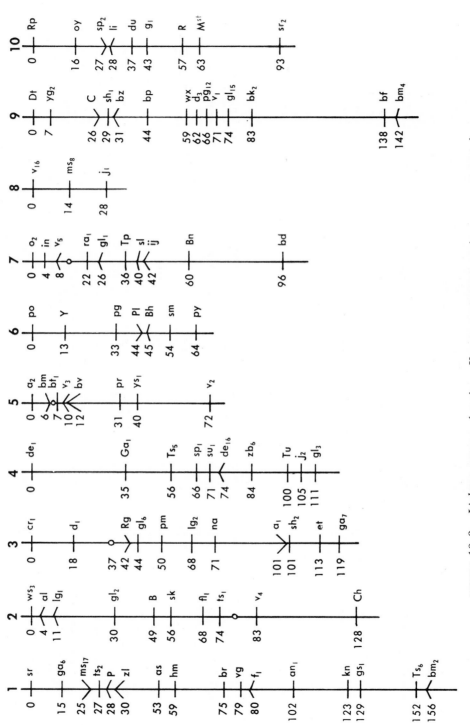

FIGURE 10–9. *Linkage groups of maize. Known centromere regions are represented by circles. The map location of most of the genes in the lower half of chromosome 9 comes from studies of E. H. Coe, Jr.* (*Courtesy of M. M. Rhoades.*)

Symbol	Name	Symbol	Name	Symbol	Name	Symbol	Name
a	anthocyanin	*d*	dwarf	*li*	lineate stripe	*sl*	slashed leaves
al	albescent	*de*	defective endosperm	*ms*	male sterile	*sm*	salmon silk color
an	anther ear	*Dt*	Dotted	M^{st}	Modifier of R^{st}	*sp*	small pollen
as	asynapsis	*du*	dull endosperm	*na*	nana plant	*sr*	striate
B	Anthocyanin booster	*et*	etched aleurone	*o*	opaque endosperm	*su*	sugary endosperm
bd	branched silkless	*f*	fine striped leaves	*oy*	oil yellow	*Tp*	Teopod
bf	blue fluorescence	*fl*	floury endosperm	*P*	Pericarp color	*Ts*	Tassel seed
Bh	Blotched aleurone	*g*	golden plant	*pg*	pale green	*ts*	tassel seed
bk	brittle stalk	*ga*	gametophyte factor	*Pl*	Purple plant color	*Tu*	Tunicate
bm	brown midrib	*Ga*	Gametophyte factor	*pm*	pale midrib	*v*	virescent
Bn	Brown aleurone	*gl*	glossy	*po*	polymitotic	*vg*	vestigial glumes
bp	brown pericarp	*gs*	green striped leaves	*pr*	red aleurone	*ws*	white sheath
br	brachytic plant	*hm*	Helminthosporium resistance	*py*	pygmy plant	*wx*	waxy endosperm
bt	brittle endosperm			*R*	Anthocyanin	*Y*	Yellow endosperm
bv	brevis plant	*ij*	iojap stripe	*ra*	ramosa ear	*yg*	yellow green
bz	bronze anthocyanin	*in*	intensifier	*Rg*	ragged leaves	*ys*	yellow stripe
C	Aleurone color	*j*	japonica stripe	*Rp*	Resistance to Puccinia	*zb*	zebra stripe
Ch	Chocolate pericarp	*kn*	knotted leaf	*sh*	shrunken	*zl*	zygotic lethal
cr	crinkly leaves	*lg*	liguleless	*sk*	silkless		

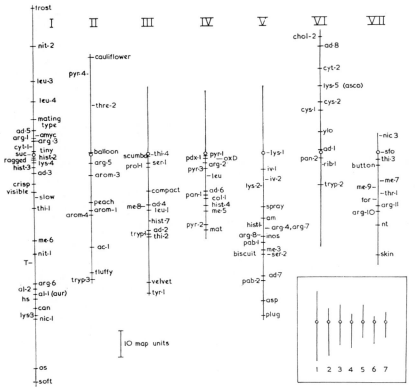

FIGURE 10–10. *The linkage groups of* Neurospora crassa. *The relative sizes and centromere positions (open circles) of the chromosomes are shown at the lower right. The chromosomes and linkage groups are numbered independently. Map distances are only approximate. (Courtesy of Blackwell Scientific Publications, Oxford, from* Fungal Genetics *by J. R. S. Fincham and P. R. Day, 1963.)*

KEY TO GENETIC SYMBOLS

Most descriptions refer to nutritional requirements of the corresponding mutants.

SYMBOL	NAME	SYMBOL	NAME	SYMBOL	NAME
a/A	mating type	cyt	altered cytochrome system	prol	proline
ac	acetate			pyr	pyrimidine
ad	adenine	for	formate	rib	riboflavin
al	albino (white conidia)	hist	histidine	ser	serine
am	α-amino nitrogen (deficient in glutamic dehydrogenase)	hs	homoserine	sfo	sulphonamide-requiring
		inos	inositol		
		iv	isoleucine + valine	su	suppressor
amyc	amycelial (an extreme morphological variant)	leu	leucine	suc	succinate or other Krebs cycle intermediate
		lys	lysine		
		me	methionine		
arg	arginine	nic	nicotinic acid	thi	thiamin
arom	aromatic (tyrosine + phenylalanine + tryptophan + p-aminobenzoic acid)	nit	non-nitrate utilizing	thr	threonine
		nt	nicotinic acid or tryptophan	tryp	tryptophan
				tyr	tyrosine
		os	sensitive to high osmotic pressure	T	modified tyrosinase structure
asp	asparagine				
aur	aurescent (probably an allele of al-1)	ox-D	deficient in D-amino acid oxidase	val	valine
				vis	visible (used for various morphological mutations)
can	canavanine resistance	pab	p-aminobenzoic acid		
chol	choline	pan	pantothenic acid		
col	colonial morphology	pdx	pyridoxine	ylo	yellow conidia
cys	cysteine				

Alfred H. Sturtevant (*in 1945*).

SUMMARY AND CONCLUSIONS

Using crossover frequency as an indication of distance between loci, linked genes are found to be arranged linearly. Observed crossover frequencies fluctuate because of variations in sample size and factors (temperature, age, nutrition, genotype) which affect either the crossing-over process itself or exert their influence after crossing over (differential viability). Standard crossover maps are made under standard (optimal for crossing over) conditions.

One crossing over (or chiasma) can interfere with the occurrence of another in the same tetrad. This crossing-over (or chiasma) interference diminishes as the distance between the two regions increases. When double crossing over occurs, the chromatids that exchange in one crossing over generally have no influence upon which chromatids exchange in the other. Consequently, there is usually no chromatid interference.

Recombination with respect to end genes is 50%, maximally, no matter how many chiasmata occur per tetrad. Although the order of linked genes is easily determined by test-crossing trihybrids, the distance between two marked loci is underestimated when multiple crossovers between them are not detected.

REFERENCES

Barratt, R. W., Newmeyer, D., Perkins, D. D., and Garnjobst, L., "Map Construction in *Neurospora crassa*," Advances in Genetics, 6:1–93, 1954.

Emerson, R. A., Beadle, G. W., and Fraser, A. C., "A Summary of Linkage Studies in Maize," Mem. Cornell Univ. Agr. Sta., No. 180, 1935.

Lewis, K. R., and John, B., *Chromosome Marker,* London: J. and A. Churchill, Ltd., 1963.

Sturtevant, A. H., "The Linear Arrangement of Six Sex-Linked Factors in Drosophila, as Shown by Their Mode of Association," J. Exp. Zool., 14:43–59, 1913. Reprinted in *Classic Papers in Genetics,* Peters, J. A. (Ed.), Englewood Cliffs, N.J.: Prentice-Hall, 1959, pp. 67–78.

See Supplement II.

QUESTIONS FOR DISCUSSION

10.1. Does the linear arrangement of the genes offer any evidence for or against the hypothesis that chromosomes are carriers of genes? Explain.

10.2. How many gene pairs must be heterozygous for you to detect a single and a double crossover in Drosophila? In Neurospora?

10.3. Suppose a pair of homologs in Neurospora have the genotypes $A\ B/a\ b$. Draw an eight-spore ascus derived from a cell that had:

(a) No chiasma between these homologs
(b) One chiasma between the centromere and the gene pair closest to it
(c) One chiasma between the two pairs of genes
(d) One two-strand double chiasmata between the two pairs of genes

10.4. What are the advantages of Neurospora over Drosophila as material for genetic studies?

10.5. Under what conditions would segregation of a pair of alleles occur during the first meiotic division? The second meiotic division?

10.6. What indications might you have that differential viability plays a role in modifying experimentally obtained crossover distances?

10.7. How many linked loci must be hybrid in a Drosophila individual and a Neurospora individual to determine from crossover data whether these loci are arranged linearly? Explain.

10.8. A test cross proves that one of the parents produced gametes of the following genotypes: 42.4% *PZ*; 6.9% *Pz*; 7.0% *pZ*; and 43.7% *pz*. List all the genetic conclusions you can derive from these data.

10.9. The trihybrid *Aa Bb Cc* is test crossed to the triple recessive, *aa bb cc*, and the following phenotypic results are obtained: abc 64; abC 2; aBc 11; aBC 18; AbC 14; Abc 17; ABc 3; ABC 71.

(a) Which of these loci are linked? Why?
(b) Rewrite the genotypes of both parents.
(c) Determine the observed map distances between all the different pairs of linked genes.

10.10. A Drosophila female with yellow body color, vermilion eye color, and cut wings is crossed with a wild-type male. In F_1 all females are wild-type and males are yellow, vermilion, cut. When the F_1 are mated to each other, the F_2 are phenotypically as follows:

1781	wild-type	1712	yellow, vermilion, cut
442	yellow	470	vermilion, cut
296	vermilion	265	yellow, cut
53	cut	48	yellow, vermilion

Construct a crossover map for *y*, *v*, and *ct* from these data, giving the map distances between loci.

10.11. Describe the practical significance of the fact that linked genes are arranged linearly.

10.12. How can you determine the position of a centromere in a linkage group of Neurospora?

10.13. Under what conditions are all eight ascospores from a single sac detectable crossovers?

10.14. In corn, virescent seedlings, glossy seedlings, and variable steriles are due to three recessives—*v*, *gl*, and *va*, respectively. G. W. Beadle test crossed a trihybrid and obtained the following phenotypic results:

235 normal	270 v gl va
40 va	48 v gl
60 v	62 gl va
7 gl	4 v va

Construct a crossover map for these three genes, giving the map distances between loci.

10.15. What effect do undetected multiple crossover strands have upon gene sequence of marked loci? Observed map distance for marked loci?

10.16. What evidence can you present that crossing over involves segments of homologs rather than individual loci?

10.17. Explain the following statement: The frequency of first division segregation of a gene pair in Neurospora is inversely related to its distance from the centromere.

10.18. How can you convert the percentage of asci showing second division segregation into map distance from the centromere?

10.19. In Neurospora, the mutant *ag* cannot synthesize the amino acid arginine, and the mutant *th* fails to synthesize the vitamin thiamin. Since both substances are needed for survival, explain how a stock pure for *ag th* is maintained and tested for the presence of these mutants.

10.20. A dihybrid for the mutants described in Question 10.19 produces asci having the following spore orders:

No. asci	Spores			
	1 + 2	3 + 4	5 + 6	7 + 8
24	*ag th*	*ag th*	++	++
27	++	++	*ag th*	*ag th*
26	*ag+*	*ag+*	*+th*	*+th*
23	*+th*	*+th*	*ag+*	*ag+*

Discuss the positions of these loci with respect to each other and their centromere(s). How would you determine the genotypes present in these spores?

10.21. Map mutant *a* relative to its centromere when Neurospora heterozygous for this mutant produces asci having the following spore orders:

No. asci	Spores			
	1 + 2	3 + 4	5 + 6	7 + 8
44	*a*	*a*	+	+
48	+	+	*a*	*a*
2	*a*	+	*a*	+
3	*a*	+	+	*a*
2	+	*a*	+	*a*
1	+	*a*	*a*	+

10.22. Suppose asci from a given Neurospora cross had spores in the following relative order:

		Spores		
% asci	or $\begin{cases} 1+2 \\ 7+8 \end{cases}$	$\begin{matrix} 3+4 \\ 5+6 \end{matrix}$	$\begin{matrix} 5+6 \\ 3+4 \end{matrix}$	$\begin{matrix} 7+8 \\ 1+2 \end{matrix}$
92	xy	xy	++	++
2	xy	++	xy	++
2	xy	++	++	xy
1	xy	x+	+y	++
1	xy	x+	++	+y
1	x+	xy	+y	++
1	x+	xy	++	+y

(a) Are *x* and *y* linked?

(b) If not linked, give the crossover distance from its centromere for each. If linked, construct a crossover map for *x* and *y* and their centromere.

(c) Are any double crossovers involved? Why?

10.23. The accompanying photograph (courtesy of R. G. Isaacson) shows asci of the fungus *Sordaria fimicola*. The asci are in various stages of maturity, the most mature containing dark ascospores. What genetic conclusions can you draw knowing that all the asci shown are products of the same parental genotype?

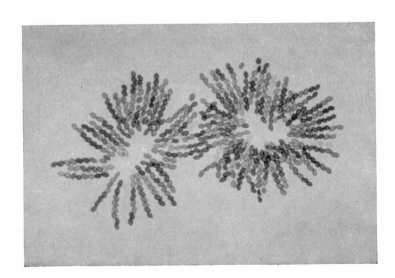

Chapter 11

CHANGES INVOLVING
UNBROKEN CHROMOSOMES

XCEPT for Chapters 6 and 8 the preceding chapters sought to determine the characteristics of the genetic material through the operation of genetic recombination. This operation revealed the existence of different recombinational units of the genetic material, which in order of size, include the genome, the chromosome, and the genes in a chromosome—the smallest recombinational unit being *the recombinational gene.*

This chapter begins a study of the genetic material through the operation of mutation. We shall be especially interested in learning the extent to which the genetic material can be divided into mutational units, always remembering that the recombinational and mutational units may or may not be materially identical.

We have been able to learn the recombinational properties of the gene only because it exerts a detectable phenotypic effect, and because it exists in an alternative state. One can readily see that if a gene were present in the same form in all organisms, it would not be detectable, since all individuals would have the same genotype and, therefore, the same range of phenotypic expression. In other words, the genes detected thus far in this book were only those that occur either in different numbers in different individuals, or have an alternate allele, or both, provided that such a genetic difference produced a detectable phenotypic change.

A great deal of genetic variation of this kind exists among living organisms. We have seen that some of the phenotypic variation attributed to genes is actually due to sexuality which by segregation, independent segregation, crossing over, and fertilization produces new combinations of already-present genes. These mechanisms of recombination shuffle the genes, just as shuffling a deck of playing cards produces the great variety of card combinations.

Detecting Mutations

We would like to learn two things concerning genetic differences; namely, what they are, and how they are produced. To do this we must first have some way to distinguish between a mutant—a really new genetic form produced by the process of mutation—and a recombinant for already-existing genes. We can use an example in Drosophila to illustrate how this distinction may be made. Suppose (as was the case at one time) none of the flies in laboratory strains has an appendage on the anterior-dorsal part of the thorax. Then a single fly occurs with an appendage in this region (Figure 11–1) and, when crossed with the wild type of a different strain (outcrossed), this trait appears in approximately one half of the progeny. How is the new phenotypic variant (*Hexaptera*) to be explained?

If the culture conditions had not changed, Hexaptera could not be due to environmental factors alone. Could Hexaptera result from a new combination of already-existing genetic units? It could not be due to the interaction between two particular alleles already present in the population which happened to combine in the same zygote at fertilization, for such a combination would have to be rare and, following segregation, this phenotype would not be expected to appear in any appreciable number of the progeny of the outcross. Moreover, it could not be due to the rare combination of two already-existing unlinked nonalleles since, at most, only one quarter of the progeny would have the novel phenotype. Consequently, neither segregation nor independent segregation could be associated with the appearance or nonappearance of Hexaptera. The new phenotype might have appeared after a rare crossing over between two very close loci brought two previously separated nonalleles into the same chromosome. Once produced, this new combination of linked genes would almost always remain intact and be transmitted to one half of the progeny. However, suppose also that the parents' chromosomes were suitably marked with genes, and it was found that the chromosome region, essential for the production of the new phenotype, was of a noncrossover type. In such a case, crossing over would not explain the results either.

The only reasonable remaining explanation would be that a novel change, a mutation, occurred in the genetic material. We see, therefore, that when the mutant produces a dominant phenotypic effect it is not too difficult to determine whether a novel phenotype is due to mutation rather than to genetic recombination.

In the case of a dominant mutant, only one parent needs to have a specific genotype to produce a dominant mutant trait in the progeny; no particular genetic recombination is a prerequisite. In other cases, the novel phenotype appears in the progeny only when both parents have specific genotypes, and genetic recombination is required for its appearance. Note that the detection of a completely recessive autosomal mutant gene is postponed for the number of generations required for two heterozygotes to mate and produce a mutant homozygote. Before a recessive mutant becomes homozygous, many generations may elapse, during which time the mutant allele may become relatively widespread in the population in heterozygous condition. When the genotype of the population is uniform or is known, it may be possible to trace back to the origin of a new recessive mutant. If, however, the population genotype is not known, it is impossible to determine when a recessive mutant first arose, and it may be considered—correctly or not—one of the genes normally present in the population.

Obviously, the detection of mutants, both recessive and dominant, would be made relatively easy by using pure lines. As mentioned in Chapter 1, suddenly-appearing phenotypic variants which are due to mutation and not to environmental fluctuation are occasionally found in pure lines of self-fertilizing bean plants. When completely

FIGURE 11–1. *The Hexaptera phenotype in* **D.** melanogaster. (*From Genetics, vol. 34, p. 13, 1949.*)

pure lines cannot be obtained because self-fertilization does not occur, detection of mutations is facilitated by knowing the pre-existing genotypes.

Although we have seen how a phenotype is proved to be the result of a mutation, we have not determined the basis for the genetic change involved. The change could conceivably encompass as much as an entire genome, or as little as the genetic material in a single gene locus. The latter type of change may not be detectable cytologically. Although a cytological study has not been made, genetic studies indicate that the chromosomal change associated with the occurrence of Hexaptera is submicroscopic. Let us now look at mutants known to be associated with a gross visible change in chromosome composition, as detected by either genetical or cytological methods, or both, and leave for later the consideration of mutations involving submicroscopic changes in chromosomes.

Heteroploidy

In the evening primrose, Oenothera, a giant type called *gigas* is found to be a mutant. Other Oenothera, like most sexually reproducing species, are diploid, having two sets of chromosomes—one genome contributed by each of the gametes. In the gigas type, cytological examination shows that there are three genomes; that is, the individuals are *triploid*. Studies of other groups of diploid plants reveal related types which prove to have four genomes (*tetraploids*), others may have six sets (*hexaploids*) or eight (*octaploids*). A chromosomal composition made up of an abnormal number of normal chromosome sets is said to be *heteroploid*. The occurrence of extra whole genomes is called *polyploidy,* a term which is applicable for multiples of the haploid number when monoploidy is the normal condition. Note that changes in genome number preserve the

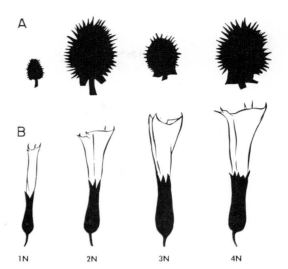

FIGURE 11–2. *Ploidy in Datura (N = 12) (silhouettes).*

same ratios that chromosomes (and genes) have to each other under normal conditions. Such changes are said to be *euploid* (right-fold).

1. *Autopolyploidy*

Different forms of the Jimson weed, Datura, carry different numbers of whole genomes, or *ploidies*.[1] Some are haploid, others diploid, triploid, or tetraploid. The flowers that each of these types produces are shown in Figure 11–2, line B (the respective seed capsules are shown in line A). Note that flower size increases with ploidy. The seed capsules illustrated are those which might have been obtained had the individual under test been fertilized by pollen from a diploid—the differences in size being due partly to the number of seeds that have set or developed.

Triploid and tetraploid embryos are found

[1] The following is based upon work of A. F. Blakeslee and J. Belling.

FIGURE 11–3. *Normal (left) and triploid (right)* D. melanogaster *females. The body of the 3N female is slightly larger than the 2N female and also has slightly larger cells. (Drawn by E. M. Wallace.)*

in a variety of mammals, and even races of some animals are polyploid. For example, tetraploids of the following are known: the water shrimp, Artemia; the sea urchin, Echinus; the roundworm, Ascaris; and the moth, Solenobia. Polyploid larvae of salamanders and of frogs also have been obtained, although races are not formed. Polyploidy is also found in Drosophila. Female Drosophila have been found that are triploid (3X + 3 sets of A) (Figure 11–3) and tetraploid (4X + 4 sets of A). Somatic parts of Drosophila individuals have been found to be haploid (1X + 1A set).

One way that ploidy can increase is by the addition of genomes of the same kind as those present—by *autopolyploidy*—as was the case with Datura. Autopolyploidy can arise several different ways:

1. Mitotic anaphase may be abnormal, so that the doubled number of chromosomes becomes incorporated into a single nucleus which thereafter divides normally to produce daughter polyploid nuclei and eventually— by asexual reproduction—polyploid progeny.

2. Sometimes two of the haploid nuclei produced by meiosis fuse to form a diploid gamete which, after fertilization with a haploid gamete, forms a triploid zygote. (Complementarily, fertilization of a gamete formed without a nucleus may initiate development of a haploid.)

3. Haploid individuals may undergo meiosis and, although this usually results in gametes containing only part of a genome, a complete haploid gamete can sometimes be produced which, upon fertilization with another haploid gamete, forms a diploid zygote.

By interfering with mitosis and meiosis, autopolyploidy can be artificially induced by: drugs like colchicine or its synthetic substitute, colcemide (which destroys the spindle, thereby preventing the anaphase movement of chromosomes); environmental stresses like starvation and cold; or energetic radiations.

Some females of Solenobia produce haploid eggs; others produce diploid eggs. Both types of eggs start development without fertilization; that is, they begin developing *parthenogenetically*. During development, however, nuclei of the respective individuals fuse in pairs to establish the diploid and tetraploid conditions. In this case, normal parthenogenesis leads to normal diploidy and tetraploidy. In many other organisms, artificially induced parthenogenesis may begin haploid development.

In the case of an ordinarily diploid individual, development as a haploid usually produces abnormalities. These must sometimes be due to the expression of detrimental genes which are not expressed in a diploid because their normal alleles are present in homologous chromosomes. However, this is not always the case. If chromosome doubling—naturally or artificially induced—occurs at an early stage, a normal diploid (and homozygous) embryo may be produced; for example, chromosome doubling has produced parthenogenetic salamanders and (female) rabbits. In these instances, at least, abnormal development as a haploid must have its basis in quite a different factor—probably one involving the surface-volume relationships within the nucleus and between the nucleus and the cytosome. These relationships are changed when cells that are adapted to be diploid are haploid. A similar explanation can be offered for the observation that development of triploid and tetraploid mouse zygotes ceases after a few days, even though initially they have a normal mitotic rate.

Ploidy changes also occur during gametogenesis and fertilization. These and certain other examples of ploidy change already discussed are normal in various organisms. (A ploidy change should be considered mutational only when it is novel.) Autopolyploidy can occur as a normal process in a portion of a multicellular organism; for example, it occurs normally in certain somatic tissues in man such as liver cells. Many of the examples of autopolyploidy mentioned involve an increase in ploidy which is accomplished by *endoreplication;* that is, the genomic contents replicate and remain in one nucleus. In these cases, the daughter chromosome strands separate to produce an increased number of separate chromosomes, each chromosome in the nucleus proceeding independently to mitotic metaphase. In another consequence of endoreplication, all daughter chromosome strands remain synapsed, so the number of separate chromosomes is not increased. Let us consider an example of this condition as found in the giant salivary gland cells of Drosophila larvae.

2. *Polynemy*

Recall that the metaphase chromosome in the usual cell of Drosophila is rod-shaped (see Figure 7–5) and contains chromatids each of which is coiled tightly in a series of spirals like those in a lamp filament, and that during interphase the chromatids unwind. The chromatids in the chromosomes of the salivary gland cell nucleus are also in an unwound state, perhaps even more so than in ordinary interphase, and undergo three special changes:

1. Each chromosome present endoreplicates synchronously a number of times in succession, so that one chromosome produces two, two produce four, four produce eight, and so on. Endoreplication can occur at least nine times, so each chromosome can produce 512 daughters.

2. All daughter strands, instead of separating, remain in contact with the homologous loci apposed, giving the appearance of a *many-threaded—polynemic or polytenic —cable.*

3. The original members of a pair of homologous chromosomes are paired at homologous loci, demonstrating what is called *somatic synapsis.* Accordingly, a double cable is formed which can contain as many as 1024 chromosomes.

When seen under the microscope (Figures 11–4 through 6), these double cables have a cross-banded appearance due to differences in density along the length of the unwound chromosomes. A band is formed by the synapsis of the same dense regions in all the strands; in this case, an interband region is also formed by the synapsis of corresponding regions of lesser density (Figure 11–5). The pattern of bands is so constant and characteristic that it is possible to identify not only each chromosome but different regions within a chromosome (Figure 11–6). The giant size of salivary chromosomes, very long because they are unwound and thick

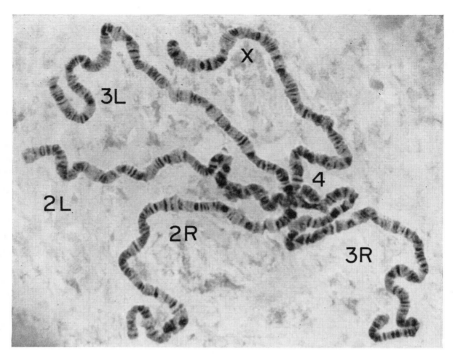

FIGURE 11–4. *Salivary gland chromosomes of a female larva of* D. melano-gaster. *(Courtesy of B. P. Kaufmann; by permission of The American Genetic Association, Journal of Heredity, Frontispiece, vol. 30, No. 5, May, 1939.)*

FIGURE 11–5. *A band (at top) and interband (below) region of a stretched Drosophila salivary gland chromosome. Photographed with the electron microscope at a magnification of approximately 12,200×. Present enlargement is about 13,000×. (By permission of The American Genetic Association, Journal of Heredity, vol. 43, p. 231, 1952.)*

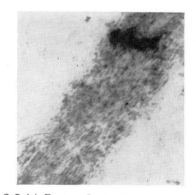

FIGURE 11–6. *The pair of fourth chromosomes as seen in salivary gland nuclei (each homolog is highly polynemic) and at mitotic metaphase (arrow), drawn to the same scale. (By permission of The American Genetic Association, C. B. Bridges, "Salivary Chromosome Maps," Journal of Heredity, vol. 26, p. 62, 1935.)*

SCALE |←—5 μ—→|

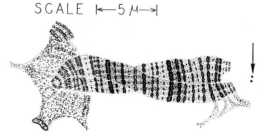

because of synapsed polynemes, offers a unique opportunity to correlate genetical and cytological events. (It should be noted that, as a rule, giant polynemic chromosomes are produced in cells which will never divide again.)

At any given stage of a cell cycle, most of the chromosomal material reacts similarly to certain staining procedures and, therefore, is called *euchromatic* (truly or correctly colored). Other portions of the chromosomes stain either darker or lighter and are said to be *heterochromatic*. Although heterochromatin may be located at various places along a chromosome arm, it is normally found adjacent to the centromere and, to a lesser extent, near the ends. Heterochromatin also has the characteristic of being less specific in synapsis than is euchromatin, different heterochromatic regions located in the same chromosome, its homolog, or in nonhomologous chromosomes often being found synapsed. In the giant salivary gland nuclei of Drosophila larvae, the heterochromatic regions nearest the centromeres of all chromosomes synapse to form one mass, called the *chromocenter*. This is the center from which the double cables radiate in Figure 11–4 and at the left of Figure 11–6. Also, the heterochromatic regions nearest the ends are sometimes found synapsed with other heterochromatic regions, especially the chromocenter. In squashing the nuclei to separate and flatten the salivary chromosomes, two synapsed heterochromatic regions may be pulled apart, but show evidence of synapsis because they are still connected by strands of apparently sticky material. The right end of the fourth chromosome polynemes in Figure 11–6 shows such glutinous matter, probably indicating synapsis with the chromocenter. Heterochromatin is chromatic and is not to be identified with the regions between bands; interband regions do not seem to contain the

Feulgen-stainable material [2] and apparently are *achromatic,* as is the spindle.

3. *Allopolyploidy*

Ploidy can increase another way besides autopolyploidy. Two species can each contribute two or more genomes to form a third species which is called an *allopolyploid*. Cultivated wheat is an allopolyploid. As expected, allopolyploids often show a combination of characteristics of their different parent species. This type of polyploidy is discussed in more detail in Chapter 18.

Changes in genome number represent the class of normal and mutational events involving the largest unit of genetic material. Although many plants are polyploid and one plant has 512 chromosomes, polyploidy will produce a chromosome number that is unwieldy in nuclear division if it occurs many times in succession. It should also be noted that certain other classes of mutation, like those involving a single locus, have greater difficulty expressing themselves in autopolyploids than they have in haploids or diploids, in which no other, or just one other, homologous locus is able to mask the mutant effect.

Aneusomy

The next category of mutations to be discussed involves the addition or subtraction of part of a chromosome set. Such mutations upset the normal chromosomal and gene balance and produce *aneuploid* ("not right-fold") chromosomal (genetic) constitutions by having the incorrect number of particular chromosomes (*aneusomy*). By what mechanisms can single whole (unbroken) chromosomes be added to or subtracted from a genome?

1. *In Drosophila*

Recall that nondisjunction in the germ line of Drosophila can produce offspring,

[2] See D. M. Steffensen (1963).

otherwise diploid, that are X0, XXX, and XXY. Nondisjunction of the small fourth chromosome can lead to the production of individuals with one fourth chromosome (haplo-IV individuals) or three (triplo-IV individuals) (Figure 11–7) being in this respect *monosomic* and *trisomic,* respectively; instead of *disomic* as is normal. Even though addition or subtraction of a chromosome IV makes visible phenotypic changes from the disomic condition as can be seen from the phenotypes, both aneusomic changes are viable. On the other hand, individuals monosomic or trisomic for either of the two large autosomes die before completing the egg stage.

When triploid Drosophila females—with all chromosomes trisomic—undergo meiosis, bundles of three homologous chromosomes (*trivalents*) may be formed at synapsis. This is because, at one place along the length of a chromosome, the pairing is between two homologs, and at another place it is between one of these two and the third homolog. In this way, although pairing is two-by-two at all levels, all three homologs are held together as a trivalent. At the first meiotic division the two homologs that are synapsed at their centromeric regions, separate, and go to opposite poles, while the third homolog goes to either one of the poles. At the end of the second meiotic division, two nuclei each have one homolog of the trivalent, and two nuclei each have two homologs. The same result is obtained when synapsis is entirely between two homologs and excludes the third. Since each of the four trisomics present at metaphase I segregates independently, eggs are produced which have one of the following:

1. Each chromosome type singly and, therefore, contain one complete genome (being haploid)
2. Two chromosomes of each type and, therefore, contain two genomes (being diploid)
3. Any combination in which some chromosomes are represented once and others twice (being aneusomic).

FIGURE 11–7. *Haplo-IV (left) and triplo-IV (right) females of* D. melanogaster. *The haplo-IV is smaller than the wild-type female shown in Fig. 2–6. (Drawn by E. M. Wallace.)*

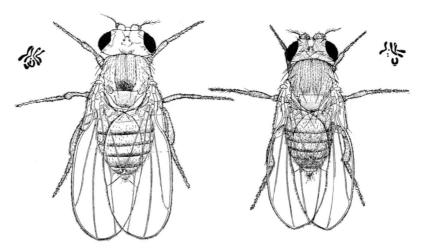

We see, therefore, that meiosis produces many aneusomic gametes when the number of homologs is odd, as it is in triploids, pentaploids, etc. In tetraploids, since each chromosome can have a partner at meiosis, the four homologs often segregate two and two. Sometimes, however, the four homologs form a trivalent and segregate three and one, so that some aneusomic gametes are produced by polyploids with even numbers of homologs.

Because the phenotypic effect of any gene depends directly or indirectly upon the phenotypic effects of most, if not all, of the other genes present, it is expected that a diploid individual contains, in its two sets of chromosomes, a proper balance of genes for the production of a successful phenotype. It is not surprising, then, that a haploid individual mated to a diploid produces very few progeny, since after fertilization most zygotes are chromosomally unbalanced by the absence of one or more chromosomes needed to make two complete genomes. Mated to a diploid the triploid individual also produces zygotes that are imbalanced but in the opposite direction, having one or more chromosomes in excess of two genomes.

In matings with diploids, however, the triploid individual usually produces more offspring than the haploid. This observation can be explained as the result of the lesser imbalance brought about by the addition of chromosomes to the diploid condition than by the subtraction of chromosomes from it. This effect can be seen by comparing how far from normality (diploidy) each of the two abnormal conditions is. When one chromosome is in excess, the abnormal chromosome number of three is one and a half times larger than the normal number of two; when one chromosome is missing, the abnormal chromosome number of one is two times smaller than the normal number. Thus, the addition of a chromo-

some makes for a less drastic change in balance than the subtraction. Accordingly, knowing that the triple dose of a large autosome is lethal in Drosophila, we can correctly predict that the single dose is lethal also. In these cases, death is attributable to genetic imbalance due to an excess of the genes present in a long autosome in trisomic individuals and to a deficiency of these genes in monosomic individuals.

2. *In Datura*

Chromosome addition and subtraction can also be studied in Datura [3] whose haploid chromosome number is twelve. It is possible to obtain twelve different kinds of individuals, each having a different one of the twelve chromosomes in addition to the diploid number. Each of these trisomics is given a different name such as "Globe." It is also possible to obtain viable plants that are diploid but missing one chromosome of a pair; these are monosomics or *haplosomics*. Individuals with two extra chromosomes of the same type (tetrasomics) or with two extra chromosomes of different types (double trisomics) are also found.

Datura enables us to test the phenotypic consequences of disturbing the normal balance among chromosomes. Compare, in Figure 11–8, the seed capsules of the normal diploid (2N) with those of diploids having either one extra chromosome (2N + 1) of the type producing Globe or two of these (2N + 2). The latter two *polysomics* can be called trisomic diploid and tetrasomic diploid, respectively. Although the tetrasomic is more stable chromosomally (each chromosome can have a partner at meiosis) than is the trisomic, the tetrasomic phenotype is too abnormal to establish a race, since it has a still greater genetic imbalance than the trisomic and produces a still greater deviation from the normal diploid phenotype.

[3] Based upon work of A. F. Blakeslee and J. Belling.

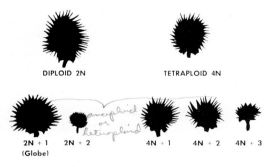

DIPLOID 2N   TETRAPLOID 4N

2N + 1   2N + 2   4N + 1   4N + 2   4N + 3
(Globe)

FIGURE 11–8. *Effect upon the capsule of Datura of the presence of one or more extra "Globe" chromosomes.*

In comparison, the tetraploid (4N) individual is phenotypically almost like the diploid, since chromosomal balance is undisturbed. The tetraploid which has one extra Globe chromosome (4N + 1, making it a pentasomic tetraploid) deviates from the tetraploid in the same direction as the 2N + 1 deviates from 2N, but does so less extremely. Hexasomic tetraploids (4N + 2) deviate from 4N just about as much as 2N + 1 deviates from 2N. It is clear, therefore, that adding a single chromosome to a tetraploid has less phenotypic effect than its addition to a diploid, since the shift in balance between chromosomes is relatively smaller in the former than in the latter. Thus, polyploids can stand whole chromosome additions and subtractions better than diploids can.

Since crosses between tetraploid Datura produce fertile seed in amounts sufficient to maintain a tetraploid race, the question arises, can a tetraploid race of Drosophila be produced? As mentioned, the gametes of a tetraploid Drosophila female contain complete genomes more often than do those of triploids. Since it produces many diploid eggs, the tetraploid female presents no difficulty for the continuity of a tetraploid race.

To be of normal sex, a tetraploid male has to carry 2X + 2Y + 4 sets of A (Chapter 8). But the X's (and Y's) in such a male usually synapse with each other during meiosis so that after meiosis each sperm carries 1X and 1Y in addition to the 2A sets. In fertilizing eggs (from tetraploid females) containing 2X + 2 sets of A, sperm of this type produce zygotes with 3X + 1Y + 4 sets of A which develop as sterile intersexes. Thus, a self-maintaining tetraploid race of Drosophila cannot be established. In fact, we can conclude that any species containing a heteromorphic pair of sex chromosomes (such as X and Y) cannot form polyploid races, since the correct balance between sex chromosomes and autosomes is upset by the meiotic divisions. This factor probably explains why polyploid races and species are rarer among animals than among plants whose sexuality (as in monoecious forms) is not associated with heteromorphic homologs.

3. *In Man*

Down's syndrome, or *mongolism,* in human beings is sometimes the result of a trisomic diploid chromosomal constitution. In this case, the trisomic is number 21 the third smallest of all human chromosomes (the smallest being the Y) (Figures 11–9, 11–10). Trisomics for several other of the smaller autosomes are also known, each producing its own characteristic set of congenital abnormalities. Trisomy for the largest autosomes is apparently lethal before birth, probably due to the imbalance of too many genes. The very severe phenotypic defects observed among the least affected autosomally trisomic individuals makes it a reasonable expectation that the monosomic condition of any autosome is lethal before birth—in accordance with the view that chromosome subtraction is even more detrimental than chromosome addition.

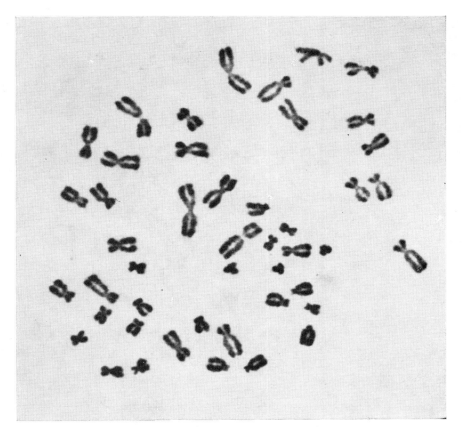

FIGURE 11–9. *The chromosomal complement of a normal human female. Cell was in mitotic metaphase (hence chromosomes appear double except at the centromere) when squashed and photographed. (Courtesy of T. C. Hsu.)*

The frequency among live births of Down's syndrome due to trisomy has been determined as approximately 0.2%. Most cases of Down's syndrome occur among the children of older mothers and are due primarily to nondisjunction during oogenesis. If other chromosomes have a similar frequency of nondisjunction, there might be a minimum of 4.4% (22 × 0.2%) of zygotes autosomally trisomic at conception. There might also be another 4.4% of zygotes that are autosomal monosomics, due to the equal chance that the haploid meiotic product complementary to the one which is disomic —the *nullosomic* one—becomes the egg. In fact, more nullosomic than disomic gametes are expected, since a chromosome left out of one daughter nucleus need not be included in the sister nucleus. Supporting a normally high frequency of aneusomy is the observation that about one quarter of aborted human fetuses show a chromosomal derangement. It is expected, moreover, that many conceptions involving aneusomy, especially monosomy, are lost so early in pregnancy that they go unnoticed.

Nondisjunction leading to aneusomy can also occur in the paternal germ line of man,

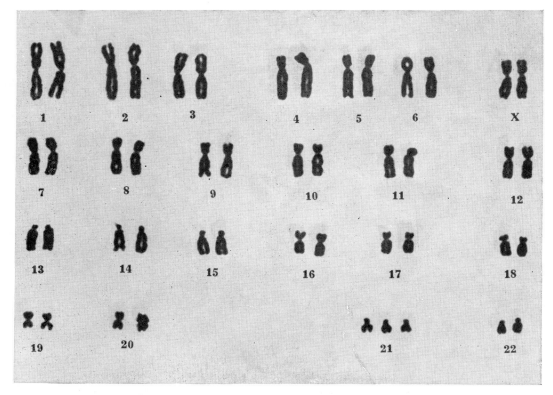

FIGURE 11–10. *Chromosomal constitution found in a female showing Down's syndrome. (By permission of M. A. Ferguson-Smith and A. W. Johnston, and The Annals of Internal Medicine, vol. 53, p. 361, 1960.) After photographing a squash preparation like that in Figure 11–10, the chromosomes are cut out and "paired" as shown here.*

although this does not seem to contribute very significantly to the total observed frequency. In man, almost all nondisjunction is associated with the aging of oocytes. The reverse is true in the mouse, however, even though mouse females—like human females—are born with all their germ cells in the oocyte stage. Thus, in the mouse, marked chromosomes show that spontaneous aneusomy almost always has a paternal origin. It should be noted that, in the mouse, viable aneusomy also occurs for the sex chromosomes and for certain small autosomes when trisomic.[4]

[4] See A. B. Griffen and M. C. Bunker (1964).

The incidence of nondisjunction can be increased by high energy radiations. Carbon dioxide, other chemical substances, and certain diploid genotypes can increase the nondisjunction rate in Drosophila. In human beings, the evidence that older women are more apt to have trisomic children suggests that some metabolic defect associated with increased age increases the chance for nondisjunction.

Although chromosome loss may result from spontaneous meiotic and nonmeiotic nondisjunction in diploids as well as from the meiotic process normally taking place in polyploids, it should not be inferred that these are the only ways entire chromosomes can be lost.

Mosaic Heteroploidy and Aneusomy

Mutations leading to heteroploidy need not involve germ cells or the entire organism, as mentioned with respect to asexually reproducing species (p. 152). Sexually reproducing species of plants and animals may also show mosaicism for ploidy involving reproductive or nonreproductive tissues, or both. In man, for example, a baby boy has been studied who is diploid in some tissues and triploid in other, normally diploid, tissues. About 3% of cells in certain human tissue cultures show such changes in ploidy.

Aneusomy can also originate at any mitotic, as well as meiotic, nuclear division. Thus, nondisjunction at the first nuclear division of a normal human zygote might produce one nucleus that is monosomic and one trisomic for chromosome 21. In this case the former nucleus is expected to die, and the latter nucleus, to produce a completely mongoloid individual.

Some of the aneusomics born of older mothers may have originated in such a post-zygotic nondisjunction, as is the case in mice. If nondisjunction occurs later in development, it produces complementary monosomic and trisomic mutant patches in a diploid background, which—in the case of autosomes in man and mouse—are usually expected to be lethal to the individual. That such nondisjunctions or chromosome losses do occur with appreciable frequency is suggested by the frequent occurrence in human adults of a few cells per hundred which are scored as having one or two chromosomes too few or too much. It is extremely unlikely that all, or even most, of these abnormal counts are due to experimental errors in preparing or in scoring the cells. Under normal circumstances one would expect the aneusomic cells produced after birth to be functionally inferior to their neighboring euploid cells and, therefore, at a selective disadvantage.

Because of the large genetic unbalance it produces, addition and subtraction of whole chromosomes is a class of mutation which involves a phenotypic change too drastic to play a very significant role in evolution.

SUMMARY AND CONCLUSIONS

The mutational events involving the largest recombinational unit of genetic material are euploid changes in the number of whole sets of chromosomes—heteroploidy. Ploidy can increase by allopolyploidy, autopolyploidy, and polynemy. The modes of origin and the breeding behavior of autopolyploids, and the origin and structure of the giant polynemic chromosomes in the salivary gland of Drosophila larvae are considered in detail.

Loss or gain of part of a genome—aneuploidy—can result from nondisjunction and the segregation of chromosomes in polyploids, especially those possessing an odd number of genomes. Not only do such mutations occur in the germ and somatic lines spontaneously, but they may be initiated or have their frequency enhanced by physical and chemical factors.

The addition or subtraction of single chromosomes results in aneusomy. The absence of a chromosome is more detrimental to survival than an excess. Aneusomy produces too drastic a phenotypic change to be as inportant in evolution as heteroploidy.

REFERENCES

Auerbach, C., *Mutation. An Introduction to Research on Mutagenesis. Part I. Methods,* Edinburgh: Oliver and Boyd, 1962.

Blakeslee, A. F., "New Jimson Weeds from Old Chromosomes," J. Hered., 25:80–108, 1934.

Blakeslee, A. F., and Belling, J., "Chromosomal Mutations in the Jimson Weed, Datura Stramonium," J. Hered., 15:194–206, 1924.

Bridges, C. G., and Brehme, K. S., *The Mutants of Drosophila Melanogaster,* Washington, D.C.: Carnegie Institution of Washington, Publ. 552, 1944.

Burdette, W. J. (Ed.), *Methodology in Mammalian Genetics,* San Francisco: Holden-Day, Inc., 1963.

Dobzhansky, Th., *Genetics and the Origin of Species,* 2nd Ed., New York: Columbia University Press, Chap. 7, pp. 223–253, 1941.

Griffen, A. B., and Bunker, M. C., "Three Cases of Trisomy in the Mouse," Proc. Nat. Acad. Sci., U.S., 52:1194–1198, 1964.

Heitz, E., and Bauer, H., "Beweise für die Chromosomennatur der Kernschleifen in den Knäuelkernen von *Bibio hortulanus* L. (Cytologische Untersuchungen an Dipteren, I)," Z. Zellforsch., 17:67–82, 1933.

Painter, T. S., "A New Method for the Study of Chromosome Rearrangements and Plotting of Chromosome Maps," Science, 78:585–586, 1933. Reprinted in *Classic Papers in Genetics,* Peters, J. A. (Ed.), Englewood Cliffs, N.J.: Prentice-Hall, pp. 161–163, 1959.

Patau, K., Smith, D. W., Therman, E., Inhorn, S. L., and Wagner, H. P., "Multiple Congenital Anomaly Caused by an Extra Autosome," Lancet, 1:790–793, 1960.

Russell, L. B., "Chromosome Aberrations in Experimental Mammals," Progress in Medical Genetics, 2:230–294, 1962.

Steffensen, D. M., "Evidence for the Apparent Absence of DNA in the Interbands of Drosophila Salivary Chromosomes," Genetics, 48:1289–1301, 1963.

Suomalainen, E., "Significance of Parthenogenesis in the Evolution of Insects," Ann. Rev. Ent., 7:349–366, 1962.

White, M. J. D., *Animal Cytology and Evolution,* 2nd Ed., Cambridge: Cambridge University Press, 1954.

QUESTIONS FOR DISCUSSION

11.1. How do we know that the genetic differences in a population today were not always present?

11.2. What have you learned in this chapter about the characteristics of mutation?

11.3. What is the relation between mutants and genes? Mutants and recombination?

11.4. From your present knowledge, how would you modify the statements on page 11 relative to the ploidy of gametes?

11.5. Describe at least two different ways that the trisomy causing Down's syndrome may originate.

11.6. The only presently known case of trisomy for a chromosome of the 19–20 group occurred mosaically in a six-year-old boy. To what do you attribute this?

11.7. Discuss the statement: All somatic cells from diploid zygotes are chromosomally identical.

11.8. Do you suppose that the human species will benefit from a discovery that certain of its members are trisomic? Explain.

11.9. What are the advantages of autopolyploidy? Of allopolyploidy?

11.10. What genetic explanation can you offer for the fact, demonstrated in Figure 11–2, that the seed capsule of the Datura haploid is smaller than that of the triploid?

11.11. What do you consider to be the advantages and disadvantages of polynemy?

11.12. Unfertilized mammalian eggs can contain ploidies of 1N, 2N, 3N, or 4N. Explain how each of these could be produced.

11.13. How can you explain the fact that persons with Down's syndrome are more susceptible to leukemia than normal diploids?

11.14. Explain why individuals with Down's syndrome show a wide variety of phenotypic differences as well as similarities in their abnormalities.

11.15. Some babies classified as normal at birth are clearly mongoloid when a year old. What would you do to assure an early diagnosis of Down's syndrome?

11.16. Would you expect a correlation between producing a child with Down's syndrome and the frequency with which the mother has abortions? Subsequent children with Down's syndrome? Explain.

11.17. Should a woman with a trisomic mongoloid sibling be more than ordinarily concerned about having a child of this type? Explain.

11.18. After examining Figures 11–8 and 11–9, discuss the precision with which a given human chromosome can be identified.

11.19. How would you proceed to determine the somatic chromosome composition of a given human individual?

11.20. Discuss the phenotypic effects of adding an N-1 genome to individuals that are normally N, 2N, 3N, or 4N.

11.21. R. A. Turpin reported two cases of monozygotic twins. One set contains an XY male and an X0 female; the other set is composed of a disomic-21 male and a trisomic-21 male. Discuss the mechanisms probably involved in producing such twins. Include in your hypothesis the additional fact that one X0 cell is also found in the first XY individual mentioned.

Chapter **12**

STRUCTURAL CHANGES
IN CHROMOSOMES

THE TWO classes of mutation dealt with in Chapter 11 involved changes in chromosomal content of unbroken individual or sets of chromosomes. In some instances, mutants are based upon the gain, loss, or shift of a part of one or more chromosomes. All such structural changes are preceded by chromosome breakage, which—ignoring chromatids for the present—results in two new, "sticky" ends. When several breaks are produced, the new ends can join together but only in pairs, any new end capable of joining any other new end. Moreover, an end produced by breakage cannot join the normal (unbroken) end of a chromosome. Thus, originally free ends of chromosomes are not sticky because they have genes, called *telomeres,* which serve to seal them off, making it impossible for a normal end to join to any other.

The two ends produced by one break usually join together in what is called *restitutional union* even when ends produced by other breaks coexist in the same nucleus. This indicates that proximity favors the union of sticky ends. Although restitutional union usually occurs and thereby restores the original linear order of the chromosome, the ends uniting may sometimes come from different breaks, so that a new chromosomal (gene) arrangement is produced. The latter union is, therefore, a *nonrestitutional,* or *exchange,* or *cross-union* type. Let us see how nonrestitutional unions

produce various structural changes in chromosomes.

Consequences of a Single Chromosome Break

Consider first the consequences of a single *chromosome break;* that is, a break through both chromatids (Figure 12–1). Diagram 1 represents a normal chromosome (its chromatids are not shown), whose centromere is indicated by a black dot. In diagram 2 this chromosome is broken. If the new chromosome ends join together, that is, restitute, no chromosomal rearrangement is produced. Although restitution usually occurs, it may sometimes fail because the new ends spring apart or are moved apart by Brownian movement or protoplasmic currents. In nonrestitution, chromosome replication produces a daughter chromosome just like the parent—with a break in the same position—as shown in diagram 3 where the two broken sister chromosomes are indicated. The union of the piece containing no centromere (a) to the centromere-bearing piece of the other sister chromosome (b′) would, in effect, be restitution as would the joining of a′ to b. (Sometimes, only one of these restitutional unions occurs.)

If restitution does not occur before or after the chromosome replicates, the ends closest together usually join together, these being the corresponding ends of the sister chromosomes (a with a′ and b with b′). As shown in diagram 4, the results of such nonrestitutional unions are one chromosome with no centromere (an *acentric chromosome*), and one with two (a *dicentric chromosome*). Note that both the acentric and the dicentric chromosomes are composed of identical halves lengthwise, each, therefore, being termed an *isochromosome.* (This diagram shows the chromosomes contracting preparatory to metaphase.)

In diagram 5 we can see that in mitotic anaphase the acentric isochromosome is not pulled toward either pole, whereas the dicentric one is pulled toward both poles at once. The acentric isochromosome is, therefore, not included in either daughter nucleus and so is lost to both. (The acentric pieces in diagram 3 will be lost in any subsequent division, whether they are joined to each other or do not join at all.) The dicentric isochromosome, being pulled to both poles at once, forms a *bridge*. A bridge can prevent any part of the chromosome from entering either daughter nucleus, so that the dicentric is lost. Alternatively, the centric regions of the dicentric piece can enter the daughter nuclei, and the bridge can either snap at any one of a number of places between the centromeres and free the daughter nuclei from each other, or it can persist, joining the daughter nuclei together.

The amount of phenotypic detriment that a single nonrestituting chromosome break will produce in the daughter cells and their progeny cells depends upon the particular chromosome involved, the place of breakage, and the fate of the dicentric piece. Suppose, for example, that chromosome IV of Drosophila (often viable as a haplo-IV individual) is the chromosome involved. The break can occur at any position in IV, and the loss of the genes in the acentric piece, though detrimental, does not usually cause

death; neither does the loss of the entire dicentric fragment if excluded from both daughter nuclei, nor, probably, does a snap in the bridge between the daughter nuclei. (In the last case, each daughter nucleus is deficient, at least for the genes in the acentric piece.)

Note what happens when a bridge, involving a dicentric isochromosome linearly differentiated as a.bcddcb.a (the centromere is between a and b), does not snap between the d's. If it breaks between b and c, one fragment is even more deficient (yet viable in this example), whereas the other contains an extra dose of the genes in the cd region (and is most probably viable). Regardless of where the bridge snaps, both daughter nuclei carry a centric fragment which, after replicating, usually forms a new dicentric isochromosome and can again form a bridge at the next mitotic division. It is possible, therefore, to have *bridge-breakage-fusion-bridge cycles* in successive nuclear generations.

When a bridge fails to break leaving the two daughter nuclei tied together, the entanglement of the nuclei may interfere with subsequent attempts at nuclear division. In our example, this interference may be of much greater importance than the presence

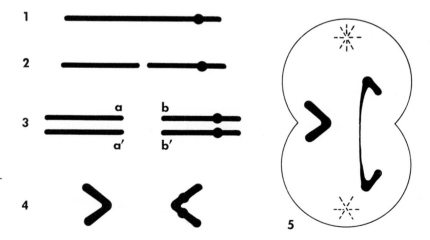

FIGURE 12–1. *Consequences of a single nonrestituting chromosome break.*

or absence of all of the genes located in the bridge.

Suppose, however, that the broken chromosome is one of the large autosomes of Drosophila. Detriment or death to one or both daughter cells may occur because of the genes lost when either the acentric or the dicentric fragment is left out of one or both daughter nuclei. In addition, successive bridge-breakage-fusion-bridge cycles may harm future cell generations via the abnormal quantities of chromosomal regions; that is, the aneuploidy, resulting from the off-center breakage of dicentric isochromosomes. Other things being equal, shorter dicentrics are expected to break more often than longer ones. Of course, any internuclear bridge that does not break may frustrate future nuclear division.

Single chromosome breaks can occur in either the somatic or the germ line. In the latter case, aneuploid gametes may be produced. Since the genes are found to be physiologically inactive in the gametes of animals, aneuploid genomes can enter the egg and sperm without impairing their functioning (as implied on p. 104). Accordingly, in animals, aneuploid genomes can be carried by unaffected gametes into the zygote, which may subsequently suffer dominant harmful or lethal effects. In many plants, however, the products of meiosis form a gametophyte generation which performs physiological functions requiring gene action, in which case, aneuploidy is usually more lethal or detrimental before fertilization than after.

Chromatid Breaks

A break can be produced in one and not the other chromatid of a chromosome. Such *chromatid breaks* are more likely to restitute than chromosome breaks, since the unbroken strand serves as a splint to hold the newly-produced ends close to each other. What appears under the microscope as a break involving only one chromatid may initially have been a *chromosome* (or *isochromatid*) *break* that was followed by restitution of one but not (yet) the other chromatid.

Nonrestituted chromatid fragments become nonrestituted chromosome fragments if they persist long enough to replicate. To be seen cytologically, a nonjoined chromatid or chromosome break produced during interphase usually has to persist until nuclear division occurs. Some chromatid and, perhaps, chromosome breaks induced in contracted (metaphase) chromosomes may not be visible, the pieces being held together without joining by the nongenetic auxiliary material in a chromosome. To detect such unjoined breaks one would have to wait until the next division. Essentially all ends produced by breaks are not sticky when the chromosome is contracted as during nuclear division; joinings are restricted largely, if not completely, to the period between late telophase and early prophase. Accordingly, the later in this period a break is produced, the less likely it is that the ends will join; broken ends produced between early prophase and late telophase have the maximum time for joining but probably also the maximum opportunity to cross-unite.

For simplicity, the discussion which follows is restricted to isochromatid breaks that fail to restitute. The reader is given the task of working out the consequences of aneuploidy resulting from single nonrestituted broken chromatids. The lack of further discussion on this type of mutation does not reflect on the relative frequency or importance of chromosome versus chromatid breaks. Agents capable of producing chromosome breaks can also produce chromatid breaks; moreover, certain agents may preferentially produce chromatid breaks.

Consequences of Two Breaks in One Chromosome

When a chromosome is broken twice, the two breaking points may be *paracentric,* that

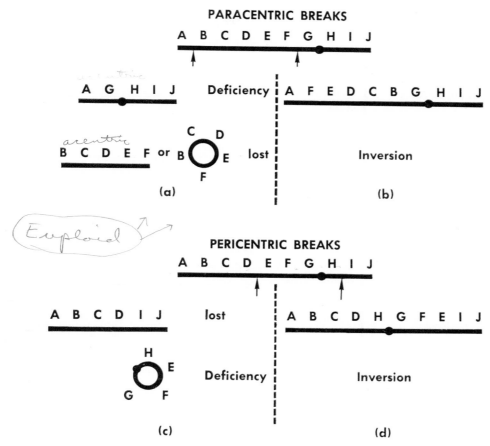

FIGURE 12–2. *Some consequences of two breaks in the same chromosome.*

is, to one side of the centromere, or *pericentric,* that is, with the centromere between them (Figure 12–2).

1. *Deficiency*

Consider a chromosome linearly differentiated as ABCDEFG.HIJ, the centromere being between G and H. When the breaks are paracentric in position (for example, between A and B, and between F and G), the fragments can unite to produce a centric chromosome (AG.HIJ, Figure 12–2a) deficient for the acentric interstitial (nonterminal) piece (BCDEF). The ends of the latter fragment may join to produce a ring

chromosome, or they may not. In either event, the acentric fragment is usually lost before the next nuclear division. When the breaks are pericentric (for example, between D and E, and between H and I), the acentric end pieces are lost, even if they join together (Figure 12–2c). The middle centric piece can survive if its ends join to form a ring and if the deficient sections are not extensive. Even if a ring survives because it is not too *hypoploid* (the aneuploid condition in which genes or chromosomal regions are missing), it is still at a disadvantage because a single crossing over either with a *nonring (rod) homolog* or with another ring results in a dicentric rod or ring, respectively, as can be seen by drawing the appropriate configurations.

Of course, a nondividing nucleus, in which breakage or another structural change occurs, is still euploid. The first occurrence of hypoploidy or *hyperploidy* (aneuploidy due to an excess of genes or chromosome parts) is in the daughter nuclei formed by such a nucleus. This delay in producing an aneuploid nucleus should be remembered when we state that chromosomes with small *deficiencies* can be lethal when homozygous, and detrimental when heterozygous; chromosomes with large deficiencies usually act as dominant lethals in the next cell generation. Remember also that we have ignored —and shall continue to do so for the rest of the chapter—the usual consequence of two breaks, that is, restitution for all ends produced by breakage.

2. *Inversion*

Another structural consequence of two breaks in the same chromosome is represented in Figure 12–2 b and d. In this case, the middle piece is inverted with respect to the end pieces and undergoes exchange unions with them. The result which is either a *paracentric* or a *pericentric inversion* (Figure 12–2 b and d), is due to the middle segment moving while the ends are relatively stationary, or the reverse. Note that inversion is a euploid rearrangement.

Structural rearrangements in chromosomes can occur in either the somatic or the germ line. An inversion which occurs in the germ line may be retained in the population long enough to become homozygous in some individuals. Meiotic behavior is normal in such *inversion homozygotes* whether or not the tetrad undergoes crossing over, since all the strands in the tetrad are identically inverted. Other individuals in the population, however, may possess one inverted and one noninverted homolog, being *inversion heterozygotes*. Provided the inversion is very small, these homologs will pair properly everywhere but in the inverted region. Because the homologs cannot twist enough to make homologous loci meet in so short a region, they will fail to synapse and no crossing over will occur. Insofar as crossing over can lead to more adaptive recombinants, such inversion heterozygotes are at a disadvantage compared to noninversion or inversion homozygotes because of the absence of recombination among genes within the inverted region. Nevertheless, very small inversions do survive in many species.

Consider the meiotic process in heterozygotes for larger paracentric inversions. In this case (Figure 12–3A), synapsis between homologs occurs for all regions except those adjacent to the points of breakage. This synapsis requires one homolog twisting in the inverted region while the other does not. The figure happens to show the inverted and not the noninverted chromosome twisting, but the reverse is equally likely to occur. If crossing over occurs anywhere outside the inverted region, each of the four meiotic products will be *eucentric* (having one centromere), as usual. If, however, a single crossing over occurs anywhere within the region inverted—as shown between C and D—the two noncrossover strands of the tetrad will be eucentric (one with and one without the inversion), and the two crossovers will be *aneucentric* (having more than one centromere or none). One of the aneucentrics will be acentric (duplicated for A and deficient for G.HIJ); the other will be dicentric (deficient and duplicated for these respective regions). If the inversion is only moderately long, only one crossing over can occur within it; if sufficiently long, double crossing over is possible. When such double crossing over is of the two-strand type, both crossover strands are eucentric.

In animals, gametes function regardless of the ploidy of the meiotic products they

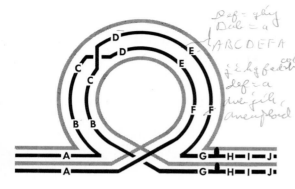

(handwritten margin notes:)
Def = ghy
Dub = a
↑ABCDEFA
j ε hg fedat
def = a
due full,
aneuploid

A. PARACENTRIC INVERSION

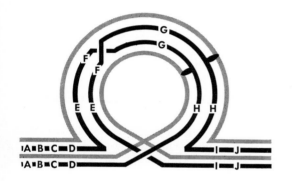

B. PERICENTRIC INVERSION

FIGURE 12–3. *A single crossing over in an inversion heterozygote. (See text for explanation.)*

contain. If a gamete contains an aneucentric produced by crossing over in a paracentric inversion heterozygote, this chromosome will usually have a dominant lethal effect after fertilization; that is, individuals heterozygous for moderate to large paracentric inversions are at reproductive disadvantage, which often leads to the elimination of the inversion from the population soon after it arises by mutation. This disadvantage is partly avoided in those species having no crossing over in one sex. For example, in the Drosophila male each homolog, inverted or not, is a noncross-

over and has the same chance of being included in the gamete. A special factor operates during meiosis in some species in which the female undergoes crossing over, occurring only if the two meiotic divisions occur in tandem, as they do in female Drosophila. In the Drosophila oocyte heterozygous for a paracentric inversion, a single crossing over within the inverted region produces the usual dicentric at anaphase I. But this dicentric serves to hold the dyads at metaphase II, so that the two eucentric monads proceed to the two outermost of the four poles. Therefore, at the end of telophase II, the centric meiotic products are arranged in a row: eucentric; part of dicentric; remainder of dicentric; eucentric. It is one of the two end eucentric-containing nuclei which becomes the egg nucleus, the others degenerate. In this way the dicentric strand is prevented from entering the nucleus that becomes gametic; the gamete, therefore, receives one of the two eucentric, noncrossover strands. That is why in Drosophila, paracentric inversions of any size rarely cause aneuploid gametes in either sex and can become established in nature.

What products result from a crossing over within the inverted region in a heterozygote for a larger pericentric inversion? As seen in Figure 12–3B, a single crossing over, such as between F and G, produces four eucentric strands: two noncrossovers (one with and one without the inversion); one with a duplication (for ABCD) and a deficiency (for IJ); the last with a deficiency and a duplication of the respective regions. All strands enter the gametes of males if crossing over occurs in the male. Each strand also has an equal chance of being present in the gametes of females capable of crossing over. This is true even in Drosophila where shunting of euploid strands into the egg nucleus does not occur because all the meiotic products are eucentric. Consequently, aneuploidy which results from crossing over within a

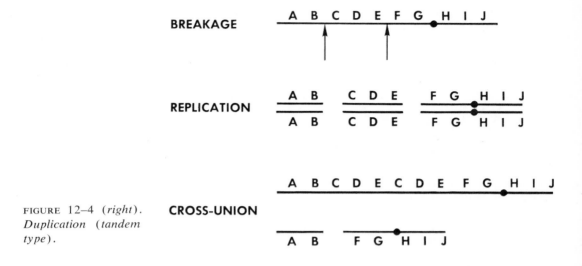

BREAKAGE

REPLICATION

CROSS-UNION

FIGURE 12–4 (*right*). *Duplication (tandem type*).

FIGURE 12–5 (*below*). *Reciprocal transloca-tion between nonhomologous chromosomes.*

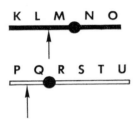

ANEUCENTRIC TYPE:

EUCENTRIC TYPE:

K L Q R S T U

P M N O

pericentric inversion always puts the hetero-zygote at a reproductive disadvantage.   For this reason, only the smallest pericentric in-versions—those which do not synapse when heterozygous—are usually able to survive in the wild.

3. *Duplication*

If, following two breaks in the same chro-mosome, joining is delayed until after the broken chromosome reproduces (Figure 12–4), the two interstitial pieces and the appropriate end pieces can join to produce a eutelomeric chromosome with the inter-stitial region repeated.   This rearrangement is called a *duplication.*   Neither, either, or both of the regions involved in the duplica-tion can be inverted with respect to the orig-inal arrangement.   The two remaining end pieces may or may not join to form a de-ficient chromosome.   (A deficiency can also be produced without a duplication when the end pieces join before chromosome replica-tion.)   Provided that the duplicated region is small enough and acentric, it can survive in nature.

Consequences of Two Breaks in Two Chromosomes

What happens when two breaks occur, one in each of two different chromosomes? In the first such case, the two broken chromosomes are nonhomologous (Figure 12–5). If the two centric pieces unite, a dicentric is formed and the two acentric pieces are lost in the next division, whether they join each other or do not join at all. If all pieces join as indicated, then there is a mutual exchange of segments between nonhomologous chromosomes, which is called a segmental interchange, or more often, a *reciprocal translocation.* This is the *aneucentric type* of reciprocal translocation and often acts as a dominant lethal in a subsequent division, particularly when the dicentric is pulled toward both poles at once.

The reverse is often just as likely, however; union occurs between the centric piece of one chromosome and the acentric piece of the nonhomolog, with the centric piece of the second joining the acentric piece of the first. This reciprocal translocation is of the *eucentric type.* In individuals heterozygous for such an exchange (Figure 12–6), having two nonhomologs translocated and two nontranslocated, gametes are formed with deficiencies and duplications if, by segregation, they receive one but not both members of the reciprocal translocation.

When the chromosomes in nuclei are compressed in a relatively small volume, no broken end is far from any other; usually,

FIGURE 12–6. *Diagrammatic representation of segregation in eucentric reciprocal translocation heterozygotes. (Chromatids not shown; the spindles—also not shown—have their poles oriented vertically.)*

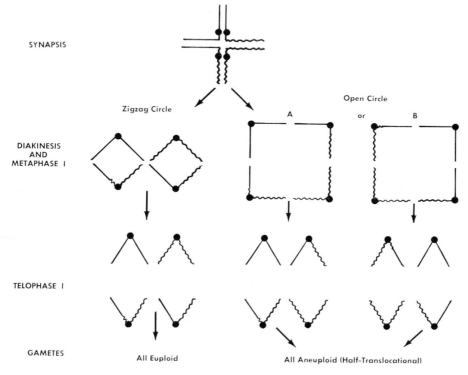

SYNAPSIS

Zigzag Circle   Open Circle

A   or   B

DIAKINESIS
AND
METAPHASE I

TELOPHASE I

GAMETES   All Euploid   All Aneuploid (Half-Translocational)

if one of the two unions needed for reciprocal translocation occurs, so does the other. Such is the case in the nucleus of the Drosophila sperm just after fertilization. In oocytes and probably in other cells that have a relatively large nuclear volume, the distance between the broken ends of nonhomologs is so great that reciprocal translocations are comparatively rare and, even if one cross union occurs, the two other broken ends usually fail to join to each other, so that only half of a reciprocal translocation—a *half-translocation*—is produced. The loss or behavior of the unjoined fragments usually causes descendent cells to die or to be abnormal, as would be expected. Half-translocations can also result when heterozygotes for a eucentric reciprocal translocation undergo segregation (see Figure 12–6), and only one of the two reciprocals is present in a gamete.

Some children with Down's syndrome have 46 chromosomes. These chromosomes include—in addition to two normal number 21's—an autosomal pair (from group 13–15 or from group 16–18) which is heteromorphic, one member being longer than usual. The extra piece is probably the long arm of 21, so that the individual is hyperploid for 21, being almost trisomic 21. In some cases the mother is phenotypically normal although she is heterozygous for a eucentric reciprocal translocation between 21 and, for example, 15. Her chromosome constitution can be represented by 15, 15.21 (centromere of 15), 21.15 (centromere of 21), 21. An egg containing 21 and 15.21 (the half-translocation) fertilized by a normal sperm (containing 21 and 15) produces the almost-trisomic-21 mongoloid under discussion. (The break in 15 must have been so close to the end that the hypoploid segment in the half-translocation mongoloid individual was not lethal.) In other cases such half-translocational mongoloids have half-translocational nonmongoloid mothers

with 45 chromosomes. These mothers have only one normal 21, one normal 15, for example, and the half-translocation 15.21. The hypoploidy for both 21 and 15 must be small enough to be viable in the mother, who can produce the aneuploid gamete that makes her child mongoloid. (Note in the cases cited above no relation exists between mother's age and the occurrence of half-translocational mongoloid children.)

In the second case in which two chromosomes are broken once, the chromosomes are homologs (ABCDEFG.HIJ). The breaks are usually at different places, for example, between A and B in one chromosome, and between D and E in the other. Here, also, reciprocal translocation can occur two ways. The aneucentric type produces a dicentric and an acentric chromosome whose fate can be readily predicted. The eucentric type produces two eucentric chromosomes, the BCD region being deficient in one and duplicated in the other.

From the preceding discussion, one would expect eucentric reciprocal translocations to tend to be eliminated from the population soon after arising by mutation, since they are usually heterozygous and cause about 50% of gametes to be half-translocational aneuploids. Certain eucentric reciprocal translocations, however, seem to be exceptions. In these cases, almost a whole arm of each chromosome is mutually exchanged. Such whole-arm reciprocal translocations—when heterozygous in Drosophila and probably in most other species—tend to synapse and disjoin in the following way: at synapsis the heterozygous reciprocal translocation forms an X configuration composed of two tetrads (Figure 12–6). Later, when homologous centromeres repel each other, alternate centromeres move toward the same pole, so that as the chiasmata move towards the ends, a zigzag arrangement of four dyads results (Figure 12–6). Because of this alternate centromeric orientation, anaphase I produces one nucleus without the translocation and the other with the full translocation. Since euploid gametes are usually formed, such translocation heterozygotes are not at an appreciable reproductive disadvantage.

Increasing Gene Number

Both here and in Chapter 11, it has been pointed out that a change in ploidy can survive in nature when it involves either no shift in chromosome balance (because it deals with whole genomes) or eucentric aneuploidy due to small segments of chromosomes which are hypo- or hyperploid. In the latter cases, the number of deficient or duplicated genes is small enough to produce a tolerable phenotypic effect. It is reasonable to assume that the greater the amount of chromosomal material, the greater the complexity possible in an organism and, consequently, the greater the diversity possible in its phenotype and adaptiveness. Accordingly, viable changes in ploidy must be particularly important in organic evolution. It is desirable, therefore, to specify some of the different ways that small numbers of genes can be added to a genome after breakage.

Two methods of increasing gene number after breakage have already been described. One requires two breaks in the same chromosome; the entire chromosome then replicates, after which the broken ends join to form a chromosome with the interstitial piece duplicated (p. 170); the other involves each member of a pair of homologs breaking once in a different region before eucentric cross union (p. 172).

A third mechanism involves three breaks in one chromosome. The two interstitial pieces exchange positions, producing what

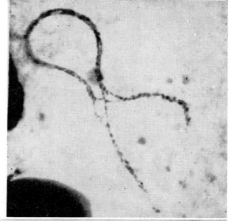

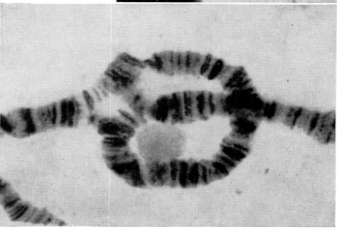

FIGURE 12–7. *Inversion heterozygotes in corn (pachynema) (courtesy of D. T. Morgan, Jr.) and in Drosophila (salivary gland) (courtesy of M. Demerec).*

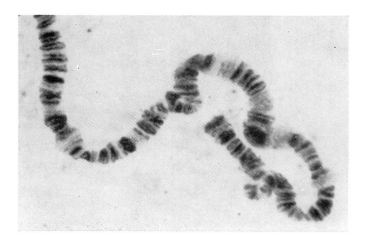

FIGURE 12–8. *Salivary gland chromosomes heterozygous for a shift within the right arm of chromosome 3 of* Drosophila melanogaster. *A piece from map region "98" is inserted into map region "91." The rightmost buckle is due to the absence of the shifted segment; the leftmost buckle is due to its presence. (Courtesy of B. P. Kaufmann.)*

is called a *shift.* If, in the heterozygote for a shift, the homologs pair up and a crossing over occurs in the region of the shift, a section of one of the crossovers will be in duplicate, as can be seen by tracing the resultant strands.

Two breaks in one chromosome and one in a nonhomolog can result in the interstitial piece of the first chromosome being inserted into the second. This result is called *transposition.* A transposition-containing chromosome can occur in subsequent generations not with the nonhomologous, deficient chromosome from which the piece was transposed, but with two normal chromosomes of that type. In this way an individual is produced containing a pair of normal homologs and a part of the normal homolog present in hyperploid condition in a nonhomolog.

The preceding indicates how the same type of structural change—duplication—can result from different types of breakage events. For this reason, one cannot always specify the particular number of nonrestituting breaks originally involved by observing the resultant rearrangement and, therefore, the explanation proposed is always the sim-

plest one. Note also that loss of an entire chromosome can occur after breakage; thus, not all such losses come from nondisjunction. Contrary to nondisjunction, however, breakage events cannot produce trisomics.

Cytogenetic Detection of Structural Changes

The question of how structural changes in chromosomes are detected may have arisen during the preceding discussions. Such mutants may be detected initially by cytological examination, or they may be noted first by their effects on the phenotype when genetic tests are made. Thus, detection and identification of structural changes can be made cytologically, or genetically, or by a combination of both methods.

When heterozygous, deficiencies can sometimes be recognized genetically since they permit the expression of all genes which are hemizygous in the nondeficient chromosome. Inversions and translocations can be suspected when mutant heterozygotes show a marked reduction in offspring carrying crossovers. Using appropriate genetic markers, inversion homozygotes show some genes in the reverse of normal order, whereas in heterozygotes or homozygotes for transloca-

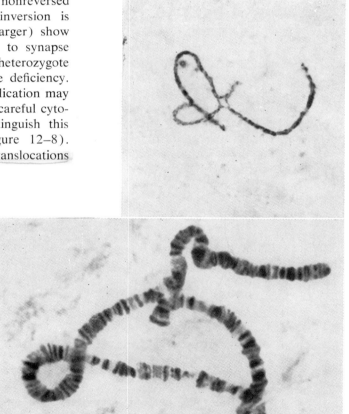

tions genes normally not linked are found linked. Sometimes a cytological study is preceded by genetic studies indicating the class of structural change involved and the particular chromosome(s) affected. Of course, detailed knowledge of the cytological appearance of the normal genome is a prerequisite for such work.

The prophase of meiosis of some organisms and the giant salivary gland chromosomes of Diptera are particularly suited for cytological studies, because in both cases synapsis between homologs helps locate the presence, absence, or relocation of chromosome parts. For example, inversion heterozygotes show either a reversed segment which does not pair with its nonreversed homologous segment (if the inversion is small), or (if the inversion is larger) show one homolog twisting in order to synapse (Figure 12–7). A deficiency-heterozygote will buckle in the region of the deficiency. Since a chromosome with a duplication may also buckle when heterozygous, careful cytological study is needed to distinguish this case from deficiency (see Figure 12–8). Heterozygotes for reciprocal translocations (Figure 12–9) show two pairs of nonhomologous chromosomes associated together in synapsis.

The present discussion should suffice as an introduction to the origin, nature, and consequences of the more common types of structural changes in chromosomes and to the methods used in identifying such mutants.

FIGURE 12–9. *Heterozygous reciprocal translocation in corn (pachynema) (courtesy of M. M. Rhoades) and Drosophila (salivary gland) (courtesy of B. P. Kaufmann).*

SUMMARY AND CONCLUSIONS

Structural change in chromosomes is a type of mutation involving the gain, loss, or relocation of chromosome parts. All such mutations require chromosome or chromatid breakage. Since proximity favors union, most of the ends produced by breakage restitute. Unions occur mainly during interphase. Nonrestitutional unions produce structural changes in chromosomes. The occurrence of one, two, or three nonrestituting breaks in one or two chromosomes is discussed in relation to the production of whole-chromosome losses, deficiencies, duplications, inversions, translocations, shifts, and transpositions.

Chromosomes that have undergone structural change may be euploid or aneuploid. The cells in which these mutations arise are euploid but can become aneuploid following mitosis, segregation, or crossing over. The structural changes most likely to be retained in the population are the smallest ones; those changes which directly or indirectly cause an increase in gene number are most likely to be important in evolution.

REFERENCES

Bearn, A. G., and German III, J. L., "Chromosomes and Disease," Scient. Amer., 205, No. 5:66–76, 1961.

Muller, H. J., "The Nature of the Genetic Effects Produced by Radiation," in *Radiation Biology,* Hollaender, A. (Ed.), New York: McGraw-Hill, 1954, Chap. 7, pp. 351–473.

Patau, K., "The Origin of Chromosomal Abnormalities," Pathologie-Biologie, 11:1163–1170, 1963.

Russell, L. B., "Chromosome Aberrations in Experimental Mammals," Progress in Medical Genetics, 2:230–294, 1962.

QUESTIONS FOR DISCUSSION

12.1. The terms *euploid* and *aneuploid* (hypo- or hyperploid) have been applied both to individual chromosomes and to whole nuclei. Give an example of:

  (a) A hypoploid chromosome in a euploid nucleus
  (b) A hyperploid chromosome in a hyperploid nucleus
  (c) An aneuploid nucleus containing all structurally normal chromosomes

12.2. As used on p. 170, what does the term *eutelomeric* mean? Name two types of aneutelomeric chromosomes.

12.3. Given the chromosome AB/CDE/F.GHI/J, where the period indicates the centromere and the slanted lines the positions of three simultaneously produced breaks, draw as many different outcomes as possible. Indicate which one is most likely to occur.

12.4. In Drosophila, the loss of a given chromosome results in monosomy; this situation is approximately three to five times as frequent as its gain, resulting in trisomy. Explain.

12.5. Discuss the origin of monosomics among human zygotes.

12.6. In human chromosomes at mitotic metaphase, discuss the detectability of the following:

    (a) Paracentric inversion   (c) Deficiency

    (b) Pericentric inversion   (d) Duplication

                                     (e) Half-translocation

12.7. What advantages may inversion provide?

12.8. What characteristics of cells undergoing oogenesis favor the production and viable transmission of half-translocations?

12.9. In Drosophila, a male, dihybrid for the mutants *bw* and *st*, when back-crossed to *bw bw st st*, normally produces offspring whose phenotypes are in a 1:1:1:1 ratio. On exceptional occasions, this cross produces offspring having only two of the four phenotypes normally obtained. How can you explain such an exception?

12.10. Is the telomere a gene? Why?

12.11. Explain how you could cytologically determine the position of the locus for *white* on the X chromosome of Drosophila by each of the following:

    (a) deficiencies of various sizes

    (b) inversions of various sizes

    (c) various reciprocal translocations

12.12. Suppose you had a self-maintaining strain of Drosophila in which all females were yellow-bodied and males, grey-bodied. How would you explain this consistency if the egg mortality were always 50%? Low, as it is normally? How would you test your hypothesis cytologically?

12.13. (a) Several X-linked mutants in Drosophila cause notched wings. One of these mutants is lethal in the male and also in the mutant homozygote female. How do you suppose such a homozygote is produced?

(b) A female heterozygous for this mutant ($N/+$) is mated to a *fa/Y* male. In F_1 all sons are normal, half the daughters are normal, and half are both notched and faceted. Explain this result showing how you might test your hypothesis.

12.14. Make a diagram of the different eucentric reciprocal translocations between autosomes 2 and 3 in Drosophila which you would expect to be lethal in the following cases:

    (a) when either half-translocation is present

    (b) when one half-translocation but not the other is present

    (c) under no circumstances

12.15. Does the absence of crossing over in male Drosophila facilitate the detection of heterozygous reciprocal translocations? Explain.

12.16. Given a Drosophila heterozygous for a eucentric reciprocal translocation between chromosomes 2 and 3 and assume both half-translocations are lethal when present separately. Discuss the nature of the linkage maps one would obtain from mating

    (a) genetically marked females of this type with appropriately marked non-translocation males

    (b) genetically marked males of this type mated to appropriately marked non-translocation females

12.17. A chromosome A.BCDEEDCFG has a reverse repeat, or duplication, for CDE. Compare the stability of this chromosome with A.BCDECDEFG, which carries a tandem repeat, or duplication, for the same region.

12.18. In Drosophila each of the genes for curly wings (Cy), plum eye color (Pm), hairless (H) and dichaete wings (D) are lethal when homozygous. A curly, hairless male mated to a plum, dichaete female produces 16 equally frequent types of sons and daughters. One curly, plum, hairless, dichaete F_1 son is irradiated with X-rays and then crossed to a plum, dichaete female. Three F_2 sons phenotypically like the father, collected and mated separately with wild-type females, produce the following males and females in the F_3 progeny.

Phenotype	Son 1	Son 2	Son 3
Cy H	140	120	76
Cy D	120	—	81
Pm H	135	—	84
Pm D	154	117	79

Explain these results, using cytogenetic diagrams for all individuals mentioned.

12.19. (a) Discuss the frequency of abortions in normal mothers who produce half-translocational children with Down's syndrome.

(b) Would you sometimes expect the occurrence of children with Down's syndrome to be correlated with the father but not with his age? Explain.

12.20. The Y chromosome is of different size in different phenotypically normal men. On the other hand, a woman with a small X chromosome is phenotypically defective. How can you explain the origin of such different Y and X chromosomes and the difference in the way they affect the two sexes?

*Chapter *13*

RADIATION-INDUCED STRUCTURAL CHROMOSOME CHANGES

I N THE preceding chapter structural changes in chromosomes were discussed with respect to types and consequences, but little was said about the events responsible for their production, namely, breakage and cross-union. Chromosomes break spontaneously; that is, they occasionally break in cells exposed to normal conditions. Because spontaneous breakage is relatively rare, agents that are able to produce great numbers of breaks are very useful in studies of chromosome breakage and its consequences. Our discussion in this chapter is restricted to one of these agents, radiation.

The process of breaking a chromosome is a chemical reaction requiring energy. The biochemical effect of radiation depends upon the type and amount of energy left in tissue. Less energetic radiations (such as visible light) leave energy in the form of *heat*; more energetic radiations (such as ultraviolet light) leave energy in the form of heat and *activation*; the latter type of energy makes an electron move from an inner to an outer orbit of an atom. The more energetic the radiation, the greater the likelihood that the energy absorbed will lead to chemical change. For example, ultraviolet light produces more breaks in chromosomes than does visible light. Radiations of energy higher than ultraviolet light (X rays and gamma rays; alpha and beta rays; electrons, neutrons, protons, and other fast-moving

particles) are even more capable of causing breaks. Although such high-energy radiations also heat and activate, most of the energy left in the cells is in the form of *ionization,* and this leads to most of the chromosome breaks. Before discussing how ionization energy leads to breakage, we should first understand what ionization is and what its consequences are.

Like visible and ultraviolet light, X and gamma rays are electromagnetic waves; however, they have relatively shorter wave lengths and can penetrate tissue more deeply than visible or ultraviolet light. When a highly energetic wave is stopped (or a fast-moving particle is captured or slowed down), energy is absorbed by the atoms of the medium. This energy can cause an atom to lose an orbital electron, creating a charged particle, or *ion,* by the process of *ionization.* Such an electron, torn free of the atom, goes off at great speed and can, in turn, cause other atoms to lose orbital electrons—to be ionized. All atoms losing an electron, of course, become *positively charged ions,* and atoms that capture free electrons become *negatively charged ions.* Since each electron lost from one atom is eventually gained by another atom, ions occur as pairs. In this way a *track* of ion pairs, or an *ion track,* is produced which often has smaller side branches. The length of the main or primary ion track and its side branches and the density of ion pairs differ with the type and energy of the radiation involved. Fast neutrons make a relatively long, rather uniformly thick ion track; fast beta rays or electrons make a relatively long, uniformly thin or interrupted track of ions; ordinary X rays make a relatively short track sparse in ions at its origin becoming only moderately dense at its end. It is sufficient to say that all known ionizing radiations produce clusters of ion pairs within microscopic distances. In other words, no amount or

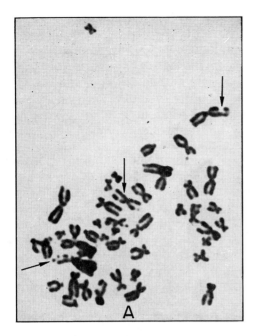

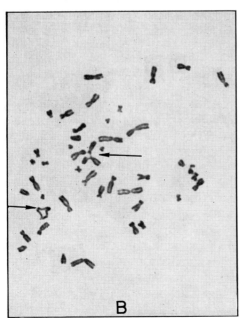

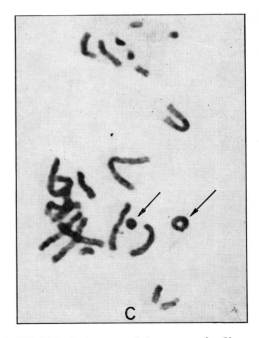

kind of high-energy radiation presently known can produce only single ions, or single pairs of ions evenly spaced over microscopic (hence, relatively large) distances. Since one ion or a pair sufficiently separated from the next does not exist, the genetic effects of ionization must be determined from the activity of clusters of negatively and positively charged ions. Ions undergo chemical reactions to neutralize their charge to reach a more stable configuration. It is during this process that ion clusters are able to produce chromosome and chromatid breaks (Figure 13–1).

The amount of ionization produced by radiation is measured in terms of an ionization unit called the *roentgen,* or *r unit,* one r being equal to about 1.8×10^9 ion pairs per cubic centimeter of air. A sufficiently

FIGURE 13–1. *Structural changes X-ray-induced (75–150 r) in normal human male fibroblast-like cells* in vitro. *Arrows show:* (A) *broken chromosomes,* (B) *translocation (center) and dicentric (lower left),* (C) *ring chromosomes. A, B are in metaphase (see Fig. 11–9); C is late prophase. (Courtesy of T. T. Puck, Proc. Nat. Acad. Sci., U.S., 44: 776–778, 1958.)*

penetrating radiation (such as fast electrons), producing this 1.8×10^9 ion pairs in a given cm^3 of air, can also produce this amount in successive cm^3 of air because only a very small fraction of the incident radiation is absorbed at successive depths. If not very energetic X rays are used ("soft" X rays of relatively long wavelength—also called Grenz rays), all radiation may be absorbed near the surface of the medium, keeping the deeper regions free from ionization. The amount of energy left at any level depends not only upon the energy of the incident radiation, but also upon the density of the medium through which the radiation passes. Thus, in tissue, which is approximately ten times as dense as air, a penetrating high-energy radiation produces about one thousand times the number of ion pairs per cm^3 as it does in air. Knowing this, it can be calculated that one r (always measured in air) produces about 1.5 ion pairs per cubic micron (μ^3) of tissue. Since the volume of the Drosophila sperm head is about 0.5 μ^3, one r is able to produce, on the average, less than one ion pair in it. Since ions occur in clusters, one r may place dozens of ion pairs in one sperm head and none in dozens of other sperm heads. The r unit measures only the absorbed energy which produces ions; another unit, the *rad,* measures the total amount of radiant energy absorbed by the medium. In the case of X rays, about 90% of the energy left in the tissue is used to produce ions; the rest produces heat and excitation. Since ultraviolet radiation is non-ionizing, its dosage is measured in rads and not r units.

The number of chromosome breaks produced by X rays increases linearly with the radiation dose (r) (Figure 13–2). This relationship means that X rays always produce at least some ion clusters large enough to cause a break. Moreover, clusters of ions from different tracks of ions do not combine their effects to cause a break. (If there were

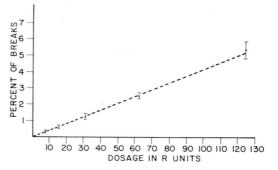

FIGURE 13–2. *The relation between X-ray dosage and the frequency of breaks induced in grasshopper chromosomes. (Courtesy of J. G. Carlson, Proc. Nat. Acad. Sci., U.S., 27:46, 1941.)*

such cooperation between clusters, the break frequency at low doses would be lower than what has been found because of the waste of clusters too small to break; the frequency at higher doses would be higher because of the cooperation among such clusters.) Certain radiations, like fast neutrons, produce fewer breaks per r than X rays because one r of these radiations produces larger—and, hence, fewer—clusters of ions than do X rays. These larger clusters more often exceed the size needed to produce a break, and therefore, are relatively less efficient in this respect.

Ion clusters can produce breaks either directly by attacking the chromosome itself, or indirectly by attacking oxygen-carrying molecules (which, in turn, react with the chromosomes) or other chemical substances (which, in turn, affect the chromosome or oxygen-carrying molecules). In any case, this indirect pathway must be of nearly submicroscopic dimensions; otherwise, different ion clusters would be able to cooperate in causing breakage. Thus, only ion clusters in or very close to the chromosome can produce breaks in it, as has been visibly demonstrated by using beams of penetrating radiation of microscopic diameter. Such a beam passing through a metaphase chromosome can break it, but fails to do so when directed at the protoplasm adjoining the chromosome.

From what has been stated, it is reasonable to assume that the number of breaks produced by a given dose of a certain radiation depends upon the volume which a chromosome occupies. This volume is different at different times in the nuclear cycle (for example, it changes during chromosome replication). Because of variations in polynemy or gene activity, the same chromosome can occupy different volumes in different tissues of an individual and the volume of the same sex chromosome can be different in the two sexes. Because breakage requires energy, it is also reasonable to assume that the number of breaks indirectly produced increases if, during irradiation, either the amount of oxygen is increased, or the cell's reducing substances are poisoned. And conversely, replacement of oxygen by nitrogen during irradiation reduces the number of breaks produced.

After this preliminary discussion of some of the factors that influence the production of radiation-induced breaks, we are ready to consider the factors that influence the fate of the ends produced by breakage. Just as breakage involves a chemical reaction, so does the union between two sticky ends. The joining of break-produced ends apparently involves adenosine triphosphate and protein synthesis.[1] Joining is enhanced by the oxygen (and inhibited by the nitrogen) present after irradiation. Accordingly, restitution is prevented if nitrogen replaces oxygen after irradiation, thus increasing the time that ends from the same break stay open, and, therefore, the chance for cross-union when the supply of oxygen is later resumed. (Note that the presence of oxygen

has two contrary effects on rearrangement frequency—during irradiation it increases the number of breaks, whereas after irradiation it increases restitution.)

Since, under given conditions, the number of breaks increases linearly with an ionizing dose—each part of the dose independently producing its proportional number of breaks—clearly, the number of breaks produced is also independent of the rate at which a given total dose is administered. It also follows that all structural changes in chromosomes resulting from single breakages are also independent of the radiation dose rate. Radiations such as fast neutrons which produce long and dense ion tracks can frequently induce two chromosome breaks with the same track. In this case, if the same chromosome—having folded or coiled tightly—is broken twice by being twice in the path of the track, then large and small structural changes of inversion, deficiency, and duplication types can be produced. The frequency of these rearrangements increases linearly with fast neutron dose and is independent of the dose rate.

A single fast neutron-induced track of ions can also break two different chromosomes when chromosomes are closely packed together, as they are in the sperm head. The linear increase with dose in the frequency of reciprocal translocations obtained after sperm are treated with fast neutrons provides evidence for concluding—as was done in Chapter 12—that proximity of sticky ends favors their union. Such a linear dose-effect can be obtained only if both breaks are produced by the same track and if the broken ends capable of exchange union are located near each other—broken ends produced by different tracks being too far apart.

When ordinary X rays are employed, however, the clusters are smaller, and the track of ions is shorter than fast neutron tracks. Accordingly, two breaks in the same chromosome are produced by the same

[1] See J. G. Brewen (1963).

X-ray ion track less frequently, and if they do occur, they are usually quite close together. Note, however, that two breaks occurring within submicroscopic distances in successive gyres of a coiled chromosome produce structural changes whose size ranges only from minute to small. Nevertheless, a small proportion of single X-ray tracks—in the treatment of sperm, for example—do cause two breaks, each in a different chromosome. Therefore, for X-ray doses that produce fewer than two tracks per sperm, gross chromosomal rearrangement frequency increases linearly with dose. So, there is actually no dose of X rays which does not have some chance of producing a gross rearrangement. In other words, no matter how small a dose of ionizing radiation is received, the possibility of a chromosomal break and a gross chromosomal mutation always exists.

In the case of X rays or fast electrons, two breaks that occur in the same nucleus usually result from the action of two ion clusters, each derived from a different, independently arising track, so that each break is induced independently. Fast electron or X-ray-induced, two-break gross rearrangements of this origin are dose dependent, for when a small enough dose is given, a nucleus is traversed by only one track, and only one-track—not two-track—gross rearrangements can result. But when the dose is large enough for a nucleus to be traversed by two separate tracks, the two breakages required for two-break gross rearrangements can be produced independently. Therefore, the higher the dose of X rays used, the greater the efficiency in producing multi-break gross rearrangements caused by breaks independently induced by separate tracks. Accordingly, for doses causing some cells to experience two such independently produced breaks and higher doses, the frequency of these mutations increases more than in direct proportion to the amount of dose. One example is the exponential rise in the frequency of reciprocal translocations obtained after treating sperm in inseminated Drosophila females with increasing dosages of fast electrons (Figure 13–3, curve T).

X-ray-induced rearrangements involving two (or more) breaks induced by separate tracks also depend upon the rate at which a given dose is administered. When a suitably large dose is given over a short interval,

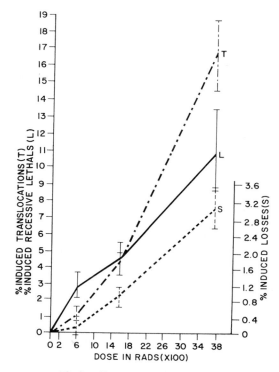

FIGURE 13–3. *Percentage of mutations, ±2× standard error, recovered from Drosophila sperm exposed to different dosages of 18 mev electrons. The sex-linked recessive lethal frequencies (L) are joined by solid lines and are adjusted for the control rate; sex chromosome loss frequencies (S) are connected by broken lines and are corrected for the control rate; reciprocal translocation frequencies (T) between chromosomes II and III are connected by dot-dash lines. (From I. H. Herskowitz, H. J. Muller, J. S. Laughlin, Genetics, 44:326, 1959.)*

the ends produced by separate breaks exist simultaneously and are able to cross-unite. But when the same dose is given more slowly, the pieces of the first break may restitute before those of the second are produced, thus eliminating the opportunity for cross-union. In this event, the same dose produces fewer gross rearrangements when given in a protracted manner than when given in a concentrated manner. Although this dose-rate dependence for X rays is true for most cells—at least during part of the interphase stage—it does not apply to mature sperm of animals, probably including man. In these gametes and during most of nuclear division in other cells, the broken pieces cannot join each other (see p. 166) and, therefore, accumulate. For this reason, it makes no difference how quickly or slowly the dose is given to the chromosomes in such a sperm head, since the breaks remain unjoined at least until the sperm head swells after fertilization.

As already mentioned, the spatial arrangement of chromosomes with respect to each other influences the number of breaks and the kinds of structural changes they produce. It should be noted that the possibilities for multiple breakages and for joinings are quite different for chromosomes packed into the tiny head of a sperm than they are for chromosomes located in a large nucleus. But even within a given type of cell, a number of other factors can influence breakage or rejoining, such as the presence or absence of a nuclear membrane, the degree of spiralization of the chromosomes, the stress or tension under which the parts of a chromosome are held, the degree of hydration, the amount of matrix in which the genes are embedded, protoplasmic viscosity and the amount of fluid and particulate movement around the chromosomes, gravity, centrifugal force, and vibration.

In cells whose chromosomes have just replicated and in somatic or meiotic cells where homologs are synapsed, a special restriction on the movements of the pieces is produced when only some of the apposed strands are broken (see p. 166). In this situation, the forces which keep parts of one strand adjacent to the corresponding parts of its sister or homolog may prevent the broken pieces from moving apart freely, so that the unbroken strand or strands serve as a splint for the broken one(s) and reduce the opportunities for cross-union. Many factors exist, therefore, which determine to what degree chromosome and chromatid fragments can move or spring apart; those affecting the distances between different chromosomes or the parts within a chromosome also affect chromosome and chromatid breakability.

The frequencies and types of structural changes depend also upon the total amount of chromosomal material present in the nucleus and the number and size of the chromosomes into which this material is divided. The rearrangements that occur in different cells of a single individual depend upon whether the cell is haploid, diploid, or polyploid, and whether or not the chromosomes are polynemic, are in the process of replication, or are otherwise metabolically active.

Radiation can produce important nonmutating effects upon the chromosomes by damaging nonchromosomal cellular components which, in turn, affect chromosomal behavior and function. If the cells are capable of repairing such nonchromosomal, structural or functional damage, they will have a longer time in which to repair when a radiation dose is given slowly than when given quickly. The most obvious example is the effect of radiation upon mitosis (and probably meiosis). Cells at about midprophase or a later stage in nuclear division usually complete the process even though irradiated. Cells no farther advanced than about midprophase often return to interphase when irradiated. For this reason, ionizing radiation causes a greater degree of synchrony in division than occurs in the absence of the radiation. Accordingly, starting with a population of cells in various stages of nuclear division, the chromosomal targets for mutation are different in the later stages of receiving a protracted dose and of receiving a concentrated dose.

The capacity to produce recoverable structural changes is not the same in euchromatic and heterochromatic chromosomal regions. Recovered radiation-induced structural changes involve heterochromatic regions more frequently than they do euchromatic ones. It has not been determined whether this excess is due to heterochromatin having a greater breakability, a lesser restitutability (which might be associated with the general ability of different heterochromatic regions to synapse with each other), or both. Nevertheless, in many rearrangements, at least one of the points of breakage is located in the heterochromatin nearest the centromere. This is one reason why whole-arm reciprocal translocation is the type most frequently observed.

The present discussion has been motivated by the ability of energetic radiations to induce many breaks and, subsequently, many structural changes. The great supply of rearrangements readily available via radiation treatment has made it possible to discover many of the factors influencing breakage and joining. Many other important discoveries were made possible by the study of structural changes, including

1. The genetic basis of the centromere
2. The reduced incidence of crossing over near the centromere
3. The genetic basis of the telomere
4. The existence in some species of genetic elements (*collochores*) near the centromere of special importance to synapsis.[2]

[2] See K. W. Cooper (1964).

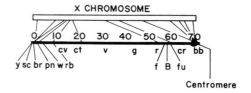

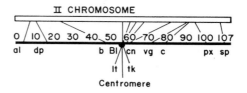

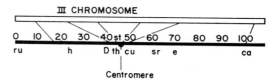

FIGURE 13–4. *Comparison of chromosome (hollow bar) and crossover (solid bar) maps in* D. melanogaster.

Perhaps the most fundamental contribution was the finding, via structural changes, that the genes have the same linear order in the chromosome, that is, in *chromosome maps,* as they have in crossover maps. The spacing of these, however, is different in the two cases (Figure 13–4). Thus, for example, because of the reduction in crossing over near the centromere, the genes nearest the centromere—spaced far apart in the metaphase chromosome map—are found to be close together in the crossover map.

Although our subject matter has been restricted to the factors influencing the origin and joining of breaks produced by ionizing radiation, these factors are expected to operate on breaks produced by any other spontaneously occurring or induced mechanism. For, in general, no matter how broken chromosomes are produced, all possess the same properties.

SUMMARY AND CONCLUSIONS

The components of structural chromosome change, breakage and cross-union, are readily studied through the use of ionizing radiations. These radiations induce breakage in chromosome strands primarily by the clusters of ion pairs they produce. These clusters form tracks of ions whose thickness and length determine the number and location of the breaks. Tracks of ions must occur very close to, or within, the chromosome that they break.

The number of breaks increases linearly with radiation dose. Whether they result from one or from two breaks, all chromosomal rearrangements induced by a single ionizing track increase linearly with radiation dose, have no threshold dose, and show no effect from protracting or concentrating the dose. Accordingly, there is no dose of ionizing radiation which does not produce breaks and at least single-track-induced rearrangements.

Two-or-more-break structural changes produced by ion clusters in separate, independently-occurring tracks increase in frequency faster than the amount of dose and do have a threshold dose. If joining of chromosome ends produced by breakage can take place during the course of irradiation, such rearrangements are reduced in frequency by protracting the delivery of the total dose.

Since both the breakage and joining processes involve chemical changes, their frequencies can be modified by the metabolic state of the cell. All types of rearrangements are expected to be affected by: the physical and chemical state of the chromosome and the amount and distribution of its euchromatin and heterochromatin; by the number and arrangement of the chromosomes present; by the presence or absence of a nuclear membrane; and by the movements of broken ends as influenced by cellular particles, fluids, and extracellular factors.

REFERENCES

Bacq, Z. M., and Alexander, P., *Fundamentals of Radiobiology,* 2nd Ed., New York: Pergamon Press, 1961.

Bender, M. A., and Gooch, P. C., "Types and Rates of X-ray-Induced Chromosome Aberrations in Human Blood Irradiated in Vitro," Proc. Nat. Acad. Sci., U.S., 48:522–532, 1962.

Brewen, J. G., "Dependence of Frequency of X-ray-Induced Chromosome Aberrations on Dose Rate in the Chinese Hamster," Proc. Nat. Acad. Sci., U.S., 50:322–329, 1963.

Chu, E. H. Y., Giles, N. H., and Passano, K., "Types and Frequencies of Human Chromosome Aberrations Induced by X-rays," Proc. Nat. Acad. Sci., U.S., 47: 830–839, 1961.

Cooper, K. W., "Meiotic Conjunctive Elements Not Involving Chiasmata," Proc. Nat. Acad. Sci., U.S., 52:1248–1255, 1964.

"Ionizing Radiation," Scient. Amer., 201:No. 3 (Sept.), 1959.

Muller, H. J., "General Survey of Mutational Effects of Radiation," in *Radiation Biology and Medicine,* Claus, W. D. (Ed.), Reading, Mass.: Addison-Wesley, Chap. 6, pp. 145–177, 1958.

Puck, T. T., "Radiation and the Human Cell," Scient. Amer., 202, No. 4:142–153, 1960.

Sobels, F. H., *Repair from Genetic Radiation,* New York: Pergamon Press, 1963.

Sparrow, A. H., Binnington, J. P., and Pond, V., *Bibliography on the Effects of Ionizing Radiations on Plants,* 1896–1955, Brookhaven Nat. Lab. Publ. 504 (L-103), 1958.

LEWIS JOHN STADLER (*1896–1954*)
*is noted for his studies on the nature
of mutation and of the gene (see p.
ix). He and H. J. Muller discovered independently the mutagenic
effect of X rays. (From Genetics,
vol. 41, p. 1, 1956.)*

QUESTIONS FOR DISCUSSION

13.1. After both are exposed to the same amount of radiation why should tissue, which is only about ten times as dense as air, contain about one thousand times more ions than air?

13.2. What evidence can you give to support the view that the ions causing breakage need not always attack the chromosome directly?

13.3. Does the observation that the volume of a chromosome is variable under different conditions mean that it has an inconstant gene content? Explain.

13.4. Do you suppose that chromosomes exposed to X rays are more likely to undergo structural change when they are densely spiralized than when relatively uncoiled? Why?

13.5. Discuss the role of heterochromatin in changes involving chromosome number and chromosome shape.

13.6. Do you suppose that the oxygen content of a space capsule can affect the mutability of Drosophila passengers? Explain.

13.7. Discuss the relative efficiency, per r, of small doses of X rays and of fast neutrons in producing structural changes in chromosomes.

13.8. Do you suppose that the mutability of ultraviolet light threatens man's survival? Explain.

13.9. Compare the number and fate of breakages induced by the same dose of X rays administered to:

(a) A polyploid and a diploid liver cell in man
(b) A diploid neuron in man and Drosophila
(c) A sperm and a spermatogonium in man

13.10. Discuss the importance of the nonmutant effects of a given dose of radiation upon the mutation frequency induced by a subsequent radiation dose.

13.11. Using Figure 13–4, discuss the likelihood of crossing over in different regions of the X chromosome of *D. melanogaster*.

13.12. Compare the roentgen unit with the rad unit.

13.13. What specific aspects of our present environment tend to reduce the number of mutations induced by penetrating radiations from the number induced when man first evolved?

Chapter *14

POINT MUTATIONS

WE HAVE already found that the mutational unit of the genotype may be a whole genome, a single chromosome, or a part of a chromosome. Perhaps a study of these units will reveal more about the mutational characteristics of a single gene; perhaps the recombinational properties of individual genes will illuminate this area of investigation. Let us consider what we already know about the mutation of single genes—the class of mutation that is probably the most important in evolution because it causes the smallest shift in gene balance.

All chromosomes are linear and unbranched whether or not they have undergone segmental rearrangement by crossing over or breakage. This linear arrangement could be due to the linkage of gene to gene directly, or indirectly by a nongenetic material which connects adjacent genes. In either case, the fact remains that a chromosome is invariably either a rod or a ring, providing almost conclusive evidence that a gene cannot be joined to other genes at more than two places, and that a mutation which permits a gene to be joined to more than two others cannot occur spontaneously or be induced. That this type of mutation is never observed regardless of the organism studied can be interpreted to mean that genes never had this property or that all existing genes have lost this property. We are led to conclude, therefore, that all interstitial genes are *bipolar,* and that mutation is incapable of

189

causing the gene to be more than bipolar.

After chromosome breakage, the "stickiness" of the new ends is evidence that almost all mutations retain the bipolarity of genes. In some relatively rare cases, however, break-produced ends (*broken ends*) are known to become permanently unsticky or *healed,* so that mutation from bipolarity to unipolarity does occur. That mutation can change genes from a bipolar to a *unipolar* type, or vice versa, is evidenced also by the presence of telomeres—unipolar genes which seal off the normal ends of chromosomes.

The chromosomal change from bipolarity to unipolarity occurs regularly in the life history of certain animals. In particular species of the roundworm Ascaris, for example, nuclei which remain in the germ line have a single pair of chromosomes. When the nuclei first enter the somatic line, however, these chromosomes break up into a number of small linear fragments whose ends are sealed off and behavior during mitosis is normal—normal mitotic behavior being possible because a germ line chromosome has numerous centromeres along its length (each surviving fragment of the chromosome in a somatic cell has at least one). In the germ-line *polycentric chromosome* all centromeres but one are suppressed. Because chromosome fragmentation in Ascaris takes place only in somatic cells, these polarity changes can be attributed to some physiological difference between cells entering the somatic line and cells remaining in the germ line. These polarity changes should be considered recombinational rather than mutational events because the changes from bipolarity to unipolarity are numerous, simultaneous, and normal—therefore lacking the novelty of mutations.

Although mutations which change polarity from bipolarity to unipolarity apparently occur, no unambiguous case has ever been reported of the reverse, that is, of a mutation from unipolarity to bipolarity. Since the chance of detecting and proving a change from uni- to bipolarity is very small indeed, the occurrence of such a change cannot, at present, be denied with certainty. Do mutations to nonpolarity occur? It is evident that a unipolar or bipolar gene that mutates to a nonpolar alternative must necessarily drop out of the chromosomal line-up. If this happens, the freed, not-at-all-sticky gene will not be linked to any chromosome. Since no evidence has yet been presented for the existence of genetic material liberated from its chromosomal locus in this way, we cannot give an affirmative answer at this point.

The gene was first identified in sexually reproducing individuals whose chromosomes synapse during meiosis. Synapsis results from the attraction between different segments of one or more chromosomes. That different degrees of specific attraction exist between genes is illustrated by the fact that genes located in heterochromatin synapse much less specifically than those found in euchromatin. Specific genes (such as one in maize called *asynaptic*) are known which not only lack synaptic attraction for their alleles but also destroy this attraction between pairs of genes at other loci, or cause general desynapsis. The occurrence of collochores—genes which assist in pairing—has already been mentioned in Chapter 13. Corresponding euchromatic loci located in homologous chromosomes synapse with each other whether or not the particular alleles contained are identical or different. Yet euchromatic genes in nonhomologs do not usually synapse with each other, although it is presumed that some presently nonallelic genes were previously allelic. Consequently, mutation must be capable of changing the synaptic specificity of a gene; and it must follow, at least in a general way, that identical genes attract each other more than non-identical ones.

Since at least some genes have multiple alleles, it is clear that different forms of a gene do exist, and mutations of such genes are not explicable merely in terms of their complete loss or inactivation. Since some mutations produce no visible change in the banding pattern of salivary gland chromosomes of Drosophila, mutations involving but a single gene, that is, *gene mutations,* can be submicroscopic. At present, we can only detect gene mutations by the phenotypic changes they produce. Consequently, the characteristics of gene mutation must be determined from the phenotypic changes produced by recombinationally detected genes. Accordingly, we are unable to determine from such phenotypic changes whether gene mutation involves the recombinational gene in toto, a one portion or site within it, or many different sites within it. If gene mutation involves a change in the entire gene, then the material composition of the genes detected by recombination and by mutation would be identical. If, on the other hand, the recombinationally detected gene contains one or more sites at which mutation can occur, the basic recombinational unit of genetic material would be larger than the basic mutational unit. Until such time as critical evidence is obtained to the contrary, we have no choice other than continuing to accept the mutational and recombinational genes as materially equivalent, an assumption (Chapter 3, p. 36) which is in accord with the law of parsimony.

As mentioned in the first chapter, any given gene is rather stable, having been faithfully replicated many thousands of times before a detectable mutation occurs. The greater the sensitivity of our tests for detecting mutations, however, the larger is the frequency of mutation observed (recall the detection of isoallelism, p. 59). It is reasonable to assume therefore that transmissible modifications of single genes do occur which escape our present means of detection. Nevertheless, within the limits of our present methods of analysis, the gene appears to be a very stable entity.

Consider the following method for obtaining information with regard to gene mutation. All mutants involving the one or more genes being investigated are collected and then analyzed. Some mutants involving a given locus prove to be based upon changes in the number of whole chromosomes; others prove to be associated with gross or small chromosomal rearrangements. All these mutants are eliminated from further consideration even though gene mutation may also have occurred. Insofar as feasible, all genetic and cytological tests known are applied to eliminate mutants involving the minutest chromosomal rearrangements including, for example, tiny duplications or deficiencies. All, or a considerable number, of the mutants remaining can then be assumed—for lack of evidence to the contrary—to have resulted from mutations involving either a single gene (gene mutations) or at most only a few genes (*intergenic mutations*). Each of the remaining mutants behaves as though it resulted from a change at a single point in the crossover and cytological maps and is, therefore, called a *point mutant*. Since at this point we have no criterion for differentiating between a mutant involving only one gene (including its complete loss) and one involving a few genes, the entire heterogeneous class of point mutants will have to be studied in the hope of revealing some of the characteristics of gene mutation.

Consider some of the characteristics of spontaneous and induced point mutations. Since point mutation of a vast number of different genes occurs, this process is not restricted to a very limited type of gene. Although the conditions causing point mutation might be of such a nature that, in the diploid cell, both members of a pair of alleles tend to mutate at the same time, actually the evidence is that only one gene of the pair is affected. Because only one member of

a pair of genes in a nucleus mutates, point mutation must be a very localized, submicroscopic event.

If point mutation usually involved either a series of stable gene changes or an instability of the gene extending over more than one cell generation, the resultant mutants would usually occur in clusters and within a cluster the same gene might not always mutate to the same allele. But many point mutants occur singly. Moreover, those which do appear in a cluster often seem to be identical. Such a cluster can usually be explained by assuming a single cell has undergone mutation, having divided a number of times before the tests to detect the mutants were performed. Although such data do not prove that point mutation is instantaneous, they indicate that it is usually completed within one cell generation and the change in this respect is quick more than it is gradual. The number of point mutations obtained from X-ray or ultraviolet ray treatments is reduced, however, if posttreatment with certain types of visible light or chemical substances is given immediately (but not if such treatment is postponed for some hours). Such immediate posttreatments produce *photo-* or *chemorecovery* from point mutation and prove that the point mutation process often does not occur or is not completed for some minutes. Certain chemical changes, which themselves may or may not be mutational, can lead to other, genetic changes such as breakage. If the first changes are repaired before they can induce the second, an apparent recovery from mutation is observed. Only after the point mutation process is completed is the new genetic alternative just about as stable as the old.

Because point mutants are just about as stable as their parent genes or other genes in the genotype, it does not necessarily mean that all allelic and nonallelic genes have the same spontaneous mutation frequency.

Study of a representative sample of specific loci in Drosophila reveals an average of one point mutation at a given locus in each 200,-000 germ cells tested. In mice the per locus frequency is about twice this, or one in 100,000. In man, by scoring the mutants detected in heterozygous condition, the per locus rate is found to be one per 50,000 to 100,000 germ cells per generation. Within a species, different loci have about the same order of mutability. Even though some genes are definitely more mutable than others, the average spontaneous point mutation rate per genome per generation can be estimated for Drosophila, mouse, and man. In one Drosophila generation, one gamete in twenty (or one zygote in ten) contains a new detectable point mutant. In mice, this frequency is about one in ten gametes, whereas in man it is about one in five gametes (or two in five zygotes).

The point mutations which occur spontaneously—that is, under natural conditions —bear no obvious relation to the environment, either with respect to the locus affected or the type of alternative produced. Modifications in the environment do, however, influence point mutation frequency. For example, in the range of temperatures to which individuals are usually exposed, each rise of 10° C produces about a fivefold increase in point mutation frequency. The magnitude of this increase is similar to, although somewhat greater than, that obtained with an increase in temperature in ordinary chemical reactions. Violent temperature changes in either direction produce an even greater effect upon point mutation frequency. Actually, detrimental environmental conditions of almost any kind increase point mutation frequency.

Physical and chemical agents which raise the mutation frequency enormously are called *mutagens*. All high-energy radiations (see Chapter 13) are mutagenic (see Figure 13–3) as are many highly reactive chemical substances including: mustard gas and its derivatives; peroxides; epoxides; and carbamates. The point mutation frequencies obtained with radiation and certain chemical mutagens can be 150 times the spontaneous frequency. One speaks of a "spectrum" of spontaneous point mutations in that, as mentioned, certain loci are normally somewhat more mutable than others. The loci affected and the types of mutant alternatives produced by ionizing radiation are not radically different from those involved in spontaneous mutation. That these radiations produce a *mutational spectrum* much like the spontaneous one is expected, since radiant energy is more or less randomly distributed in the nucleus and generally enhances many different kinds of chemical reactions. The point-mutational spectra for different chemicals are somewhat different from each other as well as from the spectra induced by radiation mutagens or by spontaneous factors. These differences can be attributed to the nonrandom penetration of these chemical substances into the nucleus, or to their specific capacities for combining with different nuclear chemicals, or both. Nevertheless, the frequency of point mutation, which increases linearly with the dose of ionizing radiation (although the frequency is influenced by the amount of oxygen present), probably also increases linearly with the nuclear dose of many different chemical mutagens. So point mutation probably has no threshold dose with chemical mutagens, and the number of point mutations produced by a given total dose is constant, other things being equal, regardless of the rate of delivery.

For ultraviolet light—which is not a highly energetic radiation—the situation is different. Here the probability for the individual unit or quantum of energy inducing point mutation is considerably less than 100 per cent. Moreover, because several quanta can cooperate to produce mutation, ultraviolet induced point-mutation frequency increases faster than linearly with dose—at least for low doses—and an attenuated dose is less mutagenic than a concentrated one.

Point mutation is not restricted to the genes of any particular kind of cell, occurring in males and females, in somatic tissues of all kinds, and in the diploid and haploid cells of the germ line. Later stages in gametogenesis and very early developmental stages—*perifertilization stages*—are found to be relatively rich in spontaneous point mutations. Despite very great differences in life span, one does not find correspondingly great differences in the spontaneous germ line mutation frequencies of flies, mice, and men. This similarity in mutation frequency is not surprising if most of these mutations occur in the perifertilization stages, since each of these organisms spends a comparable length of time in these stages. Still another similarity among these species is the comparable number of cell divisions required for each to progress from a gamete of one generation to a gamete of the next. In fact, the differences in mutation frequency for these organisms are approximately proportional to the differences in the number of germ cell divisions per generation.

When during the history of the gene does mutation occur? The finding that the point mutation frequencies in Drosophila, mouse, and man are proportional to the number of cell divisions they undergo suggests that some of these mutations occur at synthesis of the new gene, although the experimental results do not specify whether it is the old or the new gene that mutates. Aging of spermatids and sperm of Drosophila is known to increase the point mutation frequency. Since the viability of these cells is not impaired when aneuploid, the increase in point mutations may be due to an effect upon the old, physiologically quiescent gene, implying that point mutational changes can occur while a gene is linearly attached to its neighbors.

The larger number of mutations obtained from aged cells may also be explained as resulting from a mutagen accumulated over a period of time which acts on the old or the new gene once gene replication is resumed. The possibility also remains that changes can occur in the steps leading to gene synthesis—before the new gene is completed and attached to its linear neighbors; such changes could be scored later as point mutants.

Phenotypic Effects of Point Mutants

The biological fitness of a mutant gene—pure or hybrid—is best described in terms of its effect upon the organism's ability to produce surviving offspring, that is, upon *reproductive potential*. This potential includes the mutant-carrying individual's capacity to reach the reproductive stage and its fertility and fecundity during this period, as well as the viability of its offspring until sexual maturity. Although each mutant has many phenotypic effects, point mutants with small phenotypic effects occur much more frequently than those with large effects. For instance, pure (homo- or hemizygous) mutants which lower the viability of males without being lethal are at least three to five times more frequent than those which are recessively lethal (Figure 13–3).

The vast majority of point mutants have a detrimental effect on the reproductive potential; beneficial point mutants are extremely rare. In terms of the past evolutionary history of a species, it is understandable that in the great majority of cases, mutants affecting a trait or organ cause its degeneration. All the genotypes in a species have been subjected to selection for many generations, those producing the greatest reproductive potential having been retained. Although point mutation at any locus is a rare event, many of the possible alternatives for each gene must have occurred at least several times in past history. Of these alternatives, only the more advantageous alleles were retained, and these are the ones found in present populations. So, a point mutation today is likely to produce one of the genetic alternatives which occurred also in the past but had been eliminated because of its lower biological fitness, that is, its lower reproductive potential. It should be realized, moreover, that reproductive potential is the result of coordinated action of the whole genotype. The genotype may be likened to the machinery that makes modern automobiles—the automobile representing the phenotype—with the environment furnishing the necessary raw materials. Present genotypes, like the machines that manufacture automobiles, are complex and have had a long evolutionary development. The chance that a newly-occurring point mutation will increase reproductive potential is just as small as the chance that a random local change in the present machinery will result in a better automobile.

The differences between the phenotypic effect of a point mutant and its normal alternative can be studied by adding more representatives of the mutant allele to the genotype and examining the effect. In Drosophila, for example, the normal fly has long bristles when the normal, dominant gene bb^+ is present. A mutant strain has shorter, thinner bristles because of the recessive allele bb (bobbed bristles), which—it should be recalled—has a locus both in the X and the Y chromosomes. We might suppose that the male, or female, homozygous for bb has bobbed bristles because this allele results in thinning and shortening the normal bristle. Since otherwise-diploid XYY males and XXY females can be obtained which carry three bb alleles, according to this view, one would expect the bristles formed to be even thinner and shorter than they are in ordinary mutant homozygotes. But, on the contrary,[1]

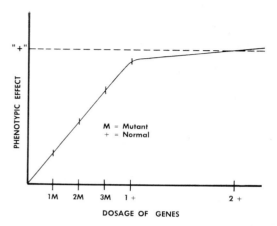

FIGURE 14–1. *The relationship between dosage of normal and mutant genes and their phenotypic effect.*

in the presence of three representatives of bb—that is, three doses of bb—the bristles are almost normal in size and shape. This finding demonstrates that bb functions in the same way as bb^+ does, but to a lesser degree. Mutants whose effect is similar but less than the normal gene's effect are called *hypomorphs*. Many point mutants are hypomorphs, since, in the absence of the normal gene, additional doses cause the phenotype to become more normal.

Of the remaining point mutants, most are *amorphs;* these produce no phenotypic effect even when present in extra dose. One example is the gene for white eye (w) in Drosophila.

Some mutants, *neomorphs,* produce a new effect—adding more doses of a neomorphic mutant causes more departure from normal, whereas adding more doses of the normal alternative has no effect.

The relationship between the normal, wild-type gene and its hypomorphic mutants is indicated diagrammatically in Figure 14–1.[2] The vertical axis represents phenotypic effect; the normal, wild-type effect is

[1] As shown by C. Stern.

[2] Adapted from H. J. Muller.

indicated by $+$. The horizontal axis refers to the dosage of either the normal gene or a hypomorphic mutant. Notice that a single $+$ gene itself produces almost the full normal phenotypic effect (and often the difference between its effect and the normal effect is not readily detected). Two $+$ genes reach the wild-type phenotypic level. In the case of the hypomorphic mutant, however, even three doses may not reach the phenotypic level produced by one $+$ gene (recall the discussion of *bb*). Note also that genetic modifiers or environmental factors, which can shift the position of the genes on the horizontal axis and thereby shift the phenotypic effect, have a decreasing influence as one proceeds from individuals carrying only one dose of mutant toward individuals carrying two $+$ genes. Natural selection would clearly favor alleles that result in phenotypic effects close to wild-type—that is, near the curve's plateau—for such alleles assure phenotypic stability. Any mutant which produced such a phenotypic effect would, in the course of time, become the normal gene in the population and would automatically be dominant when heterozygous with a hypomorphic gene alternative. This model illustrates how the heterozygote with one $+$ and one mutant gene has practically the same effect as the normal homozygote, and it seems to best explain most cases of complete or almost complete dominance. Since the normal gene alternative already produces a near-optimum phenotypic effect, this scheme also illustrates why, other things being equal, so few mutants are beneficial.

Although it is understandable from the preceding discussion that hypomorphic and amorphic mutants are usually detrimental when pure, one may still wonder what effects these mutants have when heterozygous with the normal gene. If the mutant is an amorph, the mutant heterozygote can fall short of producing the wild-type phenotypic effect and, therefore, such mutants are ex-

pected to be slightly detrimental when heterozygous. Hypomorphs are expected to be less or not at all detrimental when heterozygous, at least with respect to the trait for which they are classified as hypomorphic. But since each gene affects many different biochemical processes, a mutant hypomorphic in respect to one trait may be amorphic in respect to another. In Drosophila, for example, the normal allele *apr*$+$ which results in dull-red eye color also pigments the Malpighian tubules. One of its alleles, *apr*, causes a lighter eye color (being hypomorphic in this respect) but no color in the Malpighian tubules (being amorphic in this respect).

Experience confirms the expectation that most "recessive" lethal point mutants—these are lethal when homozygous—also have some detrimental effect on reproductive potential when heterozygous. Such mutants are not completely recessive, therefore, and when heterozygous in Drosophila cause death before adulthood in about two per cent of individuals. Usually mutants which are detrimental but not lethal when pure also show a detrimental effect when heterozygous; this effect is somewhat less than that produced by heterozygous recessive lethal point mutants. The principles of phenotypic action discussed here are expected to apply both to spontaneous and to induced point mutants.

Detection of Point Mutants in Drosophila

We have already mentioned the existence of genetic methods for collecting point mutants. Let us now consider in some detail one elegant procedure [3] employed in *Drosophila melanogaster* for this and other purposes.

The commonly-used technique for detecting recessive lethals is called *"Basc"* (see Figure 14–2) and was designed [4] to discover such mutants arising in the male germ line,

---

[3] Invented by H. J. Muller.
[4] To replace the old *"CIB"* method.

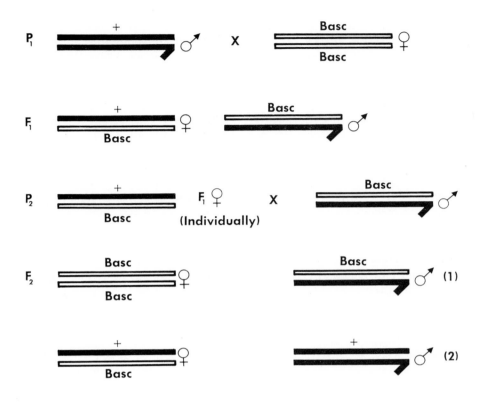

(1) is absent if the P_1 Basc chromosome contributed to the P_2 ♀ contained a recessive lethal

(2) is absent if the P_1 + chromosome contributed to the P_2 ♀ contained a recessive lethal

FIGURE 14–2. *The breeding scheme used in the Basc technique.*

in hemizygous X-chromosome loci, that is, X-loci without an allele in the Y chromosome. The males used are wild-type, having all normal characteristics including ovoid, dull-red compound eyes. The females have X chromosomes homozygous for Bar eye (*B*), for apricot eye color (*apr*), and for two paracentric *inversions* inside the left arm. The smaller inversion (*InS*) lies inside the larger inversion (*In sc*^{s1} *sc*^{s}, whose left point of breakage is designated *sc*^{s1} and right,

sc^{s}) which includes almost the entire left arm. "Basc" derives its name from *Bar, apricot, scute* inversion. Stock *Basc* females (or males) have narrow-Bar eyes of apricot color. The genotype of the *Basc* female is written

$$sc^{s1} \ B \ InS \ apr \ sc^{s}/sc^{s1} \ B \ InS \ apr \ sc^{s}$$

A wild-type male is mated with a *Basc* female and the F_1 daughters obtained are $+/sc^{s1} \ B \ InS \ apr \ sc^{s}$ and appear heterozygous (wide) Bar (and wild-type otherwise).

Since the very short right arm of the X is entirely heterochromatic, it is of no concern here. Because each F_1 female is heterozygous for two paracentric inversions, any crossing over between the left arms of her X's produces dicentric or acentric crossover strands which fail to enter the gametic nucleus (see Chapter 12). Accordingly, F_1 females produce eggs having an X that is, for our purposes, either completely maternal (sc^{S1} *B InS apr* sc^8) or completely paternal (+) in derivation. If this F_1 daughter mates with her *Basc* brothers, half of the sons in the next generation (F_2) receive the + maternal X, and half receive the *Basc* maternal X. So, if the progeny of a single F_1 female are examined, it is a simple matter to detect the presence of both types of sons among the more than 80 F_2 progeny usually produced. Note that each wild-type F_2 son carries an identical copy of the X which the mother (the F_1 female) received from her father (the P_1 male). Even when the sperm used to form the F_1 female carries an X-linked recessive lethal mutant, the F_1 female usually survives because she carries its + allele in her *Basc* chromosome. Each wild-type F_2 son, however, carries this mutant in hemizygous condition and usually dies before adulthood, so that no wild-type sons appear in F_2. It becomes clear, then, since an F_1 female is formed by fertilization with a wild-type X-carrying sperm, the absence of wild-type sons among her progeny is proof that the particular P_1 sperm carried a recessive lethal, X-linked mutant.

Such a lethal mutant must have occurred in the germ line after the fertilization that produced the P_1 male; he would not have survived had it been present at fertilization. It is unlikely that many of the X-linked lethals detected in sperm originate very early in development, for in this case a large portion of the somatic tissue would also carry the lethal and usually cause death before adulthood. Even when a few hundred sperm from one male are tested, only one is usually found to carry an X-linked recessive lethal mutant. This indicates that most X-linked lethals present in sperm involve only a very small portion of the germ line. Occasionally, however, the mutation occurs early enough in the germ line so that several sperm tested from the same male carry what proves to be the same recessive lethal.

When a thousand sperm from normal, untreated males are tested for X-linked recessive lethals by means of a thousand separate matings of F_1 females, approximately two of these matings are found to yield no wild-type sons. This X-linked recessive lethal mutation frequency of 0.2% is fairly typical in *D. melanogaster*. For every 1000 r of X rays to which the adult male is exposed, approximately 3.1% more sperm are found to carry X-linked recessive lethals (see Figure 13–3, for the similar frequency obtained after exposure to fast electrons).

When used as described, the Basc technique detects only those recessive lethals which kill before adulthood. Other recessive lethals that produce wild-type adult males which are sterile or die before they can mate are not detected. No recessive lethals are detected unless they are hemizygous in the F_2 male, as mentioned. Since a considerable number of X-linked mutants whose hemizygous lethality is prevented by genes normally present in the Y chromosome is known to occur, this group is missed because each F_2 male is normally provided with a Y chromosome. Suitable modifications of the Basc procedure can be made to detect this special kind of Y-suppressed recessive lethal. On the other hand, the advantages and applications of the Basc technique as described are numerous.

For example, the presence or absence of wild-type males in F_2 is easily and objectively determined. Since the recessive lethal detected in F_2 is also carried by the heterozygous-Bar F_2 females, further study of the recessive lethal is possible in F_2 and subsequent generations. Such studies reveal that certain lethals are associated with intergenic changes; lethals not associated with intergenic changes are designated as recessive lethal point mutants. The Basc technique can also be used to detect recessive lethals that occur in a P_1 *Basc* chromosome, the absence of *Basc* males among the F_2 progeny indicating such a mutation. Moreover, if the environmental conditions are standardized, it becomes possible to detect hemizygous mutants which either lower the viability of the F_2 males without being lethal or raise their viability above normal. The opportunity for studying the viability effects of recessive lethals in heterozygous condition is also provided by this technique.

Although the Basc technique can also be used to detect X-linked mutants producing a visible morphological change when hemizygous, all those *"visibles"* which are also hemizygous lethals are missed. The *"Maxy" technique* [5] overcomes this difficulty. In this method, the tested female has fifteen X-linked recessive point mutants on one homolog and their normal alleles on the other.

[5] See H. J. Muller (1954).

Suitable paracentric inversions maintain the identity of these chromosomes in successive generations. Mutants are detected when such females show one or more of the recessive traits. Maxy detects, therefore, any mutation involving the normal alleles of the fifteen recessives, provided that the mutant does not produce the normal phenotype when heterozygous with the recessive allele and is not a dominant lethal. Once such mutants are obtained, they can be screened for point mutants.

The study of recessive lethals in the X chromosome and in the autosomes shows that there are hundreds of loci whose point mutations may be recessively lethal. It should be noted that the recessive lethals detected by Basc and the visibles detected by Maxy are not mutually exclusive types of mutants, for some Maxy-detected visibles are lethal when hemizygous, and about ten per cent of Basc-detected hemizygous lethals show some morphological effect when heterozygous. It can be stated, in general, that any mutant in homo- or hemizygous condition which is a "visible" will produce some change in viability, and, conversely, that any mutant which affects viability will produce a "visible" effect, "visible" at least at the biochemical level.

SUMMARY AND CONCLUSIONS

The mutational units of a genotype are, in order of size: the genome; the chromosome; chromosomal segments involving more than one gene; and the gene. Since a recombinational gene can have multiple alleles, gene mutation may involve the entire recombinational unit or one or more mutational sites within it. Although the genes delimited operationally by recombination and by mutation may not be materially equivalent, we shall continue to assume that this is so until we have evidence to the contrary.

The occurrence of gene mutation is not limited by any ploidy, type of cell or gene, or effect it can have on synapsis. It is limited with respect to the effect it can have on gene polarity. Tripolar genes are excluded, bipolarity being the usual and unipolarity the less usual alternative.

Point mutations are the remainder of all mutations not identifiable as intergenic changes. Since point mutants include gene mutants, the former can be studied to reveal the mutational characteristics of the gene. The frequency of point mutants increases linearly with the dose of high-energy radiations; there is no effect from dose

H. J. MULLER, *at Cold Spring Harbor, N.Y., 1941.*

protraction and no threshold dose below which the genetic material is safe from change. Point mutations also indicate that a given gene is relatively stable over many cell generations—changes in genes resulting from very localized physico-chemical events lasting a matter of minutes, after which the new gene is stable. Point mutations are enhanced or induced by temperature changes, aging, gene replication, and physical and chemical mutagens. It is possible that changes resulting in point mutants take place in the old gene, in the new gene, or during the formation of the new gene.

Genetic schemes for the detection of X-linked recessive lethal and recessive visible mutants in Drosophila are described. A single representative of most normal genes fails to produce the full normal phenotypic effect, and most point mutants act on the phenotype in a hypomorphic or amorphic manner. The study of point mutants of these and other types reveals that almost all are detrimental to the reproductive potential of individuals when pure (not hybrid), and to a lesser extent when hybrid. Accordingly, most point mutants are not completely recessive to their normal genetic alternatives.

REFERENCES

Alexander, P., "Radiation-Imitating Chemicals," Scient. Amer., 202, No. 1:99–108, 1960.

Crow, J. F., and Temin, R. G., "Evidence for Partial Dominance of Recessive Lethal Genes in Natural Populations of Drosophila," Amer. Nat., 98:21–33, 1964.

Muller, H. J., "Variation Due to Change in the Individual Gene," Amer. Nat., 56:32–50, 1922. Reprinted in *Classic Papers in Genetics,* Peters, J. A. (Ed.), Englewood Cliffs, N.J.: Prentice-Hall, 1959, pp. 104–116.

Muller, H. J., "Artificial Transmutation of the Gene," Science, 66:84–87, 1927. Reprinted in *Classic Papers in Genetics,* Peters, J. A. (Ed.), Englewood Cliffs, N.J.: Prentice-Hall, 1959, pp. 149–155, and also in *Great Experiments in Biology,* Gabriel, M. L., and S. Fogel (Eds.), Englewood Cliffs, N.J.: Prentice-Hall, 1955, pp. 260–266.

Muller, H. J., "A Semi-automatic Breeding System ('Maxy') for Finding Sex-linked Mutations at Specific 'Visible' Loci," Drosophila Info. Serv., 28:140–141, 1954.

Muller, H. J., "The Nature of the Genetic Effects Produced by Radiation," in *Radiation Biology,* Hollaender, A. (Ed.), Vol. 1, Chap. 7:351–473, New York: McGraw-Hill, 1954.

Muller, H. J., and Oster, I. I., "Some Mutational Techniques in *Drosophila,*" pp. 249–278, in *Methodology in Basic Genetics,* Burdette, W. J. (Ed.), San Francisco: Holden-Day, 1963.

Schalet, A., "A Study of Spontaneous Visible Mutations in Drosophila Melanogaster," Proc. X Intern. Congr., Genetics, Montreal, 2:252 (Abstr.), 1958.

See Supplement III.

QUESTIONS FOR DISCUSSION

14.1. Is there a safe dose of X rays and/or ultraviolet radiation; that is, a dose that cannot produce some point mutations? Explain.

14.2. Can we be sure that any given mutation involves a single gene change rather than intergenic one? Explain.

14.3. Would we know of the existence of genes if all genes had identical mutational capacity? Explain.

14.4. Would you expect the mutation rate to polydactyly, *P,* from normal, *p,* to be greater among normal individuals in a pedigree for polydactyly than it is among normals in general? Explain. How might you test your hypothesis?

14.5. Do the mutational properties discussed suggest any limitations with respect to the chemical composition of genes? Explain.

14.6. When a chromosome is broken, is the breaking point within a gene, between genes, or both? Justify your answer.

14.7. Point mutations are sometimes called gene mutations. Do you think this is permissible? Why?

14.8. In what way is the study of mutation dependent upon genes? In what way is the reverse true?

14.9. What is your opinion regarding the validity of applying principles of point mutation directly to gene mutation?

14.10. Are all of the mutants detected by the Basc or Maxy techniques point mutants? Explain.

14.11. Suppose, in the Basc technique, an F_2 culture produced both of the expected types of daughters but no sons at all. To what would you attribute this result?

14.12. How can you determine whether a recessive lethal detected in the F_2 by the Basc technique is associated with an inversion or a reciprocal translocation?

14.13. A wild-type female produces 110 daughters but only 51 sons. How can you test whether this result is due to the presence, in heterozygous condition, of a recessive X-linked lethal?

14.14. How can you explain the phenotype of a rare female in the Maxy stock that produces only unexceptional progeny but has compound eyes distinctly lighter than normal?

14.15. Compare the relative suitability of man and Drosophila for the determination of mutation frequencies.

14.16. The genes in the X chromosomes are incompletely linked in the females of the Basc stock. Do you agree with this statement? Why?

Chapter 15

THE GENE POOL;
EQUILIBRIUM FACTORS

THE recombinational and mutational properties of the genetic material have been studied in cross-fertilizing individuals and the nature and phenotypic consequences of various genetic units have been described in terms of the traits found in such individuals and their relatives. Cross-fertilizing individuals are members of a general population. In a general population, each individual usually has an opportunity to choose a mate from a large number of the other members. The gametes of all mating individuals furnish a pool of genes, or *gene pool,* from which the genes of the next generation are drawn. Over successive generations what happens to the frequency of a particular gene in the gene pool? Let us construct a gene pool and investigate this question.

Suppose that Mars is colonized by human beings, that the population sent there is sufficiently large, and that—with respect to eye color genes—only the B (brown) allele and the completely recessive b (blue) allele are present in the gene pool in the frequencies .2 B and .8 b. Presuming that marriages are not influenced by eye color phenotype, what genotypes and phenotypes will the F_1 have? The answer can be seen in Figure 15–1. As the result of the random union of gametes, 4% of these children are BB; 32% are Bb; and 64%, bb. Phenotypically, the F_1 population is composed of 36% brown- and 64% blue-eyed people.

In the absence of mutation, what is the

201

gene pool in the gametes of the F_1? The 4% of F_1 BB individuals furnish 4% of all gametes, and these carry B. The 32% of F_1 Bb individuals furnish 32% of all gametes of which half (16%) carry B and the other half b. Therefore, the total gene pool contains 20% gametes with B. The b gametes comprise 80% of the gene pool (16% from the 32% of Bb heterozygotes and 64% from the 64% of bb individuals). Note that the gene pool of the F_1 is identical to that of the P_1. Therefore, in the F_2 and all subsequent generations, the same genotypic and phenotypic ratios are found, because the frequencies of B and b in the gene pool remain constant.

What would be the consequence if, instead of starting the Martian colony with a gene pool of 20% B and 80% b, some other proportion were used? We can generalize

FEMALE GAMETES

	.2 B	.8 b
.2 B	.04 BB Brown Eyes	.16 Bb Brown Eyes
.8 b	.16 Bb Brown Eyes	.64 bb Blue Eyes

MALE GAMETES

The F_1 Population

.04 Brown (BB) + .32 Brown (Bb) + .64 Blue (bb)

The F_1 Gene Pool

B = .04 + .16 = .2
b = .16 + .64 = .8

FIGURE 15–1. F_1 *genotypes and the gene pool these produce.*

$$(p + q)^2 = p^2 + 2pq + q^2 = 1$$

EGGS

	p B (Brown)	q b (Blue)
p B (Brown)	p^2 BB (Brown Eyes)	p q Bb (Brown Eyes)
q b (Blue)	p q Bb (Brown Eyes)	q^2 bb (Blue Eyes)

SPERMS

FIGURE 15–2. *The types and frequencies of genotypes produced by a gene pool composed of p B and q b.*

the analysis by letting p equal the fraction of male and female gametes in the population which carries *B*, and q equal the fraction which carries *b*. Naturally, for eggs, p + q = 1, as is also true for sperm. These sex cells combine at random to produce the result shown in Figure 15–2. The offspring population, then, is

$$p^2 \, BB + 2 \, pq \, Bb + q^2 \, bb$$

The fraction of brown-eyed individuals is $p^2 + 2 \, pq$, whereas q^2 is the blue-eyed fraction. The frequency of *B* and *b* among the gametes produced by the offspring population is:

$$B = p^2 + pq = p(p + q) = p$$
$$b = q^2 + pq = q(q + p) = q$$

Thus the gene frequencies have remained the same as they were in the gametes of the previous generation, and all future generations will have the same gene pool and the same relative frequencies of diploid genotypes. The formula

$$p^2 \, BB + 2 \, pq \, Bb + q^2 \, bb$$

describes the genotypic equilibrium produced by a static gene pool.[1]

[1] This is called the *Hardy-Weinberg equilibrium principle.*

It should be noted that this equilibrium principle is independent of the occurrence of dominance. Moreover, the *B* and *b* in the formula can represent any two alleles whose frequency in the gene pool is known, even if the sum of their frequencies is less than one, as in cases of multiple allelism.

If this equilibrium principle applied indefinitely, gene frequencies would remain unchanged, and the evolution of different genotypes and their resultant new phenotypes would not occur. In the Martian model described, certain conditions had to be fulfilled in order to maintain a genetic equilibrium. One condition was met by barring *mutation,* for if it were permitted, obviously the frequency of the two alleles, *B* and *b,* in the population would have been reduced, and the equilibrium upset. The frequency of any allele would also have been changed if the mutation rates to and from it were different. In either or both types of events, the genetic equilibrium is shifted until a new one is attained. Thereafter, the new equilibrium is maintained until some new factor acts on mutation rate in a directional way.

Our model also assumed that the *reproductive potential (biological fitness,* or *adaptive value)* was the same regardless of the genotype for eye color. But it is possible, under certain conditions, that persons with blue (or with brown) eyes are preferred as mates, in which case the reproductive potential of an individual is not independent of the alleles under consideration. Accordingly, if individuals with a certain genetic endowment produce more surviving offspring than those produced by a different genetic endowment, the genes which transfer this higher biological fitness tend to increase their frequency in the population, whereas those genes with lower fitness tend to decrease it. In this way *selection,* by operating on genotypes of different adaptive value, causes changes in gene frequencies and shifts in the genotypic frequencies found at equilibrium.

The Martian population was also presumed to be large. Suppose, however, that the Martian population (whose gene pool is $.2B$ and $.8b$) ran short of food, and only one couple, determined by chance, could have children. The chance that this husband and wife would be blue-eyed is $.64 \times .64$, or about $.41$. Accordingly, there is a 41% chance that the gene pool will drift at random in this particular manner, producing the new gene frequencies of 1.0 for b and 0 for B. This *random genetic drift* can also be illustrated in a less extreme situation: If a population is very large, and a certain family happens to produce a relatively large number of children for several generations, then the proportion of all individuals in the population with this family name is still very small. But if the population decreases while this family's reproductive rate is unchanged, the proportion of the population with this surname increases. Accordingly, when populations are very large, oscillations in the number of children produced by different genotypes occurring by chance are unimportant, for they do not change the gene pool. In small populations, however, such chance oscillations can change gene frequencies via random genetic drift.

In our Martian model, the possibility that the colony would have emigrants or immigrants was not considered. If the emigrants' gene frequencies are different from those remaining in the population gene pool, then the gene frequencies in the remaining population will be changed. If the immigrants' gene frequency is different from the natives', and they interbreed, the gene pool will again be changed. In this way *migration* can shift the genetic equilibrium.

We see then that a cross-fertilizing population remains static—in genetic equilib-rium—in the absence of mutation, selection, random genetic drift, and differential migration. The occurrence of one or another or all of these factors changes the frequencies of genes in the gene pool and thereby shifts the frequencies of genotypes at equilibrium. Different species possess different gene pools, and it is natural to presume that they are different species because of their different gene pools. Accordingly, the factors which change gene frequencies are considered to be the main causes of species formation. Insofar as the formation of higher taxonomic categories is, like speciation, based upon change in gene pools, the principal causes of biological evolution are:

1. Mutation (which supplies the raw materials)
2. Selection (which shapes these raw materials into the biologically fit genotypes of races and species)
3. Random genetic drift (which can produce rapid changes in gene frequency in small populations)
4. Differential migration (which can shift gene frequencies via interchange of individuals between populations).

* Selection of Genotypes

The disequilibrating effect of selection upon the gene pool has already been noted. Selection acts at the phenotypic level to conserve in the population those genotypes which provide the greatest reproductive potential. Selection takes place at all stages in the life cycle of an individual. Since it acts to preserve whole phenotypes and not single traits, selection conserves genotypes and not single genes. Sometimes selection acts upon the phenotypes produced by single genomes in haploid species or stages; at other times— in sexually reproducing organisms—it acts upon the combined phenotypic effect of two genomes. It should be noted that what is a relatively adaptive genotype at one stage of the life cycle may be relatively ill-adaptive at another whether or not these stages have the same or different ploidies. It is, of course, the total adaptiveness of all these separate features which determines the overall reproductive potential of an individual. Finally, it should be noted that in cross-fertilizing populations, selection favors genotypes which produce maximal fitness of the population as a whole. Because selection acts this way, it is possible that some portion of the population receives genotypes which are decidedly not advantageous. If this is so, the same genetic components are expected to be advantageous when present in other, more probable, combinations.

* Selection Against Mutants

Since the human being is primarily a diploid, it is upon the diploid-produced phenotype that selection principally operates. If one asks, "What is the fate of mutants in the gene pool?" the answer must include knowledge of the frequency with which the mutants arise as well as their effects upon reproductive potential in a diploid genotype. Remember that the phenotypic effect of a mutant gene depends not only upon the nature of its allele but also upon its relationship to the rest of the genotype.

Let us consider, in turn, the fate in the human gene pool of mutants whose overall phenotypic effect is: dominant lethal; dominant detrimental; recessive lethal; or recessive detrimental, as influenced by selection and mutation.

Dominant lethal mutants are lethal when heterozygous and are eliminated from the gene pool the same generation they arise. Accordingly, the biological fitness of such mutants is zero. If the normal homozygote (A_1A_1) is considered to have a selective disadvantage of zero, then the dominant lethal is at a complete selective disadvantage, and the *selection coefficient*, *s*, is one. We can readily see that the *mutation frequency*,

u, of this dominant lethal condition must equal one half the frequency of affected individuals (A_1A_2), since each affected individual has one mutant and one normal gene. In the absence of special medical treatment, *retinoblastoma,* a type of cancer of the eye, is an example of such a dominant lethal in man.

Achondroplastic (or *chondrodystrophic*) *dwarfism* is characterized by disproportion —normal head and trunk size but shortened arms and legs. This rare, fully penetrant (see p. 73) disease is attributed to the presence of a gene in heterozygous condition which therefore acts as a dominant detrimental mutant. Such dwarfs (A_1A_2) are known to produce only 20 per cent as many children as normal people. Because of this lower reproductive potential the A_1A_2 genotype selection coefficient is .8.

In one study the frequency of A_1A_2 in the population was found to be 10 dwarf babies in 94,075 births. The dwarf children in this sample must have resulted from normal parents who carried new mutations to A_2 or from one normal and one dwarf parent. The gene frequency, p, of A_2 in the population, therefore, must be 10 per 2(94,075) or .000053. From the incidence of dwarfs known to have normal parents the mutation frequency, u, to A_2 is .000042. If the value s = .8 is correct, then p = u/s, or .000042/.8, or .0000525, which is in excellent agreement with the gene frequency (p) value observed. Gene frequency for a dominant lethal equals mutation frequency (p = u) because s = 1; however, in the present case s is less than one, so the gene frequency is greater than the mutation frequency. Actually the gene frequency for dwarfism is not very much larger than the mutation frequency, demonstrating the efficiency of natural selection in eliminating such mutants from the gene pool.

The gene for *juvenile amaurotic idiocy* (a_2) has no apparent effect when heterozygous (A_1a_2); since homozygous children die, a_2 is a recessive lethal mutant. Affected individuals are found with a frequency of one per 100,000, or .00001. What is the frequency of a_2 in the gene pool? As shown in Figure 15–3, the frequency of a_2a_2 individuals at equilibrium is equal to q^2. Accordingly, the frequency of a_2 (q) must be equal to $\sqrt{q^2}$, or $\sqrt{.00001}$, or about .003, whereas the frequency of A_1 must be one minus .003, or .997. Note that heterozygotes (*carriers*) are 600 times more frequent than afflicted homozygotes. What is the mutation frequency from A_1 to a_2? Assume that the gene pool is at equilibrium; in other words, the frequency with which a_2 enters the population by mutation equals the frequency with which it leaves the population in a_2a_2 homozygotes. Accordingly, the mutation frequency to a_2 must be .00001. The selection coefficient for normal individuals (A_1A_1 and A_1a_2) is zero, and for a_2a_2 it is one. We see, therefore, that at equilibrium the frequency of a recessive

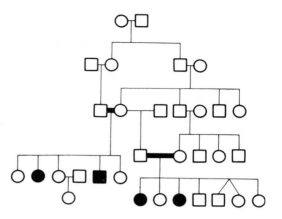

FIGURE 15–4. *Pedigree showing the occurrence of phenylketonuria among the offspring of cousin marriages (denoted by thick marriage lines).*

mutant in the gene pool can be expressed as $q = \sqrt{u/s}$, where $s = 1$ for a recessive lethal. When the homozygous recessive mutant is detrimental without being lethal, s becomes less than one (but more than zero) and the frequency of the mutant in the gene pool increases. Thus, if s were $\frac{1}{4}$ instead of one, q would be twice as large.

* Nonrandom Matings

In deriving the types and frequencies of genotypes in a population at equilibrium, we assumed that marriages were random with respect to the genotypically-determined trait under consideration. Such a randomly-mating population is said to be panmictic or to undergo *panmixis*. What happens if the different genotypes do not marry at random? Consider the disease *phenylketonuria* (Figure 15–4) which involves a type of feeblemindedness in individuals who are homozygous for a recessive gene, and who metabolize the amino acid phenylalanine to phenylpyruvic acid, which is toxic. The frequency in the gene pool of the normal gene (A) is .99 and of the abnormal gene

GENOTYPE	$A_1 A_1$	$A_1 a_2$	$a_2 a_2$
PHENOTYPE	Normal	Normal	Dies
FREQUENCY AT EQUILIBRIUM	p^2	$2pq$	q^2

u = Mutation rate from $A_1 \longrightarrow a_2$

$q = \sqrt{u/s}$ Here s = 1, hence $q = \sqrt{u}$

$u = 10^{-5} = 0.000,01$ Hence $q = \sqrt{0.000,01} = 0.003$

ACTUAL FREQUENCY AT EQUILIBRIUM	(p^2)	$(2pq)$	(q^2)
	$(0.997)^2$	$2(0.997)(0.003)$	$(.003)^2$
	0.994	0.006	0.000,01

FIGURE 15–3. *Juvenile amaurotic idiocy. (See text for explanation.)*

(*a*) is .01. In the population at equilibrium, therefore, $AA:Aa:aa$ individuals have frequencies of $9801/10,000:198/10,000:1/10,000$, respectively. Notice that Aa individuals are 198 times more frequent than aa, so that even if *every* aa did not reproduce, only one per cent of the a genes present in the gene pool would be eliminated each generation. This fact illustrates the inefficiency of selection against homozygotes for rare recessive genes, at least insofar as lowering the frequency of such genes is concerned. AA and Aa individuals apparently marry at random but feebleminded people do not. So panmixis does not occur with respect to this trait, and persons with different genotypes tend to be restricted in their marriages—all the available marriage partners making up a person's *reproductive isolate*. The occurrence of different reproductive isolates for normals and phenylketonurics has little effect on the relative frequencies of different genotypes in successive generations, because aa people have so few of all the a genes present in the population. Clearly, only marriages between two Aa individuals are of consequence, since those are the major source of aa offspring.

The example of phenylketonuria shows that when a gene is rare and apparently completely recessive, nonrandom marriage has little influence either upon gene frequency or the diploid (heterozygous or homozygous) genotypes in which it is found in the population. When the mutant is relatively frequent in the population, however, it is obvious that nonrandom marriages raise the frequencies of certain diploid genotypes and lower others. Moreover, if there are adaptive differences for the different genotypes, the composition of the gene pool can be changed in a different direction or at a different frequency than would be predicted for a population mating at random.

Consider two ways in which mating can be nonrandom. The first involves the tendency of phenotypically similar individuals (except for sex) to mate and is referred to as *assortive mating*. This kind of breeding pattern is generally true in animals including human beings. The genetic result is the production of more homozygotes than would occur by randomly-chosen matings.

The second departure from random mating involves *inbreeding,* the tendency for mates to be more closely related in descent than randomly chosen mates. What is the effect of inbreeding carried out for a single generation? This can be determined by studying what happens to genes that are heterozygous in the parent generation. There are various degrees of inbreeding, the closest form being *self-fertilization*. In self-fertilization the heterozygote for a given pair of genes, Aa, produces progeny of which one half are homozygous. In general, the decrease in heterozygosity because of self-fertilization can be expressed as follows: the chance that an offspring receives a given gene in the male gamete is $\frac{1}{2}$, and the chance that it receives the same allele in the female gamete is $\frac{1}{2}$; the chance that the offspring is a homozygote for that allele, therefore, is $\frac{1}{4}$. But there is an equal chance that the offspring becomes homozygous for the other allele, so that the total chance for homozygosis from this type of inbreeding is 50%. If all members of the population are heterozygotes and self-fertilize, then in each successive generation, half of the genes that were heterozygous become homozygous.

Suppose, on the other hand, that a portion of a population mating at random has X% homozygous individuals. These could come from matings between two heterozygotes, two homozygotes, or a heterozygote and a homozygote. If the gene pool is at equilibrium, the random matings that tend to increase homozygosis are counterbalanced by others which decrease it, so that X% homozygosis remains constant generation after generation. Consider what happens in another portion of this population which happens to practice self-fertilization for one generation. Since this segment of the population already shows X% homozygosis, its offspring will also have X% homozygosis. But, if this segment is Z% heterozygous, after self-fertilization the offspring will have only $\frac{1}{2}$ Z% heterozygosis, and, therefore, will show a total homozygosis of X% + $\frac{1}{2}$ Z%. In other words, each generation of self-fertilization makes half of all heterozygous genes homozygous, and, in a normally random-mating population, the effect of self-fertilization is to increase the random-mating frequency of homozygosis by $\frac{1}{2}$ the frequency of heterozygosis.

How much is homozygosity increased in *brother-sister (sib) matings*? The chance that a particular gene in the father is present in the male sib is $\frac{1}{2}$, and the chance that the male sib's child receives this is similarly $\frac{1}{2}$; the chance for the occurrence of both events is $\frac{1}{4}$. The chance that the female sib receives and transmits this same gene to her child is also $\frac{1}{4}$. Therefore, the chance that the child of the sib mating receives two representatives of this same allele is $\frac{1}{4}$ times $\frac{1}{4}$, or it has $\frac{1}{16}$ chance of being homozygous for this gene. Since the child has an equal chance to become a homozygote for the other allele in his grandfather and for each of the two alleles in his grandmother, this gives him 4 times $\frac{1}{16}$ or a 25% chance of homozygosis. In other words, sib matings cause $\frac{1}{4}$ of the heterozygous genes to become homozygous. This chance of homozygosis from sib mating is in addition to the chance of homozygosis from mating at random.

Matings between individuals who have one parent in common are called *half-sib matings*. In this case, the frequency with which a given allele in the common parent passes to the male half-sib is $\frac{1}{2}$, and the frequency with which an offspring of this sib receives this allele is $\frac{1}{2}$; the chance of both events occurring is, therefore, $\frac{1}{4}$. The chance is also $\frac{1}{4}$ for these events to occur through the female half-sib, so that the chance of a given allele becoming homozygous from a half-sib mating is $\frac{1}{4}$ times $\frac{1}{4}$, or $\frac{1}{16}$. Since the other allele in the common parent could, in this way, also become homozygous $\frac{1}{16}$ of the time, the combined additional chance of homozygosity for half-sib matings is $\frac{1}{8}$, or, in other words, $\frac{1}{8}$ of the heterozygous genes become homozygous because of this type of inbreeding.

The amount by which heterozygosity is reduced because of inbreeding is called the *inbreeding coefficient, F*. In a similar manner we can determine that in the case of *cousin marriage*, F is $\frac{1}{16}$. The values of F for more complicated pedigrees can be worked out accordingly.

All forms of inbreeding increase homozygosity. Let us calculate the consequence of cousin marriage upon the frequency of phenylketonuria. Its frequency of heterozygotes per 10,000 people is 198 (see p. 206). Cousin marriage reduces heterozygosity by $\frac{1}{16}$, or by twelve individuals, of which half of them are expected to be normal (*AA*) and half affected (*aa*). Since random mating produces one affected individual per 10,000, cousin marriages bring the total number of affected homozygotes in this population to seven (six from inbreeding, one from random breeding). Accordingly, there is a sevenfold greater chance for phenylketonuric children from cousin marriages than from marriages between unrelated parents.

Another example of how cousin marriages increase the risk of defect comes from a study which found that in a Japanese population (Figure 15–5) congenital malformations, stillbirths, and infant deaths were 24 to 48 per cent higher when cousins married than when parents were unrelated. Since, in some cases, defects such as these are known to be due to recessive genes in homozygous condition, these results support the view that homozygosis resulting from inbreeding can produce detrimental effects. Although inbreeding produces homozygosis and homozygosis can lead to the appearance of defects, it must not be inferred that inbreeding is disadvantageous under all circumstances. Many individuals do become homozygous for detrimental genes as a result of inbreeding, but just as many become homozygous for the normal alleles. The success of self-fertilizing species is testimony to the advantage of homozygosity at least for some types of organisms.

* Heterosis

In normally cross-fertilizing species, however, inbreeding usually results in a loss of vigor which is directly linked to homozygosis. What is the functional basis for the adaptive superiority of heterozygotes, usually known as *heterosis* or *hybrid vigor?* Consider the three genotypic alternatives, AA, AA', $A'A'$ relative to their phenotypic effects. Suppose $A'A'$ is less vigorous than AA. Whether A is completely or incompletely dominant to A' or shows no dominance to it, the AA' heterozygote will be superior to one of the homozygotes. It is also possible that the heterozygote has a greater adaptive value than either type of homozygote. To illustrate this possibility, imagine that A is pleiotropic, having a relatively great adaptive effect with respect to trait X but a relatively less adaptive effect with respect to trait Y, whereas the reverse is true of A', namely, relatively less adaptive for X and relatively more adaptive for Y. In the event of no dominance, the heterozygote is superior to either homozygote. Heterosis can be produced, therefore, when the heterozygote is superior to either one or both homozygotes.

The first type of heterotic effect can be demonstrated by crossing two pure lines, homozygous for different detrimental recessives ($AA\,bb\,CC\,dd$ by $aa\,bb\,CC\,DD$). The F_1 ($Aa\,bb\,CC\,Dd$) is uniform yet more vigorous (having normal alleles at three loci) than either parent (each of which had normal alleles at two loci) because the dominant alleles hide the detrimental effects of the recessive ones. In this case the heterozygous F_2 progeny carrying $Aa\,bb\,CC\,Dd$ are no more adaptive than the homozygotes, $AA\,bb\,CC\,DD$.

	Frequency from Unrelated Parents	Increase in Frequency with Cousin Marriage	Per cent Increase
CONGENITAL MALFORMATION	.011	.005	48
STILLBIRTHS	.025	.006	24
INFANT DEATHS	.023	.008	34

FIGURE 15–5. *Increased risk of genetic defect with cousin marriages.* (*Data from Hiroshima and Nagasaki.*)

The second type of heterotic effect can be illustrated in human beings. As mentioned on p. 71, homozygotes for the gene for *sickle cell anemia* ($\beta^s\beta^s$) usually die from anemia before adolescence. $\beta^A\beta^A$ individuals have normal blood type, whereas $\beta^A\beta^s$ individuals are either normal or have a slight anemia. In certain countries the frequency of β^s in the gene pool follows the expectation for a recessive lethal gene. In other countries, however, β^s is more frequent than expected. This difference is attributable to the $\beta^A\beta^s$ heterozygote being more resistant to certain kinds of malaria than the $\beta^A\beta^A$ homozygote. Of course, in nonmalarial countries, β^s confers no antimalarial advantage, and so the fitness of the heterozygote $(1 - s)$ is lower than that of the normal homozygote (1), whereas the $\beta^s\beta^s$ individual has a fitness of zero. As expected, therefore, sickle cell anemia is rare or absent in most of the world where certain forms of malaria are absent.

On the other hand, in certain malarial countries, even though heterozygotes may be slightly anemic, the advantage of being resistant to malaria produces a greater overall fitness than does the $\beta^A\beta^A$ genotype. Here the fitness of the heterozygote, $\beta^A\beta^s$, is maximal and therefore must be assigned the value one, whereas that of the normal homozygote, $\beta^A\beta^A$, is one minus s_1. Mutant homozygotes, $\beta^s\beta^s$, have a fitness of one minus s_2, where s_2 equals one, since all $\beta^s\beta^s$ die (even if extremely resistant to malaria). In this situation natural selection maintains both β^A and β^s in the gene pool, β^s having a frequency equal to $\dfrac{s_1}{s_1 + s_2}$. This fraction can be read as "the advantage of β^s (as shown by the advantage of $\beta^A\beta^s$ over $\beta^A\beta^A$) divided by the total disadvantage of β^A and β^s." Thus, when the heterozygote, being more adaptive than either homozygote, shows heterosis in this way, natural selection

maintains a gene such as β^s in the gene pool even though it is lethal when homozygous.

Although we have discussed heterosis in terms of the phenotypic effects of the members of a pair of alleles, it should not be inferred that the unit of heterotic action is always a single pair of genes. Since we know that different pairs of genes interact in various ways to produce phenotypes, it would not be surprising to find that heterosis results from the effects of combinations of nonalleles and alleles.

Natural populations of *Drosophila pseudoobscura* contain various paracentric inversions. Laboratory populations can be started with some individuals carrying the normal chromosome arrangement and others, a particular one of these inversions. After a number of generations has passed, in some cases the population comes to contain only normal chromosomes, because the inversion chromosome behaves like a detrimental gene which provides no advantage when heterozygous and is eliminated from the gene pool. When other particular inversions are tested this way, however, an equilibrium is reached —both the normal and inverted chromosomes are retained in the gene pool. In these cases, the inversion heterozygote is adaptively superior to either homozygote, showing heterosis just as the gene for sickling in malarial countries. It is difficult to decide the genetic basis for heterosis in such cases, however, since the hybrid vigor could be due to: the genes gained or lost at the time the inversion was initially produced; or the new arrangement of the inverted genes; or the types of genes or groups of genes contained within the inversion. Recall that individuals with paracentric inversions are not at a reproductive disadvantage in Drosophila and suppose a heterotic system exists or develops in Drosophila heterozygous for a paracentric inversion. If the heterosis is due to the action of several specific nonalleles

FIGURE 15–6. *The variability of normal corn is pointed out by* JAMES F. CROW. (*Photographed in 1959 by The Calvin Company.*)

within the inverted region, this adaptively favorable gene content tends to remain intact in the heterozygote because of the failure of single crossovers within the inverted region to enter the haploid egg nucleus.

Breeding procedures that result in hybrid vigor have been widely applied to economically important plants and animals. For example, it has been estimated that the use of hybrid corn has enriched society by more than a billion dollars. We might ask: What is wrong with normal corn? The answer is that it is too variable in quality and vigor (Figure 15–6). Inbreeding decreases variability, but unfortunately inbreeding also results in loss of vigor or other desirable traits. The way to overcome this problem

is to obtain inbred lines which are uniform (because they are homozygous) and carry different favorable dominant genes (yet are also homozygous for various undesirable recessive genes), and cross the different inbred lines to each other. Their F_1 will be multiply-heterozygous, uniform, and more vigorous than either parental inbred line.

Consequently, hybrids are made from two selected inbred lines—of corn in this case. Although the F_1 plants are vigorous and uniform, they come from kernels grown on one of the less vigorous inbred lines. For this reason, hybrid seeds are not sufficiently numerous, and consequently, commercially unfeasible. In practice this difficulty is overcome (Figure 15–7) by crossing four se-

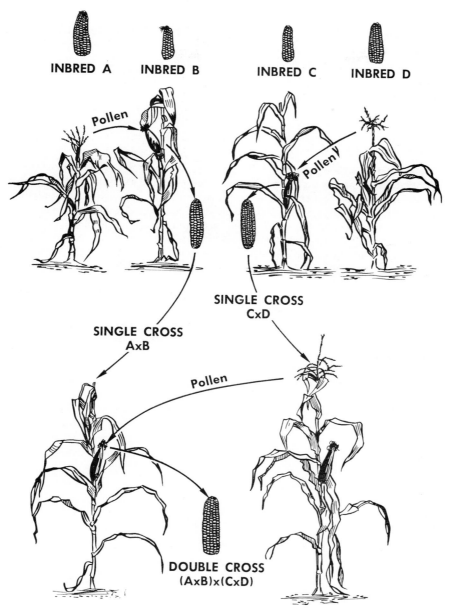

INBRED A   INBRED B   INBRED C   INBRED D

Pollen

Pollen

SINGLE CROSS
CxD

SINGLE CROSS
AxB

Pollen

DOUBLE CROSS
(AxB)x(CxD)

FIGURE 15–7. *The production of commercial hybrid corn by the "double cross" breeding procedure.*

lected inbred lines two by two and obtaining two different *single cross hybrids*. The two single cross hybrids are then crossed to each other. Since they are formed on a vigorous single cross hybrid plant, seeds produced by this *double cross* are plentiful and can be sold inexpensively. Heterosis is of great practical importance; a fuller understanding of this phenomenon requires investigation at the biochemical, molecular level.[2]

[2] See I. V. Sarkissian, M. A. Kessinger, and W. Harris (1964).

SUMMARY AND CONCLUSIONS

The gametes, whose function is to produce the next generation in a cross-fertilizing population, comprise a gene pool. The gene pool and the relative frequencies of genotypes in successive generations will remain forever unchanged if: the population (gene pool) size is so large that genetic drift does not occur; mutation does not favor any direction preferentially; no differential selection is made for genotypes; and migrants are genotypically just like the natives. If, however, any of these conditions is not satisfied, a shift in the composition of the gene pool will occur; in other words, gene frequencies will change and so will the frequencies of different genotypes until a new equilibrium is attained.

It is suggested that not only species formation but all of biological evolution is based upon changes in the gene pool.

The roles that mutation and selection have in establishing a genetic equilibrium is discussed for those rare mutants which lower reproductive fitness by being dominant lethal, dominant detrimental, recessive lethal, or recessive detrimental.

Nonrandom breeding resulting from assortive mating or inbreeding increases the frequency of homozygotes. The per generation rate of reduction in heterozygosity due to inbreeding is ½ for self-fertilization, ¼ for sib matings, ⅛ for half-sib matings, and ¹⁄₁₆ for cousin matings. Homozygosis in normally cross-fertilizing individuals leads to loss of vigor, whereas heterozygosis is accompanied by heterosis, or hybrid vigor.

Heterosis, which occurs as a phenotypic result of gene interaction because the heterozygote is adaptively superior to one or to both types of homozygote, is of great importance economically.

REFERENCES

Allison, A. C., "Sickle Cells and Evolution," Scient. Amer., 195:87–94, 1956.

Crow, J. F., *Genetics Notes,* 5th Ed., Minneapolis: Burgess, 1962.

Dobzhansky, Th., *Genetics and the Origin of Species,* 3rd Ed., New York: Columbia University Press, 1951.

Dobzhansky, Th., *Evolution, Genetics and Man,* New York: John Wiley & Sons, 1955.

Gowen, J. W. (Ed.), *Heterosis,* Ames, Iowa: Iowa State College Press, 1952.

Hardy, G. H., "Mendelian Proportions in a Mixed Population," Science, 28:49–50, 1908. Reprinted in *Classic Papers in Genetics,* Peters, J. A. (Ed.), Englewood Cliffs, N.J.: Prentice-Hall, 1959, pp. 60–62, and in *Great Experiments in Biology,* Gabriel, M. L., and S. Fogel (Eds.), Englewood Cliffs, N.J.: Prentice-Hall, 1955, pp. 295–297.

Li, C. C., *Human Genetics,* New York: McGraw-Hill, 1961.

Rasmuson, M., *Genetics on the Population Level,* Stockholm, Sweden: Svenska Bok-forlaget Bonniers; London: Heinemann, 1961.

Spiess, E. B. (Ed.), *Papers on Animal Population Genetics,* Boston: Little, Brown, 1962.

Sarkissian, I. V., Kessinger, M. A., and Harris, W., "Differential Rates of Development of Heterotic and Nonheterotic Young Maize Seedlings. I. Correlation of Differential Morphological Development with Physiological Differences in Germinating Seeds," Proc. Nat. Acad. Sci., U.S., 51:212–218, 1964.

Sprague, G. F. (Ed.), *Corn and Corn Improvement,* New York: Academic Press, 1955.

Weinberg, W., "Über den Nachweiss des Vererbung beim Menschen," Jahresh. Verein f. vaterl. Naturk. in Württemberg, 64:368–382, 1908. Translated, in part, in Stern, C., "The Hardy-Weinberg Law," Science, 97:137–138, 1943.

QUESTIONS FOR DISCUSSION

15.1. Are the causes of evolution the same in populations reproducing only asexually as in those reproducing sexually? Explain.

15.2. Suppose, in a population obeying the Hardy-Weinberg rule, mutation occurs for only one generation and changes the composition of the gene pool. How many additional generations are required before a new genetic equilibrium is established? Explain.

THEODOSIUS DOBZHANSKY *in 1957.*

SEWALL WRIGHT *is noted for his research in physiological genetics and in the mathematics of population genetics. Photograph was taken in 1954.*

15.3. Discuss the statement: "The Hardy-Weinberg Law is the cornerstone of evolutionary genetics."

15.4. Assuming that the Hardy-Weinberg principle applies, what is the frequency of the gene R if its only allele R' is homozygous in the following percentages of the population: 49%? 4%? 25%? 36%?

15.5. In the United States about 70% of the population gets a bitter taste from the drug phenyl thiocarbamide (PTC). These people are called "tasters" and the remaining 30% who get no bitter taste from PTC are called "nontasters." All marriages between nontasters produce all nontaster offspring. Every experimental result supports the view that: a single pair of nonsex-linked genes determines the difference between tasters and nontasters; dominance is complete between the only two kinds of alleles that occur; penetrance of the dominant allele is complete.

   (a) Which of the two alleles is the dominant one?
   (b) What proportion of all marriages between tasters and nontasters have no chance (barring mutation) of producing a nontaster child?
   (c) What proportion of all marriages occurs between two nontasters? Two tasters?

15.6. The proportion of AA individuals in a large crossbreeding population is .09. Assuming all genotypes with respect to this locus have the same reproductive potential, what proportion of the population should be heterozygous for A?

15.7. What do you suppose would happen to a population whose gene pool obeyed the Hardy-Weinberg rule for a very large number of generations? Why?

15.8. Can a population obey the Hardy-Weinberg rule for one gene pair but not for another? Explain.

15.9. Explain whether the mutation frequency to a particular allele is of primary importance in shifting its frequency in the population, when this gene is:

   (a) a dominant lethal in early developmental stages
   (b) a recessive lethal
   (c) phenotypically expressed only after the reproductive period of the individual
   (d) very rare
   (e) present in small cross-fertilizing populations

15.10. Can the adaptive value of the same gene (15.9) differ in:

   (a) haploids and diploids?
   (b) males and females?
   (c) two diploid cells of the same organism?

   Explain your answer in each case.

15.11. Other things being equal, what will happen to the frequency in the gene pool of a dominant mutant whose selection coefficient changes from one to ¼? If the mutant is completely recessive?

15.12. If persons carrying detrimental mutants never marry, these particular genes are removed from the gene pool. Under what conditions is the failure to marry likely to appreciably reduce the frequency of detrimental mutants in the gene pool?

15.13. Are inbreeding and assortive mating mutually exclusive departures from random mating (panmixis)? Explain.

15.14. Explain why the inbreeding coefficient, F, is ¹⁄₁₆ for cousin marriages.

15.15. Suppose the frequencies of *A* and *a* are .3 and .7, respectively, in a population obeying the Hardy-Weinberg rule and mating at random:

   (a) What per cent of the population is composed of homozygotes with respect to these genes?

   (b) What would be your answer to (a) after one generation of mating hybrids only with hybrids?

   (c) How would the conditions in (b) affect the composition of the gene pool?

15.16. Discuss, from a genetic standpoint, the advantages and disadvantages of cousin marriages in man.

15.17. In Thailand, heterozygotes for a mutant gene that results in the formation of hemoglobin E are more frequent in the population than would be expected from the Hardy-Weinberg rule. How can you explain this?

15.18. Two inbred strains of mice and their F_1 hybrids are tested for locomotor activity (measured for each subject in each group during three consecutive five-minute periods) and for oxygen consumption. In both these respects the F_1 hybrid is less variable than the parental strains. Propose a genetic hypothesis to explain these results.

15.19. Compare the reproductive isolates of people who were marrying in 1900 with those marrying today. Which factors are the same and which are different? Is the change desirable from a biological standpoint? Explain.

Chapter *16*

GENETIC LOADS AND
THEIR POPULATION EFFECTS

Genetic Loads in Drosophila

The fruit fly, *Drosophila pseudoobscura,* is commonly found in northern Mexico and the western United States. When collected in the wild, almost all its individuals are phenotypically alike, except for the sex differences, appearing wild-type or normal. We cannot accept this phenotypic uniformity as evidence of genotypic uniformity, however, since a Drosophila population appearing wild-type can conceal considerable genetic variability in the form of isoalleles, recessive point mutants, reciprocal translocations, paracentric inversions, and so on. We would like to estimate the *genetic load*—the total amount of this genetic variability present in a natural population of *D. pseudoobscura.*[1]

D. pseudoobscura has five pairs of chromosomes—the usual X and Y sex chromosomes, three pairs of large rod-shaped autosomes (II, III, IV), and a dotlike pair of autosomes (V) (Figure 16–1). Numerous laboratory strains of this species are available whose autosomes are marked by various point and rearrangement mutants. We can, therefore, make a suitable series of crosses between laboratory strains and flies collected in the wild which will yield information on the presence of autosomal mutants in the wild-type flies. In practice, autosomes II, III, and IV of individual wild-type flies are made homozygous to detect the presence of

[1] The following is based upon work of Th. Dobzhansky and collaborators.

the following recessive mutants (see Figure 6–2):

1. *Lethal* (causing death to all individuals before adulthood) or *semilethal* (causing more than ninety and less than one hundred per cent mortality before adulthood)
2. *Subvital* (causing significantly less than normal but greater than ten per cent survival to adulthood)
3. *Female sterile* (sterile to females)
4. *Male sterile* (sterile to males).

The results of this study are summarized in Figure 16–2. About 25% of all autosomes tested this way carry a recessive lethal or semilethal mutant. Recessive subvital mutants are found in about 40% of III chromosomes tested and in more than 90% of II's and IV's tested; mutants causing sterility are present in 4 to 14% of tested chromosomes. Obviously the natural population carries a tremendous load of detrimental mutants.

How is this load of mutants distributed in the fly population? Consider first one pair of the autosomes tested. Each member has a 25% chance of carrying a lethal or semilethal and a 75% chance of being free of such mutants. The chance that both members of a pair of chromosomes will carry a lethal or semilethal is $(0.25)^2$ or 6.25%. From the data presented we cannot tell whether all the lethals and semilethals found in a particular pair of autosomes are

FIGURE 16–1.
*Chromosomal
complement of*
D. pseudoobscura.

MUTANT TYPE	PER CENT OF CHROMOSOMES		
	II	III	IV
Lethal or Semilethal	25	25	26
Subvital	93	41	95
Female Sterile	11	14	4
Male Sterile	8	11	12

FIGURE 16–2. *Genetic load in natural populations of* D. pseudoobscura. *(After Th. Dobzhansky.)*

allelic (in which case up to 6.25% of zygotes in nature would be mutant homozygotes and fail to become adults), or whether all the mutants involve different loci (in which case 6.25% of zygotes would be hybrid for linked mutants of this kind), or whether some combination of these alternatives is obtained. In any case, the chance that both members of a given chromosome pair are free of lethals or semilethals is $(0.75)^2$ or 56%.

What portion of individuals in the population carry no lethal or semilethal on any member of autosomes II, III, and IV? This percentage is calculated as $(0.75)^2$ times $(0.75)^2$ times $(0.75)^2$ or about 17%. However, if one considers the X and V chromosomes which can also carry such mutants, the frequency of lethal-semilethal-free individuals in nature is still lower. Moreover, when the subvital mutants (which comprise the most frequent mutant class detected) and the sterility mutants are also considered, it becomes clear that very few, if any, flies in natural populations are free of a detrimental mutant load.

Genetic Loads in Man

What is the genetic load in man? The vast majority of mutants are detrimental in homozygous condition (as already noted in Chapter 15). Since inbreeding increases the frequency of homozygosis, a comparison of the detriment produced in an inbreeding segment with that in a noninbreeding segment of a human population may provide us with an estimate of the genetic load present in heterozygous condition. From the population records of a rural French population during the last century listing fetal deaths and all childhood and very early adult deaths we can compare the frequency of death to offspring of unrelated parents with that of cousin marriages.[2] The frequency of death to progeny from unrelated parents was .12, whereas it was .25 from cousin marriages. We are not concerned here with establishing the genetic or nongenetic cause of death in the normal outcrossed human population; however, it can be assumed that the extra mortality of .13 (.25 minus .12) has a genetic basis in the extra homozygosity resulting from cousin marriage. This assumption is reasonable in the absence of any known nongenetic factor that tends to cause death to more or fewer offspring from marriages between cousins than from marriages between unrelated parents. (These data would have a nongenetic bias if, for example, it were the custom—which it was not—that all children from cousin marriages are purposely starved.)

Apparently, then, 13% more offspring died because their parents were cousins. The total amount of recessive lethal effect present in the population in heterozygous condition can be calculated as follows: recall (Chapter 15) that of all heterozygous genes, an extra $\frac{1}{16}$ become homozygous in offspring of cousin marriages. In the model half of the $\frac{1}{16}$, or $\frac{1}{32}$, must have become homozygous for the normal genes and half of $\frac{1}{16}$, or $\frac{1}{32}$, for their abnormal alleles. Therefore, to estimate the total heterozygous content of mutants which would have been lethal if homozygous, it is necessary to

[2] Based upon an analysis of N. E. Morton, J. F. Crow, and H. J. Muller.

multiply .13 by 32. The resultant value of about 4 represents a 400% chance that the ordinary individual carried in heterozygous condition a genetic load of detrimental mutants which would have been lethal if homozygous. In other words, on the average, each person carried four *lethal equivalents* in heterozygous condition, or, four times the number of detrimentals required to kill an individual if the genes involved somehow became homozygous.

The preceding analysis did not reveal the number of genes involved in the production of the four lethal equivalents. These lethal equivalents might have been due to the presence in heterozygous condition of four recessive lethals, or eight mutants producing 50% viability, or sixteen mutants with 25% viability, or any combination of detrimental mutants whose total was four lethal equivalents. Because of environmental improvements (better housing, nutrition, and medical care) since the last century, it is likely that the effect of the same mutants in present-day society would be expressed by somewhat less than four lethal equivalents. For the same reason, the detrimental effects of these mutants in heterozygous condition are expected to be somewhat less at present than they were a century ago. For example, in the last century a particular hypothetical homozygous combination having variable penetrance and expressivity would have produced no detectable effect 25% of the time; a detrimental effect—but not death before maturity—15% of the time; and death before maturity 60% of the time; today, the respective values would be 50%; 10%; 40%. A century ago this combination would have produced .6 of a lethal equivalent; at present, the portion is .4. Notice also that the detriment not lethal before maturity would also have been reduced during this period from 15% to 10% or, speaking in terms of *detrimental equivalents,* what had been .15 would now be .10. Appar-

ently the genes responsible for lethal equivalents and for detrimental equivalents must be the same, at least in part.

It is also apparent that present-day man carries a genetic load. Some of those mutants transmitted to him arose in his parents (probably two of each five zygotes carry a newly arisen mutant, as mentioned on p. 192), and others arose in his more remote ancestry. It has been calculated [3] that, on the average, each of us is heterozygous for what is probably a minimum of about eight such mutant genes. This genetic load does not include the mutants carried in homozygous condition. What happens to this load of mutants in successive generations?

Balanced vs. Mutational Loads

To predict, in a general way, the fate of the "usual" mutant in the population, it is necessary to determine its "usual" phenotypic effect.[4] Since the typical mutant is detrimental when homozygous—at least to some degree—the homozygous condition tends to eliminate it from the gene pool. But two opposite effects are possible for mutants when heterozygous (see Chapter 15): either the heterozygote is superior to both homozygotes (as is found for the sickling-causing gene in malarial countries), or the heterozygote is somewhat inferior to the nonmutant homozygote (as is true for most point recessive lethal heterozygotes). In the former case the heterotic effect tends to increase the frequency of the mutant, and both the normal and mutant genetic variants are retained in the population gene pool at equilibrium. A population which normally retains more than one genetic (or chromosomal) alternative in its gene pool, therefore, exhibits *balanced polymorphism* in its phenotypes. This component of the genetic load is balanced, and is, therefore, a *balanced*

---

[3] By H. J. Muller and by H. Slatis.
[4] See B. Wallace (1963), J. F. Crow and R. G. Temin (1964), and Th. Dobzhansky (1964).

load. When the heterozygote is inferior to one homozygote, the heterozygous condition increases the rate at which the mutant is eliminated from the gene pool, and the population shows unbalanced polymorphism and tends to become genotypically and phenotypically monomorphic. This component of the genetic load, called the *mutational load,* is maintained in the population chiefly by recurrent mutation. Experimental evidence in Drosophila [5] and a statistical analysis of data for man [6] support the view that the great majority of point mutants are detrimental when heterozygous. We shall, therefore, consider most of the genetic load to be a mutational load.

Genetic Death

How is a mutant gene eliminated from the population? It need not be eliminated by the death of an individual, although sometimes it is. A more general way to express the removal of a mutant gene from the gene pool is by *genetic death*—the failure of a mutant-carrying individual to produce descendants carrying the mutant. Thus, all an individual's genes, whether normal or mutant, suffer genetic death if that individual fails to produce children. Since mutants are stable, they are usually removed from the gene pool by genetic death and only occasionally by mutation.

A person carrying a dominant lethal like retinoblastoma suffers genetic death (as well as physical death). In this case the mutant gene is eliminated from the population the generation in which it arises; it has, therefore, only one generation of *persistence.* A dominant detrimental mutant with a selection coefficient of .2 and, therefore, an adaptive value of .8 as compared to normal, will persist for five generations, on the average, before suffering genetic death; that is, given a population approximately the same in size for successive generations, in each generation the mutant-containing individual has a 20% chance of not transmitting the mutant. After this mutant arises, it sometimes fails to be transmitted the very first generation; it may suffer genetic death at the fifth generation or at the tenth, but, on the average, the mutant persists five generations. The principle of persistence holds even though genetic drift, migration, or other factors cause fluctuations in the frequency of the mutant.

Consider the fate in the population of a rare recessive lethal gene like the one producing juvenile amaurotic idiocy. Each time homozygosis for this gene occurs, it results in genetic death, and two mutant genes are eliminated from the gene pool. But consider the fate of heterozygotes which are 600 times more frequent (Chapter 15) and carry 300 times as many of these genes as do homozygotes. Since it is generally true that heterozygotes for a recessive lethal suffer genetic death about two per cent of the time (see p. 195), approximately .02 times 600, or twelve, heterozygous people would suffer genetic death, thus involving the removal of 24 genes, twelve of them being the recessive lethal alleles. Accordingly, six times as many of these particular recessive lethal genes suffer genetic death in the heterozygote than in the mutant homozygote, even though the reduction in reproductive potential in the former type is only $\frac{1}{50}$ of that in the latter.

It is apparent that the rarer a mutant is, the smaller will be the proportion of all genetic deaths it causes in homozygotes and the larger the proportion in heterozygotes. For rare mutants, then, natural selection removes mutant genes primarily via the genetic death of heterozygotes, the small amount of detriment being more important

[5] Based upon works of H. J. Muller and co-workers, C. Stern and co-workers, J. F. Crow and co-workers, I. H. Herskowitz and R. C. Baumiller, and others.
[6] Based upon an analysis by N. E. Morton.

when heterozygous—from the population or gene pool standpoint—than the greater detrimental effect when homozygous. However, each rare mutant, in terms of its effect on reproductive potential, is equally harmful to a constant-sized population in that each eventually causes a genetic death. Thus, hypoploidy which acts as a dominant lethal persists only one generation before it causes a genetic death; a rare point mutant whose reproductive disadvantage is only $\frac{1}{10}\%$ will persist, on the average, one thousand generations before causing genetic death.

Consider, on one hand, the gross chromosomal abnormality which kills *in utero*, destroying a life early. Neither the individual involved nor its parents suffer very long, since such deaths may occur as abortions which pass unnoticed. On the other hand, the heterozygous point mutants in individuals who are past the reproductive age—and, therefore, already have or have not suffered genetic death—will continue to subject these people to the previously and newly produced, small phenotypic detriment of heterozygosity which adds to their aches, pains, and disease susceptibility. In this respect, then, the mutant with a small effect on reproductive potential can cause more suffering than one with a large effect, for the longer the persistence, the more the damage in postreproductive life. In general, speaking not in terms of biological fitness but in terms of the total amount of suffering to which a human population is subject, point mutants with the smallest heterozygous detriment are the most harmful type of mutant.

One might at first suppose that the amount of gene-caused human suffering can be reduced by medical science. This possibility exists, particularly for an individual such as the diabetic who takes insulin; no doubt he is better off than he would be without medicine. But remember that this medicine does not cure the genetic defect.

Moreover, by increasing the diabetic's reproductive potential, the medicine serves to increase the persistence of the mutants involved, and the genetic death which must eventually occur is only postponed to a later generation—each intervening generation requiring the same medication. The total amount of human suffering would be reduced only if medicine could correct the gene-produced defect. To correct all of the multiple effects of the mutant, the medicine would have to replace the primary product of the defective gene with normal product. Insofar as most, if not all, currently known medicines act later than this earliest stage in gene action (Chapter 6), they serve to alleviate only some detrimental effects, thus causing an increase in human suffering by increasing persistence. Unfortunately, this situation will continue until medical science is much further advanced.

In view of the preceding discussion, we can assume that it is primarily the euploid or nearly euploid mutants which persist in the gene pool and are mainly responsible for changes in its composition during the course of evolution. By far the most common and most important class of such mutants is the point mutant.

Mutation and Evolution

In Chapter 15 we only suggested that mutations provide the raw materials for biological evolution. The reason for our hesitance in specifying evolution as the natural outcome of changes in gene pools was that the great majority of mutants, including point mutants, are harmful in homozygous or hemizygous condition. In this chapter and in Chapter 15, we indicated that most mutants are also detrimental when heterozygous. Under these circumstances, how can mutation provide the more adaptive genotypes postulated as necessary for evolution? It is true that for a given genotype under a given set of environmental conditions the great majority of point mutants are detrimental, and that, perhaps, only one point mutant in a thousand minutely increases the reproductive potential of its carrier. Yet, provided the mutation rate is not too large and there is sufficient genetic recombination, these rare beneficial mutants offer the population the opportunity to become better adapted. Moreover, mutants which lower biological fitness under one set of environmental conditions may be more advantageous than the normal genes under different environmental circumstances.[7] For example, a mutant producing vestigial wings in Drosophila is clearly inferior to its normal genetic alternative in an environment where flight ability is advantageous; but this mutant might be advantageous for Drosophila living on a small island where flight is not only unnecessary but harmful because insects that fly can be blown out to sea and lost. Consider a second example of this type. Several decades ago the environment was DDT-free, and mutants which confer immunity to DDT were undoubtedly less adaptive than the normal genetic alternatives present. But once DDT was introduced into the insect environment, such mutants—even if detrimental in other respects—provided such a tremendous reproductive advantage over their alternatives that they became established in the population as the new wild-type genes. Still other examples can be cited involving antibiotic-resistant mutants in microorganisms, which in an antibiotic-free environment are less adaptive than the genes normally present.

It becomes clear, then, that mutation provides the opportunity for a population to become better adapted to its existing environment. It also provides the raw materials needed to extend the population's range to different environments, either those already existing elsewhere or those that will

arise through changes. A population that is already very well adapted to its present environment is appreciably harmed by the occurrence of mutation. But environments differ, and any given environment will eventually change, so that a nonmutating population though successful at one time will, in the normal course of events, eventually face extinction. Mutation, therefore, is the price paid by a population for future adaptiveness to the same or different environments. We can now appreciate that mutation and selection, together with genetic drift and migration, are primarily responsible for the origin of more adaptive genotypes. We can also better appreciate the advantage of genetic recombination in speeding up the production of adaptive genotypes and the importance of the genetic mechanisms which regulate mutation frequency.

Somatic Mutations

In view of the preceding discussion, it is not at all difficult to predict the consequences of increasing the mutation frequency in human beings, an increase that doubtlessly is occurring as a result of our exposure to man-made penetrating radiations and certain reactive chemical substances. Man-made as well as spontaneous mutations can occur in either the somatic line or the germ line. Somatic mutants are, of course, restricted to the person in which they occur. The earlier the mutation occurs in a person's life, the larger will be the sector of somatic tissue to which the mutant cell gives rise.

When an adult is exposed to an agent which causes a mutation to occur in a certain percentage of all cells, the cells carrying induced mutants will usually be surrounded by nonmutant ones of the same tissue whose overall action produces a near-normal phenotypic effect. When an embryo is exposed, a proportionally smaller number of its cells will mutate. Mutant embryonic cells can, however, give rise later to whole tissues or

[7] See Th. Dobzhansky (1964).

organs which are defective; in such cases there is no compensatory action of normal tissue. Furthermore, since many mutants affect the rate of cell division, the earlier in development they occur, the more abnormal the size of the resulting structure will be. It is understandable, then—assuming that cells at all stages are equally mutable —that the earlier somatic mutations occur in the development of an individual, the more damaging they will be to him.

Newly arisen mutants produce almost all their somatic damage when heterozygous, since mutation involves loci which are usually nonmutant in the other genome. Although somatic mutants cannot be transmitted to the next generation, they can lower the reproductive potential of their carriers, thus affecting the gene pool of the next generation.

The damage which new mutants produce in a somatic cell depends upon whether or not the cell subsequently divides. Certain highly differentiated cells in the human body, like nerve cells or the cells of the inner lining of the small intestine, do not divide. In such cases, it is ordinarily difficult to detect mutations since the cells have no progeny classifiable as mutant or nonmutant. Nondividing cells may be more or less mutable than those retaining the ability to divide. In any event, a variety of mutations can occur in nondividing cells, including point mutations which inactivate or change the type of allele present, as well as structural rearrangements of all sizes. Nevertheless, the nondividing cell remains euploid or nearly euploid, and the phenotypic detriment produced must be due almost entirely to point mutants in heterozygous condition and to shifts in gene position. Although this may considerably impair the functioning of nondividing cells and give the impression that they are aging prematurely, their sudden and immediate death due to mutation is probably very rare.

Although the same kinds of mutations occur in somatic cells that subsequently divide and in those that do not, nuclear division can result in gross aneuploidy (Chapters 11 and 12). Accordingly, most of the phenotypic damage of induced mutants in dividing cells is the result of aneuploidy—mostly the consequence of single breakages that fail to restitute. It should be noted that all known agents causing point mutation also break chromosomes.

Germinal Mutations

Since somatic cells comprise a population produced by asexual reproduction (cell division), the preceding discussion of the effects of somatic mutation is appropriate to this chapter. Consider next, in a general way, the consequences of increasing the frequency of mutations in the human germ line. The earlier that mutation occurs in the germ line, the greater the portion of all germ cells carrying the new mutant will be. Of course, the upper limit of gametes carrying a particular induced mutant is usually fifty per cent. Consider the effect of exposing the gonads of each generation to an additional constant amount of high-energy radiation (Figure 16–3). The load of mutants produced spontaneously is presumably at equilibrium—the rate of mutant origin equals the rate of mutant loss via genetic death. Beginning with the first generation to receive the additional radiation exposure, the mutant load increases with each generation until a new equilibrium is reached; at this point the higher number of genetic deaths per generation equals the higher number of new mutants produced each generation. If the additional radiation exposure ceases at some still later generation, the mutational load will decrease gradually (because of variations in persistence) via genetic deaths, until the old spontaneous equilibrium is reached again.

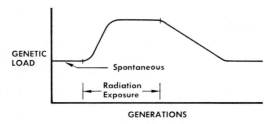

GENETIC LOAD

Spontaneous

Radiation Exposure

GENERATIONS

FIGURE 16–3. *Genetic load and exposure to radiation.*

It is clearly important to learn in detail the genetic effects of high-energy radiation to which human populations are being subjected either purposely or circumstantially. In order to make the best evaluation, we will need to know much more about: the distribution of the energy of various radiations in tissue; the exact amount of gonadal exposure to radiations of different types; the detriment of the induced mutants in hetero- and homozygous conditions; the persistence of mutants; and the different types and the frequencies of mutations that each kind of radiation produces in different stages of male and female gametogenesis.

In the last respect, it is necessary to determine for various types of mutations, the relative mutagenicity of a concentrated dose and one given in a protracted manner. It is also necessary to learn as accurately as possible the mutability of spermatogonia and oocytes, because these are the stages in which the human germ cells producing the next generation remain for the longest period of time. It is suggested that the largest number of germ-line mutations occurs in oocytes. Because spermatogonia are constantly dividing, mutants producing a detrimental effect may be selected against so that they are reduced in frequency by the time gametes are formed; the human female, however, is born with all, or almost all, her future gametes already in the oocyte stage so that there is no parallel mitotic selection in this germ line. Not only do oocytes fail to undergo mitosis, but they remain relatively inactive for decades before becoming ova; as oocytes age during this period, they become disproportionately sensitive to spontaneous mutation (at least to factors leading to aneusomy).

Although at present we do not have as much information about any one of these factors as we would like, available information along these lines already gives us approximate answers (see the references at the end of this chapter). It should be noted, therefore, that all values given in the discussion below may be in error by as much as a factor of two or more.

It has been a practice to discuss the germ-line effect of radiation in terms of the amount of increase any particular exposure would produce in our spontaneous mutation frequency. The general impression is held that, as a species, man is fairly well adapted to his spontaneous mutation rate, and that if this rate is doubled it will not threaten his survival. Accordingly, the question becomes, how much man-made radiation would produce as many mutations as occur normally? A United Nations report calculates that about 30 rads (roughly equal to 30 r) is sufficient to double the human spontaneous mutation rate—the frequency per generation. This amount is called the *doubling dose.* In a population of one million people, one rad delivered to the gonads, or sex organs, of each person is calculated to produce between 100 and 4,000 mutants which could be transmitted to future generations. Thus, one rad of gonadal exposure for one generation will result in the birth of 100 to 4,000 people with new heterozygous mutants. Affected descendants will occur for many generations, since only a small portion of the genetic deaths from these mutants will occur in the first generation. These will not be evident when added to the number of genetic deaths resulting from spontaneous mutation. If the one rad gonadal exposure were repeated every generation, an equilibrium would eventually be established in which, for every generation, 100 to 4,000 people per million would show the effects of radiation-induced mutants in the form of genetic death. However, since the kinds of phenotypic effects produced by the radiation-induced mutants would be the same as those from mutants which occur normally, we would not be able to recognize specifically those people hurt by the radiation.

What part of our normal load of mutants comes from naturally-occurring penetrating radiation? Since human beings receive about five rads in the course of a reproductive generation—that is, in 30 years—it is possible that as little as $\frac{5}{30}$, or $\frac{1}{6}$, of our mutations normally are radiation-induced.

How much additional radiation are we exposed to during medical treatment? If medical use of radiation were to continue at its present level, it has been estimated that each person in the United States would receive a total dose to the sex cells of about three r per generation. Of course, some people do not receive this amount of radiation, while others get considerably more. But this average radiation dose to the germ cells from medical uses alone is 60% of the amount received spontaneously and is raising the mutation rate about 10% above the spontaneous rate. In the years to come, with increased use of radiation for diagnosis and therapy, the average dose from medical radiation might increase greatly. Already radioactive materials have been used in one million medical treatments in a single year. Many governments as well as private dental and medical groups are investigating such radiation exposure, and many ways of reducing radiation exposure without hindering its usefulness are being instituted.

It is difficult to determine the number of germ-line mutations resulting from the radiation associated with fallout following atomic explosions, because some radiation reaching the gonads could come from fallout on the ground, breathed in, or ingested with food. In the latter case, the distribution of particular radioactive substances in the body makes a large difference in the amount of radiation reaching the sex cells. With respect to sex cells, the three most important radioactive substances in fallout are cesium-137, strontium-90, and carbon-14. Because cesium is distributed through the tissues—including the gonads—more or less evenly whereas strontium is preferentially localized in bone, we expect cesium-137 to produce more gonadal radiation damage from ingested fallout than strontium-90 produces.

The period of time over which radioactive substances produce new mutations also varies. The induction of mutations by relatively short-lived radioactive substances, like strontium-90 and cesium-137, is restricted almost entirely to a few generations. On the other hand, carbon-14—C-14—is long-lived, having a half-life of 6,000 years. So, if the exposure to C-14 in the environment does not change, there will be about half as many new mutations induced after 200 generations as there are in the first generation. Because of its abundance and long half-life, carbon-14's potential for delivering radiation to the gonads has been calculated as being 4 to 17 times more than radioactive cesium's and strontium's combined and, therefore, carbon-14 is capable of producing proportionally more point mutations.

In the United States National Academy of Sciences—National Research Council report of 1956 (see References), the gonadal dose expected from fallout—if weapons of the same type continued to be tested at the same rate—was given as about 0.1 rad in the next thirty years. On the basis of the United Nations report, we could expect approximately 10 to 400 mutations per million people. How much modification does this figure now need in order to bring it up to date? Before accurate estimates of germ-line mutational damage due to fallout can be obtained, many factors need be taken into account, among them:

1. Carbon-14, whose long half-life was not considered in this report
2. The changes in rate of testing (according to the United States Atomic Energy Commission, in 1958 alone the amount of fallout-producing radioactive material in the stratosphere was doubled by the numerous test explosions of nuclear weapons conducted by the United States and the U.S.S.R.)
3. The unequal distribution of fallout in different parts of the world
4. Reduction in decay taking place in the stratosphere since fallout is descending faster than expected
5. Changes in the nature of bombs tested and in the location of the test sites
6. The decrease in exposure as a result of the test ban treaty.

Each month brings more of the data required to estimate the fallout risk to the germ cells. Apparently, the possible damage has been underestimated. In 1953 the International Commission on Radiological Protection recommended—and various U.S. Government agencies adopted—80 units as the maximum permissible concentration of strontium-90 in food. In 1958 the Commission recommended this maximum be lowered to 33 units, and the new value has subsequently been employed as a guideline by the U.S. Government.

In principle, exposure to man-made radiation undoubtedly produces point mutants in the somatic and germ lines of man, but this possibility is not easy to demonstrate in practice principally for two reasons: The first is that the expected point mutants are not qualitatively different from those which occur spontaneously; the second is that the quantitative effect, although large in total, is small enough in any one generation to be masked by the general variability of human genotypes and environment. Through the use of improved statistical methods, however, the evidence that radiation has produced such genetic effects is becoming increasingly strong. On the other hand, clear proof that radiation can cause structural changes in human chromosomes does exist. With the recent perfection of cytological methods for studying human chromosomes and the evidence that aneusomy is a relatively frequent event in oocytes, it is likely that additional data will be forthcoming about the numbers and kinds of gross chromosomal mutations which different types and doses of radiation can induce in man.

In discussing the genetic effects of low radiation doses, we recognized a danger which is not likely to be calamitous to the human gene pool; however, the very high radiation doses from a nuclear war could be disastrous, for if the whole body receives 500 r in a short period of time, the chance is 50% that the affected person will die in a few months. If the person survives this period, his life expectancy is reduced by some years, probably because of somatic mutations, and children conceived after exposure will be handicapped by many detrimental mutants. It is even possible, but not probable, that in a nuclear war enough radiation would be released to destroy the human species.

Finally, it should be realized that we are being constantly exposed to man-made mutagenic chemical substances. Although it is very probable that we are getting fewer germ-line mutations from chemical substances than from radiation, more somatic mutants may be produced by chemical substances than by our present exposure to radiation.

SUMMARY AND CONCLUSIONS

Cross-fertilizing species carry a large load of mutants in heterozygous condition. The vast majority of them are detrimental when homozygous and—to a lesser extent—when heterozygous, although some heterozygotes are superior to either homozygote. Other things being equal, almost all mutants are harmful to the same degree in that each eventually causes genetic death. Mutants producing the smallest detriment to reproductive potential cause the greatest total amount of suffering. More detriment and more genetic deaths occur in heterozygotes than in homozygotes for rare mutants. Persistence of a mutant in the population is inversely related to its selection coefficient.

Mutation is the current price paid by a population for the possibility of having a greater reproductive potential in the same or a different environment in the future. So, despite the rarity of mutants which increase reproductive potential in a given environment, mutation provides the raw materials for evolution.

Natural and man-made penetrating radiations are undoubtedly causing mutations in our somatic and germ cells, increasing our load of detrimental mutants. This exposure, though harmful, is most likely no threat to man's survival as a species at present, although it might be in the future should the exposure become large enough. Further research is needed to accurately assess the effects of high-energy radiations and chemical substances upon man's mutation rate and well-being.

REFERENCES

Auerbach, C., *Genetics in the Atomic Age,* Fair Lawn, N.J.: Essential Books, 1956.

Background Material for the Development of Radiation Protection Standards, Report No. 1, Federal Radiation Council, Washington, D.C.: U.S. Government Printing Office, 1960.

Chu, E. H. Y., Giles, N. H., and Passano, K., "Types and Frequencies of Human Chromosome Aberrations Induced by X-rays," Proc. Nat. Acad. Sci., U.S., 47:830–839, 1961.

Crow, J. F., "Ionizing Radiation and Evolution," Scient. Amer., 201:138–160, 1959.

Crow, J. F., and Temin, R. G., "Evidence for Partial Dominance of Recessive Lethal Genes in Natural Populations of Drosophila," Amer. Nat., 98:21–33, 1964.

Dobzhansky, Th., *Evolution, Genetics, and Man,* New York: John Wiley & Sons, 1955.

Dobzhansky, Th., "How Do the Genetic Loads Affect the Fitness of Their Carriers in Drosophila Populations?" Amer. Nat., 98:151–166, 1964.

Herskowitz, I. H., "Birth Defects and Chromosome Changes," Nuclear Information, 3 (No. 2):1–2, 4, 1960.

Krieger, H., and Freire-Maia, N., "Estimate of the Load of Mutations in Homogeneous Populations from Data on Mixed Samples," Genetics, 46:1565–1566, 1961.

Morton, N. E., "The Mutational Load Due to Detrimental Genes in Man," Amer. J. Human Genet., 12:348–364, 1960.

Muller, H. J., "Mutational Prophylaxis," Bull. N.Y. Acad. Med., 2nd Ser., 24:447–469, 1948.

Muller, H. J., "Radiation Damage to the Genetic Material," Amer. Scientist, 38:33–59, 126, 399–425, 1950.

Müntzing, A., "A Case of Preserved Heterozygosity in Rye in Spite of Long-Continued Inbreeding," Hereditas, 50:377–413, 1963.

Report of the United Nations Scientific Committee on the Effects of Atomic Radiation, New York: General Assembly Official Records: 13th Session, Suppl. 17 (A/3838), Chaps. 5–6, Annexes G–I, 1958.

Selected Materials on Radiation Protection Criteria and Standards: Their Basis and Use, Joint Committee on Atomic Energy, Congress of the United States, Washington, D.C.: U.S. Government Printing Office, 1960.

The Biological Effects of Atomic Radiation, Summary Reports, Washington, D.C.: National Academy of Sciences—National Research Council, 1956 and 1960. (See Reports of the Genetics Committee.)

Wallace, B., "A Comparison of the Viability Effects of Chromosomes in Heterozygous and Homozygous Condition," Proc. Nat. Acad. Sci., U.S., 49:801–806, 1963.

QUESTIONS FOR DISCUSSION

16.1. Do you suppose that the mutations which occur in man serve a useful function? Why?

16.2. Compare the fate of a mutational load in asexually reproducing populations that are haploid, diploid, and autotetraploid.

16.3. Discuss the effect upon the gene pool of mutants restricted to the somatic line.

16.4. Can the gene that comprises part of a detrimental equivalent also comprise part of a lethal equivalent? Explain.

16.5. Give examples of balanced and unbalanced polymorphism in the genetics of man.

16.6. What is the relation between phenotypic detriment, genetic death, and genetic persistence?

16.7. Discuss the relative importance of point mutants and gross structural changes in chromosomes to the individual and to the population.

16.8. What is the difference, in terms of mutation, between a maximum permissible dose and a doubling dose of ionizing radiation? Is any dose of any radiation safe from a mutational standpoint? Explain.

16.9. Compare the genetic composition of the mutant load caused by fallout, by medical uses of radiation, and by atomic reactor accidents.

16.10. Do you believe it is essential for the general public to become acquainted with the genetic effects of radiation? Why?

16.11. What are some of the beneficial uses of radiation? Are any of these based upon the genetic effects of the radiation? If so, give one or more examples.

16.12. One of the components of fallout is radioactive iodine, I-131, which has a half-life of about a week. Discuss the genetic effects expected in the somatic and germ lines of persons exposed to fallout.

16.13. Susceptibility to leprosy may be due to a single irregularly dominant gene. S. G. Spickett notes that leprosy is increasing in some human populations that have been free of it for many generations. List some factors which may be responsible for this finding.

16.14. Is a genotype adaptive in man today, one which would have been adaptive 2,000 or 20,000 years ago? Explain.

16.15. "The danger of mutation lies primarily in the rate with which it occurs." Criticize this statement.

16.16. How can you explain the finding that in the genus Drosophila apparently the heaviest genetic loads occur in common and in ecologically most versatile species, whereas the lightest loads are found in rare and in specialized species and in marginal colonies of common species?

*Chapter *17*

CHROMOSOMAL REARRANGEMENTS IN NATURE

Oenothera [1]

The evening primrose, Oenothera (Figure 17–1), is a common weed found along roadsides, railway embankments, and in abandoned fields. It exists in nature in a number of pure breeding, self-fertilizing strains—each with a characteristic phenotype. These strains can be cross-fertilized in the laboratory. If the two strains crossed are *Lamarckiana* and *biennis* the outcome in F_1 is surprising. First, the F_1 are not all uniform in phenotype as one would expect from previous experience with crossbreeding two pure lines, but three distinct types (which we will call A, B, C). Second, upon self-fertilization each of these three F_1 types is thereafter pure breeding. If the F_1 were hybrid, we would expect self-fertilization to produce recombinants and, therefore, more than one phenotype in its progeny. These two peculiarities are summarized in Figure 17–2 where the results obtained from similar crosses with garden peas are shown side by side.

We must conclude from the Oenothera results that self-fertilizing strains cannot automatically be considered pure homozygous lines, despite any contrary impression gained in Chapter 1. In order to obtain three different genotypes in F_1, either *Lamarckiana*,

or *biennis* or both must be heterozygous. Assume that *Lamarckiana* is heterozygous for a single pair of genes. If so, how can this strain produce only *Lamarckiana* upon self-fertilization? To do this would require that the heterozygote produces only heterozygote progeny. But suppose that self-fertilization does, as expected, produce the two homozygotes, both of which are lethal. (Recall that for yellow mice—p. 69—only one homozygote is lethal; the other is viable. In the present case the two different alleles would both have to act as recessive lethals.) This hypothesis which predicts that one half of the zygotes die before becoming mature *Lamarckiana,* is supported by the finding that approximately one half of the ovules regularly fail to produce seed upon self-

FIGURE 17–1. *Oenothera.* (*Courtesy of R. E. Cleland.*)

[1] Based upon work of H. DeVries, O. Renner, R. E. Cleland, F. Oehlkers, A. F. Blakeslee, J. Belling, S. Emerson, and A. H. Sturtevant.

fertilization—evidence that in nature *La-marckiana* is a permanent heterozygote in this respect, with a *balanced lethal system.* In this case both lethals kill the individual sometime before seed formation, in fact, the lethal kills at the time of fertilization or very soon thereafter, being in effect a *zygotic lethal* (Figure 17–3).

Recall that some plants, including Oeno-thera, have a haploid gametophyte genera-tion. Permanent heterozygosis could be maintained also, if one allele were lethal to the male gametophyte and the other to the female (Figure 17–3). Consequently, *game-tophytic lethals* can also provide a balanced lethal system which prevents half of the ovules from producing seed. We have al-ready seen an example of this kind of lethal in the self-sterility gene in Nicotiana (p. 60). In general, all strains of Oenothera found in nature, including *biennis,* have *en-forced heterozygosity* due to the zygotic and gametophytic lethals which produce bal-anced lethal systems.

Does a balanced lethal system explain why the phenotype of *Lamarckiana,* for ex-ample, is the only one produced in the prog-eny after self-fertilization? Since all sexual organisms so far studied have many pairs of genes, it would not seem reasonable that Oenothera has only a single pair of recessive

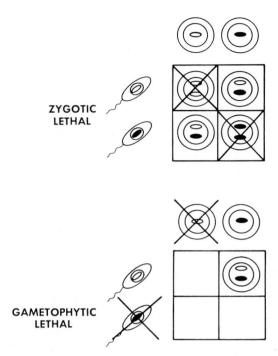

FIGURE 17–3. *Balanced lethal systems that enforce heterozygosity.*

lethal genes whose manifold (pleiotropic) effects produce the entire phenotype. It is more likely that many gene pairs exist which form a single linkage group, so that the dip-loid individual has one genome whose genes are all linked to one recessive lethal and another genome whose genes are all linked to the allelic lethal.

In other words, *Lamarckiana* behaves as though it contains two *complexes* of linked genes. Within a strain these genes are com-pletely linked by some mechanism that pre-vents recombination, leaving the gametes with only two kinds of genotypes. The two gene complexes are so constant in natural populations of a strain that in the case of *Lamarckiana* they are given the names *gau-dens* and *velans,* and identified as *gaudens. velans*; the *biennis* strain as described by its

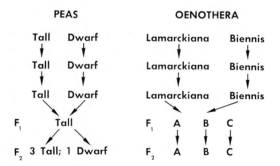

FIGURE 17–2. *Comparative breeding results from garden peas and Oenothera.*

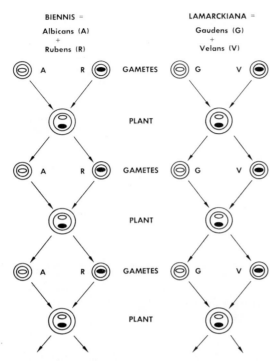

BIENNIS =
Albicans (A)
+
Rubens (R)

LAMARCKIANA =
Gaudens (G)
+
Velans (V)

FIGURE 17–4 (*above*). *Balanced lethal gene complexes in* O. biennis *and* O. Lamarckiana.

FIGURE 17–5 (*below*). *Linkage groups in hybrids from interracial crosses.*

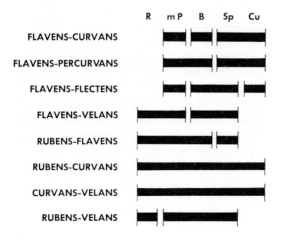

gene complexes is *albicans.rubens*. Figure 17–4 shows how these balanced lethal gene complexes are distributed generation after generation in *biennis* and *Lamarckiana*. All the recessive lethal alleles in either of the two strains cannot be identical to those in the other; if they were the F_1 from crossing them would consist of only two different phenotypes, whereas three types are actually obtained. We can conclude, therefore, that the balanced lethal system generally found in Oenothera involves either a multiple allelic series or several pairs of genes or both.

Each of the three different F_1 hybrids obtained from crossing *Lamarckiana* with *biennis* breeds true upon self-fertilization, showing that each hybrid contains two completely linked gene complexes. This conclusion may or may not be true, however, of the breeding behavior of other hybrids obtained from interracial crosses. This ambivalence is illustrated in Figure 17–5 with the gene complexes present in the different hybrids shown at the left. The distribution of the various genetic markers (top of Figure 17–5) in the gametes of these hybrids was determined from breeding tests. For example, the *curvans.velans* hybrid produced only two kinds of gametes though heterozygous for all these marker genes, the markers behaving as if they were all completely linked. On the other hand, the *flavens.velans* hybrid produced four kinds of gametes. The genes R, m, and P (all still linked to each other) segregated independently of the genes B and Sp (both still linked to each other), so that half of the gametes contained one of the two parental combinations, the other half carried one of the two recombinations. In this case, therefore, genes which belonged to a single linkage group in the parent races behaved as two linkage groups during the gametogenesis of their hybrid. Since 50% recombination occurred in gametogenesis of the hybrid, these results are not really explained by postulating that *flavens* (or *velans*) is actually a single linkage group which cannot undergo crossing over with its partner gene complex in the parent race, but which can do so when its partner is *velans* (or *flavens*).

Tests of the hybrid containing *flavens. curvans* showed *m* and *P* still completely linked but segregating independently of *B*, which was, in turn, segregating independently of *Sp* and *Cu*, so that in this case three linkage groups existed. Perhaps more linkage groups would have been found with additional genetic markers. In all cases, however, a given hybrid combination always showed the same linkage groups in its gametogenesis.

Because at least three linkage groups can be identified in certain interstrain hybrids (even though these act as one in the self-fertilizing parental strain), it is expected that the diploid Oenothera has at least three pairs of chromosomes and cytological examination confirms this genetic expectation—all of the Oenothera strains discussed in this chapter having seven pairs of chromosomes. (*Oenothera gigas,* the triploid mentioned on p. 151, has 21 chromosomes.) If the balanced lethal system is based upon a single pair of genes located on a single pair of homologs, this pair of chromosomes must be heterozygous in viable progeny. But this heterozygosity would not be expected for the other six pairs of chromosomes, if they segregated independently. Consequently, all gametes of *O. biennis,* for example, which carry the *albicans* complex recessive lethal should similarly be expected to carry the *rubens* or the *albicans* homolog in each of the other six cases of independent segregation. However, this distribution is not found. We could then suppose that each of the seven chromosome pairs is heterozygous for a different recessive lethal. Upon self-fertilization, such a genotype would produce only viable F_1 like the parent. Since this explanation predicts that only about $(\frac{1}{2})^7$ of all ovules

should develop as seeds, it cannot be the correct one for Oenothera in which, as mentioned, about 50% of all ovules mature into seeds.

A clue to the orderly segregation of complete gene complexes in Oenothera may be found by cytological study of meiosis. The typical self-fertilizing Oenothera in nature does not form seven separate bivalents as expected, but, as seen clearly at metaphase I, forms a closed circle of 14 chromosomes synapsed end to end (Figure 17–6). At ana-

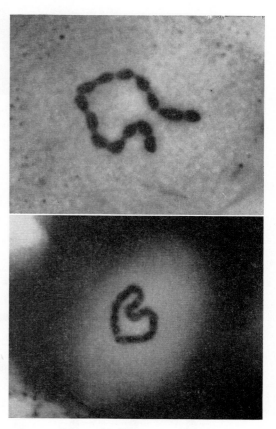

FIGURE 17–6. *Circle of 14 chromosomes in Oenothera. Chromosome number is clear in upper cell where the circle has broken open. (Courtesy of R. E. Cleland.)*

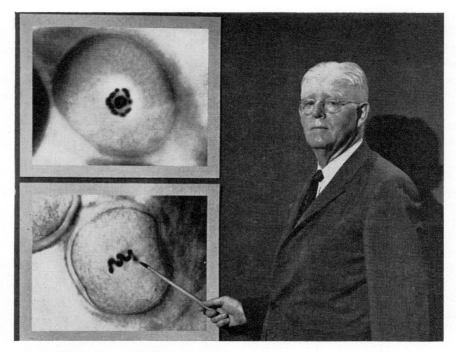

FIGURE 17–7.   RALPH E. CLELAND *points to zig-zag chromosomal arrangement at the start of anaphase I of an Oenothera having a circle of 14 chromosomes at metaphase I.   (Photograph, 1959, courtesy of The Calvin Company.)*

FIGURE 17–8.   *Manner of chromosome segregation during meiosis of Oenothera.*

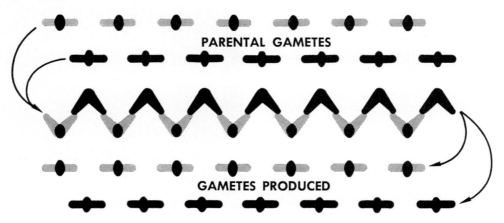

phase I, moreover, adjacent chromosomes in the circle go to opposite poles of the spindle, so that at the start of the separation the chromosomes assume a zigzag arrangement (Figure 17–7). If we assume that paternal and maternal chromosomes alternate in the circle, then all paternal chromosomes would go to one pole and all maternal chromosomes to the other. The complete linkage of all genes in a complex would be explained by such chromosome segregation (if crossing over is rare), and the gametes produced by an individual would be identical to those which united to form it (Figure 17–8).

If in an alternate segregation procedure maternal and paternal genomes separate, a circle should always contain an even number of chromosomes. Moreover, we could predict that when one gene complex no longer behaves as a single linkage group, it will also no longer form a single circle of fourteen chromosomes with the other gene complex. Fourteen chromosomes can be arranged fifteen different ways in circles (composed of even numbers of chromosomes) and pairs as shown in Figure 17–9. Indeed, when various race hybrids are made, all fifteen types and no others are found at metaphase I—any particular hybrid always forming the same meiotic configuration. (The top cell in Figure 17–7 shows an inner circle of four and an outer circle of ten chromosomes.) If what has been supposed about alternate segregation is true, it should also follow that even though alternate chromosomes within a circle show complete linkage with each other, such linkage groups should segregate independently of other linkage groups consisting of chromosomes either in separate circles or in separate pairs. This expectation can be tested by comparing the number of genetically determined linkage groups in the different hybrids of Figure 17–5 with the chromosome arrangements

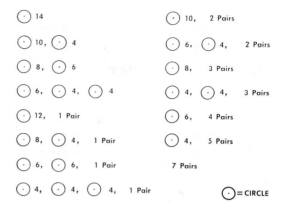

FIGURE 17–9. *Circle and pair arrangements possible for Oenothera chromosomes.*

seen cytologically during their meiosis. Such a comparison reveals that the number of separate groups of chromosomes observed in meiosis is always equal to, or greater than, the number of linkage groups detected genetically. In fact, whenever a sufficient number of genetic markers are used, the number of linkage groups always equals the number of chromosome groups.

Although the preceding discussion indicates that a rather unique segregation of alternate chromosomes in a circle and the presence of balanced lethal systems can explain most of the unusual genetic behavior of Oenothera, other matters still need explanation. What causes these chromosomes to form circles in the first place? A clue to this, contained in the observation made on p. 172 (see also Figure 12–6), is that two pairs of nonhomologs will be associated as a double tetrad during synapsis if a reciprocal translocation involving them is present in heterozygous condition. Figure 17–10 illustrates this situation in Oenothera. All Oenothera chromosomes are small, are roughly the same size, and have median centromeres. To help us identify homol-

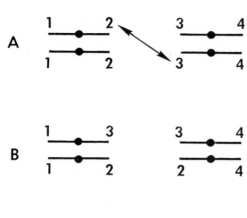

A

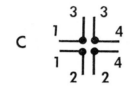

B

C

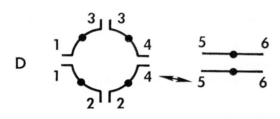

D

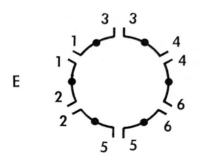

E

FIGURE 17–10. *Heterozygous reciprocal translocations and circle formation. Chromatids are not shown.*

ogous chromosomes, the ends of different chromosomes in a genome are given different numbers. Suppose, at some time in the past, a eucentric reciprocal translocation occurred between the tips marked 2 and 3 (Figure 17–10A, B). This rearrangement in heterozygous condition (B) would produce an X-shaped configuration at the time of synapsis in prophase I (C) and a circular appearance at metaphase I–early anaphase I (D). In this way a circle of four chromosomes would be produced.

If a second reciprocal translocation occurs between any chromosome arm in a circle of four and an arm of some other pair of chromosomes, a circle of six chromosomes will form in the individual heterozygous for both reciprocal translocations. This type of formation is illustrated in Figure 17–10D, E; D shows the configuration before arms 4 and 5 have exchanged, E shows the circle of six produced in meiosis after this exchange. Still larger circles can be formed by successive interchanges of this type; six such interchanges are required to form a circle of 14 chromosomes. The presence of reciprocal translocations in heterozygous condition could explain how various sized circles containing even numbers of chromosomes are produced in Oenothera.

Although the cytogenetic analysis of Oenothera is known in some detail, the picture is, however, not yet complete. One of the questions remaining is: What is the mechanism whereby alternate chromosomes in a circle proceed to the same pole during meiosis? No fully acceptable answer to this question has yet been given. A second question stems from the fact that almost all the different strains or races of Oenothera found in nature form a circle of 14. Are the six translocations involved the same in all races? No—for if they were, viable hybrids between races would form either circles of 14 or seven separate chromosome pairs at meiosis. That all the configurations in Figure 17–9 are found in meiosis of such hybrids must mean that different gene complexes differ from each other in the specific ways that their chromosome arms have become translocated. Many thousands of ways are possible for 14 ends to be arranged in seven groups of two. How can we determine the number of these different arrangements occurring in nature?

We can start by choosing a particular gene complex—calling it the "standard"—and considering its chromosome ends to be 1–2, 3–4, 5–6, 7–8, 9–10, 11–12, and 13–14. Normally, that is, in nature, this complex would form a circle of 14 with the other gene complex, which would therefore have no chromosome with the same pair of numbered ends as any chromosome in the standard complex. Proceeding further, we form a series of interracial hybrids with the standard as one of the complexes and score the meiotic chromosome arrangements of the hybrids. Suppose in one case that the hybrid forms five pairs and a circle of four. This result must mean that the ends of 5 chromosomes are in the same order in the complex under test as in the standard, but that they are in a different order in the remaining two chromosomes. Although there was previously no reason to assign ends 1–2 and 3–4 of the standard complex to any particular chromosomes, we can presently assign these ends arbitrarily to the two standard chromosomes in the circle of four. The chromosomes in the circle from the complex under test can then be called 2–3 and 4–1 (or 2–4, 1–3). In this way the composition of ends of two chromosome pairs is specified permanently. The top of Figure 17–11 shows the standard and tested complexes (of our example) synapsed according to identical numbers.

Call the complex just tested A. Suppose another complex, B, is made hybrid both

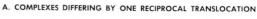

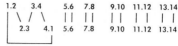

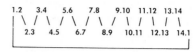

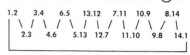

A and B are theoretical

FIGURE 17–11. *Arrangement of chromosome ends in different Oenothera complexes.*

with the standard and with A. The meiotic configuration of the hybrid may specify other ends of A, B, and the standard complexes. Such procedures can be carried out until all of the standard's chromosomes are specified and the complete order of all fourteen ends determined for any other complex. In this manner, we can verify that a circle of fourteen is produced in many different ways in nature; a hypothetical and an actual example is shown in the central and lower parts of Figure 17–11. In fact, of 350 complexes analyzed, more than 160 different segmental arrangements have been found. All these results are consistent with the hypothesis that during the course of evolution, the ends of Oenothera chromosomes have been shuffled many times in different ways by reciprocal translocation. A most convincing test of the reciprocal translocation interpretation would be the ability to predict the meiotic chromosomal arrangement to be found in a hybrid not yet formed. This type of predicting has been done many times and all such expectations have been verified.

At various points in this discussion Oenothera's behavior has seemed exceptional, apparently violating our concepts of pure lines and independent segregation. More complete analysis has shown, however, that Oenothera's failure to behave as expected was due to the operation of other, already known, genetic events. Oenothera is an exception which should be treasured; for in the exact correspondence between its atypical genetics and its atypical cytology, it is an outstanding example of the validity of the chromosome theory of transmission genetics.

Three aspects of the cytogenetic behavior of Oenothera are disadvantageous under many circumstances: reciprocal translocations; recessive lethals; and self-fertilization. By combining all three of these disadvantages in one plant, however, Oenothera's survival value is probably greater than it would be without them. The self-fertilization mechanism involves bringing the stigma down to the level of the anther, so that a much heavier pollination is attained than would be likely were the plant pollinated by insects. This self-fertilization mechanism offsets the 50% mortality due to balanced lethals. These lethals, together with the reciprocal translocations and alternate segregation, prevent the homozygosity usually consequent to self-fertilization, enforce heterozygosity, and produce maximum hybrid vigor.

The great survival value of Oenothera is demonstrated by the distribution of this genus: it can be found from the southern tip of South America to the far reaches of Northern Canada and from the Atlantic Ocean to the Pacific. It is interesting to note that the most numerous sections of the genus and those which have ranged the farthest are the ones with large circles, balanced lethals and self-pollination.

Drosophila

Although reciprocal translocations have played an important role in the evolution of Oenothera, it might be claimed that this

FIGURE 17–12. *Chromosome configurations in several Drosophila species.*

genus is an unrepresentative example of the importance of chromosomal rearrangements in evolution because its cytogenetic behavior is so unorthodox. Hundreds of different species of Drosophila occur in nature. These species can be compared ecologically, morphologically, physiologically, and biochemically. For those species able to interbreed, recombinational genetic properties can also be compared; banding patterns of salivary gland chromosomes and the appearance of chromosomes at metaphase of different species are additional areas of comparison. After all available information of this kind is gathered, it is possible to arrange the chromosomes of various species on a chart so that those closest together are more nearly related in descent—evolution—than are those farther apart.[2] This arrangement is illustrated in Figure 17–12 which shows the *karyotype*—the haploid set of chromosomes

[2] Based upon work of C. W. Metz and others.

at metaphase—including the X but not the Y chromosome for different Drosophila species or groups of species. The karyotype of the *melanogaster* species group, for example, is shown in row 2, column 1; the bottom chromosome is the rod-shaped X, the two V's are the two large autosomes (II and III), and the dot represents the tiny chromosome IV. In the other karyotypes, whole chromosomes or chromosome arms judged to be homologous are placed in the same relative positions. What can be learned from a comparison of these karyotypes?

Since the amount of detail in a metaphase chromosome is limited basically to size and shape, one cannot expect to discern any small-sized rearrangements at this stage. Accordingly, regardless of their importance, small rearrangements involving duplication, deficiency, shift, transposition, inversion, and translocation cannot be detected on the chart. Even a large paracentric inversion is undetected at metaphase, since it does not change the shape of the chromosome. Other gross structural changes, however, can be detected. In row 4 the chromosome patterns in columns 2 and 3 seem identical, except that a pericentric inversion has changed a rod to a V, or vice versa. (Pericentric inversions always change the relative lengths of the arms when the two breaks are different distances from the centromere.) Compare the karyotype for *melanogaster* (row 2, column 1) with the one to its right (row 2, column 2). A V-shaped autosome in *melanogaster* appears as two rods in its evolutionary relative. (Note also that the dot chromosome is missing.) In the next karyotype to the right (row 2, column 3), two rods have combined to form a V that is different from either of the two V's in *melanogaster*.

Other examples in this chart indicate that two rod-shaped chromosomes have formed a V-shaped chromosome, or a V has formed two rods. Consider first how a V can origi-

nate from two rods (Figure 17–13). Recall that a rod-shaped chromosome typically has two arms, though one is very short. The short arm may not be noticeable at metaphase or anaphase; however, its presence may be demonstrated either cytologically at an earlier or later stage of the nuclear cycle, or genetically by studying genetic recombination. Suppose two rods are broken near their centromeres, one in the long arm of one chromosome, the other in the short arm of the other chromosome. If the long acentric arm of the first chromosome becomes joined to the long centric piece of the second, a V is formed. Notice that this union involves the joining of two whole or almost-whole arms in a eucentric half-translocation. The remaining pieces may join together to form a short eucentric chromosome, thereby completing a reciprocal translocation; or they may not join. In either instance, if the short pieces are lost in a subsequent nuclear

HALF (OR RECIPROCAL) TRANSLOCATION

FIGURE 17–13. *Formation of a V-shaped chromosome from two rod-shaped chromosomes.*

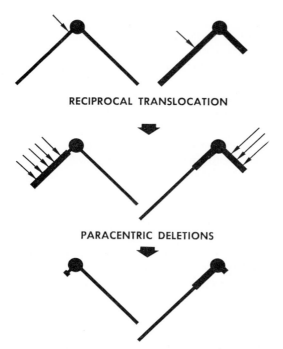

RECIPROCAL TRANSLOCATION

PARACENTRIC DELETIONS

FIGURE 17–14. *Formation of two rod-shaped chromosomes from a V-shaped chromosome and a Y chromosome.*

division and the number of genes lost is small enough, the absence of these parts may be tolerated physiologically by the organism.

The reverse process, the formation of two rods from a V, necessitates the contribution of a centromere from some other chromosome. In Drosophila, this second chromosome may be the Y (Figure 17–14). Suppose the V is broken near its centromere and the Y is broken anywhere. Should a eucentric reciprocal translocation follow, two chromosomes would be produced, each having one arm derived predominantly from the Y. If subsequent paracentric deletions occur in these Y-containing arms, rod shapes will result, thereby completing the change from a V to two rods. Note that almost every part but the centromere of the Y chro-

mosome is eventually lost in this process. But this loss may have little or no disadvantage to the Drosophila, since the Y carries relatively few loci and is primarily concerned with sperm motility. For example, this series of mutations may be initiated in the male germ line, producing two chromosomes —each containing part of the Y. Deletion of Y parts can occur without detriment if these chromosomes happen to enter the female germ line; they may stay in the male germ line provided that a regular Y chromosome is included in the genotype in due time. The small IV chromosome in *melanogaster,* whose monosomy is tolerated in either sex, may also contribute a centromere in the process of changing a V to two rods by an identical or similar series of mutational events.

Karyotype comparisons of Drosophila confirm the expectation (Chapter 12), that whole arm translocations are able to survive in natural populations. Such rearrangements and pericentric inversions are extremely useful in helping us establish evolutionary relationships among different species. But it should be emphasized that this kind of information by itself does not prove that:

1. The formation of different species is a primary consequence of the occurrence of these rearrangements
2. These rearrangements are of secondary importance in species formation
3. These mutational events occur after species formation is complete.

As exemplified by Oenothera and Drosophila, we have seen that gross chromosomal rearrangements of various types have persisted in the evolutionary course of different groups of organisms. For this reason it would perhaps be wise at this point to refrain from predicting—except generally as in Chapter 12—which, if any, structural changes might be associated with the evolution of other particular groups of organisms.

SUMMARY AND CONCLUSIONS

Although the cytogenetics of Oenothera has several unusual aspects, present knowledge renders these differences quite understandable; consequently, Oenothera provides an outstanding confirmation of the validity of the chromosomal basis for genetic material. Evolution in this genus is intimately associated with self-fertilization, balanced lethals, and numerous reciprocal translocations.

Pericentric inversions (which change chromosome shape) and whole arm reciprocal translocations (which lead to changes in chromosome number) have been frequent in the past evolutionary history of Drosophila.

REFERENCES

Cleland, R. E., "A Case History of Evolution," Proc. Indiana Acad. Sci. (1959), 69: 51–64, 1960.

Cleland, R. E., "The Cytogenetics of Oenothera," Adv. in Genet., 11:147–237, 1962.

Patterson, J. T., and Stone, W. S., *Evolution in the Genus Drosophila,* New York: Macmillan, 1952.

White, M. J. D., "Cytogenetics of the Grasshopper *Moraba scurra,* VIII." Chromosoma, 14:140–145, 1963.

HUGO DE VRIES (*1848–1935*), *pioneer in the study of mutation and Oenothera genetics. (From Genetics, vol. 4, p. 1, 1919.)*

QUESTIONS FOR DISCUSSION

17.1. What evidence can you present for saying that the genes which make up the balanced lethal system in *Lamarckiana* are different from those in *biennis*?

17.2. Discuss the following statement: "All evening primroses found in nature are constant hybrids."

17.3. With respect to chromosomes, how does the origin of a circle differ from the origin of a ring?

17.4. Can a circle contain an odd number of chromosomes? Explain.

17.5. What new investigations regarding the genetics and/or cytology of Oenothera has this chapter suggested to you?

17.6. List the genetic principles you could have deduced had Oenothera been the only organism studied so far.

17.7. If this chapter contains no new principles of genetics, why do you suppose it was written?

17.8. Curly-winged Drosophila mated together always produce some non-curly offspring. Plum eye-colored flies mated together always produce some non-plum offspring. But, when flies that are both curly and plum are mated together, only flies of this type occur among the offspring. Explain all three kinds of results and define your symbols.

17.9. (a) Draw a diagram representing a heterozygous whole-arm translocation in Drosophila at the time of synapsis. Number all chromosome arms involved. (b) What would be required for a mating between two flies with this constitution to produce offspring flies only of this type?

17.10. Do you suppose that the preservation of heterozygosity has an adaptive advantage in Oenothera? In other organisms?

17.11. Discuss the evolutionary flexibility of the genus Oenothera and Drosophila.

17.12. Is the balanced lethal system in Oenothera part of its genetic load? Explain. If so, are the lethals components of a balanced load or a mutational load? Explain.

17.13. Compare the genetic effects of ionizing radiation on populations of Oenothera and Drosophila.

17.14. Explain how a Drosophila zygote formed with a sperm carrying a centric, grossly-deleted Y chromosome can develop into a fertile male.

Chapter 18

RACES AND THE ORIGIN
OF SPECIES

In cross-fertilizing species, different individuals in a population are heterozygous for different genes (see Chapter 16), even though the gene pool is at equilibrium with the factors that cause shifts in gene frequency—namely, mutation, selection, drift, and migration. In other words, in reaching genetic equilibrium, all the members of cross-fertilizing populations do not eventually become homozygotes, nor do they all become heterozygotes. Such populations, therefore, do not become either genetically pure or uniform with the passage of time.

Although any given population is polymorphic for some genes, it is not necessarily polymorphic with regard to a particular gene. For example, Indians in South America are almost all of O blood type, being homozygous ($i\ i$) in this respect, but have a polymorphic pool with respect to other genes. Moreover, an allele, like I^B, may be rare or absent in one population, as in certain North American Indians, and relatively frequent in the gene pool of another population, as in central Asia. Thus, populations located in different parts of the world may differ both in the types and frequencies of alleles carried in their gene pools. For many purposes it is desirable to identify a population with certain gene pool characteristics as a *race*.

Races

An investigator may choose to define races only according to the distribution of the I^B gene for ABO blood type. He might define populations that do or do not contain I^B in their gene pool as different races. On this basis there would be only two races of man, the South American Indian (without I^B) and all the other people (with I^B in their gene pool).

On the other hand, an investigator may decide to define races on the basis of the relative frequency of i and I^B in the population. The frequency of these alleles in the gene pool has been determined for many populations all over the world. The results show that in western Europe, Iceland, Ireland, and parts of Spain, three-fourths of the gene pool is i, but this frequency begins to decrease as one proceeds eastwardly from these regions. On the other hand, I^B is most frequent in central Asia and some populations of India but becomes gradually less and less frequent as one gets farther away from this center. Since the change in frequency of these alleles is gradual, any attempt to sharply separate people into races having different gene frequencies would be arbitrary.

In practice, therefore, the number of races recognized is a matter of convenience. For some purposes separating mankind into only two races is adequate; for other reasons, as many as two hundred have been recognized. As a rule, most anthropologists recognize about half a dozen basic races but may increase the number to about thirty when considering finer population details. Regardless of the number of races defined, however, each is best characterized according to the genes it contains. Since the people in a population are either A, B, AB, or O in blood type and intermediates do not occur, no average genotype exists for the ABO blood group, nor is there an average genotype for any other polymorphic gene. Because a population has no average genotype, a race should be defined according to the relative frequency of alleles contained in its gene pool. Without an average genotype, a race cannot have an average phenotype; accordingly, it is futile to try to picture a typical (average) member of any race.

Other blood traits, besides ABO blood group, whose genetic basis is understood, are also useful in characterizing races. In fact, it is valid to utilize any phenotypic difference due to a genetic difference. For example, in delimiting races one can employ certain genetic differences in color of hair, eyes, and skin, and differences in stature and head shape; one should avoid using phenotypic differences whose genetic basis is unproved, for the environment itself can cause phenotypic differences (Chapter 1). Remember also that the same phenotypic result may be produced by different genotypes because of gene interaction in dominance and epistasis (Chapter 4).

Knowledge of the distribution of genes for ABO blood types in different populations provides important information to geneticists, anthropologists, and other scientists. To what can the different distributions be attributed? Since people do not choose their marriage partners on the basis of their ABO blood type, and since there does not seem to be any pleiotropic effect making persons of one blood type sexually more attractive than those of another, it is very likely that mating is at random with respect to ABO genotype. However, in other respects some evidence indicates that different ABO genotypes do not have the same biological fitness. Differential mutation frequencies can also explain part of the differences in gene distribution. During the past few thousand years the greatest shift in ABO gene frequencies of different populations has probably been the result of genetic drift and migration. In fact, the paths of past migrations can be traced by utilizing—along with other information—the gradual changes in the frequencies of ABO and other blood group genes in neighboring populations.

It has already been mentioned (p. 209) that different paracentric inversions are found in natural populations of *D. pseudoobscura*. All of these flies are very similar phenotypically, even though their chromosomal arrangements are different. Sample populations of this fly in the southwestern part of the United States (Figure 18–1) have been studied to determine the relative frequency of these inversions.[1] California populations proved to be rich in the inversion types called Standard and Arrowhead. Eastward, in nearby Arizona and New Mexico, the populations contain relatively few Standard and Pikes Peak chromosomes, most chromosomes having the Arrowhead arrangement. Finally, in still more easterly Texas, one finds almost no Standard and some Arrowhead with most chromosomes being of the Pikes Peak type.

The shift in the frequency and type of inversions in the three different geographic regions cannot be explained as the result of differential mutation, since the spontaneous mutation rate for inversions is extremely low. Moreover, since there is no indication that the gene flow among these populations has changed appreciably in the recent past, migration rates have probably had a relatively small influence upon genotypic frequencies; there is also no indication that genetic drift has had a major role in causing the differences in inversion frequency in the three areas. These observations lead us to suppose that the primary basis for these population differences lies in the different adaptive values which different inversion types confer on individuals in different territories. Despite the absence of any obvious morphological effects, these inversions prove to have different physiological effects in laboratory tests; different inversion types survive best in different experimental environments. Since

[1] Based upon work of Th. Dobzhansky and collaborators.

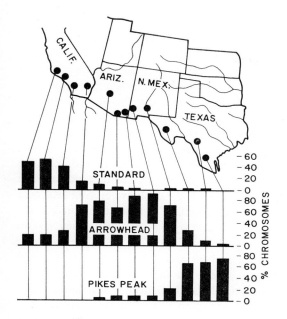

FIGURE 18–1. *Distribution of inversion types in* D. pseudoobscura *collected in the Southwestern United States. (After Th. Dobzhansky and C. Epling.)*

these inversion types show different adaptive values in the laboratory, it is reasonably certain that they do so in nature too. Accordingly, natural selection is primarily responsible for the inversion differences among the three geographic populations, which can be defined as three different races.

Similar results have been obtained with three California races of the cinquefoil plant species, *Potentilla glandulosa,* which live at sea level, mid-elevation, and the alpine zone. The sea level race is killed when grown in the alpine environment, whereas the alpine race grown at lower elevations proves less resistant to rust fungi than the lower-elevation races. Such experiments show that different races are adapted to their own habitats but not to others. The inorganic and organic environment—including its organisms—is

different in different parts of the territory occupied by a species. Clearly, then, no single genotype will be equally well adapted to all the different environments encountered within a particular territory. One way in which a cross-fertilizing species can attain maximal biological fitness as a whole is to remain genetically polymorphic and separate into geographical populations or races which differ genetically.

Whenever, as in all of the examples discussed so far, different races of a cross-fertilizing species occupy geographically separate territories, they are said to be *allopatric;* different races occupying the same territory are said to be *sympatric.* In the absence of geographical separation, what factors operate to keep sympatric races from hybridizing to become one race? One may find the answer by considering the fate of races—originally allopatric—which have become sympatric, a kind of change which has occurred in man. Several thousand years ago, mankind was differentiated into a number of allopatric races. With the development of civilization and improved methods of travel, many of these races have become sympatric. Gene exchange in the now-sympatric races, however, is sometimes inhibited by social and economic forces, so that some of these races continue to maintain their identity. Domesticated plants and animals provide another example of what can happen when allopatric races become sympatric. Many different breeds, or races, of dogs originally allopatric are now found living in the same locality. Yet these now-sympatric races do not exchange genes with sufficient frequency to form a single mongrel breed, or race, because their reproduction is controlled by man. It should be realized that, under other circumstances, such allopatric races which become sympatric can form a single polymorphic race via cross-breeding.

Speciation Involving One Species

A species of cross-fertilizing organisms usually consists of a number of races adapted to the different environments of the territories they occupy. All these races are kept in genetic continuity by interracial breeding and hybrid race types, so that the species, as a whole, has a single gene pool containing no portion completely isolated from any other. On the other hand, different cross-fertilizing species are genetically discontinuous from each other. Thus, *the gene pool of one species is so isolated from the gene pools of all other species that none can lose its identity via crossbreeding, or backcrossing subsequent to crossbreeding.* Moreover, the gene pools of different species are isolated from each other for genetic—not merely environmental—reasons.

The formation of new species, *speciation,* has occurred frequently in past evolution; since evolution is continuing, new species are still being formed. The speciation mechanism considered most common for cross-fertilizing individuals involves the production of two or more species from a single one. How can this come about?

Hypothetically, one can start with a single panmictic, genetically-polymorphic species. Since environments vary we will assume that different populations occupy different portions of a territory and, although enough interpopulation breeding takes place to form one gene pool, most of the breeding is intrapopulation. If, in the course of time, two (or more) of these populations diverge genetically—each one uniquely adapted to its own territory—these populations become different races of the same species. The differences in the gene pools of these two races may increase more and more because of mutation, natural selection, and genetic drift. As this differentiation process continues, the genes which make each of the races adaptive in their own territories may, by their mani-

fold phenotypic effects, make matings between the two races still less likely to occur or may cause the hybrids of such matings to be less adaptive than the members of either parent race. Accordingly, partial reproductive isolation may be initially an accidental or an incidental byproduct of the adaptability of genotypes to a given environment. The greater this effect, however, the greater we would expect the selective advantage to be of genes which increase the reproductive isolation between two diverging races further still. If races continued to diverge genetically in this way, they would eventually form separate and different gene pools, and instead of being two races of the same species would become two different species. Note that speciation is an irreversible process; once a gene pool has reached the species level, it can never lose its identity via cross breeding with another species.

In this generalized account of how speciation usually occurs *races have acted as incipient species.* But remember that under other circumstances two races can also crossbreed to become a single race. For example, although several thousand years ago different allopatric populations of human beings were definitely different races which might have formed different species had the same conditions of life continued, some of these races subsequently merged into one race because civilization and migration facilitated crossbreeding.

Gene exchange between races can be hindered in several ways. Those *barriers* leading to complete reproductive isolation include the following:

1. *Geographical.* Water, ice, mountains, wind, earthquakes, and volcanic activity may separate races.
2. *Ecological.* Changes in temperature, humidity, sunlight, food, predators, and parasites may alter or completely change a race's habitat.

3. *Seasonal.* Seasonal changes may cause different races to become fertile at different times even if their territories overlap, or if they are sympatric.
4. *Sexual or ethological.* Intrarace mating, due to preference or domestication effected by man.
5. *Morphological.* Incompatibility of the sex organs between some races.
6. *Physiological.* Failure of a race's sex cells to fertilize those of another, so that the hybrid zygote is formed infrequently, or not at all.
7. *Hybrid inviability.* Even when formed, the development of hybrid zygotes may be so abnormal that it cannot be completed.
8. *Hybrid sterility.* A possibility even if hybrids complete development and are hardy.

Although geographical, ecological, and seasonal differences do not automatically initiate genotypic differences, they furnish the environmental variations which select from the available genotypes those which are adaptive; that is, those with the greatest reproductive potential under the given conditions. Of course, mutation must provide the raw materials for natural selection; since no single genotype is equally well adapted to all conditions, different races come to contain different genotypes. The remaining barriers listed can complete reproductive isolation.

The many genes by which two incipient species differ may produce seasonal, sexual, morphological, and physiological barriers. Hybrid inviability may result from developmental disharmony caused by the presence of two genetically different genomes in each cell. Although hybrid sterility can be caused by such genetic action, it also results when two races become quite different with respect to gene arrangement—because of structural changes within and between chromosomes—so that during meiosis, synapsis between the two different genomes in the hybrid is irregular. Improper pairing causes abnormal segregation, which results in aneuploid meiotic products. Recall that aneuploidy in pollen is lethal, and that aneuploid gametes in animals usually result in dominant lethality of the zygotes they form. Consequently, reproductive isolation can be based upon either genetic activity or chromosomal behavior, or both.

It seems reasonable that the more morphologically divergent two forms are, the more likely it is that they will differ physiologically and that these differences will have originated in very different and isolated gene pools. Simply by comparing horse and mouse morphologies, one certainly expects them to be different species; thus the occurrence of morphological differences is sometimes a good index of a species difference. However, when the groups being compared are closely related in descent, one finds that morphology is not well correlated with reproductive isolation. For example, European cattle and the Tibetan yak are quite different in appearance and usually are placed in different genera, but these two species can be crossed. Moreover, in Tibet, many cattle have yak-like traits, so that widely different phenotypes do not necessarily result in complete reproductive isolation between closely related species. On the other hand, consider *D. persimilis* and *D. pseudoobscura.* These two species—formerly considered races of the same species—are so similar morphologically that they can be differentiated by their genitalia only if very careful measurements are made. Nevertheless, these two species have completely isolated gene pools in nature, even where their territories overlap. Such morphologically similar species are called *sibling species.* They originated from different races of a single species. Sibling species are found in mosquitoes and other insects as well as in Drosophila; they are also found in plants—among the tarweeds of the aster family and in the blue wild rye.

The study of *D. pseudoobscura* and *D. persimilis* illustrates two other principles relating to species formation. First, any particular reproductive barrier usually has a multigenic and/or a multichromosomal basis; second, any two species are separated not by one but by a number of reproductive barriers. Although each of the barriers involved is incomplete, together they result in complete reproductive isolation—there being no stream of genes between the two gene pools in nature. The known differences between these two particular sibling species include:

1. *Pseudoobscura* lives in drier and warmer habitats than *persimilis*
2. Females accept the mating advances of males of their own species more often than they do male advance of the other
3. *Pseudoobscura* usually mates in the evening, *persimilis* in the morning
4. Interspecific hybrids are relatively inviable and when viable, they are mostly sterile.

The nature and origin of the reproductive isolation mechanisms involved in forming new species from races shows that valid species originate not by a single or simple mutation, but as the result of many different, independently occurring genetic changes. Moreover, as already noted, speciation is accomplished not merely by an accumulation of mutants which distinguish races, but also by those which contribute to reproductive isolation. Usually populations are physically separated while reproductive barriers are being built up; otherwise, hybridization would break down these barriers. Experimental evidence also supports our expecta-

tion that natural selection acts to further the accumulation of the genetic factors promoting reproductive isolation between races.

The preceding discussion illustrates how one species can give rise to two or more species via races which serve as incipient species.[2] It was stated earlier that a species has an isolated gene pool, that is, a gene pool closed to individuals of some other alternative condition (species). A species is expected to undergo numerous changes in its gene pool during the course of many generations. At the end of this time, is it the same or a new species? Here is an example of one type of species formation which would not be recognized by the criterion above because the alternative state would no longer exist. Suppose some members of the original population had been (miraculously) preserved, then we might find that they were reproductively isolated from the members of the new population. In such an event we could admit the formation of a new species whose origin is dependent upon the "extinction" of the parent species. This type of speciation will become a valid subject of study once man learns how to preserve sample genotypes indefinitely.

One species can give rise to another via *autopolyploidy*—an increase in the number of genomes present in a normally cross-fertilizing species. Mechanisms for the production of autopolyploid cells, tissues, and organisms have already been described on pp. 151–153. In the genus Chrysanthemum, species occur with 2n chromosome numbers of 18, 36, 54, 72, and 90. Thus, it appears that nine is the basic n number. In the genus Solanum (the nightshades, including the potato) the basic n number seems to be twelve, since species of this genus are known

[2] See Th. Dobzhansky, L. Ehrman, O. Pavlovsky, and B. Spassky (1964).

having 24, 36, 48, 60, 72, 96, 108, and 144 chromosomes. These two examples suggest that autopolyploidy has played a role in the speciation of these two genera. Autopolyploidy, however, is not considered an important mechanism of speciation in forms reproducing primarily by sexual means, since autopolyploids having more than 2n chromosomes form multivalents at meiosis and, therefore, numerous aneuploid gametes. Autopolyploids can succeed, though, if they are propagated asexually, by budding or grafting, as in the case of the triploid apples —Gravenstein and Baldwin. Triploid tulips are also propagated asexually.

Speciation Involving Two or More Species

Many new cross-fertilizing species originate not only from a single species or its races, but—in relatively recent times—from hybridization between two or more different species, that is, via *interspecific hybridization*. Although interspecific hybrids pose no threat to the isolation of the gene pools of their parental species, they may form a successful, sexually-reproducing population that has its own closed gene pool. Interspecific hybrids, particularly of plants, can be converted into stable, intermediate types isolated from their parental species by three methods.

The first method involves *amphiploidy* (*allopolyploidy,* see p. 155). If one species has 2n = 4 and another has 2n = 6, the F_1 hybrid between them will have five chromosomes (Figure 18–2). If the hybrid survives, it may be sterile because each chromosome has no homolog and, therefore, no partner at meiosis. As a result, meiosis proceeds as if the organism were a haploid and produces mostly aneuploid gametes. If, however, the chromosome number of the F_1 hybrid is doubled—either artificially (via colchicine) or spontaneously—the individual or sector will be 2n = 10; each chromosome

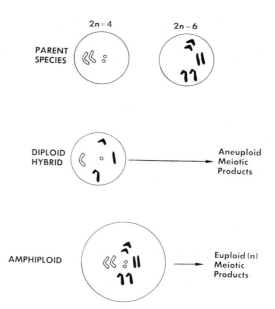

FIGURE 18–2. *Interspecific hybridization leading to new species formation via amphiploidy (allopolyploidy).*

will have a meiotic partner; and euploid gametes of n = 5 will be formed. Upon uniting, such gametes produce 2n = 10 progeny, which are fertile and more-or-less phenotypically intermediate to and isolated from both parental species.

It has been estimated that twenty to twenty-five per cent of the present flowering plant species originated as interspecific hybrids whose chromosomes doubled in number (therefore being "doubled hybrids" or amphiploids). Moreover, in the past many (or more) species originated in this way, then diverged to form different genera. Naturally-occurring amphiploidy was involved in the origin of cotton in the New World and in the appearance of new species of goatsbeard during the present century.

In the early 1800's, the American marsh grass, *Spartina alterniflora* (2n = 70), was

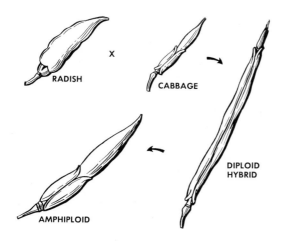

FIGURE 18–3 (above). *Seed pods of cabbage and radish, of their hybrid and amphiploid. (After G. D. Karpechenko.)*

FIGURE 18–4 (below). *Distribution of Delphinium species in California. Each species has a unique habitat.*

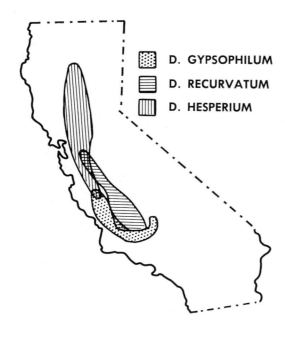

accidentally transported by ship to France and England and became established alongside of the European marsh grass, *S. stricta* (2n = 56). By the early 1900's a new marsh grass, *S. townsendii* (2n = 126), appeared and largely crowded out the two older species. Since *S. townsendii* has a chromosome number equal to the sum of the diploid numbers of the older species, is fertile, breeds true, and has an appearance intermediate between the two older forms, this species is undoubtedly an amphiploid of *S. alterniflora* and *S. stricta*. *S. townsendii* is so hardy that it has been purposely introduced into Holland (to support the dikes) and to other localities.

Amphiploidy also can be produced artificially. For example, in the greenhouse it is possible to cross radish (2n = 18) with cabbage (2n = 18) (Figure 18–3), thus producing an F_1 hybrid with 18 unpaired chromosomes at meiosis. If, however, the chromosome number of the hybrid doubles early enough in development, it can produce amphiploid progeny with 2n = 36 chromosomes (containing nine pairs each from radish and cabbage). Since the amphiploid is fertile and genetically isolated from both radish and cabbage, it constitutes a new species.

If each chromosome contributed to an interspecific hybrid is different and the hybrid's chromosome number doubles, then each chromosome would have just one partner at meiosis, and segregation would be normal. Therefore, the breeding success of the amphiploid is enhanced by greater differences between the chromosomes of the two species that contributed haploid genomes to the interspecific hybrid. It is not surprising, then, in hybridizing two chromosomally similar species, that at meiosis their amphiploid produces trivalents and quadrivalents leading to abnormal segregation and sterility.

Although amphiploidy is not successful

for hybrids between similar species, there is a second way interspecific hybrids can become stabilized as a new species, provided that the two hybridizing species are very similar chromosomally. If the two species have the same haploid number, their F_1 hybrid may have all chromosomes synapsed in pairs at meiosis. Segregation, independent segregation, and crossing over may yield progeny of the *hybrid whose recombinations can become stabilized* in nature yet are isolated from either parental species. Consider certain species in the larkspur genus, *Delphinium: D. gypsophilum* is morphologically intermediate between *D. recurvatum* and *D. hesperium;* all three species have $2n = 16$; and the "parent" species, *recurvatum* and *hesperium,* can be crossed to produce an F_1 hybrid. When the F_1 hybrid is crossed to *gypsophilum,* the offspring are more regular and more fertile than those produced by backcrossing the F_1 hybrid with either parent species. Similarly, the progeny from crosses between *gypsophilum* and either of its parent species are not as regular or as fertile as are those from the cross between *gypsophilum* and the hybrid of the parent species. These results provide good evidence that *gypsophilum* arose as the hybrid between *recurvatum* and *hesperium.* Figure 18–4 shows the distribution of these species in California.

The third way that interspecific hybrids can become stabilized as new species is by *introgression.* In this process a new type arises after the interspecific hybrid backcrosses with one of the parental types. The backcross recombinant types favored by natural selection may contain some genetic components from both species, may be true-breeding and, eventually, may become a new species.

SUMMARY AND CONCLUSIONS

A race of a cross-fertilizing species is characterized by the content of its gene pool. Each race is adapted to the territory in which it lives. Different races can be sympatric or allopatric. Races can become species by accumulating genetic differences whose end effect is genetic discontinuity—that is, the formation of isolated gene pools. Separation of two gene pools is usually accomplished by a combination of different reproductive barriers each of which is incomplete by itself and has a polygenic and/or a polychromosomal basis not necessarily correlated with morphological differences.

It is generally recognized that most cross-fertilizing species arose from the further differentiation of races. Occasionally a new species can arise via autopolyploidy, and it is possible that a new species can also arise by the gradual change of one species as a whole into another species.

Two (or more) species can give rise to a new one after interspecific hybridization. An interspecific hybrid can form a new species via amphiploidy, by selection of recombinants among its progeny, or by selection of individuals produced after introgression.

REFERENCES

Dobzhansky, Th., *Genetics and the Origin of Species,* 3rd Ed., New York: Columbia University Press, 1951.

Dobzhansky, Th., *Evolution, Genetics, and Man,* New York: John Wiley & Sons, 1955.

Dobzhansky, Th., Ehrman, L., Pavlovsky, O., and Spassky, B., "The Superspecies *Drosophila paulistorum,"* Proc. Nat. Acad. Sci., U.S., 51:3–9, 1964.

Dodson, E. O., *Evolution: Process and Product* (Rev. Ed.), New York: Rinehart, 1960.

Dunn, L. C., and Dobzhansky, Th., *Heredity, Race, and Society,* 3rd Ed., New York: New Amer. Libr. of World Lit., 1957.

Ehrlich, P. R., and Holm, R. W., *The Process of Evolution,* New York: McGraw-Hill Book Co., Inc., 1963.

Mayr, E., *Animal Species and Evolution,* Cambridge: Harvard University Press, 1963.

Merrill, D. J., *Evolution and Genetics,* New York: Holt, Rinehart and Winston, 1962.

Stebbins, G. L., *Variation and Evolution in Plants,* New York: Columbia University Press, 1950.

QUESTIONS FOR DISCUSSION

18.1. Discuss the validity of the concept of a pure race.

18.2. To use the frequencies of ABO blood types in tracing the course of past migration, what assumptions must you make?

18.3. Under what future circumstances would you expect the number of races of human beings to decrease? To increase?

18.4. Can the definition we have used for a species be applied to forms that reproduce only asexually? Why?

18.5. Differentiate between genetic sterility and chromosomal sterility. Invent an example of each type.

18.6. Discuss the hypothesis that a new species can result from the occurrence of a single mutational event.

18.7. Is geographical isolation a prerequisite for the formation of a new species? Explain.

18.8. What is the relative importance of mutation and genetic recombination in species formation?

18.9. Is a species a natural biological entity, or is it—like a race—defined to suit man's convenience?

18.10. Does the statement, "We are all members of the human race," make biological sense? Why?

18.11. Suppose intelligent beings, phenotypically indistinguishable from man, arrived on Earth from another planet. Would intermarriage with Earth people be likely to produce fertile offspring? Why?

18.12. Invent circumstances under which the present single species of man could evolve into two or more species.

18.13. The cells of triploid and tetraploid autopolyploids are usually larger than those of the diploid. What importance has this fact for fruit growers?

18.14. H. Kihara and co-workers have produced triploid (33 chromosomes) water-melons with no seeds, and tetraploid (44 chromosomes) watermelons with seeds but larger than the diploid. How do you suppose this was accomplished? How do you suppose these types are maintained?

18.15. In each of the following cases, an interspecific hybrid can be formed experi-mentally. State whether or not you would expect each of the hybrids produced from the parents described below to become established in nature.

   (a) In California, the Monterey cypress grows along the coast on the rocks, whereas the allopatric Gowen cypress grows two miles inland in the sand barrens.
   (b) Two sympatric species of pine occur in California. One of these, the Monterey pine, sheds its pollen before March; the other, the bishop pine, some time later.
   (c) The hybrid between *Crepis neglecta* (n = 4) and *C. fuliginosa* (n = 3) shows unpaired and paired chromosomes as well as multivalents during meiosis.

18.16. *Drosophila pseudoobscura* crossed with *D. persimilis* produces sterile males, but partially fertile females. Using marked chromosomes, the interspecific hybrid female can be backcrossed to *pseudoobscura*, and their progeny can have various combinations of the chromosomes of the two species. When male progeny of the backcross are examined for the length of the testis, it is found that the testis is essentially normal when the X chromosome is from *pseudoobscura;* when the X is from *persimilis,* the testis is shorter—increasing in abnormality as the num-ber of autosomes coming from *pseudoobscura* increases. What can you con-clude about reproductive barriers from these results?

18.17. The cotton species *Gossypium hirsutum* and *G. barbadense* are tetraploids (2n = 52) and are phenotypically intermediate between the diploid species *G. herbaceum* and *G. raimondii.* (Each is 2n = 26.) If cytological examination is made of meiosis in various hybrids, what would the following results reveal about the origin of these species?

   (a) *barbadense* × *raimondii* shows 13 pairs and 13 singles.
   (b) *barbadense* × *herbaceum* shows 13 pairs and 13 singles.
   (c) *raimondii* × *herbaceum* shows 26 singles.

18.18. What do the following two cases have in common?

   (a) Through artificial selection the evolution of corn, *Zea mays,* was aided by genes incorporated from teosinte, *Zea mexicana.*
   (b) Commercial wheat contains genes for rust resistance obtained from goat grass chromosomes.

Chapter 19

CHEMICAL NATURE OF GENES

I N THE preceding chapters the primary concern was with the definition of the genetic material on the basis of its capacity to recombine and mutate; our concern here will be with the chemical nature of the genetic material as revealed through chemical analyses. Let us try to determine which of the cell's chemical components are and which are not suitable to serve as genetic material. Since the nucleus contains genetic material in its chromosomes, any chemical substances located exclusively in the cytoplasm can, of course, be eliminated from consideration as the basis for nuclear genetic material. Because the genetic material seems to possess complex properties, one would expect that its chemical properties were also complex. On this basis, we can eliminate from consideration all inorganic compounds (compounds not containing carbon), since no class of inorganic compound enters into a sufficient variety of chemical reactions.

One unique feature of protoplasm is the speed and orderliness of its chemical activities. These two characteristics are due to the presence of proteins in the form of enzymes and cellular structures. Different kinds of proteins contain different numbers of amino acids. Since twenty or so different kinds of amino acids are found in the protein of organisms, the total number of different combinations is, for all practical purposes, infinite. Protein clearly possesses adequate complexity, so it is not unreason-

able to hypothesize that the genetic material is composed of protein.

If the gene were protein in nature, one would expect to find protein in the chromosomes but not, perhaps, of a type usually found in the cytoplasm. Chemical analyses of nuclei and chromosomes confirm both expectations by revealing the existence of *histones*—complex proteins which act as bases and are found primarily in chromosomes. Although the chromosomes of many cells contain histones, they are not found in the chromosomes of all cells. For example, histones are usually present in the somatic nuclei of fish; however, the sperm of trout, salmon, sturgeon, and herring instead contains *protamine,* a basic protein of simpler composition. The protamine in fish sperm is in turn replaced by histone in the somatic cells produced mitotically after fertilization. If genetic material is protein, the genetic specifications or information must be transferred from protamine to histone to protamine. At least in some organisms, then, the same genetic specifications would have to be carried in two chemical forms, protamine and histone.

Present knowledge does not prevent us from entertaining the view that alternative chemical compositions are possible for the genetic material, but any alternative must be capable of performing a number of activities in accordance with the principles already established. Nevertheless, the hypothesis that protamine and histone are both genetic material in the same organism is rather complicated, at least when one considers that there would be two chemical formulae for a single genotype. For the sake of simplicity, it would be more satisfactory if a single nuclear chemical substance were the genetic material.

Other proteins are found in chromosomes. Their quantity changes, however, according to the type and rate of metabolic activity performed by the cell. There is, therefore, no simple one-to-one relationship between their quantity and gene quantity. Consequently, additional hypotheses are required to explain genetic behavior. Despite the initial attractiveness of the hypothesis that the genetic material is proteinaceous, one can conclude that the types and amounts of nuclear protein actually found do not adequately support this view.

Chromosomes contain another chemical substance which seems to be absent in the cytoplasm (Figure 19–1). This chemical is a type of *nucleic acid* [1] called *deoxyribonucleic acid,* or *DNA,* a substance usually found combined with basic proteins like protamine and histone (by means of a chemical linkage not completely understood) to form *deoxyribonucleoproteins.* Before investigating the possibility that chromosomal DNA is genetic material, let us consider first the chemical composition of its molecule.

Chemical Composition of DNA

Organic bases. Chromosomal DNA contains organic ring compounds of which nitrogen is an integral part. The fundamental N-containing structure is a six-membered ring, as found in *benzene,* C_6H_6. Figure 19–2a shows the complete structural arrangement of benzene; Figure 19–2a′ is an abbreviated version with the carbon atoms of the ring omitted; Figure 19–2a″ is the same model condensed further by eliminating the hydrogen atoms attached to ring carbon atoms. The basic N-containing ring in DNA is a *pyrimidine.* This molecule (Figure 19–2b) has N substituted for the CH group at position 1 as well as at position 3 in the benzene ring. Figure 19–2b′ and Figure 19–2b″ show successive abbreviations of this formula corresponding to those used for benzene.

[1] Discovered by F. Miescher (1869).

The nitrogen found in DNA is also found in a derivative of the basic pyrimidine ring, called a *purine*. This molecule consists of a pyrimidine ring—minus the H atoms at positions 4 and 5—to which an *imidazole ring* (5-membered) is joined, so that the carbons at these positions are shared by both rings (Figures 19–2c, c′, and c″). Henceforth, the most abbreviated structural representation will be used for pyrimidines and purines. Since all pyrimidines and purines act chemically as bases, they are termed *organic bases.*

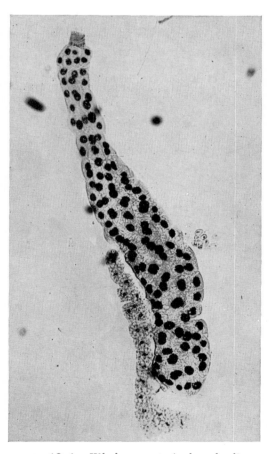

FIGURE 19–1. *Whole mount of a larval salivary gland of Drosophila. DNA stain is restricted to the nuclei. (Courtesy of J. Schultz.)*

Figure 19–3 shows the structural formulae for various types of pyrimidine. The names underlined are found in DNA. All the derivatives shown of the basic pyrimidine ring have an oxygen at position 2 replacing the H which is now at position 3. This oxygen is shown in the *keto* form (O = C<, with R representing an atom or group other than H). Two pyrimidines are commonly found in DNA: *cytosine* and *thymine*. *Cytosine* differs from the basic pyrimidine ring by having an *amino* (NH_2) group attached to the C at position 6 instead of the H. Consequently, cytosine can also be called 6-amino-2-oxypyrimidine. Replacement of the H at position 5 in cytosine by a *methyl* (CH_3) group produces *5-methyl cytosine;* this DNA pyrimidine is found in appreciable amounts

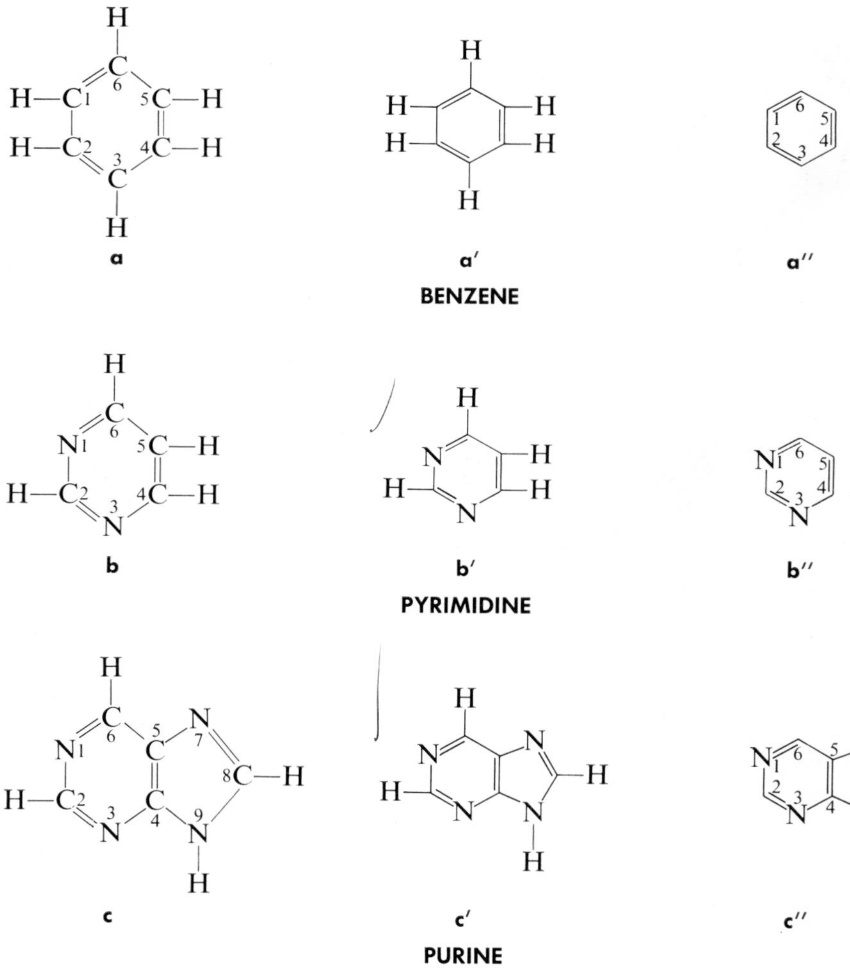

FIGURE 19–2. *Relationship between certain ring compounds.*

Pyrimidine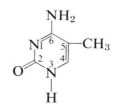

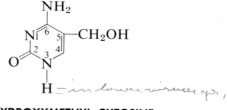

CYTOSINE
(6-amino-2-oxypyrimidine)

5-METHYL CYTOSINE
(6-amino-2-oxy-5-
methylpyrimidine)

5-HYDROXYMETHYL CYTOSINE
(6-amino-2-oxy-5-hydroxy-
methylpyrimidine)

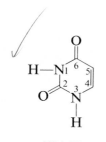

URACIL
(2,6-oxypyrimidine)

THYMINE
(2,6-oxy-5-methylpyrimidine)
(5-methyl uracil)

FIGURE 19–3. *Pyrimidines. Names of pyrimidines occurring in DNA are underlined.*

in wheat germ and in trace amounts in mammals, fish, and insects. Another pyrimidine, found only in the DNA of certain viruses attacking bacteria, has a *hydroxymethyl* (CH₂OH) group replacing the H at position 5 of cytosine, and is therefore called *5-hydroxymethyl cytosine.*

The other pyrimidine commonly found in DNA is *thymine.* Thymine is unique in having a keto group replace the H attached to the C at position 6; in addition a methyl group replaces the H at position 5. So thymine can also be called 2,6-oxy-5-methylpyrimidine. Note that all the pyrimidines shown differ primarily in the groups present at the 5 and 6 positions in the ring.

Figure 19–4 shows the structural formulae for various purines; those found in DNA are underlined. Two purines are commonly found in DNA: *adenine* and *guanine. Adenine* differs from the basic formula of purine by having an NH₂ group in place of H at position 6; therefore this compound can also be identified as 6-amino-purine. A derivative of adenine has a CH₃ substitute for an H in the NH₂ group at position 6 with *6-methylaminopurine* resulting; limited amounts of this purine have been found in DNA.

The other purine most frequent in DNA is *guanine* (Figure 19–4). Since guanine has an NH₂ group at position 2 and an O in keto form at position 6, it can also be

FIGURE 19–4. *Purines. Names of purines occurring in DNA are underlined.*

Purine

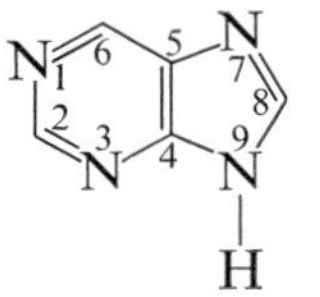

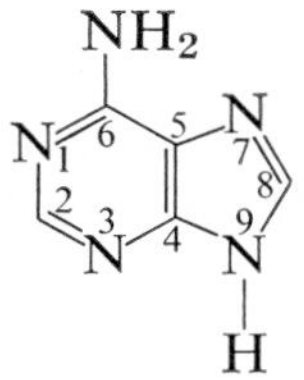

ADENINE
(6-aminopurine)

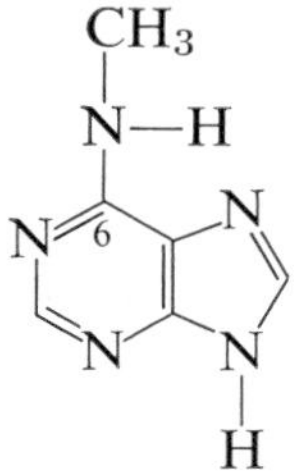

6-METHYLAMINOPURINE

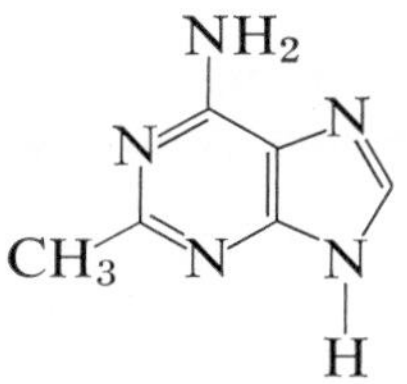

2-METHYL ADENINE
(2-methyl-6-aminopurine)

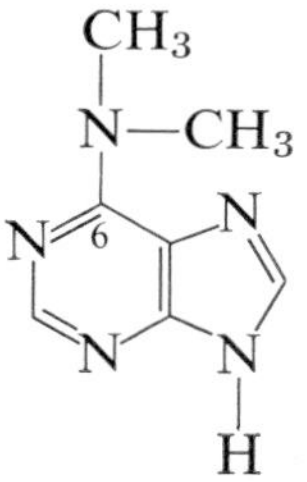

6-DIMETHYLAMINOPURINE

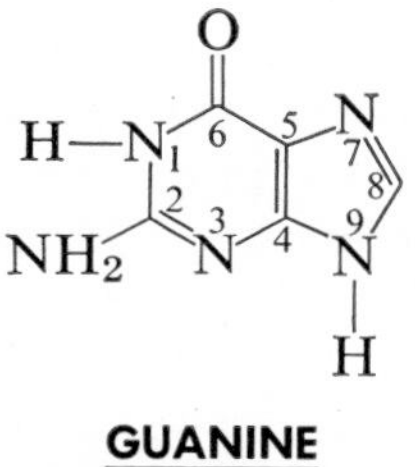

GUANINE
(2-amino-6-oxypurine)

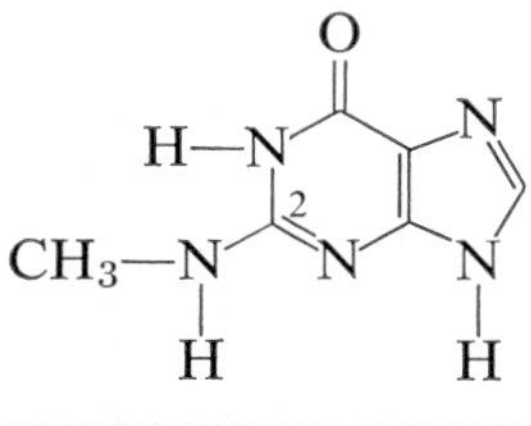

2-METHYLAMINO GUANINE

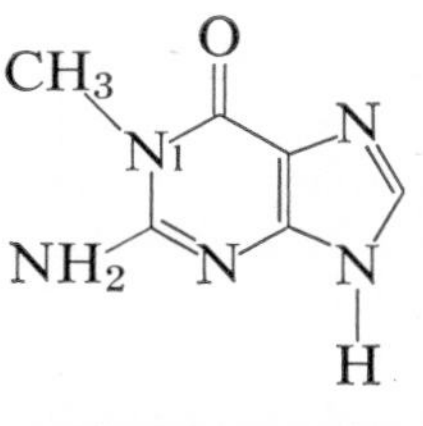

1-METHYL GUANINE

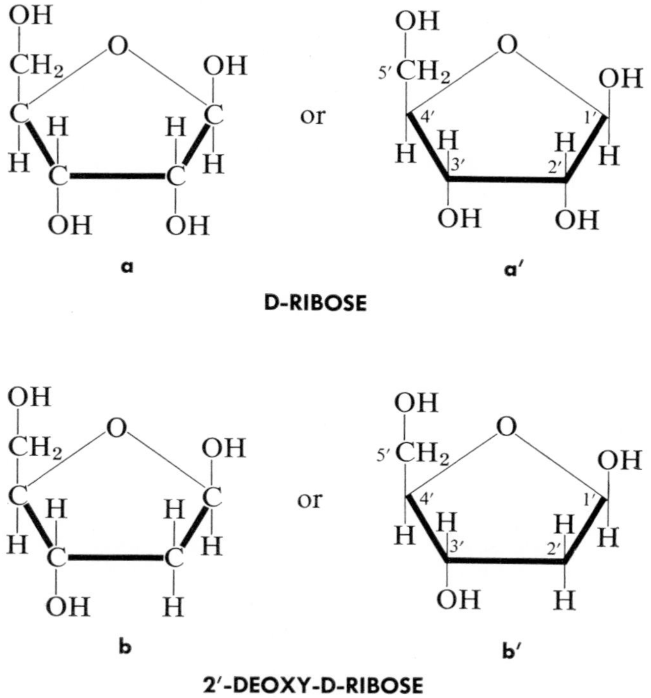

FIGURE 19–5. *Pentoses found in nucleic acids.*

called 2-amino-6-oxypurine. The purines differ largely in the groups attached at the 2 and 6 positions of the double ring.

Pentoses. *D-ribose* is a sugar (Figure 19–5a) containing five carbons (being, therefore, a *pentose*), four of which are joined with an O to form a five-membered ring. Figure 19–5a' employs the convention, used hereafter, of not showing the carbons of the ring. The carbons in pentose are given primed numbers to indicate their positions. DNA contains a pentose modified from the D-ribose structure by the absence of an oxygen at position 2', so that this sugar is named *2'-deoxy-D-ribose* and is often called *2-deoxyribose* or simply, *deoxyribose* (Figures 19–5b and b').

Deoxyribosides. Each purine or pyrimi-dine base in DNA is joined to a deoxyribose sugar to form the combination called a de-oxyribonucleoside or *deoxyriboside*. The four main deoxyribosides in DNA are: *de-oxycytidine* (for cytosine); (deoxy) *thy-midine* (for thymine); *deoxyadenosine* (for adenine); and *deoxyguanosine* (for gua-nine). The structure for these is shown in Figure 19–6. Note that the deoxyribose always joins to the organic base at its 1' position. The linkage involved occurs at position 3 in pyrimidines and at position 9 in purines.

Deoxyribotides. In DNA a *phosphate* (PO_4) group is always joined to a deoxy-riboside, forming a deoxyribonucleotide or *deoxyribotide*. The phosphate is attached either at the 3' or 5' position of the sugar

FIGURE 19–6.
Common deoxyribosides.

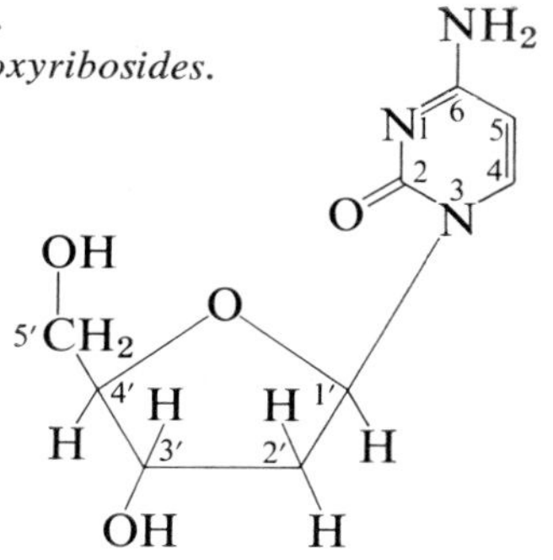

Deoxycytidine

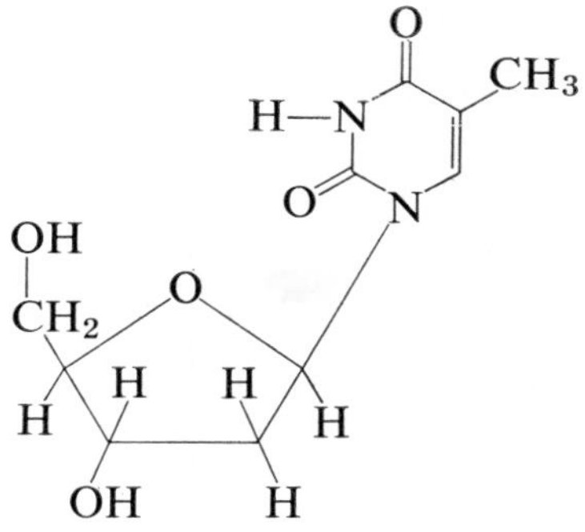

Thymidine

PYRIMIDINE DEOXYRIBOSIDES

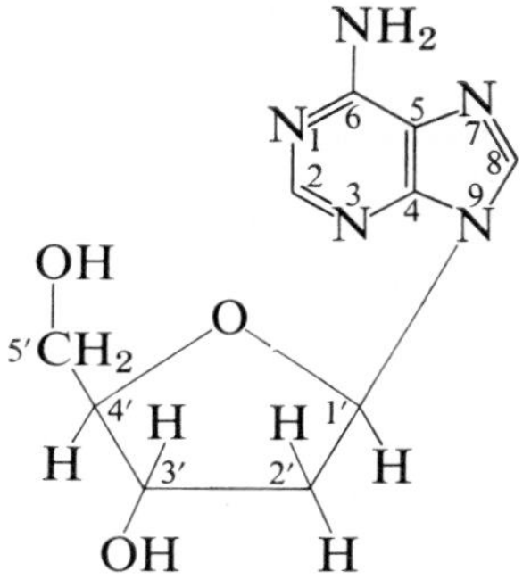

Deoxyadenosine

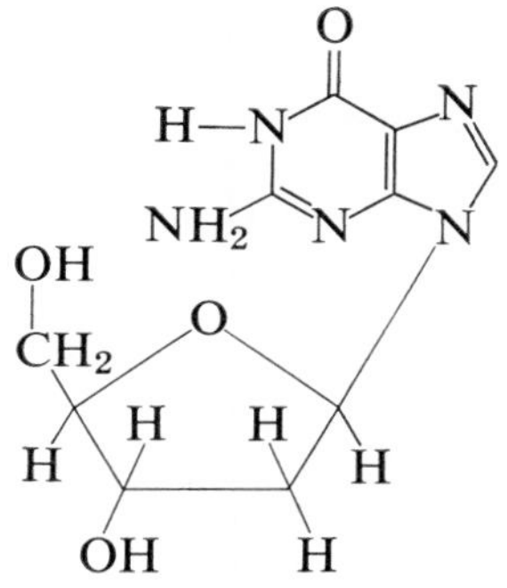

Deoxyguanosine

PURINE DEOXYRIBOSIDES

FIGURE 19–7. *Deoxyribotides.*

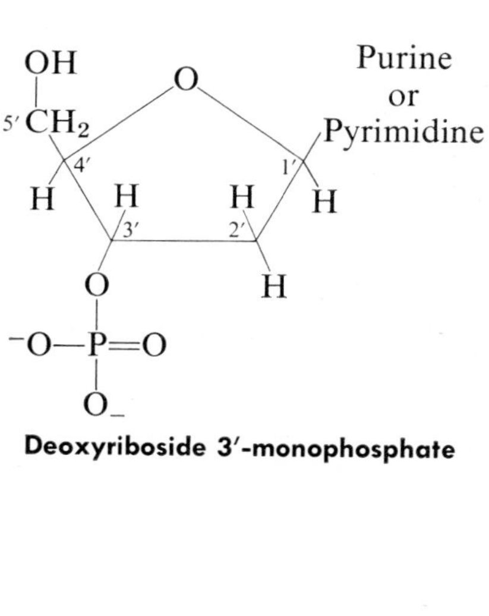

Deoxyriboside 3'-monophosphate

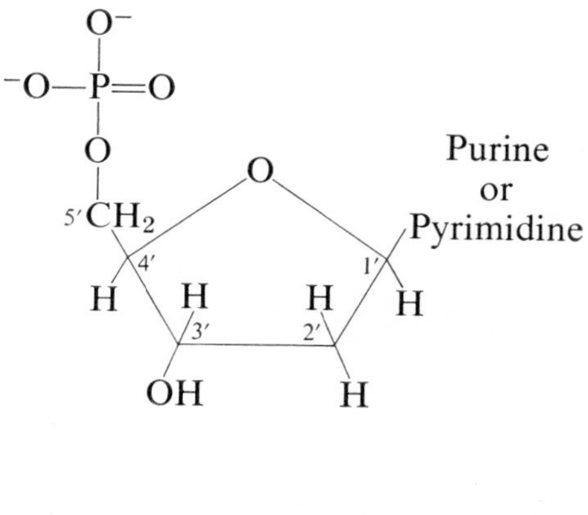

Deoxyriboside 5'-monophosphate

(a generalized form appears in Figure 19–7). This combination is shown specifically for the deoxyribotides containing the pyrimidine cytosine and the purine adenine in Figure 19–8. The deoxyriboside 5′-monophosphates of cytosine, thymine, adenine, and guanine are called, respectively, *deoxycytidylic acid, thymidylic acid, deoxyadenylic acid,* and *deoxyguanylic acid.* In summary, then, the basic unit of DNA is the deoxyribotide which is composed of a phosphate joined to a deoxyriboside; this, in turn, is composed of a deoxyribose joined to an organic base. These bases are either pyrimidines (most commonly cytosine and thymine) or purines (most commonly adenine and guanine).

Polydeoxyribotides. Chromosomal DNA occurs not as single deoxyribotides but as polydeoxyribonucleotides or *polydeoxyribo-*

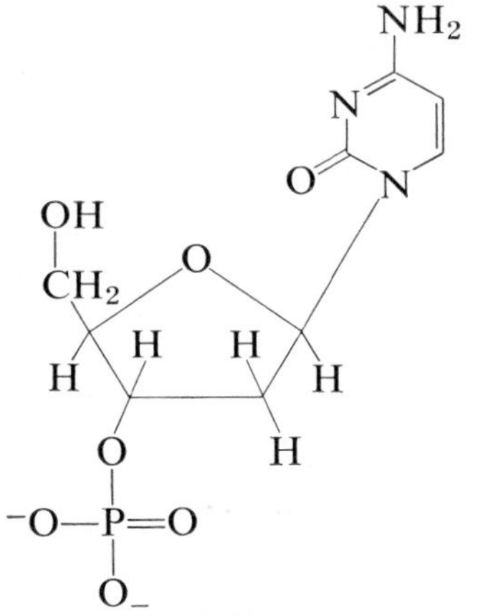

Deoxycytidine 3′-monophosphate

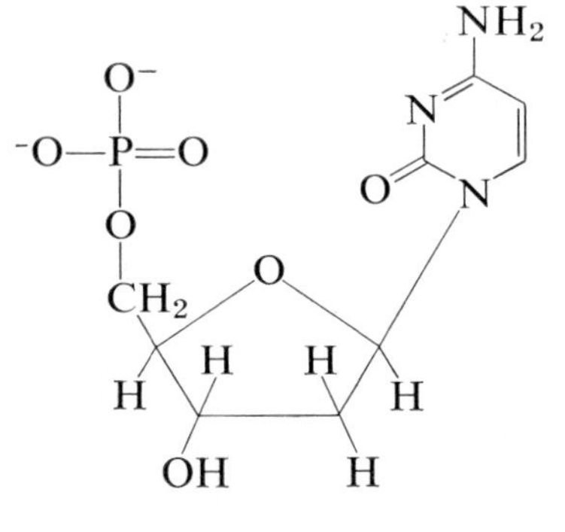

Deoxycytidine 5′-monophosphate
or
Deoxycytidylic acid

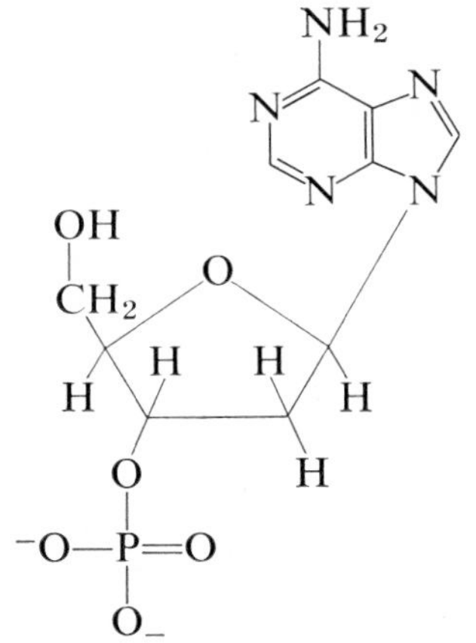

Deoxyadenosine 3′-monophosphate

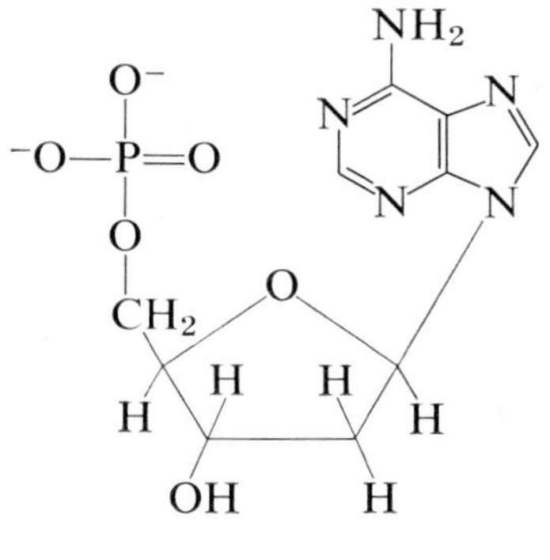

Deoxyadenosine 5′-monophosphate
or
Deoxyadenylic acid

FIGURE 19–8. *Specific deoxyribotides.*

tides. These molecules are actually chains in which the individual deoxyribotides comprise the links. The way these links are joined can be understood by examining the two separate deoxyriboside 5′-monophosphates shown at the right of Figure 19–8. These two compounds can become linked if the topmost O of the lower compound replaces the OH at position 3′ of the sugar in the upper compound. (The same reaction occurs when a phosphate is added to position 3′ of a deoxyriboside to produce a deoxyriboside 3′-monophosphate as illustrated in the two molecules shown at the left of Figure 19–8.) Since deoxyriboside 5′-monophosphates are capable of joining together by means of phosphate linkage at 3′, polydeoxyribotide chains of great length are produced. Figure 19–9 shows a portion of such a chain. Note that the polydeoxyribotide is a linear—that is, unbranched—molecule, whose *backbone* consists of sugar-phosphate linkages and whose linearity is independent of the particular bases present at any point. This independence means that the structure of the chain is uninfluenced by the sequences of bases which can be in any array. Notice, moreover, that this *polymer* (a molecule composed of a number of identical units) of deoxyribotides does not read the same in both directions. As indicated by the arrows, the sugar linkages to phosphate read 3′5′, 3′5′, and so on; whereas in the opposite direction they read 5′3′, 5′3′, et cetera. Because of this difference, the polymerized DNA molecule is said to be *polarized*.

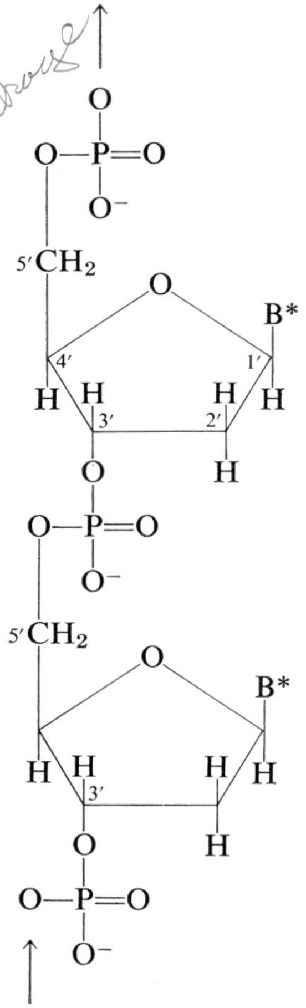

Measuring DNA Quantity

Two main methods are commonly used in determining the amount of DNA present in the nucleus: the histochemical and the cytochemical. The *histochemical method* employs whole tissues for the chemical extraction and measurement of DNA. Sometimes chemical analysis is made of masses of nuclei, from which most of the adhering cytoplasm has been removed by special treatment, to determine the average amount of DNA per nucleus. In the second, *cytochemical,* approach the DNA content of single nuclei, chromosomes, or chromosomal parts is determined. This method is based upon the finding that DNA is the only substance

* Pyrimidine or purine base of appropriate type (usually cytosine, thymine, adenine or guanine).

FIGURE 19–9. *Polydeoxyribotide.*

in the cell which stains under certain conditions. The *Feulgen technique* stains DNA purple (see p. 8), whereas the *methyl green method* stains DNA green. When properly applied, not only are these stains specific for DNA, but the amount of stain retained is directly proportional to the amount of DNA present. A given amount of dye bound by DNA will make a quantitative change in the amount of light of different wavelengths it transmits. These measurements can then be used to calculate the amount of DNA present. For example: a stained nucleus is placed under the *micro*scope; different appropriate wavelengths in the visible *spectr*um are sent through the nucleus, and a series of *photo*graphs is taken; its DNA content is *measured* by density changes of the nucleus. From the italicized portions of words comes the name of this procedure, *microspectrophotometry*.

A different application of microspectrophotometry utilizes another property of the purines and pyrimidines in DNA. These bases absorb ultraviolet light of wavelengths near 2600 A (*Angstrom units*). When other substances absorbing ultraviolet of these wavelengths are removed by enzymatic or other treatments, the quantity of DNA can be measured by its absorbence. As one test of the validity of the absorbency, one can remove the DNA from the chromosome by the use of enzymes—*deoxyribonucleases, DNAases, DNAses,* or *DNases*. These organic catalysts break the long DNA chains into short pieces which then can be washed out of the chromosomes and the nucleus. Such treatment produces the expected loss of absorbency.

DNA as Genetic Material

Having described the chemical nature and quantitative measurement of chromosomal DNA, we are in a position to consider some results bearing upon the relationship between chromosomal DNA and the genetic material of the nucleus:

1. The quantity of DNA increases during the metabolic stage until it is exactly double (within the limits of experimental error) the amount present at the beginning of this stage. Mitosis apparently distributes equal amounts of DNA to the two telophase nuclei. Therefore, when first formed, all the diploid nuclei of an individual have approximately the same DNA content.
2. The amount of DNA in a haploid gamete is roughly half that found in a newly formed diploid metabolic nucleus of the same individual. Fertilization, which restores the diploid chromosome condition, also restores the DNA content characteristic of the diploid cell.
3. Polyploid cells increase proportionally in DNA content.
4. Different cells of a tissue such as the salivary gland of larval Drosophila show different amounts of polynemy in their chromosomes. Since the DNA content of these different nuclei is found to be proportional to their volume, it is assumed to be a direct reflection of the degree of polynemy.
5. The capacity of different wavelengths of ultraviolet light to induce mutations in fungi, corn, Drosophila, and other organisms is paralleled by the capacity of DNA to absorb these wavelengths.
6. By tagging or labeling atoms (those that are radioactive or have an abnormal weight), it is found that many cellular components are being replaced continuously during metabolism. Despite this "atomic turnover," however, the total amount of cellular material does not increase. DNA is unusual because it shows little, if any, turnover; in other words, DNA maintains its integrity at the molecular level.

NUCLEIC ACID	COMMON PYRIMIDINE (PY) or PURINE (PU) BASE	PENTOSE	NUCLEOSIDE	(MONO-) NUCLEOTIDE with PO_4 at 5'
		2'-deoxy-D-ribose	deoxyriboside	deoxyribotide
DNA	Cytosine PY		Deoxycytidine	Deoxycytidylic acid
	Thymine PY		Thymidine	Thymidylic acid
	Adenine PU		Deoxyadenosine	Deoxyadenylic acid
	Guanine PU		Deoxyguanosine	Deoxyguanylic acid
		D - ribose	riboside	ribotide
RNA	Cytosine PY		Cytidine	5' Cytidylic acid
	Uracil PY		Uridine	5' Uridylic acid
	Adenine PU		Adenosine	5' Adenylic acid
	Guanine PU		Guanosine	5' Guanylic acid

FIGURE 19–10. *Terminology for nucleic acids and their components.*

7. DNA is a linear, unbranched, polymer—a reasonable finding if one expected DNA to represent a sequence of genes. Just as interstitial genes are bipolar (see p. 189), so are interstitial segments of DNA, since each deoxyriboside joins only to two other deoxyribosides via its 3' and 5' sugar linkages to phosphate.

In its cellular location and in all of the respects mentioned above, the observations are consistent with the view that *DNA either is, or is intimately associated with, the genetic material.*

Chemical Composition of RNA

In addition to DNA another type of nucleic acid is found in the chromosome. This is *ribonucleic acid* or *RNA*. Normally chromosomal RNA is found in combination with protein in the form of *ribonucleoprotein*.

Because the RNA content of chromosomes varies within a cell and among diploid cells of the same organism according to metabolic activity, RNA is unlikely to be the chemical basis of genes in typical (DNA-containing) chromosomes. Nevertheless, let us discuss the chemical composition of RNA, noting in particular its resemblance to DNA.

Chromosomal RNA, like DNA, is a long, unbranched polymer with the basic unit being a ribonucleotide or *ribotide*. The ribotide is like the deoxyribotide, for it, too, is a combination of organic base plus pentose plus phosphate; one way in which it differs is that the pentose is *D-ribose* (Figure 19–5) rather than 2'-deoxy-D-ribose. Another difference is found in RNA's pyrimidines. The two pyrimidines commonly found in RNA are cytosine (also common in DNA) and *uracil* (2,6-oxypyrimidine—not found in typical DNA). Uracil's structure is shown in Figure 19–3. The two purines commonly found in DNA, adenine and guanine, are also common in ribotides. In RNA the base plus sugar combination is called a ribonucleoside or *riboside*. Ribosides are joined together by phosphates joined both at the 3' and 5' positions of the sugar just as in DNA; consequently Figure 19–9 can represent a *polyribotide* if an O is added at each 2' position (making each sugar D-ribose), and if among the bases usually present uracil is substituted for thymine. It should be noted that RNA also absorbs ultraviolet light of 2600 A but can be removed from the chromosome by treatment with *ribonucleases* or *RNases*.

In summary, typical chromosomes contain two nucleic acids, DNA and RNA. These normally occur in combination with protein to form *nucleoproteins* (deoxyribonucleoprotein and ribonucleoprotein) in which DNA and RNA occur as *polynucleotides* (polydeoxyribotides and polyribotides). Each polynucleotide is built of (mono-) *nucleotides* (deoxy- and ribotides, respec-

tively), which in turn are composed of phosphates joined at 5' of *nucleosides* (deoxyribo- and ribosides). These nucleosides are made up of a pentose (2'-deoxy-D-ribose and D-ribose) joined to a pyrimidine (usually cytosine or thymine and cytosine or uracil) or to a purine (usually adenine or guanine). A portion of this terminology is summarized in Figure 19–10.

Although the RNA in chromosomes possesses neither the proper quantitative variation nor the constancy expected of ordinary chromosomal genes, it does have the same linear organization as DNA. Moreover, some viruses composed primarily of ribonucleoprotein (influenza, poliomyelitis, and other encephalitic viruses; plant-attacking viruses such as the tobacco mosaic virus; and certain bacteria-attacking viruses) possess genetic properties but do not contain DNA. Since DNA rather than protein is favored as being the genetic chemical under typical chromosomal conditions, it is reasonable to consider RNA rather than the protein to be the chemical basis of genetic specification in these particular viruses.

SUMMARY AND CONCLUSIONS

This chapter is an initial attempt to throw some light on the chemical nature of the genetic material. The search for chemical substances with properties of the genetic material has led to a consideration of the protein found in chromosomes, but the available evidence does not actively support such a primary role for protein.

It is hypothesized that DNA either is or, at least, is intimately associated with the genetic material in chromosomes in view of the following: the localization of DNA; its quantity and distribution in mitosis, meiosis, and fertilization; its quantity in polyploid and polynemic situations; the parallel between DNA absorption and the mutagenicity of ultraviolet light; the maintenance of molecular integrity; and its long, linear, unbranched arrangement. It is also hypothesized that RNA may assume the genetic role in certain DNA-free viruses. Some details of the chemical nature of DNA and RNA are presented.

Subsequent chapters will aim to further test the hypothesis that DNA (and RNA in special cases) is typically either the genetic material or intimately associated with it. Our ultimate objective is to determine the chemical units of the genetic material—chemical units corresponding to the genetic units of replication, mutation, recombination, and function.

REFERENCES

Chargaff, E., and Davidson, J. N. (Eds.), *The Nucleic Acids,* 2 Vols., New York: Academic Press, 1955; Vol. 3, New York: Academic Press, 1960.

Davidson, J. N., and Cohn, W. E. (Eds.), *Progress in Nucleic Acid Research,* 2 Vols., New York: Academic Press, 1963.

Miescher, F., "On the Chemical Composition of Pus Cells," translated in *Great Experiments in Biology,* Gabriel, M. L., and S. Fogel (Eds.), Englewood Cliffs, N.J.: Prentice-Hall, 1955, pp. 233–239.

Potter, V. R., *Nucleic Acid Outlines,* Vol. 1, Minneapolis: Burgess Publ. Co., 1960.

Steiner, R. F., and Beers, R. F., Jr., *Polynucleotides. Natural and Synthetic Nucleic Acids,* Amsterdam: Elsevier Publ. Co., 1961.

QUESTIONS FOR DISCUSSION

19.1. Is it simpler to postulate that DNA rather than protein constitutes the genetic material? Why?

19.2. What is the chemical distinction between:

    (a) a mononucleotide and a polynucleotide?
    (b) a nucleotide and a nucleoside?
    (c) a pyrimidine and a purine?
    (d) a ribose and a deoxyribose sugar?

19.3. Draw the complete structural formula of a polyribotide having the base sequence adenine, uracil, guanine, cytosine.

19.4. Express thymine as a derivative of uracil. What part of the term deoxythymidine is superfluous? Why?

19.5. What evidence can you provide to support the view that viruses possess genetic properties?

19.6. How would you proceed to measure the absorbency of ultraviolet light by chromosomal DNA? Chromosomal RNA?

19.7. Do you believe that the evidence so far presented provides conclusive proof that DNA is genetic material in chromosomes? Why?

19.8. What is your opinion of the hypothesis that DNA is the chemical basis for recombination, but that protein is the chemical basis for gene function?

19.9. Is DNA complex enough to serve as the chemical basis of gene action? Explain.

19.10. Do you think the term *chemon* could be defined usefully? Justify your opinion.

19.11. Discuss the similarities and the differences between DNA and RNA.

Chapter 20

ORGANIZATION AND REPLICATION OF DNA *IN VIVO*

THAT DNA serves as the chemical basis of chromosomal genetic material was supported by the indirect evidence presented in the last chapter. The *primary structure* of DNA was described as a single, long, unbranched, polarized chain of nucleotides. If the DNA polymer were genetic material, one would expect it to be linearly differentiated so that successive portions could represent different genes. This differentiation cannot be based upon either the deoxyribose sugar or the phosphate, since one of each is present in every nucleotide. Therefore, all differences in genetic information along the length of the DNA strand would have to be due to the organic bases present. Since species differ genetically, one might expect them to differ in DNA quantity and/or base content.

Figure 20–1 gives the per genome DNA content of various types of organisms. It is generally true that the higher an organism is on the evolutionary scale, the larger is its genomic DNA content. Perhaps it would be more meaningful to say that the DNA content per genome increases as the number of functions controlled by genes increases. Histochemical analyses reveal the organic base content in DNA extracted from various species. Considering the total amount of the bases in an extract as 100%, we see in Figure 20–2 the portions found as adenine (A), thymine (T), guanine (G), and cytosine (C). There is considerable variation in the relative frequency of bases, ranging from organisms relatively rich in A and T and poor in C and G (sea urchin) to those in which A and T are much less abundant than C and G (tubercle bacillus). The DNA samples taken from radically different species contained relatively different amounts of the four bases.

Do these data suggest that a shift in the sequence of bases can produce genetic differences? The assumption that different orders of the same bases might be involved in specifying different genetic units is consistent with the fact that the chicken, salmon, and locust—certainly all very different genetically—have very similar base ratios. An alternative explanation would be that these species are molecular polyploids which differ only in the multiples of a basic set of DNA molecules they contain. This possibility can be eliminated from serious consideration in light of our knowledge that chromosomal polyploidy has made a limited contribution to evolution, at least in the animal kingdom (Chapters 11, 18).

As long as relatively crude histochemical analyses are made of the total amount of DNA in cells with a large DNA content, we should expect to find roughly the same base ratios among the different members of a single species. This expectation has proved true. Moreover, the same base ratios are found in different normal and neoplastic

Man, Mouse, Maize	$5\text{-}7 \times 10^9$
Drosophila	8×10^7
Aspergillus	4×10^7
Escherichia	1×10^7
Bacteriophage T4	2×10^5
Bacteriophage X174	4.5×10^3 (Unpaired)

FIGURE 20–1. *DNA nucleotide pairs per genome in various organisms.*

	ADENINE	THYMINE	GUANINE	CYTOSINE
Man (sperm)	31.0	31.5	19.1	18.4
Chicken	28.8	29.2	20.5	21.5
Salmon	29.7	29.1	20.8	20.4
Locust	29.3	29.3	20.5	20.7
Sea urchin	32.8	32.1	17.7	17.7
Yeast	31.7	32.6	18.8	17.4
Tuberculosis bacillus	15.1	14.6	34.9	35.4
Escherichia coli	26.1	23.9	24.9	25.1
Vaccinia virus	29.5	29.9	20.6	20.3
E. coli bacteriophage T_2	32.6	32.6	18.2	16.6*

FIGURE 20–2. *Base composition of DNA from various organisms.* (*5-hydroxymethyl cytosine.*)

tissues in the same and among different human beings. Nevertheless, a genome is expected to contain many DNA molecules which differ in base content and sequence.

The variation found in $\dfrac{A + T}{G + C}$ in different species—the ratio is about 0.4 for the tubercle bacillus and about 1.8 for the sea urchin—is consistent with our chemical knowledge, since the DNA strand imposes no limitation upon either the types or the frequencies of the bases present along the length of the fiber. However, the amount of A and the amount of T in the DNA of a given species are remarkably equal as are the amounts of G and C (Figure 20–2). Since in each species A = T and G = C, it is also true that A + G = T + C; in other words, the total number of DNA purines

always equals the total number of DNA pyrimidines. Although this regularity is common to all the chromosomal DNA's listed, there is nothing in the primary structure of DNA which helps to explain this significant fact. That the primary structure of DNA is the same in all these organisms suggests, however, that these regularities may be connected with some additional, general characteristic of chromosomal DNA structure.

An understanding of the basis for the A = T and G = C relationships may come from studies of an entirely different kind. It has been known for some time that a beam of X rays is bent or refracted when it passes through material. If the material through which the rays pass is completely heterogeneous in structure and orientation,

FIGURE 20–3. *X ray diffraction photographs of suitably hydrated fibers of DNA, showing the so-called B configuration. A. Pattern obtained using the sodium salt of DNA. B. Pattern obtained using the lithium salt of DNA. This pattern permits a most thorough analysis of DNA. (Courtesy of Biophysics Research Unit, Medical Research Council, King's College, London.)*

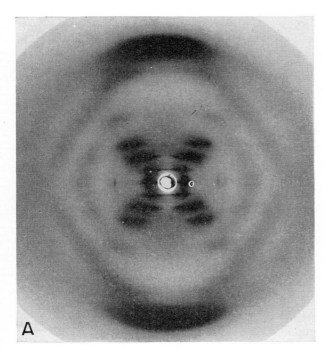

A

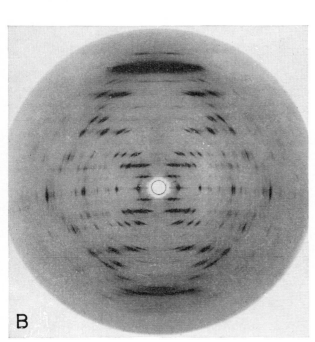

B

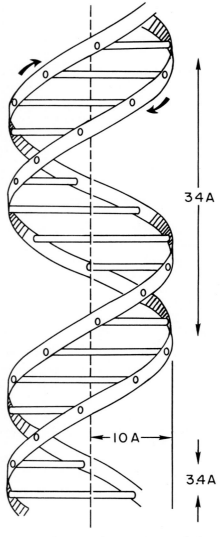

FIGURE 20–4. *The Watson-Crick double-stranded helix configuration of DNA.*

the emergent beam shows no regularity when it is refracted. But if the material is composed of macromolecular units and/or molecular subunits spatially arranged in a regular manner, then the emergent beam will form an *X-ray diffraction pattern*. This particular X-ray pattern can be used to identify units and subunits that are repeated at regular intervals. It is known that each nucleotide in a DNA chain occupies a length of 3.4 A along the chain; this repetition is detectable by the characteristic X-ray diffraction pattern it produces—the black spots located symmetrically near the upper and lower edges of both photographs in Figure 20–3.

X-ray diffraction patterns have been obtained from the DNA of numerous species. In some cases the DNA was not removed from the nucleus; in other cases it was removed and also separated from the nucleoprotein protein. The spacings between DNA parts, and hence the X-ray diffraction patterns, depend upon the degree to which the DNA is hydrated. In all cases, provided that the DNA is similarly hydrated, essentially the same patterns attributable to DNA are found (Figure 20–3). In addition to the 3.4 A repetition, a study of these common patterns shows other repeated units which can be explained only if *DNA does not usually occur as a single strand*. (On the other hand, X-ray diffraction studies show that chromosomal RNA usually is single-stranded.) Here then is clear evidence for the existence of a *secondary structure to DNA* normally found in all chromosomes. (We might infer some sort of secondary organization for DNA from the independent observation of the equivalences A = T and G = C.) The simplest explanation consistent with the diffraction results of M. H. F. Wilkins and co-workers was proposed by J. D. Watson and F. H. C. Crick (1953a). They hypothesized that *DNA is normally two-stranded* (Figure 20–4); each strand being a polynucleotide, and the two strands coiled around each other in such a manner that they cannot be separated unless the ends are permitted to revolve. This kind of coiling is called *plectonemic* (coiled like the strands of a rope) in contrast with *paranemic coiling,* which permits the separation of two coils without revolving their ends (just as two bedsprings pushed together can be separated).

The Watson-Crick model for the secondary organization of DNA macromolecules involves a double helix in which each strand is *coiled right-handedly* (clockwise). This coil direction is the same as that found in the secondary structure of amino acid chains, *polypeptides*. The model shows the pentose-phosphate backbone of each strand on the outside of the spiral (comprising the ribbon), whereas the relatively flat organic bases projecting into the center (as bars) lie perpendicular to the long axis of the fiber (indicated by a vertical interrupted line). The backbone completes a turn each 34 A. Since each nucleotide occupies 3.4 A along the length of a strand, 10 nucleotides occur per complete turn, and each successive nucleotide turns 36° in the horizontal plane (so that 10 nucleotides complete the 360° required for a complete turn).

The two helices are held together by chemical bonds between bases on different strands. The two strands can form a regular double helix with diameter uniformly about 20 A only if the bases on different strands join in pairs, each pair composed of one pyrimidine and one purine. A pair of pyrimidines (being single rings) would be too short to bridge the gap between backbones, whereas two purines (being double rings) would take up too much space. Moreover, it is found that the pyrimidine-purine pairing must be either between C and G or between T and A, for only in this way is the maximum number of stabilizing bondages between them produced. The type of stabilizing bond holding the members of a *base pair* together is called a *hydrogen bond* or *H bond*. The base pairs, their H bonds indicated by interrupted lines, are shown in Figure 20–5; the hydrogens that are removed when the base pairs join the backbones are included in the diagrams. The top half of the illustration shows the C-G (and G-C) arrangements. Note in the C-G pair that cytosine has been turned over (from left to right) relative to the way it was shown in Figure 19–3. Three H bonds are formed. Two occur between NH_2 and O (the 6—NH_2 of C with the 6—O of G; the 2—O of C with the 2—NH_2 of G). One occurs between the 1—N of C and the 1—NH of G. The G:C pair is identical to C:G shown except that, in this case, the base turned over is guanine.

The bottom half of Figure 20–5 shows the other type of base pair (T:A or A:T, in which T and A have been turned over relative to the way they were shown in Figures 19–3 and 19–4). In this pair only two H bonds are formed, one between the 6—O of T and the 6—NH_2 of A; the other between the 1—NH of T and the 1—N of A. Although the hydrogen bond is a weak chemical bond as compared to the C—C bond, there are so many H bonds along a long double helix that the entire structure is fairly rigid and paracrystalline even when moderately hydrated. Note that the region surrounding two base-paired nucleosides can be separated into two portions relative to the pentoses. The smaller portion is called the *minor groove* (the region surrounding the lower parts of the base pairs shown in Figure 20–5), and the larger portion, the *major groove* (the region surrounding the upper parts).

Recall that the double helix configuration of DNA does not dictate the sequence of bases along the length of a chain. But remember also that the sizes of the pyrimidines and purines and their H bonds do dictate

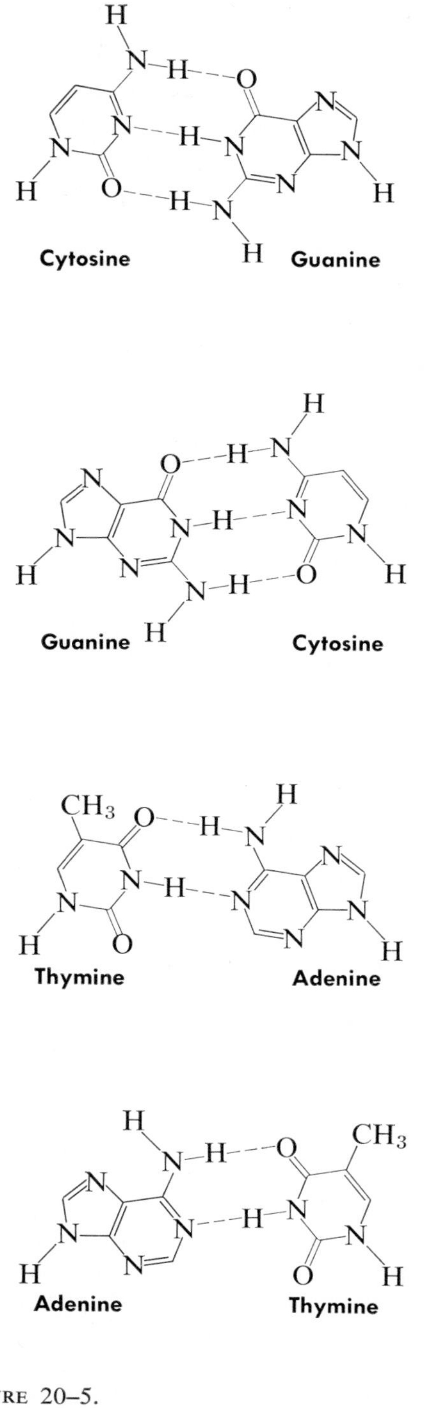

FIGURE 20–5.
Base pairs formed between single DNA strands.

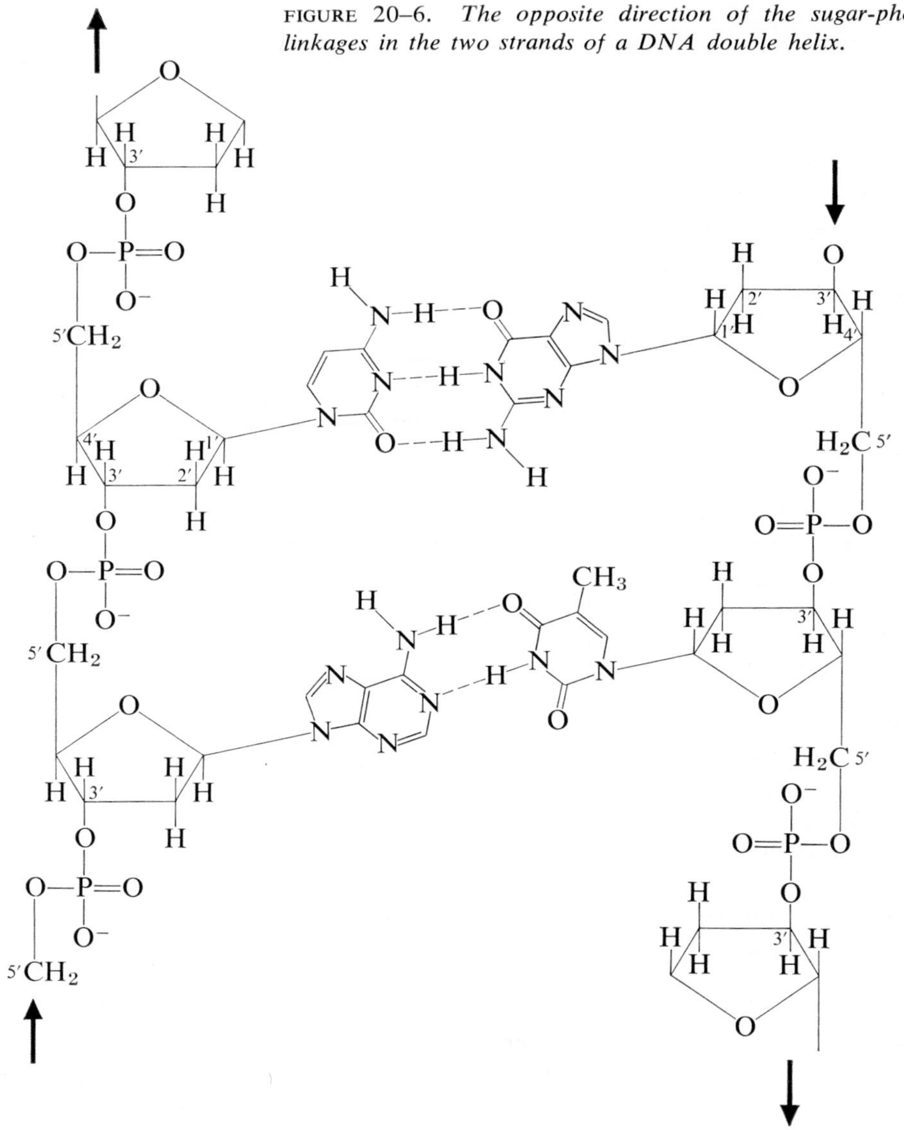

FIGURE 20–6. *The opposite direction of the sugar-phosphate linkages in the two strands of a DNA double helix.*

that A in one chain can pair only with T in the other chain—similarly C with G—to form a double helix of constant diameter whose strands are held together by the maximum number of H bonds. Since A and T always go together (as do C and G), the equivalences A = T and C = G, derived from chemical analysis of DNA, become meaningful as the direct consequence of the

secondary structure of DNA. In fact, these chemical equivalences provide the first independent test of the Watson-Crick model constructed initially on the basis of the X-ray diffraction diagrams among other considerations.

To form the maximum number of H bonds between a purine and a pyrimidine, it is necessary to represent one of the two as being turned over, so that the number 1 atoms of both face each other. This arrangement has an important consequence for the orientation of the two chains relative to each other, as represented in the two-dimensional diagram, Figure 20–6. The bases in the chain at the right all face the accustomed way; those in the left chain are all turned over. For each base to join to its sugar in the same three-dimensional way, the sugars must be arranged as shown. Notice, in proceeding downward from the top of the right chain, the $PO_4^{\equiv}$ linkages to sugar read 3'5', 3'5', and so on; reading down in the same way, however, the left chain is 5'3', 5'3', et cetera, so that *the member chains in a double helix run in opposite directions,* as indicated by the arrows.

The X-ray diffraction results, which led to the double helix hypothesis, do not tell us that all DNA in chromosomes is two-stranded, or that a double strand is never single-stranded at certain places or at certain times. Such data prove only that, in the wide variety of organisms studied, a very appreciable part of the chromosomal DNA is not single-stranded. The base content and organization of DNA in viruses attacking bacteria have also been studied by chemical analysis and by X-ray diffraction. In the varieties T_2 and T_7, for example, the data are entirely consistent with DNA's being present in the Watson-Crick double-helix configuration. In the mature bacterial virus particles of two other smaller varieties (called ϕX174 and ϕS13), however, the DNA is definitely single-stranded. This is reflected in the nonequivalence of A and T and C and G and the absence of those patterns indicating a secondary structure in the X-ray diffraction photographs.

Whenever the DNA is in the double-helix configuration, we can consider *one strand is the complement of the other,* so that if the sequence of bases in one strand is known, the composition of the other strand can be

determined. Thus, if one strand has the base sequence ATTCGAC, the other strand would have to contain TAAGCTG in the corresponding region.

If DNA is genetic material, we expect DNA to be replicated just as accurately as genetic material. Since the base sequence in one strand is complementary to the sequence in the other, we immediately see a simple way in which the double helix might be replicated: [1] the two strands separate, and then each strand builds its complement. In this explanation, called the *strand separation hypothesis of DNA replication,* each strand is visualized as a *mold* or *template.* We know that complex surfaces (like statues) can be copied exactly by making a mold which, in turn, can be used to make a second mold which is an exact copy of the original configuration. In the present case, the two complementary strands of DNA can be viewed as molds, or templates, for each other. One strand or both strands act as a mold on which the complementary strand is synthesized. Figure 20–7 shows one possible sequence of events. At the top of this figure, the two strands are coming apart due to rupture of the H bonds. At the center the two single chains exist in the presence of single nucleotides or their precursors. When the complementary free nucleotide approaches the single strand, its base is H-bonded. Then, after two or more nucleotides have bonded to the single strand, they are linked—perhaps by an enzyme—to start the new complementary strand. The bottom diagrams show sections of the complementary strands whose synthesis is already completed.

Experiments can be designed [2] to simul-

---

[1] Based upon the hypothesis of J. D. Watson and F. H. C. Crick (1953b, c).
[2] Based upon those of M. Meselson and F. W. Stahl.

taneously test the hypotheses for both the double-helix structure of DNA and its replication after strand separation. Remember that every pyrimidine or purine base normally found in DNA contains two or four N atoms, respectively. Ordinarily, these are atoms of N-14, or *light nitrogen*. It should be possible to grow bacteria in a culture medium whose only nitrogen source is in the form of a heavier isotope, N-15, or *heavy nitrogen*. If so, after a number of generations have passed, almost all of the DNA present will have been synthesized using heavy nitrogen. Suppose also that one can synchronize the multiplication of the bacteria containing heavy DNA. What will we ex-

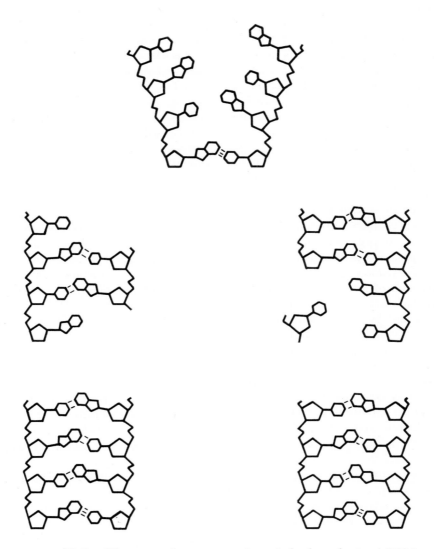

FIGURE 20–7. *Diagrammatic representation of the hypothesis of DNA replication after strand separation.*

pect to happen if these bacteria are quickly washed, placed in a culture medium containing only light nitrogen, and permitted to continue their synchronous multiplication? The DNA should replicate each time the bacteria undergo cell division. During the first replication of DNA, the two strands containing heavy nitrogen should separate, and each should synthesize a complementary strand containing only light nitrogen. Thus, after one DNA replication, the density of the DNA molecules should be exactly midway between completely light and completely heavy DNA.

To test whether or not this expectation is actually observed, DNA is extracted from "all-heavy" bacteria and also from "all-light" bacteria. These extracts, serving as controls, first are ultracentrifuged separately and then together in a fluid medium containing cesium chloride. When a solution of cesium chloride is ultracentrifuged for about twenty hours, a gradient of densities is established because the concentration of cesium chloride is greatest at the bottom of the ultracentrifuge tube and least at the top. In the ultracentrifuge tube DNA assumes the position corresponding to its own density. In the density gradient the position of the DNA can be detected by its absorption of ultraviolet light at 2600 A. Two separate bands of DNA are found in the medium, one containing the all-heavy and the other the all-light DNA. When DNA is extracted at various time intervals after the originally all-heavy bacteria have been placed in the all-light nitrogen culture medium, the DNA band in the ultracentrifuge tube is observed to move from the all-heavy DNA position to a position exactly intermediate between the all-heavy and all-light positions (Figure 20–8). This result is exactly what is expected if after one replication the DNA is "hybrid" in density.

What would one expect to find after an additional DNA replication? In this case, the two strands of the hybrid DNA should separate, and light complementary strands should be made by both the light and heavy single strands. So, after a second replication, half of the double-stranded DNA molecules should be all-light, and half should be intermediate between all-light and all-heavy (that is, they should be hybrid). In fact, the samples of DNA taken at later intervals show the single band at the intermediate position in the ultracentrifuge tube has become two bands, one at the hybrid position and one at the all-light position. It should be noted, moreover, that the time required for the change from all-heavy to all-hybrid molecules, or for the change from all-hybrid to half all-light and half hybrid molecules, is approximately the interval occupied by a bacterial generation.

Although these results are consistent with the hypothesis of replication of double-stranded DNA following chain separation, they do not automatically exclude other possible explanations. It might be claimed, for instance, that the double helix grows not by separation of strands followed by the synthesis of complementary ones, but by the addition of new double strand material to the ends of the original double strand. This alternative explanation can be tested in two ways.

If the all-heavy molecules present initially grew by adding light material to their ends, they should be composed linearly of double strands that are successively heavy and light. It should then be possible for sonic vibrations to fragment the macromolecules into smaller segments, some all-heavy and others all-light. This result should be detectable in the ultracentrifuge tube by some of the sonicated hybrid DNA assuming the all-light and some the all-heavy positions. However, nothing happens; the DNA remains in essentially the same hybrid position whether or not it is sonically fragmented.

A second test of the view that DNA syn-

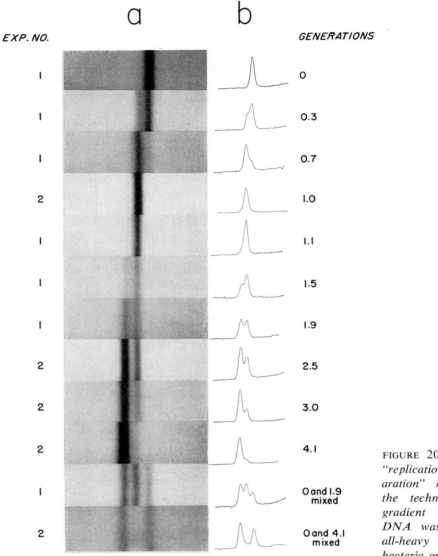

FIGURE 20–8. *Test of the "replication after chain separation" hypothesis, using the technique of density gradient centrifugation. DNA was extracted from all-heavy (N-15-labeled) bacteria grown for different generation times on all-light (N-14-containing) medium. The extracts were subjected to ultracentrifugation to position the DNA in the centrifuge tube according to its density. (Density increases to the right of the figure.) DNA absorption of ultraviolet light is indicated by the bands in different photographs under a and the height of the peaks in the corresponding densitometer tracings under b. The rightmost band in the bottom two frames and the band in the top frame represent all-heavy DNA. The leftmost band, seen clearly in all generation times after 1.5 generations, represents all-light DNA. The only other clear band is between the all-heavy and all-light ones. This is the only band present after 1.0 generations, and represents DNA which is hybrid in density. Note that at 1.9 generations, half the DNA is all-light and half is hybrid in density (see row showing 0 and 1.9 mixed). (Courtesy of M. Meselson and F. W. Stahl, Proc. Nat. Acad. Sci., U.S., 44:675, 1958.)*

thesis is at the ends of double strands involves some of the following facts: When any sample of *natural* or *native, double-stranded DNA* is heated to an appropriate temperature (near 98° C), the H bonds are broken and the complementary strands separate. Double-stranded DNA's with high $\frac{A + T}{G + C}$ ratios become single-stranded at a lower temperature than do those with low ratios. This result is expected since high-ratio DNA is richer in A-T than low-ratio DNA, each pair of which has one less H bond than a C-G pair, so that less energy is needed to break the smaller total of H bonds. If the appropriately heated mixture is cooled quickly, the chains remain single, producing *denatured DNA*. That heat denaturation followed by quick cooling produces single strands from double helices can be confirmed by the loss of that part of the DNA X-ray diffraction pattern which denotes polystrandedness. The change to single-strandedness is also accompanied by an increase of as much as 40% in the absorption of ultraviolet light of 2600 A, so that single-stranded DNA is relatively *hyperchromic*. It also is slightly denser than double-stranded DNA. If the hot mixture, containing denatured DNA, is cooled slowly, base pairing occurs and *renatured DNA* is obtained which shows a *hypochromic effect* and, from X-ray diffraction studies, evidence of double helices.

The second test of endwise DNA synthesis involves converting double-stranded, all-light and all-heavy DNA to the single-stranded condition and locating the positions of the two types of single strands in the ultracentrifuge tube. The "hybrid" double-stranded DNA is then made single-stranded and is ultracentrifuged. This preparation shows only two major components, one located at the all-light single-stranded position and the other at the all-heavy single-strand position. This result also is inconsistent with the hypothesis being tested. Not only do the two tests eliminate the view that appreciable endwise synthesis of DNA occurs in bacterial DNA, but they offer additional support for the hypothesis of replication after strand separation.

Similar experiments yielding similar results have been performed using the unicellular plant, Chlamydomonas, and higher organisms, including man. The general agreement in the results of all these experiments apparently furnishes conclusive proof of the correctness of the Watson-Crick hypotheses for the double-helix configuration of chromosomal DNA and for its replication after strand separation.

Although the nuclear DNA of most organisms is present as nucleoprotein, being combined with histones or protamines, the DNA in bacteria and in the viruses attacking them seems to exist uncombined with basic protein.[3] In the latter case, the DNA-containing fibers have a diameter of about 25 A. Ordinary chromosomes are probably polynemic with respect to DNA double helices,[4] although the exact number of double helices per chromatid is not yet known with certainty. The basic fibril in protamine-containing sperm seems to be about 40 A in diameter, containing one DNA double helix plus basic protein.[3] In cells containing histones, two DNA double helices bound side by side, plus the histone, form a fibril which is about 100 A thick.[3]

So far, the evidence presents no clue as to how either end of a DNA polymer terminates. The possibility exists that DNA is a circular molecule, although this explanation still leaves the problem of how chain separation occurs if there are no free ends to revolve. When DNA is extracted from human sperm, about 0.1% of the "purified" material is reported to be composed of amino

[3] See H. Ris and B. L. Chandler (1964).
[4] See W. J. Peacock (1963).

acids.[5] Digestion of the DNA at those points where it is joined to amino acid produces extensive depolymerization. Such results indicate that the amino acid sequence is short and, therefore, must sometimes be located internally rather than always being at the end of a DNA strand. On the average, there is a sequence of three amino acids per thousand nucleotides. The amino acid sequences appear bound to the phosphate of the DNA, not as a side chain, but as an integral part of the molecule. Thus, *the backbone of the DNA strand appears to be interrupted by short amino acid sequences.* About 33% of the amino acids in DNA are the hydroxyl amino acids, serine and threonine, and 10 to 15% are glutamic acid. As expected, available evidence indicates that the amino acid attached to the phosphate of DNA is often serine. The occurrence of amino acids in the DNA of human leucocytes, calf thymus, and the vaccinia virus has also been reported. The DNA

[5] See A. Bendich and H. S. Rosencranz (1963).

in the larval salivary gland chromosomes of Drosophila also seems to be interrupted.[6]

If confirmed, these results are significant since they involve sequences of amino acids which are so short that, when interstitial, they may be immune to the action of certain digestive enzymes. Such amino acid groups may be involved in:

1. The bending of DNA double-helices (which are rather rigid) especially where DNA is much coiled on itself
2. The mechanism by which strand separation leading to replication occurs
3. The separation of functional DNA units
4. The functioning of individual DNA units
5. The mechanism of crossing over
6. Mutagenesis by agents capable of affecting amino acids.[7]

[6] See reference to D. M. Steffensen (1963) on p. 162.
[7] See I. A. Rapoport and R. G. Kostyanovskii (1959).

SUMMARY AND CONCLUSIONS

DNA *in vivo* usually exists in the Watson-Crick double helix configuration and usually replicates, after the strands separate, by the formation of complementary strands.

In certain viruses, ϕX174 and ϕS13 for example, the DNA is single-stranded. In bacteria and bacterial viruses, the DNA exists uncombined with protein.

In ordinary chromosomes, the following are found: a basic 40 A thick fibril containing protamine and one DNA double helix; a basic 100 A thick fibril composed of histone and two DNA double helices. A chromatid probably contains a number of 100 A fibrils.

The DNA molecule seems to be interrupted periodically by short amino acid sequences.

REFERENCES

Bendich, A., and Rosencranz, H. S., "Some Thoughts on the Double-Stranded Model of Deoxyribonucleic Acid," Progr. Nucleic Acid Res., 1:219–230, 1963.

Crick, F. H. C., "Nucleic Acids," Scient. Amer., 197:188–200, 1957.

Jehle, H., Ingerman, M. L., Shirven, R. M., Parke, W. C., and Salyers, A. A., "Replication of Nucleic Acids," Proc. Nat. Acad. Sci., U.S., 50:738–746, 1963.

Luzzati, V., "The Structure of DNA as Determined by X-ray Scattering Techniques," Progr. Nucleic Acid Res., 1:347–368, 1963.

Meselson, M., and Stahl, F. W., "The Replication of DNA in *Escherichia coli,"* Proc. Nat. Acad. Sci., U.S., 44:671–682, 1958.

Peacock, W. J., "Chromosome Duplication and Structure as Determined by Autoradiography," Proc. Nat. Acad. Sci., U.S., 49:793–801, 1963.

Rapoport, I. A., and Kostyanovskii, R. G., "The Mutagenic Activity of Several Inhibitors of Cholinesterase," Doklady Akad. Nauk SSSR, 131:191–194, 1959 (in Russian).

Ris, H., and Chandler, B. L., "The Ultrastructure of Genetic Systems in Prokaryotes and Eukaryotes," Cold Spring Harb. Sympos. Quant. Biol., 28:1–8, 1964.

Sueoka, N., "Mitotic Replication of Deoxyribonucleic Acid in *Chlamydomonas reinhardi,"* Proc. Nat. Acad. Sci., U.S., 46:83–90, 1960.

Watson, J. D., and Crick, F. H. C., "Molecular Structure of Nucleic Acids. A Structure for Deoxyribose Nucleic Acid," Nature, London, 171:737–738, 1953a. Reprinted in *Classic Papers in Genetics,* Peters, J. A. (Ed.), Englewood Cliffs, N.J.: Prentice-Hall, 1959, pp. 241–243.

Watson, J. D., and Crick, F. H. C., "Genetical Implications of the Structure of Deoxyribonucleic Acid," Nature, London, 171:964–969, 1953b. Reprinted in *Papers on Bacterial Genetics,* Adelberg, E. A. (Ed.), Boston: Little, Brown, 1960, pp. 125–130.

Watson, J. D., and Crick, F. H. C., "The Structure of DNA," Cold Spring Harb. Sympos. Quant. Biol., 18:123–131, 1953c. Reprinted in *Papers on Bacterial Viruses,* Stent, G. S. (Ed.), Boston: Little, Brown, 1960, pp. 193–208.

See bibliography and all but last portion of Supplement IV.

QUESTIONS FOR DISCUSSION

20.1. Can you draw any conclusions from the observation that most of the multicellular organisms studied are richer in A + T than C + G?

20.2. Among the DNA molecules contained in a genome, why is it expected that many would differ in base sequence and content?

20.3. How many different base pairs normally occur in a double helix of DNA? What are they?

20.4. If a coil is right-handed when looked at from one end, is it also right-handed when seen from the other end?

20.5. What would you have expected to see in the ultracentrifuge tube following sonic treatment of DNA or following the conversion of DNA to its single-stranded condition, if synthesis had occurred at the ends of the double DNA helix?

20.6. What evidence can you give that heating double-helix DNA causes the strands to separate?

20.7. When is DNA single-stranded?

20.8. A double helix of DNA has a base sequence ATTAGCA on one strand. Can you complete an inversion after breaking the backbone at two places on this single strand? Explain. Can you complete an inversion if the backbone of the complementary chain is also broken at exactly the same two levels? Explain.

20.9. Given two double helices whose backbones are broken at the places indicated by periods:

ATCG.GCAT   AT.TAG

TAGC.CGTA   TA.ATC

draw the base sequences which can occur following reciprocal translocation between double helices.

20.10. In what respects is Figure 20–7 incorrect?

20.11. M. Green and M. Piña (1963) report that the $G + C$ ratio of a number of human and animal carcinogenic viruses is similar and lower than that of comparable nontumorigenic viruses. Discuss the possible implications of this anomaly for the origin and action of tumor-inducing viruses.

20.12. Locate on Figure 20–6 the minor and major grooves of the two pairs of nucleotides shown. Discuss the accuracy of this figure.

Chapter 21

REPLICATION OF DNA
IN VITRO

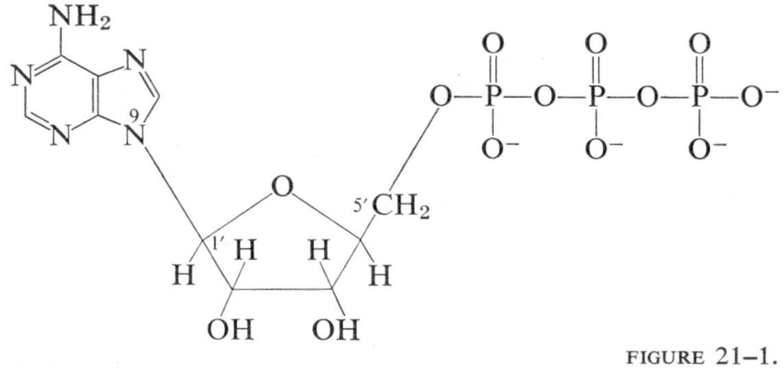

NH$_2$

$_{9}$

O

$_{5'}$CH$_2$

H $_{1'}$ H   H

H   H

OH   OH

O—P—O—P—O—P—O$^-$

O$^-$ O$^-$ O$^-$

FIGURE 21–1.
Adenosine 5'-triphosphate (ATP) (APPP).

ARLY in this book (p. 10) we assumed self-replication to be a characteristic of the genetic material. In light of the indirect evidence that chromosomal DNA is genetic material, it is of great interest to learn as much as possible about the replication of the DNA double helix. Although the evidence (Chapter 20) is fairly conclusive that complementary chains are synthesized after chain separation, no evidence has yet been presented about how this replication is accomplished. Figure 20–7 and the discussion on page 271 only postulate a mechanism which includes an enzyme that joins the nucleotides forming a new complementary strand.

Since the linear combination of nucleotides undoubtedly requires energy, consider the possible source of this energy. Considerable chemical energy is contained in the ribotide, *adenosine triphosphate* (ATP), a riboside 5'-triphosphate (Figure 21–1). The energy hitherto needed to bond two phosphates to adenosine monophosphate becomes available when ATP reacts with other nucleotides or acids and loses its two terminal phosphates as *inorganic pyrophosphate*. Because ATP is known to supply the energy for many chemical reactions in the cell, it is reasonable to suppose that it may also supply the energy needed to join individual deoxyribotides to a DNA strand during replication.

Since DNA removed from the nucleus and separated from protein still retains what appear to be its main characteristics *in situ* (in the living cell), we may well be able to study DNA synthesis under nonliving conditions. What should we extract from cells in order to study DNA synthesis *in vitro?* Basically, we ought to use all the apparatus the cell normally utilizes for this function. From the strand separation viewpoint, DNA is needed to serve as a template for DNA synthesis, so the extract should contain the cell's DNA. ATP is added to the extract as the source of energy required for the synthesis. MgCl$_2$ can also be added; since the magnesium ion, Mg^{++}, is known to activate many enzymes, perhaps it will also act on the one required for DNA strand formation.

How can we tell whether DNA is synthesized in the extract? Any crude cellular extract would be expected to contain DNases. These enzymes might depolymerize or otherwise degrade DNA as fast as—or faster than—any process synthesizing DNA. The problem of identifying DNA synthesis in the absence of a net increase in DNA quantity can be solved by preparing the deoxyriboside thymidine with radioactive C^{14} incorporated in its pyrimidine and adding this "hot" chemical to the extract. If any radioactively-labeled thymidine is incorporated into DNA, it would happen as part of the synthetic reaction, since incorporation into DNA only occurs during synthesis.

279

Finally, we ought to obtain the extract from cells that are growing and dividing rapidly, for these cells are likely to contain the greatest amount of functional apparatus for DNA synthesis. In line with this reasoning, an experiment is performed with an extract of the bacterium *Escherichia coli*.[1] ATP, Mg^{++} ions, and radioactive thymidine are added and the pH is adjusted to suit experimental conditions. After an incubation interval (about 30 minutes), the pH is made suitably acidic for precipitating a DNA polymer; single deoxyribosides—that is, *monomers*—remain soluble. The acid precipitate is washed many times until it is certain that the DNA precipitate is not contaminated by adsorbed deoxyribosides. When the DNA is examined, it is found to be only slightly radioactive (50 counts per unit time as compared with 5 million counts in the thymidine substrate added). In fact, so little thymidine is incorporated in the DNA that it is 10,000 times too small to be detected by ordinary chemical analysis. Nevertheless, the radioactivity is without doubt due to thymidine incorporated into DNA and can be released from the precipitated DNA by treatment with DNase.

Although this result is not quantitatively impressive, the process furnishes C^{14}-thymidine-labeled, acid-precipitable, DNase-sensitive DNA as the end product. The amount of this labeled material formed can be used to determine the effect of changes in the experimental procedure. This fact has already led to a change in the procedure and to a better understanding of the nature of the reaction.

Reactions that produce derivatives of adenosine commonly start with ATP as one of the reactants. Similarly, derivatives of uridine, cytidine, and guanosine involve their respective triphosphates and the liberation

[1] The preceding and following account is based primarily upon work by A. Kornberg and his associates.

of inorganic pyrophosphate. Such facts lead to the conclusion that the fundamental unit in the formation of diribotides or polyribotides is the riboside 5′-phosphate, activated in the form of riboside 5′-triphosphate. It is reasonable, therefore, to assume that the active building block of polydeoxyribotides is the deoxyriboside 5′-triphosphate.

If this molecule is the building block, the ATP added in the *in vitro* experiments may be converting various deoxyribosides—already present or added to the extract—to the 5′-triphosphate condition (making, for instance, C^{14}-thymidine 5′-triphosphate). This view is supported since DNA synthesis occurs *in vitro* when labeled thymidine 5′-triphosphate (T*PPP) is used instead of labeled thymidine (T*) + ATP (APPP).

To learn more about the ingredients essential to DNA synthesis, the initial extract, obtained from the sonic treatment of bacteria, is fractionated and its protein, concentrated. This procedure results in a nearly 4,000-fold increase in synthetic activity. From this and other evidence, it becomes clear that the presence of a protein catalyst—the enzyme *E. coli DNA polymerase* (or *DNA duplicase*)—is essential for the synthetic reaction to take place.

Once *E. coli* DNA polymerase is concentrated, it is possible to obtain a large net increase in DNA (final amount minus initial amount). Such a net increase, however, is obtained only if the 5′-triphosphates of all four deoxyribosides commonly found in DNA are added to the incubation mixture. Deoxyriboside 5′*di*phosphates are not active, nor are *ribo*side 5′-triphosphates. The other requirements for net increase in DNA amount are:

1. The presence of already-formed DNA molecules of high molecular weight
2. Mg^{++} ions
3. DNA polymerase.

The already-formed, high molecular weight

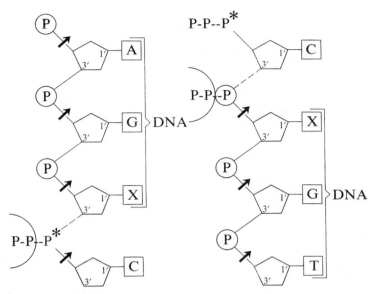

FIGURE 21–2. *Growth of a primer DNA strand at its nucleoside end (left) and nucleotide end (right). Arrows show 5′ positions of subsequent degradation by micrococcal DNase plus splenic phosphodiesterase.*

DNA may come from a plant, animal, bacterium, or virus. Similar DNA-synthesizing extracts can be prepared from other bacteria, calf thymus, and various animal tissues.

Extended and Limited Syntheses

Using *E. coli* preparations, we can obtain an *extended synthesis* of DNA which produces twenty or more times as much DNA as was initially present. In this case, therefore, 95% or more of the DNA present at the end must have been synthesized from the triphosphates added as substrate, the extended synthetic reaction proceeding until the supply of one of the four triphosphates is exhausted. One inorganic pyrophosphate is released for each deoxyribotide incorporated into DNA.

Although extensive synthesis of DNA does not occur if only one of the deoxyriboside 5′-triphosphates is added as substrate, some incorporation of this nucleotide into the

DNA strand occurs in what is called a *limited reaction*. By what mechanism does the nucleotide add on to the pre-existing DNA strand? In this case, the already-present DNA must provide a point of linear attachment for newly-forming DNA, thereby functioning as a *primer*. Suppose that the only triphosphate added to the substrate is deoxycytidine 5′-triphosphate whose innermost phosphate carries radioactive P^{32} (dCP^*PP). The two possible ways in which the DNA strand might lengthen are shown at the left and right of Figure 21–2; the DNA strand, present as primer, is shown enclosed in brackets. The primer strand can be considered to have a *nucleotide end* (top of the figure)—to which pyrophosphate, P-P, is added in the diagram to the right—and a free 3′-OH *nucleoside end* (bottom of illustration). (The removal of a sugar and base by a single break at the 5′ position involves the removal of a nucleoside at the nucleoside end and the removal of a nucleotide at the nucleotide end.) The diagram at the left of the figure shows the *d*CP* adding on to the nucleoside end by the formation of a 3′ linkage between P* and the sugar at the end of the chain, P-P being split off the *d*CP*PP. The diagram at the right shows *d*CP*PP adding on to the nucleotide end of the chain by linkage to the 5′ position of the end nucleotide which supplies the pyrophosphate that splits off. In brief, the DNA strand might be lengthened by the addition of a nucleotide at either the 3′ position of the nucleoside end or at the 5′ position of the nucleotide end.

It is possible to distinguish between these two alternatives by treating the product of a limited reaction first with *DNase from micrococci* to enhance the action of another added enzyme, *splenic phosphodiesterase*. The latter enzyme degrades DNA by breaking the strand at all the 5′ positions, so that deoxyriboside 3′-monophosphates are produced. This position of breakage is indicated by the arrows in Figure 21–2. If the strand lengthens according to the diagram at the right of the figure, radioactive P³² should be found in phosphate attached to deoxycytidine, and P* should not be part of the 3′-deoxyribotides of A, T, or G. If, on the other hand, attachment is to the 3′ position at the nucleoside end of the strand, then, as can be seen in the diagram at the left of the figure, P* should not occur in inorganic phosphates but should sometimes appear in other deoxyriboside 3′-monophosphates besides those containing C. The experiment gives the latter result; that is, not only is P* frequently present in all four kinds of deoxyriboside 3′-monophosphates, but it is absent from inorganic phosphate.

An additional test of whether the DNA strand grows at its 3′ position involves treating the limited product with a different enzyme, *snake venom diesterase*. This enzyme digests DNA by breaking the bond

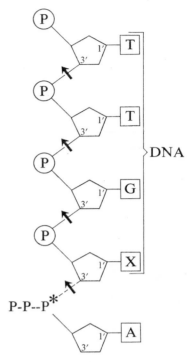

FIGURE 21–3. *Degradation of a primer DNA strand, which has grown at its nucleoside end, by snake venom diesterase. The 3′ positions of degradation (arrows) occur sequentially starting at the nucleoside end.*

between the phosphate and sugar at the 3′ position, starting at the nucleoside end of the strand and proceeding toward the nucleotide end. Thus, the DNA is gradually digested into deoxyriboside 5′-phosphates, as indicated by the arrows in Figure 21–3. When the limited product is treated this way, the result—as expected—is that almost all the radioactivity has been removed from the strand even though only a minute portion of the DNA has been digested. Other results clearly show that the product of a limited reaction is DNA with one or very few deoxyribotides added to the nucleoside end of the strand. Still other evidence supports the view that the 3′ point of lengthwise linkage is the same when net DNA is greatly increased as it is when the limited reaction occurs.

Characteristics of Synthesized DNA

That a DNA primer strand can be lengthened *in vitro,* no matter which of the four common deoxyribosides happens to be at the nucleoside terminus, is consistent with the independence of DNA primary structure upon base sequence. Consider the evidence that the DNA synthesized *in vitro* has the characteristics of DNA synthesized *in vivo.* The physical characteristics of DNA samples consisting of 90% or more of the product synthesized *in vitro* are similar to those of DNA isolated from calf thymus insofar as sedimentation rate and viscosity are concerned. Such results indicate that the product has a high molecular weight (about six million) and, usually, is not single-stranded. In support of the latter inference is the finding that the macromolecular structure of the *in vitro* product is destroyed when heated for 10 minutes at 100° C, an expected result if this treatment is to produce single strands —denatured DNA which collapses to form compact, randomly-coiled structures. Like thymus DNA, the enzymatic product shows the same type of increase in ultraviolet absorption following digestion with pancreatic DNase.

If the synthesis *in vitro* occurs as it does *in vivo,* we might expect single-stranded DNA to serve in *in vitro* synthesis as well as, or better than, double-stranded DNA. In fact, the single-stranded DNA, isolated from the virus φX174, is excellent for this purpose, and heat-treated DNA is better than unheated DNA. Moreover, the preparations containing the most active DNA polymerase do not work well with double-stranded DNA unless it is first heated or treated with DNase. The DNA produced in extended syntheses behaves as though it is primarily two-stranded, but differs from native double-stranded DNA by appearing to be markedly branched in electron micrographs and by being readily renatured after heat or alkaline denaturation. These results suggest that strand separation is usually incomplete in the *in vitro* system.

In view of these results, we can conclude that the physical characteristics of the DNA synthesized *in vitro* and *in vivo* are extremely similar, though not identical. Synthesis clearly involves single strands which produce double strands probably held together by H bonds.

One can also study the detailed chemical and physico-chemical characteristics of the *in vitro* synthesis of DNA. If single strands produce double strands by forming complementary structures, then the capacity to form a complementary strand should depend upon the presence in the substrate of purine and pyrimidine bases which can form appropriate H bonds with the bases in the added DNA. In other words, in an extensive synthesis, *pre-existing DNA should serve as a template for the synthesis of complementary DNA strands.* Figure 21–4 shows some pyrimidine and purine bases which do not naturally or frequently occur in DNA as well as the four principal types which do. The unnatural or infrequent bases include: uracil and 5-bromo uracil (both of which are expected to have the same H-bonding capacities as thymine); 5-methyl cytosine and 5-bromo cytosine (both of which are expected to have the same H-bonding capacities as cytosine); and hypoxanthine (which has two of the three H-bonding sites found in guanine). If A in the single-strand preformed DNA dictates its complement—by specifying that the complementary base is a pyrimidine that provides the proper sites for H-bonding A—then one would expect that uracil or 5-bromo (or 5-fluoro) uracil can substitute for the thymine in thymidine 5'-triphosphate.

When the substrate used contains de-

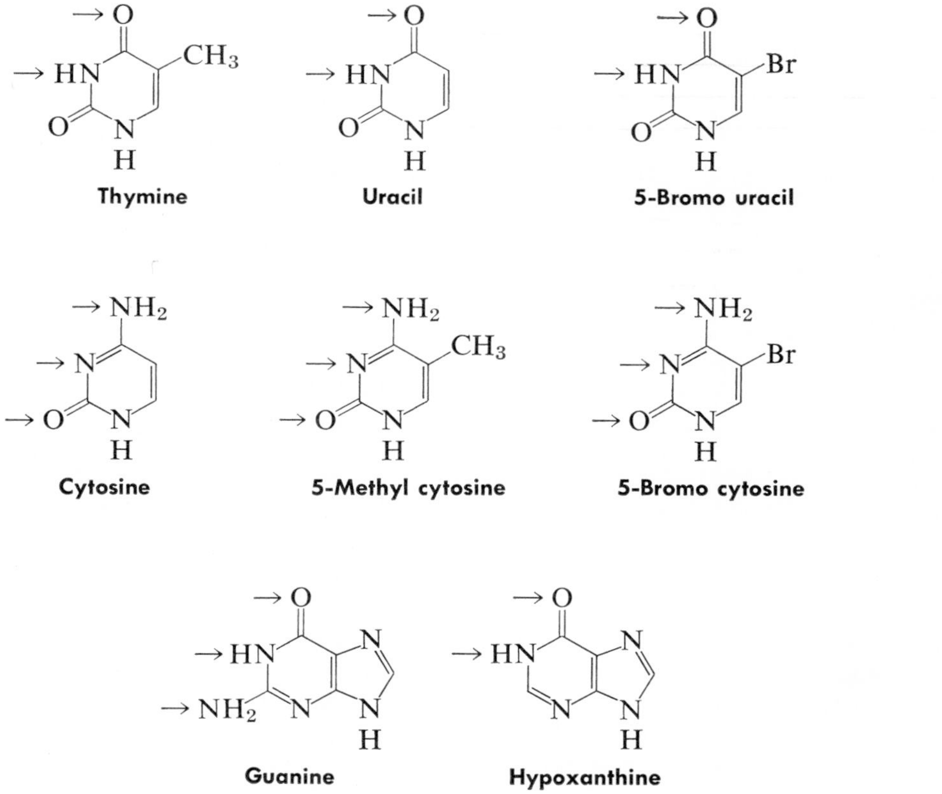

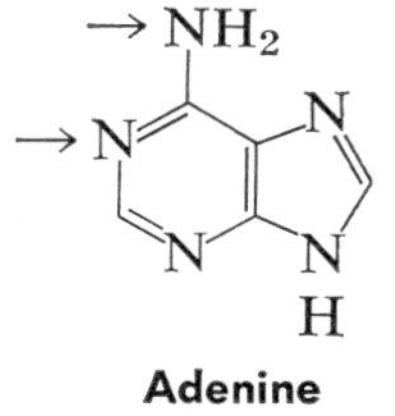

FIGURE 21–4. *Various bases utilized in* in vitro *synthesis of DNA. Arrows point to groups capable of typical H-bonding.*

oxyuridine 5'-triphosphate (or 5-bromo or 5-fluoro deoxyuridine 5'-triphosphate), dCPPP, dAPPP, and dGPPP, DNA synthesis occurs. Similarly, 5-methyl cytosine or 5-bromo or 5-fluoro cytosine can substitute for cytosine. On the other hand, the substitution of hypoxanthine for guanine does not support DNA synthesis as well as do the other substitutions mentioned. This result is expected from the hypothesis under test, since the former has one less H-bonding site than the latter. Moreover—as predicted—uracil, 5-bromo uracil, and 5-fluoro uracil will not substitute for C, A, or G in dCPPP, dAPPP, or dGPPP, respectively. Similarly, 5-methyl, 5-bromo, and 5-fluoro cytosine replace cytosine specifically; hypoxanthine replaces only guanine. Although hypoxanthine has the same H-bonding groups as thymine, it does not replace thymine, probably because the A-hypoxanthine pair, being composed of two purines, takes up too much space to fit the regular double-helix configuration. These results support the hypothesis that normally the *in vitro* synthesis of DNA is dependent upon the formation of complementary purine-pyrimidine pairs—A with T and C with G—just as is the case *in vivo*.

The DNA synthesized *in vitro* from the usual four deoxyriboside 5′-triphosphates can be analyzed chemically. The analysis shows that in the *in vitro*-synthesized DNA, A equals T and C equals G, just as they do in natural DNA, even though the relative concentration of the four triphosphates in the substrate is widely distorted. Not only do total pyrimidines equal total purines in "synthetic" DNA, as described—whether a moderate or a large amount is synthesized—but the particular $\frac{A + T}{G + C}$ ratio of the primer-template is reproduced faithfully in the synthesized product (see Figure 8 in Supplement V). In this respect, the product is a replica of the primer-template, as is strikingly illustrated by the following experiment. After a long period of incubation of all the usual components except pre-existing DNA, a linear deoxyribotide polymer composed only of A and T is formed spontaneously. When this polymer is added as the pre-existing DNA, even though all four usual triphosphates are present in the substrate, the result is an extensive synthesis of material which contains A and T only, with no trace of C and G (again see Figure 8 in Supplement V).

It has been mentioned that for each nucleotide added to the end of the DNA strand, an inorganic pyrophosphate, PP, is liberated. When PP is added to the usual synthesizing complex in great excess (about one hundred times the concentration of the triphosphates), the synthetic reaction is inhibited by about 50%. This observation implies the *reversibility of DNA synthesis in vitro*.

It was also mentioned earlier that in a limited reaction, dCP*(PP) can add onto a strand terminating in all four types of nucleotides (dCP, TP, dAP, and dGP). However, this statement does not suggest that dCP* joins linearly to each nucleotide with equal frequency, or that any nucleotide joins to all others with equal frequency. Other results indicate that the limited reaction does not add nucleotides to the end at random; this reaction probably involves the repair of the shorter strand of a double helix, the particular nucleotide added being specified in the usual way by the bases present in the longer strand. In other words, the shorter strand acts as a primer and the longer strand as a template.

Dinucleotide Sequences

What is the linear arrangement of nucleotides in the DNA synthesized in an extended reaction? If it is genetic material, different linear segments of DNA can represent different genes, and the differences among genes would lie in the sequence of their organic bases. Considering only the four usual deoxyribotides, how many different sequences of two nucleotides are possible? The first nucleotide can be one of four, and so can the second, making a possible 4 times 4, or 16 different linear arrangements in dinucleotides. The orders in dinucleotides can be determined experimentally as follows: one of the four triphosphates added as substrate is labeled with P^{32} in the innermost phosphate, the other three are not. Extended synthesis is permitted during which the P* attaches to the 3′ of the sugar of the nucleotide which is its linear neighbor (refer to the left part of Figure 21–2 and to Figure 9 in Supplement V). This linear neighbor can be identified by digesting the synthesized product with micrococcal DNase and splenic phosphodiesterase. Recall that the latter produces deoxyriboside 3'-monophosphates by breaking the chain at 5'. Consequently, the labeled phosphate (P*) is found joined at the 3' position of the deoxyriboside just anterior to the one with which it entered the DNA strand. The digest is then analyzed to see how frequently P* is part of dA 3'-P*, T 3'-P*, dC 3'-P*, and dG 3'-P*. If the P* were originally in dAP*PP, we would then know the relative linear frequencies of TA, AA, CA, and GA. By carrying out this procedure three more times, labeling a different one of the triphosphates each time, the relative frequency of all sixteen sequences can be determined.

Such *nearest-neighbor analyses* have been made of the DNAs synthesized using a number of different preformed DNAs. As already mentioned, the DNA isolated from particles of ϕX174 is single-stranded; chemical analysis reveals its base content to be A = .246; T = .328; C = .185; and G = .242. If synthesis requires the formation of complementary base pairs, an extended reaction carried out with ϕX174 DNA and all four triphosphates labeled and stopped after 20% synthesis has occurred, should produce complementary, labeled DNA composed of .328 A; .246 T; .242 C; and .185 G. The values found are exactly those expected. If both old and new strands are used as templates, one expects and finds after a 600% synthesis that A = T and C = G. Moreover, A and T are expected to have frequencies of $\frac{1}{2}$(.328 + .246), or .287, with C and G = .224. Again experimentation confirms expectation.

One can perform the 20% synthesis on four occasions, each time labeling a different triphosphate. In this way, nearest-neighbor analyses are made, and the relative frequencies of all sixteen dinucleotide sequences determined. All sequences are found and include, for instance, .054 GA; .064 TC; .052 CT; and .069 AG. Nearest-neighbor analyses can also be made after 600% synthesis.

If the complementary strand is synthesized in the same direction as the template strand, from the results of the 20% syntheses one expects that GA = CT = $\frac{1}{2}$(.054 + .052) = .053; and TC = AG = .067. If, on the other hand, the two complementary strands are synthesized in opposite directions, the expectations are GA = TC = $\frac{1}{2}$(.054 + .064) = .059; and CT = AG = .061. The values observed (.058 GA; .065 TC; .064 CT; and .058 AG) clearly follow those expected for *complementary strands synthesized* in vitro *in opposite directions,* as do the values obtained for the other dinucleotide sequences.

Chemical analysis of *Mycobacterium phlei* DNA yields .162 A; .165 T; .335 C; and .338 G. If extended syntheses permitting nearest-neighbor analyses are performed, one can determine the relative amount of base X incorporated into DNA from the sum of the separate frequencies with which XA, XT, XC, and XG occur. When X is, in turn, A, T, C, and G, the relative frequencies are found to be .162, .164, .337, .337, respectively. Thus, what is already demonstrated via chemical analyses is independently proved via nearest-neighbor analysis—namely, that the product of an extended synthesis has the same base frequencies as the natural two-stranded DNA used as primer-template.

The question of whether or not the sequences of bases along a strand is random [2] can be decided by using calf thymus DNA as primer-template and determining all the dinucleotide frequencies in the product. Among the frequencies observed, CG is .016 and GC, .044. Had these two dinucleotides occurred with equal frequency, the hypothesis of a random nucleotide sequence in a strand would have been supported. Since the frequencies are clearly different, however, base sequence in a strand is not

[2] In this connection see also J. H. Spencer and E. Chargaff (1963).

random.   The nonrandomness of base sequences is also supported by experimental results which reveal that: 70% of the bases are distributed so that three or more pyrimidines (and hence purines) occur in successive linear nucleotides; linear sequences of five successive T's exist; and 4.9% of a given DNA contains sequences of eight or more pyrimidines in succession.

Is the nearest-neighbor frequency the same when native DNA is used as primer-template as when DNA synthesized from this native DNA is used?   With synthesized calf thymus DNA as primer-template, the nearest-neighbor frequencies of the newly synthesized product are essentially the same (for example, CG is .011 while GC is .042) as they are in the product formed using calf thymus DNA as primer-template (above). Consequently, as revealed by nearest-neighbor analysis, the products of synthesis are identical when native DNA and when DNA synthesized from native DNA serve as primer-template.

The $\dfrac{A + T}{C + G}$ ratio is 1.25 for calf thymus

DNA and 1.29 for *B. subtilis*.   Even though these base ratios are very similar, it is unlikely that one of these is a molecular polyploid of the other (see p. 265).   In fact, the dinucleotide sequences determined for DNA synthesized from the bacterial DNA (for example, CG is .050 and GC, .061) are quite different from those of calf thymus (.016 and .044, respectively).   Other work generally shows that in higher plants and animals CG is lower than expected on a random nucleotide sequence, whereas the reverse occurs in bacteria.   It should also be noted that different normal or neoplastic tissues of the same individual give nucleotide neighbor frequencies which are not demonstrably different.   We conclude, therefore, that *each type of natural DNA has unique and reproducible dinucleotide sequences, not predictable from its base composition.*

De Novo Synthesis of DNA

The double-stranded polymer of A and T appearing *de novo,* referred to earlier, can be used as primer-template to study its dinucleotide sequences.   Only the AT and TA sequences are found; thus, it appears that A and T occur in perfect alternation in a strand, forming what is called a *copolymer of AT,* or *dAT(d-AT).*   The *de novo* synthesis of a dAT, sufficiently long to serve as template for extended synthesis, requires a lag period of a few hours, during which dAPPP, TPPP, Mg^{++}, and *E. coli* DNA polymerase are incubated together.   It has been hypothesized that during the lag period, the *E. coli* DNA polymerase catalyzes the *de novo* formation of single strands from single deoxyriboside 5'-triphosphates.   Once the strand is started, the short strand or *oligodeoxyribotide* can serve as a primer to lengthen itself.   In the presence of dAPPP or TPPP alone, dAT adds one or two units of dAP or TP per chain in a limited reaction.   Neither dCP nor dGP is incorporated into dAT when dCPPP and/or dGPPP are added to the substrate, whether or not dAPPP and TPPP are also present.   It is clear, therefore, that both limited and extended synthesis of dAT require base-pairing.   It is possible that a limited reaction involves a single strand of dAT which is folded so as to base-pair with itself except at the nucleotide end.   So, once the dAT strand is long enough, the polymerase can use it as a template for base-pairing synthesis.   Note that no lag period occurs in limited or extended base-pairing syntheses.

In the absence of pre-existing DNA and after a lag period, *E. coli* polymerase—in the presence of Mg^{++} and high concentrations of dCPPP and dGPPP—catalyzes the *de novo* formation of another double-stranded polymer containing only C and G.   Nearest-neighbor analysis shows only two dinucleotide sequences, CC and GG. Clearly, this polymer, called *dGdC* (or d-GC), is composed of two *homopolymers;* one strand contains only C's and the other only G's, the two strands base-pairing to form a double helix. Whereas A = T after extensive synthesis of dAT, most products of dGdC synthesis show 56 to 81% dGP.

Both dAT and dGdC illustrate that the base sequence in certain strands is not random. That such strands can have biological significance is strikingly supported by the discovery[3] of a *"natural dAT" polymer* in the sperm of a certain crab. Nearest-neighbor analysis shows that this polymer, which comprises about 30% of the total DNA content, contains A and T in strict alternation in 93% of the dinucleotide sequences. About 3% of the bases associated with this natural dAT are G or C, and all sixteen dinucleotide sequences are found. One might suspect that the G- and C-containing nucleotides are contaminants of the typical DNA comprising 70% of the total. If they are, extensive *in vitro* synthesis using natural dAT as primer-template should occur just as rapidly whether or not the substrate of dAPPP and TPPP has dCPPP and dGPPP added to it. One finds, however, that the replication rate in the absence of the latter two triphosphates is only 19% of that obtained in their presence, supporting the view that G and C bases are an integral part of the "natural dAT" polymer.

Calf Thymus DNA Polymerase

All *in vitro* DNA syntheses so far discussed, whether they occur *de novo* (by an *unprimed* initiation of single strands) or involve complementary base-pairing (as in limited and extensive syntheses), require the presence of *E. coli* DNA polymerase. The DNA polymerase isolated from calf thymus cannot form dAT or dGdC *de novo;* in other words, it is apparently incapable of unprimed DNA

synthesis.[4] Some evidence has been obtained that H-bond, base-pairing, template synthesis by calf thymus DNA polymerase begins once chain length exceeds twenty monomers. The DNA polymerase from calf thymus, like that from *E. coli,* uses DNA as a template to make DNA which resembles native DNA in primary and secondary structure, composition, sequence, and molecular size; the synthesized DNA also does not completely undergo strand separation upon heat denaturation.

Biological Replication *in Vitro*

Insofar as extensive synthesis of DNA *in vitro* is concerned, all, or almost all the physical and chemical characteristics of the product are consistent with the view that this is a biological process. However, there are several differences between the *in vitro* and the *in vivo* processes. Apparently *E. coli* DNA polymerase works more slowly *in vitro* than *in vivo.* Calf thymus DNA polymerase has a maximum yield of 100%. Both enzymes make DNA which does not strand separate completely when heat denatured; this behavior may be correlated with the branched DNA made *in vitro* by the *E. coli* enzyme. All these differences may result from contaminants *in vitro* which are not present *in vivo,* and from changes which occur in isolating the *in vivo* DNA for *in vitro* syntheses. When these possibilities are considered, there is little doubt that extensive synthesis is performed *in vitro* in essentially the same manner as in the living cell and that it produces essentially the same product.

Finally, special attention should be given to the DNA polymerases essential for the extended biological synthesis of DNA. Previously-known enzymes are specific in that they act upon one or a few particular substrates usually modified in the same way.

---

[3] By N. Sueoka.

[4] See F. J. Bollum (1963, 1964).

For example, trypsin breaks peptide bonds only at places in a polypeptide chain where lysine or arginine are present. DNA polymerases are unique in that they take directions from a long template; the strand acting as template dictates which particular monomers can be added by DNA polymerase to the strand acting as primer. It should be noted that, *in vitro,* ribonucleotides can be incorporated into terminal positions in DNA [5] and that, using DNA as a primer-template, *E. coli* DNA polymerase can use a mixture of riboside and deoxyriboside triphosphates to synthesize complementary strands that contain both ribo- and deoxy-ribotides.[6] No evidence exists, however, that such mixed RNA-DNA strands have biological or genetic significance.

DNA Synthesis from RNA

Using *poly (A + U),* the double helix composed of the homopolymer of adenylic acid base-paired with the homopolymer of uridylic acid, *E. coli* DNA polymerase activated by $MgCl_2$ can be tested [7] for ability to utilize various substrates in an *in vitro* synthesis. Using *dAPPP* and TPPP in the substrate, base-paired homopolymers of deoxyadenylic acid and thymidylic acid (designated as *poly*

[dA + T]) are synthesized without an appreciable lag period. Since each DNA strand of the product is homopolymeric (proved by nearest-neighbor analysis), it is clear that poly (A + U) is the template-primer. No evidence is found for the formation of a complex of poly A with poly T or of poly U with poly dA. Moreover, neither single-stranded poly A, nor single-stranded poly U, nor triple-stranded poly-ribotides can act as primer-template for DNA synthesis; using poly (A + U) as primer-template, no synthesis occurs with either dAPPP or TPPP alone. Finally, even after a one-fold synthesis, most—if not all— of the original poly (A + U) is present in original form. Consequently, no DNA-RNA double-helix hybrid molecules seem to be formed, no complete strand separation of poly (A + U) appears to be involved in synthesizing poly (dA + T), and both DNA strands need to be synthesized simultaneously. Other helical, double-stranded, homopolymeric polyribotides can also be used with DNA polymerase to produce other double-stranded, homopolymeric DNAs (one is probably dGdC).

Such *in vitro* studies may have important bearings upon the fate of RNA *in vivo.* Is RNA (genetic or nongenetic) ever used *in vivo* to make DNA (genetic or nongenetic)? To what extent does nucleic acid replication occur *in vivo* without complete strand separation and the formation of template-product hybrid molecules?

---

[5] See J. S. Krakow, H. O. Kammen, and E. S. Canellakis (1961).

[6] See P. Berg, H. Fancher, and M. Chamberlin (1963).

[7] See S. Lee-Huang and L. F. Cavalieri (1963), and L. F. Cavalieri (1963).

SUMMARY AND CONCLUSIONS

DNA can be synthesized *in vitro.* Extended synthesis can be obtained with pre-existing single-stranded DNA; the 5'-triphosphates of deoxyadenosine, deoxycytidine, deoxyguanosine, and thymidine; Mg^{++} ions; and a DNA polymerase. In making the product, the polymerase takes directions from pre-existing single-stranded DNA acting as a template. *In vitro,* strands lengthen at their nucleoside end, the strand lengthened serving as a primer. No lag period occurs in syntheses requiring base-pairing; the amounts of new DNA produced by these syntheses are either limited (when a pre-existing strand is lengthened slightly) or extensive (when essentially wholly-new strands are produced). After a lag period, *E. coli* DNA polymerase can synthesize dAT and dGdC *de novo; that is, in the absence of* pre-existing DNA; calf thymus DNA polymerase cannot catalyze *de novo* DNA synthesis.

Nearest-nucleotide-neighbor analysis reveals that complementary DNA strands are synthesized *in vitro* in opposite directions, and that each type of natural DNA has unique dinucleotide sequences not predictable from its base composition. Nucleotide sequences, hence, do not occur at random *in vivo*, as strikingly exemplified in a "natural dAT" DNA found in a crab.

The DNA product of an extensive synthesis *in vitro* closely resembles natural DNA in primary and secondary structure and in other physical and chemical respects. Consequently, this *in vitro* DNA synthesizing process is considered to be a biological process. These results also support the Watson-Crick structure of chromosomal DNA and its replication, after strand separation, through the formation of complementary strands.

In vitro, E. coli DNA polymerase is reported to use double-stranded RNA to synthesize complementary double-stranded DNA without involving complete strand separation.

REFERENCES

Berg, P., Fancher, H., and Chamberlin, M., "The Synthesis of Mixed Polynucleotides Containing Ribo- and Deoxyribonucleotides by Purified Preparations of DNA Polymerase from *Escherichia coli*," in *Informational Macromolecules,* Vogel, H. J., Bryson, V., and Lampen, J. O. (Eds.), New York: Academic Press, 1963, pp. 467–483.

Bessman, M. J., "The Replication of DNA in Cell-Free Systems," Chap. 1, pp. 1–64, in *Molecular Genetics, Part 1,* Taylor, J. H. (Ed.), New York: Academic Press, 1963.

Bollum, F. J., "'Primer' in DNA Polymerase Reactions," Progr. Nucleic Acid Res., 1:1–26, 1963.

Bollum, F. J., "Studies on the Nature of Calf Thymus DNA-Polymerase Products," Cold Spring Harb. Sympos. Quant. Biol., 28:21–26, 1964.

Burton, K., Lunt, M. R., Petersen, G. B., and Siebke, J. C., "Studies of Nucleotide Sequences in Deoxyribonucleic Acid," Cold Spring Harb. Sympos. Quant. Biol., 26:27–34, 1964.

Cavalieri, L. F., "Nucleic Acids and Information Transfer," J. Cell. Comp. Physiol., 62 (Suppl. 1 to No. 2):111–122, 1963.

Habermann, U., Habermannova, S., and Cerhova, M., "The Distribution of Nucleotides into Pyrimidine and Purine Nucleotide Clusters in the Polynucleotide Chain of DNA from *Escherichia coli* C.," Biochim. Biophys. Acta, 76:310–311, 1963.

Kornberg, A., *Enzymatic Synthesis of DNA,* New York: J. Wiley & Sons, 1962.

Kornberg, A., Bertsch, L. L., Jackson, J. F., and Khorana, H. G., "Enzymatic Synthesis of Deoxyribonucleic Acid, XVI. Oligonucleotides as Templates and the Mechanism of Their Replication," Proc. Nat. Acad. Sci., U.S., 51:315–323, 1964.

Krakow, J. S., Kammen, H. O., and Canellakis, E. S., "The Incorporation of Ribonucleotides into Terminal Positions of Deoxyribonucleic Acid," Biochim. Biophys. Acta, 53:52–64, 1961.

Lee-Huang, S., and Cavalieri, L. F., "Polyribonucleotides as Templates for Polydeoxyribonucleotides," Proc. Nat. Acad. Sci., U.S., 50:1116–1122, 1963.

Sinsheimer, R. L., "Single-Stranded DNA," Scient. Amer., 207 (No. 1):109–116, 1962.

Spencer, J. H., and Chargaff, E., "Studies on the Nucleotide Arrangement in Deoxyribonucleic Acids. VI. Pyrimidine Nucleotide Clusters: Frequency and Distribution in Several Species of the AT-Type," Biochim. Biophys. Acta, 68:18–27, 1963.

Richardson, C. C., Schildkraut, C. L., and Kornberg, A., "Studies on the Replication of DNA by DNA Polymerases," Cold Spring Harb. Sympos. Quant. Biol., 28:9–19, 1964.

See Supplement V. A list of references is given at the end of Dr. Kornberg's Nobel Prize lecture.

QUESTIONS FOR DISCUSSION

21.1. Has this chapter dealt with genetics? Explain.

21.2. Which single experiment described in this chapter would you consider the most important? Why?

21.3. Differentiate between the action of splenic phosphodiesterase and snake venom diesterase.

21.4. What are the requirements for the *in vitro* synthesis of DNA to proceed as a limited reaction? To proceed extensively?

21.5. What effect does the absence or presence of pre-existing DNA have upon DNA strand formation *in vitro?*

21.6. List the evidence that synthesis of DNA *in vitro* represents a biological process.

21.7. Does DNA polymerase from *E. coli* take directions only from *E. coli* DNA? Explain.

21.8. Does strand separation occur during an extended synthesis of DNA *in vitro?* Explain.

21.9. Of what significance is the nearest-nucleotide-neighbor analysis?

21.10. What is wrong with Figure 8 in Supplement V?

21.11. If substrate depletion is prevented, what would you expect to happen to the $\frac{A + T}{C + G}$ ratio when an extended synthesis is permitted to proceed for several hours?

21.12. How can you explain that an extended synthesis using dGdC as primer-template usually yields a product richer in G than C?

21.13. List the similarities and differences between the DNA polymerases isolated from *E. coli* and calf thymus.

21.14. What is meant by the statement that newly synthesized DNA is covalently linked to the primer but is not covalently linked to the template?

21.15. State three different procedures which you might use to synthesize dGdC *in vitro.*

Chapter 22

CLONES; TRANSFORMATION;
STRAND RECOMBINATION *IN VITRO*

Our present understanding of the mechanisms involved in the biological replication of DNA *in vivo* (Chapter 21) has been very significantly advanced by experiments using the DNA as well as the DNA polymerase of bacteria. Electron microscopic examination of bacteria reveals a nuclear region within which it is possible to detect a chromosome-like structure composed of DNA uncombined with basic protein (p. 275). The DNA within the bacterial nuclear body is similar to typical chromosomal DNA in the following ways: A = T and C = G; primary and secondary organization; mechanism of synthesis; and molecular integrity. Therefore, it seems justified to consider bacterial DNA as being primarily chromosomal DNA, and, despite the chemical simplicity of this structure, to use the term "chromosome" in discussing bacteria.

Since bacteria contain chromosomal DNA, one expects them also to contain chromosome-type genes according to the hypothesis —for which much indirect support has already been presented—that DNA is genetic material. How suitable are bacteria as experimental material for the study of genetics? The electron microscope reveals that each *Escherichia coli* cell contains one to four nuclear areas—usually two or four (Figure 22–1)—and that no nuclear membrane is present. Although the morphological mechanism of nuclear division is still unknown, a duplication of DNA occurs for each nuclear body division, and it can be concluded that daughter nuclear bodies are genetically identical, just as they are after a typical mitosis.

Clones

After nuclear-body replication, the bacterium divides to produce daughter bacteria. This method of increasing bacterial cell number is an asexual process called *vegetative reproduction*. Starting with a single bacterium, continuous vegetative reproduction results in a population of cells called a *clone;* barring mutations, all members of a clone are genetically identical. If mutation occurs during clonal growth, the mutant is transmitted to all the progeny of the mutant cell, thus producing a genetically mosaic clone whose proportion of mutant individuals varies, depending upon the time the mutation occurred and the relative reproductive potential of mutant and nonmutant cells. (All cells of a sexually-reproducing organism are also colonal in origin, except for fertilization and meiosis and its products, so that multicellular organisms can also be mosaic for a mutant.)

Consider the characteristics of bacteria and their clones significant for a study of mutation. The ease and speed with which large populations of bacteria can be obtained are of great advantage in mutation studies. For example, under appropriate culture conditions, *E. coli* divides about once each half hour; in fifteen hours after thirty successive generations have taken place one cell produces a clone containing about ten billion (10^{10}) individuals. The number of *E. coli* produced from a single cell after n generations (or t hours) can be calculated by the expression 2^n (or 2^{2t}) (Figure 22–2). Space is no problem in working with bacteria since 10^{10} individuals can readily be grown in liquid broth in an ordinary test tube.

However, the small size of bacteria is a

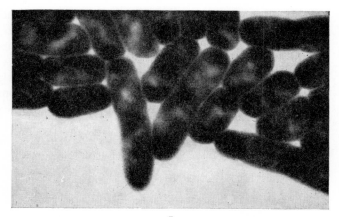

A

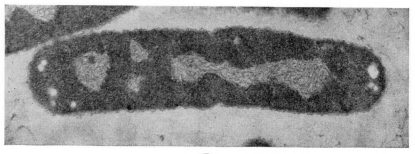

B

FIGURE 22–1 (*above*). *Electron microscope photographs of* Escherichia coli. *A. Whole cells in which nuclear bodies are revealed as less dense areas. Original magnification 3000×, present magnification about 12,000×. (Courtesy of E. Kellenberger.)* *B. Thin section showing nuclear bodies and the fine DNA-containing fibers within them. Original magnification 10,000×. Present magnification about 15,000×. (Courtesy of W. H. G. Schreil.)*

FIGURE 22–2 (*right*). *The geometric increase in the number of bacteria due to vegetative reproduction.*

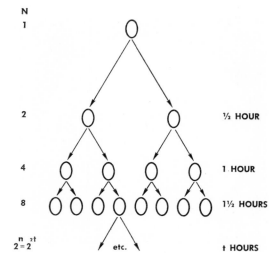

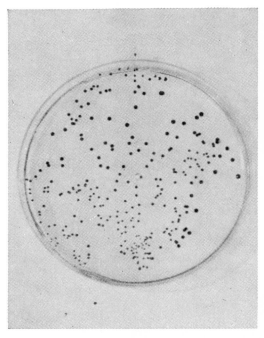

FIGURE 22–3. *Discrete clones, grow-ing on agar nutrient in a petri dish, obtained by plating a dilute culture of bacteria.*

FIGURE 22–4. *Separate bacterial clones obtained by the streaking method. (Courtesy of N. E. Mele-chen.)*

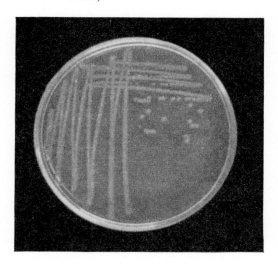

handicap in detecting phenotypic changes due to mutation. Mutants that change the morphology of bacteria must be detected by microscopic examination. Unfortunately, individual bacteria show relatively few clear-cut morphological variations—traits such as size, shape, capsule, pigment, and the presence or absence of flagella. The only mutants detected then are those which affect the relatively few morphological traits to a measurable degree, seriously limiting the detection of mutants by examination of individual bacteria.

Nevertheless, if a suspected mutant is found under the microscope, it is essential to isolate it and, from the members of the clone it produces, determine whether or not the new trait appears in the offspring. One of the several methods of isolating an individual bacterium is the tedious though exact procedure of removing a single individual from a bacterial culture with a micromanipulator and placing it in a fresh culture medium. Single bacteria can also be obtained by two indirect methods, less exact but quicker. If the bacteria are growing in a liquid medium, the culture can be sufficiently diluted so that a sample of it contains relatively few individuals. When this sample is poured onto the surface of a petri dish containing a nutrient agar medium, the individual cells are distributed on the medium at random and usually so spaced that the visible clone which each cell later produces is discrete (Figure 22–3). As an alternative, a small amount of a broth culture can be picked up in a sterile inoculating loop and the bacteria spread by streaking the loop across the surface of fresh nutrient agar medium (Figure 22–4). At some places on the medium, single bacteria will be deposited sufficiently far apart to give rise to separate colonies. Which of these methods is used depends upon the precision required.

The study of the individual bacterium is presently restricted to morphological variation, since it is not yet feasible to make physiological and biochemical studies on such a microscopic scale. One can, however, make use of the fact that, barring mutation, clones are composed of genetically-identical individuals. Genetically-different clones can show phenotypic differences in the size, shape, and color they produce on agar. Genetically-different clones can also respond differently to various dyes, drugs, and viruses. Therefore, one can also establish the genotype of a single bacterium from the phenotype of the clone it produces.

E. coli is easily cultured since it can grow and reproduce on a simple, chemically-defined food medium. Strains which grow on such a basic, minimal medium are considered to be *prototrophic,* or wild-type, capable of synthesizing the numerous metabolic components of the cell not supplied in the medium. In this respect prototrophs of *E. coli* or other bacteria are similar to the wild-type of Neurospora which also grows on a minimal, chemically-defined medium. It is not surprising, then, that in bacteria (and also in Neurospora) the richest source of mutants comes from the study of the biochemical variations which occur in different clones, particularly those involving changes in nutritional requirements. For numerous mutants to grow and reproduce—whether they arise spontaneously or after treatment with physical or chemical mutagens—one or more of a variety of chemical substances must be added to the basic medium. For example, one strain of *E. coli* requires the addition of the amino acid threonine to the minimal medium; another strain requires the amino acid methionine. Nutritionally dependent strains whose growth depends on a supplement to their basic food medium are said to be *auxotrophic.*

Transformation

As characterized by clonal phenotypes, Pneumococcus (*Diplococcus pneumoniae*)

occurs in a number of genetic types. One type, S, produces a colony whose smooth surface is directly related to the capsule of polysaccharide material each bacterium possesses. Another type of colony, R, has a rough surface because its bacteria lack this polysaccharide capsule. Moreover, several types of S colonies can be distinguished from each other because they differ antigenically; that is, different antisera can be obtained which specifically cause the clumping of each different type of S. R cells also occur in several different antigenic types, and antisera can also be produced which will clump them.

In one experiment, a large number of R cells is placed in a nutrient broth containing corresponding anti-R serum.[1] When growth continues, clumps of agglutinated R cells settle to the bottom of the test tube, and the initially cloudy supernatant fluid becomes clear. If this supernate is plated on nutrient agar, the bacteria still present form typical R colonies; any mutation from R to S must occur rarely, for it is not detected with this particular technique.

When the same experiment is performed with heat-killed (65° C for 30 minutes) S cells also present in the nutrient broth, numerous clones of S type appear on the agar after plating the supernate. This S phenotype is stable and clearly the result of a genetic change. Therefore, one is led to assume that the heat-killed S cells are acting as a mutagen in the *genetic transformation* of R to S cells. What is most surprising is that the type of S mutant produced is always identical to that of the heat-killed bacteria presumably acting as mutagen. In this apparently unique situation, the mutagen acts specifically to produce mutations in only one predictable direction (to one S type) rather

[1] The following account is based upon experiments of F. Griffith, of M. H. Dawson and R. H. P. Sia, and of O. T. Avery, C. M. MacLeod, and M. McCarty (1944).

than in several directions (to two or more S types).

To determine the chemical nature of the mutagen involved, the transforming capacity of different fractions of the heat-killed S bacteria is tested. Fractions containing either the polysaccharide coat, protein, or RNA are completely inactive; only the fraction containing DNA has the ability to transform. The purest DNA extracts retain the full transforming ability, even though they contain less than .02% protein or are treated with protein-denaturing agents or proteolytic enzymes. Chemical analyses and other tests (serological, electrophoretic, ultracentrifugal, and spectroscopic) also indicate that the active DNA is not detectably contaminated by either protein, unbound lipid, or polysaccharide. RNase has no effect on the transforming capacity of a purified DNA fraction, but the transforming factor is completely destroyed by DNase, showing that transformation requires DNA in highly polymerized form.

As revealed from its X-ray diffraction pattern, transforming DNA has the double-stranded configuration of chromosomal DNA. Since pure DNA can be used to transform, no contact need be made between the cell acting as DNA donor and the one acting as recipient. Moreover, genetic transformation does not involve the mediation of a virus. Therefore, *beyond any reasonable scientific doubt, DNA alone must be the transforming agent.*

Transformation can occur in either direction ($A \rightleftarrows A'$), and, in bacteria, any chromosomal gene can be transformed. Type A cells can be transformed to an A′ type which, in turn, provides increased amounts of A′-DNA capable of transforming other A cells to A′. So, the DNA extracted from transformed bacteria provides increased amounts of the same transforming principle.

One transforming principle (A′) can transform bacteria having any one of several alternative phenotypes (for example, A or A″). If the A′-DNA, obtained from A-type bacteria transformed to A′, is then used to transform bacteria of a third genotype, A″, only A′ transformants are found—the only transformations produced are those involving the genes of the immediate donor. This result demonstrates that transformation produces a transmissible alteration based upon the loss of host genetic material apparently at the same time as the new genetic material is acquired—not the simple addition of particular genetic material to the genotype. Thus, the genetic change in transformation is of a replacement type.

The fate of transforming DNA can be traced [2] by labeling its phosphate groups with radioactive P^{32}. At various times after exposure to such labeled DNA, one portion of the treated bacteria is killed and analyzed for the presence of P^{32} in its DNA, whereas another portion is tested to determine transformation frequency. Only after bacteria have been exposed to the DNA extract for a suitable period of time is the labeled DNA found in the extract containing the host's chromosomal DNA. Moreover, the frequency with which the host cell is transformed is directly proportional to the amount of labeled DNA so incorporated.

The preceding results demonstrate that the transforming DNA actually enters the bacterium and replaces a segment of the host's chromosomal DNA [3] (Pneumococcus contains about 6 times 10^6 deoxyribotide pairs per nuclear body), after which the newly-introduced material replicates as a normal part of the chromosome. Since it is DNA which alone carries the genetic information for transformation, *genetic transformation provides direct and conclusive evidence that DNA is genetic material.* Accordingly,

[2] Based upon work of L. S. Lerman and L. J. Tolmach (1957).
[3] See H. Ephrussi-Taylor (1951) for specific evidence on the latter observation.

chromosomal DNA contains the chemical units of the genetic material; all other transformation studies support this conclusion.

We should now re-examine the assumption, made earlier in this chapter, that transformation involves mutation. Because the first transformation studies seemed to involve novel, rare changes in the genetic material, these were called mutations (p. 149). We now know that transformation involves replacement of one segment of genetic material by another, that only a shuffling of already-existent genes occurs and not a new type of genetic material. Moreover, genetic transformation has been found not only in Pneumococcus but in Hemophilus, Xanthomonas, Salmonella, Bacillus, Neisseria, Escherichia, and other organisms as well. In Neisseria, DNA is regularly liberated (into the slime layer) by the cells which undergo self-digestion, or autolysis, in aging cultures; such DNA is effective in transformation, as is the DNA obtained from penicillin-sensitive pneumococci disintegrated or lysed after treatment with penicillin. Using different genetically-marked pneumococci, it is found [4] that genetic transformation—due to DNA liberated from one strain transforming members of the other strain—occurs spontaneously in the living mouse host.

Two lines of the human cell strain D98S maintained *in vitro* are genetically differentiated by the presence or absence of the enzyme, *inosinic acid pyrophosphorylase* (IMPPase). Since the spontaneous mutation frequency from IMPPase-negative to -positive is found to be less than one cell in 10^7, and since a culture medium can be employed which completely prevents cells of the negative line—but not those of the positive line—from forming colonies, it is possible to detect as few as one genetic transformant per 10^7 cells. Treatment of the IMPPase-negative line with DNA isolated from IMPPase-positive cells results in the appearance of IMPPase-positive, genetically-transformed cells at rates as high as 4 times 10^{-4} transformations per recipient cell (one transformation per 2500 treated cells). Such rates offer clear proof that genetic transformation of human cell lines occurs under experimental conditions.[5]

Not only is transformation widespread, but a given type can occur with a frequency as high as 25%. Such results demonstrate, of course, that transformation is not rare. Because genetic transformation is not rare and does not produce novel genotypes, it should not be considered a type of mutation. Accordingly, just as with segregation, independent segregation, crossing over, and fertilization, it is probably best to *consider genetic transformation as another mechanism for genetic recombination.*

As determined from bacterial studies, the complete transformation process requires a series of discrete stages, as follows:

Cell competence. During certain periods in cell division or in the growth of a bacterial culture, transformation does not occur; in other periods the cells are competent to react.

Binding the transforming DNA. When bacteria are in a competent stage, the transforming DNA, transiently bound to the cell at first, can be removed by several methods including exposure to DNase, before the DNA is permanently bound.

Penetration of transforming DNA. Permanently-bound DNA is considered to have penetrated the recipient bacterium. It should be noted that the success of transformation is inversely related to the thickness of a polysaccharide coat which probably acts as some kind of barrier to binding or penetration. When transforming DNA is fragmented sonically, the newly formed DNA

[4] By E. Ottolenghi and C. M. MacLeod (1963).

[5] According to W. Szybalski, E. H. Szybalska, and G. Ragni (1962); see E. H. Szybalska and W. Szybalski (1962).

particles have a molecular weight of less than 4 times 10^5, which is not sufficient to penetrate. Only high-molecular-weight DNA penetrates.

These facts should be considered with regard to the circumstances under which DNA uptake occurs in mammalian tissue culture. In this case, DNA enters by phagocytosis which occurs only when the DNA adheres to a suitably large non-DNA particle. *Pinocytosis,* similar to phagocytosis, is another process by which materials can enter ordinary cells. Although pure nucleic acids are not pinocytosed, protein is. However, if pure nucleic acid is mixed with protein, pinocytosis is stimulated, and the nucleic acid is carried into the cell with the protein. Perhaps the penetration of high-molecular-weight DNA into bacteria is dependent upon the presence of sufficient contaminating material capable of stimulating pinocytosis or some other mechanism for DNA penetration. Whatever the precise method by which transforming DNA penetrates, it is found that relatively short sequences of DNA will enter microbial cells if sufficient protein is also present.

The bacterial surface contains a finite number of sites which act as receptors for DNA. Since non-transforming DNA (such as DNA from a widely separated genus) can also penetrate readily, receptor sites can be saturated by nontransforming DNA, thereby preventing the penetration of transforming DNA.

Synapsis. Alternatives of the same trait —for example, resistance and sensitivity to streptomycin, or auxotrophy and prototrophy for a particular nutrient—can be found in different species of bacteria. Since it is a reasonable assumption that the same type of gene (and its alternatives) performs the same or similar functions in different species, interspecific transformations ought to be possible. Although this result has been achieved, in any given case the interspecific transformation is usually less frequent than the intraspecific one. Moreover, the transformation frequency is actually lower and not due to a delay in phenotypic expression which occurs in interspecific (but not in intraspecific) transformation. That interspecific transformation does take place favors the idea that the transformed locus is normally part of the genotype of both species. The relative infrequency of interspecific transformations is, therefore, not due to incompetence of the recipient cell or a failure of the foreign DNA to bind to or penetrate the recipient.

The transforming capacity of already-penetrated DNA may depend not only upon the homology of the loci transformed but upon the nature of the genes adjacent to those undergoing transformation. These neighboring genes might influence transformation by their effect upon the synapsis of the transforming DNA with the corresponding region of the host's genetic material. In intraspecific transformation, the loci adjacent to those transformed are very probably homologous in transformer and host, so that synapsis between the two segments can occur properly; in interspecific transformation, these loci are likely to be nonhomologous and, therefore, may often fail to synapse or act to prevent synapsis.

Integration. Even if the hypothesized synapsis occurs properly between host and transforming DNA, some process has yet to occur by which the host gene—whose transformation is being followed—is lost from the chromosome, and the donor's locus becomes an integral part of it. Some understanding of the mechanism of this final stage in transformation may be gained from a study of transformation frequency. First of all, different loci transform intraspecifically with different frequencies. Using genes that transform with suitably high frequencies, we are able to study the frequency of *double transformations,* that is, the frequency with which bacteria are transformed with respect to two markers present in the donor DNA. In several cases (for example, penicillin- and streptomycin-resistance), the frequency of doubly-transformed bacteria is approximately equal to (actually somewhat less than) the product of the frequencies for the single transformations. Such results probably mean that the transforming DNA carries the two loci either on separate particles or in widely separated positions on the same particle. On the other hand, the markers for streptomycin-resistance and mannitol-fermentation are transformed together with a frequency (.1%) which is about 17 times that expected from the product of the frequencies of the single transformations (.006%). This result implies that these two genetic markers are located on the same transforming particle; that is, they seem to be reasonably close together in the same bacterial chromosome.

If two loci are closely linked, how can we explain the occurrence of single and double transformations for them? Because of fragmentation during extraction, a given penetrating DNA particle may not always have the same composition relative to the two markers; it may sometimes carry only one and, at other times, may carry both of these markers. The effect of reducing the particle size of penetrating DNA upon the frequencies of single and double transformations can be tested. When particle size is reduced by DNase or sonic treatment, one expects—according to the present hypothesis—the particles sometimes to be broken between the two markers, reducing the relative frequency of the double transformation and increasing the relative frequencies of the single transformations. When the particle size is reduced, the overall rate of transformation is lower, as expected. No change is found, however, in the ratio of double to single transformations, implying that the two markers are so closely linked, they are rarely

separated when particles are fragmented. Accordingly, it seems that the penetrating particles must usually carry both markers, or neither, and the failure to obtain 100% double-transformations from the former type must be because only a small portion of a penetrating, synapsing particle is integrated.

Integration of a portion of a synapsed particle can occur in two possible ways (Figure 22–5): One involves *copy-choice* (Figure 22–5B) in which a daughter chromosome is formed by the alternate use of the host chromosome and the donor DNA as a template. When completed, the daughter chromosome is exactly like the original chromosome except for the daughter segment formed with transforming DNA as the template. One expects the recombinant chromosome produced by the copy-choice method to contain all newly-synthesized DNA.

The second method involves *breakage and exchange* of the kind that takes place in chromosomal rearrangement or in crossing over. In this case (Figure 22–5A), "breaks" have to occur on each side of the marker being integrated, so that a "double crossover" (p. 134) is produced. Although double crossovers within a short distance are expected to be extremely rare between two homologous chromosomes of higher organisms, this kind of exchange can occur under special circumstances and may be possible between the chemically less complex chromosome of bacteria and the shorter, synapsed segment of transforming DNA. Linkage of transforming DNA to host markers does not require DNA synthesis in the region involved,[6] although the integrated segment—which must be at least 900 nucleotide pairs long—appears to replicate in synchrony with the host DNA. Experiments with labeled DNA show that in transformation single-stranded donor DNA is inserted

[6] See M. S. Fox (1962).

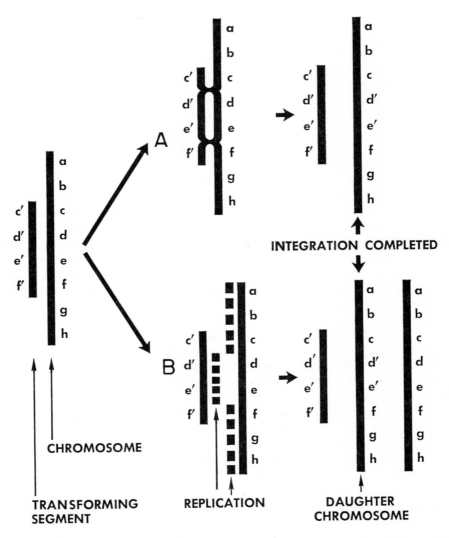

FIGURE 22-5. *Postulated mechanisms for the incorporation of a segment of genetic information into a host chromosome. A. Breakage method; B. Copy-choice method.*

into the DNA of the host, and that probably either strand of the donor DNA could be used this way.[7] Thus, the evidence favors the breakage hypothesis of integration.

It is important to note that the portion

of penetrating donor DNA which is not integrated, obviously, is also not retained or conserved as chromosomal genetic material. If integration occurs by copy-choice, the transforming segment is not conserved either; if integration occurs by "breakage-exchange," the replaced DNA segment is not conserved.

[7] See O. H. Siddiqi (1963), and M. S. Fox and M. K. Allen (1964).

Strand Recombination *in Vitro*

Heating chromosomal DNA denatures it by causing strand separation. After quick cooling, the resultant single strands of denatured DNA can fold forming a considerable number of complementary base pairs between bases at different levels of the single strand. It should be noted that, under certain conditions, homopolymers of RNA containing A, U, C, or inosinic acid are capable of base-pairing after folding, thus forming regular double-helical structures. To understand *de novo* synthesis and limited reaction *in vitro* it may be important to learn the extent to which intrastrand base-pairing occurs in DNA homopolymers containing C or G. After pneumococcal DNA is heated for ten minutes at 100° C, all strands are essentially single and all H bonds broken; [8] this denaturation, called *melting,* occurs sharply at 71° C for dAT and at 83° C for dGdC. When DNA denatured by heat is cooled slowly, only about 70% renaturation occurs for native DNA, although, as expected, dAT and dGdC apparently show 100% renaturation.

Renatured and native DNA differ from denatured DNA in several properties:

1. Under the electron microscope, renatured DNA looks very much like native DNA, whereas denatured DNA is irregularly coiled with clustered regions
2. Renatured and native DNA have similar and lighter densities than denatured DNA
3. Renatured and native DNA have about twice the molecular weight of denatured DNA
4. Although all DNA has the same absorption spectrum, renatured and na-

[8] The following account is based primarily on work reported by P. Doty, J. Marmur, J. Eigner, and G. Schildkraut (1960), and J. Marmur and D. Lane (1960).

tive DNA absorb less ultraviolet than denatured DNA.

Several factors affect renaturation:

1. *The concentration of DNA in a slowly cooling mixture.* When the concentration of single strands is high, so is the amount of renaturation; when the concentration is low, slow cooling does not produce any substantial recombination of strands.

2. *Salt concentration.* The negatively-charged phosphate groups of single strands tend to prevent union with other strands. This inhibition can be overcome by adding KCl to the solution to act as a shield against the repulsion between phosphates. Consequently, within a certain range, the more KCl present, the greater the amount of renaturation obtained by slow cooling of heated DNA.

3. *The source of DNA.* Assuming the molecular weight of native DNA to be approximately the same in all organisms, a mammalian cell, which has about a thousand times as much nuclear DNA as a bacterial cell, also has about a thousand times as many DNA molecules. Assuming that all the DNA molecules within a genome differ in base sequence, then, in a given concentration of denatured DNA, on the order of one thousand times fewer complementary strands are present in a sample from calf thymus than in one from Pneumococcus. When equal concentrations of denatured DNA are heated to 80° C, double strands are formed by a large fraction of the bacterial DNA, but by no detectable fraction of the calf thymus DNA. The concentration of complementary strands, therefore, is important in renaturation.

DNA can be denatured *in vitro* by a large number of organic chemical substances including urea, aromatic compounds, and a variety of alcohols. This finding, however, does not necessarily mean that such compounds have this function *in vivo,* or that they reveal what is responsible for holding the strands in a DNA double helix together under *in vivo* or the usual *in vitro* conditions.

Another physical-chemical change can occur when DNA is heated *in vitro*. As noted, native pneumococcal DNA has a molecular weight of about six million. When certain preparations of this native DNA are heated, the single strands obtained have a molecular weight of less than half this value. This reduction in molecular weight can be explained by the presence of DNase as a contaminant. Even though single strands in a double helix are enzymatically severed by DNase, the whole complex can still retain the double-helix configuration. Once these complementary strands are separated by heat denaturation, however, the fragments of each single strand separate.

As already mentioned, DNA from different sources and DNA particles of different sizes behave differently in various parts of the sequence leading to transformation. When DNA *in vitro* is exposed to dilute concentrations of DNase, the results [9] indicate that single strands of the double helix are attacked first, and only later—when both strands have been attacked at reasonably nearby positions—is the molecule severed. This *scission* produces smaller DNA molecules which, it should be recalled, penetrate a host cell poorly. Even if only one strand of the double helix has been attacked, however, transformation capacity declines. This effect is attributed partly to the failure of penetrant molecules to transform because the transforming locus or because a locus necessary for synapsis or integration has been inactivated.

In Pneumococcus, denatured DNA has a small amount of transforming ability. The molecular basis for this is still undetermined. On the other hand, the transforming ability

[9] Of L. S. Lerman and L. J. Tolmach.

of renatured DNA can be as much as 50% of that shown by an equivalent concentration of native DNA. An increased concentration of DNA plus a high ionic strength increase both renaturation and transforming ability.

Hybrid molecules can be made by renaturing a mixture of N-14 and N-15 DNA from *E. coli*. (Recall that these synthetic molecules can be identified by the intermediate position they assume in the ultracentrifuge tube.) Hybrid molecules can also be formed between single DNA strands from different species, but only if the species are closely related genetically (as would be suggested if they showed interspecific transformation) and, therefore, have similar base sequences. Molecular hybrids are useful for comparing base sequences in closely-related organisms even when genetic recombination between them cannot take place.

Several additional observations should be made:

1. Strand separation is accomplished by heat in a matter of a few minutes or less. One wonders if this kind of extensive strand separation occurs *in vivo*. It has been suggested that chain separation normally is produced enzymatically through the activity of *ravelase,* or better, *unravelase.*

2. The now-routine ability to separate and combine single strands should lead to a better understanding of transformation, in particular, the mechanism of integration.

3. *The smallest recombinational unit of the genetic material in bacteria can be identified as the smallest unit of DNA capable of being integrated or replaced in a host genotype in a genetic transformation.*

Although the physical and chemical properties of the DNA product of an extensive synthesis *in vitro* closely resemble those of the natural DNA used as primer-template, and although the synthesis is considered to be a biological process, it has not been demonstrated that the DNA product has biological properties, that is, functions genetically *in vivo*. When transforming DNA is used in an *in vitro* synthesis, the total transforming capacity of the incubating mixture decreases with time as the synthesis continues. It is very likely that the trace amounts of DNases present in the polymerase preparation cause the loss of overall transforming activity by interrupting the continuity of the DNA strands, so that transforming capacity is lost by DNase action faster than it is gained by means of DNA synthesis. The biological activity of newly-synthesized DNA can be detected, however, by differentially labeling the old and the new DNA and separately testing each for transforming capacity.

Consequently,[10] nonradioactive DNA containing 5-bromo uracil is used as a primer-template to synthesize radioactive DNA with no 5-bromo uracil. After synthesis, density gradient centrifugation of the DNA provides a double-stranded fraction containing essentially all newly-synthesized DNA (which is radioactive and less dense than the DNA with 5-bromo uracil). Since other explanations seem to be ruled out, and this new DNA is found capable of transforming a variety of gene loci, it apparently is proved that biologically-active genetic material, that is, *functionally-active genes, can be synthesized* in vitro.

[10] See R. M. Litman and W. Szybalski (1963).

SUMMARY AND CONCLUSIONS

Genetic recombination occurs in cells of bacteria and of other organisms by means of genetic transformation. In bacteria, transformation involves a sequence of events in which competent cells transiently and then permanently bind DNA. Once bound DNA has penetrated, it apparently undergoes a synapsis-like process with a corresponding segment of the bacterial genome. Transformation is completed when a small segment of donor DNA becomes integrated and replaces a similar segment of the host genome.

Transformation provides direct and conclusive evidence that chromosomal DNA is genetic material. In bacteria, the smallest recombinational unit of the genetic material is the smallest unit of DNA integrated or replaced in transformation.

Strand separation and recombination *in vitro* produce denatured and renatured DNA, respectively.

Strong evidence has been obtained that functionally-active genes, introduced into bacteria via transformation, can be synthesized *in vitro*.

REFERENCES

Akinrimisi, E. O., Sander, C., and Ts'o, P. O. P., "Properties of Helical Polycytidylic Acid," Biochemistry, 2:340–344, 1963.

Avery, O. T., MacLeod, C. M., and McCarty, M., "Studies on the Chemical Nature of the Substance Inducing Transformation of Pneumococcal Types," J. Exp. Med., 79:137–158, 1944. Reprinted in *Papers on Bacterial Genetics,* Adelberg, E. A. (Ed.), Boston: Little, Brown, 1960, pp. 147–168, and in *Classic Papers in Genetics,* Peters, J. A. (Ed.), Englewood Cliffs, N.J.: Prentice-Hall, 1959, pp. 173–192.

Doty, P., Marmur, J., Eigner, J., and Schildkraut, C., "Strand Separation and Specific Recombination in Deoxyribonucleic Acids: Physical Chemical Studies," Proc. Nat. Acad. Sci., U.S., 46:461–476, 1960.

Ephrussi-Taylor, H., "Genetic Aspects of Transformations of Pneumococci," Cold Spring Harb. Sympos. Quant. Biol., 16:445–456, 1951.

Fox, M. S., "The Fate of Transforming Deoxyribonucleate Following Fixation by Transformable Bacteria, III," Proc. Nat. Acad. Sci., U.S., 48:1043–1048, 1962.

Fox, M. S., and Allen, M. K., "On the Mechanism of Deoxyribonucleate Integration in Pneumococcal Transformation," Proc. Nat. Acad. Sci., U.S., 52:412–419, 1964.

Gellert, M., Lipsett, M. N., and Davies, D. R., "Helix Formation by Guanylic Acid," Proc. Nat. Acad. Sci., U.S., 48:2013–2018, 1962.

Herriot, R. M., "Formation of Heterozygotes by Annealing a Mixture of Transforming DNAs," Proc. Nat. Acad. Sci., U.S., 47:146–153, 1961.

Hotchkiss, R. D., "Transfer of Penicillin Resistance in Pneumococci by the Desoxyribonucleate Derived from Resistant Cultures," Cold Spring Harb. Sympos. Quant. Biol., 16:457–461, 1951. Reprinted in Papers on Bacterial Genetics, Adelberg, E. A. (Ed.), Boston: Little, Brown, 1960, pp. 169–176.

Hoyer, B. H., McCarthy, B. J., and Bolton, E. T., "A Molecular Approach in the Systematics of Higher Organisms," Science, 144:959–967, 1964.

Lerman, L. S., and Tolmach, L. J., "Genetic Transformation. I. Cellular Incorporation of DNA Accompanying Transformation in Pneumococcus," Biochim. Biophys. Acta, 26:68–82, 1957. Reprinted in Papers on Bacterial Genetics, Adelberg, E. A. (Ed.), Boston: Little, Brown, 1960, pp. 177–191.

Levine, L., Gordon, J. A., and Jenks, W. P., "The Relationship of Structure to the Effectiveness of Denaturing Agents for Deoxyribonucleic Acid," Biochemistry, 2:168–175, 1963.

Litman, R. M., and Szybalski, W., "Enzymatic Synthesis of Transforming DNA," Biochem. Biophys. Res. Commun., 10:473–481, 1963.

Marmur, J., Falkow, S., and Mandel, M., "New Approaches to Bacterial Taxonomy," Ann. Rev. Microbiol., 17:329–372, 1963.

Marmur, J., and Lane, D., "Strand Separation and Specific Recombination in Deoxyribonucleic Acids: Biological Studies," Proc. Nat. Acad. Sci., U.S., 46:453–461, 1960.

Marmur, J., Rownd, R., and Schildkraut, C. L., "Denaturation and Renaturation of Deoxyribonucleic Acid," Progr. Nucleic Acid Res., 1:231–300, 1963.

Ravin, A. W., "Experimental Approaches to the Study of Bacterial Phylogeny," Amer. Nat., 97:307–318, 1963.

Roger, M., "Fractionation of Pneumococcal DNA Following Selective Heat Denaturation: Enrichment of Transforming Activity for Aminopterium Resistance," Proc. Nat. Acad. Sci., U.S., 51:189–195, 1964.

Siddiqi, O. H., "Incorporation of Parental DNA into Genetic Recombinants of E. coli," Proc. Nat. Acad. Sci., U.S., 49:589–592, and 50:581, 1963.

Szybalska, E. H., and Szybalski, W., "Genetics of Human Cell Lines, IV. DNA-Mediated Heritable Transformation of a Biochemical Trait," Proc. Nat. Acad. Sci., U.S., 48:2026–2034, 1962.

QUESTIONS FOR DISCUSSION

22.1. Which single characteristic of bacteria provides the greatest advantage for genetic studies? Why?

22.2. Assuming that all members of a clone are genetically identical, could sexual processes have influenced the results of any of the experiments described in this chapter? Explain.

22.3. Distinguish between auxotrophic and prototrophic bacteria.

22.4. Design an experiment to test whether the dye, acriflavin, is mutagenic in *E. coli*.

22.5. Compare the "chromosome" of bacteria with that of man.

22.6. Is the use of the phrase "bacterial chromosomal DNA" justified even though bacteria do not contain typical chromosomes? Explain.

22.7. What is meant by integration in genetics? Without using diagrams, describe the mechanisms by which it may occur.

22.8. List those features of crossing over which are difficult to explain on a copy-choice basis.

22.9. Discuss the genetic control of gene synthesis and gene degradation.

22.10. Criticize the statement (p. 5) that genetic transmission can occur between generations only by means of a cellular bridge.

22.11. On what basis is transformation classified as a type of genetic recombination rather than as a mutation? Do you agree with this interpretation? Why?

22.12. Devise an experiment to detect whether chain separation occurs during extensive *in vitro* synthesis of DNA.

22.13. Do the studies on transformation offer any clues as to the ploidy of Pneumococcus? Explain.

22.14. What kinds of problems would you investigate if you had a feasible method of studying the fate of individual cells exposed to transforming DNA?

22.15. What do studies of genetic transformation reveal regarding the genetic nature of conserved and nonconserved chromosomal DNA?

22.16. Redraw Figure 22–5 showing hypothetical base sequences in double-stranded DNA. Has your drawing any bearing on your answer to question 22.8? Explain.

22.17. How can you explain the finding (p. 299) that the frequency of double transformations for certain markers is sometimes somewhat less than the product of the frequencies of the single transformations?

22.18. Interspecific transformation in bacteria is rare or absent when the relative $G + C$ contents of host and donor differ. When the $G + C$ contents are the same, donor-host hybrid DNA's can form even when interspecific transformation is rare. Discuss the relative values of $G + C$ content, hybrid DNA formation, and interspecific transformation in taxonomic studies of bacteria.

Chapter 23

BACTERIAL MUTATION
AND CONJUGATION

Mutation

Practically all of the mutants produced after treatment with a mutagenic agent have non-adaptive or detrimental phenotypic effects (Chapter 16). The detriment produced by these mutants clearly is not dependent upon the mutagen's continued presence in the environment. Similarly many of the rare mutants that increase adaptability continue to be beneficial in the absence of the mutagen which induced them. On rare occasions, however, a mutagen (like X rays) produces a mutant with an adaptive advantage in the presence of the mutagen (for example, resistance to the genetic or nongenetic detrimental effects of X rays). Is such an adaptive mutant produced by chance, or is it a special genetic response elicited by the mutagen? The same question can be raised about adaptive mutants that occur "spontaneously." Are these mutants produced as an adaptive genetic response to unidentified factors in the environment?

This general problem can be illustrated with a particular strain of *E. coli* which apparently has never been exposed to the drug streptomycin. If such a strain is plated onto an agar medium containing this drug, almost all the individuals will not grow and, therefore, will not form colonies. These individuals are *streptomycin-sensitive*. However, about one bacterium in ten million does grow on this medium and forms a colony composed of *streptomycin-resistant* individuals, the basis for this resistance

clearly being transmissible. Is the adaptive, resistant mutant produced in response to the streptomycin exposure, with the streptomycin acting as a directive mutagenic agent? Or, do streptomycin-resistant mutants occur in the absence of streptomycin, spontaneously, with the streptomycin acting only as a selective agent to reveal the prior occurrence (or nonoccurrence) of resistant mutants? Or, are both explanations true? Restating the problem more generally, we ask whether mutants adapted to a treatment are *postadapted* (having arisen after treatment), *preadapted* (having already been present before treatment), or of both types.

Clearly, an ambiguous decision results so long as it is necessary to treat the individuals scored with what is being tested—streptomycin, in this example—for, under these conditions, one cannot decide whether the resistant mutant had a post- or preadaptive origin. This difficulty can be resolved. If streptomycin-resistant mutants are preadaptive, they should occur in the absence of the drug and give rise to clones all of whose members are resistant. It should be noted again that the mutation to streptomycin-resistance is a very rare event however it originates. Consequently, one must grow about ten million clones on streptomycin-free agar medium and test each clone for streptomycin resistance by placing a sample of each on a streptomycin-containing medium. After this transfer, part or all of one sample is expected to be resistant to the drug. If resistance is due to a preadapted mutant, one can return to the appropriate original clone—which has never been exposed to streptomycin—and readily obtain other samples which prove to be resistant. If, on the other hand, the mutant is post-adaptive, additional samples of the original clone will have no greater chance of furnishing resistants than additional samples taken from different clones.

Three *clone-sampling procedures* are

available for testing the preadaptive or post-adaptive origin of mutants. The first method starts with growing a single (presumably) streptomycin-sensitive clone in liquid medium and then plating it on an agar medium to produce a large number of separate colonies. A sample of each colony is then streaked across an agar medium perpendicular to a strip in the agar containing streptomycin. Where there is no streptomycin, each streak of bacteria will grow on the agar and, if enough clones are tested, at least one streak will also grow in the streptomycin region (Figure 23–1). If streptomycin-resistant mutants are postadaptive in origin, the growth on the streptomycin-containing area will be sharply discontinuous, since the members of the clone streaked across the streptomycin were originally sensitives, and only rarely will more than one of these bacteria respond to streptomycin by post-adaptive mutation. Moreover, other samples from the original clone will succeed in growing on streptomycin only to the same limited degree as did the first sample. If, on the other hand, the mutation is preadaptive, the growth across the streptomycin will be practically as continuous as after streak-ing the drug with a pure clone of resistant bacteria or with a mixture of bacteria rich in resistant individuals. The proof that the parental clone contained a spontaneous, preadaptive, streptomycin-resistant mutant will be complete if other samples of that clone also grow readily when streaked across this drug.

Considering the rarity of mutation from streptomycin-sensitivity to -resistance in this strain (one per 10^7 cells), the labor involved in testing the preadaptive or postadaptive nature of streptomycin-resistant mutants by this clone-sampling technique is prohibitive. (Nevertheless, the method has numerous uses in other genetic studies of bacteria.)

The second method which can be used to sample clones involves *replica plating*.[1] As before, this procedure starts by spreading the members of a single clone on streptomycin-free agar in a petri dish. As many as a thousand separate colonies can form after the plate is incubated and by pressing this *master plate* on the top of a sheet of velvet, a sample of almost every colony can be obtained simultaneously. The velvet—whose fibers pick up 10 to 30% of each colony— is then used to plant a corresponding pattern of growth on a series of additional *replica plates* (Figure 23–2). Preliminary control tests show that the velvet makes several excellent replicas of the master plate, and that both streptomycin-resistant and -sensitive clones can be replicated this way. The first replica is made on drug-free medium, whereas the second and later ones are made with streptomycin-containing plates on which, obviously, only streptomycin-resistant bacteria can grow into colonies. If the postadaptive view is correct, the chance that cells from one colony will grow on two replicas in the presence of streptomycin is the same as it is for two colonies to grow on the same replica. In other words, the

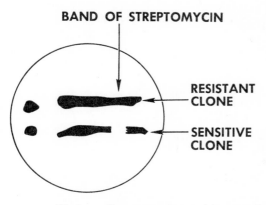

BAND OF STREPTOMYCIN

RESISTANT CLONE

SENSITIVE CLONE

FIGURE 23–1. *Streptomycin-sensitive and streptomycin-resistant* E. coli *as determined by streaking individual clones.*

[1] Based upon work of J. Lederberg and E. M. Lederberg.

positions of the resistant colonies on different replicas are random. If the mutants are preadaptive, however, all replicas probably will be resistant in the same position (although some exceptions can occur if the velvet fails to place a portion of the same colony on every replica plate). Of course, one also readily finds resistant bacteria in the corresponding position on the master plate. Although this clone-sampling technique is advantageous for many other purposes, it is still too laborious for testing the preadaptation or postadaptation hypothesis, since replicas of about ten thousand master plates are required to be reasonably sure of finding one clonal streptomycin-resistant mutant.

This difficulty can be avoided by using a third method for clone-sampling that involves replica-plating contiguous colonies. A billion or so bacteria (from a streptomycin-sensitive clone) plated on drug-free agar will produce small clones so closely spaced that they grow together and form a *bacterial lawn* (Figure 23–3A). Nevertheless, replicas of this growth can be made on strepto-

mycin-containing agar and will show growth wherever drug-resistant mutants occur (Figure 23–3B, C, D). One can then turn to the corresponding regions on the master plate to obtain samples to be tested for resistance to the drug. If such samples are no richer in resistant mutants than samples from randomly-chosen sites on the master plate corresponding to those which are not mutant on any replica, the postadaptive view is proved. When the experiment is actually performed, the master plate is found to be much richer in mutants at replica sites that are mutant than at those that are nonmutant. Moreover, replicas tend to have mutant clones at corresponding positions on all replica plates (Figure 23–3B–D). Accordingly, most mutants are clearly preadaptive. Other experiments show conclusively, in the case of streptomycin, that almost all, if not all, mutants resistant to the drug are preadaptive—that is, streptomycin does not induce a detectable number of resistant mutants. Since the same results are obtained with the drug chloramphenicol, one can extrapolate and conclude that, *in general, the*

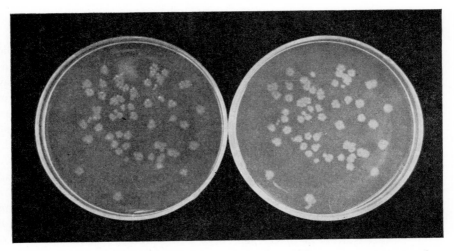

FIGURE 23–2. *Separate colonies replica-plated* (right) *from a master plate* (left). (*Courtesy of N. E. Melechen.*)

*resistant mutants on drug plates arise spon-
taneously, prior to exposure to the drugs
and, therefore, are preadaptive in origin.*

Large numbers of bacteria can be easily
tested for mutations. For example, a billion
drug-sensitive individuals can be plated on
agar containing the drug, and the number
of resistant mutant clones detected by counting the colonies formed; or, similarly, the
number of mutants to prototrophy can be
scored by plating auxotrophs on agar which
lacks the nutrient required for their growth
and counting the number of colonies formed.
To give information in terms of a *rate of
mutation,* however, it is necessary to state
the number of mutants occurring per unit
event. In multicellular organisms, mutation
rate is usually expressed in terms of mutations per cell, per individual, or per generation. This definition can be applied to bacteria also. Thus, the mutation rate from
streptomycin-sensitivity to -resistance in one
particular strain of *E. coli* (a different strain
from that used previously) is one per billion
bacteria—one of the lowest mutation rates
so far measured in any organism.

It is sometimes desirable to express mutation rate in terms of mutations per unit time;
for example, in describing the increase in
mutations obtained by aging Drosophila
spermatids or sperm (Chapter 14). In bacteria, one can considerably vary the length
of time required to complete a generation.
For generation times between 37 minutes
and two hours, the shorter the generation
time, the larger the mutation rate per hour.
When generation time is lengthened from
two to twelve hours, the rate of mutations
per hour is constant—each hour of delay
increasing the number of mutants by the
same amount. (Thus, in the two- to twelve-
hour range, the number of mutations increases linearly per generation.) Even when
the generation time is extended from twelve
hours to infinity (the nondividing cells kept
alive in a medium which provides a source

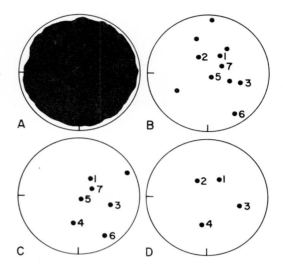

FIGURE 23–3. *Replica-plating a bacterial lawn
for the detection of mutants to streptomycin-
resistance. (After J. Lederberg and E. M.
Lederberg.)*

of energy), some mutations are found to
take place.

It becomes apparent, therefore, that *mutation rate is best defined as the chance of
a mutation per cell (or individual) per unit
time.* When, however, each of the division
cycles or generations requires the same
length of time (as would be true for bacteria
under optimal environmental conditions),
mutation rate is usually measured with one
generation as the unit of time.

Conjugation

Genetic recombination in bacteria may occur
as a result of genetic transformation. The
transformation process has two features
hitherto unencountered in discussions of genetic recombination in multicellular organisms:

1. The donor DNA enters the host bacterium without intervention of any other organism, as is shown by the infectivity of pure
DNA. (Although transformation involves

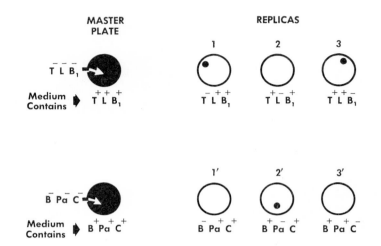

FIGURE 23–4. *Use of replica-plating (shown diagrammatically) to detect spontaneous mutations in* E. coli. *Replica 1 detects one mutant to* T+, *replica 3 detects one mutant to* B₁+, *and replica 2′ detects one mutant to* Pa+.

the genetic material of two different cells, it is not a typical sexual process, since transformation does not depend upon contact between donor and recipient cells.)

2. The integration process leading to genetic recombination requires the presence of only a portion of the entire genome of the donor cell. (Integration results in a small segment of the penetrant donor DNA replacing a small homologous segment of the host genome.)

At this point it does not seem unreasonable to hypothesize that any homologous DNA penetrating a bacterial cell can integrate by the same mechanism involved in transformation. Of course there may be other means of introducing DNA into a cell and, consequently, experiments are now designed to test whether or not DNA passes from one bacterium to another when two are in contact.

One such experiment [2] starts with a prototrophic strain (K12) of *E. coli* treated with

[2] Based upon work of J. Lederberg and E. L. Tatum (1946).

a mutagen (like X rays or ultraviolet light) to obtain single auxotrophic mutants which require different nutritional supplements in order to grow. The mutagenic treatment is repeated—first on the single and then on the double mutant auxotrophs—eventually obtaining two lines which differ from each other by three nutritional mutants, all six mutants having arisen independently. One triple mutant strain is auxotrophic for threonine (T^-), leucine (L^-), and thiamin (B_1^-); the other triple mutant is auxotrophic for biotin (B^-), phenylalanine (Pa^-), and cystine (C^-). The genotypes of these two lines can be given, respectively, as

$$T^-L^-B_1^-B^+Pa^+C^+$$

and

$$T^+L^+B_1^+B^-Pa^-C^-.$$

Of course, the given gene sequence may be different in the linkage map.

The pure lines are grown separately on *complete* liquid *culture medium,* that is, one which contains all nutrients required for growth and reproduction. To form a bacterial lawn, about 10^8 bacteria from one line are plated onto agar containing complete medium. Then three replica plates are made for the $T^-L^-B_1^-$ line (Figure 23–4), each plate contains complete medium deficient in a different single nutrient (T, L, and B_1, respectively). Occasionally, a replica shows a clone that is able to grow because a pre-adaptive mutant produces prototrophy for the nutrient missing from the medium. However, such clonal growth is not found in the corresponding position on all three replicas (or even on two) with greater than chance frequency. The same results are obtained when an equal number of bacteria of the $B^-Pa^-C^-$ line are plated on complete medium and tested on appropriate replicas. We may conclude, therefore, that on relatively rare occasions mutants to prototrophy for one nutrient do occur singly, but double or triple mutants do not occur with detectable frequency.

In another test, the preceding experiment is repeated exactly, with the exception that the same numbers of the two triply-mutant strains are mixed in the liquid medium *before* being plated on agar containing complete medium. In this case (Figure 23–5), six replicas are made with medium which is complete except that three lack B, Pa, and C in addition to lacking T, L, or B_1; the other three lack T, L, and B_1 and also B, Pa, or C. Individuals of the $T^-L^-B_1^-$ strain cannot grow on the first three replicas mentioned because a single required nutrient is missing; they cannot grow in the last three because all three required nutrients are missing. Individuals of the $B^-Pa^-C^-$ strain cannot grow on the first three replicas because all three required nutrients are missing; they cannot grow on the last three because one of the three is absent. If the master plate contains a mutant preadaptive to nutritional independence for one of the nutritionally dependent loci, in only one of the six replicas will the mutant form a colony.

For example, if a T^+ mutant occurs among the individuals of the $T^-L^-B_1^-$ strain on the master plate, a colony will grow only on the replica lacking B, Pa, C, and T. Actually, about a hundred different positions on the master plate show growth on the replicas. This number is very much larger than that found in the two groups of three replicas made after plating the two lines separately. In the present case, some positions show growth only on one of the six

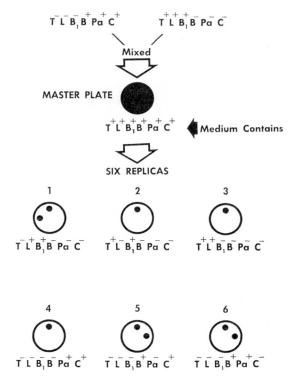

FIGURE 23–5. *Replica-plating (shown diagrammatically) to detect genetic recombination in E. coli. A completely prototrophic recombinant is found at 12 o'clock in all replicas. A recombinant for both* Pa *and* C *is found at 3 o'clock on replicas 5 and 6. Replica 1 has a clone growing at 9 o'clock which may be due either to recombination or to mutation to* T+.

replicas. Many positions, however, show growth on two replicas suggesting that these clones must have gained nutritional independence at two loci. Finally, at many positions growth occurs on all six replicas, each position of growth representing the occurrence of a complete prototroph ($T^+L^+B_1^+B^+Pa^+C^+$). A study of these clones on the replicas and on the master plate shows that the changes involved are transmissible and preadaptive. When tested, such clones prove to be pure; that is, the nutritional independence gained is not attributable to any type of physical association between two or more different auxotrophs. Since the findings that large numbers of clones grow on the replicas and many are either complete prototrophs or auxotrophs for only one nutrient cannot be due to spontaneous mutation, they must be attributed to some type of genetic recombination.

Could this genetic recombination be the result of transformation? Recall that most transformations involve single loci, and that the frequency of double transformations is much lower than the frequencies of single transformations even when the loci are apparently very close together, while double recombinants are common in the present experiment. In fact, certain recombinations for two loci (for example $T^+L^+B_1^-B^+Pa^+C^+$) occur more frequently than do recombinations for these loci singly

$$T^+L^-B_1^-B^+Pa^+C^+$$

and

$$T^-L^+B_1^-B^+Pa^+C^+.$$

Transformation explains even less readily the large number of triple recombinants— the complete prototrophs. Nevertheless, some additional experiments are performed to test the transformation explanation. The number of prototrophs obtained by recombination is found to be uninfluenced by addition of DNase to the medium in which the bacteria are mixed or on which the bacteria are plated. No transformation occurs when one culture of *E. coli* is exposed to filtrates or autolysates of another. Therefore, the genetic recombination detected in *E. coli* is not due to transformation.

In still another experiment, the base of a U-tube is filled with sintered glass to separate the arms; broth is then added, and each of the two bacterial strains placed in different arms. Since the sintered glass acts only as a bacterial filter, the nutrient medium, soluble substances, and small particles (including viruses) can be shuttled back and forth. Yet, when platings are subsequently made from either arm, no recombinants are found. Consequently, the recombinations observed are not dependent upon a virus. Moreover, after plating a mixture of three different mutant lines of K12, we can explain all the different recombinants obtained as resulting from recombination between any two lines; no individuals obtained are recombinant with respect to markers in all three lines. Apparently, *this type of genetic recombination depends upon conjugation; that is, it involves actual cell-to-cell contact of bacteria in pairs and is, therefore, a sexual process.*

The frequency of sexual recombination in the first experiment discussed is only about one per million cells (100 clones of recombinants per 100 million bacteria placed on the master plate). At this point in the investigation, the rarity of such events makes it fruitless to search for microscopic evidence of bacterial mating. (The importance of a new phenomenon should not be judged by the frequency with which it occurs in experiments first detecting it. Recall, for example, that the quantity of DNA first synthesized *in vitro* was infinitesimal compared with the amount synthesized in later work; and the rate of transformation observed initially was very much smaller than the 10–25% rate currently obtained with modified techniques.)

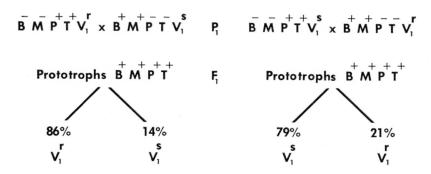

FIGURE 23–6. *Genetic recombinations obtained in reversed crosses involving unselected markers.*

The type of nutrient medium used in the experiments described permitted the detection of certain recombinants and not others. In the first recombination experiment, only *selective markers*—only those alleles which provided nutritional independence—were selected for detection. Thus, though the prototroph $T^+L^+B_1^+B^+Pa^+C^+$ was detectable, it was not possible to test for the occurrence of the complementary polyauxotroph $T^-L^-B_1^-B^-Pa^-C^-$. Since no test was made for the multiple auxotroph, one could doubt its occurrence. It is entirely reasonable that the immediate product of mating is a zygote containing part or all of the genotypes of both of the parental cells. Although it is assumed that integration can take place as it does in transformation (if DNA passes from one conjugant to another), no evidence that it does has been presented so far. In other words, the possibility remains, at least with respect to the genes showing recombination, that the recombinant produced by conjugation may be partially or completely diploid.

Although it is not feasible to find zygotes microscopically, one can look for them genetically. After mating, certain clones behave as though they are mosaic for a number of markers. When a single cell from such clones is isolated, grown, and tested, it is found [3] that some of its progeny possess the original genotype of either parent and that others are recombinants. Clearly, the single-cell isolates were derived from more or less persistent heterozygotes—individuals diploid for various markers. Thus, the haploid recombinants within a clone offer unambiguous proof that they were derived from a true zygote. Haploid recombinants are also called *segregants,* although this term does not imply that they were the result of a meiotic process. One concludes, therefore, that the (partially or completely) diploid zygote produced after bacterial conjugation usually has a temporary existence—just as in the case of transformation—which terminates in the production of haploid progeny. In other words, all the genes in a nuclear body of *E. coli* are usually haploid.

At the same time that certain genetic markers are used selectively—to detect recombinant prototrophs, for example—other markers may be present that are not subject to selection. Such genes are called *unselected markers*. *E. coli* is available in two genetic forms: V_1^r is resistant to infection by the bacterial viruses T_1 and T_6; V_1^s is sensitive to infection by these viruses. Infection is followed by death of the bacteria.

[3] By J. Lederberg and M. Zelle.

Using this marker and the auxotrophic mutants P^- (proline-requiring) and M^- (methionine-requiring), we can make the cross [4] $B^-M^-P^+T^+V_1^r$ by $B^+M^+P^-T^-V_1^s$ and select for the prototrophs $B^+M^+P^+T^+$. Since the medium employed is virus-free, the V_1 locus is used as an unselected marker.

The number of prototrophs thus obtained are subsequently tested for sensitivity and resistance to virus T_1, and 86% are found typically resistant, V_1^r, and 14% typically sensitive, V_1^s (Figure 23–6). Note that both these alternatives are recombinant relative to some of the markers for prototrophy.

When the reverse cross is made, V_1^r entering with the $B^+M^+P^-T^-$ parent and V_1^s with $B^-M^-P^+T^+$, the percentages of prototrophs sensitive and resistant to T_1 are found to be approximately reversed. In other words, the parent that provides P^+ and T^+ to the prototroph also contributes the V_1 locus which it contains 79–86% of the time. The imbalance in the frequency of resistants and sensitives among prototrophs (that is, their ratio is not 50% : 50%), and its reversal when the V_1 markers are reversed in the parent cells, provide clear evidence that the V_1 locus does not integrate and segregate independently of the other markers with which it enters the zygote and which, subsequently, are present in the haploid prototroph. As a consequence V_1 must be

[4] See J. Lederberg (1947).

linked to P and T and segregated from these loci (or fail to be integrated in the same segment with them) only about 20% of the time.

The linkage relationships for auxotrophic markers can also be determined, as follows: the cross $T^+L^+B_1^-B^-$ by $T^-L^-B_1^+B^+$ is made on a complete medium, plated on a complete medium, and replicated four times on a complete medium without T, or L, or B_1, or B. As a result, prototrophic recombinants grow on all four replicas and single auxotrophs grow on three, whereas double auxotrophs grow on two of the replicas. Since prototrophs are found to be more frequent than either $T^+L^-B_1^+B^+$ or $T^-L^+B_1^+B^+$, T and L must be linked. A further analysis of the results, for other markers and other experiments, reveals that all the genetic markers tested in E. coli are linked to each other and on a map can be arranged in a linear order according to their recombination (segregation or integration) distances. In all likelihood, this analysis indicates, that E. coli has a single "chromosome."

Genetic recombination by the sexual process of conjugation is known to occur in bacteria like Pseudomonas, and—under special conditions—in Serratia and Salmonella, as well as in Escherichia. Intergeneric conjugation between Escherichia and Salmonella has been observed to occur in a mammalian host.

SUMMARY AND CONCLUSIONS

Bacterial clones are excellent experimental material for the study of the mutation process and its rate. Techniques for detecting and isolating mutants are described. Mutants occur spontaneously, independent of the factors to which they may be adaptive.

Genetic recombination occurs in *Escherichia coli* and other bacteria after the sexual process of conjugation. *E. coli* normally has a haploid nuclear body, in which all tested genes belong to a single linear linkage group.

REFERENCES

Lederberg, J., "Gene Recombination and Linked Segregation in Escherichia Coli," Genetics, 32:505–525, 1947. Reprinted in *Papers on Bacterial Genetics,* Adelberg, E. A. (Ed.), Boston: Little, Brown, 1960, pp. 247–267.

Lederberg, J., "Bacterial Reproduction," Harvey Lect., 53:69–82, 1959.

Lederberg, J., and Lederberg, E. M., "Replica Plating and Indirect Selection of Bacterial Mutants," J. Bact., 63:399–406, 1952. Reprinted in *Papers on Bacterial Genetics,* Adelberg, E. A. (Ed.), Boston: Little, Brown, 1960, pp. 24–31.

Lederberg, J., and Tatum, E. L., "Gene Recombination in Escherichia Coli," Nature, London, 158–558, 1946. Reprinted in *Classic Papers in Genetics,* Peters, J. A. (Ed.), Englewood Cliffs, N.J.: Prentice-Hall, 1959, pp. 192–194.

QUESTIONS FOR DISCUSSION

23.1. In previous chapters, has any evidence been presented that spontaneous mutations are preadaptive? If so, state where.

23.2. Suppose one thousand streptomycin-free test tubes are each inoculated with one bacterium from a streptomycin-sensitive clone, and growth is permitted until about one billion bacteria are present in each tube. When the contents of each tube are plated on streptomycin-containing agar, what kind of result would you expect if the mutations to streptomycin-resistance were postadaptive in origin? Preadaptive in origin? From the expected results can you distinguish between these two alternatives? How?

JOSHUA LEDERBERG *and* ESTHER MARILYN LEDERBERG *about 1951.* (*Courtesy of The Long Island Biological Association.*)

23.3. From our discussion of drug-resistant mutants, is it valid to conclude that no drugs are mutagenic? Explain.

23.4. Criticize an attempt to prove the occurrence of genetic recombination by conjugation in which two bacterial strains, each singly auxotrophic for different nutrients, are mixed and subsequently tested for prototrophs.

23.5. Why is it futile to search cytologically for bacteria in the process of conjugation?

23.6. Differentiate between and give an example of a selective and an unselected marker; a singly auxotrophic and a prototrophic bacterium.

23.7. In this chapter, what is the evidence that the two auxotrophs which produced prototrophic progeny did so by conjugation rather than by mutation, genetic transformation, or viral infection?

23.8. In what ways does genetic transformation differ from conjugation?

23.9. Invent suitable genotypes for parents, a zygote, and its clonal progeny, and prove the existence of the zygote from the genotypes of the members of the clone it produces.

23.10. Ignoring the centromere, draw all the different ways you can represent a chromosome whose recombination map is linear.

23.11. Do you suppose that the discovery of sexuality in bacteria has important implications for the practice of medicine? Why?

Chapter 24

THE EPISOME F

ARE THE members of a pair of conjugating bacteria equivalent in that DNA from one can go into the other, each bacterium capable of acting either as donor or recipient? Let us take a look at two streptomycin-sensitive and auxotrophically different lines able to conjugate with each other to produce recombinant progeny. If both lines are exposed to streptomycin before—but not after—being mixed and plated, none of the pretreated individuals can divide. In fact, all eventually die, and no recombinant clones are formed. When one of the two parental lines is pretreated with streptomycin, again no recombinants are detected. But when the other parental line is pretreated, prototrophic recombinants do occur.[1] This finding demonstrates that the two parents are not equivalent. The parent giving no recombinants when pretreated acts as the DNA-receiving cell which normally would become the zygote after conjugation. When this parent is killed by streptomycin, it is impossible to obtain recombinant clones. The other type of parent must always serve as DNA donor in conjugation. After acting as donor, the death of this parent has no effect upon the zygote and subsequent recombination. The parent acting as genetic donor is called F^+ (for "fertility"); the parent acting as genetic recipient is called F^-. These types serve, so to speak, male and female functions, respectively. In bacterial conjugation, there-

fore, the genetic transfer is a one-way process.

In the discussion on pages 310 through 312, the original wild-type strain of *E. coli* K12 was F^+, and an F^- variant must have arisen while one of the triply auxotrophic lines was being prepared. F^+ by F^- crosses are fertile (show recombination); F^- by F^- crosses are sterile (show no recombination). F^+ by F^+ crosses can be fertile because F^+ cells can, on occasion, spontaneously change to F^- or because F^+ cells—acting as F^- phenocopies—can occasionally behave like F^- phenotypically, despite being genetically F^+. If one F^+ cell is placed in a culture of F^- cells, all the F^- cells will be rapidly converted to F^+ type. F^- cells converted to F^+ produce F^+ progeny. The rapidity of change from F^- to F^+ is such that the causative agent of F^+ must multiply at least twice as fast as the typical cell (and, therefore, twice as fast as chromosomal DNA). Consequently, in *E. coli*, F^+ *male sexuality is an infectious phenomenon due to a factor or particle called F.*

Several properties of F are known:

1. F is transferred from male to female only upon contact and cannot be isolated as a cell-free particle retaining sex conversion potency. (Accordingly, it does not give evidence of being a typical virus.)

2. Only one particle of F is transferred per mating.

3. Matings that transfer F are more frequent but less stable than matings involving chromosomal transfer. In fact, the transient conjugations which transfer F do not transfer known chromosomal markers.

4. Exposure of F^+ individuals to the dye acridine orange inhibits the replication of F so that F^- cells appear among the progeny. Acridine dyes also inhibit the synthesis of chromosomal DNA although not as completely as they inhibit F factor replication. Thus, acridine "curing" is really a differen-

[1] See W. Hayes (1953).

tial phenomenon. In stable F⁺ cultures, F multiplication proceeds at exactly the same rate as does chromosomal multiplication. This means that there is precise regulation of the number of F particles per chromosome and it is only when this regulation is inoperative—when a population of F⁻ cells is being converted to F⁺ by a few F⁺ cells, for example—that one sees the explosive multiplication of F.

These evidences are sufficient to conclude that *F is an extrachromosomal particle.* F not only makes a cell a potentially fertile male—that is, potentially capable of acting as chromosomal donor—but it affects the cell harboring it in several ways:

1. It changes the surface of a male cell so that on contact, it can recognize and react with a female cell.

2. It must be the cause of some kind of bridge between the male and female cell through which F or the chromosome is passed to the F⁻ cell.

3. It must also cause the formation of a receptor at the surface of the cell for viruses that attack males only.[2]

4. Finally, F has the ability to initiate, at a low frequency, the transfer of random chromosomal markers during F⁺ by F⁻ crosses. This phenomenon has been termed *Lfr* (*low frequency of recombination*).

So far we have found *E. coli* to have two mating types, F⁻ and F⁺. Another mating type can arise from F⁺ cells. This type produces a rather *high frequency of recombination* of chromosomal genes; hence its name, *Hfr*. Since the fertility of Hfr cells is unaffected by pretreatment with streptomycin, Hfr cells are donors. These cells can mate with F⁻ cells, and—although fertility is low—with cells in F⁺ cultures (which have either changed spontaneously to F⁻ or act as F⁻ phenocopies). Crosses

of Hfr with F⁻ produce 100 to 20,000 times as many recombinants as F⁺ by F⁻ crosses. Since the progeny of Hfr by F⁻ are typically F⁻ and rarely Hfr, Hfr does not usually carry infective F particles. Hfr can, however, revert to F⁺ strains apparently showing all the characteristics of F⁺, including infective F. Since Hfr can only come from F⁺ and can only revert to F⁺, it is concluded that *F must be retained in masked or bound form in Hfr strains.* When F is present in this masked condition, the replication of any extrachromosomally located F capable of infection is suppressed.

Using an Hfr strain, the cytological search for conjugating pairs is successful. Figure 24–1 is an electron micrograph showing conjugation between an F⁻ cell and an Hfr cell. The Hfr cell has ultraviolet-killed bac-

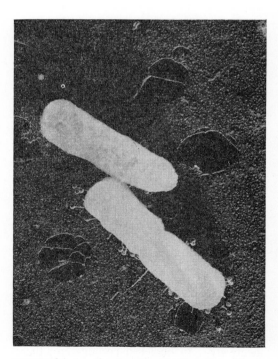

FIGURE 24–1. *Conjugation in* E. coli. (*Courtesy of T. F. Anderson.*)

[2] According to T. Loeb and N. D. Zinder (1961).

terial virus particles (tadpole-shaped objects) adsorbed on its surface; the F⁻ cell does not, since it is genetically resistant to this virus. The cytoplasmic bridge between the conjugants is clearly shown. When exconjugants of such visibly marked pairs of Hfr and F⁻ cells are isolated by micromanipulation and are cultured, only the clones from the F⁻ partner yield recombinants. Note, in passing, that these findings again demonstrate how genetics and cytology have aided each other's advancement.

In studies of Hfr by F⁻ crosses, it is commonly found that most of the unselected markers in recombinant progeny are those derived from the F⁻ parent. This result may be explained either by the transfer of the entire genome of the male to the female followed by the integration of only a portion of it, or by the transfer of only a portion of the male genome and its integration *in toto,* or by a combination of the two. Experiments have been designed to test one or more of these possible explanations.[3]

Particular strains of Hfr and F⁻, both marked with suitable genetic factors, are grown separately and then mixed in the proportion of 1:20, respectively, to assure rapid contact of all Hfr with F⁻ cells. At various time intervals, ending roughly two hours after mixing, samples are withdrawn and subjected to a strong shearing force in a Waring blendor. This treatment is a very efficient means of separating bacteria in the act of conjugation and does not affect either the viability of the bacteria, their ability to undergo recombination, or the expression of the various chromosomal genotypes under test. Once separated, the bacteria are plated and scored for male markers which have integrated. As expected, zero minutes after mixing no recombinants for male markers

[3] The following discussion is based principally upon work of E. L. Wollman and F. Jacob (see references at the end of this chapter).

MINUTES	RECOMBINANTS HAVING Hfr MARKERS
0	None
8	T
8½	T, L
9	T, L, Az
11	T, L, Az, T_1
18	T, L, Az, T_1, Lac
25	T, L, Az, T_1, Lac, Gal

FIGURE 24–2. *Recombinants obtained when conjugation is artificially interrupted at various times after mixing F⁻ and Hfr strains. The Hfr strain has markers for T, L, Az, T_1, Lac, Gal. (After W. Hayes.)*

are obtained; to obtain recombinants for all the male markers, conjugation must last for about 107 minutes. The time at which different male markers enter the female cell, however, varies widely within this time interval (Figure 24–2). For example, T and L markers of the Hfr do not enter F⁻ until after about 8.5 minutes of conjugation, whereas the *Gal* marker (for galactose) requires about 25 minutes of conjugation before it is transferred. T and L are known to be close together and widely separated from *Gal* in the recombination map of F+ (p. 314); consequently, a definite relationship exists between time of transfer from Hfr to F⁻ and the location of the marker on the Hfr chromosome.

Had different portions of the Hfr chromosome entered the F⁻ cell at random times, the above results would not have been obtained. It can be concluded, therefore, that the Hfr chromosome is transferred in a specific manner: one particular end of the DNA string usually enters the F⁻ cell first, since *the loci that transfer do so in a regular linear procession* (Figure 24–2). Other experiments reveal that energy is required for the transfer process, and that the entrance rate is uniform from the first part of the chromosome to be transferred, O (representing the "origin"), up to and including the locus of *Lac* (for lactose).

Whether or not they receive or lose a segment of an artificially ruptured chromosome, both the female and male cells are able to survive. Chromosome rupture may also occur spontaneously. Because of such breakage, the spontaneous transfer of the Hfr chromosome is usually partial. Consequently, a piece of chromosome, called a *merogenote,* of variable size is sent into the recipient cell. As a resut, the zygote of an Hfr cross is a partial diploid—a *merozygote* —produced by a process of partial genetic exchange, *meromixis.* These three new terms are applicable also in transformation.

The frequency of recombination is relatively low for all chromosomal genes in an F+ strain. In Hfr, however, this frequency is high for those markers nearest O, although it decreases as the distance of the markers from O increases, and is only 0.001–0.01% for the markers furthest from O. As mentioned previously, only rarely is an offspring of Hfr by F− itself Hfr. An Hfr offspring arises only when the marker furthest from O—the terminal marker—has also been transferred. This fact leads us to believe that the locus responsible for Hfr is located in the chromosome. Moreover, since no chromosomal locus is found transferred after the Hfr locus, we can conclude that *Hfr is always located at the terminus of a chromosome being transferred.*

Several Hfr strains derived from F+ cultures show a very high frequency of recombination.[4] In these strains, recombination rates for the markers furthest from O occur with a frequency of one to two per cent— a rate at least one hundred times that found

[4] See A. L. Taylor and E. A. Adelberg (1960).

SELECTED MARKER	STRAIN		
	AB-311	AB-312	AB-313
his+	42	2.5	—
gal+	12	4	—
pro+	—	8	—
met+	4	22	—
mtl+	3.7	25	49
xyl+	2.8	26	43
mal+	1.5	40	32
ade+	—	—	15
try+	—	—	6
arg+	—	—	0.3

FIGURE 24–3. *Recombination percentages for certain Hfr strains. 0 = point of origin; − = untested. (After A. L. Taylor and E. A. Adelberg, 1960. See References.)*

in other Hfr strains. Even so, less than about one per cent of the progeny from mating these Hfr with F− are Hfr. By artificial rupture experiments, the sequence of certain marker genes can be determined for each of the three independently-arisen Hfr strains of this type.

These sequences are shown in Figure 24–3 together with the frequency of recombinants per one hundred Hfr cells in the mating mixture.

The results show that the markers held in common by the three different Hfr strains are in the same sequence. The O point, however, is in a different position in each case! Accordingly, so is the position of the

Hfr locus at the end of the linkage map. These results suggest [5] that:

1. *The linkage group of* E. coli *is normally circular.*

2. *The Hfr-causing factor can locate itself at various places on the chromosome during the genetic event by which Hfr strains are formed.*

3. *At the time of chromosome transfer, the linkage group is open adjacent to the point of Hfr attachment so that the Hfr locus is at the end opposite the O point.*

Studies of other Hfr strains [6] confirm all these assumptions, including various positions for Hfr—which consequently determine different O points and sequences of entry.

When DNA synthesis occurs in the presence of radioactive thymidine, autoradiographs of replicated DNA strongly suggest the presence of a single, circular, double-helix chromosome in E. coli. The single chromosome may be, in fact, a single DNA molecule or it may be composed of a series of DNA molecules held end-to-end by non-nucleic acid links. There is no definitive evidence which allows us to decide between these two alternatives. It has been found, however, that the chromosome tends to fragment at certain predetermined points during the growth of particular bacterial viruses in infected cells. If the chromosome is actually composed of an assemblage of DNA molecules and if breakage does occur at all non-nucleic acid links, then the DNA molecules would have a molecular weight of 10^7 or contain about 16,000 nucleotide pairs. Other evidence suggests that the linkage group of Hfr is usually circular, though the linkage group transferred during conjugation is open at the Hfr locus.

Since an Hfr male strain always has the same chromosomal marker leading the others

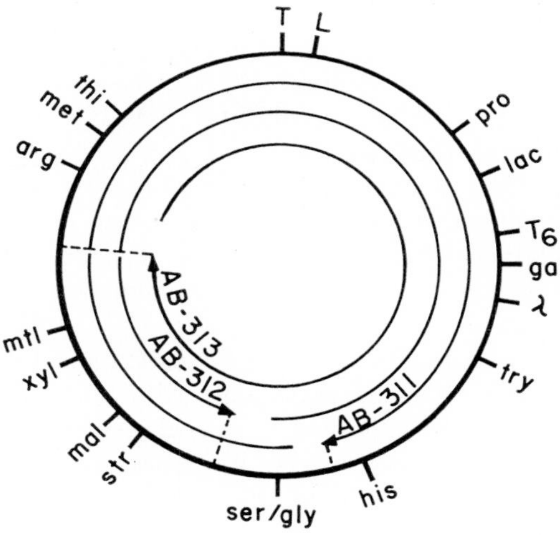

FIGURE 24–4. *Linear chromosomes of three Hfr strains. Arrows show direction of chromosome penetration during conjugation. (After A. L. Taylor and E. A. Adelberg, 1960. See References.)*

in transfer, Hfr apparently causes the ring chromosome to open at only one of the two regions immediately adjacent to it. That the entry sequence is different in different strains (the chromosome of AB-312 enters in the reverse direction from that of AB-311 or AB-313, as can be seen in Figures 24–3 and 24–4) may be due to an inversion of Hfr when it locates itself at different chromosomal positions.

Since the ring chromosome of E. coli is opened when the Hfr chromosome is transferred, one might question whether these two new ends are able to join in restitution. When considering whether the two new ends rejoin, one must distinguish between what goes into the recipient cell and what is left behind in the donor cell. There is little evidence about how much chromosome is left behind—whether, in fact, there is or is not a complete chromosome—in the donor

[5] Following F. Jacob and E. L. Wollman.
[6] See A. L. Taylor and E. A. Adelberg (1961).

after conjugation. Thus, the question of whether the ends of the remnant can rejoin or not in the donor cannot be answered at present. It is clear that the donated chromosome remains linear and open during the process of conjugation. One can, however, legitimately ask whether the two ends of this chromosome or chromosome segment can rejoin in the recipient after conjugation has terminated. Again, if one believes in synapsis as a requirement for recombination, this question can be asked only with regard to those recipients which receive a complete donor chromosome. In this case, since linkage of the Hfr locus and point of origin is rapidly re-established in such cells, the answer is that ends do rejoin, and quickly.

The recombination frequencies observed after conjugation depend, of course, upon both the frequency of a marker's penetration and the efficiency with which it is integrated. Interrupted-mating experiments reveal the sequence of markers, regardless of the frequency (greater than zero) with which their integration occurs. Once the marker sequence is known, integration efficiency can be studied. If, for example, matings are permitted to continue long enough so that just about all F^- cells are penetrated by the marker under test, the percentage of zygotes producing recombinants for that marker will indicate the efficiency of integration. If 50% of the recipient cells show integration of a transferred marker, this locus has an integration efficiency of .5. One can also test whether recombinants for a given locus are recombinants for markers transferred earlier. By these and other methods, the integration efficiency after penetration can be determined for various markers. On the average, the integration efficiency is about .5 for each marker. Therefore, because of differences in penetration, the closer a gene is to O, the greater is its overall chance for integration. Recall that when one strand of a double helix of donor DNA

is broken by DNase activity, incorporation of donor DNA into the recipient DNA fraction is unaffected but transformation rate is drastically reduced. Accordingly, it is theoretically possible that the decreases in the overall chance for integration with distance from O may sometimes be associated with the breakage of one strand of double-helix DNA and not the other. In this event, backbone defects might affect not only chromosomal breakage (by scission of the DNA double chain), but also integration (by breaking only one strand of the two at any given level).

Although the donor DNA rate of penetration is approximately constant for the first half of the chromosome, it is slower for the second half. Since the bacterial chromosome is about 10^7 nucleotide pairs long and the entire chromosome is transferred in about two hours, about 10^5 nucleotide pairs (about 34μ) are transferred in one minute at $37°$ C. This transfer rate is slower at lower temperatures. Taking into account variations in rate of penetration and integration efficiency, it is possible to construct, from interruption experiments using Hfr males, a genetic map of *E. coli* markers whose relative distances are expressed in minutes. Such a map is shown in Figure 24–5.

It was mentioned that F is transferred from F^+ to F^- even when known chromosomal markers are not. When an interrupted-mating experiment is performed to determine the time when the F particle in F^+ males is transferred, it is found that F is first transferred about five minutes after mixing F^+ and F^- or several minutes earlier than any known marker in the chromosome is transferred. We, therefore, have additional evidence that F is extrachromosomal in nature.

As already mentioned, Hfr strains are always derived from F^+ strains. It was also noted that Hfr strains can revert to F^+, indicating that Hfr harbors a latent F particle. Since the fertility of Hfr is unaffected by exposure to acridine orange, the latent F particle is probably not located extrachromosomally. This contention is supported by the fact that maleness is not infective; that is, maleness is not transmitted to F⁻ cells after short mating intervals with Hfr males. Consequently, *the latent F particle in Hfr must be located chromosomally.* Since, at this point, F is the only known factor essential for maleness, *the chromosomal locus assigned to the Hfr must be that of chromosomal F.* Once F enters the chromosome, as mentioned, replication of any remaining cytoplasmic F particles normally is prevented or repressed.

What happens in those few cells of an F⁺ clone which transfer chromosomal material, causing the F⁺ clone as a whole to give a low frequency of recombination? Suppose that for an F⁺ cell to transfer its chromosome, an F particle must attach to the chromosome, making it an Hfr chromosome. This hypothesis can be tested as follows.[7] After mixing suitably marked F⁺ and F⁻ and plating them on a complete medium, appropriate replica plates are made to detect the positions where recombination has taken place. A search is then made for Hfr strains among the cells on the master plate. Although new Hfr strains rarely occur, they are found most frequently on the master plate at positions where replicas show that recombination has taken place. Moreover, the Hfr strains discovered often produce a high frequency of recombination of the same markers that show recombination in the corresponding positions in the replicas. In other words, *it seems* valid to believe *that to transfer chromosomal material, an F⁺ individual must first change to an Hfr condition.* It is the Hfr which produces the recombination detected on the replica, its clonal members on the master plate yielding the same type of Hfr.

Some evidence exists, however, that not all recombinants in F⁺ by F⁻ crosses result from the formation of stable Hfr cells. For example, UV radiation enhances the ability of an F⁺ culture to give chromosomal recombinants by 30- to 50-fold but this enhancement is not the result of stable integration of F into the chromosome since it only persists for one or two generations. Furthermore, all attempts to isolate stable Hfr from other bacteria harboring other types of fertility factors have been unsuccessful. Apparently, some sort of temporary or "abortive" Hfr state is sometimes—if not always—produced in F⁺ cells which transfer chromosomal markers.

Since F⁺ males rarely become Hfr, we conclude that extrachromosomal *F has a low affinity for the chromosome;* and, since F⁺ males produce Hfr strains having any one of various O points, we conclude that *F has no preferential site of attachment. F is composed of DNA* (F transferred to Serratia gives a satellite DNA band in CsCl not found in Serratia alone) and contains roughly 2.5 times 10^5 base pairs, or about 3.7% of the amount present in a nuclear body. Although F has a considerable number of sites at which it can integrate, this number is by no means unlimited in view of the repeated isolation of strains with Hfr mapping in the same region. In any case, if one accepts the idea that naturally-occurring F possesses regions which are homologous to certain chromosomal regions and that integration is in fact the result of a recombinational event between F and the chromosome, then it is reasonable that F, because of its size, could carry genetic regions homologous to only a small fraction of all chromosomal sites.

The bacterial chromosome always replicates in a polarized manner, starting at one point and continuing to the end. Although

[7] Based upon work of F. Jacob and E. L. Wollman.

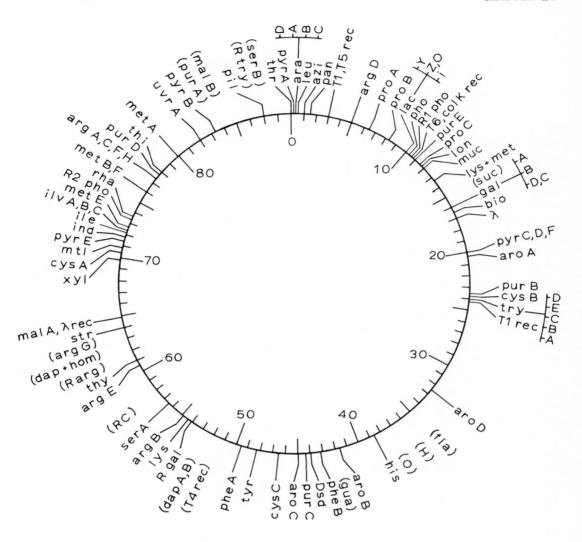

FIGURE 24–5.
Genetic map of E. coli,
*drawn to scale. A key to
the genetic symbols appears
in the accompanying chart. The map
is graduated in one-minute intervals
(89 minutes total). Markers enclosed
in parentheses are only approximately
mapped; the exact sequence of markers
in crowded regions is not always known.
(Courtesy of A. L. Taylor and
M. S. Thoman, 1964. See References.)*

LIST OF CHROMOSOMAL MARKERS OF *E. coli*

Key to genetic symbols *		Activity affected
araD	arabinose	L-ribulose 5-phosphate 4-epimerase
araA	arabinose	L-arabinose isomerase
araB	arabinose	L-ribulokinase
araC	arabinose	unknown
argB	arginine	N-acetylglutamate synthetase
argC	arginine	N-acetyl-γ-glutamokinase
argH	arginine	N-acetylglutamic-γ-semialdehyde dehydrogenase
argG	arginine	acetylornithine-δ-transaminase
argA	arginine	acetylornithinase
argD	arginine	ornithine transcarbamylase
argE	arginine	argininosuccinic acid synthetase
argF	arginine	argininosuccinase
aroA,B,C	aromatic amino acids and vitamins	shikimic acid to 3-enolpyruvylshikimate-5-phosphate
aroD	aromatic amino acids and vitamins	biosynthesis of shikimic acid
azi	azide	resistance or sensitivity to sodium azide
bio	biotin	
cysA	cysteine	unknown
cysB	cysteine	3'-phosphoadenosine 5'-phosphosulfate to sulfide †
cysC	cysteine	sulfate to sulfide; four known enzymes †
dapA	diaminopimelic acid	dihydrodipicolinic acid synthetase
dapB	diaminopimelic acid	N-succinyl-diaminopimelic acid deacylase
dap + hom	diaminopimelic acid + homoserine	aspartic semialdehyde dehydrogenase
Dsd	D-serine	D-serine deaminase
fla	flagella	
galA	galactose	galactokinase
galB	galactose	galactose 1-phosphate uridyl transferase
galD	galactose	uridinediphosphogalactose 4-epimerase
galC	galactose	operator mutants
gua	guanine	
H	H antigen	flagellar antigen
his	histidine	ten known enzymes and an operator †
ile	isoleucine	threonine deaminase
ilvA	isoleucine + valine	α-hydroxy β-keto acid reductoisomerase †
ilvB	isoleucine + valine	α,β-dihydroxyisovaleric dehydrase †
ilvC	isoleucine + valine	transaminase B
ind	indole	tryptophanase
λ	prophage λ	
lac Y	lactose	galactoside permease
lac Z	lactose	β-galactosidase
lac O	lactose	operator mutants
leu	leucine	three known enzymes and an operator †
lon	long form	filament formation and radiation sensitivity
lys	lysine	diaminopimelic acid decarboxylase
lys + met	lysine + methionine	unknown
λ*rec,malA*	λreceptor and maltose	maltose permease and resistance to phage λ
malB	maltose	probably amylomaltase
metA	methionine	synthesis of the succinic ester of homoserine †
metB	methionine	succinic ester of homoserine + cysteine to cystathionine †

(*Continued on next page*)

LIST OF CHROMOSOMAL MARKERS OF *E. coli*—CONTINUED

Key to genetic symbols *		Activity affected
metF	methionine	probably 5,10-methylene tetrahydrofolate reductase
metE	methionine or cobalamin	unknown
mtl	mannitol	probably mannitol dehydrogenase
muc	mucoid	regulation of capsular polysaccharide synthesis
O	O antigen	somatic antigen
pan	pantothenic acid	
pheA,B	phenylalanine	
pho	phosphatase	alkaline phosphatase
pil	pili (fimbriae)	
proA	proline	
proB	proline	supports syntrophic growth of *proA* mutants
proC	proline	supports syntrophic growth of *proA* mutants
purA	purine	adenylosuccinic synthetase
purB	purine	adenylosuccinase
purC,E	purine	5-aminoimidazole ribotide(AIR) to 5-aminoimidazole 4-(N-succinocarboxamide) ribotide
purD	purine	biosynthesis of AIR
pyrA	uracil + arginine	carbamate kinase
pyrB	uracil	aspartate transcarbamylase
pyrC	uracil	dihydroorotase
pyrD	uracil	dihydroorotic acid dehydrogenase
pyrE	uracil	orotidylic acid pyrophosphorylase
pyrF	uracil	orotidylic acid decarboxylase
R arg	repressor	arginine repressor
R gal	repressor	galactose repressor
R1 pho, R2 pho	repressor	alkaline phosphatase repressor
R try	repressor	tryptophan repressor
RC	RNA control	regulation of RNA synthesis
rha	rhamnose	utilization of D-rhamnose
serA	serine	3-phosphoglycerate dehydrogenase
serB	serine	phosphoserine phosphatase
str	streptomycin	resistance, sensitivity, or dependence on streptomycin
suc	succinic acid	
T1,T5 rec	phage receptor site	resistance to phages T1 and T5
T1 rec	phage receptor site	resistance to phage T1
T6, colK rec	phage and colicine receptor site	resistance to phage T6 and colicine K
T4 rec	phage receptor site	resistance to phage T4
thi	thiamine	
thr	threonine	
thy	thymine	thymidylate synthetase
tryA	tryptophan	tryptophan synthetase, A protein
tryB	tryptophan	tryptophan synthetase, B protein
tryC	tryptophan	indole 3-glycerolphosphate synthetase
tryE	tryptophan	anthranilic acid to anthranilic deoxyribulotide
tryD	tryptophan	3-enolpyruvylshikimate 5-phosphate to anthranilic acid
tyr	tyrosine	
uvrA	ultraviolet radiation	reactivation of UV-induced lesions in DNA
xyl	xylose	utilization of D-xylose

* Established systems of genetic nomenclature are retained wherever possible, except that capital letters beginning with the letter A are arbitrarily assigned to functionally related gene loci which do not conform to the system of bacterial genetic nomenclature proposed by M. DEMEREC (1963).

† Denotes enzymes controlled by the homologous gene loci of *Salmonella typhimurium*.

the starting point of replication in F⁻ is possibly random, some evidence indicates that replication starts at the F-containing end in Hfr strains.[8] Chromosome transfer in Hfr lines may require initiation of a new replication of the chromosome.[9]

The chemical composition, genetic alternatives,[10] capacity for autonomous self-duplication, and "suicide" due to incorporated P^{32} after transfer to F⁻, demonstrate that the *male fertility factor, F, of* E. coli *must be composed of genetic material*. Since F is probably neither lytic nor otherwise rapidly lethal to F⁻ cells, and since F has a stable relationship with the F⁺ cell, it can be considered a "normal" cellular component, when present. Because it can function and reproduce in an autonomous manner when located extrachromosomally, *F furnishes the first example so far presented of "normal," extrachromosomal genetic material.* When extrachromosomal F is lost—either spontaneously or after treatment with acridine orange—it represents genetic material not conserved for future generations. Since F is genetic material, its transmission

from F⁺ to F⁻ is an example of genetic recombination.

F also has the ability to assume a regular locus on a chromosome. When stably attached to or integrated in the chromosome, F functions and replicates just as any other ordinary chromosomal locus. In regular vegetative reproduction, chromosomal F is transmitted to all progeny; that is, F is conserved. In conjugation, however, chromosomal F may not be conserved, for integrated F is not transmitted to the zygote with appreciable frequency except in the case of certain Hfr strains, and—even when transmitted—may fail to be integrated. In such cases, the nonconservation of F in F⁻ cells is no different from the nonconservation of other chromosomal loci.

The only type of genetic elements discussed in detail prior to this chapter were those restricted to the chromosome. To these can now be added the male fertility factor, F, which may or may not be present in the cell, and, when present, can be either autonomous extrachromosomally or integrated in the chromosome. Such genes which can participate in the cell either as extrachromosomal or as chromosomal elements are called *episomes*.[11]

[8] See J. Cairns (1964), T. Nagata (1964), and N. Sueoka and H. Yoshikawa (1964).

[9] See J. Roeser and W. A. Konetzka (1964).

[10] See E. A. Adelberg and S. N. Burns (1960).

[11] See F. Jacob and E. L. Wollman (1958).

SUMMARY AND CONCLUSIONS

E. coli has only one female mating type (genetic recipient)—F⁻—but two male mating types (genetic donors)—F⁺ and Hfr. Male mating type depends upon the presence and location of F.

F, an episome, is infective when present extrachromosomally. Thus, F⁺ males donate F only. F can assume a chromosomal locus and produce the Hfr male. When the Hfr male conjugates, the ring chromosome of *E. coli* is open near the locus of F. The end opposite the F locus proceeds into the recipient conjugant first, in the linear transfer of part—or sometimes all—of the opened ring chromosome. Thus, Hfr males mobilize and donate chromosomal loci.

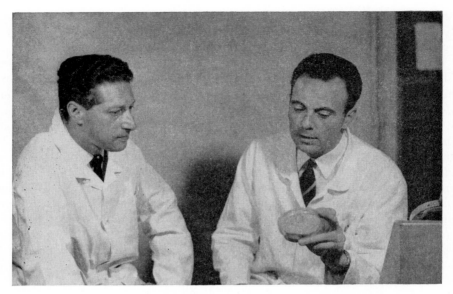

ELIE L. WOLLMAN (*left*) *and* FRANÇOIS JACOB (*right*) *in 1961*.

REFERENCES

Adelberg, E. A., and Burns, S. N., "Genetic Variation in the Sex Factor of Escherichia Coli," J. Bact., 79:321–330, 1960. Reprinted in *Papers on Bacterial Genetics,* Adelberg, E. A. (Ed.), Boston: Little, Brown, 1960, pp. 353–362.

Cairns, J., "The Chromosome of *Escherichia coli,*" Cold Spring Harb. Sympos. Quant. Biol., 28:43–46, 1964.

Clark, A. J., and Adelberg, E. A., "Bacterial Conjugation," pp. 289–319, in *Annual Review of Microbiology,* 16, Palo Alto, Calif.: Annual Reviews, Inc., 1962.

Hayes, W., "The Mechanism of Genetic Recombination in *Escherichia coli,*" Cold Spring Harb. Sympos. Quant. Biol., 18:75–93, 1953. Reprinted in *Papers on Bacterial Genetics,* Adelberg, E. A. (Ed.), Boston: Little, Brown, 1960, pp. 268–299.

Hayes, W., *The Genetics of Bacteria and Their Viruses,* New York: J. Wiley & Sons, 1964.

Jacob, F., and Wollman, E. L., "Episomes, Added Genetic Elements" (in French), C. R. Acad. Sci. (Paris), 247:154–156, 1958. Translated and reprinted in *Papers on Bacterial Genetics,* Adelberg, E. A. (Ed.), Boston: Little, Brown, 1960, pp. 398–400.

Jacob, F., and Wollman, E. L., "Genetic and Physical Determination of Chromosomal Segments in Escherichia Coli," Sympos. Soc. Exp. Biol., 12:75–92, 1958. Reprinted in *Papers on Bacterial Genetics,* Adelberg, E. A. (Ed.), Boston: Little, Brown, 1960, pp. 335–352.

Jacob, F., and Wollman, E. L., *Sexuality and the Genetics of Bacteria,* New York: Academic Press, 1961.

Nagata, T., "The Sequential Replication of *E. coli* DNA," Cold Spring Harb. Sympos. Quant. Biol., 28:55–57, 1964.

Roeser, J., and Konetzka, W. A., "Chromosome Transfer and the DNA Replication Cycle in *Escherichia coli,*" Biochem. Biophys. Res. Commun., 16:326–331, 1964.

Sueoka, N., and Yoshikawa, H., "Regulation of Chromosome Replication in *Bacillus subtilis,*" Cold Spring Harb. Sympos. Quant. Biol., 28:47–54, 1964.

Taylor, A. L., and Adelberg, E. A., "Linkage Analysis with Very High Frequency Males of Escherichia Coli," Genetics, 45:1233–1243, 1960.

Taylor, A. L., and Adelberg, E. A., "Evidence for a Closed Linkage Group in Hfr Males of *Escherichia coli* K-12," Biochem, Biophys. Res. Commun., 5:400–404, 1961.

Taylor, A. L., and Thoman, M. S., "The Genetic Map of *Escherichia coli* K-12," Genetics, 50:659–677, 1964.

Wollman, E. L., Jacob, F., and Hayes, W., "Conjugation and Genetic Recombination in *Escherichia coli* K 12," Cold Spring Harb. Sympos. Quant. Biol., 21:141–162, 1956. Reprinted in *Papers on Bacterial Genetics,* Adelberg, E. A. (Ed.), Boston: Little, Brown, 1960, pp. 300–334.

QUESTIONS FOR DISCUSSION

24.1. What events do you suppose occur from the time donor DNA enters a female conjugant to the appearance of a segregant haploid for a segment of the donor DNA?

24.2. What is the evidence that F can integrate in a chromosome? That it can do the reverse (deintegrate)?

24.3. What properties are attributable to F when integrated at a chromosomal locus?

24.4. Does the occurrence of spontaneous ruptures of the donor bacterial chromosome interfere with mapping the linear order of genes via artificial interruptions of mating? Explain.

24.5. Assume (correctly) that the decay of P^{32} incorporated into DNA can break the *E. coli* chromosome, and that this decay is temperature-independent. Devise an experiment to determine the gene order in this bacterium.

24.6. What kinds of evidence can you present that a nuclear body of *E. coli* normally contains a single chromosome? A ring chromosome?

24.7. Give the genotypes of parents and recombinants and the specific culture conditions you would employ in searching the progeny of F^+ by F^- crosses for Hfr lines.

24.8. What relationships exist between episomes and genetic recombination?

24.9. Transforming DNA is isolated from cultures of *Bacillus subtilis* in a stationary (nonreplicating) phase and in an exponentially-growing and nonsynchronously-reproducing phase and tested with respect to eleven genetic markers. Invent quantitative results expected if the chromosome replicates in a polarized manner.

Chapter 25

TRANSDUCTION

T HE THREE preceding chapters dealt with recombination of genetic material in bacteria by mechanisms usually involving relocation of only a portion of a bacterial genome. In transformation, the presence of a donor organism is unnecessary for the entrance of donor DNA; in conjugation, however, a segment of chromosomal DNA passes from donor to recipient bacterium through a cytoplasmic bridge effected by the presence of an F particle. The F particle itself undergoes recombination not only when it is infectious but when it enters and leaves the bacterial chromosome.

As already noted (p. 310), it is expected that any homologous segment of DNA, no matter how introduced into a bacterium, can pair with and integrate into a bacterial chromosome. A third possible mechanism exists for introducing homologous DNA into bacteria. *Bacteriophages* or *phages* [1] are viruses that attack bacteria. After these viruses become attached to the bacterial surface (see Figure 24–1), all or part of the phage remaining external to a bacterium can be shaken off by the shearing action of a blendor. Such treatment does not alter the course of the infection, however; that is, the virus still produces its characteristic effect on the bacterium. We can infer that the part of the virus essential for this effect actually enters the bacterial protoplasm,

whereas the part of the phage that remains attached to the bacterial surface is unnecessary. These observations suggest a new way by which homologous DNA may enter a phage-infected cell. The virus might carry a segment of DNA derived from a previous bacterial host. This piece could penetrate the new host at the same time as part of the phage does, the phage's entry providing the opening for the bacterial DNA.

With this possibility in mind, consider a series of experiments [2] involving the mouse typhoid organism, *Salmonella typhimurium*. This bacterium, like its close relative *E. coli,* can also be cultured on a simple nutrient medium. A large number of auxotrophic strains of Salmonella are available, including one that requires methionine (M^-T^+) and another that requires threonine (M^+T^-). When these two strains are mixed and plated on a culture medium lacking both methionine and threonine, prototrophic colonies appear in such large numbers that they cannot be explained entirely as the result of mutation. Prototrophs are also obtained when a liquid culture of the M^+T^- strain is centrifuged (to remove most of the bacteria), the supernatant liquid heated for 20 to 30 minutes (to kill any remaining bacteria), and this liquid added to the M^-T^+ strain. This procedure demonstrates that living M^+T^- donor cells are not required to furnish the M^+ factor needed to establish prototrophy. So here the production of prototrophs clearly does not result from conjugation. Moreover, the filtrate retains its full M^+ capacity after treatment with DNase. Accordingly, this is not a case of genetic recombination via transformation. Since the M^+ factor can pass through filters that hold back bacteria but not viruses, the factor is a "filterable agent." The reverse experiment—using fil-

---

[1] The Greek letter ϕ (phi) is used to denote phage.

[2] The following discussion is based upon the work of N. D. Zinder and J. Lederberg (1952).

trates of the M^-T^+ strain on M^+T^- cells —does not produce recombinants. The two strains differ, therefore, in donor capacity.

The M^+T^- donor strain (but not the M^-T^+ strain) is found to harbor a phage. This virus, P22, is said to be *nonvirulent* or *temperate*. Nevertheless, about one in a thousand times this phage replicates and *lyses* or bursts the host cell, liberating up to several hundred progeny phage. Accordingly, a culture of bacteria harboring temperate phage does not show a conspicuous amount of lysis. Because each cell of the M^+T^- strain carrying P22 is potentially subject to lysis, the strain is said to be *lysogenic*. (The lysogenic bacterium, or *lysogen*, is *immune* to new infection—that is, to superinfection—by identical or homologous phage.) On the other hand, the M^-T^+ strain normally lacks P22 and is a *nonlysogenic* or *sensitive* strain. When a sensitive strain is exposed to temperate phage, a relatively large fraction of the newly-infected cells lyse and liberate phage. But a small fraction is able to survive, become lysogenic, and give rise to lysogenic progeny. If lysogens are lysed artificially and tested for phage, none are detected. Apparently, the phage in a lysogen is converted to a new form, called *prophage*, which reproduces at the same rate as the host chromosome. Usually, to lyse a lysogen, prophage must first rapidly replicate a number of times to produce the infective phage liberated at the time of lysis.

What is the relationship between the filterable M^+ factor and the phage P22?

1. Both are unaffected by RNase and DNase.

2. Both show the same inactivation pattern with temperature changes.

3. Both have the same susceptibility to an antiserum that blocks the attachment of phage to the bacterium.

4. Both become attached to susceptible cells simultaneously.

5. Both have the same size and mass as determined by filtration and sedimentation tests.

6. Both appear in the medium at the same time and in a constant ratio.

7. Both retain this ratio even though various purification and concentration procedures are applied.

From these results, it is evident that M^+ is associated with the phage. Since the genetic material of Salmonella is known to be composed of DNA, it is likely that the genetic factor M^+ is also composed of DNA. Moreover, because the M^+ genetic factor cannot be located on the outer surface of the phage particle, the M^+ gene must be located in the interior of the virus.

Genetic transduction is the process of genetic recombination made possible by a virus particle introducing homologous DNA into a recipient cell.

Are there any restrictions on the genetic material of Salmonella which can be transduced by P22? This virus can be grown on sensitive bacteria genetically marked $M^+T^+X^+Y^-Z^-$; the crop of phage produced after this infection can be harvested, and a portion tested on sensitive indicator strains (M^-, T^-, X^-, Y^-, Z^-) one at a time. The results of such tests show transduction of M^+, of T^+, and of X^+—but not of Y^+ or Z^+. Another portion of the harvested phage is grown on another genetically-marked, sensitive strain—$M^+T^-X^+Y^+Z^-$, for example. When the new phage crop is harvested and then tested on the indicator strains already mentioned, it is found now that the new crop of phage has lost T^+ but has gained Y^+ transducing ability. These results demonstrate that a phage filtrate has a range of transduceable markers exactly equal to that of the markers present in the bacteria on which the phage was last grown.

In other words, the phage is passive with respect to the content of genes it transduces and retains no transducing memory of any hosts previous to the last. Since additional tests demonstrate that every locus in Salmonella is transduceable by P22, we can call this a case of *unrestricted* or *generalized transduction*. In generalized transduction one cell is transduced for a given marker for about each 10^6 infecting phage particles.

Any chromosomal marker is transduceable by P22, but is it possible to transduce more than one at a time? P22 can be grown on $M^+T^+X^+$, harvested, and then grown on $M^-T^-X^-$. The latter bacteria are replica-plated on three different media —one selecting only for M^+ recombinants (it contains T and X), another only for T^+, and the third only for X^+. When the M^+ clones are further typed, they are still T^-X^-. Similarly, T^+ clones are still M^-X^-, and X^+ clones are still M^-T^-. These results show that only a single bacterial marker or a relatively short DNA segment is transduced at one time. In this respect, transduction is similar to transformation but different from conjugation, in which —especially in Hfr strains—large sequences of genes can be transmitted and integrated.

In Salmonella, however, examples are known of several genetic markers transduced together in what is called *linked transduction* or *cotransduction*. Other work has established that the biological synthesis of the amino acid, tryptophan, is part of a sequence of genetically-determined reactions that proceed from anthranilic acid through indole to tryptophan. Different genes controlling different steps of this biosynthetic sequence are cotransduced[3]; this finding suggests such genes are closely linked to each other. The biosynthesis of histidine in Salmonella is known to involve at least eight loci, four of which produce identifiable ef-

fects on the sequence of chemical reactions involved. Linked transductions have been found between two or more of these loci.[4] In fact, using the relative frequencies of different cotransductions and other evidence, all eight loci are found to be continuous with each other and to be arranged linearly (see Figure 25–1). Using cotransduction, one can build up a complete and detailed genetic map of Salmonella which proves to be a single circle. Cotransduction of closely-linked markers is also known to occur[5] in *E. coli* by phage P1.

In a generalized transduction experiment, when a prototroph is obtained by transducing an auxotroph, the new prototroph is usually stable and produces clones phenotypically identical to typical prototrophs. This process is called *complete transduction*. In this case, the prototrophic gene introduced must have integrated into the Salmonella chromosome in place of the recipient's auxotrophic allele. However, in addition to the large prototrophic colonies formed on selective agar (each of these clones represents a complete transduction), on occasion about ten times as many minute colonies are present (see Figure 25–2). These minute colonies do not appear in platings of auxotrophic mutants on minimal medium and, also, are not the result of an interaction between auxotrophs and colonies of normal or transduced prototrophs located elsewhere on the plate. Minute colony formation is explained as follows: Through phage infection the cell initiating the minute colony receives the segment of DNA containing the gene for prototrophy under test. This gene, however, fails to be integrated and fails to replicate but retains its functional ability to produce a phenotypic effect. Consequently, a hybrid merogenote or *heterogenote* is produced in which the dominant injected gene for prototrophy is func-

---

[3] As shown by M. Demerec and coworkers.

[4] By M. Demerec, P. E. Hartman, and coworkers.
[5] From the work of E. Lennox.

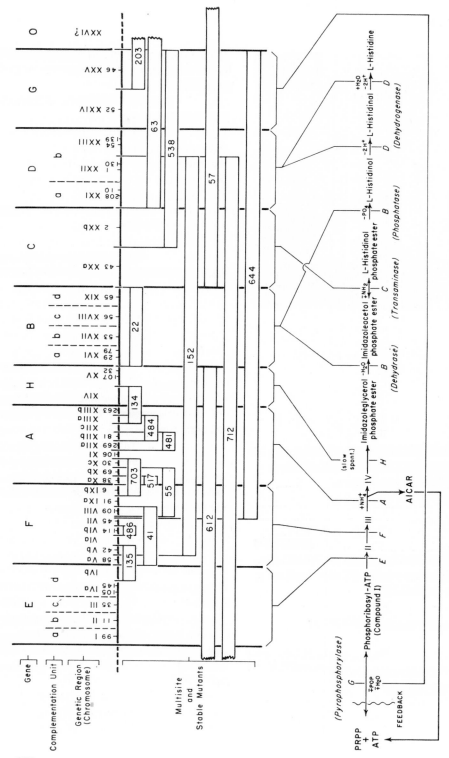

FIGURE 25–1. *The histidine region in Salmonella.* (*Courtesy of P. E. Hartman.*)

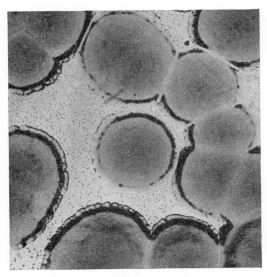

FIGURE 25–2. *Large and minute (period-sized) colonies of Salmonella, representing complete and abortive transductions, respectively. (Courtesy of P. E. Hartman.)*

tional. Because the prototrophic gene product is made, the cell is able to grow and divide. Only one of the first two daughter cells, however, receives the added chromosomal fragment, the *exogenote*. The daughter cell without the exogenote is able to grow and divide only until the prototrophic gene product received from the parent becomes too scarce; on the other hand, the heterogenotic daughter cell can continue to grow and divide, in turn producing only one heterogenotic daughter cell. In this way a minute colony is produced which contains a single genetically-prototrophic cell. This has been proved in a variety of cases and by various methods.[6] This consequence of the failure of complete transduction is called *abortive transduction*.

Hypothetically, the exogenote in an abortive transduction has two possible fates: the

exogenote might eventually be lost; or it might be integrated, resulting in a complete transduction. Regardless of its ultimate fate, the exogenote is considered to be genetic in nature, even though it does not self-replicate. Remember, however, that self-replication is an assumed characteristic of the total genetic material; this capacity was not required when a gene was first defined (p. 33).

In most transduction studies, an excess of phage is used; that is, each cell is infected with more than one phage particle. In such experiments, it is always found that transduced cells become lysogenic simultaneously. Thus, the cell transduced receives not only the exogenote but an apparently-complete genome of a phage as well—the former resulting in genetic recombination for one or more host markers; the latter in lysogeny and immunity. The phage particle whose contents make the host cell lysogenic need not be the same particle which introduces the exogenote, since high concentrations or multiplicities of infecting phage are used, and, on the average, each host cell is penetrated by the contents of two or more phage particles. Consequently, one particle might furnish the exogenote, and another might cause lysogeny and immunity. Using low concentrations of phage to obtain low multiplicities so that almost no bacterium can be infected by more than one phage, it is possible to prove that, at least in some cases, only one phage particle is needed per transduction. It is found,[7] moreover, that when a single phage attacks a susceptible bacterium, the virus can usually produce only one of three mutually-exclusive effects on its host—namely, lysis, lysogeny, or transduction.

E. coli strain K12 is normally lysogenic for the temperate phage *lambda* (λ). Another strain of *E. coli* is nonlysogenic, that

[6] By B. A. D. Stocker, J. Lederberg, and N. D. Zinder, and by H. Ozeki (1956).

[7] By J. N. Adams and S. E. Luria.

is, sensitive to lambda. This phage can be collected from a culture of lysogenic bacteria in great quantities a few hours after a brief exposure of these cells to ultraviolet light. Such *UV-induction* causes the prophage to replicate, and the progeny phage lyse the cell. Using λ phage collected from lysogenic cultures, one finds that only a very limited number of different bacterial markers can be transduced. They are restricted to a region that controls galactose fermentation, the *Gal locus,* whose markers are known from conjugation studies to be very closely linked. Lambda is therefore capable only of *restricted* or *specialized transduction*.

As mentioned, lysis of a lysogen and the consequent liberation of infective phage can be induced by ultraviolet light. When lysogenic Hfr conjugate with sensitive F⁻, a number of zygotes are induced to lyse and liberate infective phage. Initiated by conjugation this method of inducing prophage to produce infective phage and lysis, is called *zygotic induction*. Moreover, zygotic induction by λ occurs, with a given Hfr strain, at a specific time after the start of mating. This precise timing suggests that the chromosome has a locus with which lambda prophage is physically associated during lysogeny. In a nonlysogenic cell, no prophage is attached to or associated with this site. When the site with the prophage enters a sensitive F⁻ cell, zygotic induction occurs. When crosses are made between nonlysogenic Hfr (without prophage) and lysogenic F⁻ (with prophage), however, zygotic induction does not occur, and the nonlysogenic locus is transferred and segregates in the heterogenotes just as any other genetic marker. From these results and others, the locus for lambda prophage maintenance is found to be closely linked to the *Gal* locus which lambda can transduce (see Figure 24–5, p. 324, in which the attachment locus is given as λ).

The original lambda-containing lysogenic K12 bacterium is stable and haploid with respect to the *Gal* locus and produces only about one *Gal*-carrying lambda per 10^6–10^7 phage. A lysate made by inducing such λ lysogens is capable of producing only a *low frequency of transduction (LFT)*. Some of the cells transduced by an LFT lysate form clones unstable with respect to *Gal,* that is, that segregate out cells with the *Gal* genotype of the recipient cell. In other words a *Gal⁻* bacterium, transduced by an LFT lysate of lambda carrying *Gal⁺*, is usually an unstable heterogenote being diploid and heterozygous for *Gal* and occasionally segregating *Gal⁻* progeny. The merozygote produced by lambda transduction differs from that produced by P22 in an abortive transduction. In the latter case, the transduced segment cannot replicate; in the former case, the transduced segment can replicate, so that clones of merozygotes can be produced. When infective lambda is induced from a lysogenic host merozygotic for *Gal,* the lysate contains one hundred times as many phage which carry a *Gal* locus as does the lysate of haploids. Such a *Gal*-rich crop of phage is capable of a *high frequency of transduction* (*HFT*).

In the case of phages capable of generalized transduction, transducing phage can be obtained from the lysate of sensitive cells infected with free phage; for phage capable only of restricted transduction, transducing phage cannot be obtained this way. Therefore, in lambda, transducing phage are not found in the lysate of infected nonlysogenics and are released only from lysogenic (haploid or merozygotic) bacteria.[8]

By employing different multiplicities and combinations of transducing lambda (collected from lysogenic cells) and nontransducing lambda (collected soon after nonlysogenic cells are infected), it is possible to

---

[8] The preceding account is based largely upon the work of J. Lederberg, E. M. Lederberg, and M. L. Morse, and of E. L. Wollman and F. Jacob.

prove[9] that transducing lambda is defective for a portion of the lambda genome. The *Gal* locus being transduced replaces a variably-sized segment of the lambda genome. The *d*efective *Gal*-transducing lambda particle, λ*dg,* retains certain phage properties and loses others. λdg has lost the ability to replicate and produce infective phage progeny and the prophage it forms must be defective; the host cell infected with a single λdg particle is never lysogenized. A cell infected by λdg, therefore, can be superinfected with a nontransducing phage whose additional presence makes the host lysogenic and contributes a function which permits the defective prophage to multiply after induction. At the time of lysis of such a doubly-infected cell, infective phages of both nontransducing and transducing types are liberated. This situation parallels that already described for Salmonella which cannot be lysed or lysogenized if infected by a single transducing P22 phage, but which shows one of these characteristics if the host is also infected with one or more normal, nontransducing P22 phage particles.

Transformation does not ordinarily occur in *E. coli,* probably because of difficulty in DNA penetration. If the DNA of λdg were isolated and somehow introduced into the bacterium, however, one would expect this DNA to behave as a transforming principle with respect to the *Gal* locus. Even if DNA does not penetrate *E. coli* by itself, it might be capable of entering with infecting whole phage. Indeed, this does occur[10]; that is, using nontransducing lambda as a carrier or "helper," DNA isolated from λdg is capable of *Gal* transformation.

From the discussion of nontransducing P22 and lambda, it should be clear that such temperate phages have two alternative pathways of action open to them upon infecting a sensitive bacterium: the phage either lyses or lysogenizes its bacterial host. As clearly shown in the case of lambda, the infecting phage either remains in the cytoplasm where it replicates faster than the chromosome and eventually lyses and liberates progeny phage, or it integrates in the chromosome where it resides as prophage and is replicated as a regular chromosomal marker. Accordingly, lambda and *most* other *temperate phages are episomes.*

What is the basis for the difference between the temperate phages capable of generalized and those capable of restricted transduction? A restrictive-transducing phage usually has a specific chromosomal locus for attachment to the host chromosome, a generalized-transducing phage has not. Assuming—correctly—that the phage genome is nucleic acid, it can be suggested that the nucleotide sequence held in common between prophage and chromosome is shorter for the generalized-transducing phage than it is for the specialized transducer. In this connection it is noteworthy that evidence has been obtained[11] that a portion of the lambda genome is homologous to the *E. coli* chromosome, as revealed by the ability of their denatured DNAs to base pair with each other. Several experiments suggest that a prophage makes the host cell immune to further infection by homologous phage, by preventing not the penetration of the DNA but its replication. This action parallels the suppression of free-F replication by integrated F.

Transduction by temperate phages has been found to occur also in Pseudomonas, Vibrio, Staphylococcus, and Proteus, and it would not be surprising to find transduction occurring in a wide variety of other types of cells, including human.

[9] See W. Arber, G. Kellenberger, and J. Weigle (1957), and A. Campbell (1964).
[10] See A. D. Kaiser and D. S. Hogness (1960).

[11] By D. B. Cowie and B. J. McCarthy, and by M. H. Green.

SUMMARY AND CONCLUSIONS

Genetic recombination of loci of the bacterial chromosome can be mediated by temperate bacteriophages in the process of genetic transduction.

The transduced segment can be derived from any region of the bacterial chromosome (as in generalized or unrestricted transduction) or from a narrowly limited region (as in specialized or restricted transduction). The DNA segment transduced may, by integration, replace a chromosomal marker of the host (as in complete transduction), or it may produce a merozygote, in which case the exogenote can still function, whether it can replicate (as *Gal* exogenotes in *E. coli*) or not (as the exogenote in abortive transduction in Salmonella).

A transducing φ lambda is defective in its own genome. The deficient portion is replaced by a small segment of bacterial DNA acquired at the time the prophage was induced in its last host.

Most temperate phages are episomes which, when attached to the chromosome, have some characteristics resembling those of integrated F.

NORTON D. ZINDER, *about 1954.*

REFERENCES

Arber, W., Kellenberger, G., and Weigle, J., "The Defectiveness of Lambda-Transducing Phage" (in French), Schweiz. Zeitschr. Allgemeine Path. und Bact., 20:659–665, 1957. Translated and reprinted in *Papers on Bacterial Genetics,* Adelberg, E. A. (Ed.), Boston: Little, Brown, 1960, pp. 224–229.

Campbell, A., "Transduction," pp. 49–89, in *The Bacteria,* Vol. 5, *Heredity,* Gunsalus, I. C., and Stanier, R. Y. (Eds.), New York: Academic Press, 1964.

Jacob, F., and Wollman, E. L., "Spontaneous Induction of the Development of Bacteriophage λ in Genetic Recombination of Escherichia Coli K 12" (in French), C. R. Acad. Sci. (Paris), 239:317–319, 1954. Translated and reprinted in *Papers on Bacterial Viruses,* Stent, G. S. (Ed.), Boston: Little, Brown, 1960, pp. 336–338.

Jacob, F., and Wollman, E. L., "Genetic Aspects of Lysogeny," pp. 468–500, in *A Symposium on the Chemical Basis of Heredity,* McElroy, W. D., and Glass, B. (Eds.), Baltimore: The Johns Hopkins Press, 1957.

Kaiser, A. D., and Hogness, D. S., "The Transformation of Escherichia Coli with Deoxyribonucleic Acid Isolated from Bacteriophage λdg," J. Mol. Biol., 2:392–415, 1960.

Morse, M. L., Lederberg, E. M., and Lederberg, J., "Transduction in Escherichia Coli K-12," Genetics, 41:142–156, 1956. Reprinted in *Papers on Bacterial Genetics,* Adelberg, E. A. (Ed.), Boston: Little, Brown, 1960, pp. 209–223.

Ozeki, H., "Abortive Transduction in Purine-Requiring Mutants of Salmonella Typhimurium," Carnegie Inst. Wash. Publ. 612, *Genetic Studies with Bacteria,* 97–106, 1956. Reprinted in *Papers on Bacterial Genetics,* Adelberg, E. A. (Ed.), Boston: Little, Brown, 1960, pp. 230–238.

Stent, G., *Molecular Biology of Bacterial Viruses,* San Francisco: Freeman & Co., 1963.

Wollman, E. L., and Jacob, F., "Lysogeny and Genetic Recombination in Escherichia Coli K 12" (in French), C. R. Acad. Sci. (Paris), 239:455–456, 1954. Translated and reprinted in *Papers on Bacterial Viruses,* Stent, G. S. (Ed.), Boston: Little, Brown, 1960, pp. 334–335.

Zinder, N. D., " 'Transduction' in Bacteria," Scient. Amer., 199:38–43, 1958.

Zinder, N. D., and Lederberg, J., "Genetic Exchange in Salmonella," J. Bact., 64:679–699, 1952.

QUESTIONS FOR DISCUSSION

25.1. How would you define the term *provirus?* How do the terms *merozygote* and *heterogenote* differ? How would you define a *homogenote?*

25.2. What characteristics are conferred upon a host cell infected by a nontransducing temperate phage which becomes a prophage? Does not become a prophage?

25.3. How would you prove that only one exogenote exists in a microcolony of Salmonella produced by an abortive transduction?

25.4. Discuss the statement: "Temperate phage has chromosomal memory, and the chromosome has temperate phage memory."

25.5. F particles are known which carry the prophage of λ as "memory." How could you prove the existence of such a particle?

25.6. Describe the procedure and genotypes you would use in demonstrating that *E. coli* can undergo genetic transformation with respect to *Gal.*

25.7. Is there any reason to believe that the close linkage of genes with related effects might be more advantageous in microorganisms than in higher organisms? Explain.

25.8. List the different ways that the *Gal* locus in the *E. coli* chromosome can undergo recombination.

25.9. Are temperate phages good or bad for bacteria? Explain.

25.10. Is a cell which has presumably stopped undergoing mutation, genetic recombination, and self-replication of its DNA still considered to contain genetic material? Explain.

25.11. Discuss the origin and relative numbers of λdg present among the phages in LFT and HFT lysates.

Chapter 26

BACTERIOPHAGE: RECOMBINATION AND GENETIC MAPS

THE morphology of the T-even group (T2, T4, T6) of phages that attack *E. coli* has been studied in some detail.[1] Its members are tadpole shaped, 0.1 to 0.2 μ long—roughly a tenth the bacterial diameter (Figure 26–1). The surface of the head has a hexagonal outline and facets like a crystal. The *head membrane* is composed of numerous subunits each having a molecular weight of about 80,000. The *tail* is cylindrical and is used by the phage for attachment to the host cell. The outer *sheath* of the tail, composed of about 200 spirally-arranged subunits each having a molecular weight of approximately 50,000, forms a hollow cylinder. The sheath can contract, shortening its length while increasing its diameter without changing its volume appreciably. Beneath the sheath is the *core,* a hollow cylinder with a central hole about 25A in diameter. At the distal end of the core is a *hexagonal plate* to which six *tail fibers* are attached; each is bent in the middle and seems to contain subunits with molecular weight of not less than 100,000 a piece. The subunits of the head membrane, sheath, and tail fibers are composed of protein. When digested with trypsin, each of these subunits produces a unique set of peptides indicating that each is different. The core is also protein. A serologically distinct protein, 4 to 6% of the total phage protein, is found in the interior of the phage par-

[1] See S. Brenner *et al.* (1959).

339

ticle; polyamines, putrescine, spermadine, lysozyme, and a minor polypeptide are also reported in the phage interior.

In addition to these components, the T-even phage interior contains DNA whose volume is approximately the same as that of the total protein. This DNA is composed of a single double helix about 200,000 nucleotides long. Since such a polynucleotide would be about 68 μ long, the DNA inside the phage must be highly coiled.[2] No RNA has been reported in DNA-containing phages.

Not all phages contain DNA; several bacteriophage contain RNA and no DNA. Moreover, the physical and chemical complexity of the T-even phages is not typical

[2] See R. Kilkson and M. F. Maestre (1962).

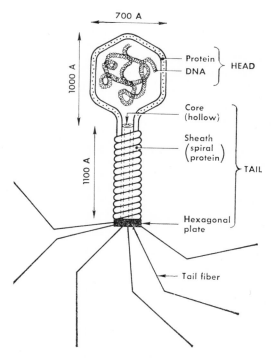

FIGURE 26–1. *Diagrammatic representation of the structures observed in intact and triggered T-even phages of* E. coli.

of all viruses. Certain plant viruses, such as the tobacco mosaic and turnip yellow mosaic, are relatively simple helical or spherical structures. Although ϕX174 seems to have a simple spherical structure, ϕR, a closely related single-stranded DNA phage, shows a small knob which may function as a tail.

Identification of the genetic material in DNA-containing phages is made somewhat easier because DNA contains no sulphur and T2 phage protein contains no phosphorous. The DNA in one sample of phage can be labeled by feeding the *E. coli* host cells radioactive P[32], while the protein in another phage sample is labeled by feeding the host cells radioactive S[35]. Each sample of radioactive phage is then permitted to infect nonlabeled cells.[3] The following results are obtained: in one sample all of the P[32] (hence all of the DNA) enters the bacterium; in the other all but about 3% of the S[35] (hence almost all the protein) remains outside and is removed by blendor treatment. As implied earlier (p. 330), when most of the protein of an attached phage is removed from the host cell by blendor treatment the normal outcome of infection remains unaffected. These results are consistent with the view that DNA and not protein is the carrier of phage genetic information.

[3] This account follows the work of A. D. Hershey and M. Chase (1952).

Recall (p. 336) that pure DNA does not penetrate normal *E. coli* unassisted. The cell wall of *E. coli* can be removed by suitable culture conditions, leaving a *protoplast* that can be penetrated by purified DNA. After phenol, $CaCl_2$, or other treatments, the entire protein coat of phage can be removed, leaving pure DNA. When protoplasts of *E. coli* are mixed with such pure, single-stranded DNA of phage X174 (which has only about 4,500 deoxyribotides per particle), typical ϕX174 progeny, including the characteristic protein envelope are produced.[4] Consequently, *the only genetic material in DNA-containing phage is DNA.*

The course of events leading to lysis of a phage-infected bacterium can be summarized as follows (Figure 26–2): The phage becomes attached tail-first to specific receptors on the bacterial surface. All the DNA and a small amount of protein are injected into the host; probably, the injection is assisted by the contraction of the spiral sheath protein. An *eclipse period* follows (Figure 26–2, B–D), during which no infective phage can be recovered if the host cell is artificially lysed. During this eclipse period, the infected cell is said to carry *immature phage,* and the phage DNA is replicating to produce a pool of phage DNA units. Starting at the end of the eclipse period (Figure 26–2E), a fraction

[4] This has been shown by G. D. Guthrie and R. L. Sinsheimer.

FIGURE 26–2 (*opposite*). *Electron micrographs of growth of T2 virus inside the* E. coli *host cell. A. Bacillus before infection. B. Four minutes after infection. C. Ten minutes after infection. The thin section photographed includes the protein coat of T2 which can be seen attached to the bacterial surface. D. Twelve minutes after infection. New virus particles are starting to condense. E. Thirty minutes after infection. More than 50 T2 particles are completely formed and the host is about ready to lyse. (Courtesy of E. Kellenberger. Reprinted from the Scientific American, 204:100, 1961.)*

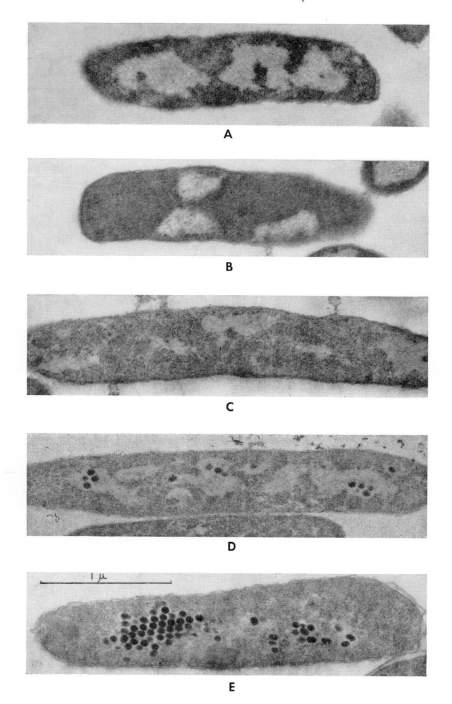

of this DNA pool is assembled into mature phage, each genome surrounded by a newly synthesized coat (head and tail) (Figure 26–2D). About 20 to 40 minutes after infection, the infected bacteria produce enzymes called *endolysins* which rupture the bacterial cell wall and liberate infective phage into the medium.

This last step completes the *lytic cycle* of a bacteriophage—the only one possible for *intemperate* or *virulent* phages, such as T. For temperate phages, this is one of the two possible cycles—upon entering a bacterium, the alternative is integrating with the bacterial chromosome as a prophage, thereby making the bacterium lysogenic and immune. Even in this event, remember, prophage occasionally dissociates from the chromosome and replicates to produce infective phage liberated by lysis of the host cell.

Virulent Phages

Methods for assaying the amount of phage present in a solution are based upon the virus's capacity to lyse sensitive bacteria. In one commonly-used method, the surface of an agar-containing plate is heavily seeded with sensitive bacteria which, upon incubation, will grow to form a continuous and somewhat opaque lawn. When a few intemperate phage particles are mixed with the sensitive bacteria before incubation, each particle enters a different bacterium, grows there, subsequently lyses the host, and releases up to several hundred daughter phage. These particles proceed to attack bacteria near the original host, causing them to lyse later. The repetition of this cycle produces a progressively increasing zone of lysis that is detected as a *clearing* or *plaque* in the bacterial lawn. Under these conditions each plaque is derived from one ancestral phage and a count of plaques therefore corresponds to a count of phage in the infecting sample.

The detailed appearance of a plaque depends upon the medium, host, and phage. When other factors are controlled, different mutants of a phage may produce plaques with characteristically different morphology. Plaque differences can involve size, turbidity, presence or absence of a halo, nature of the edges, and—when a dye is added to the agar in the plate—color. The investigator can, therefore, detect and maintain phage mutants affecting plaque type. Ge-

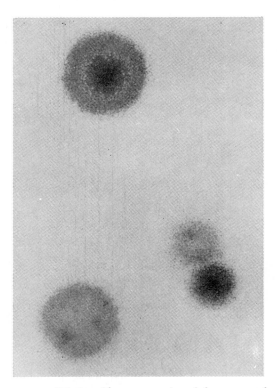

FIGURE 26–3. *Plaques produced by parental and recombinant phage types. Progeny phage of a cross between* h r+ *and* h+ r *were tested on a mixture of suitable indicator bacteria. The small clear and the large turbid plaques are made by the parental types of phage progeny (*h r+ *and* h+ r, *respectively). The large clear and the small turbid plaques are produced by the recombinant types of progeny (*h r *and* h+ r+, *respectively). (Courtesy of A. D. Hershey.)*

netically, phages can differ according to the hosts they are able to infect, and mutants occur which change the range of hosts attacked. Therefore, phage mutants affecting host range can also be detected and maintained.

One can obtain a strain of intemperate T phage that is mutant both for *host range, h,* and *plaque type, r.* Sensitive bacteria are infected by a single phage particle containing both markers to determine the mutation frequencies to the wild-type alleles (h^+

and r^+); wild-type phages are used to determine the mutation rates to each of the two kinds of mutant alleles. When the sensitive bacterial strain is exposed to a highly concentrated mixture of the double mutant ($h\,r$) and wild-type ($h^+\,r^+$) phages, so that some of the multiply-infected cells carry both phage types, not only do the parental types ($h\,r$ and $h^+\,r^+$) occur among the progeny, but the recombinant types ($h^+\,r$ and $h\,r^+$) occur in frequency too high to result from mutation (Figure 26–3). Con-

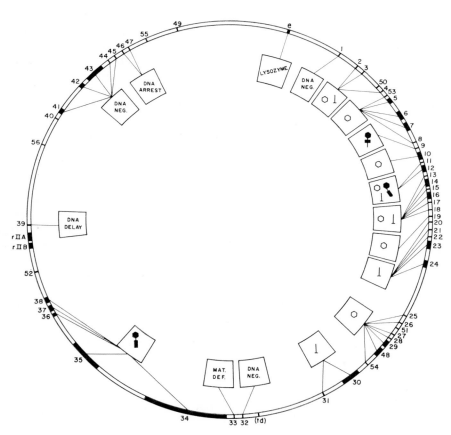

FIGURE 26–4. *A recombination map of T4D. Filled-in areas represent minimal lengths for genes. The symbols for phage components represent the typical morphological products present in lysates of mutant-infected E. coli. (Courtesy of R. S. Edgar; see F. W. Stahl, et al., Genetics, 50:539–552, 1964.)*

sequently, such experiments [5] prove that *ge-netic recombination occurs between phage particles in a multiply-infected cell.* From the relative frequencies with which different recombinants appear among phage released from cells multiply-infected with a series of different mutants (this procedure is known as "crossing" genetically-different phages), the genetic map of a phage can be constructed. When this is done for T4, the mutant loci are found to be arranged in a single closed linear order, that is, a circle (Figure 26–4).

Because the T4 plaque mutant *r* lyses rapidly, it produces a larger plaque with sharper margins than the phage with the wild-type allele, r^+. Mixed infections with *r* and r^+ phages usually yield progeny that produce plaques of one or the other type. Two per cent of the observed plaques, however, are *mottled;* that is, they appear partly r and partly r^+. When *mottled plaques* are picked and their phage content tested, they produce progeny that make either r or r^+ type of plaque. Since both parental types are present, the mottled plaque could not have been initiated from a single phage haploid for the *r* locus. Mottled plaques are not caused by infection with clumps of phage particles; moreover, these plaques are not initiated by a phage carrying an unstable *r* mutant, since unstable *r* phages produce phenotypically—and genotypically—*sectored,* not mottled, *plaques.* From these results and others, it has been proved [6] that the two per cent of T4 phage producing mottled plaques in mixed infections are heterozygous for a short region of the phage genome that includes the *r* locus.

A single phage particle can be heterozygous for several loci, provided they are

GENOTYPE	PLAQUES FORMED ON HOST STRAIN	
	B	**K**
r I or r III **Mutants**	r	r
r II **Mutants**	r	**None**
r^+	+	+

FIGURE 26–5. *Behavior of* r *mutants of T-even phages in the B and K strains of* E. coli.

located far enough apart. In fact, it is unlikely that any phage is completely haploid. Regions present in diploid condition are said to be *redundant.* Redundancy appears to be accomplished in two ways [7]: Either both regions are part of one DNA double-helix (*terminal redundancy*) or the extra region is present as a separate segment of double-helix DNA (*internal redundancy*).

Genetic Fine Structure of ϕT4 [8]

The *r* mutants occur in three distinct regions of the T4 genetic map—rI, rII, and rIII. The *r* mutants in all three regions produce plaques when *E. coli* strain B is used as host. However, mutants in the rII region are unique in that they cannot form plaques when their host is strain K12 of *E. coli* (which happens to be lysogenic for lambda), whereas the *rI* and *rIII* mutants and r^+ phages can (Figure 26–5). Thus, among *r* mutants, only those in region II have this restriction in host range.

The host-range restricted *rII* mutant is useful since it can be employed as a selective marker. The mutation frequency from

[5] After the work of M. Delbrück and W. T. Bailey, and of A. D. Hershey and R. Rotman.
[6] See A. D. Hershey and M. Chase (1951); see also A. H. Doermann and L. Boehner (1963).
[7] See G. Streisinger, R. S. Edgar, and G. H. Denhardt (1964).
[8] The following discussion is based mainly upon the work of S. Benzer (1955, 1957).

rII to *rII*⁺ can be determined readily by plating T4*rII* on strain K12, since only mutants to r⁺ will form plaques (r⁺ is "selected" on strain K12). A large number of *rII* mutants that have a low mutation frequency (sometimes as low as one per 10^8 phages) can be obtained. T4*rII* mutants can be divided into two classes, A and B, on the basis of their behavior after mixed infection of strain K12. When K12 is infected with an *rII* phage from each class, growth of the phage and lysis of the host occurs. This behavior suggests that the rII region is composed of two subregions, A and B, and the products of both are required to produce the normal r⁺ phenotype. Mutants defective only in the A subregion presumably can still make normal B product, and vice versa. In a bacterium multiply-infected with one phage mutant in A and another in B, the B and A products produced by the mutants can cooperate—that is, show *complementation*—to produce the r⁺ phenotype (Figure 26–6).

If the two different *rII* mutants in a multiple infection of strain K12 are located in the same subregion—region A, for example—they will be unable to produce the r+ phenotype by complementation since neither phage can produce normal A product. In such cases the phage cannot grow and the host will not lyse unless the infecting mutants have lesions far enough apart in region A to permit wild-type progeny to result from recombination between them.

Two mutants, *r1* and *r2*, arising independently in the same subregion, may fail to recombine with each other; however, *r1* may recombine with a third independent mutant, *r3*, even though mutant *r2* does not. These results suggest that mutant *r2* has a long deficiency or deletion that includes all or part of the region defective in *r1* and *r3*. Such deletion mutants are never found to revert to r⁺. Other mutants which do revert and which give no evidence of having long deficiencies are considered to be point mutants. Of the more than 1500 spontaneously-occurring *rII* mutants which have been typed,

FUNCTIONAL COMPLEMENTATION

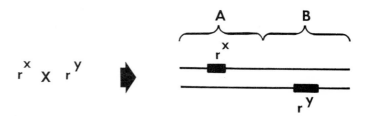

NO COMPLEMENTATION

FIGURE 26–6. *The occurrence or nonoccurrence of complementation between different rII mutants.*

FIGURE 26–7. *Genetic map of the rII region of phage T4. The breaks in the map indicate segments as defined by the ends of deletions. The order of the segments has been determined as shown. The order of mutants within any one segment has not been determined, but all give recombination with each other. The hollow circles and other filled-in symbols represent different types of phenotypic effects. (Courtesy of S. Benzer and S. P. Champe, Proc. Nat. Acad. Sci., U.S., 47:1030–1031, 1961.)*

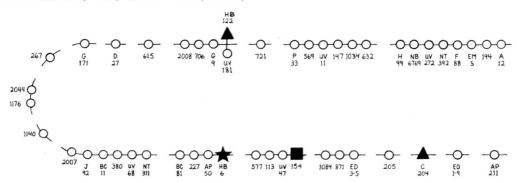

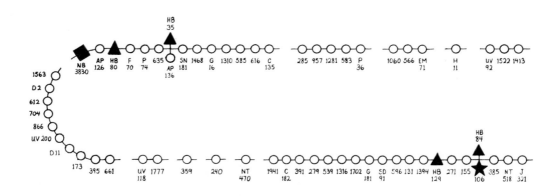

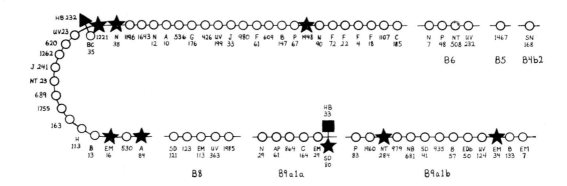

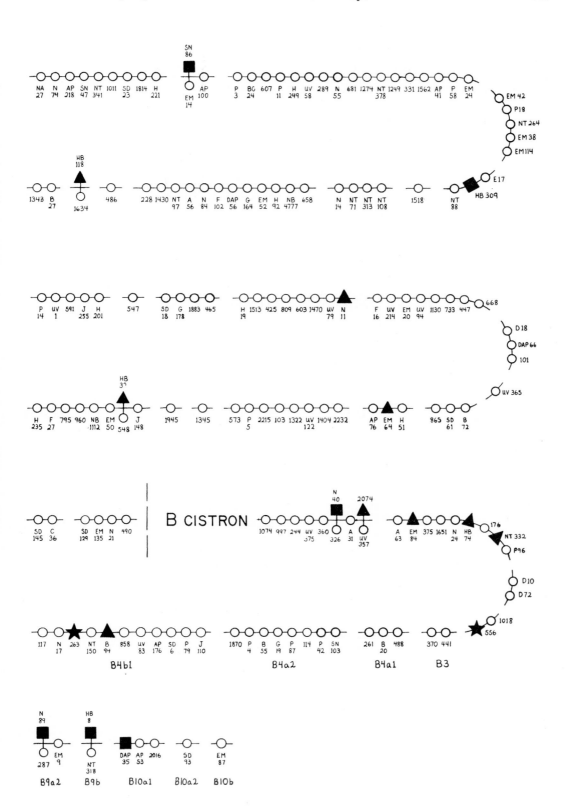

about 300 are different; that is, each is separable from all the others by recombination (Figure 26–7). Using overlapping deficiencies and point mutants, it is possible to arrange all the mutant loci of the A and B subregions in a single linear sequence with distances between mutants being approximately additive. Thus, *even in its fine structure* (*within one "gene"*) *the genetic recombination map of bacteriophage is linear.*

The ability to select for r^+ reversions by plating *rII* mutants on strain K12 permits the detection of mutation frequencies as low as one in 10^8. This method also has approximately the same efficiency for detecting recombinants. Although numerous mutants were crossed with each other, the smallest reproducible frequency of recombination found between two mutants (0.02%) was relatively large, being at least one hundred times greater than the lowest frequency detectable. For recombination, therefore, 0.02% seems to be close to the lower limit, a value which may be useful in estimating how finitely divisible DNA is for purposes of recombination.

To calculate the smallest nucleotide distance between two markers of T4 which are able to recombine with each other, we must assume that:

1. The probability of genetic recombination is constant per molecular distance on the phage genetic map.
2. The genetic markers studied are representative of all other loci.
3. The total length of the genetic map is accurately estimated by the summation of a number of small distances.

Based on these assumptions, the total genetic map of phage T4 is calculated to be approximately 2500 recombination units long; that is, it shows 2500% recombination with respect to its total genetic content. (Remember that a recombination map based upon crossing over can be longer than one

hundred recombination units—in this case, crossover units.) The molecular weight of the DNA of T4 is 130 to 160 times 10^6 which means T4 contains about 400,000 nucleotides. These are arranged in the form of a single double helix of 200,000 linearly-arranged nucleotides.

The fraction $\dfrac{2500\% \text{ recombinants}}{200{,}000 \text{ nucleotides}}$ equals 0.0125% and expresses the percentage of recombination per nucleotide pair. Assuming that recombination cannot take place within a nucleotide pair, a phage genome has 200,000 internucleotide points where exchanges can occur. Thus, we can say that if two *r* mutants—different from wild-type in single, adjacent nucleotides—are crossed, r^+ recombinants are expected to occur among $\dfrac{0.0125\%}{2}$, or 0.00625%, of their progeny (the undetected double mutant recombinant also occurring with this frequency).

Suppose that the lowest r^+ recombinant frequency observed, 0.02%, is actually the minimal rate. This might mean that recombination could occur in each internucleotide position, but that the closest of the numerous mutants tested still would be separated by about three nucleotides (.02/.00625). Supposing the mutants actually affect adjacent nucleotides, then only about every third internucleotide point, on the average, would be capable of undergoing recombination, and an estimate of the average unit of recombination would be three nucleotides in length. Because the observed value of 0.02% is a maximum value for the least amount of recombination, and uncertainties exist concerning the length of the genetic map and the number of nucleotides in the phage genome, the average nucleotide length between phage recombination events is subject to considerable error. Since the DNA backbone does not seem to have any structural feature which occurs only every third nucleotide, it is reasonable to accept as a working hypothesis that *the smallest recombinational unit in phage equals one nucleotide.*[9]

The entire rII region contains about 2000 linearly-arranged nucleotides. Consider the functional characteristics of this region. If only the production of the r and r+ phenotypes were considered, the rII region would behave as a single functional unit. The rII region, however, is composed of two sub-regions, A and B, which show complementation. Such a division suggests that A and B are independent, separate units at the functional level.

When *E. coli* strain K12 is doubly-infected with wild-type (++) and T4 doubly-mutant (a_1a_2) in the A (or B) region, the r+ phenotype is produced. In this case, the mutants are present in the same DNA double helix, being in the *cis position* (Figure 26–8). When the strain K12 bacterium is doubly-infected and each virus particle carries one of these mutants (a_1+, $+a_2$), the mutants are in the *trans position*. No complementation occurs, and no plaque is produced. When such a *cis-trans test* gives this result, the two mutants failing to complement in the trans position are said to belong to the same functional (A or B) unit, or *cistron*. The closest mutational sites between the A and B cistrons (Figure 26–6) are no more than 0.4 map units apart, indicating that the two cistrons are not separated by a large amount of DNA within which recombination can occur.

Temperate Phages

Genetic recombination also occurs between temperate phages. From the frequencies of genetically-recombinant phages occurring among the progeny of sensitive cells multiply infected with different mutants of lambda, it is possible to arrange the mutants on a single linkage map, just as is done for different mutants in the virulent T phages. The

[9] Support for this view is found in work by D. R. Helinski and C. Yanofsky (1962).

map for λ, however, is (like T5) not circular as is the map for T4.

The difference between a temperate and an intemperate phage is that the former can lysogenize its host. When temperate phages infect sensitive bacteria, the plaques produced have a turbid center caused by the growth of the bacteria that were lysogenized —not lysed. In such a temperate strain, mutants occur whose capacity for lysogenization is either decreased or lost (in which case the phage become virulent) and are detectable because they form less turbid or clear plaques. Matings between phages that carry mutants with different degrees of virulence and other markers show that the loci controlling ability to lysogenize are a regular part of the phage genetic map.

Some mutants seem to affect the very process by which phage is converted to prophage. Mutants of the latter type are called *c (clear) mutants* and occur in a cluster of loci within the phage genetic map. In lambda, three groups of *c* mutants occur in the sequence of c_3, c_1, c_2 (Figure 26–9). Mutants in the c_1 segment no longer have any measurable ability to lysogenize and, therefore, cause completely-clear plaques, whereas those in c_3 and c_2 have about .1 to .01 of the lysogenization ability of wild-type lambda. It has been demonstrated, furthermore, that these three loci act at different times after infection.

More than a dozen temperate phages in

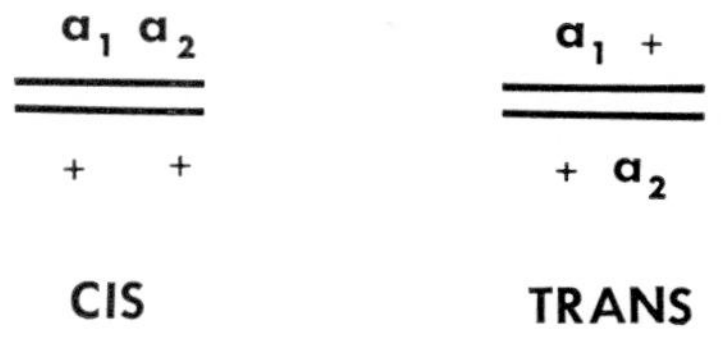

FIGURE 26–8. *Cis and trans positions for two mutants in cistron rIIA.*

E. coli have been isolated. Some of these are ultraviolet inducible, others are not. All (seven) of the viruses whose prophages are inducible occupy different chromosomal loci located in one region of the host chromosome (Figure 26–10). These phages also differ from each other in that a host lysogenic for one can still be infected by any of the others.[10]

Hemophilus influenzae is transformable and can also be infected by the UV-inducible, temperate phage HP1. The genetic material of this phage can be introduced into nonlysogenic Hemophilus competent for transformation in three ways: by injection from intact phage; by infection with pure phage DNA; and by infection with pure bacterial DNA

carrying the prophage, isolated from lysogens. In each case, the host cell either becomes lysogenic or lyses and liberates mature phage progeny.[11]

Although the immunity properties of prophage are controlled by a small portion of the phage's total DNA content—the c_1 region—this region alone does not include all the genetic information or specifications needed for prophage to become mature, infective phage. Presumably most, if not all, the other phage loci are essential for the production of mature phage, complete with its protein parts.

Using unlabeled host cells, crosses can be made between genetically-different strains of lambda, one unlabeled and the other labeled with the isotopes C^{13} and N^{15}. Following density-gradient ultracentrifugation, the dis-

[10] The preceding discussion is based primarily upon work of F. Jacob and E. L. Wollman (1957), of A. D. Kaiser and F. Jacob (1957), and of F. Jacob and A. Campbell.

[11] See W. Harm and C. S. Rupert (1963).

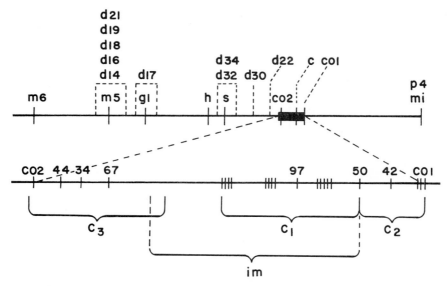

FIGURE 26–9. *Diagrammatic representation of the linkage group of the temperate bacteriophage* λ. *The upper diagram shows the linear arrangement of various markers for host range or plaque size or type. The d symbols refer to specific defective mutants. The c region is marked by a thicker line and is shown enlarged in the lower diagram. It is composed of three sub-regions, c_3, c_1, c_2. Im refers to the segment controlling immunity. (After F. Jacob and J. Monod.)*

tribution of labeled parental DNA is determined both among the parental and the recombinant genotypes. In such experiments,[12] discrete amounts of the original parental DNA are found in the recombinant

[12] See M. Meselson and J. J. Weigle (1961), and G. Kellenberger, M. L. Zichichi, and J. J. Weigle (1961).

phages. The simplest explanation for this result is that recombinants are formed after breakage and rejoining of the parental DNA strands. Such results do not support—but do not exclude—phage recombinations occurring via a copy-choice mechanism according to which recombinant phage DNA is expected to be made of entirely new, unlabeled material.

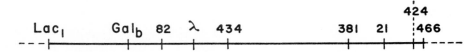

FIGURE 26–10. *Part of the* E. coli *linkage map showing the location of certain inducible prophages.*

SUMMARY AND CONCLUSIONS

The morphology and lytic cycle of the virulent T-even phages of *E. coli* are discussed, and their genetic material identified chemically as DNA. After multiple infection with T4 phages carrying different genetic markers, genetic recombinants are found among the progeny.

From the results of such phage crosses, a recombination map can be constructed for T4 in which the genes are arranged linearly in a single circle. Recombinant phages are often diploid for a short region between the recombinant markers.

The genetic fine structure of the rII region of ϕT4 is revealed by studies of mutation, complementation, and genetic recombination. Their data suggest the hypothesis that the smallest recombinational unit in phage is one nucleotide.

Genetic recombination also occurs between mutants of a temperate phage. The single linkage group of lambda is not circular. Immunity to superinfection is determined by the c_1 region of the phage genetic map. Sometimes, if not always, phage recombination involves parental strands which have broken and rejoined.

REFERENCES

Benzer, S., "Fine Structure of a Genetic Region in Bacteriophage," Proc. Nat. Acad. Sci., U.S., 41:344–354, 1955. Reprinted in *Papers on Bacterial Viruses*, Stent, G. S. (Ed.), Boston: Little, Brown, 1960, pp. 209–219.

Benzer, S., "The Elementary Units of Heredity," pp. 70–93, in *A Symposium on the Chemical Basis of Heredity*, McElroy, W. D., and Glass, B. (Eds.), Baltimore: Johns Hopkins Press, 1957.

Benzer, S., "On the Topography of the Genetic Fine Structure," Proc. Nat. Acad. Sci., U.S., 47:403–415, 1961.

Benzer, S., "The Fine Structure of the Gene," Scient. Amer., 206 (No. 1):70–84, 1962.

Brenner, S., Streisinger, G., Horne, R. W., Champe, S. P., Barnett, L., Benzer, S., and Rees, M. W., "Structural Components of Bacteriophage," J. Mol. Biol., 1:281–282, 1959.

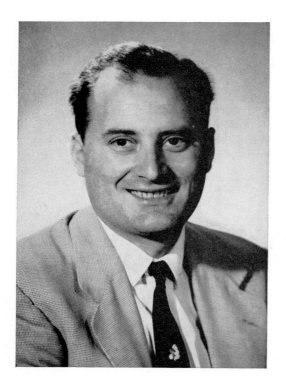

A. D. HERSHEY, *about 1960.*

SEYMOUR BENZER, *in 1961.*

Davidson, P. F., Freifelder, D., Hede, R., and Levinthal, C., "The Structural Unity of the DNA of T2 Bacteriophage," Proc. Nat. Acad. Sci., U.S., 47:1123–1129, 1961.

Doermann, A. H., and Boehner, L., "An Experimental Analysis of Bacteriophage T4 Heterozygotes, I.," Virology, 21:551–567, 1963.

Guthrie, G. D., and Sinsheimer, R. L., "Observations on the Infection of Bacterial Protoplasts with the Deoxyribonucleic Acid of Bacteriophage ϕX174," Biochim. Biophys. Acta, 72:290–297, 1963.

Hanafusa, H., Hanafusa, T., and Rubin, H., "The Defectiveness of Rous Sarcoma Virus, II. Specification of RSV Antigenicity by Helper Virus," Proc. **Nat. Acad.** Sci., U.S., 51:41–48, 1964.

Harm, W., and Rupert, C. S., "Infection of Transformable Cells of *Haemophilus influenzae* by Bacteriophage and Bacteriophage DNA," Zeit. f. Vererbungsl., 94: 336–348, 1963.

Hayes, W., *The Genetics of Bacteria and their Viruses,* New York: J. Wiley & Sons, 1964.

Helinski, D. R., and Yanofsky, C., "Correspondence between Genetic Data and the Position of Amino Acid Alteration in a Protein," Proc. Nat. Acad. Sci., U.S., 48:173–183, 1962.

Hershey, A. D., and Chase, M., "Genetic Recombination and Heterozygosis in Bacteriophage," Cold Spring Harb. Sympos. Quant. Biol., 16:471–479, 1951. Reprinted in *Papers on Bacterial Viruses,* Stent, G. S. (Ed.), Boston: Little, Brown, 1960, pp. 179–192.

Hershey, A. D., and Chase, M., "Independent Functions of Viral Protein and Nucleic Acid in Growth of Bacteriophage," J. Gen. Physiol., 36:39–54, 1952. Reprinted in *Papers on Bacterial Viruses,* Stent, G. S. (Ed.), Boston: Little, Brown, 1960, pp. 87–104.

Jacob, F., and Wollman, E. L., "Genetic Aspects of Lysogeny," pp. 468–500, in *A Symposium on the Chemical Basis of Heredity,* McElroy, W. D., and Glass, B. (Eds.), Baltimore: Johns Hopkins Press, 1957.

Jacob, F., and Wollman, E. L., "Viruses and Genes," Scient. Amer., 204 (No. 6): 92–107, 1961.

Kaiser, A. D., and Jacob, F., "Recombination Between Related Temperate Bacteriophages and the Genetic Control of Immunity and Prophage Localization," Virology, 4:509–521, 1957. Reprinted in *Papers on Bacterial Viruses,* Stent, G. S. (Ed.), Boston: Little, Brown, 1960, pp. 353–365.

Kellenberger, G., Zichichi, M. L., and Weigle, J. J., "Exchange of DNA in the Recombination of Bacteriophage λ," Proc. Nat. Acad. Sci., U.S., 47:869–878, 1961.

Kilkson, R., and Maestre, M. F., "Structure of *T*2 Bacteriophage," Nature (Lond.), 195:494–495, 1962.

Meselson, M., and Weigle, J. J., "Chromosome Breakage Accompanying Genetic Recombination in Bacteriophage," Proc. Nat. Acad. Sci., U.S., 47:857–868, 1961.

Mosig, G., "Genetic Recombination in Bacteriophage T4 during Replication of DNA Fragments," Cold Spring Harb. Sympos. Quant. Biol., 28:35–42, 1964.

Rubenstein, I., Thomas, C. A., Jr., and Hershey, A. D., "The Molecular Weights of T2 Bacteriophage DNA and its First and Second Breakage Products," Proc. Nat. Acad. Sci., U.S., 47:1113–1122, 1961.

Stahl, F. W., Edgar, R. S., and Steinberg, J., "The Linkage Map of Bacteriophage T4," Genetics, 50:539–552, 1964.

Streisinger, G., Edgar, R. S., and Denhardt, G. H., "Chromosome Structure in Phage T4. I. Circularity of the Linkage Map," Proc. Nat. Acad. Sci., U.S., 51:775–779, 1964.

See last portion of Supplement V.

QUESTIONS FOR DISCUSSION

26.1. Is the hole in the tail of T-even phages large enough for the passage of one or two double helices of DNA? Explain. In what respect does your answer concern the manner in which phage DNA enters into a bacterial host?

26.2. In studying phages, what are the advantages of using bacteria growing on a solid, rather than in a liquid, culture medium?

26.3. Do you think it would be feasible to study the genetic basis for different morphological or for different protein components of a phage? Explain.

26.4. What is meant by a phage cross? Describe how you would know that you made one.

26.5. Does the finding—that complete progeny phages are liberated after pure DNA from ϕX174 infects a protoplast—mean that all the information for making ϕX174 DNA and ϕX174 protein is contained in the phage's DNA? Explain.

26.6. Are the hypotheses of phage recombination by breakage and by copy-choice mutually exclusive? Explain.

26.7. In what respects is $\phi\lambda$ similar to and different from an F particle?

26.8. A temperate phage able to transduce any known chromosomal marker in *E. coli* is known. Would you be able to locate the chromosomal site for its prophage? Explain.

26.9. Does the finding—that a single phage particle can transduce a bacterial fragment carrying not only a bacterial marker but two linked prophages—have any bearing upon the essentiality of the entire phage genome being present for infection and/or the production of phage progeny? Explain.

26.10. How can you distinguish a ϕT4 mutant in the rII region from one in the rI or the rIII region?

26.11. Describe how the cis-trans test is used to show functional complementation between two mutants in phage.

26.12. What would you expect to be the near-maximum number of nucleotides transduceable by a phage still capable of phage activity? On what is your opinion based?

26.13. If the average protein-specifying gene were 2000 nucleotides long, how many different proteins could be specified by ϕT4? By ϕX174?

26.14. What do you consider to be the most remarkable feature of ϕX174?

26.15. Mutants which show functional complementation in the *pan-2* region of Neurospora can be arranged in the same linear order by complementation and by genetic recombination. Is it necessarily true that both maps will also be identical for other regions? Explain.

26.16. What is a functional genetic unit, or cistron? How is your answer related to its length in nucleotides?

26.17. What have you learned in this chapter regarding the chemical scope of the genetic unit of recombination? Of function?

Chapter **27**

BACTERIAL EPISOMES AND
GENETIC RECOMBINATION

T HE LOCATION and genotype of F determines the kind of male sexuality which occurs in Escherichia. In this bacterium, conjugation leads to new combinations of either or both the chromosomal genes and the extrachromosomal episomal genes.

Let us consider the sequence of events in F's genetic recombination. When an Hfr strain reverts to F+, the F particle integrated into the Hfr chromosome is somehow liberated from it, or *deintegrated*. The particle then enters the cytoplasm, replicates, and thereafter is infectious. In some subsequent generation, the F particle may reintegrate into a chromosome, making it Hfr. Before an F particle can integrate, it apparently must synapse with the chromosome—the attraction between F and the chromosome probably being the same as between a segment of donor chromosome and the host chromosome in transformation, conjugation, or transduction. In transformation, the integrating donor loci must be homologous to those replaced in the recipient cell. (Most likely, this homology is also required for the integration of chromosome fragments introduced by conjugation or transduction.) Since F can integrate at a variety of loci, it appears likely that F has segments of DNA homologous to a variety of chromosomal regions. The homologous segments which F presumably contains may have been present "ini-

tially," or they may have been obtained at the time of previous deintegrations. (It is not known whether the first F originated as an offshoot of the bacterial chromosome or entered the bacterium from the outside.) If a free F particle sometimes carries an extra segment of chromosomal DNA somehow obtained at the time of deintegration, one should be able to find a type of free F particle which, when introduced into an F− strain, shows a high affinity for a specific chromosomal region. Recall that temperate phages capable only of restricted transduction show such a restriction, although the wild-type F particles do not.

Consider next the following results from experiments [1] concerned with the expectations mentioned. An F+ strain (carrying F extrachromosomally) gave rise to an Hfr strain, P4x, whose chromosomal markers were arranged in the following sequence: O (origin or lead point)-*Pro-TL-Thi* . . . -*Gal-Lac-SF* (sex factor place of attachment). Crosses of P4x by F− produced F− progeny, except for *Lac* recombinants (which are usually Hfr males because of the close linkage of F and *Lac*).

From P4x arose a new strain, P4x-1, having these characteristics:

1. With respect to chromosomal loci, it was identical to P4x in the order of arrangement and in the times of entry (determined by interrupted conjugation). For example, both transferred *Pro* at about six minutes, *TL* at about twenty minutes, and *Lac* last.

2. Recipients showed a frequency of recombination for chromosomal loci lower than the frequency of recombination when P4x was the donor. For example, *Pro* recombinants were 0.3 to 0.5% with P4x-1 as donor and 4.8% with P4x as donor.

3. Interrupted conjugations revealed that

---

[1] The following discussion is based primarily upon the work of E. A. Adelberg and S. N. Burns (1960), and F. Jacob and E. A. Adelberg (1959).

many of its recombinants for *Pro* or *TL* behaved as males.

4. The male factor was linked neither to the above-mentioned loci nor to any other chromosomal marker showing recombination.

5. Like free F, the male factor entered the F⁻ cell about five minutes after conjugation began.

6. Treatment with acridine orange eliminated the male sex factor, converting the cells to F⁻.

These findings prove that the P4x-1 male sex factor—called F′—is located extrachromosomally.

Although F could attach at any one of a number of different chromosomal sites producing Hfr chromosomes differing in O point position and in direction of transfer, F′ attached at a particular locus near *Lac* in such a way that chromosomal loci were always transferred in the same order and direction. Since P4x-1 transferred its chromosome more frequently than the typical F⁺ (F-containing) male, the chance of F′ associating with the chromosome near *Lac* seems to be greater than the total chance of F integrating at any one of numerous different loci. P4x-1, on the other hand, transferred the chromosome less frequently than P4x, suggesting the possibility that F is not fully integrated in P4x-1 ordinarily, although it is in P4x. This difference would also explain why P4x-1 had free F′, whereas P4x did not, since chromosomal F prevented the establishment of free F. Ordinarily, F′ seems to exist as a kind of exogenote which synapses with the chromosome just before or after conjugation is initiated. The mechanism of chromosome mobilization seems to involve a recombinational event between the episome F′ and the chromosome.

When F′ was transferred to F⁻ cells as an extrachromosomal particle, the recipient cells were converted to males that, relatively often, could transfer their chromosome in the same sequence as P4x and P4x-1 males, suggesting that the chromosome of the ordinary F⁻ cell has a segment of DNA near *Lac* homologous to a segment carried by F′; that is, F′ possesses a chromosomal segment which can pair with a particular chromosomal locus.

As mentioned, treatment with an acridine dye eliminated the extrachromosomal F′ particles from the P4x-1 strain and converted it to F⁻. Such an F⁻ strain conjugates with males carrying either F or F′ extrachromosomally. In both cases the F⁻ strain was relatively often converted into a donor (male) that transferred its chromosome in the same sequence as P4x and P4x-1 males. Clearly, then, the F⁻—derived from P4x-1 via acridine orange—carries a chromosome which has retained a segment of F near *Lac*, the portion retained held in common by F and F′. In so far as the F portion of the particle is concerned, then, F and F′ were not detectably different in these experiments. Since F′ is found to be approximately twice the size of F, one can think of F′ as being an F particle with an extra, particular piece of chromosome attached.

The preceding suggests that F′ can carry chromosomal DNA apparently still capable of replication in its new location. Let us suppose that this chromosomal segment is also still able to function normally. F′ may fail to show a phenotypic effect for a normal chromosomal locus because it contains one or more (as yet unidentified) chromosomal markers. (Probably less than 1% of the chromosomal loci have been identified; moreover, there may be chromosomal regions whose only function is the maintenance of and recombination with episomes.) The very existence of F′, however, encourages a search for still different F particles to which a known chromosomal marker might be attached.

Using Lac^-F^- cells and a Lac^+ strain of Hfr with F integrated very close to Lac^+, rare recombinants are obtained from interrupted conjugations which receive Lac^+ too early. Certain of these recombinants have the following properties:

1. They receive only F and Lac^+.

2. They are unstable and, occasionally, give rise to Lac^-F^- individuals; hence, the original recombinant must be a merozygote carrying both Lac^+ and Lac^- alleles.

3. When crossed to Lac^-F^- cells, they simultaneously transfer both F and Lac^+ with 50% or higher frequency. This transfer starts soon after conjugation begins, just as in the case of free F (or F′), and is unlinked to other chromosomal markers. Thus, F-Lac^+ behaves as a free single unit.

4. The recombinant transfers its chromosome in the same sequence as, but with a lower frequency ($\frac{1}{10}$) than, the original Hfr line. These frequencies are exactly those found in comparing P4x-1 with P4x.

5. The F-Lac^+ element can be transmitted in a series of successive conjugations, each recipient possessing the properties of the original recombinant.

All these characteristics are most simply explained by an F particle which carries a chromosomal piece bearing Lac^+ deintegrating in the original Hfr strain. The attached Lac^+ piece is known, moreover, to contain three cistrons governing the synthesis of β-galactosidase, β-galactoside permease, and the repressor for this system. From subsequent integrations and deintegrations, one can also obtain F-Lac^- particles—composed of F-Lac with a Lac^- point mutation. Finally, another Hfr, with F integrated close to *Pro,* is found to produce an F-*Pro* particle whose properties are analogous to those of the F-*Lac* particle. If, however, an F-Lac^+ particle enters a cell containing a deletion in the *Lac* region, the particle, besides transferring Lac^+, behaves like F in that it transfers random chromosomal markers with the low frequencies characteristic of ordinary F^+ by F^- crosses.

Since F can integrate at a variety of loci, these results suggest (and it turns out to be true) that upon deintegration any one of a variety of normal chromosomal loci can become a part of the genotype of cytoplasmic F and can replicate and function in the extrachromosomal state.

Particles like F′ and F-*Lac*—substituted *sex factors*—represent a third type of male sex factor characterized by serving as *intermediate donors* of the usual chromosomal markers. It can be hypothesized that F, F′ and other substituted sex factors are normally small, double-helix, DNA ring chromosomes. If such small ring chromosomes were integrated in the *E. coli* chromosome by a single crossing over, the product would be a bigger (Hfr) ring. The now-integrated F particle would cause the enlarged ring chromosome to be open, usually at one end of F, and would mobilize the chromosome during conjugation. If the chromosome were opened at some internal position in F, part of F would be at the O point and part at the opposite terminus. Some evidence suggests that openings of this type sometimes occur. F may deintegrate by an internal crossing over, producing free ring F and the ring *E. coli* chromosome. It should be emphasized that the suggested circular model of F is based upon no evidence and is nothing more than speculation at present.

When F is not integrated, only one or a few F particles are present per *E. coli* chromosome—at least in cells that have carried F for some time. (This case is similar to the situation in which organisms with more than one chromosome are regulated by some mechanism in the cell which permits each chromosome to replicate only once a generation.) Populations of donors, grown to saturation density in aerated broth or cultured on agar overnight, can lose their donor phenotype temporarily and behave as genetic recipients. Since they retain their sex factor yet behave as F⁻ cells, they are known as *F⁻ phenocopies* (see p. 317). If a *Lac⁻*F⁻ phenocopy carrying F is mated with an F⁺ male carrying F-*Lac⁺*, exconjugants can be obtained that carry both types of F. Soon, however, in some experiments, one or the other F particle persists in the progeny. This adjustment shows that there is some regulation of the number of F particles per nuclear body. Hfr which are F⁻ phenocopies, do not tolerate the presence of an introduced autonomous sex factor.

F not only mobilizes the entire chromosome in Hfr cells, but it also mobilizes merogenotes—in an *F-merogenote transfer* [2]—as shown in the preceding discussion. This latter process has also been called *sex-duction, F-duction,* or *F-mediated transduction.* With respect to such transduction, substituted sex factors resemble λdg, just as F resembles λ. One can construct a haploid Hfr containing two attached F factors so integrated that, upon mating, the chromosome is present in two pieces—⅓ and ⅔ its length—each with an F at the end, and both merogenotes capable of being transferred to the F⁻ cell. An F-merogenote carrying the markers *Pur, V6,* and *Lac* transfers the merogenote so that the entry order—determined by studies of spontaneous and artificial interruptions of mating—is O-*Pur-V6-Lac*-F. In all these respects, then, whole chromosome and merogenote mobilization by F appear identical, differing only with regard to the length of the genetic segment transferred.

Although the merogenote markers can

sometimes integrate into the chromosome, F-linked merogenotes can also persist and replicate without integration, forming clones of merozygotes or partial diploids. The longer the merogenote—when it consists of 4% or more of the genome—the more unstable it is.

Extrachromosomal F can pass from male to female during conjugation. Deintegration and integration of F can result in a two-directional flow of chromosomal genes between F and the chromosome in the same cell. When F is at a chromosomal locus, the chromosomal genes are rendered mobile so that chromosomal genes can be transferred to another cell. F can also enter an F⁻ cell by transduction, in which case it is recovered only in the free state, even if the donor was Hfr. (During phage growth, fragmentation of the chromosome takes place at or close to the ends of the integrated F element.) Consequently, the F particle is directly involved in genetic recombinations within and between bacteria which involve F itself and chromosomal genes.

Promoters

A *promoter* is a genetic element which provides one or more of the special conditions needed for genetic transfer via conjugation. If a genetic element (like F) performs all the functions of a promoter, including mobilization of the entire chromosome or of a merogenote, it is called a *sex factor.* Sometimes a promoter (such as F) promotes only its own transfer (into F⁻ cells). At other times a promoter and a whole chromosome or a merogenote are transferred in linkage.

F-*Lac* promotes the transfer of both the merogenote and the chromosome. After ultraviolet treatment of F-*Lac* heterogenotes, some individuals are found no longer able to transfer *Lac* or chromosomal markers. Apparently a mutation in F resulted in a loss of one or more promoter functions. When

[2] The remainder of this section is based upon A. J. Clark and E. A. Adelberg (1962), A. M. Campbell (1962), and W. Hayes (1964).

Salmonella or Shigella act as recipients in crosses with F^+ or Hfr *E. coli*, F is transferred but sometimes is unable to act as a sex factor until it is sent back into F^- *E. coli*. Such results show that promoter functions can be temporarily inhibited or unexpressed, depending upon the host genotype.

* Resistance Transfer Factors

A genetic agent—the *resistance transfer factor, RTF*—has been found in Shigella.[3] RTF is a promoter which causes conjugation and the transfer of a series of different, linked, drug-resistance genes; it is, therefore, a sex factor. Under special circumstances, RTF can mobilize chromosomal loci. It can be transferred from Shigella to Escherichia or Salmonella independently of the chromosome, and such recipients can be cured of RTF by acridine dyes. RTF promotes its own transfer which starts within one minute of mixing the parents, and it replicates autonomously. Although RTF remains transferrable when introduced into an F^+ or Hfr cell, F-promoted chromosome transfer in Hfr cells is reduced one hundredfold, and F-promoted merogenote transfer and the transfer of free F are completely inhibited by certain RTFs. When RTF is spontaneously lost, these F functions are restored. Other RTF strains have no effect on F function.

F produces an antigen on the cell surface which must be present for $\phi f2$ to attack males. When RTF and F are both present, a new RTF-antigen replaces the F-antigen. When a cell is infected by RTF its chromosomal markers are mobilized one hundred times more frequently when its chromosome carries a segment of F than when it does not. These observations suggest that at least a partial genetic homology exists between RTF and F. In view of this and other evidence, it is concluded that RTF has some relationship with the chromosome, although it may

[3] See T. Watanabe (1963).

not be able to assume a stably integrated state. RTF has been called an episome by its discoverers.

* Colicinogenic Factors [4]

Many strains of enteric bacteria (Escherichia, Salmonella, Shigella, for example) produce one or more highly-specific, antibiotic substances called *colicins*. Colicins are bactericidal but not bacteriolytic agents; a thousandth of a microgram of colicin can kill a million sensitive *E. coli* cells. More than a dozen groups of colicins are known; each group is designated by a different capital letter; each adsorbs to a different receptor site at the cell surface. Different colicins belonging to the same group can be distinguished by other characteristics. Colicins have a high molecular weight; two of them, colicin K and colicin V, have been purified and identified as lipocarbohydrate-proteins. These purified colicins seem to be the same as the O antigen of the bacteria.[5] The antigen molecule can be separated into a lipocarbohydrate and a protein fraction, the latter having all the colicidal activity.

A cell able to produce a colicin is *colicinogenic;* one without this ability is *noncolicinogenic*. Colicinogeny is stable and can be transmitted through thousands of cell generations. Although it can be lost spontaneously, spontaneous acquisition of colicinogeny has never been observed. Consequently, it is reasonable to suppose that colicinogenic bacteria possess genetic material—*colicinogenic (col) factors*—that govern the synthesis of different colicins. Not only are these factors transmitted to progeny via vegetative reproduction, but new strains can become colicinogenic through bacterial conjugation or phage-mediated transduction.

Only a small fraction of the bacteria in a

[4] This section follows the work of P. Fredericq (1963). See also W. Hayes (1964).
[5] See W. F. Goebel (1962).

colicinogenic culture actually produce coli-cins. Colicin is lethal to the bacterium syn-thesizing it, but colicinogenic cells which do not yield colicin are viable and immune when exposed to corresponding colicin. Colicin synthesis can be induced in nearly all cells of a colicinogenic culture after exposure to ultraviolet light, nitrogen mustard, or hydro-gen peroxide. Thus, in several of the prop-erties mentioned, colicinogeny and lysogeny are similar, the col factors behaving in these properties like the prophages of temperate phage. When a strain is both lysogenic and colicinogenic, induction often releases either phage or colicin but not both.

Bacteria can be protected against colicins via *immunity* or *resistance*. A colicinogenic bacterium, although immune to the corre-sponding colicin, can possess receptor sites which make it susceptible to colicins of other groups. Certain other genes confer resist-ance to whole groups of colicins by causing the loss of receptors.

As noted, colicin K and the O antigen are apparently identical. When the receptor sites for colicins and for virulent phages are studied, in a number of cases colicin and phage are found to share receptor sites; for example, receptor sites are shared by colicin K and ϕT6; colicin E and ϕBF-23; colicin C and ϕT1 or ϕT5. Since virulent phage attach to receptors by means of a protein located at the tip of their tails, *colicin and tail-tip protein appear to be very similar.* In serological tests, however, colicin and phage sharing a common receptor have not been found to exhibit any cross reaction, and colicinogeny does not confer immunity to infection by a site-sharing phage. When bacteria are exposed to the protein coat, or phage ghost, of ϕT2, all protein synthesis (and possibly that of RNA and DNA, too) is halted. The same effect is produced by colicin. Bacteria, however, may recover after exposure to phage ghosts or to colicin (if the latter is removed by enzymatic diges-

tion). Sometimes, virulent phage can kill its host without reproducing; in such cases, the constituent responsible for lethality is a tail-tip protein. When ϕT6 is the killer, the lethal protein has the same X-ray inactiva-tion curve, specificity, and receptor site as colicin K.

Since the lethal protein of T6 is very simi-lar to colicin K, it seems reasonable that T6 and col K are homologous with respect to at least one gene. Col K can be thought of as a virulent phage missing that portion of the genome required to lyse the cell and to give rise to particles whose infectivity is inde-pendent of conjugation, yet with enough of the phage genome persisting to make the cell colicinogenic. Labeling experiments show that three col factors studied contained DNA in the amount of 4 to 7 times 10^4 nucleotide pairs—about one-tenth the amount in F or phage.

During conjugation, *E. coli* F$^+$ cells trans-fer col E1 with high frequency, so that col E1 can exist autonomously. Autonomous col factors can arrive in the F$^-$ cell as early as $2\frac{1}{2}$ minutes after conjugation is initiated. Since Hfr *E. coli* carrying col V, col I, or col E2 do not transfer them in linkage, these col factors give no evidence for an attached state.

In Salmonella, col I in the absence of F is transferable via conjugation. Although cells carrying only col E1 cannot transfer it during conjugation, col E1 cells infected by col I transfer both col factors. Consequently, col I promotes the transfer of col E1. When Salmonella harbors only col I, transfer of the chromosome in conjugation occurs but is rare. When such cells are also infected with col E1, chromosome transfer increases one hundredfold. As a result, in Salmonella col I promotes the transfer of col E1, and col E1 promotes the transfer of the chromosome. Col I is, therefore, a sex factor. Although they do not cure colicinogeny, acridine dyes inhibit the transfer of col factors.

When F$^+$ *col$^-$* is crossed with F$^-$ *col I,*

F is transferred to the F⁻ *col I* conjugant, and *col I* is transmitted to the F⁺ *col⁻* conjugant with high efficiency. However, when F⁺ *col I* is crossed with F⁻ *col⁻*, *col I* is transferred at a low rate, so that F interferes with transfer of *col I* from the same parent.

The preceding shows a number of similarities among temperate and virulent phages,[6] F factors, RTF factors, and col factors. It is still too early, however, to make any kind of definite suggestion as to the precise nature of the evolutionary interrelationships, if any, among these various types of episomal elements.

[6] See also E. Seaman, E. Tarmy and J. Marmur (1964).

SUMMARY AND CONCLUSIONS

A two-directional flow of F and chromosomal genetic material occurs between extra-chromosomal F and the chromosome. Chromosomal markers carried by free F retain their capacity for replication and phenotypic action.

F′, other F-merogenotes, RTF factors, and some col factors behave like episomes.

Col factors have several characteristics in common with F and the provirus stage of temperate phages. Their products, colicins, resemble the lethal, tail-tip protein of virulent phages. Accordingly, it is possible that F, temperate phage, virulent phage, and col factors are related in evolution.

Certain bacterial episomes promote their own transfer and/or transfer of other genetic material via conjugation. In Salmonella, col I promotes the transfer of col E1 which, in turn, promotes the transfer of the chromosome. RTF promotes the transfer of linked drug resistance markers and can inhibit certain promoter functions of F.

Since they can initiate conjugation, F and its derivatives, col I, and RTF are sex factors.

REFERENCES

Adelberg, E. A., and Burns, S. N., "Genetic Variation in the Sex Factor of Escherichia Coli," J. Bact., 79:321–330, 1960. Reprinted in *Papers on Bacterial Genetics*, Adelberg, E. A. (Ed.), Boston: Little, Brown, 1960, pp. 353–362.

Campbell, A. M., "Episomes," Advances in Genetics, 11:101–145, 1962.

Clark, A. J., and Adelberg, E. A., "Bacterial Conjugation," Ann. Rev. Microbiol., 16:289–319, 1962.

Fredericq, P., "On the Nature of Colicinogenic Factors: A Review," J. Theoret. Biol., 4:159–165, 1963.

Goebel, W. F., "The Chromatographic Fractionation of Colicine K," Proc. Nat. Acad. Sci., U.S., 48:214–219, 1962.

Hayes, W., *The Genetics of Bacteria and their Viruses*, New York: J. Wiley & Sons, 1964.

Jacob, F., and Wollman, E. L., "Episomes, Added Genetic Elements" (in French), C. R. Acad. Sci. (Paris), 247:154–156, 1958. Translated and reprinted in *Papers on Bacterial Genetics*, Adelberg, E. A. (Ed.), Boston: Little, Brown, 1960, pp. 398–400.

Maas, R., "Exclusion of an F Lac Episome by an Hfr Gene," Proc. Nat. Acad. Sci., U.S., 50:1051–1059, 1963.

Seaman, E., Tarmy, E., and Marmur, J., "Inducible Phages of *Bacillus subtilis*," Biochemistry, 3:607–613, 1964.

Watanabe, T., "Infectious Heredity of Multiple Drug Resistance in Bacteria," Bact. Rev., 27:87–115, 1963.

QUESTIONS FOR DISCUSSION

27.1. Do all matings transfer F particles of one genotype or another? Explain.

27.2. Discuss the relationship between the transmission of free F particles and a segment of the male chromosome.

27.3. Discuss the reality of a bacterial "chromosome" and its linear arrangement.

27.4. By what series of events can you explain the origin of strain P4x-1 from P4x?

27.5. From which particular Hfr strain of *E. coli* could you obtain an F-*Pro* (proline) merogenote? How?

27.6. How do you suppose episomes originate?

27.7. Are integrated episomes and episomal derivatives generally able to break chromosomes? Explain.

27.8. It has been found that ϕP2, a temperate phage which normally integrates at a particular chromosomal locus, position I, loses the extreme preference for position I when liberated from a strain carrying it in position II. How can you explain this finding?

27.9. Discuss the statement: "The ability to pass from the integrated to the free state or vice versa is possessed by every gene in a bacterial cell."

27.10. A transducing phage can carry two closely-linked prophages obtained from a doubly-lysogenic host. What conclusions can you draw with regard to the nucleotide content of a mature phage and a prophage?

27.11. The *Lac* gene can either be chromosomal when integrated into the chromosome, or extrachromosomal when attached to free F. Should such a gene be considered an episome? Why?

27.12. How would you locate the position of the UV-inducible prophage of ϕ434 in the *E. coli* linkage map?

27.13. How would you locate the prophage site of a noninducible (by ultraviolet light or zygote formation) phage?

27.14. Lactic dehydrogenase contains a single-strand sequence of about 33 deoxyribotides. Should this portion of the enzyme be considered genetic material? Explain.

27.15. During conjugation, F is reported to enhance the transfer to the F$^-$ cell such substances as lactose, ultraviolet-irradiation products that induce λ prophage, and a λ repressor. Is F acting as a promoter in these cases? Explain.

Chapter 28

RNA AS GENETIC MATERIAL

IN PREVIOUS CHAPTERS, the DNA-containing phages were the only viruses discussed in detail. In this chapter, we study another group—viruses that contain no DNA and are entirely, or mainly, ribonucleoprotein in content. Members of this group include many of the smaller viruses that attack animals (causing poliomyelitis, influenza, and encephalitis, for example), many viruses that attack plants (such as the tobacco mosaic and the turnip yellow mosaic viruses), and the small RNA-containing bacteriophages [1] (f2, MS2, R17, and others). These phages are all extremely similar, but not identical. They are the same size, shape, and molecular weight; they cross react serologically, having similar coat proteins; all attack only male (Hfr or F+) E. coli.

The usual host for the influenza virus is the mammalian cell. This virus consists of a helical ribonucleoprotein core surrounded by a lipoprotein membrane. It was shown that the lipids in the envelope of the influenza virus are derived mainly from pre-existing lipids of the host cell, and that the composition of the lipids varies with the strain of the host cell. The outer membrane of the virus is apparently derived from the cell membrane and applied when the virus leaves the cell. After infection by the virus, normal cellular growth continues for several hours. There-fore, most of the RNA, protein, and DNA synthesized are normal cellular products and bear little relation to the growth of the virus. Using the drug, actinomycin-D, to inhibit normal cellular RNA synthesis, one can demonstrate a specific synthesis of viral RNA. Moreover, with the closely related Newcastle disease virus, which grows in the cytoplasm, one can show that the new (viral) RNA appears in the cytoplasm and not, as in normal cells, in the nucleus. It is probable, therefore, that the internal viral RNA and protein, as well as other viral antigens, such as the hemagglutinating factors, are made under the direction of the virus inside the cell.

Several genetically-different, haploid strains of influenza virus have been isolated; for example, SWE (with markers, $a\,c$) and MEL (with markers, $A\,C$). When a mixture of the two strains is used to multiply-infect a chick's egg membranes, the mixed infections give progeny particles which, when tested, yield pure clones not only of the parental genotypes but also of stable recombinant types ($A\,c$ or $a\,C$). Since other explanations can be excluded, the results prove that *genetic recombination occurs* also *between RNA-containing viruses*.[2] Genetic recombination has also been demonstrated for the *poliomyelitis virus*. Whereas the occurrence of genetic recombination in influenza may require incorporation of two or more pieces of viral RNA into a single particle, recombinant polio-virus RNA seems to occur in one piece.[3] Consequently, although the details of recombination between RNA viruses are unknown, more than one mechanism may be involved.

No evidence has been obtained for the occurrence of genetic recombination among viruses that attack plants. In the case of the *tobacco mosaic virus (TMV)*, infection is

---

[1] See T. Loeb and N. D. Zinder (1961), J. E. Davis and R. L. Sinsheimer (1963), and S. Mitra, M. D. Enger, and P. Kaesberg (1963).

[2] Based upon the work of F. M. Burnet and others.

[3] See G. K. Hirst (1962).

brought about experimentally by rubbing a sample of virus on the leaf surface. Even when a high concentration of virus is used, only a small fraction of the virus particles (one in 10^6) find and penetrate susceptible cells and give rise to a detectable lesion. For

FIGURE 28–1. *Electron micrographs of to-bacco mosaic virus (TMV) showing its general configuration (top) and its hollow core (middle). The bottom photo shows a particle whose protein has been partially removed by treatment with detergent, leaving a thinner strand of RNA. (Courtesy of R. G. Hart.)*

this reason, it is difficult to multiply-infect a tobacco cell, and experiments testing for genetic recombination are probably negative due to the lack of mixed infections.

The TMV particle is a cylinder 3000A long and about 80A in radius (Figure 28–1, top). It has a molecular weight of about 40 times 10^6, of which 38 times 10^6 is protein and 2 times 10^6 is RNA. The outer dimensions of TMV are attributed to the helical aggregation of about 2200 identical protein subunits, each of which has a molecular weight of about 18,000 and contains 158 amino acids in a single polypeptide chain (Figure 28–2). A cross section of the TMV particle shows a hollow core about 20A in radius (Figure 28–1, middle); the protein subunit, therefore, adds about 60A to the radius. The RNA in a particle (Figure 28–1, bottom) is typically a single, unbranched strand consisting of some 6400 nucleotides threaded through the protein subunits at a radius of 40A. Internally the RNA is normally covered by about 20A and externally by about 40A of protein subunit. Since the protein subunits are arranged in a gently-pitched helix (49 subunits per three turns), the RNA forms a helix of the same pitch.

When TMV in water is treated with phenol, the protein of the virus is extracted into the phenol, leaving the single RNA molecule intact in the water. If the tobacco plant is exposed to RNA molecules with protein thus removed, the frequency of infection is about 500 times less than the frequency obtained with an equal number of whole virus particles; typical TMV progeny (complete with TMV protein coats) are produced. Repeated phenol treatments do not further decrease the infectiveness of the RNA, and no amount of protein can be detected in the preparations. RNase, on the other hand, completely destroys the infectiveness of the RNA fraction but not the infectiveness of the whole virus. It must be concluded,

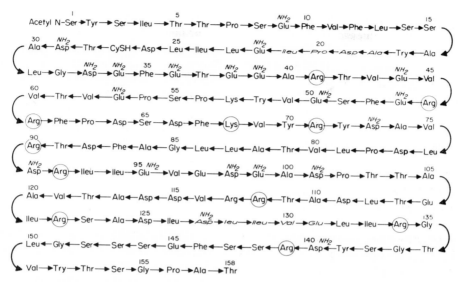

FIGURE 28–2. *Amino acid sequence in the protein building block of tobacco mosaic virus (TMV). There are 158 amino acids in the sub-unit, the encircled residues indicate the points of digestion by trypsin. (Courtesy of A. Tsugita, D. T. Gish, J. Young, H. Fraenkel-Conrat, C. A. Knight, and W. M. Stanley, Proc. Nat. Acad. Sci., U.S., 46:1465, 1960.)*

therefore, that *pure virus RNA is infective and carries all the genetic information necessary for its replication.*[4] These experiments also prove that TMV protein plays no part—other than protecting the RNA and increasing the infectivity—in the replication either of the RNA genetic material or of itself. This conclusion is tested by what is called *reconstitution experiments* in which, under appropriate conditions, we can first separate the protein and RNA of TMV and then have them recombine and demonstrate the high infectiveness of the original virus. Using two genetically-different strains of this virus —the standard (TMV) and Holmes rib grass (HR)—a highly-infective virus con-

taining the RNA of TMV and the protein coat of HR can be constructed. The progeny obtained are typically TMV with both TMV RNA *and* protein coat. The reciprocal construct, a virus with HR RNA and TMV protein, produces HR progeny typical in both RNA and protein. Thus, *only the RNA of a TMV particle specifies the RNA and protein of the progeny virus.*[5] Mutations can be induced in TMV by many of the agents known to be mutagenic for DNA. Such results and others prove that the biological activity of the RNA depends upon its primary (nucleotide content) and not its secondary (coiling pattern) structure.

The complete amino acid sequence in the protein building block of tobacco mosaic

[4] RNA isolated from a number of small animal viruses and from coliphages f2, MS2, etc., is also infective. (See Vol. 27, Cold Spring Harb. Sympos. Quant. Biol., 1962, and D. E. Engelhardt and N. D. Zinder, 1964.)

[5] The genetic experiments described for TMV are based largely upon work of H. Fraenkel-Conrat and R. C. Williams (1955), A. Gierer (1960), G. Schramm, and others.

virus is known (Figure 28–2); much less is known about the sequence of ribotides in TMV. One can visualize TMV as a polymer of 3′ mononucleotides ending in a nucleoside —shown to be adenosine.[6]

Snake venom phosphodiesterase (see p. 282) splits off 5′-nucleotides one at a time starting at the free 3′-OH end—called the 3′ or nucleoside end—of TMV, revealing that the terminal base sequence is —UACUA (or possibly —UAUCA). The sedimentary behavior of TMV RNA from which one to three nucleotides have been enzymatically removed does not change, implying that the enzyme primarily acts at the end of the RNA molecule as an *exonuclease*. The intrinsic integrity of the molecule is further demonstrated by the infectivity of such terminally-deleted TMV and the production of progeny TMV. When the progeny TMV are in turn treated with the same diesterase, they are found to release first A, then U, and then C. Thus, when RNA, from which several terminal nucleotides have presumably been removed, replicates, the original nucleotide sequence seems to be restored in the progeny.[7] It is possible that the sequence occurs in the progeny by chance; it is also possible that the free 5′-OH end—called the 5′ or nucleotide end—can normally base-pair for some distance with the 3′ end of TMV. If diesterase does remove the terminal —CUA, the shortened 3′ end could be repaired by making the complement of a UAG— sequence (which

we would presume starts the 5′ end). On the other hand, it seems more likely that the infectivity of these degraded RNAs, which is about 10% of normal, is due to residual undegraded RNAs, which, of course, infect perfectly normally. The degradation with snake venom diesterase is very likely not synchronous, so that some molecules can have several nucleotides removed before others lose any.

Results obtained with TMV and other RNA-viruses show that complementary RNA strand formation occurs during replication of RNA genetic material. *RNA-dependent RNA polymerase, RNA synthetase,* or *RNA replicase,* an enzyme which utilizes riboside triphosphates and takes directions from RNA to make complementary RNA, has been isolated and purified.[8] One RNA synthetase uses the single-stranded RNA of the ϕMS2—called the "plus" strand —as a template to synthesize the complementary "minus" RNA strand *in vivo.* The double-stranded product—called the replicative form—is used *in vitro* as a natural template by the same or another RNA synthetase to synthesize "plus" strands.[9] In this connection it should be noted that the infective forms of a *wound virus* obtained from sweet clover and a *reovirus* associated with the respiratory and enteric tracts of animals, including man, have *double-stranded RNA as their genetic material.*[10]

---

[6] From work of T. Sugiyama and H. Fraenkel-Conrat (1961).
[7] See B. Singer and H. Fraenkel-Conrat (1963).

[8] By I. Haruna, K. Nozu, Y. Ohtaka, and S. Spiegelman (1963), and by C. Weissmann, L. Simon, and S. Ochoa (1963). See D. Baltimore (1964).
[9] See C. Weissmann *et al.* (1964).
[10] See P. J. Gomatos and I. Tamm (1963).

SUMMARY AND CONCLUSIONS

RNA is the sole carrier of genetic properties in certain viruses. Some animal RNA viruses can undergo genetic recombination. Mature RNA viruses carry either single-stranded or double-stranded RNA. Viral RNA replication involves RNA synthetase and the formation of complementary RNA chains.

REFERENCES

Baltimore, D., "*In vitro* Synthesis of Viral RNA by the Poliovirus RNA Polymerase," Proc. Nat. Acad. Sci., U.S., 51:450–456, 1964.

Burnet, F. M., and Stanley, W. M. (Eds.), *The Viruses;* Vol. 1, *General Virology,* 609 pp.; Vol. 2, *Plant and Animal Viruses,* 408 pp.; Vol. 3, *Animal Viruses,* 428 pp., New York: Academic Press, 1959.

Davis, J. E., and Sinsheimer, R. L., "The Replication of MS2. 1. Transfer of Parental Nucleic Acid to Progeny Phage," J. Mol. Biol., 6:203–207, 1963.

Engelhardt, D. E., and Zinder, N. D., "Host-Dependent Mutants of the Bacteriophage f2. III. Infective RNA. Virology, 23:582–587, 1964.

Finch, J. T., "Resolution of the Substructure of Tobacco Mosaic Virus in the Electron Microscope," J. Mol. Biol., 8:872–874, 1964.

Fraenkel-Conrat, H., and Ramachandran, L. K., "Structural Aspects of Tobacco Mosaic Virus," Advances in Protein Chemistry, 14:175–229, 1959.

Fraenkel-Conrat, H., and Williams, R. C., "Reconstitution of Tobacco Mosaic Virus from Its Inactive Protein and Nucleic Acid Components," Proc. Nat. Acad. Sci., U.S., 41:690–698, 1955. Reprinted in *Classic Papers in Genetics,* Peters, J. A. (Ed.), Englewood Cliffs, N.J.: Prentice-Hall, 1959, pp. 264–271.

Gierer, A., "Ribonucleic Acid as Genetic Material of Viruses," in *Microbial Genetics,* Hayes, W., and Clowes, R. C. (Eds.), Cambridge: Cambridge University Press, 1960, pp. 248–271.

Gomatos, P. J., and Tamm, I., "Animal and Plant Viruses with Double-Helical RNA," Proc. Nat. Acad. Sci., U.S., 50:878–885, 1963.

Hirst, G. K., "Genetic Recombination with Newcastle Disease Virus, Polioviruses, and Influenza," Cold Spring Harb. Sympos. Quant. Biol., 27:303–309, 1962.

Horne, R. W., "The Structure of Viruses," Sci. Amer., 208 (No. 1):48–56, 170–171, 1963.

Hudson, W. R., Kim, Y. T., Smith, R. A., and Wildman, S. G., "Synthesis of Tobacco Mosaic Virus Infectivity by Cell Free Extracts," Biochim. Biophys. Acta, 76:257–265, 1963.

Loeb, T., and Zinder, N. D., "A Bacteriophage Containing RNA," Proc. Nat. Acad. Sci., U.S., 47:282–289, 1961.

Mitra, S., Enger, M. D., and Kaesberg, P., "Physical and Chemical Properties of an RNA from the Bacterial Virus R17," Proc. Nat. Acad. Sci., U.S., 50:68–75, 1963.

Reddi, K. K., "Studies on the Formation of Tobacco Mosaic Virus Ribonucleic Acid, V. Presence of Tobacco Mosaic Virus in the Nucleus of the Host Cell," Proc. Nat. Acad. Sci., U.S., 52:397–401, 1964.

Richter, A., "Structure of Viral Nucleoproteins," Ann. Rev. Microbiol., 17:415–428, 1963.

Shipp, W., and Haselkorn, R., "Double-Stranded RNA from Tobacco Leaves Infected with TMV," Proc. Nat. Acad. Sci., U.S., 52:401–408, 1964.

Singer, B., and Fraenkel-Conrat, H., "Studies of Nucleotide Sequences in TMV-RNA. I. Stepwise Use of Phosphodiesterase," Biochim. Biophys. Acta, 72:534–543, 1963.

Spirin, A. S., "Some Problems Concerning the Macromolecular Structure of Ribonucleic Acids," Progr. Nucleic Acid Res., 1:301–345, 1963.

Tsugita, A., Gish, D. T., Young, J., Fraenkel-Conrat, H., Knight, C. A., and Stanley, W. M., "The Complete Amino Acid Sequence of the Protein of Tobacco Mosaic Virus," Proc. Nat. Acad. Sci., U.S., 46:1463–1469, 1960.

Weissmann, C., Borst, P., Burdon, R. H., Billeter, M. A., and Ochoa, S., "Replication of Viral RNA, IV. Properties of RNA Synthetase and Enzymatic Synthesis of MS2 Phage RNA," Proc. Nat. Acad. Sci., U.S., 51:890–897, 1964.

QUESTIONS FOR DISCUSSION

28.1. What conclusions can you draw from the observation that within a day or so after infection with a single particle of TMV, the cell can produce about 50,000 viral nucleic acid molecules and about 100×10^6 protein subunits?

28.2. Using pure TMV RNA for infection, how could you test whether this RNA contains information for manufacturing TMV protein?

28.3. Compare transformation with infection by pure virus nucleic acid.

28.4. Discuss the view that cancerous growths may originate as a result of virus infection activating RNA replication.

28.5. What conclusions can you draw from the observation (see reference to J. E. Davis and R. L. Sinsheimer) that the RNA of the parental MS2 phage is routinely excluded from the progeny phage?

28.6. What are the similarities and differences in the behavior of DNA polymerase and RNA synthetase?

28.7. Discuss the possible advantages and disadvantages of double-stranded rather than single-stranded RNA as the genetic material of a mature virus.

Chapter 29

EXTRANUCLEAR GENES

THE DNA RABBIT POXVIRUS and certain RNA viruses, which are restricted to the cytoplasm of cells normally possessing a definite nuclear membrane (and hence a definite nucleus), are clearly autonomous extranuclear genes. To what extent do extranuclear genes occur and what is their relationship with particular chromosomal genes?

Various operational tests—chemical, recombinational, mutational, phenotypical, and replicative—can be applied to identify an extranuclear component as genetic material. Recombination is the first operational method used in our search for extranuclear genes. To detect recombination, the extranuclear gene must produce a recognizable phenotypic effect. To provide the required phenotypic alternatives, changes involving either the kind or the quantity (or both) of such a gene must occur.

Drosophila

How do we actually proceed to look for an extranuclear gene in Drosophila? Starting with different nonoverlapping phenotypic alternatives which occur generation after generation under the same environmental conditions, a series of crosses is made to test whether the occurrence of the alternatives is associated with the presence of one or more particular chromosomes (X, Y, II, III, IV). If it is, the phenotypic alternatives are probably due to some genetic factor linked to, and hence located in, a chromosome. (Additional appropriate crosses and cytological

studies will reveal the precise nature of the nuclear gene change. Since the vast majority of carefully analyzed gene-based traits are located in chromosomes, the search for an extranuclear gene will usually be unsuccessful.)

But consider the genetic alternatives for *resistance and susceptibility to* CO_2 (gas). Although wild-type Drosophila adults can be exposed to pure CO_2 for as long as 15 minutes and recover without apparent effect, flies of other strains almost invariably are killed by such exposure. Using marked chromosomes, CO_2-sensitivity is found to be unlinked to any chromosome of the normal genome. In fact, by appropriate crosses it is possible to replace each of the chromosomes in the sensitive strain by a corresponding chromosome of the resistant strain. After this is done, the flies produced are still sensitive to CO_2! Possibly, the sensitive strain carries an additional nonhomologous nuclear chromosome which it transmits independent of the usual ones. In the progeny of hybrids derived from sensitive and resistant lines the CO_2-sensitivity trait does not segregate, which indicates that if such a supernumerary chromosome exists, it cannot occur singly (in the individual hybrid for sensitivity) or as a pair (in flies of the pure sensitive strain). Although cytological examination reveals no additional nuclear chromosome, this finding is not a conclusive argument against a nuclear locus for CO_2-sensitivity, for, according to recombinational evidence, "chromosomes" so small they escape cytological detection are known to exist. (A phenotypic change in corn is associated with the presence of readily detectable, supernumerary, heterochromatic, "B" chromosomes.)

Although the sensitive female regularly transmits CO_2-sensitivity to some progeny, the sensitive male does so only under special circumstances. It might be possible that a nuclear gene for sensitivity is somehow excluded from a nucleus destined to be in a sperm but not from one destined to be in an egg, although it seems much more reasonable to attribute the nontransmission of CO_2-sensitivity through the sperm to the rather minute amount of cytoplasm in a sperm as compared with the amount in an egg. It is therefore highly probable that CO_2-sensitivity in Drosophila is due to the presence of a particle called *sigma*. Other studies show that sigma contains DNA,[1] is mutable, and has many of the characteristics of a virus including infectivity by experimental means.[2] Since sigma is not visible, its location within the cell remains somewhat of a mystery. Certain sigma and episome characteristics are similar. (Melanotic tumor incidence in Drosophila may also depend upon the presence of an episome-like particle.[3])

Consider another trait of Drosophila (p. 110)—females mated to normal males giving rise almost entirely to females. This trait has a genetic basis; is not transmitted by males; is infective; is not linked to the usual chromosomes; and proves to be intimately associated with the presence of a spirochaete in the blood.

Maize

None of the examples just mentioned demonstrates conclusively the existence of both intracellular and extranuclear genes. They do serve to illustrate, however, possible results of a search for such genes which starts with a study of genetic recombination. The desirability of making a direct correlation between potentially extranuclear genes and objects observable in the cytoplasm is clear.

Continuing the search for extranuclear genes, let us restrict our attention to cytoplasmic components which seem to be nor-

mal constituents of present-day cells, disregarding their normality when they or their precursors first arose.

Many plant cells contain cytoplasmic bodies called *plastids*. Green plastids (due to chlorophyll) are called *chloroplasts;* white plastids are called *leucoplasts*. Immature plastids are small and colorless. In the absence of sunlight, chloroplasts lose their pigment and become leucoplasts; the process is reversed when the plastids are again exposed to sunlight.

In corn, mutants of chromosomal genes can interfere with the sequence of reactions leading to the manufacture of chlorophyll. One such nuclear gene prevents plastids from producing any chlorophyll at all, so that a type of leucoplast incapable of becoming green occurs. A seedling that possesses the appropriate mutant nuclear genotype will not be green; will grow only until it exhausts the food supply in the seed; will die because photosynthesis of sugar cannot occur in the absence of chlorophyll. Nuclear genes that produce albino seedlings act, therefore, as lethals.

Certain corn plants have mosaic leaves, with stripes of green and white (Figure 29–1).[4] Although the leucoplasts of the white parts are incapable of becoming green, the white parts survive by receiving nourishment from the green parts. Is this mosaicism based upon nuclear genes causing different portions of the leaf to follow different paths of development? Were striping due to a nuclear gene acting upon differentiation, such a gene would have to be transmitted through the male or female gamete independent of the whiteness or greenness of the tissue giving rise to the reproductive structures.

Sometimes an ear of corn is derived from an ovary that is expected to be mosaic be-

---

[1] See N. Plus (1963).
[2] Much work on sigma has been done by P. L'Héritier, G. Teissier, and co-workers.
[3] See C. Barigozzi (1963).

[4] The following account is based primarily upon work of M. M. Rhoades.

FIGURE 29–1. Marcus M. Rhoades (*in 1959*) *examines striped corn plants in the foreground. Unstriped corn plants are in the background.*

cause it originated partly from green and partly from white tissue. When the kernels in such an ear are planted in rows corresponding to their positions in the cob, the result is not all green, all white, all striped, nor a random mixture of these types, but groups of green and albino seedlings (Figure 29–2). This outcome suggests that striping actually occurs in the ovary and persists in the cob. Other tests of this strain show that the greenness or whiteness of a seedling is independent of the color of the parental part forming the pollen used to produce the seed. Moreover, appropriate crosses show that none of the genes in the paternal or maternal chromosomes is involved. The striping effect, therefore, is not due to a nuclear gene acting differently in different tissues. Since the pollen grain is not known to carry plastids, and since the only deciding factor proves to be the color of the tissue giving rise to the ovary, it can be concluded that only the nature of the plastids within different ova is important in determining seedling color in this case. All these facts suggest that plastids are derived only from pre-existing plastids and that daughter plastids have the same color capacities as the parent plastid.

This hypothesis is subjected to further test by examining the cytoplasm of cells located at the border between white and green tissue.

These cells are found to contain mature plastids of both fully green and completely white types, whereas cells within a green sector contain only green mature plastids, and cells in a white sector contain only leucoplasts. Thus, even when the two kinds of mature plastids are present in the same cell, they have no influence upon each other but develop according to their innate capacities. If a zygote (or other cell) containing both kinds of plastids produces daughter cells which happen to receive only "white" or only "green" plastids, these daughter cells will give rise to sectors of white and of green tissue. From the results presented (in addition to other evidence not mentioned) it can

FIGURE 29–2. *Groups of albino and non-albino seedlings from kernels planted in rows corresponding to their positions in a cob produced on a green-white striped plant.*

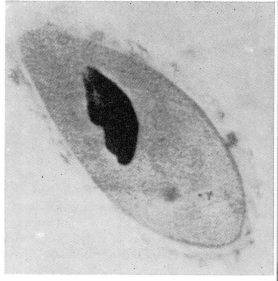
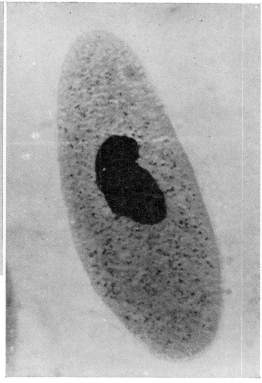

FIGURE 29–3. *Normal (above) and kappa-containing (right) Paramecium. (Courtesy of T. M. Sonneborn.)*

be concluded that plastids do not arise except from plastids. Consequently, *since they are self-replicating, mutable, and capable of replicating their mutant condition, plastids apparently contain at least one cytoplasmic gene.* Although DNA is present in chloroplasts,[5] this substance has not yet been proved to be the basis for the genetic alternatives under discussion. As already mentioned, the chlorophyll trait is also influenced by nuclear genes. Thus, this trait is controlled by both the plastid and the nuclear genotypes.

In another study, a cross of two all-green corn plants gives some progeny which are green-and-white striped. The striped plants

prove to be homozygous for a recessive nuclear gene, *iojap (ij)*, for which their parents were heterozygous. Since colorless plastids in ova of striped plants remain colorless in subsequent generations, even in homozygotes for the normal allele, the colorless plastid is not due to interference by *ij ij* in the biosynthetic pathway leading to the production of chlorophyll pigment. The only simple explanation for this effect is that, in the presence of *ij ij,* an extranuclear gene located in the plastid and essential for chlorophyll production is somehow induced to mutate to a form no longer able to perform this function. The results convincingly demonstrate that *mutation of an extranuclear gene can be induced by a nuclear gene.* A similar case, in which a nuclear gene controls chlorophyll production by mutating plastid genes, is known in the catnip, Nepeta.

[5] See R. Sager and M. R. Ishida (1963), and M. Edelman, C. A. Cowan, H. T. Epstein, and J. A. Schiff (1964).

374 CHAPTER 29

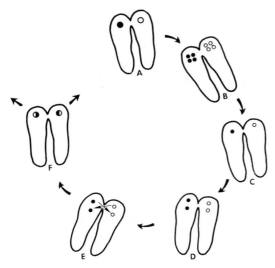

FIGURE 29–4. *Simplified representation of micronuclear events occurring during conjugation in Paramecium. Each conjugant has a single diploid micronucleus (A), which following meiosis produces four haploid nuclei (B). Three of these disintegrate (C), and the remaining nucleus divides once mitotically (D). The conjugants exchange one of the haploid mitotic products (E), after which fusion of haploid nuclei occurs (F) so that each of the conjugants, which later separate, contains a single diploid micronucleus.*

Paramecium [6]

Kappa particles (and the similar lambda or mate-killer particles) are located in the cytoplasm of certain strains of the protozoan Paramecium. Hundreds of kappa particles can easily be seen in a single cell (Figure 29–3). They contain DNA (and very probably RNA) and are self-reproducing. Individuals containing kappa are called *killers,* since animal-free fluid obtained from cultures of killer paramecia will kill sensitive (kappa-free) individuals.

[6] The following discussion of Paramecium is based mainly upon the work of T. M. Sonneborn and co-workers.

Mutant kappa particles are known to produce modified poisons. Kappa is liberated into the medium once it develops a highly refractile granule which sometimes appears as a "bright spot" under the microscope. One "bright spot" kappa particle is enough to kill a sensitive individual. Kappa has a specific relationship to its host, in that a particular dominant host gene (K) must be present for kappa to maintain itself, that is, reproduce. Killer individuals homozygous for the recessive host allele (k) cannot maintain kappa, and after 8 to 15 divisions, kappa particles are lost and sensitive individuals result. Because it is infective and not typically found in paramecia, kappa seems to be a foreign organism of some kind. Since lambda can be grown *in vitro,* lambda and kappa are considered to be bacterial endosymbiotes of Paramecium.[7]

Although the cytoplasmic bacterial endosymbiote kappa can be transmitted from one generation of Paramecium to the next, its distribution to the next generation depends upon the mechanism by which the new generation is initiated. Two such mechanisms —asexual and sexual—are described briefly with special reference to kappa-transmission.

A typical Paramecium contains a diploid *micronucleus* and a highly polyploid (about 1000N) *macronucleus* (or *meganucleus*). When the parent divides asexually by *fission,* two daughter paramecia are produced. Both micronucleus and macronucleus replicate and separate; when fission is completed, both daughter cells are chromosomally identical to each other and to their parent cell. Although the cytoplasmic contents are not equally apportioned to the daughters, a killer parent will normally produce two killer daughters since each receives some of the hundreds of kappa particles present in the parental cytoplasm. Successive fissions by the killer daughters will produce a clone of chromo-

[7] See W. J. van Wagtendonk, J. O. D. Clark, and G. A. Godoy (1963).

somally identical killer individuals. Similarly, successive fissions of a sensitive Paramecium will produce a clone of sensitive individuals.

A new generation can also be formed sexually. All members of a clone are of the same mating type. When different mating-type clones are mixed, a *mating reaction* occurs which involves individuals of different mating types sticking together to form larger and larger clumps of paramecia. After this clumping, pairs—each member a different mating type—undergo *conjugation*. During conjugation (Figure 29–4) the micronucleus of each mate undergoes meiosis to produce four haploid products, three of which subsequently disintegrate. The remaining nucleus divides mitotically to produce two haploid nuclei. Next, one of the two haploid nuclei in each conjugant migrates into the other conjugant where it joins the nonmotile haploid nucleus to form a single diploid nucleus in each conjugant. The macronucleus disintegrates during conjugation.

After conjugation the two paramecia separate and produce the exconjugants of the next generation. Since each conjugant contributes an identical haploid nucleus to each fertilization micronucleus, both exconjugants are chromosomally identical—as can be proved by employing various marker genes. (When the conjugants are homozygous for different alleles, the exconjugants are identical heterozygotes.) The diploid micronucleus in each exconjugant divides once mitotically; one product forms a new macronucleus, while the other remains as the micronucleus.

Since all conjugants happen to be resistant to killer action, we can study the consequence upon kappa-transmission of mating a killer with a sensitive individual. The cytoplasmic interiors of conjugants are normally kept apart by a boundary probably penetrated only by the migrant haploid nuclei so that little or no cytoplasm is exchanged. Consequently, the exconjugants have the same

kappa-condition as the conjugants; namely, one is a killer and one is a sensitive individual. Under special conditions, however, a wide bridge forms between the conjugants allowing the cytoplasmic contents of both mates to flow and mix (Figure 29–5). The extent of the cytoplasmic mixing can be controlled experimentally. When cytoplasmic mixing between killer and sensitive conjugants is sufficiently extensive, kappa particles flow into the sensitive conjugant and both exconjugants are killers.

Consider how specific nuclear genes are distributed in conjugation. If each conjugant is a micronuclear heterozygote, *Aa*, which one of the four haploid nuclei produced by meiosis—*A, A, a,* or *a*—will survive depends on chance. Accordingly, whether the cytoplasms of the conjugants mix or not, *both* exconjugants will be *AA* 25% of the time, *Aa* 50% of the time, and *aa* 25% of the time. Note again that both exconjugants are identical with respect to micronuclear genes, and that both will give rise to clones phenotypically identical with respect to the micronuclear gene-determined trait under consideration. When dealing with a trait determined by a cytoplasmic particle like kappa, however, the result can be different. In this particular example, the cross of a

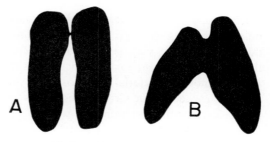

FIGURE 29–5. *Silhouettes of conjugating Paramecium. A. Normal, no cytoplasmic mixing. B. Wide bridge, permitting cytoplasmic mixing.*

sensitive individual with a killer produces exconjugants whose type depends upon the occurrence or nonoccurrence of cytoplasmic mixing.

Kappa has special significance because it shows how a symbiotic microorganism can become so well adapted to its host, that it becomes part of the host's genetic system and determines some of the host's traits. Like kappa, the rickettsial organism causing Rocky Mountain spotted fever is visible and transmitted through the cytoplasm of carrier cells. These rickettsiae, as well as sigma and the spirochaete already discussed, also determine certain traits of their hosts. Even though each of these organisms seems to be foreign to its host, we cannot be sure whether it was originally a parasite or symbiont. Could some of the now-foreign organisms located intracellularly have been originally part of the normal gene content of a cell?

This question is particularly pertinent when viruses are considered. From what has been discussed in previous chapters, it is clear that all viruses cannot be classified as either being or arising from foreign infective agents. Present-day virulent phages seem to be acting as foreign organisms when they lyse their bacterial hosts. But, the lytic capacity of a phage depends upon both its genotype and its host's, and, under some genotypic conditions, lysis is quite rare. Determining the normality or abnormality of present-day viruses is even more difficult when temperate phages are considered; not only are they less lytic (yet capable of transduction), but the very genes characterizing their prophages seem to be associated with part of a normal bacterial chromosome. As more is learned about viruses, and phage in particular, our understanding of what is genetically "normal," and what is "foreign," will undoubtedly undergo drastic revision.[8] As knowledge of the genetics of viruses and

their "hosts" increases, we will be in a better position to postulate how they originated.

Chlamydomonas

Chlamydomonas reinhardi is a unicellular plant with two flagella and a single chloroplast. By means of mitotic cell division, it can reproduce asexually to produce clones. No sexual reproduction is observed between members of a clone, but if members of two different clones are mixed together, individuals from different clones may pair, fuse, and produce zygotes. After two divisions, the zygote produces four cells, each of which can be isolated to give rise to separate clones. When a sample from each of the four clones is mixed with different portions of a fifth clone, two of the four show mating (and are called sexual type $+$) and two do not (being, therefore, of $-$ sex). Moreover, when portions of the four sibling cultures under test are combined in pairs, we find that individuals of any $+$ culture can mate with individuals in any $-$ culture. Combinations of two $+$ or two $-$ cultures, however, show no mating. No morphological difference between $+$ and $-$ individuals has been detected.

Among the first four cells produced from a zygote, two are $+$ and two are $-$. This outcome suggests that the zygote is diploid; that it carries a pair of genes for sex (which we can call mt^+ mt^-); and that meiosis occurs in the next two divisions. As a consequence of this meiosis, a $1:1$ ratio of mt^+: mt^- is found among the haploid products. Mating type, therefore, behaves like a trait based upon two different alleles of a single nuclear gene.

The wild-type Chlamydomonas is sensitive to streptomycin. After exposure to streptomycin, a number of preadaptive mutants are found which make the individual resistant to 100 μg streptomycin per vial, although they are still sensitive to 300 μg per vial. Since crosses with a streptomycin-

---

[8] See A. Campbell (1961).

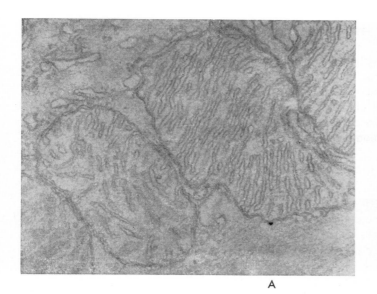

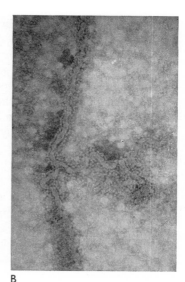

A   B

FIGURE 29–6. *Electron micrographs of (A) mouse heart mitochondria (×60,000), (B) Neurospora mitochondria prepared to show cristae with elementary particles attached (×67,200), and (C) the outline of Neurospora mitochondrial DNA (×29,300). (Courtesy of Dr. Walther Stoeckenius, The Rockefeller Institute, New York.)*

C

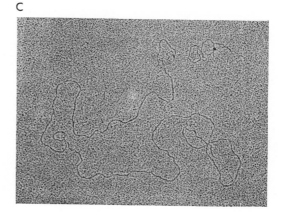

sensitive strain segregate two sensitive to two resistant—just as the alleles for mating type segregate—a chromosomal basis for the mutation is indicated. These chromosomal mutants are of the *sr-100* class. Streptomycin also acts not as a selective agent but as a mutagen to produce individuals—called *sr-500* mutants—resistant to 500 µg streptomycin per vial. Sr-500 mutants do not show meiotic segregation in the haploid F_1 or the backcross progeny. Moreover, in crosses with *ss* (streptomycin-sensitive) individuals, the sr-500 factor is usually received by all progeny when the sr-500 parent is of mating type + (mt^+), and by none of the progeny when the sr-500 parent is − (mt^-). These and other characteristics demonstrate that sr-500 is caused by a "nonchromosomal" gene; that is, a gene which does not comply with the usual transmission rules for chromosomal genes in sexually reproducing individuals. Streptomycin also induces a large number of auxotrophic mutants whose basis also proves to be in nonchromosomal genes.

Exceptional zygotes occur which contain the nonchromosomal genes from both parents. Using such zygotes, the results of single factor crosses and of reciprocal two-factor crosses show that the nonchromosomal genes recombine in postmeiotic divisions.

These studies [9] suggest the existence of an extensive extrachromosomal gene system in Chlamydomonas. Some of these genes may be located in the DNA of the chloroplast; this DNA is reported to have a base ratio distinctly different from Chlamydomonas nuclear DNA.

Mitochondria

Mitochondria (Fig. 29–6) are organelles consisting of a smooth continuous outer membrane and an inner membrane which folds inward to form double layers or *cristae*.[10] The outer membrane probably controls permeability; the inner membrane, its cristae, and elementary particles contain most of the insoluble respiratory enzymes whose function provides the main source of energy for the cell. Mitochondria which appear to be dividing transversely have been observed; it is very likely that most, if not all, mitochondria arise from the division of pre-existing mitochondria.[11] DNA is a normal component of mitochondria.[12] This DNA (Figure 29–6) has a unique buoyant density and is probably double-stranded.[13]

Certain strains of yeast produce *tiny* colonies on agar. When such organisms are crossed with normal-sized individuals, we obtain a two normal to two tiny ratio in the meiotic products after segregation. Such tiny strains due to mutant nuclear genes are called *segregational petites*. When normal yeast cells are treated with an acridine dye (euflavin), numerous petite colonies arise.[14] When these strains, called *vegetative petites*, are crossed with normal yeast, the petite phenotype does not segregate regularly. The ease with which vegetative petites are produced by acridine dyes and their subsequent failure to segregate properly provide good evidence that they are caused by extrachromosomal mutants. The characteristic slow growth of petites is attributable to the absence of respiratory enzymes known to reside in the mitochondria. Although no change in mitochondrial morphology has been detected in petites, it is clear that the presence of certain mitochondrial enzymes is controlled by chromosomal as well as by extrachromosomal genes. It has not yet been proved, however, that these extrachromosomal genes are located in the mitochondrial DNA.

In Neurospora a slow-growing strain, *poky,* when crossed with a wild strain, fails to show segregation and is unlinked to any chromosome.[15] The poky phenotype is apparently due to a mutant of an extrachromosomal gene. In poky individuals certain enzymes normally present in the mitochondria are altered and so is mitochondrial morphology. Fusion of hyphae from wild type and poky strains produces a *heterocytosome*—a mixture of the two kinds of cytoplasm. Such fused hyphae are wild-type at first but later become poky, with the nuclear genotype having no effect upon the outcome. Is this outcome due to selection favoring an apparently detrimental extrachromosomal gene? We do not know. As in the case of petites, the location of the extrachromosomal genes involved in poky is unknown.

Centrosomes, Kinetosomes, and Kinetoplasts

The *centrosome* is an organelle often found at each pole of a spindle, particularly in animal cells. A granular structure—the *centriole*—is sometimes seen within it; similar granules can sometimes be seen within the centromere (Figure 29–7). The granules

[9] See R. Sager (1965).
[10] See D. F. Parsons (1963), and D. E. Green (1964).
[11] See D. J. L. Luck (1963).
[12] See M. Chèvremont (1963), and G. Schatz, E. Haslbrunner, and H. Tuppy (1964).
[13] See D. J. L. Luck and E. Reich (1964).
[14] See B. Ephrussi (1953).

[15] See M. B. Mitchell and H. K. Mitchell (1952).

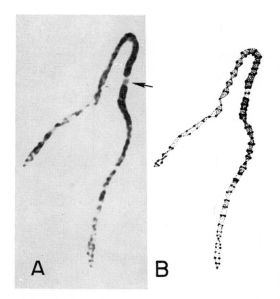

FIGURE 29–7. *The centromere and its granules in corn.* (*Courtesy of A. Lima de Faria, "Compound Structure of the Kinetochore in Maize," J. Hered., 49:299, 1958.*)

in the centromere and centrosome stain the same (both seem to contain DNA); so does the material surrounding these granules. In the living cell centromere and centrosome have a similar appearance. The granules within the centromere are apparently thickenings of the DNA thread which passes from one chromosome arm to the other.

Centromeres are sometimes attracted to each other and to the centrosomes, and at anaphase the centromeres migrate toward the centrosomes. The centrosome, too, has the capacity to move, as demonstrated by its preanaphase movement and its behavior after a sperm has penetrated an egg. Thus we see that the morphological similarity of centromere and centrosome is paralleled by their behavioral similarities.

From these facts some sort of kinship is suggested [16] between centrosome and centro-

mere. This view is strikingly supported by the finding [17] that during the meiotic divisions leading to the formation of certain mollusc sperms, certain chromosomes degenerate and release "naked" centromeres. These now-free centromeres group together with the centrosome and thereafter duplicate centrosomal behavior and appearance exactly. In effect, then, the freed centromeres become extra centrosomes. The preceding circumstances suggest that the centromere and centrosome may be two states of a presently—or previously—existing episome. The change from one episomal state to another is probably influenced by the presence of a nuclear membrane and by various other genetic factors present in highly organized cells, as well as by the occurrence of mutations in the autonomous or integrated state of the episome.

At the base of each cilium or flagellum is a granular body, the *kinetosome,* which is responsible for the motion of the organelle. Considerable evidence has been brought forth that kinetosomes contain DNA and are homologous to centrioles (or centrosomes). Perhaps kinetosomes, too, are episomes or episomal derivatives. It has been suggested that the episome F functions like a centromere. Could it be that the movements attributed to F and the centromere and centrosome have the same basis as the flagellar and ciliary movement produced by kinetosomes?

In Trypanosoma, DNA and a histone-like protein are found in the *kinetoplast,* a large cytoplasmic organelle associated with motility as well as mitochondria. DNA replication occurs synchronously in nucleus and kinetoplast. Kinetoplasts can be damaged irreversibly if treated with acridine dyes. Since the kinetoplast apparently has an appreciable DNA content, additional molecular information about it should prove quite valuable.

[16] Originally by C. D. Darlington, F. Schrader, and others.

[17] See A. W. Pollister and P. F. Pollister (1943).

Tracy M. Sonneborn, *about 1960.*

SUMMARY AND CONCLUSIONS

Nucleated cells may contain an extensive system of extranuclear genes. In some cases the extranuclear genes seem to be foreign organisms (viruses, kappa, and probably sigma); in other cases they appear to be associated with normal constituents of the cell (plastids, mitochondria, centrosomes, kinetosomes, and kinetoplasts). The characteristics of centrosomes, kinetosomes, and centromeres suggest a past or present episomal interrelationship. The DNA in plastids and mitochondria has yet to be directly connected with the activity of specific genes.

Nuclear and extranuclear genes are already known to be interrelated in two ways: the former can mutate the latter, and both may interact in the production of a particular phenotype.

REFERENCES

Barigozzi, C., "Relationship Between Cytoplasm and Chromosome in the Transmission of Melanotic Tumours in Drosophila," in *Biological Organization,* pp. 73–89, New York: Academic Press, 1963.

Beale, G. H., *The Genetics of Paramecium Aurelia,* Cambridge: Cambridge University Press, 1954.

Campbell, A., "Conditions for the Existence of Bacteriophage," Evolution, 15:153–165, 1961.

Chèvremont, M., "Cytoplasmic Deoxyribonucleic Acids: Their Mitochondrial Localization and Synthesis in Somatic Cells Under Experimental Conditions and During the Normal Cell Cycle in Relation to the Preparation for Mitosis," Sympos. Int. Soc. for Cell Biol., 2:323–331, 1963.

Edelman, M., Cowan, C. A., Epstein, H. T., and Schiff, J. A., "Studies of Chloroplast Development in *Euglena,* VIII. Chloroplast-Associated DNA," Proc. Nat. Acad. Sci., U.S., 52:1214–1219, 1964.

Ephrussi, B., *Nucleo-Cytoplasmic Relations in Micro-Organisms,* Oxford: Clarendon Press, 1953.

Green, D. E., "The Mitochondrion," Scient. Amer., 210 (Jan.):63–74, 152, 1964.

L'Héritier, P., "The Hereditary Virus of Drosophila," Adv. Virus Res., 5:195–245, 1958.

Jinks, J. L., *Extrachromosomal Inheritance,* Englewood Cliffs, N.J.: Prentice-Hall, Inc., 1964.

Luck, D. J. L., "Genesis of Mitochondria in *Neurospora crassa,"* Proc. Nat. Acad. Sci., U.S., 49:233–240, 1963.

Luck, D. J. L., and Reich, E., "DNA in Mitochondria of *Neurospora crassa,"* Proc. Nat. Acad. Sci., U.S., 52:931–938, 1964.

Mitchell, M. B., and Mitchell, H. K., "A Case of 'Maternal' Inheritance in *Neurospora crassa,"* Proc. Nat. Acad. Sci., U.S., 38:442–449, 1952.

Parsons, D. F., "Mitochondrial Structure: Two Types of Subunits on Negatively Stained Mitochondrial Membranes," Science, 140:985–987, 1963.

Plus, N., "Action de la 5-Fluoro-Desoxyuridine sur la Multiplication du Virus σ de la Drosophile," Biochim. Biophys. Acta, 72:92–105, 1963.

Pollister, A. W., and Pollister, P. F., "The Relation Between Centriole and Centromere in Atypical Spermatogenesis of Viviparid Snails," Ann. N.Y. Acad. Sci., 45:1–48, 1943.

Rhoades, M. M., "Plastid Mutations," Cold Spring Harb. Sympos. Quant. Biol., 11:202–207, 1946.

Rhoades, M. M., "Interaction of Genic and Non-Genic Hereditary Units and the Physiology of Non-Genic Inheritance," in *Encyclopedia of Plant Physiology,* Ruhland, W. (Ed.), Vol. 1, pp. 19–57, Berlin: Springer Verlag, 1955.

Sager, R., "Genes Outside the Chromosome," Scient. Amer., 212 (No. 1):70–79, 134, 1965.

Sager, R., and Ishida, M. R., "Chloroplast DNA in *Chlamydomonas,"* Proc. Nat. Acad. Sci., U.S., 50:725–730, 1963.

Schatz, G., Haslbrunner, E., and Tuppy, H., "Deoxyribonucleic Acid Associated with Yeast Mitochondria," Biophys. Biochem. Res. Commun., 15:127–132, 1964.

Seecof, R. L., "CO_2 Sensitivity in Drosophila as a Latent Virus Infection," Cold Spring Harb. Sympos. Quant. Biol., 26:501–512, 1962.

Sonneborn, T. M., "The Role of the Genes in Cytoplasmic Inheritance," Chap. 14, pp. 291–314, in *Genetics in the 20th Century,* Dunn, L. C. (Ed.), 1951.

Sonneborn, T. M., "Kappa and Related Particles in Paramecium," Adv. Virus Res., 6:229–356, 1959.

Sonneborn, T. M., "The Gene and Cell Differentiation," Proc. Nat. Acad. Sci., U.S., 46:149–165, 1960.

van Wagtendonk, W. J., Clark, J. A. D., and Godoy, G. A., "The Biological Status of Lambda and Related Particles in *Paramecium aurelia,"* Proc. Nat. Acad. Sci., U.S., 50:835–838, 1963.

QUESTIONS FOR DISCUSSION

29.1. What is revealed about nucleocytoplasmic interrelationships from the study of F? Of temperate phages?

29.2. What evidence can you present that CO_2-sensitivity is due to a virus rather than a normal chromosomal gene?

29.3. In proving the existence of extranuclear genes, which operations (recombinational, mutational, functional, chemical) were utilized? Did our decision include their capacity for self-replication? Why?

29.4. Discuss the genetic control of chlorophyll production in corn.

29.5. Do you think that the study of nucleocytoplasmic interrelations in Paramecium has any bearing upon differentiation processes in multicellular organisms? Explain.

29.6. As an experimental organism for genetic investigation, what are the unique advantages of Paramecium?

29.7. Certain paramecia are thin because of a completely recessive nuclear gene, *th*. What is the phenotypic expectation for the clones derived from exconjugants of a single mating of ++ by +*th*? How would cytoplasmic mixing affect your expectation? Why?

29.8. According to the definition of a chromosome given on page 8, would you consider kappa to be or to contain a chromosome? Explain.

29.9. Keeping in mind the difficulties of proving the existence of extranuclear genes, which do you think represents the primary genetic material in cellular organisms, nuclear or extranuclear genetic material? Explain.

29.10. Discuss the statement (p. 253) that DNA "seems to be absent in the cytoplasm."

29.11. Do you think the evidence presented that sex in Chlamydomonas is based primarily upon a single pair of genes is conclusive? Justify your answer.

29.12. Report any evidence obtained since this account was written (November, 1964) that the DNA in chloroplasts or in mitochondria has a phenotypic effect.

Chapter **30**

THE GENETIC CONTROL
OF MUTATION

CHAPTERS 11, 12, and 14 dealt with different units of mutation, ranging from the largest—genomic—changes to the smallest—gene—changes. Although various externally-applied environmental agents can produce mutations of all kinds (Chapters 13 and 16), we would like to know to what extent the genotype regulates its own mutability.

Mitosis is so precise that ordinarily the genotype prevents the occurrence of genomic and single, whole-chromosome changes in successive generations of cells. Mitotic rate and spindle orientation are controlled by genes, just as are other aspects of mitosis. In Ascaris, the genotype seems to prevent mutation in a polycentric chromosome by suppressing the action of all but one centromere.

In meiosis, crossing over occurs at points that correspond precisely in two nonsister strands, so that crossovers containing deficient or duplicated segments are avoided.[1] In this way intrachromosomal euploidy is maintained even though recombination between homologs is permitted. Synapsis and chiasma formation in meiosis help distribute the homologs in a way that prevents the gain or loss of whole chromosomes, that is, aneusomy. Evidence for the genetic control of synapsis is provided by collochores in Drosophila (p. 185) and by the genes for asynapsis found in maize (p. 190), many other

plant species, and Drosophila. Genes producing spindles that diverge at the poles during meiosis are known in both Drosophila and maize. In general, the synthesis of new genes is usually regulated to prevent substitution of improper genetic raw materials for the proper ones, assuming both types are present in the cell at the same time.

It might be argued that the examples given demonstrate only that reduced mutability is an inevitable consequence of normal cell operation. Although present genotypes may appear to play a passive role, mitosis and meiosis are not intrinsic properties of genes or cells, and, therefore, during the course of evolution the selection of genes for carrying out these activities must have been an active process aimed at reducing mutability; that is, genes that could maintain genetic stability and permit replication and genetic recombination via sexuality must have been favored.

Though the genetic controls so far mentioned lead to a reduction in mutability, it should be realized that the genotype also permits genetic changes to occur in the following controlled or regulated ways:

1. The ploidy changes in a sexual cycle —from diploid to haploid and back again— are under genetic control.

2. Mutational changes increase with mitotic activity (p. 193); since the rate of mitosis is under genetic control (many cancer cells are mutants whose mitotic rate has increased), the genotype controls mutability in this way.

3. We have already mentioned (Chapter 11) certain modifications of meiosis—undoubtedly under genetic control also—leading to ploidy changes in the next generation.

4. Even within the somatic tissues of a multicellular organism, controlled genetic change is permitted in cells whose chromosomes become polyploid (as in human liver), or highly polynemic (as in the Dipteran larval salivary gland).

---

[1] See, however, G. E. Magni (1963).

5. We have also noted that in Ascaris (p. 189) changes occurring in somatic tissues lead to the formation of a number of small chromosomes from a single large one.

6. The frequency of nondisjunction leading to aneusomy has been shown to depend both on the amount and distribution of heterochromatin and on the types of chromosomal rearrangements present. Therefore, to the extent that the genotype regulates its heterochromatin and rearrangements, it is also regulating the incidence of nondisjunction.

7. Similarly, the arrangement of meiotic products in Drosophila oogensis (Chapter 12) acts to eliminate dicentrics produced by crossing over in paracentric-inversion heterozygotes.

8. Finally, the arrangement of the chromosomal material and the metabolic activity of the cell (as it influences the amount of water and oxygen present, for example) are other ways in which mutability is influenced or regulated by the genotype itself.

The preceding discussion dealt mainly with the prevention or regulated occurrence of intergenic changes. Does the genotype regulate the occurrence of point mutation? Consider the spontaneous point-mutation frequencies for two lines of the same species of Drosophila—one living in a tropical and the other in a temperate climate. If the genotype were at the mercy of temperature in the wild, we would expect the tropical form to have a higher frequency of spontaneous point mutation than the temperate form. However, when both lines are grown at the same temperature in the laboratory, the tropical form has a lower mutation rate than the temperate one. This result provides good evidence that the tropical form has genetically suppressed (or the temperate form has genetically enhanced) its mutational response to temperature. Consequently, in nature the two forms probably show less differ-

ence in mutation frequency than would be expected with the differences in temperature. Other strains of Drosophila melanogaster collected from various regions have different spontaneous point-mutation frequencies. Some of this may be due to differences in the mutability of their isoalleles (p. 59); part may be due also to a general control of mutability by the genotype, for some strains contain mutator genes which can increase the general point-mutation frequency as much as tenfold. Of course, other alleles of mutator genes can be considered general suppresssors of point mutability. Certain organisms (bacteria, for example) have mutants which make the individual generally less mutable to a given mutagen. Since the organisms most advanced in evolution contain more genetic material per cell than less advanced forms, the most advanced forms probably have selected genotypes which reduce their spontaneous mutation rate to avoid overmutation.

Activator and Dissociation in Maize [2]

The triploid endosperm (p. 26) in kernels from some corn plants are white, others are colored, and still others are white with colored speckles. At first, it might seem as if we were dealing with a high mutation frequency of a gene from a "colorless" to a "colored" allele. It is found, however, that the white phenotype results from the presence of two genes adjacent to or very near each other on the same chromosome. If these two loci are separated or dissociated from each other by chromosomal breakage that removes a particular one of the two loci, the mutant cell and all its daughter cells with the remaining locus will be colored. The locus removed, called Dissociation, Ds, causes breakage in chromosome regions near it and is probably in a heterochromatic portion of the chromosome. If Ds is never dissociated from the adjacent locus, the kernel

[2] Based upon work of B. McClintock.

is white; if it dissociates during kernel formation, the kernel shows colored sectors or dots on a white background; if *Ds* is moved before the kernel forms, the kernel and later generations of plants are completely colored. In some plants the colored specks are large, due to the movement of *Ds* early in development; in other plants they are small due to the movement of *Ds* later in development, when very few additional cell divisions take place. The mutation involved here is the loss or removal of *Ds* via breakage. The change in color apparently is not a mutational but a phenotypic event which enables the detection and proof of the mutational event. This phenotypic effect is dependent upon the relative position of genes; that is, it is a *position effect;* the presence of *Ds* next to the gene for color suppresses color formation; its absence permits the gene for color to produce color.

Although the breaks which *Ds* causes are usually near *Ds* in the chromosome, they are not always at the same locus. For this reason and also because breaks can occur simultaneously in other chromosomes (due to spontaneous events or to the presence of other *Ds* genes located in them), *Ds* need not be lost after breakage but may transfer from one chromosomal position to another in the same or a different chromosome. As the result of the movement of *Ds* to new positions, the number of *Ds* factors present in the endosperm can increase in successive generations. When the number of *Ds* genes in a given region of a chromosome increases, the region breaks more and more frequently.

Ds transposed to another chromosome can cause breaks near its new location. Thus, whenever *Ds* moves, a mutation has occurred. Such relocations of *Ds* often suppress the phenotypic effect of a gene located near the new locus of *Ds*. As long as *Ds* remains in its new position, the new phenotype is produced, thereby simulating a stable point mutation of the gene near *Ds*. More-

over, each time *Ds* is lost from such a location, the new phenotype of the adjacent gene reverts to the old phenotype. If these transpositions are frequent, they may be incorrectly scored as point mutations of an unstable, mutable allele of the neighboring gene. If *Ds* rarely moves, one might incorrectly score the new phenotype produced by its neighboring gene as a rare mutational change in the neighboring gene. Although it is still not definite how many events scored as point mutations of a given gene are position effects due to suppression or release resulting from a change in linear gene neighbors, not all point changes can be such position effects, of course, since differences among the genes involved in position effects must first arise by mutation.

The ability of *Ds* to cause breaks in chromosomes is controlled by *Activator, Ac,* genes. *Ac* does not have to be on the same chromosome as *Ds* and usually is not; it also seems to be located in heterochromatin. By appropriate crosses kernels can be obtained whose endosperm contains none, one, two, or three *Ac* genes in addition to one *Ds* gene located near a pigment-producing gene (Figure 30–1). In the absence of *Ac,* no specks are produced, and the kernel is completely white. This observation proves that *Ds* cannot cause chromosome breakage (and is not relocated in other ways) in the absence of *Ac.* Moreover, as the dosage of *Ac* increases from one to three, the colored spots become smaller and smaller. Thus, *Ac* also acts to delay the time of *Ds* action. Here, then, is a case in which the genotype regulates its own mutability—*Ac* not only determines the ability of *Ds* to produce breakages but regulates the time in development when breakage is to occur. *Ac* is clearly acting as a *regulator gene.* This kind of gene may be important in cyclical metabolic processes as well as in cellular differentiation and embryonic development. Factors like *Ac* are fairly common in maize, and the phenotypic

instability of various loci in other flowering plants, ferns, fungi, and bacteria may be
due to similar factors.

* Segregation Distortion in Drosophila

Drosophila melanogaster homozygous for the
II chromosome mutants, *cinnabar* (*cn*) and
brown (*bw*), have white eyes because *cn*/*cn*

and *bw*/*bw* prevent the formation of the
brown and the red pigments, respectively,
which together comprise the dull-red eye
color of the wild type. When the test cross
$+ +$/*cn bw* ♂ by *cn bw*/*cn bw* ♀ is made,
the progeny typically occur in the approximate phenotypic ratio of one white to one
$+$. If, however, the unmarked II chromo-

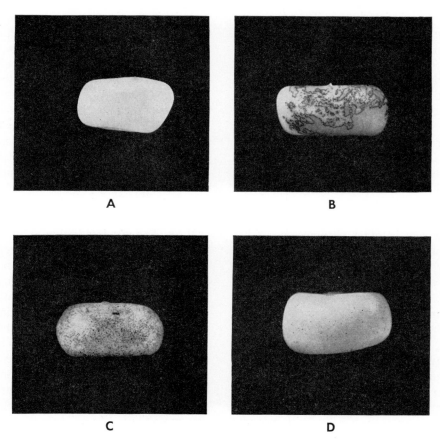

A   B

C   D

FIGURE 30–1. *The effect of* Activator *on the action of* Dissociation. (*A*)
No Ac is present. The kernel is colorless due to the continued presence of
Ds, *which inhibits the action of a neighboring pigment-producing gene.*
(*B*) *One Ac factor is present. Breaks at* Ds *occur early in kernel devel-
opment, leading to large colored sectors.* (*C*) *Two Ac factors are present.
Time of* Ds *action is delayed, producing smaller sectors which appear as
specks.* (*D*) *Three Ac factors are present.* Ds *action is so delayed that
relatively few and tiny specks are produced.* (*Courtesy of B. McClintock.*)

some comes from certain natural populations, this cross [3] produces 93 to 99% (instead of about 50%) + progeny. Moreover, this atypical ratio is not associated with any increase in egg mortality. It is concluded, therefore, that the two kinds of male gametes (+ + and *cn bw*) must be functionally unequal in number at the time of fertilization, suggesting that the segregation ratio 1 + +:1 *cn bw* is somehow distorted prior to gamete formation. Analysis of the *segregation distortion* phenomenon reveals a genetic factor, *Segregation-Distorter, SD*— present in the otherwise wild-type II chromosome—located in the heterochromatic region of the right arm near the centromere of II. The *cn bw*-containing chromosome, therefore, carries *SD+*. *SD* causes some kind of genetic change, probably at or near *SD+* in the homologous chromosome, which results either in the loss of the *cn bw*-containing homolog or the inability of sperm carrying that chromosome to be used in fertilization. The net result is that the *SD*-containing chromosome is recovered in excess in the F_1.

When, however, the *SD+*-containing chromosome carries certain inversions involving IIR absent in the homolog, the *SD/SD+* male shows no segregation distortion. Consequently, for *SD* to prevent the appearance of *SD+* in the progeny, *SD* and *SD+* must "pair." *SD+* alleles vary in their sensitivity to any particular *SD; SD* alleles differ in their ability to affect a given *SD+* region.

The original *SD/SD+* combination gives a constant amount of distortion, indicating that the *SD* line is stable. Every *SD*-bearing chromosome recombinant for the (probably heterochromatic) tip of the right arm of the II chromosome becomes less stable. The decrease in stability is reflected by variations in ability to distort. Consequently, the

stable line must have a modifying gene, *Stabilizer of SD, St(SD)*, at the tip of the right arm of II. Stabilization occurs whether *St(SD)* is in cis or trans position relative to *SD*.

Since the markers *purple (pr)* and *cn* closely span both the centromere and the *SD* locus, one can study recombinants for the regions near *SD*. The results show that a locus is present in the right arm of II—near *SD* but farther from the centromere—whose presence is essential for *SD* operation. This locus is *Activator of SD, Ac(SD)*, which must be in cis position for *SD* to function. Since it is found that crossing over in the *SD-Ac(SD)* region is reduced, it is hypothesized that a small rearrangement exists in this region. Usually, *SD-Ac(SD)* causes a genetic change in the corresponding—presumably nonrearranged—*SD+* segment of the homolog. An individual can be synthesized, however, with one II chromosome, containing almost all the hypothesized rearrangement without *SD*, whose homolog carries *SD, Ac(SD)* and a segment of the nonrearranged region. Under these conditions, segregation distortion occurs against the *SD*-containing chromosome instead of against its homolog.

Although the F_1 of the usual heterozygous *SD* male occur in a distorted ratio (*the father distorts, or shows segregation distortion via his progeny*), the F_1 from heterozygous *SD* females do not. An *SD/SD+* male can distort when outcrossed to an attached-X female. Surprisingly, when his *SD*-containing sons are tested (these received the father's X), they do not distort. It would appear that a distorting male conditions his X chromosome so that sons receiving it cannot distort. When a distorting male is mated to an unrelated *SD+/SD+* female having separate X's, all the *SD*-containing sons can distort since each received an unchanged maternal X. (Note that the daughters carry one unchanged maternal and

---

[3] As noted originally by Y. Hiraizumi and J. F. Crow.

one changed paternal X.) Among the *SD*-containing sons the daughters produce, the half receiving the unchanged maternal X can distort, whereas those receiving the changed paternal X cannot. When either of these kinds of males are outcrossed to SD^+/SD^+ females, all *SD*-containing sons receive an unchanged maternal X and, therefore, can distort. Females producing *SD*-carrying sons of which only half distort, are said to be *conditioned* and to show *conditional distortion;* the mechanism of conditional distortion is unknown.

The case of *SD* shows some similarity to the *Ac-Ds* example discussed.[4] *SD* causes some kind of genetic change regulated by *Ac*(*SD*). The activity of *SD* is modified by *St*(*SD*) and is also conditioned by the X chromosome. *SD* provides an excellent example of the genetic control of mutability.

SD was initially obtained from a natural population that showed no distortion because *SD*'s detrimental effect on the transmission of its homolog was suppressed by a combination of factors. One was X-chromosome conditioning fostered by inbreeding. In this population selection apparently favored the retention of SD^+ alleles resistant to distortion as well as inversions or other structural changes involving IIR which, in heterozygous condition, prevented pairing and, hence, distortion. *SD* is an example of *meiotic drive,* a force capable of altering gene frequencies in natural populations by the production of functional gametes which do not carry segregants in a one-to-one ratio.

Episomes and Viruses as Mutagens

Suppressed or variegated phenotypic effects are known which are due to the placement of heterochromatin near euchromatin. In Drosophila, such position effects are frequent after structural changes in chromosomes.

Some cases of phenotypic suppression involve special genetic elements—for example, *Segregation Distortion* in Drosophila and *Dissociation* in corn—associated with heterochromatin. Some of these genetic factors are capable of causing breakage and of changing their location in the genome. Since such factors and episomes have certain characteristics in common, both should be studied and compared with regard to phenotypic suppression, organelle movement, and chromosomal breakage.

The spontaneous mutation frequency from auxotrophy to prototrophy is known for a large number of alleles for various markers in Salmonella. When auxotrophic bacteria are infected with transducing phage grown on the same genetic strain or on a bacterial strain carrying a deletion (deficiency) for the gene under test, the frequency of prototrophs is significantly increased.[5] Genes induced to revert to prototrophy in this way are called *selfers*. Although the mechanism of reversion is not fully understood, the presence of a transducing fragment which synapses in a region near a selfer gene somehow stimulates the mutability of the selfer. Consequently, phage enhances the mutability of bacterial genes. We have already seen (p. 373) that the mutability of an extranuclear gene is under control of nuclear genes.

In this connection we should also note the following results involving the higher animals, including man:

1. The addition of Rous sarcoma virus to normal rat cells in tissue culture produces an increased incidence of chromosome breakage over the control level.

2. After herpes simplex virus is innoculated into established human tissue-culture lines, the incidence of chromosomal breakage increases.

---

[4] See L. Sandler and Y. Hiraizumi (1961).

[5] See M. Demerec (1963), and A. L. Taylor (1963).

3. All patients [6] with clinical measles (rubeola) have a high incidence of chromosome breakage in the white blood cells by the fifth day after onset of the rash. Chromosome breaks occur in 33 to 72% of the cells examined, and all chromosomes are breakable at numerous positions, although the unions between ends produced by breakage resulting in structural rearrangements are of low frequency.

4. After infection of human cell lines *in vitro* with the simian virus SV_{40}, large numbers of chromosomal mutants are detected [7] including chromosome loss, chromosome breakage, and gross rearrangements like dicentrics, rings, and (probably) translocations. The frequency with which these involve different chromosomes is apparently not random. At least seven other viral infections in man are associated with an increased incidence of various chromosomal rearrangements in white blood cells.

We do not know whether these effects are due to a general metabolic effect of the presence, functioning, or replication of viral nucleic acids; to a specific episomal-like feature of these viruses; or to some other factor or combination of factors. In any case, viruses can induce mutations in cells of higher organisms *in vivo* and *in vitro,* and it is possible that normally-present extranuclear genes can also do so. Clearly then, the genetic control of mutability involves extranuclear genes, episomes, and ordinary chromosomal genes; each is hypothetically capable of affecting its own mutability as well as each other's.

[6] Studied by W. W. Nichols, A. Levan, B. Hall, and G. Östergren (1962).
[7] See P. S. Moorhead and E. Saksella (1963).

SUMMARY AND CONCLUSIONS

The spontaneous occurrence of genomic and of single, whole-chromosome mutations is suppressed by the genotypic control of the processes of mitosis and meiosis. Structural rearrangements in chromosomes are suppressed by the precision of synapsis and crossing over. Such controls are possible because of the linear arrangement of genes in the chromosomes. In certain cases involving the production of polyploid and polynemic chromosomes and several monocentric chromosomes from a polycentric chromosome, genetic change is genotypically regulated.

Point-mutation frequencies also are regulated genotypically, as shown by the general control of mutation response to temperature changes or to mutagenic agents; by the occurrence of mutator genes; and by genes which produce chromosome breakages that can lead to losses, shifts, and transpositions and, therefore, position effects. Regulator genes control the operation of genes that cause breakages or other mutations. Transducing phages induce point mutations; viruses that attack higher animals can also effect chromosomal breakage.

REFERENCES

Demerec, M., "Selfer Mutants of *Salmonella typhimurium,*" Genetics, 48:1519–1531, 1963.

Magni, G. E., "The Origin of Spontaneous Mutations During Meiosis," Proc. Nat. Acad. Sci., U.S., 50:975–980, 1963.

McClintock, B., "The Origin and Behavior of Mutable Loci in Maize," Proc. Nat. Acad. Sci., U.S., 36:344–355, 1950. Reprinted in *Classic Papers in Genetics,* Peters, J. A. (Ed.), Englewood Cliffs, N.J.: Prentice-Hall, 1959, pp. 199–209.

McClintock, B., "Controlling Elements and the Gene," Cold Spring Harb. Sympos. Quant. Biol., 21:197–216, 1956.

Moorhead, P. S., and Saksela, E., "Non-Random Chromosomal Aberrations in SV$_{40}$-Transformed Human Cells," J. Cell Comp. Physiol., 62:57–83, 1963.

Nichols, W. W., Levan, A., Hall, B., and Östergren, G., "Measles-Associated Chromosome Breakage. Preliminary Communication," Hereditas, 48:367–370, 1962.

Peterson, P. A., "The Pale Green Mutable System in Maize," Genetics, 45:115–133, 1960.

Sandler, L., and Hiraizumi, Y., "Meiotic Drive in Natural Populations of Drosophila Melanogaster. VIII. A Heritable Aging Effect on the Phenomenon of Segregation-Distortion," Canad. J. Genet. Cytol., 3:34–46, 1961.

Taylor, A. L., "Bacteriophage-Induced Mutation in *Escherichia coli,*" Proc. Nat. Acad. Sci., U.S., 50:1043–1051, 1963.

QUESTIONS FOR DISCUSSION

30.1. How is the precision of the mitotic and meiotic processes related to the mutability of the genetic material?

30.2. Defend the statement that meiosis and mitosis are not intrinsic properties of genes.

30.3. If whole genome changes represent a class of mutation, should the changes in ploidy which occur in gametogenesis and fertilization be considered mutations? Why?

30.4. Does the activity of *Dissociation* provide evidence for the genetic control of mutability? Explain.

30.5. What evidence can you present that variegation is not always due to the effect of a single pair of genes, one with unstable alleles?

30.6. What characteristics of *Dissociation* resemble those of the episome F?

30.7. Discuss the mechanisms by which segregation distortion is suppressed in natural populations of Drosophila.

30.8. Discuss the hypothesis that the *SD* phenomenon involves an episome-like agent.

30.9. In what respects is *SD* similar to and different from *Ds?*

30.10. Do you suppose that all viruses cause a significant increase in the frequency of chromosomal breakage? Explain.

Chapter 31

THE MOLECULAR BASIS
OF MUTATION

THE SPONTANEOUS mutation frequency is influenced by naturally-occurring physical mutagens such as ultraviolet light and ionizing radiations (Chapter 13) and probably by naturally-occurring chemical mutagens (Chapter 14); mutability is also under considerable genetic control (Chapter 30). The correlation found betwen mutagenicity and the wavelength of ultraviolet light suggests that nucleic acids are involved in the mutation process (p. 261). What, then, is the detailed molecular basis of spontaneous and induced mutation?

Mutagens and Antimutagens

In *E. coli* auxotrophic for tryptophan, the spontaneous mutation rate from sensitivity to resistance to infection by ϕT5 or ϕT6 is found to depend upon whichever component of the nutrient medium is made the limiting factor for growth.[1] The highest rate is obtained when the growth-controlling factor in the medium is tryptophan; the lowest rate is obtained when the growth-controlling factor is lactate.

This result indicates that the spontaneous mutation rate depends upon the physiological or biochemical state of the organism—a view also supported by the effect of temperature changes upon the spontaneous mutation rate (p. 192)—and suggests that chemical substances added to a culture of *E. coli* growing in a medium limited in one essential nutrient would have a pronounced mutagenic effect.

By testing various substances in concentrations that produce no appreciable killing of tryptophan-limited bacteria, many *purines and purine derivatives are found to be mutagenic*. The most mutagenic is caffeine; theophylline is nearly as effective; azaguanine is mutagenic, and—to a lesser degree—adenine. In contrast, no pyrimidines or their derivatives are mutagenic under the same conditions. If purine ribosides such as adenosine or guanosine are added to the medium containing any one of several purine mutagens, the mutagenic activity is completely suppressed.[2] Thus, for example, adenosine completely suppresses the mutagenicity of adenine or caffeine. Clearly the *purine ribosides* are acting as *antimutagens*—just as anoxia or catalase are antimutagens so far as chromosomal breakage (p. 182) or point mutations (p. 192) produced by X rays are concerned—and are not acting as selective agents against induced mutants. On the other hand, pyrimidine ribosides, deoxyadenosine, and deoxyguanosine either are not at all antimutagenic to purines and their derivatives, or they are much less efficient than the purine ribosides.

Theophylline is mutagenic under aerobic but not anaerobic conditions. Adenosine, however, is present in significant concentrations in bacteria growing anaerobically but not detectable in bacteria growing aerobically. Under anaerobic conditions, adenosine is apparently a normally-present antimutagen that counteracts the effect of purines added in the medium. Note that anaerobiosis has no effect on the ultraviolet-induced mutation rate and makes gamma radiation less effective only because of the reduction in oxygen; such a result is consistent with the finding that extra adenosine has no antimutagenic effect on either ultraviolet or gamma radiation mutagens.

[1] Based upon work of A. Novick and L. Szilard (1951).

[2] See A. Novick (1956).

The *spontaneous mutation rate* is reduced by the presence of purine ribosides (adenosine or guanosine) but not pyrimidine ribosides (uridine or cytidine) in the medium. With adenosine in the medium, the spontaneous rate is reduced to about one third its original value. Moreover, the spontaneous rate is lower under anaerobic than aerobic conditions, as would be expected from the metabolic production or lack of utilization of adenosine. Finally, it should be noted that all the purine mutagens increase the mutation rate to T5 resistance more than to T6 resistance, although the reverse is true for ultraviolet and gamma radiation.

From these results it seems reasonable to distinguish two kinds of mutagens—a purine type and a radiation type—which produce two different kinds of mutations. We can postulate that under the experimental conditions described, about two thirds of the spontaneous mutation rate is produced by the action of some purine type of substance produced spontaneously during the normal metabolism of the cell. It may seem surprising that only purines, their analogs, and purine ribosides affect the mutation rate. This finding, however, may be related to the particular mutants studied—namely, those resistant to phages T5 or T6. Such mutations may depend more upon changes in purines than pyrimidines; other mutations may prove to be relatively pyrimidine-sensitive and purine-insensitive.

Even though it is not clear how the purines and their ribosides accomplish their mutagenic and antimutagenic effects, two general conclusions are warranted:

1. A considerable portion of the spontaneous mutation rate is the normal consequence of the cell's biochemical activity in producing mutagens and antimutagens.
2. A connection exists between mutation rate and nucleic acid metabolism.

Though the mutation rate is directly connected only with purines and their ribosides, supported by the fact that thymine is mutagenic when withheld from bacteria requiring it, it is reasonable to suppose that an indirect connection also exists with DNA and its precursors.

Mutational Spectra

In discussing the genetics of the rII region of the ϕT4 genetic map, it was mentioned (p. 345) that the more than 1500 spontaneously-occurring mutants tested involved changes in one or more of about 300 different sites in the rII region. This statement, of course, implies that some mutation sites must have been involved more than once. In fact, the number of times different sites are involved in mutation varies considerably. In terms of DNA, this variability must mean that certain nucleotides, singly or in groups, are much more likely to undergo spontaneous mutation than others, so that *mutational "hot spots"* must occur.

Since recombination studies permit the analysis of the rII region at the level of the nucleotide, the DNA of T4 can serve as material for studies leading to a clearer definition of mutation on the molecular level. Note that even-number T phages (T2, T4, T6) have 5-hydroxymethyl cytosine (Figure 19–3 on p. 255) or a derivative of it, instead of cytosine in their DNA; in all other respects this DNA is typical. It has already been noted (p. 283) that 5-bromo uracil (Figure 21–4) can substitute for thymine—and only thymine—in the synthesis of DNA *in vitro*. What will be the mutational consequences of incorporating 5-bromo uracil into T4 DNA? [3]

Addition of 5-bromo uracil to the normal culture medium of *E. coli* before infection with T4, does not necessarily result, after

---

[3] The discussion following is based largely upon the work of S. Benzer and E. Freese (1958), and subsequent work by E. Freese and co-workers.

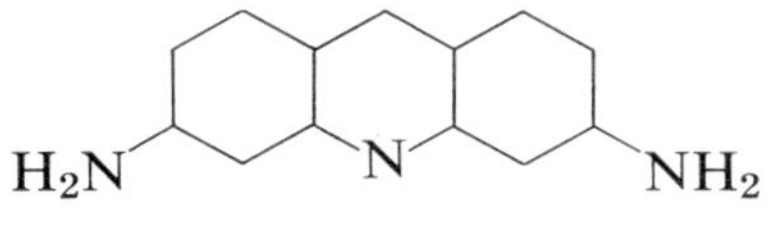

FIGURE 31–1. *Two acridine dyes.*

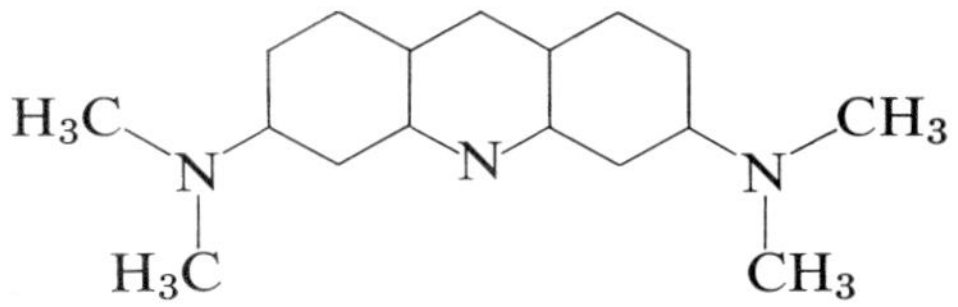

infection, in the incorporation of this base analog in T4 DNA, since thymine can be synthesized by the bacterium and it—rather than the analog—may be used preferentially or exclusively in the synthesis of phage DNA. Sulfanilamide, itself not mutagenic, inhibits synthesis of folic acid, which in its reduced form (tetrahydrofolic acid) is required for enzymatic methyl transfer reactions. Therefore, sulfanilamide is added to the culture medium to assure that no thymine is synthesized from uracil. The medium is supplemented with a variety of essential chemical substances already containing methyl and hydroxymethyl groups but not with the deoxyribotides of thymine or of 5-hydroxymethyl cytosine. (The deoxyribotide of 5-hydroxymethyl cytosine is omitted to prevent its possible conversion to an analog of thymine which might be incorporated in preference to the 5-bromo uracil.) In this way, the bacterium can function properly as a phage host.

Under these conditions, 5-bromo uracil is highly mutagenic in the rII region. A comparison of 5-bromo uracil-induced and spontaneously-occurring rII mutants reveals that the induced mutants also occur in clusters on the genetic map, although the hot spots are in different positions. Moreover, contrary to the spontaneous mutants, very few of those induced are of the gross (internucleotide) type, and almost all are subsequently capable of reverse mutation to, or near the r+ phenotype.

Although the *mutational spectra* (p. 192) for 5-bromo uracil, other chemical mutagens, and spontaneous mutants are all different at the nucleotide level, the exact chemical basis for the induced mutations cannot be specified with any certainty, because any given mutagen may be producing its effect via any of several different metabolic pathways. Clearly, the molecular basis for mutagenic action is best studied using the shortest possible physical pathway between chemical mutagen and gene.[4] Thus, it is preferable to treat sperm rather than oocytes with a chemical mutagen, and more desirable to expose phage or transforming DNA to the mutagen directly, rather than indirectly, via its host.

Mutation Involving Whole Nucleotides

Since the genetic material is a linear array of nucleotides, let us consider the possible changes to whole nucleotides at the basis of mutations. One or more nucleotides can be added, deleted, substituted for, inverted, or transposed to a new position with or without inversion. All these nucleotide rearrangements ought to be possible for single-stranded nucleic acid, except inversion, which requires double-stranded nucleic acid to maintain strand polarity. Whole-nucleotide changes can be produced by breaking the polynucleotide backbone at two or more places, followed by rearrangement of the fragments. Breakage of the backbone (and loss of DNA's ability to act as primer-template) occurs especially often after exposure to an ionizing physical mutagen, and leads to deletions and other rearrangements

[4] As noted by I. H. Herskowitz (1955).

Uracil

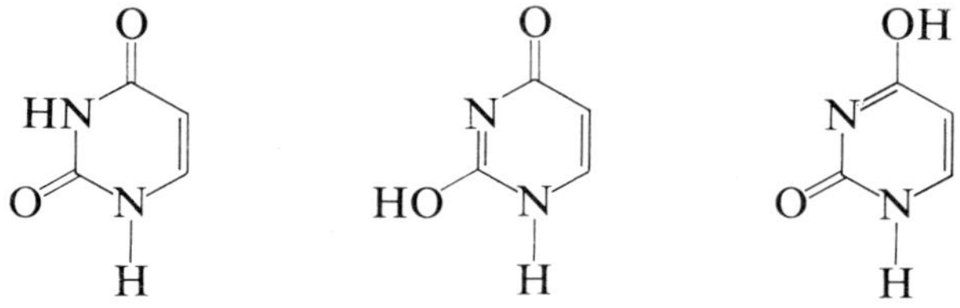

Adenine

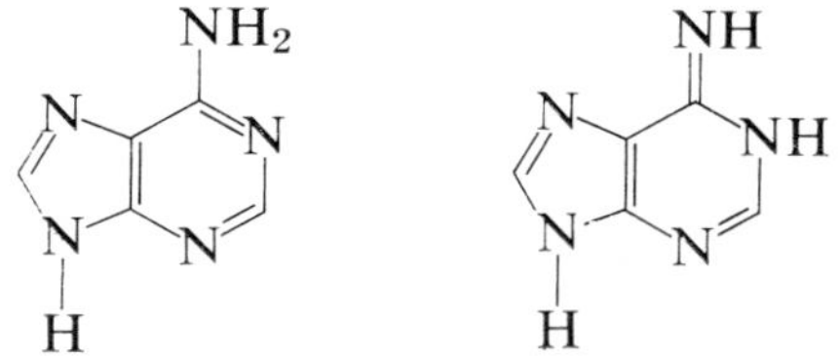

FIGURE 31–2. *Tautomers of uracil and adenine.*

of the already-formed, "old" gene material.[5] Single, whole-nucleotide changes can also be produced by chemical mutagens without involving breakage. Molecules of chemical mutagens such as the *acridines* (Figure 31–1) can be inserted between successive nucleotides of a strand.[6] A single, intercalated molecule of chemical mutagen is apparently able to spread the strand lengthwise 3.4A. When this chain is used as template, an entire nucleotide may be added to the complementary chain at the position occupied by the molecule of mutagen. The possibility also exists that an unbound nucleotide or other naturally-occurring substance may intercalate with similar results. This mutagenic mechanism involves changes both in the old and the new DNA strands.

In the presence of Mn^{++}, the complementary strand made by DNA polymerase from a DNA template *in vitro* is a mixture of deoxyribo- and ribotides,[7] provided, of course, that the appropriate riboside 5′ triphosphates are included as substrates. The incorporation of U and ribose into a complementary strand is expected to be mutational. Since salts of manganese are highly mutagenic in bacteria,[8] it appears that such an incorporation may occur *in vivo*.

Sub-Nucleotide Mutations

Mutation can involve the sugar, phosphate, or base portions of a nucleotide. Although deoxyribose is the only sugar detected in the DNA of microorganisms, one cannot exclude the possibility that an occasional ribose occurs in an otherwise typical DNA strand. Ribose can be part of a DNA chain synthesized *in vitro* if whole ribotides are incorporated by the method described in the preceding paragraph. Some evidence has been obtained for the incorporation of arabinose into DNA of mammalian cells in culture. As mentioned, ribosides give no evidence of acting as DNA mutagens; in fact, purine ribosides are sometimes antimutagenic. Nevertheless, we cannot rule out the possibility that some agents act as mutagens either by adding an O at the 2′ position of deoxyribose in an already-formed DNA sequence

[5] See H. Harrington (1964), and C. G. Mead (1964).
[6] See L. S. Lerman (1963).
[7] As shown by P. Berg and co-workers (see reference on p. 290).

[8] As shown by M. Demerec and co-workers.

or by removing the 2' O of ribose in an RNA sequence.

The phosphate part of a nucleotide can be changed by substituting P^{32} for P. When single-stranded DNA viruses such as ϕX174 and ϕS13 incorporate P^{32}, a single radioactive decay of P^{32} to S is sufficient to inactivate them. On the other hand, about ten decays are required to inactivate ϕT2 and similar phages containing double-stranded DNA. One simple explanation of such *suicide experiments* is that each decay breaks the backbone of the polynucleotide in which it occurs, a single decay in one backbone sometimes leading to a nearby break in the backbone of a complementary strand if one is present. According to this explanation, scission of single- or double-stranded DNA (or RNA, presumably) is sufficient for inactivation.

Base changes in old genes. Consider, next, changes involving the base portion of a nucleotide. We have already seen that base changes can result from the substitution of one whole nucleotide for another. We are now interested in the possible ways the base portion of a nucleotide already in a genetic sequence may be changed chemically.

Certain atoms in each of the bases in DNA and RNA can assume several different arrangements; that is, each base can exist in several *tautomeric forms*. In previous discussions and diagrams, the most likely tautomer of each base—that is, its (=O) keto or amino (NH_2) form—was assumed to occur. In the tautomers of uracil and adenine shown in Figure 31–2, the alternatives differ in the positions at which a hydrogen atom is attached. The *less likely tautomers exist in the* (—OH) *enol or imino* (NH) *form.* Although the usual amino tautomer of adenine pairs with thymine, one of its less common imino tautomers can pair with cytosine (Figure 31–3). Reciprocally, a rare imino tautomer of C can pair with A,

forming two H bonds. A rare enol tautomer of T can pair with G, forming three H bonds, and the same T:G pair can be formed when the purine is in an uncommon tautomeric state. In each of these cases, then, a *tautomeric shift has made a new purine-pyrimidine base pair possible.*[9] Tautomeric shifts may play an important role in spontaneous mutation. The relative frequencies of the different tautomeric alternatives depends upon several factors, including pH. The unusual base pairs, A:C and T:G, can also occur after ionization of any one of the bases.

Chemical changes in the old bases can also occur after treatment with chemical

[9] See reference on p. 277 to J. D. Watson and F. H. C. Crick (1953c).

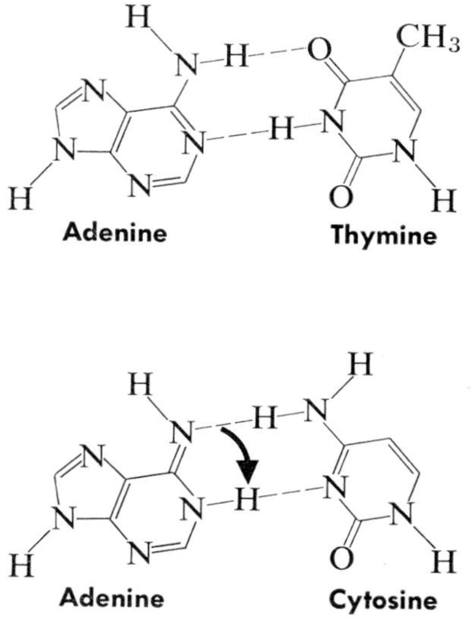

FIGURE 31–3. *Tautomeric shift of adenine which could change its complementary base from thymine to cytosine. Upper diagram shows adenine before, and lower diagram after, undergoing a tautomeric shift of one of its hydrogen atoms. (After J. D. Watson and F. H. C. Crick.)*

mutagens. *Nitrous acid* (HNO$_2$) is mutagenic to TMV, T2 and T4 phages, bacteria, yeast, and to transforming DNA. This mutagen removes NH$_2$ from—that is, *deaminates*—purines and pyrimidines both in DNA and RNA. Deaminated A becomes hypoxanthine (Figure 21–4) (which then pairs with C); deaminated C becomes U (which then pairs with A); and deaminated G becomes xanthine (which still pairs with C but with only two H bonds).

Exposure of ϕT4 to low pH induces point mutations. *In vitro,* low pH causes *depurination*—the complete removal of all G and A—which results in *apurinic acid*. Although the backbone of apurinic acid may break after a return to higher pH, it is likely that the point mutations produced in ϕT4 by low pH are caused either by an incorrect replacement of bases or by the formation of a complement with the complementary nucleotide deleted.

The absorption of *ultraviolet* (UV) *light* by nucleic acids depends primarily upon the presence of *chromatophoric groups* (special groups containing double bonds). When free bases are treated with UV, pyrimidines are found to be more liable to chemical change than purines. One common change is the addition of water to the double bond between the number 4 and 5 carbon atoms of pyrimidines. The *photoproduct* in the case of cytosine is shown in Figure 31–4A. Although the photoproduct reverts to cytosine upon heating or acidification, it may persist frequently enough *in vivo* to weaken H-bonding between C and G, thereby leading to localized areas of strand separation or denaturation. Supporting this view is the observation that UV disrupts H-bonding in native double-stranded DNA.

UV also changes thymine at the same position as cytosine, by breakage of the 4-5 double bond; in this case two thymines unite to form a *dimer* (Figure 31–4B). The UV-initiated hydration of C is expected—via the weakening of H-bonding between C and G—to increase the likelihood of T dimerization. *Thymine dimers* form not only between T's on different strands—thereby producing cross links between DNA chains—but also between adjacent T's on the same strand. (Interchain crosslinking is also produced by the mutagenic antibiotic, *mitomycin C.*) Interchain dimerization prevents chain separation and also blocks replication,

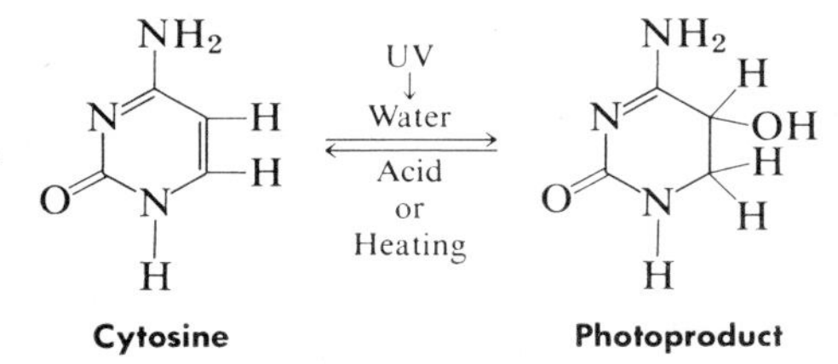

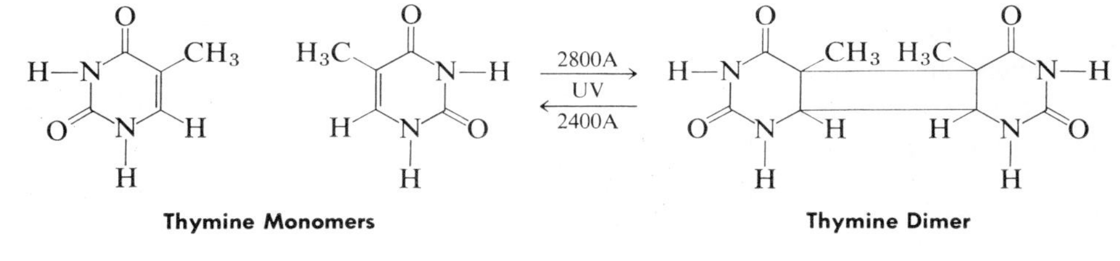

FIGURE 31–4. *Effect of ultraviolet light upon DNA pyrimidines. (The H atoms attached to ring C atoms are shown.)*

whereas intrachain dimerization interferes with the proper base-pairing of T with A, leading eventually to the formation of incorrect complements.

Dimerization may explain how UV destroys the primer-template activity of single-stranded DNA, causes mutations in φX174, and destroys transforming DNA. UV radiation has two opposite effects, however, depending upon the wavelength employed: At 2800A UV radiation tends to form dimers from monomers, whereas at 2400A it tends to form monomers from dimers. In fact, DNA inactivated as primer-template by 2800A UV radiation is partially restored to activity by subsequent exposure to 2400A radiation. Similarly, the transforming activity of Hemophilus DNA inactivated by 2800A can be partially reactivated by subsequent irradiation at 2390A. With large doses of 2800A, about 50% of the biological inactivation—as measured by transforming ability—can be attributed to T dimer formation, one inactivating "hit" being equivalent to one dimer formed for each 160 nucleotides.[10]

The replicational consequences of intrastrand dimer formation can be studied *in vitro*.[11] After various single-stranded DNA primer-templates are exposed to 2800A radiation, the products of synthesis are subjected to nearest-neighbor analysis. As expected, the frequency of the AA sequence decreases in proportion to the TT sequences dimerized; the dinucleotide sequences containing G, especially GG, increase in frequency. These results strongly indicate that T dimers *in vivo* decrease the chance that the complementary AA sequence will incorporate opposite a TT sequence in the template and suggest—but do not prove—that these A's are often replaced by G's.

As mentioned, *photorecovery* from UV-induced dimer formation occurs after exposure to UV radiation of shorter wavelength. In the presence of light of certain longer wavelengths—blue light—a particular enzyme system has been found which can break T dimers—including those which are interchain—into monomers. Such a case illustrates *chemophotorecovery* (p. 191). Since recovery from a mutagenic UV treatment is only about 50%, UV radiation probably produces mutations in other ways than dimer formation. Since large doses of UV can cause breaks in the DNA backbone *in vitro*, this effect is probably another mutagenic pathway *in vivo*.

Although thymine dimers block DNA synthesis *in vitro* and *in vivo*, certain strains of *E. coli* are UV-radiation-resistant and even in the dark can recover to resume DNA synthesis. Such a recovery in these cells does not involve the splitting of thymine dimers; instead, the dimers are, by some mechanism, removed from the DNA (the acid-insoluble fraction) and appear in the acid-soluble fraction. In an irradiated, sensitive strain, which cannot synthesize DNA in the dark, the dimers remain in the insoluble phase and remain photorecoverable.[12] Other work [13] suggests that intrastrand thymine dimers are removed from the DNA of resistant cells enzymatically, and that corrected DNA is reconstructed from information on the complementary strand. Such an error-correcting mechanism would be biologically important for the preservation of DNA.

Finally, it should be noted that although dimerization of 5-bromo uracil is difficult, if not impossible, uracil dimers can be made by UV irradiation. Consequently, UV is expected to be mutagenic to RNA by the same mechanisms as it is to DNA.

Tautomeric shifts, physical and chemical

[10] As found by R. B. Setlow and J. K. Setlow (1962).
[11] As shown by R. B. Setlow, W. L. Carrier, and F. J. Bollum (1963).

[12] See R. B. Setlow and W. L. Carrier (1964).
[13] See R. P. Boyce and P. Howard-Flanders (1964).

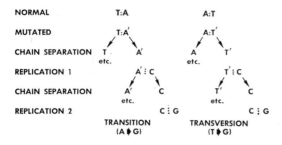

NORMAL	T:A		A:T	
MUTATED	T:A′		A:T′	
CHAIN SEPARATION	T · etc.	A′	A etc.	T′
REPLICATION 1		A′ : C		T′ : C
CHAIN SEPARATION	A′ etc.	C	T′ etc.	C
REPLICATION 2		C : G		C : G
	C : G		C : G	
	TRANSITION (A ♦ G)		TRANSVERSION (T ♦ G)	

FIGURE 31–5. *One postulated sequence of events leading to transition or transversion.*

mutagens, and low pH may ultimately cause base substitution. Replacement of one purine by another purine (A ↔ G) or one pyrimidine by another pyrimidine (T ↔ C) is called *transition;* replacement of a purine by a pyrimidine or the reverse (for example A ↔ C or T ↔ G) is called *transversion.*[14] Both kinds of substitution should be possible at the nucleotide and subnucleotide level.

What is the sequence of events involved in a transition or transversion? A particular base pair, T:A, exposed to a mutagen may become T:A′ (Figure 31–5). For example, suppose that at the time of strand separation, A′ specifies C (instead of T), and at the next division C acts normally to specify G. The net result is that the original A strand eventually produces a second-generation strand carrying G; this is a transition. (Or, given the original pair G:C, a mutagen may produce C′ which specifies A instead of G which, in turn, specifies T. The net change from C to T in this example is also a transition.) If A:T becomes A:T′, T′ specifies C, and C specifies G, the overall result is that T is replaced by G, and a transversion occurred.

Another possible mechanism for intranu-

[14] Following the terminology of E. Freese.

cleotide base changes requires the members of a base pair to undergo *rotational substitution* by breaking their bonds to sugar, rotating 180°, and rejoining.[15] Thus, after rotational substitution, which may be a frequent consequence of ion action, C:G becomes G:C, the resultant double transversion being mutant. Note that in all the mechanisms mentioned for producing base changes, the transitions and transversions were initiated by a change in the old base.

Base changes in new genes. Base analogs are incorporated into DNA *in vitro* when they are present as deoxyriboside 5′-triphosphates (p. 284). For example, uracil (U), 5-bromo uracil (BU), or 5-fluoro uracil (FU) can be substituted for T only; 5-methyl, 5-bromo, or 5-fluoro cytosine can be substituted for C only; hypoxanthine can be substituted for G only. BU, 5-chloro uracil, and 5-iodo uracil can replace some of the T in DNA of bacteria, phages, and human cell lines and are also highly mutagenic. 5-Bromo deoxyuridine (BUdR) is a more efficient mutagen than BU, probably because it is more readily converted to the triphosphate condition and interferes less with the formation of U or C.

Consider the kinds of mistakes which may occur involving BU. Since the usual tautomer of BU (like T) is in the keto state, this tautomer is usually incorporated as the complement of A. The rare enol tautomer of BU (like T), however, can pair with G, forming BU:G. Consequently, two kinds of *mistakes of incorporation* of BU are possible: formation of the A:BU and the G:BU pairs. Once part of a DNA strand, the BU of an A:BU pair can continue to specify A, so that no *mistakes in replication* occur. If, however, such a BU assumes its rare enol state and accepts G as its complement, the grandparental A will be replaced

[15] See H. J. Muller, E. Carlson, and A. Schalet (1961).

by G in a transition resulting from a mistake in replication. Since the BU in G:BU is usually in the keto form at the time of the next replication, it usually accepts A as its complement, resulting in the G to A transition. Therefore the pyrimidine BU is expected to produce purine transitions in both directions $(A \leftrightarrow G)$.

Errors involving BU can be studied *in vitro*. The *copolymer of A and BU, dABU,* can be made and used as primer-template in an extended 30 to 100% synthesis with TPPP, *d*APPP, and *d*GPPP in the substrate. Under these conditions, G is incorporated at the rate of one G residue per 2000 to 25,000 A and T residues. (On the other hand, dAT does not incorporate G.) Using *d*GP*PP, *d*APPP, and *d*BUPPP as a substrate for the dABU primer-template, an extended synthesis is performed and a nearest-neighbor analysis is carried out on the product, thus permitting detection of any BUG, GG, and AG dinucleotide sequences. The primer-template presumably has a strict alternation of BU and A. Consequently, when a G residue appears in the product, it is expected to be attached to a BU residue, and to produce the BUG dinucleotide sequence. However, all three sequences for the G residue are found. In fact, G is incorporated next to BU or G (the BUG and GG dinucleotide sequences) with about the same frequency but less often next to A (the AG sequence). Because sequences other than BUG are found, the results cannot be explained only by mistakes in replication made by the BU in the primer-template. It should be noted that the behavior of BU in dABU *in vitro* may or may not be identical to that of BU present in native DNA *in vivo*.

2-Aminopurine induces point mutations. In its normal tautomeric form, it can pair with T (by two H bonds) or with C (by one H bond). In its rare tautomeric form, it can also bond with C (by two H bonds).

As a consequence, pyrimidine transitions $T \leftrightarrow C$ can eventually result.

A considerable amount of work has been carried out to identify the particular base changes occurring in point mutation.[16] One technique is to produce a mutation with a mutagen whose action is expected to produce a specific transition or transversion. Evidence that the change expected has occurred can subsequently be obtained by studying the reversional mutation rate induced by chemical mutagens expected and not expected to cause the reverse transition or transversion.

Mutation

It is easy to identify the completed transition, transversion, or whole nucleotide change as mutant. But at what point in a series of changes should one consider that a mutation has first been produced?

We consider the mutation accomplished when, as in one of the mechanisms discussed, A is permanently changed to A'. One might object to this answer on the basis that A' may never be reproduced in a future replication; however, to be considered mutant the product of a novel change need not be replicated or transmitted. The novel product, A', need only be more or less permanently different from A in one or more of five ways (as identified by five different operational procedures):

1. A' may have a different chemical composition
2. It may have a different rate of change to a new chemical or physical form
3. It may not specify T at all or not to the same extent as A did
4. It may change the phenotypic effect of the cistron in which it is located

---

[16] See E. Freese (1963), and E. B. Freese and E. Freese (1964).

5. It may affect the recombination rate of its own or another recombinational unit.

Operationally, then, it is desirable to classify a *mutation as any one or a combination of novel, identifiable changes in the chemical or physical, mutational, replicative, functional, or recombinational properties of one or more nucleotides.* This operational definition of mutation includes all aspects of the previous one ("a novel qualitative or quantitative change in the genetic material"). Of course, at the present time, certain of the changes (listed above) that identify a mutant cannot be detected in specific individual nucleotides for technical reasons. Nevertheless, it seems important to indicate the various possible operational ways in which a mutant can be identified. Subnucleotide components should not be considered the smallest units of the genetic material capable of mutation, since the nucleotide is the smallest significant chemical unit of the genetic material. Since the smallest part of the genetic material whose change gives rise to a mutant is presumably smaller than a nucleotide (and, therefore, smaller than a recombinational unit) it is probably more meaningful to speak of subnucleotide parts as furnishing *a number of mutational sites within the nucleotide.*

The word, "novel"—used in our operational definition of mutation—requires some additional consideration. It would have been entirely correct to consider the first case of segregation as being a mutation, since it certainly was a novel—never before recognized—change in the genetic material. However, once it was found that segregation was not a novelty but the rule for paired nuclear genes, segregation was classified as a means of genetic recombination, not of mutation. Similarly, genetic transformation was first considered to be mutation, but after further study it is more properly considered

a mechanism for genetic recombination. Consider the discussion of *Dissociation* whose breakages were called mutations. Since more and more *Dissociation*-type genes are being discovered, are we still justified in thinking the breakages they produce are mutations? In the future we may conclude that such genes provide another mechanism for genetic recombination, at least in certain organisms. Finally, recall that the integration and deintegration of F were classified as genetic recombinations and not as mutations. This interpretation was given in the light of knowledge (but not yet presented) that other types of episomes are known. In this case, the evolution in terminology, from mutation to recombination, was purposely shortcut.

Since what first appears to be a novel genetic change may prove, upon further investigation, not to be novel, we are always subject to reclassifying mutation as genetic recombination. Today's mutations, therefore, are possibly tomorrow's new mechanisms for genetic recombination.

The type of mutational change which seems to be the most immune to reclassification as recombination is subnucleotide change. Clearly, a substitution of 5-bromo uracil for thymine is a mutation, but even at this level, such immunity to reclassification is not absolute. Rotational substitution (A:T becomes T:A)—now considered a possible type of mutation—might be a normal mechanism of genetic recombination in some organisms.

It seems desirable, therefore, to restrict the term, *mutation, to describe nucleotide changes which are unnatural* rather than novel. For this reason, we have already refrained from calling mutations certain genetic changes normally part of the life cycle (polyploidy in liver cells, chromosome fragmentation in Ascaris), although these same changes are considered mutations when they are abnormal or induced.

SUMMARY AND CONCLUSIONS

A considerable portion of the spontaneous mutation rate is based upon the intracellular production of mutagens and antimutagens. For this reason, spontaneous mutation is in many respects an incident of the normal metabolism of the cell in which nucleic acids are specifically implicated.

Mutational "hot spots" found at the nucleotide level are different for mutants occurring spontaneously and those induced by various chemical mutagens.

Mutation is defined operationally as any detectable, unnatural change affecting the chemical or physical constitution, mutability, replication, phenotypic function, or recombination of one or more nucleotides. One or more whole nucleotides can be added, deleted, substituted for, inverted, or transposed to a new position with or without inversion. Chemical and physical mutagens capable of such mutations are discussed.

The components of a nucleotide serve as sites for mutation. Mutations involving the phosphate portion are described, and those affecting the sugar portion are hypothesized. Base changes in the old gene may be produced in a number of ways, including tautomeric shifts, deamination, depurination, rotational substitution, and dimerization. Base changes in new genes can result—for example, after treatment with chemical analogs—from mistakes in incorporation and replication. Eventually, base changes can result in deletion, transition, or transversion.

REFERENCES

Benzer, S., and Freese, E., "Induction of Specific Mutations with 5-Bromo-uracil," Proc. Nat. Acad. Sci., U.S., 44:112–119, 1958. Reprinted in *Papers on Bacterial Viruses,* Stent, G. (Ed.), Boston: Little, Brown, 1960, pp. 220–227.

Boyce, R. P., and Howard-Flanders, P., "Release of Ultraviolet Light-Induced Thymine Dimers from DNA in *E. coli* K12," Proc. Nat. Acad. Sci., U.S., 51:293–300, 1964.

Deering, R. A., "Ultraviolet Radiation and Nucleic Acid," Scient. Amer., 207 (Dec.): 135–144, 1962.

Freese, E., "The Difference Between Spontaneous and Base-Analogue Induced Mutations of Phage T4," Proc. Nat. Acad. Sci., U.S., 45:622–633, 1959.

Freese, E., "Molecular Mechanism of Mutations," Chap. 5, pp. 207–269, in *Molecular Genetics, Part I,* Taylor, J. H. (Ed.), New York: Academic Press, 1963.

Freese, E. B., and Freese E., "Two Separable Effects of Hydroxylamine on Transforming DNA," Proc. Nat. Acad. Sci., U.S., 52:1289–1297, 1964.

Harrington, H., "Effect of X Irradiation on the Priming Activity of DNA," Proc. Nat. Acad. Sci., U.S., 51:59–66, 1964.

Herskowitz, I. H., "The Production of Mutations in Drosophila Melanogaster with Substances Administered in Sperm Baths and Vaginal Douches," Genetics, 40:76–89, 1955.

Krieg, D. R., "Specificity of Chemical Mutagenesis," Progr. Nucleic Acid Res., 2:125–168, 1963.

Kubitschek, H. E., "Mutation Without Segregation," Proc. Nat. Acad. Sci., U.S., 52:1374–1381, 1964.

Lerman, L. S., "The Structure of the DNA-Acridine Complex," Proc. Nat. Acad. Sci., U.S., 49:94–102, 1963.

McLaren, A. D., and Shugar, D., *Photochemistry of Proteins and Nucleic Acids,* New York: Macmillan, 1964.

Mead, C. G., "The Enzymatic Condensation of Oligodeoxyribonucleotides with Poly-deoxyribonucleotides," Proc. Nat. Acad. Sci., U.S., 52:1482–1488, 1964.

Muller, H. J., Carlson, E., and Schalet, A., "Mutation by the Alteration of the Already Existing Gene," Genetics, 46:213–226, 1961.

Novick, A., "Mutagens and Antimutagens," Brookhaven Symposia on Biology, 8:201–215, 1956. Reprinted in *Papers on Bacterial Genetics,* Adelberg, E. A. (Ed.), Boston: Little, Brown, 1960, pp. 74–90.

Novick, A., and Szilard, L., "Experiments on Spontaneous and Chemically Induced Mutations of Bacteria Growing in the Chemostat," Cold Spring Harb. Sympos. Quant. Biol., 16:337–343, 1951. Reprinted in *Papers on Bacterial Genetics,* Adelberg, E. A. (Ed.), Boston: Little, Brown, 1960, pp. 47–57.

Setlow, R. B., and Carrier, W. L., "The Disappearance of Thymine Dimers from DNA: An Error-Correcting Mechanism," Proc. Nat. Acad. Sci., U.S., 51:226–231, 1964.

Symposium on Molecular Action of Mutagenic and Carcinogenic Agents, J. Cell. Comp. Physiol., 64 (Suppl. 1), 191 pp., 1964.

Tergazhi, B. E., Streisinger, G., and Stahl, F. W., "The Mechanism of 5-Bromo-uracil Mutagenesis in the Bacteriophage T4," Proc. Nat. Acad. Sci., U.S., 48:1519–1524, 1962.

Trautner, T. A., Swartz, M. N., and Kornberg, A., "Enzymatic Synthesis of Deoxyribonucleic Acid, X. Influence of Bromouracil Substitutions on Replication," Proc. Nat. Acad. Sci., U.S., 48:449–455, 1962.

Wacker, A., "Molecular Mechanisms of Radiation Effects," Progr. Nucleic Acid Res., 1:369–399, 1963.

QUESTIONS FOR DISCUSSION

31.1. Discuss the causes of the "spontaneous" mutation rate.

31.2. Does this chapter offer any new evidence that the genotype regulates its own mutability? Explain.

31.3. What, if any, new information does this chapter present regarding the genetic or chemical basis of mutation?

31.4. Would you expect the mutational hot spots in the rII region to be different after exposing T4 to 5-bromo uracil from what they would be after exposing T4 to nitrous acid? Why?

31.5. In 1959 I. Tessman found that after nitrous acid treatment ϕT2 gave mottled plaques whereas ϕX174 gave only nonmottled plaques. What do these results suggest about DNA structure and the molecular basis of mutation?

31.6. S. Zamenhof and S. Greer found that heating *E. coli* to 60° C is mutagenic. What molecular explanations can you suggest for this result?

31.7. Chemical substances carrying one, two, or more reactive alkyl groups (C_nH_{2n+1}) are called mono-, bi-, or polyfunctional alkylating agents; many of these are mutagenic. Depending upon the particular alkyl group, DNA can be altered in its phosphate or base portions. Under what circumstances would you expect the use of alkylating agents as mutagens to be unsuitable for determining the molecular basis of mutation?

31.8. How permanent must a change in a nucleotide be before it can be considered a mutant?

31.9. Would you consider the substitution of P^{32} for P in the phosphate of a nucleotide a mutation? Why?

31.10. What do you think of the statement that the only way we have of detecting changes in individual genes is by the phenotypic changes they produce?

31.11. *E. coli* contains a locus capable of conferring resistance to ϕT1 irradiated with ultraviolet light. Substituting 5-bromodeoxyuridine for the thymidine in the phage, however, removes this protection. What do you suppose is the product and mechanism of action of the bacterial locus involved?

Chapter 32

GENE ACTION
AND POLYPEPTIDES

URING interphase, the nucleus plays a very active and essential role in the normal metabolism of the cell. Let us make the oversimplified assumptions that chromosomal genes are the only nuclear components essential for normal metabolism, and that all of the features of metabolism unique to cells are the consequence of gene action. On this basis, then, all aspects of the phenotype that are genetic in origin result from biochemical effects of the genes. Because a cell contains a great variety of chemical substances, we expect one gene-initiated biochemical reaction to lead to others which, in turn, will lead to still others, forming a kind of tree whose branches represent successive chemical reactions. Since all the branches would be affected by the initial, gene-caused biochemical change, we should find many different chemical, physiological, and morphological consequences of the initial change in the fully-developed cell or individual. It is not surprising, therefore, that a given genetic change usually has many different effects upon the phenotype and that most, if not all, mutants have manifold or *pleiotropic* effects (Chapter 6). In tracing these pleiotropic effects back toward their origin, we would expect the many different end effects to be the consequence of fewer earlier-produced effects. Moreover, we would expect their more primary causes to be based upon metabolic changes—changes sometimes identifiable with modifications of particular

404

chemical substances such as hemoglobin or pituitary hormone (Chapter 6).

With this orientation in mind, we can begin a study of the biochemical basis of gene action—*biochemical genetics*. Information regarding the biochemical basis of gene action may be gained by studying a trait such as pigmentation, which, because it is describable in chemical terms, may require relatively few steps back to arrive at or near the primary, gene-caused biochemical changes.

Alcaptonuria

In man, a rare condition detectable at birth affects the color of urine. Though normal in color when passed, it soon darkens on contact with air and turns from light to dark brown and finally to black. This characteristic persists throughout the life of the individual.

Family, pedigree, and population studies reveal that normal parents can have affected children of either sex, and that affected children appear with a much higher incidence when their parents—both normal—are related. From the frequency of those affected within families, and the finding that the blackening of the urine is expressed fully or not expressed at all, we can conclude that affected individuals are homozygous for a single pair of completely-recessive, autosomal genes.

The blackening is due to the oxidation of a substance in urine called *alcapton* or *homogentisic acid* whose chemical description is 2,5-dihydroxyphenylacetic acid (Figure 32–1). The disease is called *alcaptonuria* [1] and affected individuals, *alcaptonurics*. It should also be noted that several pedigrees have been found in which apparently the same phenotype is attributable to the action of a single, dominant gene. Since biochemical studies of dominant alcaptonuria have not been extensive, our attention is

[1] The account following is based upon the work of A. E. Garrod and subsequent investigators.

henceforth restricted to the recessive form of this disease.

Alcaptonuria is clearly an *inborn error of metabolism* and results in the daily excretion of several grams of alcapton. A study of the biochemistry of alcaptonurics shows that, of numerous substances tested, only alcapton appears in abnormal quantities in the urine or blood, and that the reducing properties of the urine can be attributed entirely to the alcapton it contains. These results suggest that we have traced the pedigree of causes back to, or very close to, the primary effect of the gene.

If alcapton is a substance produced by the abnormal gene, it should be absent in homo-

FIGURE 32–1. *Sequence of chemical substances involved in the formation and metabolism of alcapton. 4 = homogentisic oxidase, 5 = isomerase, 6 = hydrolase. 3 involves two reactions—first an oxidation to 2,5-dihydroxyphenylpyruvic acid, then oxidative decarboxylation.*

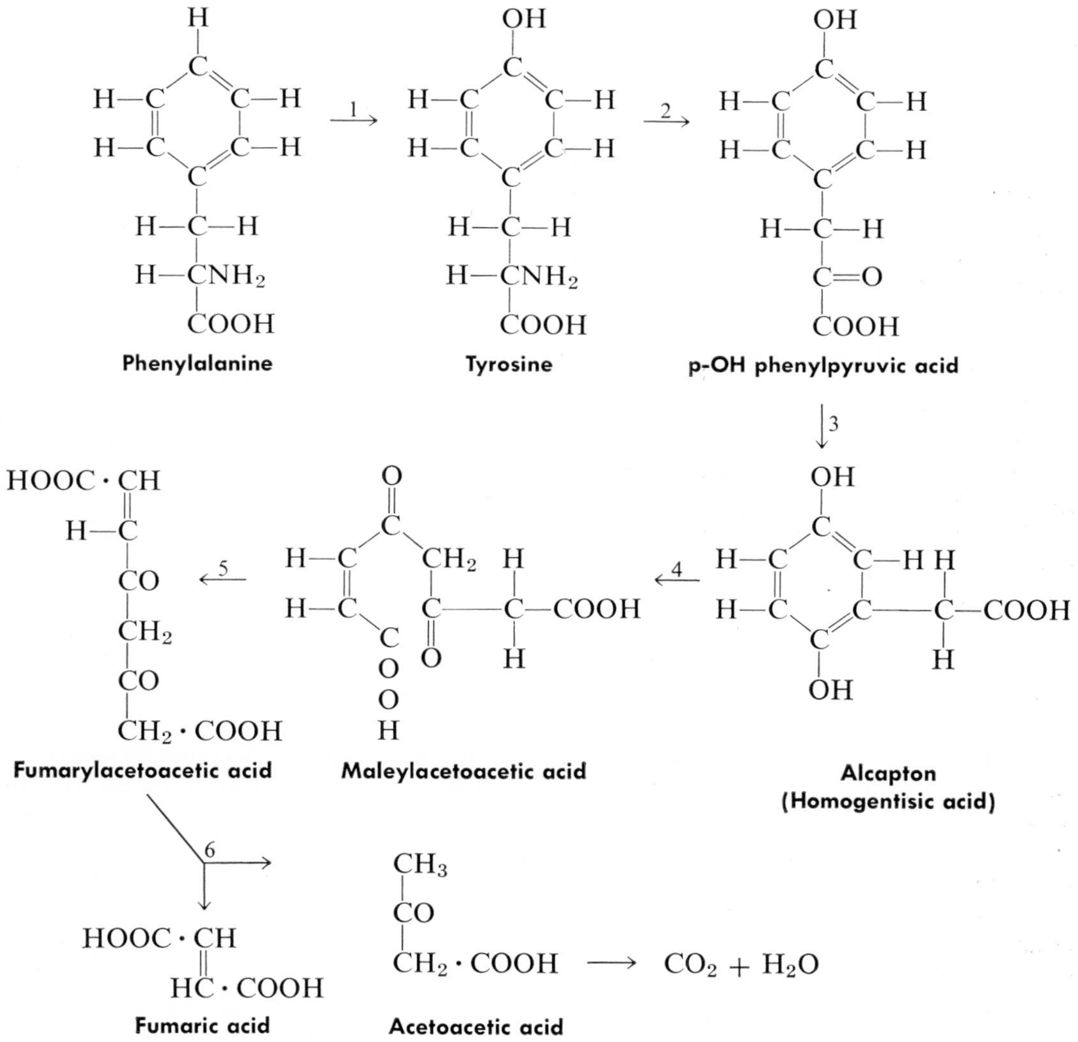

Phenylalanine → (1) → Tyrosine → (2) → p-OH phenylpyruvic acid → (3) → Alcapton (Homogentisic acid) → (4) → Maleylacetoacetic acid → (5) → Fumarylacetoacetic acid

Fumarylacetoacetic acid → (6) → Fumaric acid + Acetoacetic acid

Acetoacetic acid (CH_3—CO—$CH_2 \cdot COOH$) → $CO_2 + H_2O$

zygotes for the normal allele. When alcaptonurics are fed five grams of alcapton, approximately this additional amount is excreted in the urine. But when normal individuals are fed the same quantity of alcapton, none is found in the urine. If, however, normal individuals are fed eight grams of alcapton, some is found in the urine. We can conclude from these observations that normal people have the ability to metabolize alcapton to another form which does not change color upon exposure to air and that this ability has been lost, apparently completely, by alcaptonurics. The abnormal gene, therefore, does not produce its effect by forming alcapton as a unique substance. Alcapton seems to be a normal metabolic product which does not accumulate in normal individuals because it is rapidly metabolized, but which does accumulate in alcaptonurics. The blood of alcaptonurics proves to be deficient in a normally present enzyme which catalyzes the conversion of alcapton by oxidation to a noncolor-producing substance. This enzyme, *homogentisic oxidase,* is, in fact, missing in the liver of the alcaptonuric; thus, it must be this enzyme which is changed in alcaptonurics.

It is clear, therefore, that alcapton is not produced by the gene for alcaptonuria but is a normal metabolic intermediate. Since it is not part of the normal diet, alcapton should have chemical precursors. If such a precursor of alcapton is added to the diet of alcaptonurics, it should be converted to alcapton which, in turn, would be excreted in increased amounts. When alcaptonurics are fed an excess of glucose, the amount of alcapton found in the urine is unchanged, indicating that glucose is not a precursor of alcapton. But, if p-OH phenylpyruvic acid or if either of the amino acids, tyrosine or phenylalanine, is increased in the diet of alcaptonurics, their excretion of alcapton is increased almost correspondingly. We can, therefore, postulate that alcapton has a series

of chemical precursors (Figure 32–1). In the scheme illustrated, phenylalanine is converted to tyrosine by the addition of an oxygen to the top carbon; tyrosine is converted to p-OH phenylpyruvic acid by replacing the amine (NH_2) group by an oxygen; p-OH phenylpyruvic acid is converted by still other chemical reactions to alcapton. Normally, alcapton is converted to acetoacetic acid by a process which involves the oxidation and splitting-open of the benzene ring; it is the first step in this conversion which fails in alcaptonurics. This hypothesized pathway from phenylalanine through alcapton to acetoacetic acid has been confirmed in subsequent work and seven enzymatically-catalyzed steps have been identified.

It should be realized, however, that tyrosine, an essential component of protein, can also partake in biochemical pathways other than the one leading to alcapton (Figure 32–1). For example, tyrosine is part of the pathway of chemical reactions leading to melanin formation; and so tyrosine, by a different chemical pathway, is also a precursor of melanin. Albinism (lack or absence of melanin) could be caused genetically by the defective production of an enzyme necessary for the conversion of tyrosine to melanin.

In another disease due to a single, rare, recessive gene, affected individuals are feebleminded or of lower than normal mental ability and have other phenotypic changes including light pigmentation. This pleiotropism is directly correlated with the presence of phenylpyruvic acid in the urine of affected individuals. The normal conversion of phenylalanine to tyrosine fails to occur in such individuals; instead, the amine in phenylalanine is replaced by an oxygen (thus forming a keto group), so that phenylpyruvic acid is produced (Figure 32–2). Diseased persons are therefore called *phenylpyruvics* or *phenylketonurics* (Chapter 15). The disease, *phenylketonuria,* can be partially allevi-

H
|
C
H—C   C—H
H—C   C—H
C
|
H—C—H
|
C=O
|
COOH

FIGURE 32–2.
Formula for phenylpyruvic acid.

ated or circumvented if phenylalanine—which is essential to proteins—is reduced in the diet to an amount sufficient for protein synthesis but insufficient for any appreciable quantity to be converted into phenylpyruvic acid. Since tyrosine is also needed for human protein, it must be present in sufficient quantity in the diet of phenylketonurics. Finally, it should be noted that a *parahydroxylase*, which converts phenylalanine to tyrosine and is normally present in the liver (where most of the phenylalanine is normally metabolized and oxidized), has not been found in phenylketonurics.

Inborn metabolic defects are of great help in identifying the places where genes direct metabolic processes. They also permit the determination of precursors of a genetically-defective step and aid in the study of chains of biochemical reactions and metabolic pathways. For example, if mutant 1 cannot form substance Y but accumulates substance X, and if mutant 2 can only form Y when X is supplied, then X must be a precursor of Y (Figure 32–3).

Biochemical genetics is of special interest in another respect. In the cases most thoroughly investigated, one can trace the pedigree of causes back to a point where only one effect of the gene is detected, for example, as in alcaptonuria. It is quite improbable that further study of the gene for al-

captonuria will reveal another phenotypic effect which, when tested adequately, will prove to be produced independent of the effect upon homogentisic oxidase. Present findings suggest, therefore, that this gene acts upon the phenotype only in one, primary way.

One Gene-One Primary Effect Hypothesis

The study of biochemical genetics in this chapter (and also in Chapter 6) leads us to hypothesize that each gene has only a single, primary, phenotypic effect and that all the pleiotropic effects of a gene stem from this single activity. If the hypothesis of *one gene-one primary phenotypic effect* is substantiated, we may be able to determine the size or scope of the genetic material whose action produces a single, primary effect. Such information would reveal the nature of the functional genetic unit, but it should be realized that this kind of information will de-

FIGURE 32–3.
Determination of precursors using mutant genes.
A accumulates X but makes no Y.
B makes no X but will make Y if X is supplied.
C is the normal pathway.

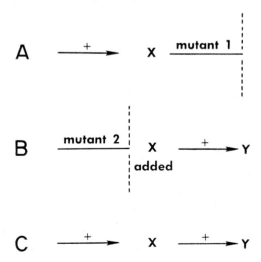

pend upon what is considered to be primary and what is identified as a phenotypic effect.

An additional implication of the one gene-one primary effect hypothesis is that if we know the nature of a primary effect, it should always be the result of one gene. To test this prediction, it is necessary to decide which particular aspects of the phenotype are primary effects of gene action.

The cases just discussed indicate that a mutant gene has a primary effect upon the catalytic ability of an enzyme. If we assume that the catalytic abilities of all enzymes result from the primary action of genes, it should be possible to study any particular enzyme and find that its catalytic ability can be altered or abolished as the result of mutation. Experimental support for this *one enzyme-one gene hypothesis* would also provide specific—though limited—support for the more general concept of one gene-one primary phenotypic effect.

One Enzyme-One Gene Hypothesis

Not only is Neurospora a good organism for studying genetic recombination (p. 124), but it has certain very favorable characteristics for biochemical studies. Neurospora can manufacture all the components it needs to exist and to reproduce from a basic, very simple, food medium consisting of water; an array of inorganic salts; sources of nitrogen, phosphorus, sulfur; various trace elements; a carbon and energy source such as a sugar; and a single vitamin, biotin. From these raw materials it can synthesize all twenty different amino acids, all essential vitamins (except biotin), purines and pyrimidines, and everything else needed for its total activity. According to the hypothesis under consideration, it should be possible to induce mutants that change the catalytic ability of enzymes, thereby blocking various chemical syntheses.

Previous work has established that the last step in the synthesis of *vitamin B_1*, or *thiamin,* is normally accomplished by the enzymatic combination of a particular thiazole with a particular pyrimidine. If the catalytic action of every enzyme depends upon the primary action of genes, it should be possible to induce a mutation in the gene that normally specifies this B_1-forming enzyme. If the mutant no longer produces the active B_1-forming enzyme, no B_1 will be made. Since B_1 is required for growth, the mutant mold will be auxotrophic and require B_1 in its diet to grow.

An experiment can be performed [2] in which asexually-produced, haploid spores (p. 26) are treated with a mutagenic agent such as X rays or ultraviolet light. The treated spores are then grown on the basic medium supplemented with vitamin B_1. The spores that grow include prototrophs for B_1 as well as auxotrophs which obtain their B_1 from the culture medium. Once the spores have grown sufficiently, a portion of each of the growths is placed on a basic, minimal medium supplemented with the particular thiazole and pyrimidine that are the immediate precursors of vitamin B_1. (All other imaginable nutritional factors except B_1 itself can also be added, but they will have no effect on the outcome.) Cultures which fail to grow on a medium which contains the immediate precursors of B_1 are clearly defective for the enzyme that catalyzes the last step in B_1 synthesis. Stocks of such cultures are made from samples growing in the presence of B_1. To test for and localize the genetic basis for the B_1 auxotrophy, each of these haploid strains is crossed to a haploid strain normal for B_1 synthesis. The diploid hybrid is formed and undergoes meiosis (pp. 124–126), producing a sac containing eight haploid ascospores. Each spore is removed and grown on a B_1-supplemented minimal medium. If the haploid strain under test were B_1-deficient because of a mutation, transplants of each of the eight haploid cul-

[2] Based upon work of G. W. Beadle and E. L. Tatum.

tures to a B_1-free minimal medium would produce exactly four that can grow and exactly four that cannot. As expected from our hypothesis, mutants are found which lack B_1 and do not contain this final enzymatic activity.

If for a given mutant, a number of spore sacs are tested as described, the locus of the mutant relative to the centromere of the chromosome in which it is located can be mapped (see Figure 9–10, p. 125). When no chiasma occurs between the loci of the mutant and the centromere, segregation of normal $(+)$ and mutant (th) alleles occurs at the first meiotic division and—because the last two divisions in the ascus are tandem to the first—the eight ascospores occur in the relative order,

$$+ + + + \; th \; th \; th \; th.$$

However, when a single chiasma occurs between the mutant and the centromere, segregation occurs in the second meiotic division, and the ascospores occur in the relative order,

$$+ + \; th \; th \; + + \; th \; th.$$

If a record is kept of the order of the spores in each ascus, the first and second division segregation arrangements can be identified after the spores are grown and their genotypes determined. It should be recalled that if 20% of all sacs show second-division segregation (two $+$ spores alternating with two th spores), then 20% of the tetrads had a chiasma between the mutant and the centromere, and the mutant is located ten map units from the centromere.

When a number of separately-occurring point mutants, defective in the enzyme which catalyzes the last step in B_1 synthesis, are localized this way, all are found to be on the same chromosome and approximately the same distance from the centromere. This result suggests that the catalytic ability of a particular enzyme is the result of the action of a particular gene.

For the efficient detection of biochemical mutants in Neurospora, certain modifications are made in the procedure already outlined. Potentially-mutant spores are grown on a medium supplemented with all substances which might conceivably be involved in biochemical mutation. Growing cultures are then transferred to a basic (minimal) medium containing no additions, where failure to grow indicates that the mutant culture has lost the ability to synthesize some component added to the basic medium. The specific ability lost is determined by testing for growth in a basic medium supplemented, in turn, with the individual enriching components of the complete medium. Techniques have been developed also to eliminate nonmutant strains selectively. Thus, spores given an opportunity to grow for a short time on a minimal medium can be subjected either to filtration, which separates the larger, (growing) nonmutant cultures from the smaller, (nongrowing) mutant ones, or to an antibiotic which kills actively-growing cultures but has less or no effect on nongrowing ones. In this way, the sample later tested for mutants can be mutant-enriched. It is even possible to find mutants for unknown growth factors by supplementing the culture medium with extracts of normal strains of Neurospora containing various substances, both known and unknown, needed by the mold. The same mutants requiring unknown growth factors can then be used in the specific assays needed for the isolation and identification of such substances.

Such improvements in the techniques for detecting biochemical mutants in Neurospora expedite additional tests of the postulated enzyme-gene relationship. Two more tests are described briefly. The first deals with the final step in the synthesis of the amino acid tryptophan and involves the catalyzed union of indole (in the substrate indole-glycerol phosphate) and the 3-carbon amino acid, serine, by the enzyme, *tryptophan syn-thetase*. Separately occurring tryptophan-requiring point mutants are obtained which are blocked in the final synthetic step. All of 25 mutants qualifying prove to be located on the same chromosome and at about the same locus. The second test involves the final step in the synthesis of adenine, catalyzed by the enzyme, *adenylosuccinase,* which removes succinic acid from adenylo-succinic acid to leave adenine. Of 137 independently occurring point mutations with little or no adenylosuccinase activity, all prove again to be on the same chromosome and at about the same locus. The genes specifying different enzymes are different, each occupying separate loci in the genome.

These results and similar ones for other enzymes in Neurospora offer strong support for the hypothesis that the catalytic ability of all enzymes is under gene control. Moreover, the addition of B_1, tryptophan, or adenine to the diet of mutants defective in the enzymes directly responsible for their respective syntheses makes the mold completely or almost completely normal, providing good evidence that the genes involved have only one function to perform—determining the catalytic ability of one enzyme. If a gene had more than one primary effect, nutritionally overcoming one defect would not be expected to produce normality or near-normality in all cases. Because in all these cases the enzymatic defect is due to a defect only in one specific, localized area of the genetic map, the total catalytic ability of an enzyme seems to be the result of the primary action of a single gene.

One Gene-One Polypeptide Hypothesis

All enzymes are protein, at least in part, and the catalytic ability of an enzyme is known to be due to its protein content and often added co-factors. Proteins are composed of amino acids (Figure 32–4) linked to each other by peptide bonds between carboxyl and amino groups to form polypeptide chains. The catalytic ability of an enzyme depends upon the number and kinds of amino acids contained, their order in the polypeptide, the number of polypeptide chains, the way in which the parts of a polypeptide chain are arranged relative to each other, and the way in which the different polypeptide chains in a protein are arranged relative to each other.

The enzyme, tryptophan synthetase, found in *Escherichia coli,* can be treated *in vitro* so that it dissociates into two proteins, that is, two polypeptide chains. Neither single chain has the usual enzymatic activity but, when the two chains are reassociated, normal enzymatic activity is restored. Clearly, to have the specific enzymatic action both chains need to be joined. Since the two chains are so easily dissociable and reassociable, probably no complex gene-directed physical or chemical change is needed to join them together. Therefore, the basis for the catalyzing ability of the enzyme must reside primarily in the nature of the polypeptide chains which, when joined, make not just any enzyme, but tryptophan synthetase in particular. This reasoning leads to the suggestion that each chain might be the result of the primary action of a different gene.

A number of bacterial mutants lacking tryptophan synthetase activity can be obtained.[3] Some of them are defective in one polypeptide chain, and others are defective in the second. All the mutants causing defects in one chain are found to be recombinationally separable from those producing defects in the other, although adjacent areas of the genetic map are involved. In this case we have the choice of considering the two adjacent areas either as a single functional gene or as two separate genes. Because the nature of this enzyme seems to

[3] Based upon the work of C. Yanofsky.

depend upon what each of these two genetic areas does individually, it is considered that two genes are involved, and that each gene completely specifies a polypeptide chain.

The union of the two chains comprising tryptophan synthetase may somehow be related to the two genes involved being adjacent.

FIGURE 32–4. *The twenty types of common amino acids.*

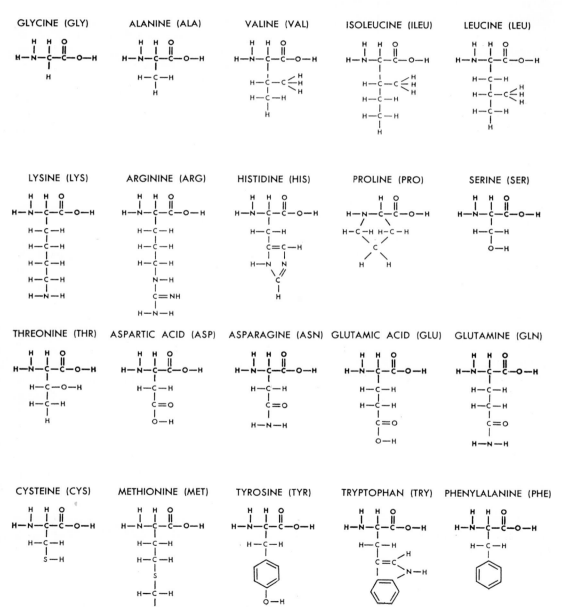

What bearing have these results upon the general hypothesis of one gene-one primary phenotypic effect? Although the general hypothesis is unaffected, the specific hypothesis to test it—one enzyme-one gene—should be made more comprehensive and should be stated as *one polypeptide-one gene,* meaning that the composition of a polypeptide chain is completely determined by one gene. According to the general hypothesis, then, *the primary effect of at least some genes is to specify completely the amino acid content of a polypeptide.* If the one polypeptide-one gene hypothesis is correct, we expect *every polypeptide chain* in every protein—including proteins that are not enzymes—to be completely *specified by the primary and solitary action of a single gene.*

Biochemical Genetics of Hemoglobin

In man, hemoglobin [4] is a protein with a molecular weight of about 66,700. In the horse (and probably in man) the shape of the molecule is spheroidal; its dimensions are 55 by 55 by 70 A; and it is composed of two dimers. Each dimer is composed of two identical polypeptide chains and the polypeptides in the two dimers are usually different. Each of the four monomeric chains contains about 140 amino acids and has a molecular weight of about 17,000. The chains partly coil to form what are called right-handed helices, and different chains are coiled about each other in a regular way. An iron-containing heme group fits into a pocket on the outer surface of the coil of each chain. In the whole hemoglobin molecule, therefore, there are four heme groups—one for each of the chains—and a total of about 560 amino acids. Since the heme groups are not involved in the variations to be considered, we shall henceforth be concerned only with the protein, or globin, part of the molecule.

Hemoglobin isolated from normal adults contains three components: A (or A_1), A_2, and A_3. The A component, called *hemoglobin A* (*Hb-A*) comprises about 90% of the total hemoglobin and the A_2 component (*Hb-A_2*) about 2.5%. The remaining percentage of about 7.5 is due to the A_3 component, probably Hb-A that has become chemically altered during aging of the red blood corpuscles.

Hemoglobin A. In vitro, Hb-A can be dissociated into the two kinds of homodimer, and can be reassociated to reform the Hb-A tetramer.[5] Since the monomers are called α^A and β^A, the reversible reaction can be written $\alpha_2^A \beta_2^A \rightleftharpoons \alpha_2^A + \beta_2^A$. The globin part of the molecule can also be partially digested with trypsin, which specifically cleaves the peptide bonds between the carboxyl group of lysine or arginine and the amino group of other amino acids. This digestion produces 28 smaller polypeptides, or peptides, in duplicate (since there are two chains of each type), plus an undigested core composed of about 25% of the original globin. The 28 peptides can be separated from each other since, on filter paper, they migrate at different rates when the digest containing them is subjected to an electrical field and various solvents. This treatment results in separate spots—"fingerprints"—on the filter paper for each of the peptides (Figure 32–5); each peptide (fingerprint) is given a different number and then analyzed for amino acid content. Peptide 4, for example, normally contains eight amino acids in the following sequence: Val-His-Leu-Thr-Pro-*Glu*-Glu-Lys. . . .[6] The core of globin can be digested with chymotrypsin and fingerprints obtained of

---

[4] Based upon the work of V. M. Ingram, L. Pauling, H. A. Itano, H. Lehrmann, J. V. Neel, M. F. Perutz, and others.

[5] See also G. Guidotti, W. Konigsberg, and L. C. Craig (1963).

[6] These abbreviations are explained in Figure 32–4.

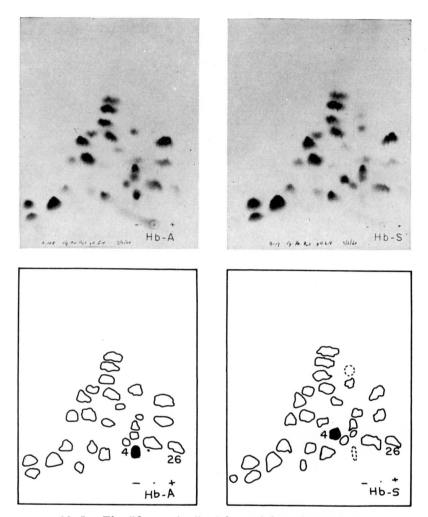

FIGURE 32–5. *The "fingerprints" of hemoglobin obtained after trypsin treatment. (Courtesy of V. M. Ingram, from C. Baglioni, Biochim. Biophys. Acta, 48:392–396, 1961.)*

its peptides. When these and other analytical procedures are carried out, the sequence of all the amino acids in the α^A and β^A chains can be determined (Figure 32–6). Note that the Val in peptide 4 is at the N-terminus of the β^A chain.

Persons heterozygous for the *gene for sickling* have the "sickle cell trait," readily detected when their red blood corpuscles

are exposed to an oxygen pressure very much lower than normal; persons homozygous for this mutant have "sickle cell anemia," and their red cells sickle even when the oxygen pressure is not so drastically reduced. The hemoglobin of both types of persons has been fingerprinted and analyzed for amino acid content. The hemoglobin of the mutant homozygote is identical with

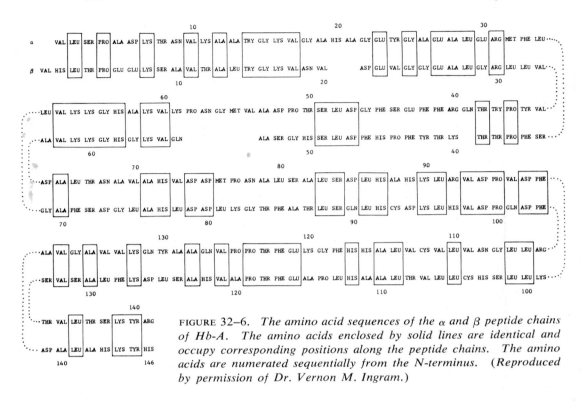

FIGURE 32–6. *The amino acid sequences of the α and β peptide chains of Hb-A. The amino acids enclosed by solid lines are identical and occupy corresponding positions along the peptide chains. The amino acids are numerated sequentially from the N-terminus. (Reproduced by permission of Dr. Vernon M. Ingram.)*

hemoglobin A, with the exception that the sixth amino acid in peptide 4 has valine substituted for glutamic acid (the particular amino acid italicized in the sequence given earlier in the text) (see also Figure 32–5). The heterozygote produces both this type of abnormal hemoglobin, called *hemoglobin S* (*Hb-S*) and hemoglobin A. Other studies of the gene for sickling (see Chapter 6 and p. 209) show that all of its manifold phenotypic effects are traceable through a pedigree of causes to this single amino acid substitution in the β^A chain.

Another mutant, known to be located on the same chromosome as the gene for sickling, produces *hemoglobin C* which differs from hemoglobin A by replacing the same glutamic acid in the β^A chain, this time with lysine. Still another genetic change produces another hemoglobin, *hemoglobin G*.

The amino acids in all the trypsin-produced peptides are the same as in hemoglobin A, except that the seventh one from the N-terminus in peptide 4 is glycine instead of glutamic acid. In this case, then, the amino acid sequence in peptide 4 is: Val-His-Leu-Thr-Pro-Glu-*Gly*-Lys. . . . Here, an amino acid in a different position—position 7—in the β^A chain is changed. In *hemoglobin E* a glutamic acid—normally found in position 26 on the β^A chain (see Figure 32–6)—is replaced by lysine; this probably is the only change in the whole molecule.

The preceding is evidence that different mutants cause single amino acids located in different positions in the β^A chain to be replaced by other single amino acids. Although the precise genetic basis for the different mutants is unknown, the available evidence strongly indicates that all these mutants are on the same chromosome. In fact, the simplest explanation is that the β^A chain is specified by a single gene whose various mutants cause the different single amino-acid substitutions mentioned.

Still other kinds of adult hemoglobin A are found. In some cases the amino acid sequence in the α chain is modified, as in *hemoglobin I* (in which a change occurs in position 16) and in *hemoglobin "Hopkins-2."* Since an adult homozygous for hemoglobin A has a molecule describable as $\alpha_2^A \beta_2^A$, an individual homozygous for the gene for sickling can have its hemoglobin described as $\alpha_2^A \beta_2^S$, and one homozygous for the production of hemoglobin I can have its molecule written $\alpha_2^I \beta_2^A$. A list of some of the genetically-determined chemical variants of Hb-A is given in Figure 32–7. In each case a single amino acid replacement is involved.

The biochemical genetics of Hb-A strongly supports the view that the synthesis of the nonenzymatic protein globin is a pri-

FIGURE 32–7. *Genetically determined variants of Hb-A.*

Hb Type		Amino Acid Position	Change Involved
β Chain	S	6	Glu ⟶ Val
	C	6	Glu ⟶ Lys
	G San José	7	Glu ⟶ Gly
	E	26	Glu ⟶ Lys
	M Saskatoon	63	His ⟶ Tyr
	Zürich	63	His ⟶ Arg
	M Milwaukee-1	67	Val ⟶ Glu
	O Arabia	121	Glu ⟶ Lys
	D Punjab (= D Cyprus)	121	Glu ⟶ Glu-NH$_2$
α Chain	I	16	Lys ⟶ Asp
	G Honolulu	30	Glu ⟶ Glu-NH$_2$
	Norfolk	57	Gly ⟶ Asp
	M Boston	58	His ⟶ Tyr
	G Philadelphia (= G Azakuoli)	68	Asp-NH$_2$ ⟶ Lys
	O Indonesia	116	Glu ⟶ Lys

mary effect of gene action. We would also like to decide whether one or more genes are involved in hemoglobin A synthesis. Several lines of evidence point to an independent specification of α and β chains:

1. Mutants that change the β chain (producing hemoglobins S, C, E, or G) produce no change in the α chain.
2. Mutants that change the α chain (producing hemoglobins I or Hopkins-2) produce no change in the β chain.

Further evidence consistent with the independent specification of α and β chains comes from the study of individuals possessing both Hopkins-2 and S hemoglobins. Such known individuals have one parent like themselves and the other of normal blood type (hemoglobin A). Also, these individuals have siblings with Hopkins-2 but not S hemoglobin, and others with the reverse. Consequently, such Hopkins-2 + S persons cannot be monohybrid and must be dihybrid, since the abnormal hemoglobins can occur separately or together in different siblings. Because the number of siblings who must be recombinant is quite large, the two loci are either unlinked or, if linked, cannot be very close together. We can write the genotype of these dihybrids as $\alpha^{\text{Ho-2}}\alpha^{A}\ \beta^{S}\beta^{A}$.

The two α and the two β chains in a given globin molecule are identical, even in heterozygotes. Since the Hopkins-2 + S individuals are dihybrid for mutants at widely separated loci, it seems reasonable that the two α chains specified by gene $\alpha^{\text{Ho-2}}$ (that is, $\alpha_2^{\text{Ho-2}}$) or by gene α^{A} (α_2^{A}) are produced independently of the two β chains specified by gene β^{S} (β_2^{S}) or by gene β^{A} (β_2^{A}). If so, either product of the two different α-specifying genes should be found joined to either of the two different products of the β-specifying genes. Accordingly, the dihybrid under discussion is expected to have all four of the following types of globin: $\alpha_2^{\text{Ho-2}}\beta_2^{S}$, $\alpha_2^{\text{Ho-2}}\beta_2^{A}$, $\alpha_2^{A}\beta_2^{S}$, $\alpha_2^{A}\beta_2^{A}$. This is found to be the case.[7]

Hemoglobin A_2. The Hb-A_2 tetramer present in normal adults can be dissociated into two dimers and fingerprinted separately. One dimer is identical with α_2^{A}; the other dimer is called $\delta_2^{A_2}$. The δ^{A_2} chain is very similar to the β^{A} chain, only 4 (or possibly 8) amino acid differences occurring among the 146 residues. Hb-A_2 is represented as $\alpha_2^{A}\delta_2^{A_2}$. Certain individuals are found[8] to produce only about half the normal amount of Hb-A_2. In place of the missing component is an equal amount of a new hemoglobin *Hb-B_2*. When fingerprinted, the chains of Hb-B_2 prove to have two α and two δ chains in the tetramer. Further analysis shows that the α chains are α_2^{A}—that is, normal—but a single amino acid is substituted in the δ chain which probably involves a change of Gly $\rightarrow$ Arg at position 16. Hb-B_2 can, therefore, be written $\alpha_2^{A}\delta_2^{B_2}$.

It should be noted that a person with Hb-B_2 makes normal Hb-A, thus leaving the β^{A} chain unaffected. The δ chain is presumably specified by a gene, δ, which is nonallelic to either the α^{A} or β^{A} genes. Moreover, a person that makes both Hb-A_2 and Hb-B_2 presumably is genetically hybrid —$\delta^{A_2}\delta^{B_2}$.

One study involved a man who made some Hb-S ($\alpha_2^{A}\beta_2^{S}$) and Hb-B_2 ($\alpha_2^{A}\delta_2^{B_2}$) and married a normal woman (with Hb-A, Hb-A_2). They had six children; those that made Hb-S did not make Hb-B_2, and vice versa. Since one of the hemoglobin defects in the father's hemoglobin was present in each of his parents, the simplest explanation is that the δ and β genes are linked and that no crossover recombinants occurred in

[7] See H. A. Itano and E. A. Robinson (1960), and C. Baglioni (1963).
[8] By R. Ceppellini.

his children. The father's genotype would be, therefore, $\frac{\alpha^A}{\alpha^A} \frac{\beta^S \delta^{A_2}}{\beta^A \delta^{B_2}}$. As expected, he actually made four kinds of hemoglobin— Hb-A, Hb-S, Hb-A$_2$, Hb-B$_2$. Finally, we find that, as expected, heterozygotes for Hb-I make not only Hb-A and Hb-I but also make Hb-A$_2$ and a defective Hb-A$_2$ composed of $\alpha_2^I \delta^{A_2}$. Dimers of the α chain apparently combine in a random way with dimers of the β and δ chains.

Hemoglobin F. The hemoglobin of the fetus *hemoglobin F* has two α chains like those in adult hemoglobin A. Accordingly, persons with mutant α^A genes make Hb-F whose α chains have the same abnormality as has Hb-A. The other two chains in Hb-F are different from the β, δ, and α chains and are called γ chains; thus, normal hemoglobin F is $\alpha_2^A \gamma_2^F$. The amino acid sequence in the γ^F chain of Hb-F is given in Figure 32–8. Homozygotes for the sick-ling gene can make hemoglobin F which is apparently normal, $\alpha_2^A \gamma_2^F$, so that a change in the β chains has no effect on the γ chains. Some known abnormal types of Hb-F are believed to be altered in the γ chain. It is very likely, therefore, that a separate gene, γ^F, specifies γ^F chains and has allelic alternatives. Hb-A appears in the fetus as early as the 20th week and gradually replaces Hb-F; even at parturition, however, there is still some Hb-F in the blood. The change from Hb-F to Hb-A means that during development the γ^F gene has its action turned off, so to speak, and gene β^A has its action turned on.

The preceding evidence indicates that four genes are involved in the manufacture of fetal and adult hemoglobin, namely—α, β, δ, and γ. All results support the view that each kind of polypeptide chain in hemoglobin is completely specified by a unique gene. Because heterozygotes for mutants

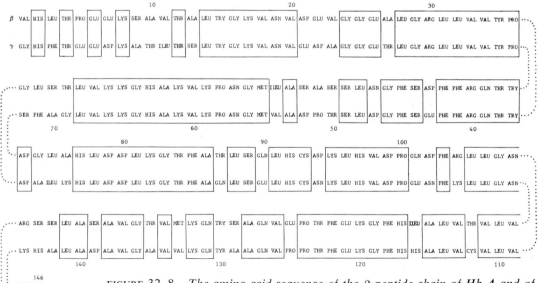

FIGURE 32–8. *The amino acid sequence of the β peptide chain of Hb-A and of the γ peptide chain of Hb-F. The amino acids enclosed by solid lines are identical and occupy corresponding positions along the peptide chains. The amino acids are numerated sequentially from the N-terminus. (Reproduced by permission of Dr. Vernon M. Ingram.)*

Present Genes

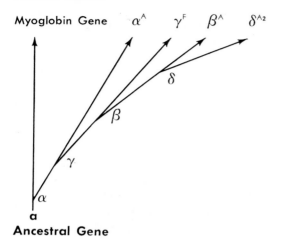

FIGURE 32–9. *Gene duplication and intragenic mutation hypothesis for the molecular evolution of myoglobin and hemoglobin.*

which specify hemoglobin are rare, and because the linkage maps of man are so incomplete, it is difficult to learn the precise relative positions of the various nonalleles. For the same reasons, it is difficult to study the allelism of hemoglobin mutants which affect the same chain.

* Molecular Evolution of Hemoglobin [9]

Present-day *myoglobin,* a protein in muscle, is composed of a single chain of 155 amino acids which partly forms a right-handed α helix and carries a single heme group on its surface. When the amino acid sequence of myoglobin is compared with that of the α or β chain of hemoglobin, a large number of differences are found. After accounting for the difference in chain length, however, a number of places still remain where the same amino acid occurs on both types of chain. These similarities probably explain why both types of chain have the same three-dimensional arrangement. Though it

[9] See V. M. Ingram (1961), and C. B. Anfinsen (1959).

is possible that some, if not all, of these similarities are due to convergent evolution by unrelated genes, we can postulate as the basis for the observed chain similarities that the genes specifying these present-day chains have a common gene ancestor (Figure 32–9).

According to this hypothesis, an ancestral gene, *a,* must have been duplicated in the genome by one of the mechanisms discussed in Chapter 12, since present-day species have separate loci for the specification of myoglobin and hemoglobin. Subsequent mutations of one gene could give rise to the present-day locus for myoglobin production, whereas mutations of the other gene could give rise to the ancestral locus for hemoglobin chains. Such mutations might result in the addition or—more likely—the removal or substitution of amino acids singly or in groups. This common-origin hypothesis is supported by the finding that the hemoglobin of the lamprey consists of a single polypeptide chain with a molecular weight of about 17,000 and that hagfish hemoglobin appears to be a similar monomer or possibly a dimer with a molecular weight of about 34,000.

Since all known hemoglobins of vertebrates, except for the lamprey, have a hemoglobin chain that starts with a Val-Leu sequence, they may all be products of mutants of α. Accordingly, it is suggested that the ancestral gene for hemoglobin is α and that after α arose, it mutated to an allele whose polypeptide product could form a dimer, since dimerization enhances α's efficiency as an oxygen carrier. Suppose, next, that the α locus became duplicated and that one of the resultant loci mutated to γ, which produced γ chains, which, in turn, formed not only dimers but also tetramers with the α dimers. The tetramer would be a fetal-type hemoglobin $\alpha_2\gamma_2$. Tetrameric hemoglobin is presumably more efficient than dimeric hemoglobin.

From which gene, α or γ, did the gene for β chains arise? Since the β^A chain is known to differ from both the α^A and γ^F chains by about 21 to 23 amino acids, we are told nothing about which of the last two was the ancestral type of the β chain. Although just about as many mutants involving the α as the β chain have been discovered, only those affecting the β chain occur in the population with any appreciable frequency. This finding, together with the similarities between vertebrate α chains mentioned earlier, suggests that in the tetramer changes in the α dimer produce a greater selective disadvantage than those in the β chain. Remember that a change in gene α^A modifies both fetal and adult hemoglobin. It may also be that certain α chain changes result in loss of ability to form tetramers. The homotetramer of α, α_4^A, may not be possible, although β chains can form β_4^A and γ chains can form γ_4^F. We, thus, conclude that the ancestral β gene was probably derived from one of the products of a duplication of the γ gene.

As mentioned previously, the β^A and δ^{A_2} chains differ in less than ten amino acids. Presumably, the β gene was duplicated in the genome, and one of the two resultant genes mutated to become the δ gene; that the duplication is recent is suggested by the small number of amino acid differences between the β^A and δ^{A_2} chains; by the apparent persistence of linkage of the β^A and δ^{A_2} genes; and by the restriction in the occurrence of A_2-like hemoglobin to the primates. In summary, it is likely that by means of gene duplication and intragenic mutations, the ancestral gene, a, gave rise to the myoglobin gene on one hand and the gene sequence, $\alpha \rightarrow \gamma \rightarrow \beta \rightarrow \delta$, on the other. Since polypeptides are apparently primary products of gene action, the study of polypeptides should considerably advance our understanding of the molecular basis of evolution.

SUMMARY AND CONCLUSIONS

The biochemical activities necessary for the existence of protoplasm are controlled by the nucleus, presumably by the genes it contains. These chemical reactions occur in sequences that form many-branched, metabolic pathways leading to the chemical, physical, physiological, developmental, and morphological aspects of the phenotype. Because of this branching most, if not all, genes have pleiotropic effects.

The phenotypic differences produced by different alleles can be traced back toward the gene by a pedigree of causes. Such studies demonstrate that genes produce their effects at the metabolic level.

The study of inborn errors of metabolism in man demonstrates that by their influence upon enzymes genes control various steps in biochemical sequences, and in these cases, the effect on enzymes appears to be the primary and the only consequence of gene action.

In view of these experimental results, a one gene-one primary effect relationship is hypothesized—that a gene produces only one primary effect and that any primary effect is the result of the action of a single gene. The specific hypothesis, one enzyme-one gene, proposed as a test of the general hypothesis, is supported by biochemical and genetic studies of auxotrophy (for B_1, tryptophan, adenine, and other nutrients) in Neurospora.

The biochemical genetics of tryptophan synthetase in *E. coli* and of hemoglobin require that the hypothesis of "one enzyme-one gene" be generalized to "one polypeptide-one gene." Thus, we consider that the amino acid content of each polypeptide is specified completely by the primary action of a single gene. The one gene-one primary effect hypothesis is therefore supported, and it is concluded that one way for a gene to act in a primary way is to specify polypeptide amino acid content. Consequently, the way is opened for the study of evolution at the biochemical level. The molecular evolution of hemoglobin is discussed.

REFERENCES

Anfinsen, C. B., *The Molecular Basis of Evolution,* New York: J. Wiley & Sons, 1959.

Baglioni, C., "Correlations between Genetics and Chemistry of Human Hemoglobins," Chap. 9, pp. 405–475, in *Molecular Genetics, Part I,* Taylor, J. H. (Ed.), New York: Academic Press, 1963.

Beadle, G. W., and Tatum, E. L., "Genetic Control of Biochemical Reactions in Neurospora," Proc. Nat. Acad. Sci., U.S., 27:499–506, 1941. Reprinted in *Classic Papers in Genetics,* Peters, J. A. (Ed.), Englewood Cliffs, N.J.: Prentice-Hall, 1959, pp. 166–173.

Bearn, A. G., "The Chemistry of Hereditary Disease," Scient. Amer., 195:126–136, 1956.

Bonner, D. M., and Mills, S. E., *Heredity,* 2nd Ed., Englewood Cliffs., N.J.: Prentice-Hall, Inc., 1964.

Guidotti, G., Konigsberg, W., and Craig, L. C., "On the Dissociation of Normal Adult Hemoglobin," Proc. Nat. Acad. Sci., U.S., 50:774–782, 1963.

Harris, H., *Human Biochemical Genetics,* Cambridge: Cambridge University Press, 1959.

Hsia, D. Y.-Y., *Inborn Errors of Metabolism,* Chicago: Year Book Publishers, 1959.

Human Genetics, Cold Spring Harb. Sympos. Quant. Biol., 29, 1965.

Ingram, V. M., "Gene Evolution and the Haemoglobins," Nature, 189:704–708, 1961. Reprinted in *Papers on Human Genetics,* Boyer, S. H., IV (Ed.), Englewood Cliffs, N.J.: Prentice-Hall, 1963, pp. 164–175.

Itano, H. A., and Robinson, E. A., "Genetic Control of α- and β-Chains of Hemoglobin," Proc. Nat. Acad. Sci., U.S., 46:1492–1501, 1960.

Kendrew, J. C., "Myoglobin and the Structure of Proteins," Nobel Prize Talk, Science, 193:1259–1266, 1963.

Nance, W. E., "Genetic Control of Hemoglobin Syntheses," Science, 141:123–130, 1963.

Wagner, R. P., and Mitchell, H. K., *Genetics and Metabolism,* 2nd Ed., New York: J. Wiley & Sons, 1964.

Yanofsky, C., and Crawford, L. P., "The Effects of Deletions, Point Mutations, Reversions and Suppressor Mutations on the Two Components of the Tryptophan Synthetase of Escherichia Coli," Proc. Nat. Acad. Sci., U.S., 45:1016–1026, 1959. Reprinted in *Papers on Bacterial Genetics,* Adelberg, E. A. (Ed.), Boston: Little, Brown, 1960, pp. 384–394.

See Supplement VI and the first portion of Supplement VII.

Harriet Ephrussi-Taylor (*see p. 296*), Boris Ephrussi, *and* Leo Szilard (*see p. 391*) *at Cold Spring Harbor, N.Y. in 1951.* (*Courtesy of the Long Island Biological Association.*)

QUESTIONS FOR DISCUSSION

32.1. List five diseases in man caused by inborn errors of metabolism.

32.2. In what respect can an inborn error of metabolism be cured?

32.3. Do all mutations produce inborn errors of metabolism? Explain.

32.4. What evidence can you present that genes control different steps of a biosynthetic sequence of reactions?

32.5. Is a study of mutation completely or partially dependent upon the concept of a functional genetic unit? Explain.

32.6. Do you suppose that proof of the one gene-one primary effect hypothesis would reveal anything about the chemical properties of a gene? Explain.

32.7. From which of these areas of investigation would you expect to obtain the most information regarding the gene—morphology, physiology, biochemistry? Why?

32.8. Do you think that the concept of a functional genetic unit has any consequences for the practice of medicine? Explain.

32.9. In what way is the study of a functional genetic unit related to or dependent upon mutation and the genetic recombinational unit?

32.10. Is it a significant fact that a glutamic acid in hemoglobin A is replaced by another amino acid (valine, lysine, or glycine) in hemoglobins S, C, G, and E? Explain.

32.11. What are the disadvantages of using human beings as material for investigation of the gene?

32.12. Using Neurospora, design an experiment to detect crossing over within a gene.

32.13. Is the one gene-one primary function hypothesis equivalent to the one polypeptide-one gene hypothesis? Why?

32.14. What evidence can you give for rejecting the hypothesis that a functional genetic unit is equivalent to a single genetic recombinational unit?

32.15. Would you expect a chemical substance specified in a primary way by a gene to be composed of linearly-arranged parts? Why?

32.16. Can you apply the term cistron to the one or more recombinational units that determine whether glutamic acid or lysine is located at a particular place in hemoglobin? Why?

32.17. What do genes actually do?   Has your answer any bearing upon the concept of a gene?   Explain.

32.18. Is it proper to use the term, allele, to describe functional genetic units rather than recombinational genetic units?   Explain.

32.19. What conclusions can you draw from the observation that most of the amino acid substitutions involved in abnormal hemoglobins appear to lie on the surface rather than in the interior of the fully-folded hemoglobin molecule?

32.20. How do you interpret the finding that during hemoglobin synthesis, short-term exposures to the isotope Fe^{59} reveal its incorporation into Hb-A and Hb-A_2 but not into Hb-A_3?

32.21. As indicated by arrows in the upper row of the accompanying diagram, transplantation of eye anlage (imaginal discs) between *D. melanogaster* larvae pure for dull-red (+) or bright-red—vermillion (v) or cinnabar (cn)—eye color genes produces adults with the eye colors indicated in the lower row.   From these results what can you conclude about the biochemical reactions leading to the production of brown eye color pigment?

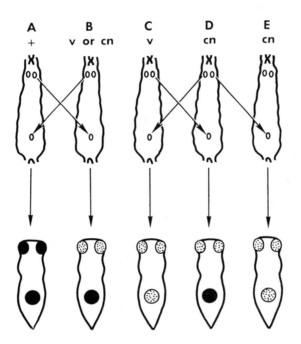

Chapter 33

POLYPEPTIDE
SYNTHESIS AND RNA

THE metabolism of an organism is regulated primarily by proteins whose purposes are both structural (to make subcellular organelles), and catalytic (to make enzymes). Since the structure and function of an organism is so dependent upon protein, it is not surprising that one of the primary effects of genes is to specify the amino acid content of polypeptides (Chapter 32).

Restricting our attention to DNA—the genetic material in most kinds of organisms—we ask, what can DNA do, or have done to it, which will result in the formation of particular polypeptide chains? Since we are dealing with *conserved DNA,* that is, DNA which remains part of a chromosome or other structure, whatever DNA does must happen *in situ.* Since DNA is not protein, it cannot be an enzyme and probably does not act as a catalyst in producing its effect on polypeptide formation. However, DNA might possibly serve as a kind of template for specifying a polypeptide. Because ribose is more reactive than deoxy-D-ribose, RNA is less stable than DNA. Consequently, being more inert, DNA is a more stable template than RNA.

We already know that after strand separation, each DNA strand serves as a template for the formation of a complementary strand. If DNA is also used as a template for gene functioning, then the four different bases—A, T, G, C—usually found in DNA must play a role in determining the nature of the

423

templates formed. In other words, the information for the genetic specification of a polypeptide by a template mechanism would have to be contained in the bases of DNA. The nature of a polypeptide depends ultimately upon its amino acid content. Many polypeptide chains contain one or more of each of the twenty amino acids commonly found in organisms (Figure 32–4, p. 411), and the number and sequence of these building blocks of polypeptides vary. Since both polypeptides and DNA are linear structures, the mechanism by which a sequence of DNA nucleotides serve as a template for specifying an amino acid sequence may be relatively simple to visualize.

Ribosomes

The synthesis of hemoglobin occurs in the cytoplasm of mammalian red blood corpuscles—cells which no longer have a nucleus. Since the cytoplasm is the only site for protein synthesis in this case, it is desirable to consider the structural components of the cytoplasm in some detail. For all cells which have been examined—plant, animal, and microorganismal—electron micrographs reveal numerous bodies, called *ribosomes* (see Figure 1–3 and Suppl. IX Fig. 2), in their cytoplasm. These are particularly abundant in cells actively synthesizing protein and are also found in the nucleus and in chloroplasts. Ribosomes isolated from ruptured cells are characterized by their sedimentation rate—measured in the ultracentrifuge and expressed in terms of *sedimentation units, s.* The fewer the s units, the smaller the particle, although the relationship is not linear; therefore, s values reflect ribosome size. *E. coli* has four discrete ribosomal units: 30s, 50s, 70s, and 100s. The two basic sizes are 30s and 50s, the larger units being composites of the basic ones, as indicated in Figure 33–1. Both the 30s and 50s particles contain about 64% RNA and 36% protein by weight. (Animal ribosomes are

WHOLE PARTICLE	O	O	OO	OOOO
Size	2(30s) +	2(50s) ⇌	2(70s) ⇌	1(100s)
Molecular Weight x 10⁶	0.85 ± 0.15	1.80 ± 0.15	2.8 ± 0.2	5.9 ± 1.0

RNA CONTENT		
Size	16s	23s
Molecular Weight x 10⁶	0.55 + 0.10	1.15 + 0.20

FIGURE 33–1. *Characteristics of* E. coli *ribosomes.*

50% RNA by weight.) The smaller units aggregate to form the larger ones when Mg^{++} or other divalent cations are added. Mammalian ribosomes behave similarly, although the basic particles, 40s and 60s, are somewhat larger than those in *E. coli*. The mammalian 80s particle (homologous to the *E. coli* 70s particle) results from the combination of one 40s and one 60s ribosome.

About 80% of the RNA in a cell is contained in ribosomes. (Small amounts of RNA are also reported in mitochondria.) Ribosomal RNA is single-stranded and has a relatively high molecular weight: $0.55 \pm 0.10 \times 10^6$ for the 16s RNA component of the 30s particle and $1.15 \pm 0.20 \times 10^6$ for the 23s RNA in the 50s particle; the number of nucleotides in 16s and 23s RNA is about 1000 and 2000. The 23s RNA, however, is not to be considered a dimer of 16s RNA because of evidence [1] that their genetic derivations are different. Moreover, the RNA of ribosomes complexes best with denatured homologous DNA, suggesting that the ribosomal RNA of different organisms differs in base sequence, if not base content.

The synthesis of the RNA of certain mammalian viruses is similar to 18s and 30s ribosomal RNA of mammalian cells in that both viral RNA replication and ribosomal RNA synthesis are inhibited by the drug *puromycin.* On the other hand, RNA viruses such as TMV are ribonucleoproteins whose protein portion is composed of a number of identical subunits (Figure 28–2), whereas the 30s ribosome contains ten, probably all different, polypeptide chains with a molecular weight of about 30,000. Clearly, the protein structure of ribosomes is more complicated than that of RNA viruses.

After radioactive amino acids are injected into the body, tissues which synthesize proteins rapidly can be examined at intervals.[2] When a large dose of labeled amino acid is injected, the ribosomes are labeled almost immediately. When a minute dose of labeled amino acid is injected it is expected to be used up rapidly in protein synthesis; the label in the ribosome increases quickly at first but then decreases. Finally, the labeled amino acid which moves out of the ribosomes is actually incorporated into protein, for example, hemoglobin. These experiments give us clear evidence that ribosomes are associated with protein synthesis. Since the amino acid sequence in hemoglobin is found to be a primary effect of the func-

[1] See S. A. Yankovsky and S. Spiegelman (1963), and S. Spiegelman (1964).

[2] The following is based on the work of P. C. Zamecnik and co-workers, and of M. Rabinovits and M. E. Olson.

tioning of DNA genes (Chapter 32), it is necessary to understand how a DNA template that remains in the nucleus of a reticulocyte orders the amino acid sequence of hemoglobin manufactured in the cytoplasm. Clearly, if the DNA functions as a template in this respect, it must be doing so indirectly.

DNA might be used to make another template, neither DNA nor protein, which can leave the nucleus and enter the cytoplasm where it will be used for protein synthesis. RNA fits this description, being a nucleic acid which also has a four-symbol code (A, U, C, and G) in which uracil (U) occurs in place of thymine (T). Such a mechanism would require the four-symbol code of DNA to be transcribed directly into the four-symbol code of RNA—that is, it would involve a problem of *transcription.* It would also require RNA to carry information translated into polypeptide sequences—that is, it would involve a problem of *translation.* Therefore, the multiple hypothesis is suggested that *DNA nucleotide sequence is transcribed into RNA nucleotide sequence which, in turn, is translated into amino acid sequence.*

Messenger RNA

Under normal circumstances, a considerable amount, if not all, of the RNA in higher organisms is synthesized in chromosomes and then transferred to the nucleolus. Subsequently, using radioactive tracers, RNA can be detected entering the cytoplasm. On the other hand, no evidence is found for a flow of RNA from the cytoplasm to the nucleus. These results are consistent with the hypothesis under consideration.

The relationship between RNA synthesis and DNA can be studied in bacteria. RNA is synthesized in bacteria after infection with a DNA phage whose base ratio differs from that of the host DNA. The RNA manufactured after phage infection is different from the RNA manufactured prior to infection; its base ratio depends upon that of phage, since only the RNA synthesized after infection can base pair *in vitro* with strand-separated phage DNA to form a hybrid double strand—one RNA and one DNA. (Hybrid RNA-DNA molecules have a unique specific density and, therefore, can be identified in the ultracentrifuge tube; they are also relatively resistant to RNase.) Also, freshly-made nuclear RNA from normal cells can form a complex with chromosomal deoxyribonucleoprotein.[3] Such results suggest the existence of a direct base-for-base dependence of nucleus-synthesized RNA and nuclear DNA.

As mentioned, RNA complementary to phage DNA is made after a DNA phage infects its host. This phage-specific RNA is found to attach to a small percentage of already-formed ribosomes, suggesting that at least some ribosomes do not permanently carry a template of RNA (obtained from the DNA template) containing information for the specification of an amino acid sequence. Such ribosomes are capable of receiving segments of RNA which carry the information for making phage-specific polypeptides. Thus, a type of RNA, called *messenger RNA* or *mRNA,* is synthesized. mRNA carries information for gene action from phage DNA to the ribosome. Presumably the messenger RNA causes the assembly of various amino acids at the ribosome where they are joined to form polypeptides. Messenger RNA is also found and functions in normal, uninfected cells.[4] The RNA genetic material of MSφ2 which infects *E. coli* is conserved during all replications (by RNA synthetase) and translations (by serving as a messenger RNA) which occur during a lytic cycle.[5]

[3] As shown by J. Bonner, R. C. Huang, and N. Maheshwari (1961).
[4] M. Hayashi and S. Spiegelman (1961); see S. Spiegelman (1964).
[5] As shown by A. H. Doi and S. Spiegelman (1963).

Messenger RNA can be made using DNA located in the cytoplasm as template; for instance, the DNA of the vaccinia virus in human-tissue culture cells.[6]

mRNA Synthesis

How is messenger RNA synthesized? DNA can replicate *in vitro* in the absence of RNA; such a replication probably also occurs in the nucleus, although there might be subtle, secondary interactions with RNA or protein. The evidence mentioned proves that mRNA synthesis is intimately related to DNA. It is found [7] that the nucleus normally contains an enzyme, *DNA-dependent RNA polymerase,* necessary for RNA synthesis. This enzymatic RNA synthesis can be performed *in vitro* and requires the presence of DNA as well as all four riboside triphosphates. Under certain conditions, the RNA synthesized has the same base ratio as its DNA primer-template (except, of course, that T is U). This situation is reminiscent of the synthesis of DNA, in which the DNA polymerase is directed by single-stranded DNA. *In vitro,* however, double-stranded DNA is a more effective primer in making RNA polymer than single-stranded DNA.

The DNA in mature ϕX174 is in the form of a single-stranded ring. In *E. coli,* ϕX174 in its *replicative form* (RF) is a double-stranded, circular, DNA helix. If the double ring is broken, RNA polymerase *in vitro* makes RNA complementary to both single-stranded DNA rods. If, however, the phage DNA is extracted carefully so that the circle or ring is not broken, the results indicate that only one of the two DNA strands will serve as template. Moreover, it is found *in vivo* as well as *in vitro* that the DNA circle serving as template for RNA polymerase is the same one used to produce the single-

stranded DNA found in the mature phage.[8] This finding not only proves the occurrence of *one-complement transcription* but seems to indicate that the control mechanism in this case at least requires the circular DNA double helix to be intact.

Not all RNA is made from a DNA template. We have already noted (p. 366) that, *in vivo,* viral RNA is used as a template by RNA synthetase (RNA-dependent RNA polymerase) to make complementary RNA. Moreover, *in vitro,* homopolyribotides of A, U, and C can also serve as templates in the synthesis of complementary RNA by an RNA polymerase.[9]

At low concentrations, *actinomycin D* binds with G-containing sites in DNA, thus selectively suppressing the synthesis of messenger RNA by RNA polymerase. Interference with DNA synthesis also occurs but at much higher concentrations. Experimental evidence suggests [10] that:

1. Actinomycin lies in the minor groove of DNA
2. The minor groove is the specific template site for DNA-dependent RNA polymerase
3. The major groove is the site for DNA polymerase action.

Ribosomal RNA

Since the typical chromosome of higher organisms contains RNA, some of the newly-synthesized RNA appears in the nucleus as part of parent and daughter chromosomes. Most of the newly-made RNA, however, leaves the chromosomes, and a considerable portion is presumably used in the manufacture of new ribosomes. Studies with *Bacillus*

[6] See Y. Becker and W. K. Joklik (1964).
[7] From the work of J. Hurwitz, of A. Stevens, of S. B. Weiss, their colleagues and others.

[8] See M. Hayashi, M. N. Hayashi, and S. Spiegelman (1963, 1964), B. Chandler, M. Hayashi, M. N. Hayashi, and S. Spiegelman (1964), and M. H. Green (1964).
[9] See J. S. Krakow and S. Ochoa (1963).
[10] See E. Reich (1964).

megaterium furnish evidence [11] that different segments of DNA are complements of 16s and 23s ribosomal RNA. Although completely-formed ribosomes do not accept large quantities of newly-formed RNA, labeling experiments show that a small amount of RNA turnover is associated with complete ribosomes. This turnover RNA is mRNA. Accordingly, the greater part of the RNA in ribosomes—*ribosomal RNA*—is usually incorporated at the time of ribosome formation. The precise mechanism by which RNA is incorporated into new ribosomes as ribonucleoprotein is still unknown.

The wild type of the toad *Xenopus laevis* usually has two nucleoli in its diploid cells. A recessive lethal mutant, called *anucleolate,* has one nucleolus when heterozygous and none when homozygous in which case the mutant has many small, nucleolar "blobs" instead of typical nucleoli. The mutation apparently involves the nucleolus organizer [12]—the region of the chromosome responsible for nucleolus formation (p. 11). The homozygous mutant also fails to synthesize ribosomal RNA which, in this organism, includes 18s and 28s types although small RNA molecules (4s), probably other RNA, and DNA continue to be made. Homozygous mutants, just as the normal homozygotes, conserve and apparently utilize the ribosomes contributed in the egg. The heterozygote produces the same amount of 28s and 18s ribosomal RNA as the normal homozygote. Since these two kinds of ribosomal RNA differ in base composition, they are probably products of separate DNA sequences. The synthesis of both types, however, is prevented by the single mutant whose molecular basis is unknown.

Since ribosomal RNA is complementary to about 0.6% of deoxyribotide pairs in bacteria and the mouse, many genes apparently are involved in the synthesis of ribosomal RNA. The results with anucleolates suggest that these genes are linked closely and can be controlled by a single genetic change. The DNA attached to nucleoli isolated from Hela human-tissue culture cells can be collected and heat denatured. Such single-stranded DNA forms molecular hybrids with ribosomal RNA. This result (together with others) shows that a concentration of DNA complementary to ribosomal RNA occurs in the nucleolus organizer region.

Transfer (Soluble or Adapter) RNA

As already mentioned, ribosomal RNA has a relatively high molecular weight (about one-half to one million). The cytoplasm contains another kind of RNA which has the relatively low molecular weight of about 18,000 and consists of about 67 nucleotides. Since this RNA is soluble in $\sim$ 1M NaCl and ribosomal RNA is not, it is called *soluble RNA or sRNA*. sRNA is probably also derived from nuclear RNA.[13] The use of radioactively-labeled amino acids shows that the amino acids arrive at the ribosomes individually, each attached to a molecule of soluble RNA. All the soluble RNA molecules are similar in their terminal nucleotides, one end terminating with the base G and the other end with the base sequence —C—C—A, and X-ray diffraction studies show them to be primarily in double-helix condition.[14] Since each sRNA is composed of a single strand, the molecule must be in the shape of a twisted "bobby pin" (Figure 33–2 and Suppl. IV, Fig. 12) or some similar highly base-paired configuration. The bobby pin terminates unevenly at the ends,

[11] See S. A. Yankovsky and S. Spiegelman (1963), and S. Spiegelman (1964).
[12] The subsequent discussion follows D. D. Brown and J. B. Gurdon (1964), and E. H. McConkey and J. W. Hopkins (1964).
[13] See M. I. H. Chipchase and M. L. Birnstiel (1963).
[14] See G. Zubay (1963), and Suppl. IV.

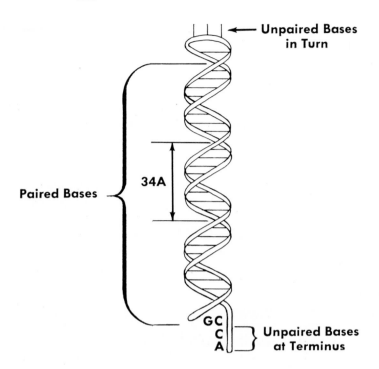

Unpaired Bases in Turn

Paired Bases

34A

G C
C
A

Unpaired Bases at Terminus

FIGURE 33–2.
*Proposed structure
for adapter RNA.*

and its sides contain about thirty base-pairs. It is calculated that no less than three unpaired nucleotides are needed to make the turn. Each of these RNA molecules is also similar, being about 100A long and 20A wide. In other respects, they are dissimilar: they are believed to differ internally in base content or sequence, and comprise about twenty different types, each capable of carrying a different one of the amino acids typically found in protein. Since sRNA forms base pairs best with denatured homologous DNA, the sRNAs of different species probably vary in their nucleotide sequences.[15] Because sRNA acts to transport the amino acids to the ribosomes, it is also called *transfer RNA.*

It is found that to form the amino acid-transfer RNA complex, each of the twenty acids must be activated before it is attached

to its particular transfer RNA. Activation involves the combination of the amino acid at its carboxyl end to the 2' or 3' hydroxyl group of adenosine triphosphate (ATP) with the removal of two phosphates as pyrophosphate. This reaction can be summarized as: amino acid + ATP $\rightleftharpoons$ amino acid adenylate + pyrophosphate. The attachment reaction can be summarized as: sRNA + amino acid adenylate $\rightleftharpoons$ amino acyl sRNA + adenylic acid. Both the activation of an amino acid and its attachment to soluble RNA may involve the activity of a single enzyme, probably a different one for each kind of amino acid.[16]

Each amino acid to be incorporated into a polypeptide is attached to a specific sRNA when it arrives at the ribosome. Since sRNA is probably not completely base-paired with itself, we can suppose that three (or more)

15 See D. Giacomoni and S. Spiegelman (1962), and S. Spiegelman (1964).

16 See A. T. Norris and P. Berg (1964).

unpaired bases (such as those making a bobby-pin turn) in sRNA H-bond with complementary bases in messenger RNA. Transfer RNA would, therefore, also function as an adapter, *adapter RNA,* leaving the end which carries the transported amino acid—A—C sequence sufficiently flexible to reach a similar region and make a peptide union.

About 2% of the purine and pyrimidine bases in sRNA are methylated. The methyl groups have their origin in the amino acid methionine (see Figure 32–4, p. 411), which becomes homocysteine upon losing the methyl group. Methylation occurs in bases which are already part of the polyribotide of sRNA. Several different enzymes, called RNA methylases, are involved in the synthesis of 1-methyl guanine, thymine, 5-methyl cytosine, 2-methyl adenine, 6-methylaminopurine, and 6-dimethylaminopurine. RNA methylase is found in the nucleolus and is different in different species. It has been suggested that the methylated bases occupy specific sites in sRNA and somehow play a role in sRNA function. In this connection it should be noted that methylated RNA is more resistant to a potassium-dependent ribo-exonuclease than unmethylated RNA. Some of the bases in ribosomal RNA are methylated. It should be recalled, with respect to DNA, that 5-methyl cytosine is present only in plants and animals, and 6-methyl adenine only in bacteria. DNA can also be methylated as a polydeoxyribotide, different enzymes being used to form 5-methyl cytosine (from C) and 6-methylaminopurine (from A).[17]

Polypeptide Synthesis

The 70s ribosome seems to be the smallest unit capable of participating in polypeptide synthesis, and observations indicate that the messenger RNA is bound to the 30s subunit. Messenger RNAs of various sizes can associate with a ribosome. It is likely, however, that only part of a messenger RNA is bound at one time, since ribonuclease in small amounts destroys messenger RNA but not ribosomes. When protein-synthesizing ribosomes are treated with RNase, the protein being synthesized remains attached to the ribosome. Therefore, the nascent protein is attached to the ribosome, not to messenger RNA.

Polypeptide chain formation is found [18] to proceed by the step-by-step addition of individual amino acids, beginning at the amino (or N-) terminal end. Consequently, the growing polypeptide chain should end at its carboxyl (or C-) terminal end with an sRNA molecule. Each ribosome has only two sites—both on the 50s subunit—for the attachment of sRNA. When no protein is being made, only one site can hold an sRNA molecule. When protein is being made, however, the second site holds the growing polypeptide chain, which terminates in an sRNA molecule [19] (Figure 33–3). Consequently, each functioning ribosome makes only one polypeptide chain at a time and receives only one messenger RNA at a time.

How does the ribosome function? Since transfer RNAs apparently form base-pairs with different parts of a messenger RNA strand, it becomes necessary to assume—using the present hypothesis—that each portion of messenger RNA carries its information in unpaired bases at the proper time. The 30s subunit apparently provides an adapter capacity which guarantees that successive segments of messenger RNA are single-stranded and have their bases prop-

---

[17] See articles by E. Borek; M. Gold and J. Hurwitz; and U. Z. Littauer, K. Muench, P. Berg, W. Gilbert, and P. F. Spahr in Cold Spring Harb. Sympos. Quant. Biol., 28:139–159, 1963.

[18] From work of H. Dintzes and of R. Schweet and collaborators.
[19] See J. R. Warner and A. Rich (1964).

erly exposed. The 50s subunit holds the recently-made portion of a polypeptide which ends in an sRNA molecule in such a way (see Figure 5, p. s-126) that:

1. The next correct, free amino acid-sRNA combination can pair—probably via the nucleotides at the bend of the sRNA molecule—with the next sequence in the messenger RNA
2. An enzyme can link the amino part of the free amino acid-sRNA complex to the carboxyl portion of the

amino-acid sRNA complex at the end of the polypeptide chain, liberating the sRNA molecule formerly bound to the end of the chain
3. The liberated sRNA is then free to accept another one of its specific amino acid molecules for transport.

It is not known how the sRNA at the end of a completed polypeptide is removed. It should also be noted that since the growing polypeptide chain appears attached to the 50s particle only at its growing end (this

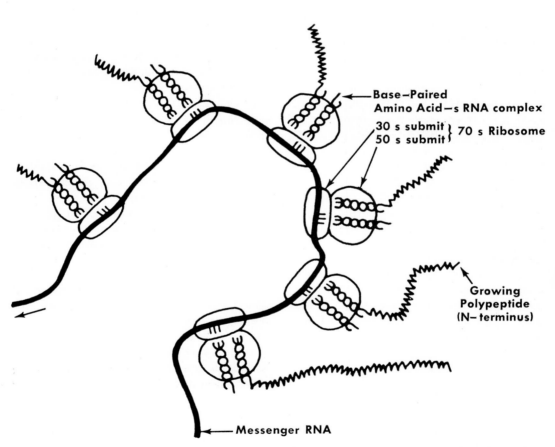

FIGURE 33–3. *Schematic representation of the hypothesized relation between messenger RNA, adapter RNA, ribosomes, and growing polypeptide chains.*

attachment requiring the presence of gua-nosine triphosphate), much of the final, three-dimensional configuration of the poly-peptide may be attained before its synthesis is completed.

Since only one specific ribosomal site ex-ists for peptide bond formation, the mes-senger RNA cannot remain in a constant position on a ribosome. Consequently, the messenger RNA template must move over or through the ribosomal surface. The di-ameter of a 70s ribosome is only about 230A. Messenger RNAs containing more than 1500 nucleotides have been detected; if the average internucleotide distance is 3.4A, this RNA would extend lengthwise more than 5000A. These facts suggest that several ribosomes can utilize the same messenger RNA simultaneously, the poly-peptide that each is making being at differ-ent stages of growth (Figure 33–3). Sup-porting this hypothesis is evidence that in some systems protein synthesis occurs among aggregates of five to eight 70s (or 80s) ribosomes. Such protein-synthesizing ribosomal aggregates—*polyribosomes* or *polysomes (ergosomes)*—can be seen in electron micrographs. When long messen-ger RNAs are involved, polysomes can con-tain dozens of ribosomes. Ribosomes that have completed a polypeptide synthesis are free to start the process again; each ribo-some is available for protein synthesis sev-eral times. Since ribosomes are found in the nucleus, it is not surprising that some protein synthesis occurs there.[20] Data ob-tained from *in vitro* studies suggest an in-termediate stage in protein synthesis in which DNA is joined to functionally com-petent ribosomes by means of mRNA. Such an intermediate stage *in vivo* would have important implications for the stabili-zation of mRNA and polarity of mRNA

attachment to the ribosome, as well as the regulation of protein synthesis.[21]

The synthesis of all normal bacterial pro-tein ceases within several minutes after the addition of the base analog, 5-fluoro uracil, to the medium in which the bacteria are be-ing cultured. Since this analog is quickly incorporated into the RNA being synthe-sized, the analog is expected to be incor-porated into new messenger RNA; to lead subsequently to the acceptance of incorrect adapter RNAs; and, therefore, to lead the manufacture of defective proteins. This expectation suggests that, in bacteria, fresh messenger RNA is made continuously and that old messenger RNA does not persist very long. As noted earlier, the synthesis of new messenger RNA from DNA is blocked by the addition of the antibiotic *actinomycin D*. Studies of bacteria treated with actinomycin D show that messenger RNA has a half-life of about two minutes and is available as a template only ten to twenty times. In other organisms, certain messenger RNAs—the one for hemoglobin, for example—persist for a longer period. The mechanism by which messenger RNA is degraded is still unknown. Perhaps ribo-nuclease is involved in this degradation, for much, if not all, of the bacterial cell's RNase is found, in latent form, attached to the 30s particle.[22] Moreover, where messenger RNA does not appear to be degraded, as in reticulocytes whose mRNA shows little turnover, there is also no evidence for a latent structural RNase on the ribosome. On the other hand, some evidence [23] indi-cates that *polynucleotide phosphorylase* de-stroys messenger RNA in microorganisms.

[20] As shown by A. E. Mirsky, V. G. Allfrey, and others.

[21] See R. Byrne, J. G. Levin, H. A. Bladen, and M. W. Nirenberg (1964).
[22] See M. Tal and D. Elson (1961), and also I. D. Raacke and J. Fiala (1964).
[23] Obtained by M. Sekiguchi and S. S. Cohen (1963); see also W. C. Hymer and E. L. Kuff (1964).

SUMMARY AND CONCLUSIONS

Under typical circumstances, RNA is synthesized in the chromosomes, and many—but not all—polypeptides are synthesized in the cytoplasm. DNA-dependent RNA polymerase transcribes the information in one strand of double-stranded DNA into complementary, single-stranded, messenger RNA. This mRNA becomes attached, probably at one end, to a ribosome. The ribosome functions to orient successive groups of bases in the messenger RNA, one group at a time, so that they can pair with unpaired complementary bases present in adapter RNA, each type of which transports a single different amino acid. Since a protein-synthesizing ribosome only accepts amino acid-adapter RNA molecules one at a time, the polypeptide chain grows by single amino acid steps (beginning at the N-terminus). As the messenger RNA is translated, it passes over (or through) the ribosomal surface, liberating the starting point to accept another ribosome at that position. Consequently, a number of ribosomes, comprising a polysome, simultaneously translate the same messenger RNA.

Ribosomes can be used a number of times; a given messenger RNA may be used ten to twenty times, and under some circumstances, many more; once liberated from the growing polypeptide chain, adapter RNA is free to accept another amino acid for transport.

REFERENCES

Allfrey, V. G., and Mirsky, A. E., "How Cells Make Molecules," Scient. Amer., 205: 74–82, 1961.

Bautz, E. K. F., and Hall, B. D., "The Isolation of T4-Specific RNA on a DNA-Cellulose Column," Proc. Nat. Acad. Sci., U.S., 48:400–408, 1962.

Becker, Y., and Joklik, W. K., "Messenger RNA in Cells Infected with Vaccinia Virus," Proc. Nat. Acad. Sci., U.S., 51:577–585, 1964.

Brenner, S., Jacob, F., and Meselson, M., "An Unstable Intermediate Carrying Information from Genes to Ribosomes for Protein Synthesis," Nature, London, 190: 576–581, 1961.

Brown, D. D., and Gurdon, J. B., "Absence of Ribosomal RNA Synthesis in the Anucleolate Mutant of Xenopus laevis," Proc. Nat. Acad. Sci., U.S., 51:139–146, 1964.

Byrne, R., Levin, J. G., Bladen, H. A., and Nirenberg, M. W., "The in vitro Formation of a DNA-Ribosome Complex," Proc. Nat. Acad. Sci., U.S., 52:140–148, 1964.

Chandler, M., Hayashi, M., Hayashi, M. N., and Spiegelman, S., "Circularity of the Replicating Form of a Single-Stranded DNA Virus," Science, 143:47–49, 1964.

Chipchase, M. I. H., and Birnstiel, M. L., "Synthesis of Transfer RNA by Isolated Nuclei," Proc. Nat. Acad. Sci., U.S., 49:692–699, 1963.

Crick, F. H. C., "Nucleic Acids," Scient. Amer., 197:188–200, 1957.

Crick, F. H. C., "On Protein Synthesis," Symp. Soc. Exp. Biol., 12:138–163, 1958.

Davidson, J. N., and Cohn, W. E. (Eds.), Progress in Nucleic Acid Research, Vol. 2, New York: Academic Press, 1963.

Furth, J. J., Hurwitz, J., and Goldman, M., "The Directing Role of DNA in RNA Synthesis," Biochem. Biophys. Res. Commun., 4:362–367, 1961.

Gay, H., "Nuclear Control of the Cell," Scient. Amer., 202 (No. 1):126–136, 1960.

Geiduschek, E. P., Moohr, J. W., and Weiss, S. B., "The Secondary Structure of Complementary RNA," Proc. Nat. Acad. Sci., U.S., 48:1078–1086, 1962.

SOL SPIEGELMAN,
in 1964.

Geiduschek, E. P., Nakamoto, T., and Weiss, S. B., "The Enzymatic Synthesis of RNA, Complementary Interaction with DNA," Proc. Nat. Acad. Sci., U.S., 47:1405–1415, 1961.

Giacomoni, D., and Spiegelman, S., "Origin and Biologic Individuality of the Genetic Dictionary," Science, 138:1328–1331, 1962.

Green, M. H., "Strand Selective Transcription of T4 DNA *in vitro,*" Proc. Nat. Acad. Sci., U.S., 52:1388–1395, 1964.

Gross, F., Hiatt, H., Gilbert, W., Kurland, C. G., Risebrough, R. W., and Watson, J. D., "Unstable Ribonucleic Acid Revealed by Pulse Labelling," Nature, London, 190:581–585, 1961.

Hall, B. D., and Spiegelman, S., "Sequence Complementarity of T2-DNA and T2-Specific RNA," Proc. Nat. Acad. Sci., U.S., 47:137–146, 1961.

Hayashi, M., Hayashi, M. N., and Spiegelman, S., "Restriction of *in vivo* Genetic Transcription to One of the Complementary Strands of DNA," Proc. Nat. Acad. Sci., U.S., 50:664–672, 1963.

Hayashi, M., Hayashi, M. N., and Spiegelman, S., "DNA Circularity and the Mechanism of Strand Selection in the Generation of Genetic Messages," Proc. Nat. Acad. Sci., U.S., 51:351–359, 1964.

Hoagland, M. B., "Nucleic Acids and Proteins," Scient. Amer., 201 (No. 6):55–61, 1959.

Hurwitz, J., and August, J. T., "The Role of DNA in RNA Synthesis," Progr. Nucleic Acid Res., 1:59–92, 1963.

Hurwitz, J., and Furth, J. J., "Messenger RNA," Scient. Amer., 206 (No. 2):41–49, 1962.

Hymer, W. C., and Kuff, E. L., "Enzymatic Breakdown of Rapidly Labeled Nuclear RNA and its Inhibition by Cytoplasmic Soluble Fraction," Biochem. Biophys. Res. Commun., 15:506–512, 1964.

Kurland, C. G., "Molecular Characterization of Ribonucleic Acid from *Escherichia Coli* Ribosomes," J. Mol. Biol., 2:83–91, 1960.

Krakow, J. S., and Ochoa, S., "Ribonucleic Acid Polymerase of *Azotobacter vinelandii,* I. Priming by Polyribonucleotides," Proc. Nat. Acad. Sci., U.S., 49:88–94, 1963.

Leboy, P. S., Cox, E. C., and Flax, J. G., "The Chromosomal Site Specifying a Ribosomal Protein in *Escherichia coli,*" Proc. Nat. Acad. Sci., U.S., 52:1367–1374, 1964.

Lipmann, F., "Messenger RNA," Progr. Nucleic Acid Res., 1:135–161, 1963.

McConkey, E. H., and Hopkins, J. W., "The Relationship of the Nucleolus to the Synthesis of Ribosomal RNA in Hela Cells," Proc. Nat. Acad. Sci., U.S., 51:1197–1204, 1964.

Norris, A. T., and Berg, P., "Mechanism of Aminoacyl RNA Synthesis: Studies with Isolated Aminoacyl Adenylate Complexes of Isoleucyl RNA Synthetase," Proc. Nat. Acad. Sci., U.S., 52:330–337, 1964.

Raacke, I. D., and Fiala, J., "Polyribosome-Bound Nucleoside Triphosphatases in *Escherichia coli,*" Proc. Nat. Acad. Sci., U.S., 51:323–329, 1964.

Reich, E., "Actinomycin: Correlation of Structure and Function of Its Complexes with Purines and DNA," Science, 143:684–689, 1964.

Rich, A., "Polyribosomes," Scient. Amer., 209 (No. 6):44–53, 178, 1963.

Schulman, H. M., and Bonner, D. M., "A Naturally Occurring DNA-RNA Complex from *Neurospora crassa,*" Proc. Nat. Acad. Sci., U.S., 48:53–63, 1962.

Smellie, R. M. S., "The Biosynthesis of Ribonucleic Acid in Animal Systems," Progr. Nucleic Acid Res., 1:27–58, 1963.

Spiegelman, S., "Hybrid Nucleic Acids," Scient. Amer., 210 (No. 5):48–56, 150, 1964.

Spirin, A. S., *Macromolecular Structure of Ribonucleic Acids,* New York: Reinhold, 1964.

Stevens, A., "Net Formation of Polyribonucleotides with Base Compositions Analogous to Deoxyribonucleic Acid," J. Biol. Chem., 236:(No. 7), PC 44, 1961.

Synthesis and Structure of Macromolecules, Cold Spring Harb. Sympos. Quant. Biol., 28, 1964.

Tal, M., and Elson, D., "The Reversible Release of Protein, Ribonucleic Acid and Deoxyribonuclease from Ribosomes," Biochim. Biophys. Acta, 53:227–229, 1961.

Warner, J. R., and Rich, A., "The Number of Soluble RNA Molecules on Reticulocyte Polyribosomes," Proc. Nat. Acad. Sci., U.S., 51:1134–1141, 1964.

Yankofsky, S. A., and Spiegelman, S., "Different Cistrons for the Two Ribosomal RNA Components," Proc. Nat. Acad. Sci., U.S., 49:538–544, 1963.

Zamecnik, P. C., "The Microsome," Scient. Amer., 198 (No. 3):118–124, 1958.

Zamecnik, P. C., "Historical and Current Aspects of the Problem of Protein Synthesis," Harvey Lect., 54:254–281, 1960.

Zubay, G., "Molecular Model for Protein Synthesis," Science, 140:1092–1095, 1963.

See Supplement IX and the last part of Supplement IV. A list of references can be found after Dr. Wilkins' and Dr. Watson's Nobel Prize lectures.

QUESTIONS FOR DISCUSSION

33.1. What conclusions can you draw from the observation that under a variety of conditions, the rate of protein synthesis is proportional to ribosome concentration?

33.2. What can happen to an 80s ribosome that has just completed synthesis of a polypeptide?

33.3. Discuss the hypothesis that ribosomes are viruses.

33.4. Since seventeen leucine molecules occur in reticulocyte hemoglobin, how can you explain J. R. Warner's finding an average of 7.4 leucine molecules per ribosome in a polysome synthesizing hemoglobin?

33.5. To what do you attribute the difference between polysomes composed of five or six ribosomes (in reticulocytes making hemoglobin) and fifty to seventy ribosomes (in a mammalian cell infected by poliomyelitis virus)?

33.6. In what respects would you expect the properties of sRNA to be changed or unchanged by methylation?

33.7. The non-α dimer in Hb-Lepore seems to consist of an N-terminal portion of the δ chain joined to a C-terminal portion of the β chain. This "hybrid" δ-β chain is the same length as the δ or β chain. Recall that the genes for δ and β chains are closely linked, and that the δ gene probably originated as a duplication of the β gene. Discuss the acceptability of the following genetic explanations for the origin of Hb-Lepore:

   (a) Two-break deletion of parts of the β and δ genes and the region separating them

   (b) Incorrect synapsis between the β and δ genes followed by a crossing over which produces one crossover whose gene sequence is β, β-δ, δ (phenotypic effect, unknown) and the complementary crossover whose gene content is δ-β.

How does your evaluation of these genetic explanations compare with that of C. Baglioni, Proc. Nat. Acad. Sci., U.S., 48:1880–1886, 1962?

33.8. Suggest a mechanism by which both DNA strands of ϕX174 can be present in the RF and only one in the mature phage.

33.9. Compare the terminal nucleotides of TMV and sRNA. What can you infer from this comparison?

33.10. What conclusions can you draw from the observation that although the ribosomal RNAs from *Pseudomonas aeruginosa* and *Bacillus megaterium* are indistinguishable, the DNA is 64% G + C in the former, and 44% in the latter?

33.11. Although the average cell of the adult rat liver probably divides less often than once a year, it synthesizes an amount of protein equivalent to its own content every six or so days. In bacteria, on the other hand, the time required to double the protein content is roughly equal to the generation time. Compare the turnover of messenger RNA in bacteria with that expected in adult rat liver cells.

33.12. When native RNase is treated with urea and sulfhydryl reagents, its disulfide bonds are broken and the enzyme unfolds into an inactive linear form. When O_2 is bubbled slowly through a solution of this denatured enzyme, the disulfide bonds reform and enzymatic activity resumes. What do these results tell you about the genetic basis for the folding of polypeptides?

Chapter 34

GENETIC AMINO ACID CODING

I F SINGLE ribotides in messenger RNA were translated into different amino acids, only four amino acids would be specified or coded. Since there are twenty common amino acids, we are presented with the *problem of how RNA codes for amino acids*. To resolve this problem, we can assume that an amino acid is coded by a sequence of two nucleotides— a situation comparable to having an alphabet of four letters and a language of two-letter words. In this case, assuming the RNA code can be read only in one direction, we would have four times four, or sixteen, possible doublets (words). (Unidirectional reading seems reasonable since a single strand of RNA is polarized just as a single strand of DNA.) However, sixteen doublets are still too few to specify twenty amino acids, so other assumptions must be made. We might hypothesize that a given doublet encodes more than one kind of amino acid, in which case the code would be *ambiguous*. Alternatively, we could assume an amino acid is coded by a sequence of three messenger ribotides—a triplet. Such a triplet code would give us four times four times four, or sixty-four, different, unidirectional sequences—more than enough to encode twenty amino acids. Should more than one triplet encode the same amino acid, the code would be *degenerate*. Thus, this introductory discussion suggests that a sequence of two or three ribotides encodes an amino acid—that is, acts as a *codon*.

Other characteristics of messenger RNA may affect amino acid coding. For example, since the number of consecutive ribotides can be in the hundreds or thousands, no spacing—that is, no non-nucleotide punctuation—is provided to indicate where one codon stops and the next begins. Consequently, we are dealing with what is called a *comma-free code*. Suppose six ribotides are arranged linearly in positions 123456. If triplet 123 specifies amino acid A and 456 specifies amino acid B, errors are possible due to overlapping triplets 234 or 345. The problem of overlapping codons can be avoided if only successive doublets or triplets are read starting at one distinct point on messenger RNA. In this case, the punctuation is provided by the mechanism for reading the code.

The rII Region and the Code

The genetic fine structure of the rII region of φT4 has already been discussed in Chapter 26. We recall that the rII region is composed of two genes (or cistrons), A and B, both of which must function correctly to yield the r+ phenotype. From the last chapter, it is inferred that these genes produce messenger RNA which specifies the two different polypeptide chains required for the r+ phenotype. In the case of hemoglobin, the protein gene product is readily collected and analyzed, but the genetic basis for globin variants is difficult to study; the converse is true for the r+ phenotype. In other words, even though the presumed polypeptide chains involved in producing r+ have not been detected, the genetic basis for rII mutants can be readily determined. We would, of course, prefer to study a system whose genetic and polypeptide consequences both are easily investigated; nevertheless, other genetic studies [1] of the rII

[1] The discussion follows the work of F. H. C. Crick, L. Barnett, S. Brenner, and R. J. Watts-Tobin (1961), and of others.

436

region may reveal additional information about gene action and the RNA code.

The A gene has been mapped into six major segments (A_1 through A_6); the B gene into ten (B_1 through B_{10}), all numbered consecutively from left to right. Since complementation occurs, a point mutant in any one of the A segments has no effect on B function, and vice versa. A large number of point mutants can be induced in the B_1 and B_2 regions by chemical mutagens expected to cause transitional or transversional base substitutions. In some of these mutants all B activity is lost, and in others some product with B activity is detected. As expected, those mutants assumed to involve base substitutions can be reverted to normal B activity by subsequent treatment with chemical mutagens which should produce the reverse transition or transversion. On the other hand, B_1 or B_2 mutants produced by acridines always completely inactivate B gene function and are not reverted by mutagens assumed to cause base substitutions. Such an occurrence is expected if acridines usually act as mutagens by causing the addition or loss of one or more whole nucleotides (see p. 394).

A large number of B-inactivating, acridine-induced mutants located in the B_1 and B_2 segments are obtained. After recombination between such mutants, progeny phage which carry two to six different acridine-induced point mutants are recovered. Some of the doubly-mutant phages still show no B activity, but others do. If a complete series of different double-mutant combinations is made, a consistent pattern is observed. To interpret it we shall assume that a given single mutant is either + or −, that is, has either gained or lost one or more nucleotides. We shall also assume that a codon has more than two nucleotides and that the code is nonoverlapping; in other words, it is read in successive codons. Operationally, one isolates a "−" mutant

as a suppressor mutant of a presumed "+" mutant, and vice versa. By isolating a series of "suppressors" and a series of "suppressors of suppressors," one gets a series of + and of − mutants. It is not known whether "+" mutations or "−" mutations represent nucleotide additions. Accordingly, a double mutant of − − or + + still causes B to have no B activity, since the reading of codons starts to be out of phase with the first mutant and continues out of phase even beyond the second mutant. If the mutant loci are widely separated, we do not expect a double-mutant combination of + − or − + to produce any B activity, since all the codons between the mutants are read incorrectly—out of phase, even though we expect those before the first and after the second mutant to be read correctly—in phase. If, however, a + − or − + mutant combination involves nearby nucleotides, it is possible that one or only a few codons—those between and including the mutants—will be read incorrectly. The pattern reveals that any given mutant can be classified either as + or − and that only double-mutant combinations of + − or − + produce some B activity —provided that the two mutants in the B_1-B_2 segments are near each other. These assumptions can be tested another way. If a few incorrect codons still permit some B activity, it should be possible to increase the number of mutational errors of the same type (all − or all +) until the number of nucleotides subtracted or added equals the number in a codon. Should this point be reached, the nucleotides beyond the last mutated codon would be read correctly—in phase—and some B activity might be restored.

Accordingly, phages carrying three, four, five, and even six different − (or +) mutants are constructed. Some of the three or six multiple − (or +) mutants have B activity; other combinations, like four −

and one + (or four + and one −) mutants also show B activity. None is found if the mutants fail to add up to three or a multiple of three. These results demonstrate that the message from gene B is *translated via successive, nonoverlapping codons and that a codon is most probably three successive nucleotides*. The proposed molecular model of sRNA whose turn is presumably made by three unpaired nucleotides (see Figure 33–2, p. 428) is consistent with this statement. Apparently, the triplet codon of DNA is transcribed into a complementary triplet codon of messenger RNA, which, in turn, is translated into an amino acid brought into position by an sRNA molecule bearing a complementary triplet codon. The triplet codon in DNA and a unique triplet in sRNA are therefore expected to be identical, except that T in the former is U in the latter.

In r^+, genes A and B are separated by a spacer which results either in separate messenger RNAs for each gene or a nonmeaningful segment between the A and B parts of a single messenger RNA. One particular deletion, number 1589, removes most of region A_5 and all of regions A_6, B_1, and B_2. Such phage particles show no A but partial B activity. Whether or not r^+ makes separate messenger RNAs for the A and B genes, the spacer denoting the end of the A message and the start of the B message (or the reverse, the end of B message and the start of A message) may be absent in phages carrying deletion 1589. Consequently, this mutant may make only one continuous strip of messenger RNA containing the base complements of those parts of the A and B genes still present. This possibility can be tested as follows: single + (or −) acridine-induced mutants in the A region are introduced by recombination into phages carrying deletion 1589. In each case the B gene is rendered inactive. In other words, B gene activity is now vulnerable to mutants in the A gene. This finding supports the view that deletion 1589 enables two genes to form one messenger RNA (whether or not they do so in r^+) and that if the reading is out of phase due to a nucleotide addition or subtraction in A, all subsequent codons—that is, those in gene B—will be misread. This result also suggests that the *codons in rII messenger RNA are always read from A toward B,* the order in which the genes are usually represented in genetic maps (as in Figure 26–4, on p. 343). Other evidence supports this interpretation. For example, when we make deletion 1589 phage doubly-mutant in the A region, the B gene is inactivated in some cases, but in others some B activity is detected. When + and − are assigned the mutants, we find that only + − double mutants in A can restore B activity; − − or + + combinations cannot. Moreover, as expected, the sequence + − or − + and the distance between these two mutants make no difference.

Since deletion 1589 has some B activity, it must be associated with the deletion of some multiple of three nucleotides. Although the codon cannot be less than three nucleotides, it can be a multiple of three if, for example, each + (or −) mutation added (or lost) two nucleotides. In this case the codon will be six nucleotides. We can test for the size of the codon by combining mutant 1589 with different medium-sized deletions in the A gene. Assuming that the two breakage points involved in such deletions occur at random, then only one third of the A deletions should remove exact multiples of three nucleotides, only one sixth should remove exact multiples of six, and so on. Therefore, a test of these deletions should show one sixth which permit the B gene to function if the codon is six nucleotides long; one third should permit B to function if the codon is three nucleotides long. Tests show, in fact, that a little more than one third of these moderate-sized A deletions permit 1589 mutants to show B activity. Consequently, these results strongly suggest that the coding unit is a triplet.

What can we hypothesize about the nature of the spacer that normally interrupts the A and B genes in r^+? If the DNA sequence is interrupted at the ends of each gene, A and B, by short amino acid sequences (see p. 276), transcription will be physically interrupted, thereby furnishing a starting and a stopping point for the formation of messenger RNA and, similarly, polypeptides. Another possibility is the occurrence in the DNA between the A and B genes of a sequence (or a multiple) of three nucleotides whose complement in messenger RNA has no complement in the presumed unique triplet of any sRNA. This untranslatable mRNA codon would make no amino acid sense and is, therefore, called a *no sense* or *nonsense codon*. According to this hypothesis, genes A and B normally form one continuous strip of messenger RNA, whose translation produces two separate polypeptides.

How many of the 64 triplet codons are nonsense? Genetic studies of the rII region strongly suggest that relatively few triplets are nonsense. Consequently, most triplets probably code for amino acids, and, since only twenty kinds of amino acids commonly occur, the same amino acid can be coded by more than one codon. Thus, we are apparently dealing *in vivo* with a degenerate triplet code. If the base-pairing of sRNA with messenger RNA is strictly accurate—that is, exactly complementary—there will be more than twenty kinds of sRNA, several of them carrying the same amino acid. Alternately, if there are only twenty sRNA types, and the base-pairing with messenger RNA triplets is inaccurate, a given sRNA will base-pair with different (but somewhat similar) messenger RNA tri-

plets. Both of these mechanisms for degeneracy may apply. In any event, most mutants involving base substitutions probably produce sense—that is, code for a different amino acid—and therefore produce *missense codons*.

It is possible to determine the nucleotide basis for certain point mutants in the rII region.[2] Suppose that the DNA strand used to make messenger RNA in r^+ has a G replaced by A in a particular r point mutant. If this mutant phage does not lyse the K12 strain of *E. coli* because its messenger RNA, containing a U instead of a C, is abnormal, a defective r^+ product results. Although 5-fluoro uracil (FU) is not mutagenic when added to the diet of K12, it can be used as a substitute for U when RNA is synthesized. When FU substitutes for U in messenger RNA, an sRNA molecule may *sometimes* mistake it for C (see discussion of BU on p. 398). If such a mistake is made, the sRNA paired with abnormal messenger RNA will contain G and be the sRNA that transports the amino acid normally found in r^+ product. Consequently, the amino acid correct for r^+ will be incorporated to form some r^+ product, and the host cell will lyse. Therefore, r mutants which can lyse only when FU is added most probably have G on their r^+ DNA strand used to make messenger RNA, and C on the complementary strand. Those mutants which do not lyse in the presence of FU may have T, A, or C at this locus in the DNA strand used for transcribing messenger RNA. Using various chemical mutagens as well as FU, it is often possible to determine when T, A, or C is present in the transcribed strand.

Sometimes a single bacterial mutant simultaneously suppresses the effects of point mutants at a number of other nucleotide sites. Suppose that in some of these cases, all the suppressed point mutants have the

[2] See S. P. Champe and S. Benzer (1962).

same triplet modified by the same base substitution, resulting in the incorporation of the same incorrect amino acid into the different polypeptide products. These effects can be suppressed by a mutant which modifies the specificity of an enzyme responsible for activating and attaching an amino acid to sRNA. Such a modification may sometimes cause the sRNA to transport an incorrect amino acid to the ribosome carrying the abnormal messenger RNA; this amino acid may be the one normally incorporated at that position in the polypeptide product. Consequently, mutants which make incorrect messenger RNA may still form the correct protein product, if compensated by the additional error of having sRNA carry a specific wrong amino acid. In a limited way, such suppressor mutants cause an alteration in the code for amino acids.[3]

Identification of Codons

The mechanism of protein synthesis can be studied *in vitro* by using a suspension of ruptured cells. Such a cell-free system is prepared from *E. coli* plus the addition of triphosphates of the ribosides of A, G, C, and U as well as all twenty of the amino acids in their L forms. The synthesis of protein can be readily detected if one of the added amino acids is radioactive—valine, for example, which becomes incorporated into protein. This incorporation can be stopped by the addition of DNase, which halts the production of messenger RNA by destroying the DNA. In the absence of new messenger RNA, protein synthesis stops.

That the DNase effect concerns the production of messenger RNA is demonstrated by the absence of valine incorporation when sRNA or ribosomal RNA is added to the system and by the resumption of valine incorporation when messenger RNA obtained from washed ribosomes is added to the system. This added messenger RNA can also come from other sources. For example, *E. coli* extracts can be used to synthesize hemoglobin under the direction of RNA from rabbit reticulocytes, and the RNA of coliphage f2 will stimulate amino acid incorporation into protein, part of which at least is the coat protein of the phage.[4]

Using such a cell-free system derived from bacteria, we can also study whether the addition of synthetic polyribotides has any effect on protein synthesis. First, a homopolyribotide containing U is added; the polyuridylic acid causes L-phenylalanine to be incorporated into protein.[5] Moreover, it is found that:

1. The protein formed is poly-L-phenylalanine
2. No other amino acid is incorporated in substantial amounts (However, if the Mg^{++} concentration is altered or if streptomycin is added, significant amounts of leucine are incorporated. The explanation for this is unknown.)
3. Phenylalanine linked to sRNA is an intermediate in this process.

These results surely mean that wherever an appropriate sequence of U's appears in normal messenger RNA, the protein being synthesized will usually incorporate L-phenylalanine. This discovery is *the first crack in the RNA code;* in other words, this is the first determination of a sequence of messenger RNA nucleotides which specifies the incorporation of a particular amino acid into protein.

When the synthetic polyribotide of U is mixed with the synthetic polyribotide of A in a way likely to make the strands base-

[3] Such mutants are reported by S. Benzer and S. P. Champe and by A. Garen and O. Siddiqi in Proc. Nat. Acad. Sci., U.S., 48:1114–1127, 1962.

[4] See D. Nathans, G. Notani, J. H. Schwartz, and N. D. Zinder (1962).
[5] See M. W. Nirenberg and J. H. Matthaei (1961).

pair or wrap about one another, incorporation of phenylalanine is partially or completely reduced. Thus, the synthetic polymer is most effective *in vitro* when single-stranded,[6] as is messenger RNA *in vivo*.

How the presence of different bases in the same synthetic polyribotide affects amino acid incorporation into protein can also be studied. Using *polynucleotide phosphorylase,* which has riboside diphosphates as substrate, polyribotides containing two or more different ribotides can be synthesized *in vitro.* Nearest-neighbor analysis of the heteropolymer confirms that the ribotides are actually in a random linear array. The early analyses [7] were greatly expedited because polyphenylalanine is insoluble in the cell-free system. In practice, then, an excess of uridylic acid was used in the synthesis of any mixed polynucleotide to obtain the later-synthesized protein as a precipitate from which the amount and kind of amino acids—in addition to phenylalanine—could be analyzed. Thus, to synthesize polyuridylic-adenylic acid, polyuridylic-cytidylic acid, and polyuridylic-guanylic acid, five times as much uridine diphosphate was used as the diphosphates of adenosine, cytidine, or guanosine, respectively. To make mixed polynucleotides containing UAC, UCG, or UGA, ten times as much uridine diphosphate was used as the riboside diphosphates of A, C, or G.

For example, when a mixed polyribotide containing U and C is added to the cell-free system which is then tested to determine whether an amino acid besides phenylalanine is incorporated into protein, proline and serine are among the amino acids incorporated. The code letters for these amino acids include, therefore, at least one ribotide of C. In the same way, we can

also determine the effects of other mixed polyribotides on amino acid incorporation. Some amino acids such as alanine and arginine require the use of three different nucleotides for coding; thus, the coding ratio (the number of nucleotides required to code one amino acid) is at least three. No amino acid is found which requires the presence of all four types of nucleotides. From these results, it is hypothesized that triplets of nucleotides in synthetic messenger RNA are translated into amino acids; that is, a triplet RNA code occurs also in the *in vitro* studies.

When the proportions of uridylic acid and cytidylic acid in a mixed polynucleotide are varied, more serine than proline is incorporated when there is an excess of uridylic acid. However, when the excess is cytidylic acid the reverse occurs—more proline than serine is incorporated. In terms of triplets, serine must be specified by 2U 1C and proline by 1U 2C. Note that neither the sequence of nucleotides in the triplet nor the order in which they are read is determined from such results. In other words, although the messenger-RNA triplet code letters are 1U 2C for proline, we cannot say whether the sequence is UCC, CUC, or CCU. (The first and last triplets are different, since the single-stranded messenger RNA molecule is translated in one direction only.)

Starting with ribotides of U and C in the relative frequencies 5:1, the relative frequencies of different triplets in the synthesized polymer can be predicted. UUU should occur with a frequency of $\frac{5}{6}$ times $\frac{5}{6}$ times $\frac{5}{6}$, or $\frac{125}{216}$. Although three arrangements are possible for the code letters 2U 1C, any particular sequence should occur with a frequency of $\frac{5}{6}$ times $\frac{5}{6}$ times $\frac{1}{6}$, or $\frac{25}{216}$; any one of the three possible arrangements of 1U 2C should occur with a frequency of $\frac{5}{6}$ times $\frac{1}{6}$ times $\frac{1}{6}$, or $\frac{5}{216}$, whereas CCC should occur with a

---

[6] See M. F. Singer, O. W. Jones, and M. W. Nirenberg (1963).

[7] By S. Ochoa and co-workers, and by M. W. Nirenberg and co-workers.

frequency of $\frac{1}{216}$. These particular sequences are, respectively, in the relative frequencies 125:25:5:1. Consequently, if a triplet code is the correct one, studies of this particular polyribotide for protein synthesis, should reveal incorporation of five times more phenylalanine than serine and twenty-five times more phenylalanine than proline. Although the results obtained using various synthetic polymers sometimes differ by a factor of two or so from those presently expected, the overall agreement is excellent and offers very strong support for a triplet RNA code. The existence of a triplet code is also supported by the finding that the messenger RNA is approximately 450 ribotides long [8] while the α or β chain which it specifies in hemoglobin is 150 or so amino acids long.

All the synthetic polyribotides tested thus far for messenger RNA activity in protein synthesis contain an excess of U for technical reasons. As mentioned earlier, the protein product is mainly polyphenylalanine, insoluble in the cell-free system and therefore readily collected and quantitatively analyzed for phenylalanine as well as other amino acids. Such studies reveal triplet code letters for nineteen amino acids. For example, three triplets code for leucine—1A 2U, 1C 2U, and 1G 2U—demonstrating, as expected from our previous discussion, that *in vitro,* at least, the code is degenerate. Degeneracy also occurs for asparagine which has 2A 1U and 1C 1A 1U as codons, and isoleucine with codons 1A 2U and 2A 1U.

The triplet code letters for tyrosine are 1A 2U. But is the actual sequence AUU, UAU, or UUA? Short sequences of ribotides (oligoribotides) can be lengthened at their nucleoside (3′) ends by polynucleotide phosphorylase. A mixture of AUU and AAU oligoribotides (the base at the

5′ end is always written first in the sequence) is lengthened at the 3′ end with uridylic acid residues. When the lengthened, mixed polyribotide—AUUU . . . U or AAUUU . . . U—is tested for polypeptide synthesis, it is found that phenylalanine and tyrosine are incorporated in significant amounts and that no significant amounts of isoleucine (which also has the code letters 1A 2U) or of asparagine and lysine (whose code letters are 2A 1U) are incorporated. Therefore, the code sequence for tyrosine is probably AUU.

Another method of attack for determining base sequence in codons makes use of the mutations causing single amino acid substitutions in hemoglobin (see Figure 32–7, p. 415), TMV, tryptophan synthetase, and other proteins. Those mutations occurring spontaneously or with mutagens expected to produce single base substitutions are assumed to involve single base changes. In TMV, a mutant causes tyrosine (AUU) to be replaced by phenylalanine (UUU); the mutant apparently causes a single base change from A to U. In tryptophan synthetase, a mutant replaces tyrosine (AUU) by cysteine (GUU) and presumably involves a change from A to G. In hemoglobin-M_{Boston}, the α chain (see p. 414) has the histidine (1A 1U 1C) at position 58 changed to tyrosine (AUU). If only a single base change—from C to U—has occurred, then the codon for histidine must start with A and is either ACU or AUC. In hemoglobin Zürich, the amino acid at position 63 is changed from histidine (ACU or AUC) to arginine (1G 1C 1U). This change is probably from A to G, so that the first base in the arginine codon is G, and the codon is either GCU or GUC. A continuation of this kind of analysis has made it possible [9] to assign complete U-containing nucleotide sequences to the codons for nineteen of the twenty amino acids. These sequences (listed

[8] As shown by T. Staehlin, F. O. Wettstein, H. Oura, and H. Noll (1964).

[9] For T. H. Jukes.

in the second column of Figure 34–1) are consistent with the triplet code letters, base sequence studies *in vitro,* and 87 of 93 known single amino acid substitutions assumed to have resulted from single base changes. The disagreements with respect to amino acid replacements are relatively few, and for the most part are probably due to an incomplete knowledge of all triplet code letters and to the inclusion of cases in which two or three base changes occurred successively or simultaneously in replacing one amino acid by another.

The ability of synthetic polyribotides without U to result in amino acid incorporation can also be studied using agents (trichloracetic acid, for example) that precipitate proteins otherwise soluble in the *in vitro* system. When homopolyribotides of A, C, or G and mixed polymers with these bases are synthesized and tested, a large number of new triplet code letters without U's are found. For example, poly A makes polylysine; poly C makes polyproline. Guanine-rich polynucleotides do not work well, probably because of the secondary structure due to guanine-guanine interactions. Based on the nucleotide sequences given to the U-containing codons and using sequences which will not duplicate those given to the codons of other amino acids, the base sequences in these new triplets without U's are assigned and listed in the third column of Figure 34–1.

In studying the incorporation of amino acids into protein *in vitro,* one must use very

Amino Acid	U-containing codons[1]	Non U-containing codons[2]	Shared doublets
Ala	CUG	CAG, CCG	C·G
Arg	GUC	GAA, GCC	G·C
Asn	UAA, CUA	CAA	·AA, C·A
Asp	GUA	GCA	G·A
Cys	GUU		
Glu	AUG	AAG	A·G
Gln		AGG, AAC	
Gly	GUG	GAG, GCG	G·G
His	AUC	ACC	A·C
Ileu	UUA, AAU		
Leu	UAU, UUC, UGU		U·U
Lys	AUA	AAA	A·A
Met	UGA		
Phe	UUU		
Pro	CUC	CCC, CAC	C·C
Ser	CUU	ACG	
Thr	UCA	ACA, CGC	·CA
Try	UGG		
Tyr	AUU		
Val	UUG		

[1]Sequence proposed by T. H. Jukes.

[2]Sequences given are fitted to those in footnote 1, or avoid duplication of a sequence for another amino acid.

FIGURE 34–1. *Tentative* in vitro *messenger RNA codons for amino acids.* (*After Wahba, A. J., et al., 1963; see reference at end of chapter. See also M. R. Bernfield and M. W. Nirenberg,* Science, *147:479–484, 1965.*)

long oligoribotides, for example, a chain of 500–1000 uridylic acids. Although poly U greatly stimulates phenylalanine incorporation into protein, the single trinucleotide UUU does not. Recall, however, that early steps in protein synthesis require the activation and attachment of the amino acid to a specific sRNA molecule. This "charged" sRNA binds to the ribosome and, as directed by the messenger RNA, is incorporated at the end of the growing peptide chain. Poly U causes Phe-sRNA to be bound to ribosomes; other polynucleotides cause other specific charged sRNAs to be bound.

One can synthesize or isolate oligoribotides and test them for their *in vitro* ability to bind specifically charged sRNAs to ribosomes.[10] (According to convention, a triribotide of U with a 3'-terminal phosphate is designated UpUpUp and one with a 5'-terminal phosphate, pUpUpU.) When pUpUpU, pApApA, and pCpCpC are tested, they are found to direct the binding of Phe-, Lys-, and Pro-sRNA, respectively; dinucleotides have no effect. Moreover, trinucleotides with 5'-terminal phosphate are more active than those with no terminal phosphate, and trinucleotides with 2'-(3')-terminal phosphate are inactive.

From other work 2U 1G is known to be a code word for valine. The order of the bases can be investigated using poly UG, dinucleotides, the trinucleotide GpUpU, and its sequence isomers UpGpU and UpUpG. The binding of C^{14}-Val-sRNA to ribosomes is found to be directed both by poly UG and GpUpU but not by UpGpU, UpUpG, or dinucleotides. GpUpU has no effect upon the binding of sRNAs, corresponding to 17 other amino acids, to ribosomes. Therefore, we conclude from these results that a code word for valine is GpUpU, and we predict that a GUUGUUGUU . . . GUU polymer will stimulate only valine incor-

poration into protein. Similar work showed that UpUpG is a code word for leucine and possibly UpGpU a code word for cysteine.

Although there will undoubtedly be corrections and additions to the codons in Figure 34–1 (some contradictory base sequence results are obtained using the different *in vitro* methods described), examination of the codons listed reveals a common feature to some of the degeneracy already detected. For example, two of the codons for leucine have U at both ends. In other words, they share the same doublet, so that their codons can be written U · U, in which · can be A or G. Although the base sequences in alanine's two codons without U are postulated, both contain a C and a G, as does the U-containing sequence, so that one can refer to a C · G shared doublet, in which · probably can be U, A, or C. These and other doublets are listed in the figure. The meaning of such shared doublets in the degenerate *in vitro* RNA code is not yet clear, nor is it known to what extent triplets without U code in messenger RNA *in vivo*.

That the frequency of some of the amino acids in protein remains nearly constant when there are large shifts in the $\dfrac{A + T}{C + G}$ ratio is evidence for the existence of degeneracy *in vivo*. Leu-sRNA of *E. coli* can be separated into three types, each with different coding properties *in vitro*.[11] The first type responds preferentially to poly UC, the second type responds to poly U and copolymers rich in U (including poly UC), and the third responds preferentially to poly UG. The discovery that leucine is carried by different sRNAs provides an explanation for the observations *in vitro* that the coding unit for leucine is degenerate (at least four different triplets serve to encode it) and that the UUU codon is ambiguous (since it is a codon for both leucine and phenylalanine). Assuming that there is only one DNA locus

---

[10] See M. Nirenberg and P. Leder (1964), and P. Leder and M. W. Nirenberg (1964).

[11] See G. von Ehrenstein and D. Dais (1963).

per type of sRNA molecule, the finding [12] of approximately forty sites in *E. coli* DNA which are complementary to sRNA indicates not only the presence of degeneracy at this level but the extent to which it occurs. Already twenty-nine specific sRNAs for sixteen amino acids have been detected in *E. coli*.[13]

Although DNA and the polypeptides it specifies are both linear, it is important to determine whether the exact linearity of the polypeptides is dependent upon the exact linearity of the DNA; that is, whether *colinearity* exists. This possibility can be tested using ten ϕT4 mutants that produce incomplete head protein molecules. These mutants map in a linear sequence, as determined by recombination studies. When the head protein of each mutant is analyzed, the length of the portion of the molecule made is exactly proportional to the map distance from one end of the gene. This finding [14] is proof of colinearity.

[12] By H. M. Goodman and A. Rich (1962), and D. Giacomoni and S. Spiegelman (1962) (see reference on p. 433).

[13] See J. Goldstein, T. P. Bennett, and L. C. Craig (1964).

[14] By A. S. Sarabhai, A. O. W. Stretton, and S. Brenner (1964); see C. Yanofsky, B. C. Carlton, J. R. Guest, D. R. Helinski, and U. Henning (1964), and M. E. Reichmann (1964).

Despite the degeneracy and ambiguity noted, is the code basically the same for all organisms; that is, is the code essentially universal? It was already mentioned that something very similar to rabbit hemoglobin can be synthesized in a cell-free system derived partly from rabbit reticulocytes and partly from *E. coli*. As also mentioned, RNA isolated from phage f2 directs the synthesis of its coat protein in extracts of *E. coli*. This RNA also leads to the synthesis of f2 coat protein in extracts of *Euglena gracilis*. The DNA from the animal viruses polyoma and vaccinia is infective in competent *Bacillus subtilis;* that is, mixing the virus DNA with the bacteria produces intact virus particles which can infect the normal animal host. In certain animal cell-free systems which are stimulated by exogenous RNA messages, synthetic polynucleotides have many of the incorporation properties that they have in bacterial cell-free systems. Finally, a marked correlation exists between C + G content and the percentages of certain amino acids incorporated into protein in a variety of organisms. All these results support the hypothesis that even if there are mutational modifications, only *one basic code for polypeptide synthesis exists in all present-day organisms.*

SUMMARY AND CONCLUSIONS

In vivo study of the rII region of ϕT4 reveals that the genetic code for amino acids is read in one direction—probably from one fixed point of messenger RNA—very likely in successive triplets. Such work suggests that the code is degenerate and almost all of the possible codons make sense.

Studies of polypeptide synthesis *in vitro* using natural and synthetic messenger RNA, of mutants involving single amino acid substitutions, and of sRNA binding to ribosomes *in vitro* support these hypotheses. Such work also permits the assignment of base sequences to the triplets which code *in vitro*.

In vivo, DNA and the polypeptide it specifies are colinear; the RNA code is basically universal.

REFERENCES

Campbell, A., "Fine Structure Genetics and its Relation to Function," Ann. Rev. Microbiol., 17:49–60, 1963.

Champe, S. P., and Benzer, S., "Reversal of Mutant Phenotypes by 5-Fluorouracil: An Approach to Nucleotide Sequences in Messenger-RNA," Proc. Nat. Acad. Sci., U.S., 48:532–546, 1962.

Crick, F. H. C., "The Genetic Code," Scient. Amer., 207:66–74, 176, (Oct.) 1962.

Crick, F. H. C., "The Recent Excitement in the Coding Problem," Progr. Nucleic Acid Res., 1:163–217, 1963.

Fraenkel-Conrat, H., "The Genetic Code of a Virus," Scient. Amer., 211 (Oct.):47–54, 142, 1964.

Goldstein, J., Bennett, T. P., and Craig, L. C., "Countercurrent Distribution Studies of E. coli sRNA," Proc. Nat. Acad. Sci., U.S., 51:119–125, 1964.

Goodman, H. M., and Rich, A., "Formation of a DNA-Soluble RNA Hybrid and its Relation to the Origin, Evolution, and Degeneracy of Soluble RNA," Proc. Nat. Acad. Sci., U.S., 48:2101–2109, 1962.

Grunberg-Manago, M., "Polynucleotide Phosphorylase," Progr. Nucleic Acid Res., 1: 93–133, 1963.

Jukes, T. H., "Coding Units and Amino Acid Substitutions in Proteins," pp. 485–497, in Informational Macromolecules, Vogel, H. J., Bryson, V., and Lampen, J. O. (Eds.), New York: Academic Press, 1963.

Leder, P., and Nirenberg, M. W., "RNA Codewords and Protein Synthesis, III. On the Nucleotide Sequence of a Cysteine and a Leucine RNA Codeword," Proc. Nat. Acad. Sci., U.S., 52:1521–1529, 1964.

Nathans, D., Notani, G., Schwartz, J. H., and Zinder, N. D., "Biosynthesis of the Coat Protein of Coliphage f2 by E. coli Extracts," Proc. Nat. Acad. Sci., U.S., 48:1424–1431, 1962.

Nirenberg, M. W., "The Genetic Code: II," Scient. Amer., 208 (March):80–94, 190, 1963.

Nirenberg, M., and Leder, P., "RNA Codewords and Protein Synthesis," Science, 145: 1399–1407, 1964.

Nirenberg, M. W., and Matthaei, J. H., "The Dependence of Cell-Free Protein Synthesis in E. Coli upon Naturally Occurring or Synthetic Polyribonucleotides," Proc. Nat. Acad. Sci., U.S., 47:1588–1602, 1961.

Reichmann, M. E., "The Satellite Tobacco Necrosis Virus: A Single Protein and its Genetic Code," Proc. Nat. Acad. Sci., U.S., 52:1009–1117, 1964.

Singer, M. F., Jones, O. W., and Nirenberg, M. W., "The Effect of Secondary Structure on the Template Activity of Polyribonucleotides," Proc. Nat. Acad. Sci., U.S., 49:392–399, 1963.

Synthesis and Structure of Macromolecules, Cold Spring Harb. Sympos. Quant. Biol., 28, 1964.

von Ehrenstein, G., and Dais, D., "A Leucine Acceptor sRNA with Ambiguous Coding Properties in Polynucleotide-Stimulated Polypeptide Synthesis," Proc. Nat. Acad. Sci., U.S., 50:81–86, 1963.

Wahba, A. J., Gardner, R. S., Basilio, C., Miller, R. S., Speyer, J. F., and Lengyel, P., "Synthetic Polynucleotides and the Amino Acid Code, VIII," Proc. Nat. Acad. Sci., U.S., 49:116–122, 1963.

Speakers (l. to r.) M. W. NIRENBERG, F. LIPMANN, *and* S. OCHOA *at a symposium on the RNA code held January, 1962, at Indiana University.*

Weisblum, B., Gonano, F., von Ehrenstein, G., and Benzer, S., "A Demonstration of Coding Degeneracy in the Synthesis of Protein," Proc. Nat. Acad. Sci., U.S., 53:328–334, 1965.

Woese, C. R., Hinegardner, R. T., and Engelberg, J., "Universality in the Genetic Code," Science, 144:1030–1031, 1964.

Yanofsky, C., Carlton, B. C., Guest, J. R., Helinski, D. R., and Henning, U., "On the Colinearity of Gene Structure and Protein Structure," Proc. Nat. Acad. Sci., U.S., 51:266–272, 1964.

See Supplement X. Other references can be found at the end of Dr. Crick's Nobel Prize Lecture.

QUESTIONS FOR DISCUSSION

34.1. Do you expect the genetic code for amino acids to be the same in all free-living organisms? Explain.

34.2. Compare the replication of an RNA virus with the replication of a polypeptide chain.

34.3. Prepare a report on advances in our understanding of the genetic code since the present account was written (November 1964).

34.4. What evidence can you present that the attachment of messenger RNA to the ribosome does not involve extensive complementary base pairing?

34.5. Give evidences that messenger RNA is single-stranded.

34.6. What raw materials are needed to make a mixed polyribonucleotide in the absence of a primer? In the presence of a primer?

34.7. Do you suppose the first genetic code was or was not degenerate? Explain.

34.8. Work out the relative frequencies of the triplet code letters, UUU, UUA, AAU, UAC, AAA, CCC, in the specific sequences given from a polymer synthesized from ribotides of U, A, and C in the relative amounts of 6, 1, and 1, respectively.

34.9. Using large quantities of riboside diphosphates of A, U, G, and C in the relative proportions of 4, 3, 2, 1, and polynucleotide phosphorylase to synthesize a mixed polyribotide, give the proportion of sequences in the polyribotide for the following types (all read in one direction only):

  (a) doublets AU; AC; CA
  (b) homotriplets; heterotriplets
  (c) quadruplet AUCG

34.10. Make a list of the minimal requirements for the functioning and reproduction of the simplest free-living organism you can imagine; estimate the minimum number of nucleotides required to perform these functions assuming the genetic material is RNA; assuming it is DNA. Compare your estimates with the number of nucleotides in TMV and ϕX174. What are your conclusions?

34.11. Devise experiments which permit the collection of essentially pure sRNA carrying phenylalanine; sRNA carrying lysine.

34.12. Cysteine, while still attached to its normal sRNA type, is converted to alanine by reduction with Raney Nickel. Using synthetic polyribotides, design a direct test of the hypothesis that sRNA functions as an adapter in specifying the fit of amino acids on a template.

34.13. How can you explain the observation by L. Grossman that ultraviolet irradiation of polyuridylic acid not only results in a marked depression in incorporation of phenylalanine in an *in vitro* protein synthesis but is accompanied by an increased incorporation of serine? What relation has your explanation to the observation that polyuridylic acid can normally code not only for phenylalanine but for leucine?

34.14. How can you explain the observation by G. E. Magni (see reference on p. 389) that normad mutations (reversions) for certain UV-induced mutants in yeast occur six to twenty times more frequently during meiosis than mitosis?

34.15. A number of rII point mutants can be classified as resulting from transitions A:T → G:C or G:C → A:T according to their reversibility after treatment with various chemical mutagens. Addition of FU to the nutrient medium does not produce the r+ phenotype in any of the mutants which supposedly carry the G:C pair at the mutant DNA site. On the other hand, some r+ phenotype is produced by FU in 17 of the 46 mutants presumed to carry A:T at the mutant site. What conclusions can be drawn?

34.16. What bearing does the observation that a hemoglobin chain is always synthesized beginning at the N-terminus have upon the alternatives of one-complement and two-complement transcriptions?

34.17. Of the possible 64 unidirectionally-read triplets using AUGC, how many have one or more U's? No U's?

Chapter **35**

REGULATION
OF GENE SYNTHESIS

A REVEALED by *in vitro* studies, DNA synthesis in biological systems requires the following: primer-template DNA; the nucleoside 5′-triphosphates of A, T, C, and G; Mg⁺⁺ ions; and DNA polymerase in an aqueous solution of proper pH and temperature. In an extended *in vitro* synthesis of DNA using *E. coli* DNA polymerase, we permit the reaction to proceed in a largely uncontrolled, unregulated manner until the supply of one of the raw materials is exhausted or until some other factor becomes limiting. The synthesis of DNA *in vitro* can be controlled, however, by changing one or a combination of the required factors. For example, we may choose to omit one of the triphosphates containing a base present in the primer-template. Reducing the amount of such a triphosphate or utilizing one which contains a base analog can control the rate and/or amount of DNA synthesized. The synthetic reaction can be slowed down or even partly reversed by excessive additions of pyrophosphate. In other words, there are a large number of ways by which the biochemist can regulate the synthesis of DNA *in vitro*. Such knowledge should be quite valuable in helping us answer the question: In present-day organisms how is gene synthesis regulated *in vivo*?

This question presupposes that DNA synthesis *in vivo* is regulated, and ample evidence, some of it already presented, supports such a view. The regulation of DNA synthesis at the cellular level is revealed by observations that DNA synthesis occurs during interphase and ceases during nuclear division. Evidence of regulation at the genomic level is provided by the fact that when DNA synthesis stops, the nucleus is euploid for DNA ($\pm$ about 10%)—even if the nucleus fails to divide and comes to contain a multiple (polyploid or polynemic) genome content. DNA synthesis is also regulated chromosomally since largely heterochromatic chromosomes replicate at a different time than largely euchromatic ones, and intrachromosomally since the heterochromatic and euchromatic regions within a chromosome are synthesized at different times during interphase. It should be noted that the occurrence and amount of "natural dAT" in different crabs is probably gene controlled.[1]

DNA Synthesis in Uninfected and Phage-Infected Bacteria

Let us discuss further the regulation of gene synthesis by exploring the biochemical pathways (summarized in Figure 35–1) so important in the synthesis of the four usual types of deoxyriboside triphosphates in uninfected *E. coli*. Since the hypothesis that genes specify all protein synthesis in an organism is now generally accepted, whenever these reactions involve enzymes, the control of gene synthesis by gene action is also involved.

In the presence of *deoxyribosidase* or *reductase,* the riboside diphosphates of A, G, C, and U are converted to the corresponding deoxyriboside diphosphates by removal of the O at the 2′ position.[2] The energy source for this reaction is ATP. The *d*TP is synthesized from *d*UP by adding a methyl group at the 5 position in the presence of *thymidylate synthetase.* (A thymine-requiring strain of *E. coli* lacking this enzyme is known.

[1] See M. Smith (1963).
[2] See A. Larsson (1963).

449

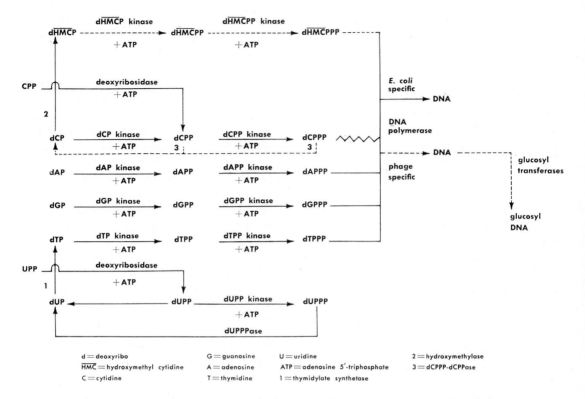

FIGURE 35–1. *Enzymatic pathways leading to DNA synthesis in* E. coli. *Interrupted arrows denote reactions occurring and wavy line to reaction blocked in cells infected with T-even phages. (After M. J. Bessman, 1963.)*

Such T-requiring *E. coli* can, however, synthesize thymidylic acid—thymidylate—when infected with φT2 because, as was proven, T2 carries the information to make a chromatographically different but similar-acting thymidylate synthetase.) The *d*UP involved has at least two sources. One source, *d*UPPP, loses pyrophosphate through the action of *d*UPPPase; another, *d*UPP, loses one phosphate (orthophosphate) and becomes *d*UP. The deoxyriboside 5′-monophosphates of C, A, G, and T are phosphorylated to the 5′-diphosphate condition by specific phosphorylating enzymes—*nucleoside monophosphate kinases*—in the following reaction:

$$dXP + ATP \xrightarrow{\text{nucleoside monophosphate kinase}}$$
$$dXPP + ADP \text{ (adenosine 5′-diphosphate)}$$

where X is the nucleoside of C, A, G, or T. (It should be noted that the *d*GP, *d*TP, and *d*CP kinases formed in *E. coli* infected with virulent phage are different from those produced in uninfected cells.) The deoxyriboside 5′-diphosphates produced are most probably converted to the 5′-triphosphate condition by means of other specific phosphorylating enzymes—*nucleoside diphosphate kinases*. The reaction is as follows:

$$dXPP + ATP \xrightarrow{\text{nucleoside diphosphate kinase}}$$
$$dXPPP + ADP.$$

This formula completes a summary of the pathways involved in producing the deoxyriboside triphosphates required for replication of *E. coli* DNA.

In the preceding discussion we noted that an infecting virulent phage carries specifications for the manufacture of a specific thymidylate synthetase and probably for specific nucleoside monophosphate kinases. This conclusion suggests that virulent phages carry instructions for making a number of specific proteins. Within two minutes after injection of T phage DNA, phage specific RNA appears; within four minutes phage specific proteins appear; and within six minutes phage DNA is synthesized—five times faster than is DNA in uninfected cells. Host DNA is destroyed soon after infection by T-even phages. Although the mechanism is not completely clear, it is thought to involve a new DNase that appears after phage infection. Roughly half an hour after infection 100 to 200 new phages are produced and liberated by lysis. These activities lead us to hypothesize that, after virulent phage infection, all DNA and messenger RNA synthesis in the bacterial cell is directed by the phage DNA. That *E. coli* DNA contains C, whereas the T-even phages contain *5-hydroxymethyl cytosine* ($\overline{HMC}$) to which glucose is attached in different ratios for different T-even phages, suggests another test of this hypothesis.

Within several minutes after infection with T-even phage, *d*CP is converted to *d*$\overline{HMCP}$ by a *hydroxymethylase*. This enzyme is newly produced, since uninfected cells or cells infected with T5 (which has no $\overline{HMC}$ in its DNA) have no hydroxymethylase activity. Through the action of kinase—also produced only in T-even infected cells—*d*$\overline{HMCP}$ is phosphorylated to *d*$\overline{HMCPPP}$. All the nucleoside monophosphate kinase activity for G, T, and $\overline{HMC}$ in phage-infected cells may be due to a sin-

gle new enzyme. In T2-infected cells another new enzyme appears which splits pyrophosphate away from *d*CPPP and orthophosphate away from *d*CPP converting these to *d*CP which, as described, is the substrate for making *d*$\overline{HMCP}$. The dephosphorylating activity of this enzyme, *dCPPP-dCPPase,* is 60 times greater than the kinase phosphorylating activity and has no effect upon *d*$\overline{HMCPPP}$. Such a mechanism seems to be adequate in excluding C from T-even phage DNA.

The biochemical pathways described in uninfected and T-even infected cells result in the synthesis of *d*$\overline{HMCPPP}$, *d*APPP, *d*GPPP, and *d*TPPP—the raw materials required for DNA polymerase action in the synthesis of T-even phage DNA. As is true for other phage-induced enzymes, DNA polymerase shows a high level of activity in phage-infected cells. Is a new DNA polymerase developed in response to T2 phage infection, a different one from the *E. coli* DNA polymerase formed in uninfected cells? The DNA polymerases in samples from uninfected and T2-infected cells are found to differ in antigenic properties, migration during chromatography, and inactivation sensitivity to specific chemicals. Moreover, *E. coli* DNA polymerase can use native, double-stranded DNA as primer-template, whereas the polymerase from the infected cells is virtually inert. Given single-stranded primer-template, *E. coli* polymerase can increase the amount of DNA ten- to twentyfold, whereas the polymerase from infected cells produces less than 100% increase. We may conclude, therefore, that a new DNA polymerase, *T2 DNA polymerase,* is formed in T2-infected *E. coli.*

As mentioned, T2, T4, and T6 have distinctly different glucose distributions in the $\overline{HMC}$ of their DNAs. The glucose residues are added to $\overline{HMC}$ in the DNA polymer through the action of enzymes called *glu-*

cosyl transferases. These enzymes transfer glucose from uridine diphosphate glucose (UPP glucose)—not shown in Figure 35–1—to $\overline{\text{HMC}}$ residues in DNA. Such enzymes are not found in uninfected or T5-infected cells and are clearly phage-induced. Note again that the glucosyl transferases act on polydeoxyribotides.

We have seen, therefore, that after T-even phage infection, new enzymes are induced to carry out syntheses unique to viral DNA production and to neutralize host enzymes which would be antagonistic to this process. New enzymes are also known to supplement the action of the host's enzymes to speed up synthesis of viral DNA. (For example, phages induce production of a different thymidylate synthetase than their host's.) These results not only indicate that viral DNA leads to the destruction of the host's DNA, but they provide us with some insight as to where DNA synthesis is regulated genetically in the T-even phage-*E. coli* system.

Variation in Genetic Nucleic Acid Components

The base-ratio of double-stranded DNA containing A, T, C, and G can be estimated from its buoyant density in the ultracentrifuge and from its denaturation (melting) temperature. A discrepancy in the base-ratios found by these methods [3] for the DNA of *phage PBS 1* (and also PBS 2) is explained by the finding that all the T in the phage DNA is replaced by U, the base composition frequencies being A = 0.359, U = 0.359, G = 0.134, and C = 0.147. The host of this phage, *Bacillus subtilis,* has T not U in its DNA. Apparently information which the phage carries in its own genome incorporates *d*UP into its DNA to the exclusion of *d*TP.

PBS 1 can transduce several of the genetic markers of its host. Transducing

phages like P22 and λ have a DNA base composition similar to their host's DNA. In the present case, the G + C content of host and phage are quite different—43% and 28%, respectively. Consequently, the PBS 1(PBS 2)-Bacillus system seems to offer an unusual opportunity to study the mechanism of transduction as well as the genetics, biosynthesis, and homology of host and phage DNA.

$\overline{\text{HMC}}$ (with or without attached glucose) and U are not the only genetically-determined variations which occur in the bases incorporated into DNA. (Various bases found in native DNA have already been mentioned on pp. 254–255.) Still other pyrimidines appear in DNA. 5-Methyl cytosine occurs in higher organisms like wheat, mammals, fish, and insects, with higher percentages of this base found in plants than in animals. On the other hand, 5-methyl cytosine is absent from many microorganisms—bacteria, actinomycetes, yeasts and their relatives, algae, and protozoa. Trace amounts of 5-ribosyl uracil are reported to occur in DNA. Finally, thymine is probably replaced by 5-bromo uracil in *infectious bovine rhinotracheitis virus* [4] and by 5-hydroxymethyl uracil in a phage.[5]

DNA can contain a variety of purines. Although 5-methylaminopurine (6-methyl adenine) is not found in the DNA of actinomycetes, yeast, higher plants, or higher animals, it is found in some bacteria—for example, *E. coli, Aerobacter aerogenes, Diplococcus pneumoniae,* and *Mycobacterium tuberculosis bovis*—and related bacteriophages. Not more than 0.7% of all bases is made up of 5-methylaminopurine. Trace amounts of 2-methylamino guanine, 6-dimethylaminopurine, 1-methyl guanine, and 2-methyl adenine are reported to occur in DNA. Unlike the findings for pyrimidines,

[3] See I. Takahashi and J. Marmur (1963).

[4] See J. G. Stevens and N. B. Groman (1963).
[5] See D. H. Roscoe and R. G. Tucker (1964).

in DNA made under normal conditions no example is known of a usual purine (A or G) being replaced completely or in appreciable quantity by another purine.

Large scale incorporation of 5-bromo uracil, 5-chloro uracil, 5-iodio uracil, 5-fluoro uracil, thiouracil, or 8-azaguanine into DNA may occur when tissue culture cells or bacteria are grown in media containing these compounds. Abnormal nutritional conditions must be employed to obtain such incorporation, the amount of incorporation depending partly upon the particular compound under test. Since incorporation also depends upon the strain tested, this kind of investigation may contribute to our understanding of the genetic control of DNA synthesis. 5-Iododeoxyuridine is incorporated into the root tip chromosomes of the broad bean plant, *Vicia faba*.

A number of analogs of adenosine occur naturally.[6] These include α-ribosyl dimethylbenzimidazole, nebularine, psicofuranine, cordycepin, tubercidin, and puromycin aminonucleoside. Although some of these compounds can be phosphorylated, none has yet been found in either genetic or nongenetic polynucleotides. It would be of great interest to know how the cell genetically controls the production of these ribosides yet manages to keep them out of nucleic acid polymers.

It is not too soon to wonder what the genetic basis may be for the amino acid interruptions which have been reported to occur periodically along some DNA strands. Such information would be appropriate in the present context, since these interruptions may be serving as natural termini for genetic nucleic acid molecules. *In vitro,* it is possible (p. 289) to add a ribotide to the terminus of a DNA molecule and to synthesize a mixed polynucleotide—part DNA and part RNA—using a DNA template and

DNA polymerase activated by Mn^{++}. Do such reactions take place *in vivo?* It would be valuable to learn the basis for the regulation which results in some mature phage containing double-stranded DNA and other mature phage containing single-stranded DNA.

Answers to some of these questions may go a long way toward explaining the mechanism of *E. coli* chromosome replication. As mentioned on p. 323, the circular *E. coli* chromosome starts replicating *in vivo* from a fixed position. *Synthesis of the two new strands apparently occurs in parallel;* that is, one complement grows at the nucleoside end and the other at the nucleotide end.[7] This situation is *contrary to the antiparallel synthesis of complementary DNA strands* in vitro. A second problem with the *in vivo* synthesis entails uncoiling. It has been suggested that the starting point of DNA synthesis serves as a kind of swivel whose rotation permits uncoiling.

Regulation of Synthesis of RNA Genes

RNA viruses (f2, TMV, poliovirus) serve as messenger RNA to form RNA synthetases needed for replication *in vivo* of complementary RNA from RNA. We would like to know if genetic RNA is variable in the respects mentioned for DNA, and to what extent this variability is regulated by the genotype. In this connection we note that poliovirus infection inhibits the synthesis of host RNA and induces the synthesis of poliovirus RNA that is infectious. Guanidine at concentration 0.001 M inhibits the synthesis of the latter type of RNA.[8] After infection with TMV, cytoplasmic ribosomal RNA is broken down, and the ribosides liberated are utilized in the synthesis of TMV-RNA.[9] On the other hand, neither host protein nor host RNA is in-

[6] See S. S. Cohen (1963).

[7] See J. Cairns (1964), and P. Fong (1964).
[8] See J. J. Holland (1963).
[9] See K. K. Reddi (1963).

corporated into the progeny of ϕR17,[10] an RNA phage.

Genetic DNA $\xrightarrow[\text{Transcription}]{}$ Genetic RNA

The *mate-killer* (*mu*) particle in Paramecium, like the similar bacterial endosymbiotes lambda and kappa (see p. 374), depends upon the micronuclear genes of its host for its maintenance. In this case, two unlinked dominant genes, M_1 and M_2, are involved, either one independently capable of supporting growth and replication of the mu particles. Sensitive, non-mate-killer individuals containing either M_1, M_2, or both do not spontaneously generate mu particles, so these genes do not form mu particles directly. If after conjugation of a mate-killer, its M dominant genes are replaced and the resulting exconjugant is $m_1 m_1 m_2 m_2$, the mu particles (which are visible and contain DNA) and the mate-killer phenotype are lost some 8 to 18 fissions later. This delayed loss of mu particles is abrupt, since a cell has either a large number of particles or none. Consequently, it is suggested that the M genes control mu particle existence by their gene products, called *metagons*.

Numerous tests of this hypothesis yield confirmative results. It has also been found in Paramecium that:

1. A single metagon is sufficient to support numerous mu particles
2. Metagons rarely, if ever, replicate
3. Metagons can be transferred via a cytoplasmic bridge from one member of a conjugating pair to the other
4. In the absence of an M gene, the metagons are diluted in successive fissions
5. Normally, about 1,000 metagons are present in each mate-killer individual.

Moreover, since ribonuclease destroys them, RNA is an essential constituent of metagons. Mu particles are destroyed exactly one fission after the metagons are eliminated from a cell by ribonuclease. Metagons can be synthesized two fissions after ribonuclease treatment, provided an M gene is present.[11] Subsequent evidence shows that metagons are messenger RNA with a high proportion of $G + C$. Accordingly, the existence of an endosymbiont is regulated by its host's messenger RNA. Not only can other paramecia be infected with metagons, but the very different protozoan Didinium can acquire both metagons and mu by eating paramecia which contain them. Metagonic RNA recovered from Didinium or paramecia can hybridize with DNA from M-containing paramecia and, to a lesser extent, m-containing paramecia but not with DNA from Didinium. Therefore, we conclude that Didinium contains no M genes. Nevertheless, the metagons not only persist but multiply in Didinium.[12] These results suggest that in Paramecium, metagonic RNA is somehow inhibited from replicating although it persists as a messenger for a rather long time. In this respect the RNA metagon resembles the DNA in an abortive transduction. In Paramecium, the RNA metagon is behaving like an RNA virus generated but incapable of replication; in Didinium, like one incapable of being generated but capable of being replicated. It is important for us to learn as much as possible about the nature and origin of the metagon-replicating enzyme and the mechanism that inhibits or prevents metagon replication under particular circumstances. A host's genetic control of RNA replication may sometimes involve the action of *interferons*—proteins (presumably synthesized through the intermediary functioning of messenger RNA) which prevent replication of certain viruses.[13]

[10] See D. B. Ellis and W. Paranchych (1963).

[11] The preceding discussion is based upon work of I. Gibson and G. H. Beale (1963).
[12] See I. Gibson and T. M. Sonneborn (1964).
[13] See R. Z. Lockhart, Jr. (1964).

The preceding evidence indicates that *in vivo* transcription of genetic DNA can produce genetic RNA. We have already noted that RNA can produce DNA by transcription *in vitro* (p. 289). The *Rous sarcoma virus* (RSV) infects chick embryo cells; this is an RNA virus, and infectious RNA can be isolated from Rous sarcoma cells. When DNA synthesis is inhibited soon after exposure of cells to RSV, the production of progeny virus is prevented; if the inhibition occurs later, however, virus progeny are produced. RNA-DNA hybridization experiments reveal that upon infection with RSV, the chick cell synthesizes DNA homologous to the viral RNA.[14] This DNA is not present before infection and is not homologous to RNA unrelated to RSV RNA. It has been suggested that this new DNA is the *provirus* stage of RSV and is comparable to the prophage stage of lambda. This is apparently a case of *in vivo* transcription from genetic RNA to genetic DNA, and perhaps also of transcription in the reverse direction.

[14] See H. M. Temin (1964).

SUMMARY AND CONCLUSIONS

Some of the biochemical pathways leading to the synthesis of bacterial and phage DNA are outlined. These pathways involve a large number of specific enzymes. Since enzymes are directly specified by gene action, we have gained some insight into the genetic control of gene synthesis. The occurrence in DNA of bases other than A, T, C, and G has given, or is expected to give, further insight into this matter. Further investigation of factors which determine polynucleotide composition, length, and single- or double-strandedness are also needed before we can fully understand how genetic nucleic acids are regulated *in vivo*.

In vivo, genetic DNA can be transcribed to genetic RNA (metagons) and genetic RNA (Rous sarcoma virus) can be transcribed into apparently-genetic DNA.

REFERENCES

Bessman, M. J., "The Replication of DNA in Cell-Free Systems," Chap. I, pp. 1–64, in *Molecular Genetics, Part I*, Taylor, J. H. (Ed.), New York: Academic Press, 1963.

Cairns, J., "The Chromosome of *Escherichia coli*," Cold Spring Harb. Sympos. Quant. Biol., 28:43–47, 1964.

Cohen, S. S., "On Biochemical Variability and Innovation," Science, 139:1017–1026, 1963.

Ellis, D. B., and Paranchych, W., "Synthesis of Ribonucleic Acid and Protein in Bacteria Infected with an RNA Bacteriophage," J. Cell. Comp., Physiol., 62:207–213, 1963.

Fong, P., "The Replication of the DNA Molecule," Proc. Nat. Acad. Sci., U.S., 52: 641–647, 1964.

Gibson, I., and Beale, G. H., "The Action of Ribonuclease and 8-Azaguanine on Mate-Killer Paramecia," Genet. Res. (Camb.), 4:42–54, 1963.

Gibson, I., and Sonneborn, T. M., "Is the Metagon an m-RNA in Paramecium and a Virus in Didinium?," Proc. Nat. Acad. Sci., U.S., 52:869–876, 1964.

Holland, J. J., "Depression of Host-Controlled RNA Synthesis in Human Cells During Poliovirus Infection," Proc. Nat. Acad. Sci., U.S., 49:23–28, 1963.

Kornberg, A., *Enzymatic Synthesis of DNA,* New York: J. Wiley & Sons, 1962.

Larsson, A., "Enzymatic Synthesis of Deoxyribonucleotides, III.   Reduction of Purine Ribonucleotides with an Enzyme System from *Escherichia coli* B," J. Biol. Chem., 238:3414–3419, 1963.

Lockhart, R. Z., Jr., "The Necessity for Cellular RNA and Protein Synthesis for Viral Inhibition Resulting from Interferon," Biochem. Biophys. Res. Commun., 15:513–518, 1964.

Reddi, K. K., "Studies on the Formation of Tobacco Mosaic Virus Ribonucleic Acid, III.   Utilization of Ribonucleosides of Host Ribonucleic Acid," Proc. Nat. Acad. Sci., U.S., 50:419–425, 1963.

Roscoe, D. H., and Tucker, R. G., "The Biosynthesis of a Pyrimidine Replacing Thymine in Bacteriophage," Biochem. Biophys. Res. Commun., 16:106–110, 1964.

Smith, M., "Deoxyribonucleic Acids in Crabs of the Genus Cancer," Biochem. Biophys. Res. Commun., 10:67–72, 1963.

Stevens, J. G., and Groman, N. B., "A Nucleic Acid Analogue Dependent Animal Virus," Biochem. Biophys. Res. Commun., 10:63–66, 1963.

Takahashi, I., and Marmur, J., "Replacement of Thymidylic Acid by Deoxyuridylic Acid in the Deoxyribonucleic Acid of a Transducing Phage for *Bacillus subtilis,*" Nature, London, 197:794–795, 1963.

Temin, H. M., "Homology between RNA from Rous Sarcoma Virus and DNA from Rous Sarcoma Virus-Infected Cells," Proc. Nat. Acad. Sci., U.S., 52:323–329, 1964.

QUESTIONS FOR DISCUSSION

35.1. Why should Kornberg and his associates fail to observe extended DNA synthesis in extracts of T2-infected cells to which the deoxyriboside 5'-triphosphates of A, T, G, and C had been added?   How would you proceed to obtain the desired synthesis?

35.2. What have we learned about the genetic control of nucleic acid synthesis from *in vitro* studies?

35.3. Do you suppose there is a genetic control over the tautomeric states a base in DNA may exhibit?   Justify your opinion.

35.4. Whereas laboratory synthesis of nucleosides can produce a mixture of α and β configurations (which differ in the way the parts are folded or pointed relative to each other), all the nucleosides in DNA have the β configuration.   How can you explain this difference?

35.5. Outline experiments designed to throw light upon the genetics of

　　(a) DNA polymerase
　　(b) RNA synthetase
　　(c) RNA polymerase
　　(d) polynucleotide phosphorylase

35.6. Which do you think came first in evolution, biochemical pathways leading to DNA or to RNA synthesis?   Explain.

35.7. Many mutants induced by nitrous acid in TMV show a mutant phenotype but no change in the amino acid sequence of their protein coat.   Suggest ways in which such mutants produce their phenotypic effects.

35.8. Does the work with metagons suggest an origin for viruses?   Explain.

Chapter 36

REGULATION OF GENE ACTION—OPERONS

EXTENSIVE study of any organism reveals a large number of alternative traits with a genetic basis. Some of these alternatives result from the presence or absence of genetic material (for example, in Paramecium "cytoplasmic DNA" can depend upon the presence of kappa); other alternative traits involve the relocation of genetic material (for example, changes in episomal state or the inversion of a chromosomal segment). But the presence, absence, and location of genetic material do not describe the mechanism operating on the affected cell or organism, or the ways genetic material performs a function.

We are, therefore, especially interested in studying those alternative traits resulting from some action by or involving genetic material. Self-replication, one action typical of what has been defined as genetic material, must have some phenotypic consequences due to the removal of gene precursor material from the pool of metabolic substances and to the presence of new genetic material. (Gene control mechanisms which act via gene replication were considered in the previous chapter.)

Evidence for the occurrence of gene action without gene replication is provided in numerous cases, including abortive transduction and highly functional cells which never divide again (neurons, for example). We already know that whenever phenotypes are dependent upon protein synthesis, gene action requires the formation of messenger RNA. Using DNA to make complementary DNA—that is, for gene replication—may inhibit its use in making complementary messenger RNA—that is, for gene functioning via polypeptide synthesis. This may be true even if DNA polymerase uses the major groove and RNA polymerase the minor groove of double-helix DNA. That gene action is sometimes controlled by genetic means was demonstrated by finding *regulator genes* (such as *Activator* in maize, p. 385). We should not exclude the possibility that DNA genes can produce phenotypic effects using mechanisms other than DNA replication and messenger RNA formation.

Gene action can be controlled nongenetically. A series of enzymatic reactions is usually required to produce a particular metabolic end product. In many cases the end product inhibits the functioning of one of the first enzymes in the pathway. Such *end product inhibition* of an enzyme, very widespread in bacteria, provides immediate and sensitive control of the rate of synthesis of many metabolites. Enzyme inhibition by end product is one example of controlling gene action by a *feedback mechanism*. The possibility also exists that gene action can be regulated more directly—at a stage prior to protein synthesis.

Recall (p. 357) that the *Lac* segment of the *E. coli* genetic map contains three recombinationally separate genes. The y^+ gene specifies the structure of the enzyme β-galactoside permease; z^+ specifies the structure of the enzyme β-galactosidase (certain alleles of z cause the synthesis of a modified, enzymatically inactive protein, called Cz, identified by its specific antigenic characteristics); the third gene, i^+, specifies the synthesis of a *repressor substance* which prevents y^+ and z^+ from producing permease and galactosidase. In the presence of lactose (which supplies the substrate upon which these enzymes act), however, the repressor substance made by i^+ is inactivated, so that the formation of enzymes by y^+ and z^+ becomes possible. *Lactose functions as an inducer*. Therefore, *E. coli* of genotype $y^+ z^+ i^+$ cannot produce permease or galactosidase *constitutively* (in the absence of lactose) but can do so *inductively* (in the presence of lactose). This example serves as a model to explain the genetic basis for many cases of induced enzyme formation. In this instance, the *feedback system controls the production* but not the activity *of certain enzymes*.

The order of these genes in the linkage map is: *TL . . . Pro . . . (Lac) y z i . . . Ad . . . Gal*. Note that all three *Lac* genes specify unique substances. Because i^+ produces a repressor substance which, in the absence of lactose, is capable of pleiotropic effects—that is, of phenotypic suppression of both y^+ and z^+—i^+ can be called a *regulator gene*.

Consider the consequences of certain mutations in the *Lac* region. Mutants capable of synthesizing permease and galactosidase constitutively can have the genotype $y^+ z^+ i$ in which the specific repressor is not produced, and their y^+ and z^+ genes can act under all circumstances. *E. coli* hybrid for the *Lac* region can be produced by introducing into F^- cells, F merogenotes carrying the *Lac* region (p. 357). Thus, we can obtain an *E. coli* individual whose chromosome is $y^+ z i$ (which by itself would make permease and Cz protein constitutively), and whose F-*Lac* particle is $y^+ z^+ i^+$ (which by itself would make permease and galactosidase only inductively). In the hybrid, no products are formed in noninduced bacteria (in the absence of lactose), although all three (permease, galactosidase, and Cz protein) are formed in induced bacteria (exposed to lactose). We can conclude, therefore, that a single i^+ gene can manufacture a repressor substance which

prevents the products of both normal and mutant *y* and *z* genes from being formed constitutively but not inductively, whether or not these genes are located in the same chromosome segment. In other words, the repressor substance is diffusible and can act at a distance. Various lines of evidence indicate that the repressor substance is protein.[1] An allele of i^+, i^s—called a *superrepressor*—prevents the *y* and *z* loci from functioning even in the presence of lactose. Apparently the superrepressor substance is insensitive to lactose, and the *y* and *z* loci cannot be *derepressed*.

Another mutant has been found which permits both y^+ and z^+ products to form constitutively, and may, therefore, be a mutation of i^+. Let us call this mutant allele i^x. When an F-*Lac* particle of the genotype $y^+ z^+ i^x$ is placed in a cell with a chromosome $y^+ z i$ (which by itself is found to produce permease and Cz protein constitutively), no Cz protein is formed constitutively in noninduced bacteria. Contrary to the assumption that i^x is a mutant of i^+, i^x must actually be i^+ since it produces a repressor capable of repressing Cz protein formation constitutively. In what respect, then, is the F-*Lac* particle mutant? Suppose the F-*Lac* particle is mutant at an additional locus, o^+. The new allele, o^c, would permit only the *y* and *z* loci in the same chromosome (or particle) to act constitutively regardless of which allele of *i* is present in the cell. Assuming this is so and ignoring gene order for the present, then the F-*Lac* particle is genotypically $y^+ z^+ o^c i^+$, while the genotype of the chromosome can be written $y^+ z o^+ i$. According to this new hypothesis, the hybrid ought to produce permease and galactosidase constitutively and, in addition, to produce Cz protein inductively. This is found to be true;

[1] See A. Garen and N. Otsuji (1964), and M. E. Balis, J. S. Salser, and A. Elder (1964).

the results obtained with this genotype are summarized in Figure 36–1 along with those of other hybrids which contain both the o^c and o^+ alleles. For example,

$$y^+ z\ o^+ i^+ / F\text{-}Lac\ y^+ z^+ o^c i^+$$

produces y^+ and z^+ enzymes but no Cz substance constitutively, and it produces all three in induced bacteria. Partial phenotypic analyses are available for two other genotypes. Thus,

$$y\ z^+ o^+ i^+ / F\text{-}Lac\ y^+ z\ o^c i^+$$

produces Cz protein but no galactosidase in noninduced bacteria, but it produces both of these in induced bacteria;

$$y^+ z\ o^+ i^+ / F\text{-}Lac\ y\ z^+ o^c i^+$$

produces galactosidase constitutively, and galactosidase and permease inductively.

We may conclude, therefore, that these results confirm the hypothesized existence of an *operator gene*, o^+, and that this gene is the one sensitive to the repressor substance produced by the regulator gene, i^+.

When the repressor substance is produced and not rendered inactive by lactose inducer, the repressor reacts with o^+; this reaction prevents both y and z alleles from operating. When the mutant allele i is present, no repressor is produced, o^+ is unaffected, and y and z alleles are capable of acting constitutively. However, a mutant allele of o^+, namely o^c, is insensitive to the repressor substance. Consequently, regardless of the genotype with respect to i, the y and z alleles can act constitutively. Note that the behavior of the y and z alleles depends on which particular allele of o is in the same chromosome or F particle; in other words, it depends on which allele of o is linked in the *cis position*. Thus, the *constitutive mutant of operator*, o^c, has a pleiotropic effect only on other genes in the cis position. Recombinational studies show that the locus of o^c is between z and i.

The operator gene does not seem to produce any unique product which can be detected cytoplasmically. Therefore it can be considered a gene whose primary job is not

GENOTYPE		NON-INDUCED BACTERIA			INDUCED BACTERIA		
Chromosome	F-Lac	P	G	Cz P	P	G	Cz P
$y^+ z^+ o\ i^+$	$y^+ z^+ o^c i^+$	33	36	nd	100	270	100
$y^+ z^+ o\ i^+$	$y^+ z^+ o^c i^+$	50	110	nd	100	330	100
$y\ z^+ o^+ i^+$	$y^+ z\ o^c i^+$	—	<1	30	—	100	400
$y^+ z\ o^+ i^+$	$y\ z^+ o^c i^+$	nd	60	—	100	300	—

P = Permease

G = Galactosidase

Cz P = Cz Protein

FIGURE 36–1. *Crosses, and their results, involving the* Lac *region of* E. coli. *nd = not detectable, — = not tested.*

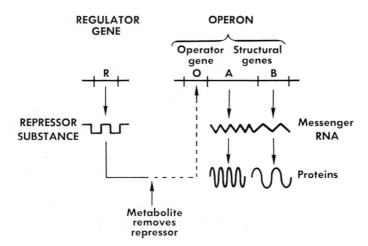

FIGURE 36–2. *Relationships between a regulator gene and the operator and structural genes of an operon.*

to specify a chemical product (such as an amino acid sequence in a polypeptide) but to control the function of other genes. Consequently, operator genes can be called *genes for function* in contrast to those which specify chemical structures and are accordingly called *genes for structure* (Figure 36–2).

An operator gene coordinates the expression of linear gene neighbors. In our model the genes controlled are related in that both structural genes affect the biochemical pathway involving lactose utilization. This situation suggests that there is, at least in some cases, a unit of gene function, intermediate in size between the gene and the chromosome, which can be called an *operon*. An operon is *a linear group of genes whose structural activity is coordinated by a functional gene, or operator, located at one end.*[2] An operon probably represents the length of genetic material whose complementary RNA comprises one strip of messenger RNA; *the operon, therefore, may well be a unit of transcription.* When the operon

is functioning, a strip of messenger RNA is produced containing information for all the structural genes in the operon. The messenger RNA is then translated starting from one end.

A leucine auxotroph, leu 500, is caused by an operator mutant, o^x, in the *leucine operon* of *Salmonella typhimurium*.[3] Using transduction to replace this mutant with the wild-type operator o^+ restores leucine prototrophy. When leu 500 (o^x) individuals are plated on complete medium without leucine, some large colonies are formed as a result of reverse mutation to o^+. Some small colonies, however, are also produced. When tested by transduction, the small colonies all prove to have a common property —all are mutant at the same locus, *suppressor of leu 500 (su leu 500)*, located outside the leucine operon between the tryptophan and cysteine operons. These mutants of *su leu 500* are of point mutation or deletion type; they no longer completely suppress o^x, and, consequently, partial leucine prototrophy is restored. *Su leu 500* is not the normal regulator gene for the leucine operon; when *su leu 500* is deleted,

[2] The discussion of operons and operator genes is based mainly upon work of F. Jacob, D. Perrin, C. Sanchez, and J. Monod (1960), and F. Jacob and J. Monod (1961).

[3] See F. H. Mukai and P. Margolin (1963).

the normal regulatory factors for leucine apply demonstrating that the normal leucine regulator gene is still present. It is hypothesized that normally *su leu 500* is a regulator gene for one or more other operons. When the leucine operon is o^+, the suppressor substance made by *su leu 500* has no effect on the operon. The mutation to o^x makes the leucine operon susceptible to the foreign repressor produced by *su leu 500,* the repressor acting here as a super-repressor. Mutation at the *su leu 500* locus partially restores the susceptibility of o^x to its own repressor and, it is inferred, also permits the operons normally regulated by *su leu 500* to act constitutively.

The mutant o^x first appeared in a culture treated with 5-bromo uracil. Its pattern of reverse mutation by 2-aminopurine strongly suggests that the production of o^x involved the transition of a single base-pair. Induction of mutations in *su leu 500* by 2-aminopurine indicates that simple base alterations may result in a change in the nature of the *su leu 500* repressor so that o^x is no longer repressed by it. These conclusions lead us to believe that:

1. Regulator genes for different operons differ from one another by relatively few nucleotides in the region that specifies their repressor's action upon an operator
2. Operator genes for different operons differ from one another by relatively few nucleotides.

Operons (such as *Lac*) whose gene products are proteins needed for special digestive or catabolic reactions, or for special structural or other biological purposes, are often normally repressed by repressor substances produced by regulator genes. To function, such operons must be derepressed. Other operons, however—particularly those whose enzyme products are used more routinely in metabolism, especially in synthetic or anabolic reactions—apparently are not ordinarily repressed but are functional. In such cases regulation of operon function is sometimes accomplished by a repressor produced when the end product of operon action combines with the gene product of a regulator gene. Other mechanisms of controlling operon action via feedback systems have been suggested.

At the level of the gene, we see that any structural gene in an operon can be permanently "turned off" by mutations within it. In such a gene, deletions which do not involve three or groups of three nucleotides are also expected to turn off other structural genes in the operon whose translation on the ribosome occurs later. We have seen that the functioning of an entire operon can be regulated or changed by the alleles present at the operator locus or at normal and foreign regulator loci. In principle, such operon regulation could occur either at its transcription or translation stage. For example, a DNA base substitution at the end where messenger RNA synthesis starts might cause that end to be susceptible to its own or another repressor substance and prevent transcription. A deletion which does not comprise a multiple of three nucleotides might occur at the end of the operon whose messenger RNA sequence is translated first. In this instance, the messenger RNA would be produced but would make complete nonsense. After normal messenger RNA is formed the operon might also be turned off by digestion of the messenger, by a suppressor which blocks translation of the messenger,[4] or by failure of the translated proteins to be liberated from the ribosome. Intraoperon regulation can occur at the translation stage,[5] since different proteins

---

[4] See E. Orias and T. K. Gartner (1964).

[5] See Y. Ohtaka and S. Spiegelman (1963), B. N. Ames and P. E. Hartman (1964), and the references to R. Byrne, *et al.* (1964) on p. 432, and to M. Nirenberg and P. Leder (1964) on p. 446.

encoded in a messenger RNA are produced in different quantities.

The "operator" gene might sometimes prove to be nothing more than the nucleotide sequence which begins a series of structural genes in an operon. However, the question remains: What is it in messenger RNA which serves as "spacer"—that is, what marks the termination of one polypeptide and the start of another? This spacing might be attributed to a nonsense triplet or to an intramolecular base-pairing that results in segments of a single-stranded messenger RNA having a secondary structure (being "double-stranded" as in sRNA).[6]

[6] See M. F. Singer, O. W. Jones, and M. W. Nirenberg (1963).

SUMMARY AND CONCLUSIONS

DNA genes can be classified as genes for structure or genes for function. A gene for function serves as an operator controlling the expression of the structural genes which are its linear neighbors. This whole complex of genes comprises an operon which is probably a unit of transcription. Some operons are normally nonfunctional; they are controlled by a regulator gene which produces a repressor which, in turn, represses the operator and hence, the operon. Derepression of such operons can be accomplished by:

1. An inducer (often the substrate for the first enzyme) which removes the repressor
2. Mutation of the regulator gene (which changes the repressor)
3. Mutation of the operator (which renders it insensitive to the repressor).

Other operons are normally functional and are rendered nonfunctional by repressors. Repression may result from mutations in regulator or operator genes which make an operator gene susceptible to the repressor of a foreign regulator gene.

Regulator genes, inducers, and operons interact at both the transcriptional and translational levels in feedback systems of various types to regulate the production of proteins.

REFERENCES

Allen, J. M. (Ed.), *The Molecular Control of Cellular Activity,* New York: McGraw-Hill, 1961.

Ames, B. N., and Hartman, P. E., "The Histidine Operon," Cold Spring Harb. Sympos. Quant. Biol., 28:349–361, 1964.

Balis, M. E., Salser, J. S., and Elder, A., "A Suggested Role for Amino-acids in Deoxyribonucleic Acid," Nature, London, 203:1170–1171, 1964.

Cellular Regulatory Mechanisms, Cold Spring Harb. Sympos. Quant. Biol., 26, 1962.

Gallant, J., and Spottswood, T., "Measurement of the Stability of the Repressor of Alkaline Phosphatase Synthesis in *Escherichia coli,*" Proc. Nat. Acad. Sci., U.S., 52:1591–1598, 1964.

Garen, A., and Otsuji, N., "Isolation of a Protein Specified by a Regulator Gene," J. Mol. Biol., 8:841–852, 1964.

JACQUES MONOD, *in 1964.*

Gorini, L., "Antagonism Between Substrate and Repressor in Controlling the Formation of a Biosynthetic Enzyme," Proc. Nat. Acad. Sci., U.S., 46:682–690, 1960.

Jacob, F., and Monod, J., "Genetic Regulatory Mechanisms in the Synthesis of Proteins," J. Mol. Biol., 3:318–356, 1961.

Jacob, F., Perrin, D., Sanchez, C., and Monod, J., "The Operon: A Group of Genes Whose Expression is Coordinated by an Operator" (in French), C. R. Acad. Sci. (Paris), 250:1727–1729, 1960. Translated and reprinted in *Papers on Bacterial Genetics,* Adelberg, E. A. (Ed.), Boston: Little, Brown, 1960, pp. 395–397.

Mahler, I., Neumann, J., and Marmur, J., "Studies of Genetic Units Controlling Arginine Biosynthesis in *Bacillus subtilis,*" Biochim. Biophys. Acta, 72:69–79, 1963.

Mukai, F. H., and Margolin, P., "Analysis of Unlinked Suppressors of an o^o Mutation in Salmonella," Proc. Nat. Acad. Sci., U.S., 50:140–148, 1963.

Ohtaka, Y., and Spiegelman, S., "Translational Control of Protein Synthesis in a Cell-Free System Directed by a Polycistronic Viral RNA," Science, 142:493–497, 1963.

Orias, E., and Gartner, T. K., "Suppression of a Class of rII Mutants of T4 by a Suppressor of a *Lac*-'Operator Negative' Mutation," Proc. Nat. Acad. Sci., U.S., 52:859–864, 1964.

Riley, M., and Pardee, A. B., "Gene Expression: Its Specificity and Regulation," Ann. Rev. Microbiol., 16:1–34, 1962.

Singer, M. F., Jones, O. W., and Nirenberg, M. W., "The Effect of Secondary Structure on the Template Activity of Polyribonucleotides," Proc. Nat. Acad. Sci., U.S., 49:392–399, 1963.

Stent, G., "The Operon: On its Third Anniversary," Science, 144:816–820, 1964.

Sypherd, P. S., and Strauss, N., "The Role of RNA in Repression of Enzyme Synthesis," Proc. Nat. Acad. Sci., U.S., 50:1059–1066, 1963.

QUESTIONS FOR DISCUSSION

36.1. What evidence can you cite that one strip of messenger RNA can be long enough to contain several structural genes of an operon?

36.2. In what respects are the alleles o^x, o^+, and o^c similar? In what respects are they different?

36.3. How does an operator gene differ from a regulator gene?

36.4. Do you suppose that the nucleotide sequence is longer in an operator gene than in other genic members of an operon? Why?

36.5. Does prophage behave as though it contains one or more regulator genes? Does prophage behave as a repressed operon? Explain.

36.6. Some workers classify genes into three types: those for structure; those for regulation; and those for operation. Do you believe this distinction is basic? Do you believe it is useful? Explain.

36.7. What specific kinds of phenotypic effects may operons produce in man?

36.8. In what ways do genes function?

36.9. What is your present concept of the "gene"?

36.10. Discuss the view that in *E. coli*, rII deletion 1589 involves an operon.

36.11. What conclusions could you draw from the report that with respect to the bacterial linkage map certain operons are arranged clockwise and others counterclockwise?

36.12. What support can you give to the hypothesis that o^c mutants involve nucleotide deletions?

36.13. Apply the operon concept to hemoglobin production in man.

36.14. Are all regulator genes suppressor genes? Explain.

Chapter *37

REGULATION OF GENE ACTION—GENE CONTROL SYSTEMS IN MAIZE

IN DISCUSSING the genetic control of mutation (Chapter 30), we considered the case of *Activator* and *Dissociation* in maize (pp. 384–386). The control of chromosomal breakage in the *Ac-Ds* system was found to be associated with the way this system controls the functioning of genes located in cis position near *Ds*—*Ds* being controlled by *Ac,* a regulator gene. Based on our knowledge of regulator gene-operator gene systems in bacteria, we can postulate that *Ds* functions as an operator gene for the *Ac* regulator gene.

Let us analyze another case [1] of what originally appeared to be an unstable gene in maize. The pericarp of a corn kernel encloses the seed containing the embryo (Figure 2–8, p. 25). Although embryo tissue is formed by the offspring generation, the pericarp is formed by the parental generation. Some plants are completely red and produce completely red pericarps; other plants are striped with red, and striping appears also in the pericarp; still others are completely nonred. A plant which shows medium variegation of red (therefore called *medium variegated*) produces kernels of the type shown in Figure 37–1. In the random sample of kernels shown, about 6% have full red color. From this result (and others) it appears that the parent of a medium variegated pericarp has about 6% mutant

[1] Based upon work of R. A. Brink and co-workers.

465

kernels. Genetically, these results can be attributed to mutation at a locus P on chromosome 1, and we can expect nonred individuals to be $P^w P^w$, and medium variegated individuals producing some full red kernels to be heterozygous for P^w. The other allele, P^v, would be unstable and in somatic cells frequently mutate to a red-producing gene. If we accept this hypothesis, large red sectors of the stem and leaves would be due to mutations of this unstable allele which occur early in development of the shoot; small sectors would be due to later mutations.

It has been found, however, that medium variegated individuals produce not only red but also light variegated mutants. The parental type and the two mutant types of ears can be seen in Figure 37–2. The *light variegated kernels* (*lights*) have about half as many sectors mutant as have the *medium variegated kernels* (*mediums*).

The results of test crossing mediums ($P^v P^w$) are shown in Figure 37–3. As expected, half the offspring are nonred

FIGURE 37–1. *A random sample of kernels from a medium variegated pericarp ear. (Courtesy of R. A. Brink; photograph by The Calvin Company reprinted by permission of McGraw-Hill Book Co., Inc., from* Study Guide and Workbook for Genetics *by I. H. Herskowitz. Copyright, 1960.)*

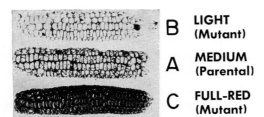

B **LIGHT** (Mutant)

A **MEDIUM** (Parental)

C **FULL-RED** (Mutant)

FIGURE 37–2. *Corn ears showing medium variegated pericarp (parental type) (A), and the mutant types light variegated (B) and full red (C). (Courtesy of R. A. Brink; reprinted by permission of McGraw-Hill Book Co., Inc., from* Study Guide and Workbook for Genetics *by I. H. Herskowitz. Copyright, 1960.)*

($P^w P^w$). In the remaining half, of those with various degrees of red, 90% are mediums ($P^v P^w$); about 6% are *full red* (*reds*); and 4% are lights. The similar frequency of reds and lights indicates that these two mutants may somehow be related in origin. Reds by $P^w P^w$ produce offspring which are all red, if colored at all. The red allele is stable in this cross.

Occasionally, medium ears show the two mutants, light and red, as twin patches of kernels (Figure 37–4). This situation suggests that reds and lights are not merely related to one another in origin but that they are complementary. In other words, one has gained something the other has lost in the mutation process. In view of the results with *Ac* and *Ds,* a new genetic hypothesis can be presented to explain pericarp variegation (Figure 37–5). Note that the gene symbols are changed. The way stocks of these strains are maintained, all variegated

genotypes are heterozygous for P^w, the stable gene (on chromosome 1) for nonred pericarp. The variegated allele is considered a dual structure, containing P^r, the top dominant allele for red and *Mp, Modulator,* which suppresses red pigment production.

Since a $\overline{P^r\,Mp}$ combination suppresses red pigmentation, mediums are produced. P^r alone produces stable, full red; $\overline{P^r\,Mp}$, plus an additional *Mp* somewhere else (*transposed Modulator*), produces lights. Consider the results obtained when certain lights ($\overline{P^r\,Mp}/P^w$ plus transposed *Mp*) are test crossed by $P^w P^w$. Half the offspring are nonred ($P^w P^w$); the other half are colored —about half of them lights (genetically similar to the light parent), half mediums (similar to the light parent but lacking the transposed *Mp*) with a few reds (cases where *Mp* is transposed from $\overline{P^r\,Mp}$, leaving P^r alone). The mechanism for transposing *Mp* away from $\overline{P^r\,Mp}$ is considered the same as

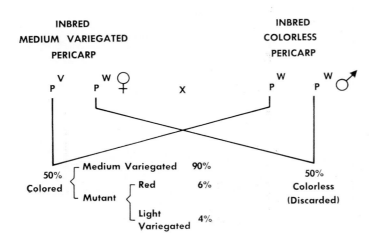

INBRED
MEDIUM VARIEGATED
PERICARP

INBRED
COLORLESS
PERICARP

FIGURE 37–3. *Results of test crossing medium variegated pericarp with colorless pericarp.*

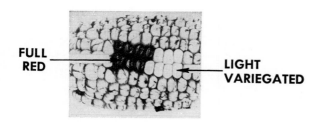

FULL RED — **LIGHT VARIEGATED**

FIGURE 37–4. *Twin patch of mutant kernels, full red and light variegated, in a medium variegated pericarp ear. (Courtesy of R. A. Brink; photograph by The Calvin Company reprinted by permission of McGraw-Hill Book Co., Inc., from* Study Guide and Workbook for Genetics *by I. H. Herskowitz. Copyright, 1960.)*

that for transposing *Ds*. This situation is illustrated in Figure 37–6, where the medium parent cell chromosomes ($\overline{P^r\,Mp}$ and P^w) are shown already divided, but daughter strands are still connected at the centromere. Normal division would have produced two daughter cells—each carrying $\overline{P^r\,Mp}/P^w$, each giving rise to medium sectors. But when transposition occurs as a result of two or more breaks or some other mutational mechanism, and, consequently, the *Mp* in one daughter strand is transposed into a nonhomologous chromosome (hollow bar), then the daughter cell which receives the transposed *Mp* may be the one carrying $\overline{P^r\,Mp}$, while the other daughter cell will carry only P^r. Thereafter, normal mitosis of the cell containing P^r alone will produce reds; and mitosis of the sister cell will produce lights. These cells will then become adjacent mutant patches in a medium background (Figure 37–4).

Red by nonred ($P^r/P^w \times P^w/P^w$) should produce roughly one-half nonred and one-half red. As mentioned previously, it does. Reds do not have *Mp* adjacent to P^r. Light by nonred ($\overline{P^r\,Mp}/P^w$ plus transposed $Mp \times P^w\,P^w$) always produces half nonred. When transposed *Mp* is located in a nonhomologous chromosome, about one quarter of F_1 will be light and one quarter will be medium, as mentioned in the previous paragraph. *Mp* can move away from $\overline{P^r\,Mp}$ yet remain in the same chromosome at a new position, so lights may still have their transposed *Mp* on chromosome 1. In this instance, backcrossing will produce more than one quarter lights in F_1 and correspondingly fewer mediums.

Other properties of *Mp* have been discovered. *Mp* may become fixed at the *P* locus so that a medium becomes a stable nonred form. Transposed *Mp* may occupy a variety of sites; two of these have already been mentioned (linked and no-longer-linked to chromosome 1). In 57 out of 87 cases, transposed *Mp* was found still linked to

PHENOTYPE	GENOTYPE
Medium Variegated	$= \overline{P^r\,Mp} / P^w$
Mutants { Red	$= P^r / P^w$
Mutants { Light Variegated	$= \overline{P^r\,Mp} / P^w$ + Transposed Mp / —

FIGURE 37–5. *New genetic hypothesis for pericarp variegation.*

chromosome 1, the allele having moved less than 50 crossover units from *P*. In the remaining 30 cases *Mp* was found transposed to one of five different nonhomologous chromosomes. Of the 57 cases where transposed *Mp* was still linked to chromosome 1, 37 showed *Mp* within five crossover units of *P*; 10 showed *Mp* within 5 to 15 units; and the remainder showed *Mp* to be farther away. Hence, *Mp* tends to move from the *P* locus by short rather than by long jumps. This situation suggests that contact between old and new sites may be required for shifts and transpositions of *Mp*.

Reds sometimes revert to variegated. In such cases an *Mp* is found transposed near *P^r*. The frequency of such reversions from red to variegated can be studied after introducing an *Mp* locus various distances from *P^r* in a *P^r*-containing chromosome. As shown in Figure 37–7, the closer to *P^r* the introduced *Mp* is, the greater is the frequency of reversions. In summary, medium mutates to red by loss of *Mp* from its position near the *P^r* locus. In this process, complementary lights are produced possessing an extra *Mp*—a transposed *Mp*. The medium

type is reconstituted by the return of a transposed *Mp* near the *P^r* locus.

Two additional points need to be made. Changes in phenotype involving reds, mediums, lights, and nonreds are not mutations at the *P* locus. These changes are the phenotypic consequences of mutations involving the transposition of *Mp* and are, in this respect, much like the changes which follow the transposition of *Ds*. Transposition of *Mp* to another locus may change the phenotype the recipient locus produces. For example, a "mutation" to the waxy phenotype was observed in a particular medium variegated individual whose chromosome 9 carried an allele for the starchy phenotype. The waxy phenotype was unstable and frequently "mutated" back to starchy. Tests showed that *Mp* had been transposed to the starchy locus, which then produced the waxy phenotype; furthermore, the reversions to starchy were the result of *Mp*'s transposition away from this locus. All the phenotypic changes dependent upon the presence of *Mp* (and *Ds*) strongly resemble position effects.

No evidence has been presented thus far that the transposition of *Mp* is genetically

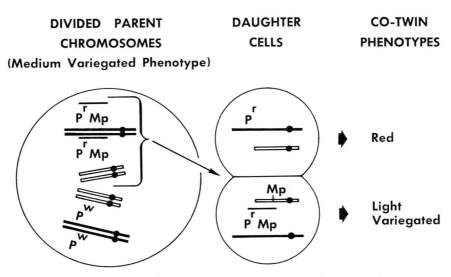

FIGURE 37–6. *Transposition of* Modulator *and the origin of twin sectors.*

controlled. It has been found, however, that the relative frequency with which Mp transposes away from $\overline{Pr\ Mp}$ is 100 in the absence of a transposed Mp; about 60 in the presence of one transposed Mp; and about 5 in the presence of two transposed Mp's. Thus, the transposition of Mp from $\overline{Pr\ Mp}$ is controlled by the presence of transposed Mp.

Topographical Relations of Controlling Elements [2]

In the Ac-Ds system, Ac controls Ds not only by regulating Ds transposition by breakage or some other mechanism which may involve contact, but in other ways, as detected by the kind of phenotypic effect Ds produces on its linear gene neighbor to one side. The capacity for transposition is possessed by both the regulator gene (Ac) and the operator gene (Ds), a feature unknown in the bacterial systems.

In bacterial systems the regulator and operator genes may be close to each other or they may be a considerable map distance apart. In view of the transposability of both elements in maize, it can be hypothesized that both elements are at times adjacent or in close linkage. Consequently, $\overline{Pr\ Mp}$ can be interpreted $Pr\ op^{Mp}\ R^{Mp}$ where op^{Mp} is the operator and R^{Mp} the regulator gene. In general, it can be hypothesized that both an operator gene and a regulator gene are located close to a structural gene when only the presence of the regulator gene is known with certainty.

This general hypothesis is tested in the following way. The gene for bronze, Bz, is located in chromosome 9 and has a completely recessive allele, bz, which produces no color. If a transposition of Ac occurs near Bz, resulting in a variegated bronze color, this locus is now assumed to be $Bz\ op^{Ac}\ R^{Ac}$. If a two-element control sys-

[2] This section is based upon the work of B. Mc-Clintock (1961, 1962, 1963).

PER CENT RECOMBINATION P - Mp	VARIEGATED SECTORS PER 1000 KERNELS
2.6	15
4.3	11
7.6	8
12.0	3
42.0	0.2

FIGURE 37–7. *Effect of distance of* Mp *from* P *upon transposition rate of* Mp *to* P.

tem actually exists at this locus, three kinds of subsequent transpositional events are possible:

1. Transposition of both op^{Ac} and R^{Ac}. (This operation should release Bz from the control system, and R^{Ac} should prove absent from the vicinity of Bz.)
2. Transposition of op^{Ac} only. (This should also release the Bz gene from control by R^{Ac}; but the latter should still be near Bz and capable of regulating op^{Ac} located at other sites in the genotype.)
3. Transposition of R^{Ac} only. (This should leave the $Bz\ op^{Ac}$ locus still under the control of R^{Ac} in its new location.)

Experimental results confirm these expectations. (Were there a one-element control system, the third alternative could not occur.) Since other results demonstrate that R^{Ac}, R^{Mp}, and still other R genes are different (each regulates its own type of op gene), numerous and different op-R systems occur in maize. The transposability of op explains why a given op can become the operator gene of a variety of loci previously uncontrolled by that op. Additional work with corn is needed to determine:

1. Whether transposition of op or R involves an addition or a replacement of an already present op or R locus

2. How the two kinds of controlling loci arise, and whether their origin is interdependent

3. Whether the two elements of a controlling system usually are adjacent or separate

4. The nucleotidic basis for and the biochemical mode of action of, *op-R* gene-controlling systems.

Paramutation [3]

The *R* locus in chromosome 10 of maize produces anthocyanin pigment in the aleurone and certain vegetative parts of the plant. Two alleles—stippled, R^{st}, and marbled, R^{mb}—are aleurone-spotting genes found occasionally in strains of corn native to Peru and neighboring countries. Heterozygotes for one of these mutants are phenotypically as expected if the other *R* allele is also from one of these South American countries. Mutant homozygotes are also as expected. However, when the other *R* allele in a heterozygote with these mutants is native to other countries, exceptional phenotypes result. This suggests that a control system has evolved in populations where R^{st} or R^{mb} occur which does not operate properly when these mutants are heterozygous with foreign *R* alleles.

The exceptional result from "foreign *R*" R^{st} hybrids is that pigmentation is reduced or suppressed in 100% of the *R*-containing progeny of a test cross. Moreover, all of the *R*-containing descendants continue to show the same pigment suppression—even though R^{st} is no longer present. For this reason, R^{st} and R^{mb} are said to be paramutagenic. They induce foreign *R* alleles to undergo *paramutation* to form *paramutant* alleles. Paramutation can occur somatically. An *R* factor which becomes a paramutant may itself become weakly paramutagenic to other *R* alleles. The pigment spotting action

of R^{st} and R^{mb} is separable from their paramutagenic ability. The paramutagenic action of R^{st} is not depleted by exercising this function repeatedly in $R R^{st}$ plants; nevertheless, no evidence has been found for the occurrence of a cytoplasmic element released by a paramutagenic allele and taken up at the paramutable locus.[4]

Paramutational events may occur in organisms other than maize. The conditional segregation-distortion phenomenon observed in Drosophila (pp. 387–388) resembles paramutation. Since it is considered to involve a system which controls gene action, paramutation does not imply a modification of the chemical composition of genetic material. Additional studies should further elucidate the nature of paramutation.

Superregulatory Mechanisms [5]

A single control system is capable of regulating the action of many genes in development. One of the systems studied—(*Spm, Suppressor-mutator*)—according to B. McClintock (1963) ". . . serves as a model of the mode of operation of one type of superregulatory mechanism. Such a system can activate or inactivate particular genes in some cells early in development, and activate or inactivate other genes later in development. It can turn on the action of some genes at the same time that it turns off the action of others. It can adjust the level of activity of a particular gene in different parts of an organism. . . . The controlling elements of the examined systems may represent foreign, nonessential, episomelike components that have been integrated into the maize genome; or, on the other hand, they may be true chromosomal components of present-day maize, whatever their evolutionary origins and histories may have been."

---

[3] See R. A. Brink (1960).

[4] See R. A. Brink, J. L. Kermickle, and D. F. Brown (1964).
[5] See B. McClintock (1963).

SUMMARY AND CONCLUSIONS

A large number of cases involving the control of gene action in maize are known. Those analyzed prove to comprise several regulator gene-operator gene systems comparable to those found in bacteria. In maize both genes of this two-element control system are transposable to new loci. Paramutation probably involves a gene control system. Other, more complicated, control systems (superregulatory, for example) also exist.

Royal Alexander Brink, *in 1961.*

REFERENCES

Brink, R. A., "Very Light Variegated Pericarp in Maize," Genetics, 39:724–740, 1954.

Brink, R. A., "Paramutation and Chromosome Organization," Quart. Rev. Biol., 35: 120–137, 1960.

Brink, R. A., Kermickle, J. L., and Brown, D. F., "Tests for a Gene-Dependent Cytoplasmic Particle Associated with R Paramutation in Maize," Proc. Nat. Acad. Sci., U.S., 51:1067–1074, 1964.

McClintock, B., "Some Parallels between Gene Control Systems in Maize and Bacteria," Amer. Nat., 95:265–277, 1961.

McClintock, B., "Topographical Relations between Elements of Control Systems in Maize," Carnegie Inst. Wash. Yearb., 61(1961–1962):448–461, 1962.

McClintock, B., "Further Studies of Gene-Control Systems in Maize," Carnegie Inst. Wash. Yearb., 62(1962–1963):486–493, 1963.

van Schaik, N. W., and Brink, R. A., "Transpositions of Modulator, A Modifier of the Variegated Pericarp Allele in Maize," Genetics, 44:725–738, 1959.

QUESTIONS FOR DISCUSSION

37.1. Could you detect the transposition of a *Modulator* to a locus near P^w? Explain.

37.2. Why does a light variegated individual of maize, with a transposed *Modulator* on the same chromosome as $\overline{Pr\ Mp}$ produce among the F_1 offspring more than one quarter lights and less than one quarter mediums when this individual is back-crossed to nonred ($P^w\ P^w$)?

37.3. Could genes similar to *Modulator* be the cause of relatively rare "mutants" of amorphic, hypomorphic, and neomorphic types? Upon what do you base your opinion?

37.4. Do experimental results with corn have any bearing upon the hypothesis that the operator gene is nothing more than the initial portion of the nucleotide sequence of a transcriptional unit of DNA? Explain.

37.5. Is paramutation a normal mechanism for controlling gene action? Explain.

37.6. Compare the mechanisms for controlling gene action in maize and Salmonella.

Chapter 38

REGULATION OF GENE ACTION—POSITION EFFECT IN DROSOPHILA

Some of the chromosomal rearrangements induced in Drosophila by ionizing radiations have the same, or nearly the same, points of breakage, and many nearly-identical rearrangements are associated with the occurrence of the same phenotypic change. Moreover, the new phenotype is transmitted whenever the rearrangement is, and is often similar to that produced by a known allele located at or near one of the breakage points. In such cases, the change in phenotype seems to be directly connected with the mutation of a gene known to be located at or near a point of breakage.

We cannot claim that chromosome breakage in or adjacent to a gene automatically changes it to a particular allele because other breaks at this locus partake in other types of rearrangements which do not produce such a phenotypic change. For the same reason, it is untenable to presume that the radiation which caused the break, simultaneously produced a minute deficiency or duplication of the affected locus. An important feature of this phenotypic change, therefore, is its disassociation with breakage. However, the change may have something to do with the broken ends that join—occurring only when the broken end carrying a given locus unites with the broken ends

from certain specific loci in the genome. If we accept this view, then we would expect the gene at the broken end to produce one phenotypic effect when united with certain broken ends and another phenotypic effect when joined to others. In other words, the phenotypic effect of a gene may be modified when it has new linear neighbors. Such a phenotypic change is called *position effect* (pp. 384–385). Presumably position effect changes the working of a gene without changing the gene itself. Position effect, therefore, may be one of the phenotypic consequences of mutations involving structural rearrangements, even though not a mutation itself.

A gene showing position effect is presumed to be chemically and physically unchanged in any permanent way. Since genes located some distance from a point of breakage sometimes show position effects, position effect can spread somehow along the chromosome and affect the functioning of a gene whose immediate linear neighbors have not been switched. This *spreading effect* is further reason for dismissing explanations of position effect based solely upon breakage or upon other mutational changes connected with ionization.

If the physico-chemical nature of a gene showing position effect is unchanged, two predictions can be made. First, the gene in a position-effect rearrangement should resume its original function upon being placed near its former genic neighbors in the chromosome. This can be tested experimentally either by irradiating individuals carrying rearranged chromosomes and examining the progeny for structural changes that reverse this rearrangement, or by moving (by crossing over) the gene showing position effect to a normal chromosome. In both cases it is found that the gene returns to its original position and phenotypic effect. The second prediction is that a normal gene placed in the rearranged position by means of crossing over should exhibit the position effect. It does.

In Drosophila, position effects often accompany rearrangements that bring genes in euchromatin close to those in heterochromatin. Placing a gene normally located in a euchromatic region near or in a heterochromatic region often produces a special, wavering position effect which is expressed in the phenotype as a mosaic or variegated characteristic. Thus, for example, if by paracentric inversion, the gene for dull-red eye color on the X chromosome, w^+ (normally located in euchromatin) is placed in the heterochromatin near the centromere, the result is mottled eye color, white and dull-red speckles. Such variegation is reduced, however, if, by breeding, an extra Y chromosome or another heterochromatin-rich chromosome is added to the genotype. It is not altogether clear yet how this suppression of variegation is brought about.

The only requirement for the occurrence of position effect is an appropriate change of a gene's linear neighbors. Breakage merely provides a way of obtaining such changes. Other mechanisms—such as crossing over—which change the relative positions of genes should also reveal position effects. Let us see if a crossover system [1] which will produce a position effect can be devised.

An X-linked mutant in Drosophila, Bar (B), reduces the number of facets (ommatidia) in the compound eyes, thereby narrowing the normally ovoid eye to a slit. When the normal and the Bar-containing chromosomes are studied in nuclei of larval salivary glands, it is found that about seven successive bands in the normal chromosome are duplicated in tandem in the Bar chromosome. Let us designate such a single region as abcdef. Consequently, a normal

---

[1] Based upon investigations of A. H. Sturtevant, H. J. Muller, C. B. Bridges, and others.

female contains abcdef/abcdef and a homozygous Bar female abcdef abcdef/abcdef abcdef. In normal $(+/+)$ females, homologous letters (parts) of the two homologs synapse and crossing over takes place between corresponding letters. In homozygous Bar (B/B) females, proper synapsis and normal crossing over can also occur, but in this case a potentially different sequence of events will cause synapsis to occur incorrectly—the left region in one chromosome will pair with the right region of the second (Figure 38–1), leaving the other two regions unsynapsed. If this *oblique synapsis* is followed by normal crossing over anywhere in the paired region (as shown between b and c in the figure), the crossover strands will be abcdef and abcdef abcdef abcdef. The former strand has this region only once—and will therefore be normal $(+)$—whereas the latter has this region three times. If an egg containing the one-region crossover is fertilized by an X-bearing sperm of a normal-eyed male, the zygote will produce a daughter having normal eye shape, thereby demonstrating that Bar has reverted to $+$. This result can be checked in a subsequent generation by examining the salivary gland chromosomes.

If an egg containing the three-region crossover is similarly fertilized, a female will be produced having four of these regions, three in one homolog and one in the other. What will be the phenotype of such a female? Does it make any difference phenotypically whether these regions are grouped two and two (as in homozygous Bar) or three and one? Note that the genic neighbors of the four regions are different when two regions are present on each homolog than they are when one homolog has three regions and the other has one. Since position effect occurs, this gene neighbor difference may result in different phenotypes.

Although we do not know what the potential position effect phenotype should be, we can look for any significant variation from the number of eye facets expected. The normal ovoid eye of females and males ($+/+$ and $+/Y$) contains more than 200 facets. The homozygous *Bar* female (B/B) and hemizygous *Bar* male (B/Y) have about 68 ommatidia per eye. The heterozygous female ($+/B$) has about 150; *Bar* on one chromosome is incompletely dominant to $+$ in the homolog. From the cross $+/Y$ ♂ by B/B ♀, the typical F_1 females are $+/B$ with about 150 ommatidia per eye. As mentioned earlier, reversions to the $+$ condition by crossing over in an obliquely synapsed tetrad could be detected as a $+/+$ female. The complementary crossover—a triple re-

gion chromosome—with a normal chromosome would produce a female whose eye might have less than 68 facets or have more than 68 but less than 150 facets.

The design of the experiment is not yet complete, however. Since we do not know how often a chromosome showing the potential position effect will be produced in meiosis, two other possible causes of exceptional eye shape must be eliminated. If the cross made is $+/Y$ by B/B, a sperm carrying two X's (because of nondisjunction in the father) that fertilizes an egg with no X (because of nondisjunction in the mother) will produce a $+/+$ daughter counted as one of the exceptional types. Although such zygotes would be extremely rare, they would

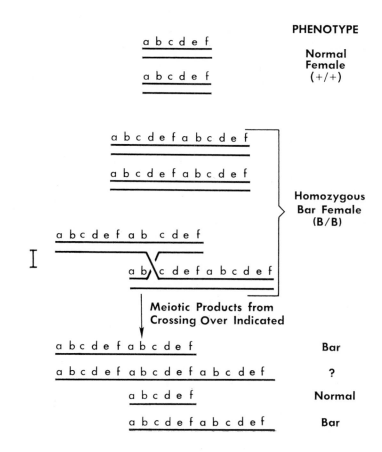

PHENOTYPE

a b c d e f
—————————
a b c d e f

Normal
Female
($+/+$)

a b c d e f a b c d e f
—————————————
a b c d e f a b c d e f

Homozygous
Bar Female
(B/B)

a b c d e f a b c d e f

a b c d e f a b c d e f

Meiotic Products from
Crossing Over Indicated

a b c d e f a b c d e f — Bar

a b c d e f a b c d e f a b c d e f — ?

a b c d e f — Normal

a b c d e f a b c d e f — Bar

FIGURE 38–1.
Diagrammatic representation of the normal and the Bar region of the X chromosome and the consequences of crossing over after oblique synapsis (I).

be recognized, however, if the + chromosome carried as a marker the gene for yellow body color, *y*; such nondisjunctionally produced daughters would be yellow, not gray, in body color. (In this way we would also be able to recognize any female progeny resulting from cultures contaminated by flies of the yellow stock.) Consequently, the cross that should be made is $y +^B/Y$ by $y^+ B/y^+ B$. For clarity the gene symbol for ovoid eye is now given as $+^B$.

The other event that should not be allowed to confuse the results is mutation at or near the *B* locus. The exceptional phenotypes sought (ovoid and unknown eye shapes) will always be produced after crossing over in the region of *Bar*. The *B/B* female can be made dihybrid for genes near and on either side of *B*—near enough (less than ten crossover units apart) to avoid double crossovers between them. On the X chromosome linkage map *Bar* is located at 57.0; *forked bristles* (*f*) at 56.7; and *carnation eye color* (*car*) at 62.5. Accordingly, the females constructed are:

$$y^+ f^+ B car/y^+ f B car^+$$

We can now eliminate from further consideration any unusual eye shape that is non-crossover between the loci for *f* and *car*. All exceptional phenotypes of interest will be crossovers between *f* and *car*; normally, crossovers in this region will be present in 5.8% (62.5 minus 56.7) of F_1 daughters. To identify the crossover daughters (which will be either nonforked noncarnation or forked carnation), the males used will have to be $y f +^B car/Y$. The actual cross then is:

$$y f +^B car/Y \text{ ♂ by}$$
$$y^+ f^+ B car/y^+ f B car^+ \text{ ♀}$$

When the experiment is performed, about one daughter in two thousand is ovoid-eyed and carries a crossover between *f* and *car*; a similar percentage of crossover daughters have very narrow eyes, called *Ultrabar* (Figure 38–2), each eye containing about 45 facets. The two types of exceptional flies are equally frequent, as would be expected of the reciprocal products of the hypothesized crossing over. Moreover, Ultrabar females contain a triple region in one X and a single region in the other X, as predicted and revealed by examining the salivary glands of their F_1. Any argument that the Ultrabar phenotype results from a mutation—not a position effect—that is somehow dependent upon a simultaneously-occurring crossing over is disqualified by obtaining females which carry both exceptional types of X and by occasionally finding perfectly typical *Bar* chromosomes in their progeny. These *Bar* chromosomes prove to be the product of a crossing over between the single region of one chromosome and the middle region of the triple-dose homolog (Figure 38–3). We may conclude, therefore, that four regions aligned in different ways—by crossing over

FIGURE 38–2. *Compound eye of Drosophila. Left: Ultrabar; center: Bar; right: normal.*

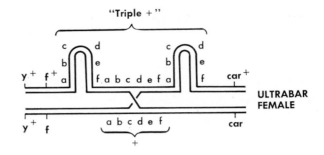

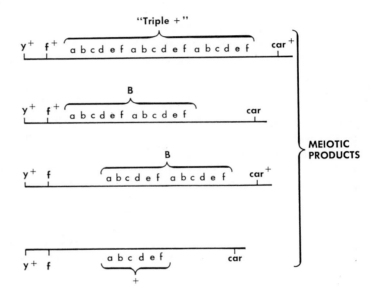

FIGURE 38–3.
*Production
of Bar chromosomes
by crossing over
in Ultrabar females.*

and not by mutation-producing chromosome breaks––produce different phenotypes.

From a *B* (double region) chromosome, it is also possible to obtain a few chromosomes nonrecombinant for bordering markers but + (single region) or *Ultrabar* (triple region). This unusual circumstance is brought about by an intrachromosomal exchange within the double loop that is formed when the two members of the tandemly duplicated region synapse with each other. Similarly, intrachromosomal exchange within an Ultrabar chromosome can yield + and *B* chromosomes.[2]

[2] See H. M. Peterson and J. R. Laughnan (1963).

Another way of detecting position effects involving crossing over is possible. If the genotype of a Drosophila female is *y a+b spl/y+a b+spl+*, both the *a* and *b* loci are heterozygous and the mutants are in different homologs or in *trans position* (Figure 38–4). If crossing over occurs between these loci, the resulting crossover chromosomes would be *y a+ b+ spl+* and *y+a b spl*. When both these crossover chromosomes are present in the same individual, both mutants (*a* and *b*) are in the same homolog or in *cis position*. Both the trans and cis heterozygotes have the same number of loci on each chromosome. In the former instance, however, *a* and *b+* (and *a+*

CIS	TRANS
+ +	+ b
═══	═══
a b	a +

FIGURE 38–4. *Cis and trans positions for dihybrid linked genes.*

and *b*) would be linear neighbors; in the latter case *a* and *b* (and a^+ and b^+) would be linear neighbors. If the trans dihybrid had one phenotypic effect, the cis dihybrid obtained from it by crossing over had another, and if, by crossing over, the cis form reverted to the trans form and restored the old phenotypic effect, position effect would be considered proved.

This *cis-trans test for position effect* should have the best chance of yielding a positive result when the two pairs of genes involved are adjacent to or very close to one another. If the genes are very close together, crossing over will rarely occur between them; large numbers of progeny would have to be scored to assure at least one crossover.

The members of the multiple allelic series at the white locus on the X chromosome of Drosophila are all located at approximately 1.5 on the crossover map. Although the hybrid composed of w^a (apricot) and *w* (white), $w^a w$, produces pale apricot eye color, this result does not prove that w^a and *w* are alternatives of the same gene. Suppose w^a and *w* are mutants of separate but similarly-acting genes located close together, one at position 1.49 (w^{a+}) and one at 1.51 (w^+). The crossover data, being finite and somewhat variable, could accidentally have placed them both at locus 1.5. If w^{a+} and w^+ are close but separate loci, the trans dihybrid should yield the cis dihybrid by crossing over.

To test whether w^{a+} and w^+ are sepa-rate loci,[3] Drosophila females which carry an attached-X chromosome with *y w spl* on one arm and $y^+ w^a spl^+$ on the other are bred. Recall that the use of attached-X's permits the recovery of two of the four strands involved in each crossing over (p. 122). The attached-X genetic system sometimes yields both complementary crossover types in the same gamete. Figure 38–5 (left side) shows schematically a portion of this attached-X as it would appear in the tetrad stage at the time of the crossing over and indicates the standard genetic map location of the *y* and *spl* markers. When a female with pale (dilute) apricot eye color and this chromosome is crossed with a *Bar*-containing male, the non-Bar F_1 daughters (who carry a paternally-derived Y) are usually noncrossovers and have pale apricot-colored eyes like their mother. Crossovers between the region containing the white locus and the centromere produce either white or apricot daughters. Barring mutation, these phenotypes would be the only ones expected if w^a and *w* were alternatives of the same gene.

But if w^{a+} is separate from w^+, the former can be distinguished by a new symbol, apr^+. If apr^+ lay to the left of w^+ (as shown in the left portion of the figure), *apr* and *w* would each have its own + allele in the other arm of the parental attached-X and, consequently, the female parent would have to be a trans heterozygote with respect to these loci. A rare crossing over between these loci would produce the crossover attached-X shown at the right of the figure. As a result, the two mutants would be in the cis position.

When large numbers of daughters from the attached-X females are examined, several are found to have dull-red eyes. It is essential to determine whether these flies are mutant or the result of a change from the

[3] Based on the work of E. B. Lewis.

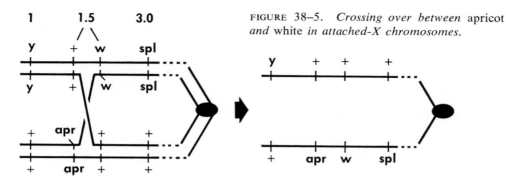

FIGURE 38–5. *Crossing over between* apricot *and* white *in attached-X chromosomes.*

trans to the cis form. To do this, we detach—that is, separate the arms of—the attached-X's in the dull-red-eyed exceptional flies (by collecting the products of the occasional crossing over that occurs between the attached-X and the Y in the heterochromatic regions near their centromeres) and determining the genes carried in each detached arm. The finding that one arm can always be represented as *y apr+ w+ spl+* and the other as *y+ apr w spl* offers strong support for the view that the dull-red exceptional females were cis heterozygotes, and that *apr* lies to the left of *w* on the X chromosome, as shown in the figure. (It is instructive to work out the arrangement of the markers after crossing over between *apr* and *w* on the assumption that *apr* is to the right of *w*.)

Proof that the exceptional dull-red females result from position effect rather than mutation is obtained by mating these exceptional females and occasionally obtaining daughters with pale apricot eye color. In these new exceptional daughters the original gene arrangement is found restored by crossing over.

The phenotypic difference between pale apricot and dull red is undoubtedly the result of position effect, since the only difference between the cis and trans conditions is in the arrangement of the genetic mate-

rial. This phenomenon is therefore termed a *cis-trans position effect.* To detect such an effect it is necessary to separate two very closely linked genes. Prior to the experiment the genes used had been considered alleles because of their closeness on the genetic map and their similar phenotypic effects, but observing their cis-trans position effect proved they were nonalleles occupying different loci. When the other genes making up the "white multiple allelic series" (Chapter 5) are investigated, some are found to be allelic to *w* and others to *apr.* Some, however, are allelic to neither, and appropriate crossing over studies show that the "white region" on the X is a nest of five (perhaps more) separate, linearly arranged genes with similar effects.

Other regions in the genome are now known where two or more genic alternatives —previously considered allelic—prove to be *pseudoallelic,* that is, prove to be nonallelic when subjected to the cis-trans test. In addition to pseudoallelism in Aspergillus, other microorganisms, and corn, examples of pseudoallelism include cases involving color in cotton; lack of tails in mice; lozenge and vermilion eye colors in Drosophila.

Another case of pseudoallelism in Drosophila [4] involves nonalleles whose functions differ somewhat more than *apr* and *w.*

[4] See E. B. Lewis (1963) for complete discussion.

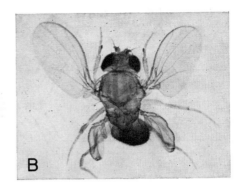
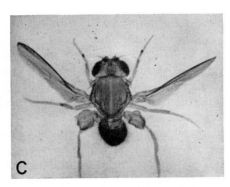

FIGURE 38–6.   Drosophila melanogaster *males: normal* (*A*), *bithorax* (*B*), *postbithorax* (*C*), *and bithorax postbithorax* (*D*).   (*Courtesy of E. B. Lewis; reprinted by permission of McGraw-Hill Book Co., Inc., from* Study Guide and Workbook for Genetics *by I. H. Herskowitz.   Copyright, 1960.*)

The normal, wild-type fly (Figure 38–6A) has small club-shaped *balancers* (*halteres*) located on the posterior part of the thorax. One of the pseudoalleles, *bithorax* (*bx*), converts the haltere into a large wing-like structure (Figure 38–6B); another, called *postbithorax* (*pbx*), appears to do much the same thing (Figure 38–6C). But close examination reveals that these two recessive pseudoalleles really have different functions. Bithorax converts the front portion and postbithorax the hind portion of the haltere into a wing-like structure. Flies homozygous for both mutants demonstrate

these changes in a fully developed second pair of wings (Figure 38–6D).

What are the cis-trans effects for *bx* and *pbx?* The cis form (+ +/*bx pbx*) has normal balancers, whereas the trans form (*bx* +/+ *pbx*) shows a slight postbithorax effect, providing another example of cis-trans position effect and demonstrating the nonallelism of these genes. The map distance between these loci is 0.02.

These examples of pseudoallelism apparently involve separate but closely linked functional genes; they do not seem to involve intragenic recombination of the type that occurs within the A or B cistron of the rII region of φT4. The possibility exists, however, that recombination does occur within [5] as well as between functional gene units in Drosophila, although mechanisms other than crossing over may also be involved.

Consider the morphology of Drosophila chromosome regions which contain pseudo-alleles. The white series is associated with a double band (*doublet*) in the salivary gland chromosome; *apr* may be in one band, *w* in the other. The vermilion series is associated with another doublet in the X chromosome, whereas the bithorax series (composed of five separate pseudoallelic loci) is connected with two doublets. (This last fact demonstrates what is proved by other data—that a band may contain more than a single gene.) The great number of doublets in salivary chromosomes suggests that genes located in these regions are pseudo-allelic.

The origin of adjacent loci with similar types of action can be accounted for in several ways. One explanation is that during the course of evolution, adjacent genes producing different effects mutated to alleles which performed similar, presumably advantageous, functions. A second explanation might be that rearrangements brought together widely separated nonalleles with similar functions. Though both of these explanations may be sufficient for some of the cases found, it seems more likely that most adjacent and similar genes arose as duplications that occurred one or more times (as in the bithorax case) in the ways described in Chapter 12 (see also pp. 418–419). After duplication linearly adjacent genes—originally identical—would have become somewhat different from each other functionally by mutation.

[5] See W. J. Welshons and E. S. Von Halle (1962), and A. Chovnick, A. Schalet, R. P. Kernaghan, and M. Krauss (1964).

What causes position effects? With respect to gene action, genes that are linear neighbors are perhaps more likely to be dependent upon each other than upon their alleles in a homologous chromosome (usually located a considerable distance away). This kind of dependency might be subject to position effect when the relative positions of heterochromatin and euchromatin are shifted by breakage. Position effects due to structural changes might be particularly common in species whose chromosomes or chromosome parts take on special positions in the nucleus relative to each other. Two facts—that during nuclear division Drosophila chromosomes show somatic synapsis, and that somatic synapsis is found in the giant interphase nuclei of salivary gland and other cells—suggest that at the time of gene action different chromosomes and their parts are arranged so that the products of gene action may be formed or used in particular sequences. Due to the presence of heterozygous reciprocal translocations in Oenothera (Chapter 17), chromosomal parts show a very orderly arrangement in the circle of 14 chromosomes formed during meiosis. Here also, a new arrangement of chromosomal parts might disturb functional sequences and produce position effects. As a matter of fact, position effect is known to occur in Oenothera.

The molecular basis for position effects in Drosophila is yet to be established. In studying systems that control gene action the results with bacteria and maize lead us to hypothesize that position effects in Drosophila can result if the production or the translation of messenger RNA for a given cistron is influenced by a change in its gene neighbors. Since protein synthesis occurs in the nucleus, the possibility also exists that position effects can result from sequential intranuclear reactions which are influenced by the diffusion and, hence, the concentration of the protein products of gene action.

SUMMARY AND CONCLUSIONS

Phenotypic changes can result when the same genetic material is arranged in different ways. The shuffling of genes which produces such position effects may be brought about by structural changes in chromosomes and by crossing over.

Linear nests of genes with similar effects have probably arisen by one or more duplications *in situ* of an ancestral gene, followed by mutations that led to differentiation in their effects.

Position effect is attributed to a change in one or more of the following:

1. Production of a given messenger RNA
2. Translation of this messenger RNA
3. Interactions between proteins resulting from the intranuclear translation of messenger RNAs.

REFERENCES

Bridges, C. B., "The Bar 'Gene' a Duplication," Science, 83:210–211, 1963. Reprinted in *Classic Papers in Genetics,* Peters, J. A. (Ed.), Englewood Cliffs, N.J.: Prentice-Hall, 1959, pp. 163–166.

Chovnick, A., Schalet, A., Kernaghan, R. P., and Krauss, M., "The Rosy Cistron in *Drosophila melanogaster:* Genetic Fine Structure Analysis," Genetics, 50:1245–1259, 1964.

Lewis, E. B., "The Pseudoallelism of White and Apricot in Drosophila melanogaster," Proc. Nat. Acad. Sci., U.S., 38:953–961, 1952.

Lewis, E. B., "Genes and Developmental Pathways," Amer. Zool., 3:33–56, 1963.

Muller, H. J., Prokofyeva-Belgovskaya, A. A., and Kossikov, K. V., "Unequal Crossingover in the Bar Mutant as a Result of Duplication of a Minute Chromosome Section," C. R. (Dokl.) Acad. Sci., U.R.S.S., N.S., 1(10):87–88, 1936.

Peterson, H. M., and Laughnan, J. R., "Intrachromosomal Exchange at the Bar Locus in Drosophila," Proc. Nat. Acad. Sci., U.S., 50:126–133, 1963.

Sturtevant, A. H., "The Effects of Unequal Crossingover at the Bar Locus in Drosophila," Genetics, 10:117–147, 1925. Reprinted in *Classic Papers in Genetics,* Peters, J. A. (Ed.), Englewood Cliffs, N.J.: Prentice-Hall, 1959, pp. 124–148.

Welshons, W. J., and Von Halle, E. S., "Pseudoallelism at the Notch Locus in Drosophila," Genetics, 47:743–759, 1962.

QUESTIONS FOR DISCUSSION

38.1. If a previously unknown phenotype appears at the same time as a qualitative or quantitative change in the genetic material, can you determine whether the effect is due to mutation or to position effect? Explain.

38.2. Would you expect to find position effects in most sexually reproducing organisms? Why?

38.3. Is crossing over ever unequal? Explain.

38.4. Should pseudoalleles be considered subgenes (parts of one gene) rather than separate, nonallelic genes? Explain.

38.5. Does position effect require pseudoallelism for its detection? Explain. Is the reverse true? Explain.

38.6. What genotypic steps are required to prove that a region shows a cis-trans position effect? Explain.

38.7. Can one of the steps in question 38.6 be a lack of all or part of the region under investigation? Why?

38.8. What crosses would you make to test whether two recessive mutants in Drosophila, apparently alleles of the X-linked gene v^+ (normal allele of vermilion eye color), are pseudoalleles?

38.9. Using appropriate genetic markers, draw a tetrad configuration which would permit you to identify strands which have undergone intrachromosomal exchange in the *Bar* region of the X chromosome of *Drosophila melanogaster*.

38.10. Using the operon concept, explain how a paracentric inversion in the X chromosome of Drosophila might result in a mottled eye color phenotype.

38.11. Suggest a molecular explanation for the cis-trans position effect observed in the white region of the X chromosome in Drosophila.

38.12. Can position effect occur in haploids? Why?

Chapter *39

REGULATION OF GENE ACTION—DOSAGE COMPENSATION

Mammals

BECAUSE DNA synthesis occurs almost without interruption in the relatively uncoiled chromosome of *E. coli,* we may suppose that, in general, uncoiled chromosomes can synthesize complementary DNA and RNA. On the other hand, DNA synthesis does not occur during mitosis or meiosis when the chromosomes are highly condensed. Consequently, we may hypothesize that a chromosome cannot function in DNA or RNA synthesis while coiled. If these premises are acceptable, we may consider that during interphase the presence of heavily Feulgen stained, clumped, chromosomal material (chromatin knots or *karyosomes*) is an indication of coiled chromosomal material and, therefore, the total absence of genetic activity in such bodies.

That certain chromosomes or chromosomal regions are highly clumped or coiled while others are not is probably correlated with their different times for DNA replication. Chromosomes or chromosomal regions which are normally coiled and stained (*eupycnotic*), relatively overcoiled and overstained (*hyperpycnotic*), and relatively undercoiled and understained (*hypopycnotic*) differ in their time of DNA replication. Abnormal staining, *heteropycnosis,* is one of the characteristics of heterochromatin (p. 155).

The gene action hypothesis presented

484

above can be tested by comparing the interphase activity of genes when a given chromosomal region is normally coiled and when it is overcoiled. Many of the diploid interphase nuclei in human males show a small karyosome touching the nuclear membrane; in the human female the same cells show a similar but much larger karyosome. Because the size of this chromatin knot differs in each sex, the extra karyosome material in the female is called *sex chromatin,* or the *Barr body* (after its discoverer). The presence of sex chromatin in individuals aneusomic with regard to sex chromosomes has been investigated. The maximum number of separate Barr bodies found are: none in XY and X0 individuals; one in XX, XXY, XXYY; two in XXX, XXXY; and three in XXXX individuals. Cells with less than the maximum number have fewer and, accordingly, larger Barr bodies. We may conclude, therefore, that the maximum number of Barr bodies is one less than the number of X chromosomes in a diploid individual. Tetraploid cells of a male probably have no valid Barr body; the larger karyosome reported is attributed to the union between the small karyosomes of the two X's. That tetraploid cells of a female have two Barr bodies suggests the maximum number of Barr bodies is determined by the balance between the number of X chromosomes and the number of autosome sets. One X chromosome balanced by two sets of autosomes does not give rise to a Barr body. However, each X in excess of this balance clumps and is either detected as a separate Barr body or is fused with other excess X's to form larger bodies. Hence the maximum number of Barr bodies is equal to x-(p/2), where x is the number of X chromosomes, and p is the ploidy or number of sets of autosomes.[1] Note that the Y chromosome has no influence upon

[1] According to D. G. Harnden.

the number of Barr bodies. Consequently, the genes for sex, particularly those located in the Y, do not suppress Barr body formation in normal or abnormal males.

According to the hypothesis under discussion, each excess X is rendered hypercoiled and functionally inactive. It is, however, still capable of being replicated during interphase, although the replication is delayed.[2] That no normal tissue in a female ever has 100 per cent of its nuclei showing a Barr body may very well be partly due to errors in cytological observation. It is also possible that some of the cells that fail to show a Barr body are replicating the X chromosome involved. As a consequence of Barr body formation, males and females—whether normal or abnormal—apparently have similar numbers of functional X chromosomal genes per diploid number of autosomes.[3] In other words, basically males and females may not be very different after all, at least at the functional X chromosome level.

The human X chromosome (Figure 10–7, p. 139) contains a gene necessary for production of the enzyme *glucose-6-phosphate dehydrogenase (G-6-PD)*. One X chromosomal mutant fails to produce this enzyme. Males with the normal X therefore can and those with the mutant X cannot make this enzyme. Since the Y chromosome has no effect on the production of this enzyme it carries no allele for this gene. When individually tested,[4] red blood corpuscles of genetically pure, normal males and females show the same amount of G-6-PD activity. If both normal alleles operated in the female as they did in the male, we would expect the red blood corpuscles of a normal female to produce twice as much enzyme as those of a normal male. When the red blood cells of females heterozygous for the X-linked mutant are studied, however, some are found to be normal and others deficient with respect to G-6-PD; no corpuscles of intermediate activity are found. These results prove that such *human females are functional mosaics* for this locus. Some of their red blood corpuscles are derived from nucleated cells in which the normal gene is nonfunctional, the defective locus functional; others come from cells in which the mutant gene is nonfunctional, the normal locus functional. The already-mentioned results obtained with normal females support the general conclusion that euploid females can express only one allele of this locus in any cell, with sometimes the maternally-derived, sometimes the paternally-derived locus being operational. In support of this conclusion is the finding that in human females not carrying the G-6-PD mutant, otherwise diploid cells, either X0, XX, XXXY, or XXXX, all produce the same amount of G-6-PD.

Since *X-linked muscular dystrophy* is due to a rare mutant of an X-limited gene, usually only males have this disease. Muscular dystrophy is closely associated with certain enzymatic and histological abnormalities. Studies of females known to be mutant heterozygotes and showing subclinical and clinical muscular dystrophy[5] reveal two populations of muscle fiber—one normal and the other dystrophic, a result best attributed to functional mosaicism, just as described for the G-6-PD locus. The same kind of result is obtained for at least five other X-linked genes. On the basis of these genetic results and the cytological studies of Barr bodies, we can conclude that a female normally has an appreciable portion of one X chromosome inactivated in many diploid so-

[2] See M. M. Grumbach, A. Morishima, and J. H. Taylor (1963).
[3] See M. F. Lyon (1962).
[4] See E. Beutler, M. Yeh, and V. F. Fairbanks (1962), and D. R. Davidson, H. M. Nitowsky, and B. Childs (1963).

[5] See C. M. Pearson, W. M. Fowler, and S. W. Wright (1963).

matic cells. Since the normal male has no Barr body, it is the condensed X which is inactivated. Human sex chromatin is not present at fertilization; it first appears at about the twelfth day of development.

From Barr body cytology and the inactivation of a half dozen or so different loci, we cannot determine how much of an X chromosome is inactivated in a normal human female. Still other X chromosome loci whose gene action can be studied in separate individual cells, need to be discovered. A gene whose action gives rise to a product diffusible between cells will be of little or no use in determining the length of the inactivated segment.

Sex chromatin occurs in many mammals [6] besides human beings. In the mouse, although sex chromatin is absent one of a female's X's is heteropycnotic during mitosis. One locus has been found which fails to show the inactivation expected,[7] suggesting the presence of an X chromosome region not heteropycnotic in the female and, therefore, not routinely inactivated. Since reciprocal X-autosome translocations occur in mice, we may ask whether such rearrangement has any effect upon the functioning of the rearranged autosomal genes. This question can be studied in females heterozygous for such a translocation when the nontranslocated autosomal homolog carries suitable recessive alleles of genes whose loci span a large portion of the linkage group. In some cases the phenotype is that of the normally dominant allele present in the structurally rearranged autosome; in others, a mottled or variegated phenotype results. Moreover, according to studies of different rearrangements between a given autosome and the X, in the latter cases, the portion of the body showing the recessive phenotype decreases as the distance from the au-

tosomal locus to the point of union with the X increases. Consequently, autosomal loci can be inactivated by translocation to the X, the greater the distance from the breaking point, the less inactivation. Since breakage in an autosome occurs at several positions, the decreasing strength of inactivation has been found to proceed in either direction. Thus, inactivation of autosomal loci in X-autosome rearrangements can explain cases of *variegated-type (V-type) position effects.*

In two instances, the autosomal break points involved in rearrangement with the X were located in slightly different positions; both, however, were close to a given gene. In one case, the normal autosomal allele was inactivated and produced variegation; in the other no variegation occurred. Results from the investigation of the latter case strongly suggest the nonsuppressed wild-type gene was in an autosomal fragment which had joined an X region incapable of causing inactivation. These studies also suggest—as does the already-mentioned finding of an apparently unsuppressible X locus—that, normally, in the segment replaced by the autosomal fragment some X chromosome genes near the point of breakage are always functional. There are, then, two possible reasons for nonvariegation of an autosomal gene attached to the X chromosome: attachment to a portion of X incapable of causing inactivation and excessive distance from a portion of X capable of causing inactivation.

In light of the preceding discussion, perhaps the same genetic material can be heterochromatic or euchromatic, the primary determinant being the degree of coiling. Chromosome hypercoiling during interphase seems to prevent the functioning of the gene contents. In mammals, this system apparently compensates for the difference in gene dosage existing between male and female.

[6] See M. L. Barr (1959).
[7] See L. B. Russell (1963).

That is, the system provides *dosage compensation* with respect to some X-limited loci.[8]

Note that in mammals parts of certain chromosomes can become more or less permanently fixed in their functioning.[9] The mosaicism just discussed in mice results in patches of tissue of different phenotypes. When a chromosome segment is functionally turned off (or on) in a given cell, the descendant cells are similarly turned off (or on), despite the intervening occurrence of mitosis. Consequently, the result is a patch of tissue of similar phenotype. This turning off occurs more than a week after fertilization in mice and, as mentioned, in human beings. Moreover, it at least sometimes fails to occur in the germ line. For example,[10] although one X in an adult female rat is hyperpycnotic in somatic tissues, the XX-bivalent in the oocyte is *isopycnotic;* that is, both members stain similarly. It is therefore hypothesized [11] that a gene can exist in two functional forms, active or inactive, and that one form will persist despite intervening nuclear divisions until specific conversion to the other. For some maize genes, it is found that a given state during gametogenesis is continued in the zygote. In the endosperm, for example, a maternally-derived gene has been found to continue activity whereas the paternally-derived allele is inactive.

Drosophila

In Drosophila, as in man, typical males have one X chromosome and typical females two. Many of the X chromosome loci have essentially the same phenotypic effect in males as in females; that is, many loci show dosage compensation. Thus, the eye color of the *apr*/Y male and *apr*/*apr* female is essentially identical. Dosage compensation applies not only to hypomorphic mutants (p. 194) like apricot but also to their wild-type alleles. Consequently, both wild-type males and females have, for example, the same dull-red eye color. Other X chromosome loci in *D. melanogaster* showing dosage compensation are *y; ac; sc; sn; g; f;* and *B.* Only partially compensated for, however, is *fa,* since females show somewhat more effect than males. *Hw* (*hairy wing*), *w^e* (*eosin*), and *w^i* (*ivory*) show no compensation, nor do any autosomal genes, nor *bb* which has a locus in both the X and the Y chromosomes and, therefore, is usually present in paired condition in both males and females.

The cytological basis for dosage compensation is difficult to study in ordinary somatic cells of Drosophila because of the small size of diploid nuclei. Since the somatically synapsed polynemic X's in the female larval salivary gland and other nuclei appear identical, dosage compensation in Drosophila does not seem to be based upon differences in chromosome coiling between homologs. Perhaps this means that the alleles on both X chromosomes of a female are equally functional, and that in Drosophila dosage compensation is accomplished by a somewhat different mechanism than it is in mammals. Whereas the single X and the paired X's in salivary cells of males and females have DNA in approximately a one-to-two ratio as expected, the single X seems to contain just about as much RNA and protein as the double X. Dosage compensation therefore involves the "stepping-up" of gene action by single X's, the suppression of gene action by double X's, or both. A number of genetic studies throw some light upon dosage compensation in Drosophila, and their results can be

[8] See M. F. Lyon (1962).
[9] See also R. DeMars (1963).
[10] See S. Ohno, W. D. Kaplan, and R. Kinosita (1960).
[11] By M. Lyon and by D. Schwartz.

described in terms of the *apr* allele. Females having *apr* in triple dose (the extra *apr* locus is carried in another chromosome) have darker apricot eyes than *apr/apr* females, demonstrating not only the hypomorphic nature of the mutant but also the direction of dosage compensation—namely, suppression of eye pigment formation in *apr/apr* females and the consequent leveling-off of pigment formation at the level produced by one *apr* locus present in the X chromosome of a male. Males carrying an extra *apr* locus have apricot eyes even darker than those of females with triple *apr*.

Since X0 and XY males and XX, XXY, and XXYY females—all pure for *apr*—have the same eye color, the Y chromosome cannot be responsible for dosage compensation. In addition, males transformed from females (X^{apr} X^{apr}, *tra tra*) with or without a Y chromosome have the same eye color as an X^{apr} Y male. If maleness as such prevents the suppression of gene action leading to dosage compensation, the transformed-from-female male with a double dose of *apr* should have a darker apricot eye than a male with a single dose of *apr*. Thus, dosage compensation is not dependent upon male or female phenotype.

What is the genotypic basis for dosage compensation in Drosophila? That the male (transformed female) with two full X chromosomes shows dosage compensation, while the male with one X^{apr} and another *apr*—either in a grossly deleted X or inserted into an autosome—does not, suggests that the X chromosome itself contains *dosage compensator genes,* a single dose of such genes present in males and a double dose in females. One complete X chromosome apparently carries several dosage compensators to suppress one *apr* gene. In a regular X^{apr} Y male, this suppression permits only apricot eye color. Note that females with the *apr* region in one X deleted, and *apr* present in the other have a light apricot eye color.

Pure *apr* males or females hyperploid for different short segments of X can be obtained and scored for eye color and sex. Such experiments show that:

1. Different X segments have a positive or negative dosage compensating effect on eye color with an overall effect of suppression
2. The effects of these segments on eye color are not correlated with their effects on sex differentiation.

Moreover, the net dosage compensation effects exerted by individual segments are different when other loci showing dosage compensation are investigated. In conclusion, therefore, we find:

1. No correlation between a set of compensator genes and their effect on sex differentiation
2. Suppression of different genes exhibiting dosage compensation either by different groups of dosage compensator genes or by the same groups of compensator genes whose action varies with the locus to be compensated.

X-linked genes or alleles without dosage compensation may be so new in terms of evolution that dosage compensator genes may not yet have had an opportunity to become established. Supporting this view is evidence that *eosin* (w^e) and *ivory* (w^i) which do not show dosage compensation are nonallelic to *apr* [12] and, therefore, may be mutants of a more recently-evolved locus. Additional support comes from the study of mutants in the X chromosome of *D. pseudoobscura* which is V-shaped with one arm homologous to the X, the other to the left arm of chromosome III of *D. melanogaster*. If we assume that most mutants are hypomorphs, we find more mutants in the arm homologous to the *melanogaster* X showing

[12] From work of M. M. Green (1959).

the same degree of phenotypic effect in both males and females (probably representing dosage compensation) than we find in the arm homologous to the *melanogaster* III L.[13]

As a working hypothesis we can suggest that the suppression involved in dosage compensation in Drosophila is closely associated with messenger RNA. The messenger RNA (or the protein product) of compensator genes could either interact with and inac-

tivate messenger RNA of the genes they compensate, or they could act directly upon the gene to be compensated interfering with its production of messenger RNA. This suppression might be based upon the messenger RNAs of all dosage compensators having some common nucleotide sequence (p. 461), either the complement or the equivalent of a deoxyribotide sequence in the locus being suppressed. Perhaps the operator genes of the loci being compensated are suppressed by the regulator dosage compensator genes.

[13] The preceding discussion of dosage compensation in Drosophila to a great extent follows the work of H. J. Muller (1950).

SUMMARY AND CONCLUSIONS

Dosage compensation for X-linked genes is accomplished by suppression of gene function.

In human beings, in mice, and probably in all mammals having sex chromatin, this suppression is associated with heteropycnosis and, hence, chromosome coiling. Although some differentiation in a chromosome is temporary, dosage compensation and other nuclear phenomena demonstrate that the chromosome can become more or less permanently fixed in some way related to its function.

In Drosophila, another mechanism is responsible for the regulation of gene action leading to dosage compensation. It is hypothesized that this process involves the transcription, translation, or protein products of messenger RNA; perhaps dosage compensator genes are regulator genes which control operator genes of the loci being compensated.

REFERENCES

Barr, M. L., "Sex Chromatin and Phenotype in Man," Science, 130:679–685, 1959.

Beutler, E., Yeh, M., and Fairbanks, V. F., "The Normal Human Female as a Mosaic of X-Chromosome Activity; Studies Using the Gene for G-6-PD-Deficiency as a Marker," Proc. Nat. Acad. Sci., U.S., 48:9–16, 1962.

Cock, A. G., "Dosage Compensation and Sex-Chromatin in Non-Mammals," Genet. Res. (Camb.), 5: 354–365, 1964.

Davidson, R. G., Nitowsky, H. M., and Childs, B., "Demonstration of Two Populations of Cells in the Human Female Heterozygous for Glucose-6-Phosphate Dehydrogenase Variants," Proc. Nat. Acad. Sci., U.S., 50:481–485, 1963.

DeMars, R., "Sex Chromatin Patterns and the Lyon Hypothesis," Science, 141:649–650, 1963.

Grumbach, M. M., Morishima, A., and Taylor, J. H., "Human Sex Chromosome Abnormalities in Relation to DNA Replication and Heterochromatinization," Proc. Nat. Acad. Sci., U.S., 49:581–589, 1963.

Human Genetics, Cold Spring Harb. Sympos. Quant. Biol., 29, 1965.

Lyon, M. F., "Sex Chromatin and Gene Action in the Mammalian X-Chromosome," Amer. J. Hum. Genet., 14:135–148, 1962.

McKusick, V. A., *On the X Chromosome of Man,* Washington, D.C.: American Institute of Biological Sciences, 1964.

Muller, H. J., "Evidence of the Precision of Genetic Adaptation," *The Harvey Lectures*
(1947–1948), Ser. 43:165–229, Springfield, Ill.: Chas. C. Thomas, 1950. Ex-
cerpted in Muller, H. J., *Studies in Genetics,* Bloomington, Ind.: Indiana Univ.
Press, 1962, pp. 152–171.

Ohno, S., Kaplan, W. D., and Kinosita, R., "On Isopycnotic Behavior of the XX-
Bivalent in Oocyte of *Rattus norvegicus,*" Exp. Cell. Res., 19:637–639, 1960.

Pearson, C. M., Fowler, W. M., and Wright, S. W., "X-Chromosome Mosaicism in
Females with Muscular Dystrophy," Proc. Nat. Acad. Sci., U.S., 50:24–31, 1963.

Russell, L. B., "Mammalian X-Chromosome Action: Inactivation Limited in Spread
and in Region of Origin," Science, 140:976–978, 1963.

Russell, L. B., "Another Look at the Single-Active-X Hypothesis," Trans. N.Y. Acad.
Sci., Ser. II, 26:726–736, 1964.

Russell, L. B., "Genetic and Functional Mosaicism in the Mouse," Sympos. Soc. Study
Devel. and Growth, 1964.

Stern, C., "Dosage Compensation—Development of a Concept and New Facts," Canad.
J. Genet. Cytol., 2:105–118, 1960.

Welshons, W. J., "Cytological Contributions to Mammalian Genetics," Amer. Zool.,
3:15–22, 1963.

QUESTIONS FOR DISCUSSION

39.1. If essentially all of one X chromosome in a human female is functionally turned
off in somatic tissues, what is the disadvantage of having $♀ = X\,0$ and $♂ = X\,Y$?

39.2. Almost without exception, piebald or tortoise-shell cats are females. Explain.

39.3. What kind of autosomal genes would be unsuitable for the experiments with mice
described on p. 486?

39.4. Discuss the phenotypes expected among females heterozygous for the X-linked
mutant for hemophilia.

39.5. Compare the dosage compensation mechanism in mice with that in Drosophila.

39.6. How can studies of twins test the hypothesis of dosage compensation?

39.7. What explanations can you give for the occurrence of females heterozygous for
the X-linked mutant for red-green colorblindness but who are colorblind only
in one eye or in portions of one eye? For identical female twins, one colorblind
and one not colorblind?

39.8. Ocular albinism is an X-linked mutant that causes the retina of human males
to be colorless. What phenotype would you expect in heterozygous females if
the mutant is

(a) Completely recessive?
(b) Completely dominant?
(c) Partially dominant?

Such females actually contain patches of both albino and normally pigmented
retina. What bearing does this finding have upon questions (a), (b), (c) above
and to your answers?

39.9. An X-linked mutant in the human male prevents perspiration in any part of the body. What do you suppose would happen to a heterozygote for this mutant who dusted her body with a dry mixture of starch and iodine and then entered a hothouse?

39.10. How can you account for the fact that X0, XX, and XXX women (or XY and XXY men) are not phenotypically equivalent? Does your answer hold true for the female mouse (the X0 is usually fertile)?

39.11. What do you think of the hypothesis that dosage compensation in mammals starts because one chromosome (or part of one) is precociously used as template?

39.12. What can you conclude from the observation that in human females heterozygous for an abnormal X—the mutant X being either rod shaped but shorter or longer than normal, or ring shaped—the abnormal X appears in Barr bodies more frequently than the normal X homolog?

39.13. Discuss the significance of work with the toad Xenopus (discussed on p. 427) relative to dosage compensation.

Chapter 40

REGULATION OF GENE ACTION—ITS MOLECULAR BASIS IN HIGHER ORGANISMS

Ｎｏｎｅ of the cases discussed in Chapters 37 through 39 have yet been analyzed far enough to specify the biochemical elements of the control mechanisms involved in the regulation of gene activity. In this chapter, additional examples of gene action regulation in higher organisms are explored in an effort to gain some insight into its molecular basis.

Dipteran Polynemic Chromosomes [1]

Evidence obtained from radioautography strongly suggests that the ordinary chromosome of higher organisms is polynemic or polytenic; that is, it contains more than one double helix of DNA per chromatid.[2] Interphase chromosomes of larval Diptera which are highly polynemic may be considered merely more extreme examples of a normal tendency toward polynemy.

At various times during the growth and differentiation of a dipteran cell containing highly polynemic chromosomes, different cross-bands "puff out" (Figure 40–1) and later "unpuff" in a regular sequence. Although the sequences vary, they are characteristic of different larval tissues. Puffing may be interpreted as a local unwinding of the chromosome and its DNA. In Drosophila and the midge Chironomus, a puff region

[1] See W. Beermann (1962), W. Beermann and U. Clever (1964), and H. J. Becker (1964).
[2] See W. J. Peacock (1963).

492

synthesizes more RNA than an equivalent nonpuff region; in the salivary gland cells of Rhyncosciara and Glyptotendipes larvae, the amount of DNA synthesized in puffed regions is greater than in equivalent nonpuffed regions.

In certain species of Chironomus, the cytoplasm of cells in one lobe of the larval salivary gland contains (protein secretion?) granules due to a gene located near one end of chromosome IV. Such granules are absent in other species. In cells forming granules, a puff is also found near the tip of chromosome IV but none is found in nongranule containing cells not even those of the same gland. Moreover, larvae produced by an interspecific mating of granule formers and nonformers have some granules and are cytogenetically hybrid; in other words, one homolog does and the other does not have this puff.

Injecting larvae with the pupation hormone ecdysone causes specific bands to puff and others to unpuff. It has also been shown that the RNA synthesized in a puff does not have A = U or C = G (in terms of quantity) and is probably messenger RNA. We may conclude, therefore, that puffing (unwinding DNA) is directly associated with gene activity. In a dipteran salivary cell, only about 20 per cent of the bands ever seem to puff, which indicates that not all genes are functional in every nucleus.

Conserved vs. Nonconserved DNA

What is the nature and fate of DNA synthesized in "excess"? The following evidence indicates that DNA can leave the nucleus because it is in excess or for other reasons:

1. In certain organisms (for example, the fungus gnat Sciara) some chromosomes are regularly eliminated from the nuclei of certain cells.

2. In Drosophila, DNA is extruded from the nuclei of nurse cells in the ovary.

SEGMENT   **CHROMOSOME   B**

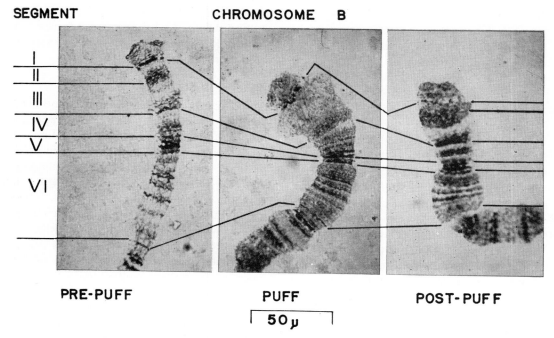

PRE-PUFF   PUFF   POST-PUFF

|‾ **50 μ** ‾|

FIGURE 40–1.   *Puffing and unpuffing in a region of a salivary gland chromosome of Rhyncosciara.   (Courtesy of G. Rudkin.)*

3. All the cells in certain testicular tubes of the grasshopper *Melanoplus differentialis* normally disintegrate and liberate large quantities of DNA.[3]

4. The oocyte of a newt appears to have in its nucleoplasm and nucleolus DNA —unassociated with the nucleolus organizer—which presumably is not retained in the nucleus.[4]

5. A similar situation is reported [5] in the oocyte of the dipteran Tipula: Within this cell's nucleus is a body which contains about 50 per cent of all the nuclear DNA present. Not only is this DNA synthesized at a different time from the DNA in the chromosomes, but this body and its DNA contents disappear at diplonema.

6. Germinating wheat seeds and growing roots of wheat and corn contain a double-stranded DNA of low molecular weight (10^5) which shows turnover; that is, it is metabolically labile.[6] Such DNA differs from stable, high molecular weight DNA by its higher G + C content.

Though it may be concluded that DNA is sometimes released to the cytoplasm, no data from the studies mentioned indicate that this material has any of several known or assumed properties of genetic material

[3] See A. Lima de Faria and T. Nordqvist (1962).
[4] See M. Izawa, V. G. Allfrey, and A. E. Mirsky (1963).
[5] See A. Lima de Faria (1962).

[6] See M. Sampson, A. Katoh, Y. Hotta, and H. Stern (1963).

(replication, mutation, recombination) once it has left the chromosome. As a result, whether this DNA is genetic material remains an open question.

It should be realized that DNA which leaves the nucleus may serve an extranuclear function quite different from the function DNA performs within the nucleus. For example, nucleus-derived, cytoplasmically located DNA may serve as raw material for synthesis of nuclear DNA. Such may be the fate of the DNA in nonfertilizing sperm which disintegrate in the cytoplasm of insect eggs fertilized by polyspermy (more than one sperm entering but only one fertilizing the egg). In Drosophila, the DNA of the nurse cells which surround the developing oocyte enters the cytoplasm of the oocyte and presumably serves as raw material for future DNA synthesis. The same fate is suggested for DNA phagocytosed by fibroblasts and white blood cells *in vivo,* since phagocytosis of DNA by mammalian cells in tissue cultures is followed by the appearance of this DNA in the nucleus. That DNA loss may be associated with differentiation is indicated by: the loss of some chromosomal material during chromosome diminution in Ascaris; the differential elimination of chromosomes by the two sexes of Sciara; and the decrease in DNA in the salivary gland cells of the snail Helix as the secretion product is manufactured. It has also been suggested [7] that cytoplasmic DNA may act as a messenger.

It is clear from the preceding discussion that all the DNA in a nucleus may not always remain there to perform the usual functions of nuclear genetic material. In this respect, then, there are *two kinds of DNA:* the *one conserved* as part of the chromosome (which serves as genetic material); the *one not conserved* (which may or may not be genetic material). In bacteria, the

nonconservation of nonintegrating or deintegrating DNA involved in transformation, conjugation, or transduction has already been mentioned.

Lampbrush Chromosomes [8]

Amphibian oocytes have giant "lampbrush" chromosomes (Figure 40–2), whose appearance is due to the lateral projection of numerous pairs of loops from the main chromosomal axis. Each loop is asymmetric—one end being thicker than the other. In addition to normal pairs of loops, some giant granular loops are found which contain a thin axial thread continuous with the main chromosomal axis and having a dense, contorted region at the thinner end of the loop; a coarsely granular matrix at the thicker end.

When newt lampbrush chromosomes are exposed to tritium-labeled (H^3) uridine, autoradiographs reveal that incorporation into a pair of giant granular loops occurs in a definite sequence, starting at the thin end of the loop and proceeding around the loop in about 10 days. These results demonstrate the sequential synthesis of RNA by different portions of the loop. Other evidence proves that:

1. The loops contain DNA
2. The RNA synthesis observed is DNA-dependent
3. Agents which inhibit nuclear RNA synthesis (such as actinomycin D) lead to disappearance of the loops (and inhibition of puffing in insect polynemic chromosomes).

Such results lead to the hypothesis that a loop (like a puff) is a temporarily unwound portion of the chromosome thread. As the thick portion of a loop completes its synthetic activity, it presumably winds up and

---

[7] See P. B. Gahan (1962), and J. J. Holland and B. J. McCarthy (1964).

[8] Based upon work of W. R. Duryee, of J. G. Gall and H. G. Callan (1962), and of M. Izawa, V. G. Allfrey, and A. E. Mirsky (1963).

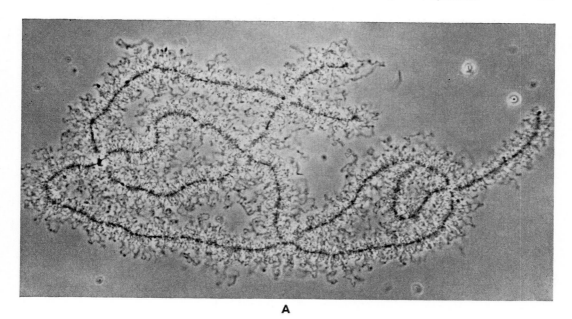

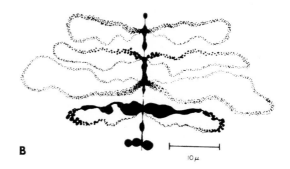

FIGURE 40–2. *Giant "lampbrush" chromosomes of the amphibian oocyte. A. Unfixed chromosomes of* Triturus viridescens *in saline solution, phase contrast, 540×. B. Semidiagrammatic view of the central chromomere axis with paired lateral loops. (Courtesy of J. G. Gall.)*

reforms part of the main nonsynthesizing chromosome axis. At the same time more of the main axial thread unwinds to produce the thin end of the loop which proceeds to synthesize RNA. In any event, it is clear that the morphology of a chromosomal site is closely related to its ability to synthesize RNA.

The large number of loops present in lampbrush chromosomes indicates that a large number of chromosomal sites are synthesizing RNA. Although almost all the granules (*chromomeres*) that occur along the main axis of lampbrush chromosomes have loops, at any given time only about 2 per cent of the bands (comparable to chromomeres) show puffs in giant polynemic chromosomes. A comparison of the protein, the DNA, and the RNA content of liver, dipteran salivary, and lampbrush chromosomes also suggests that the oocyte chromosome is synthetically active at many loci. It is noteworthy that the DNA content of a lampbrush chromosome is about four times that of a regular chromosome from a diploid cell of the same newt, and that the nucleoplasm and nucleoli of the oocyte contains an amount of nonconserved DNA equal to that present in the chromosomes. Most of the RNA present in the mature amphibian oocyte is synthesized in the lampbrush stage, over 90 per cent being ribosomal RNA. The lampbrush type of chromosome structure has also been reported in the growing oocytes of animals ranging from mollusks to mammals, in the pigeon, in the onion,[9] and in the Drosophila spermatocyte Y chromosome.[10] It may well be more widespread than previously suspected.

Histones

The evidence presented strongly suggests that in a large variety of organisms, chromosome uncoiling and consequent DNA unmasking are requisites for the utilization of DNA as a template. The DNA of a mature T phage is highly coiled in the phage head. After T-phage attachment the DNA unwinds and enters the host, where it is immediately available for use as a template. Thus, phage DNA when functional is probably uncoiled and not complexed with protein. These conditions probably also hold true for functional chromosomal DNA in *E. coli*. In contrast to bacterial and phage DNA, the chromosomal DNA of most types of cells is usually joined with basic proteins (such as histone or protamine) to form deoxyribonucleoproteins (p. 253). According to the view already presented, perhaps the union of DNA with histone causes coiling, which, in turn, results in gene inactivation. The influence of histones on gene action will be considered further after we have explored some of their properties.

When DNA has been removed from nucleohistone, the histone can be separated by electrophoresis, ultracentrifugation, and chromatography into numerous subfractions,

indicating that a given type of cell probably contains a heterogeneous population of hundreds of kinds of histone molecules. These molecules are relatively small—having a molecular weight of 3,500 to 74,000—and differ in amino acid composition. One class is relatively rich in lysine (and proline) and poor in arginine; another is relatively rich in arginine and poor in lysine. DNA can combine with these histone fractions to reconstitute nucleohistone whose DNA seems to be as fully complexed with histone as the DNA in native nucleohistone.

The deoxyribonucleohistone reconstituted by combining pure DNA and purified chromosomal histones is about 35A in diameter. The histone in such a nucleohistone seems to cover the DNA uniformly; it may be bound spirally around the DNA and occupy one if not both the grooves of the DNA double helix. Other arrangements, however, have not yet been ruled out.

Interphase chromatin of somatic cells seems to contain a uniform structural unit. As seen through the electron microscope, this unit is a rod approximately 160A in diameter containing two double helices of DNA (each 20A in diameter). The two double helices are coiled about each other paranemically (p. 268) and the histone seems to occupy the space between and around them.[11] Histones are probably synthesized in the nucleolus, which is reported to contain ribosomes.

When DNA is complexed with histones its melting or denaturation temperature rises. In this respect, then, histones stabilize DNA.[12] Lysine-rich histones increase the temperature required to melt half the DNA of a pea from 70°C to 81°C; arginine-rich nucleohistones half-melt their DNA at 71°C. An approximately linear relation exists be-

---

[9] See B. R. Nebel and E. M. Coulon (1962).
[10] See W. Beermann, O. Hess, and G. F. Meyer (1963).

[11] See V. Luzzati, and A. Nicolaïeff (1963), and J. Bonner and P. O. P. Ts'o (1964).
[12] See also S. Felsenfeld, G. Sandeen, and P. H. von Hippel (1963).

tween the lysine content of a histone and the melting temperature of the DNA in a nucleo-histone. DNA fully complexed with prota-mine (salmine or clupein) melts at the same temperature as pure native DNA.

Since an appreciable portion of chromo-somal DNA must be used to carry informa-tion for the synthesis of non-histone pro-teins, not every portion of this DNA can be complexed with a specific type of histone. Consequently, a given type of histone must be able to complex with several different sequences of DNA.

Although the DNA of duck erythrocytes appears to be almost completely complexed with histone, not every cell has all its DNA histone-complexed. In peas, the fraction of the total DNA not complexed with histone is 5% for the developing cotyledon; 20% for the embryo; 30% for the apices. These results suggest that actively-growing and protein-synthesizing cells have more non-complexed DNA than differentiated cells. The stabilizing effect that histones have upon DNA may involve the suppression of DNA as a template, perhaps by inhibiting DNA strand separation.

Isolated nuclei can synthesize comple-mentary RNA by using the DNA as a tem-plate; much of this synthesized RNA is mes-senger RNA; some of it is transfer RNA. In isolated calf thymus nuclei, arginine-rich histone added to the incubation medium not only reduces the uptake of thymidine into DNA, but strongly inhibits the synthesis of RNA; [13] lysine-rich histones are much less inhibiting. Selective removal of histones from isolated nuclei results in a two- to four-fold increase in RNA synthesis; the newly made RNA is probably messenger RNA, although its base composition is different from that of the messenger RNA normally synthesized. These results strongly indi-cate that the use of DNA as template for

both DNA and RNA synthesis is inhibited by histones, and the release of DNA from histones can lead to the production of hitherto-repressed messenger RNA.

Some evidence [14] suggests that the histone control of genetic activity *in vivo* is essen-tially preserved not only in isolated nuclei but in isolated chromatin as well. Chro-matin isolated from pea embryos, 20 per cent of which is not complexed with his-tone, is able to carry out DNA-dependent synthesis of RNA from the four usual ribo-side triphosphates through the action of RNA polymerase; removal of histone in-creases RNA synthesis about 500 per cent. Fully complexed DNA in a reconstituted nucleohistone either does not support DNA-dependent RNA synthesis at all or does to a considerably reduced extent. Finally, it should be noted that DNA fully complexed with arginine-rich protamine is fully active in DNA-dependent RNA synthesis.

Pea cotyledons synthesize a specific *pea seed reserve globulin* not produced in other pea plant tissues such as buds or roots. Chromatin isolated from pea cotyledons will, *in vitro,* produce the messenger RNA used in a ribosomal system to manufacture this globulin. On the other hand, chromatin isolated from pea buds will not lead to synthesis of this protein; removal of histone from pea bud chromatin, however, yields DNA which supports globulin synthesis. Thus, we see that the gene for globulin syn-thesis is normally repressed in the bud by histone.[15]

Histones may affect gene action by an-other mechanism.[16] When already-formed histones are acetylated at their ends, they permit complementary RNA synthesis *in*

[13] See V. G. Allfrey, V. C. Littau, and A. E. Mirsky (1963).

[14] From work of J. Bonner, R. C. C. Huang, R. V. Gilden and co-workers.
[15] See J. Bonner, R. C. C. Huang, and R. V. Gilden (1963).
[16] See V. G. Allfrey, R. Faulkner, and A. E. Mirsky (1964).

vitro, whereas nonacetylated histones suppress RNA synthesis. That *histone acetylation* may be a mechanism for controlling gene action *in vivo* is supported by the finding [17] that clumped (nonfunctioning) chromatin contains a smaller percentage of acetylated histone than dispersed (functioning) chromatin.

[17] By V. C. Littau, V. G. Allfrey, J. H. Frenster, and A. E. Mirsky (1964).

SUMMARY AND CONCLUSIONS

Puffs in dipteran polynemic chromosomes and loops of lampbrush chromosomes in amphibian oocytes are unwound, genetically active regions.

From the standpoint of behavior, two kinds of DNA occur. One type is conserved as a regular part of the chromosome and is genetic material; the other type is not conserved—although nucleus-derived—and may be found in the cytoplasm or in the nucleus. No clear evidence exists that nonconserved DNA has genetic properties.

Basic proteins form complexes with DNA. These complexes are either deoxyribonucleohistones or deoxyribonucleoprotamines. Noncomplexed DNA and nucleoprotamines support the synthesis of DNA-dependent RNA. On the other hand, different histones have different capacities to inhibit DNA synthesis and DNA-dependent RNA synthesis when complexed with DNA as nucleohistones. Nonfunctioning chromatin contains a smaller percentage of acetylated histone than functioning chromatin. Inhibition of gene action by histones may be accomplished by increasing the denaturation temperature of DNA; by causing chromosome coiling; or by other, presently-unknown means. In any event, it is likely that in higher organisms, the use of DNA as a template is regulated to a large extent by histones.

REFERENCES

Allfrey, V. G., Faulkner, R., and Mirsky, A. E., "Acetylation and Methylation of Histones and Their Possible Role in the Regulation of RNA Synthesis," Proc. Nat. Acad. Sci., U.S., 51:786–794, 1964.

Allfrey, V. G., Littau, V. C., and Mirsky, A. E., "On the Role of Histones in Regulating Ribonucleic Acid Synthesis in the Cell Nucleus," Proc. Nat. Acad. Sci., U.S., 49: 414–421, 1963.

Allfrey, V. G., and Mirsky, A. E., "Evidence for the Complete DNA-Dependence of RNA Synthesis in Isolated Thymus Nuclei," Proc. Nat. Acad. Sci., U.S., 48:1590–1596, 1962.

Becker, H. J., "Die genetischen Grundlagen der Zelldifferenzierung," Naturwissenschaften, 51:205–211, 230–235, 1964.

Beermann, W., *Reisenchromosomen,* Protoplasmologia, 6:1–160, 1962.

Beermann, W., and Clever, U., "Chromosome Puffs," Scient. Amer., 210 (April): 50–58, 156, 1964.

Beermann, W., Hess, O., and Meyer, G. F., "Structure and Function of the Y Heterochromatin in Drosophila," Proc. XVI Int. Congr. Zool., 4:283–288, 1963.

Bloch, D. P., "On the Derivation of Histone Specificity," Proc. Nat. Acad. Sci., U.S., 48:324–326, 1962.

Bonner, J., Huang, R. C. C., and Gilden, R. V., "Chromosomally Directed Protein Synthesis," Proc. Nat. Acad. Sci., U.S., 50:893–900, 1963.

Bonner, J., and Ts'o, P. O. P. (Editors), *Nucleo-Histones: First World Conference.* Holden-Day, 1964.

Davidson, E. H., Allfrey, V. G., and Mirsky, A. E., "Gene Expression in Differentiated Cells," Proc. Nat. Acad. Sci., U.S., 49:53–60, 1963.

Davidson, E. H., Allfrey, V. G., and Mirsky, A. E., "On the RNA Synthesized during the Lampbrush Phase of Amphibian Oögenesis," Proc. Nat. Acad. Sci., U.S., 52:501–508, 1964.

Felsenfeld, G., Sandeen, G., and von Hippel, P. H., "The Destabilizing Effect of Ribonuclease on the Helical DNA Structure," Proc. Nat. Acad. Sci., U.S., 50:644–651, 1963.

Frenster, J. H., Allfrey, V. G., and Mirsky, A. E., "Repressed and Active Chromatin Isolated from Interphase Lymphocytes," Proc. Nat. Acad. Sci., U.S., 50:1026–1032, 1963.

Gahan, P. B., "The Possible Genetic Significance of Cytoplasmic Deoxyribonucleic Acid" (Abstr.), Heredity, 17:603, 1962.

Gall, J. G., and Callan, H. G., "H³ Uridine Incorporation in Lampbrush Chromosomes," Proc. Nat. Acad. Sci., U.S., 48:562–570, 1962.

Holland, J. J., and McCarthy, B. J., "Stimulation of Protein Synthesis *in vitro* by Denatured DNA," Proc. Nat. Acad. Sci., U.S., 52:1554–1561, 1964.

Horn, E. C., "Extranuclear Histone in the Amphibian Oocyte," Proc. Nat. Acad. Sci., U.S., 48:257–265, 1962.

Huang, R. C. C., and Bonner, J., "Histone, A Suppressor of Chromosomal RNA Synthesis," Proc. Nat. Acad. Sci., U.S., 48:1216–1222, 1962.

Izawa, M., Allfrey, V. G., and Mirsky, A. E., "The Relationship between RNA Synthesis and Loop Structure in Lampbrush Chromosomes," Proc. Nat. Acad. Sci., U.S., 49:544–551, 1963.

Izawa, M., Allfrey, V. G., and Mirsky, A. E., "Composition of the Nucleus and Chromosomes in the Lampbrush Stage of the Newt Oocyte," Proc. Nat. Acad. Sci., U.S., 59:811–817, 1963.

Lima de Faria, A., "Metabolic DNA in *Tipula oleracea,*" Chromosoma, 13:47–59, 1962.

Lima de Faria, A., and Nordqvist, T., "Disintegration of H³-Labelled Spermatocytes in *Melanoplus differentialis,*" Chromosoma, 13:60–66, 1962.

Luzzati, V., and Nicolaïeff, A., "The Structure of Nucleohistones and Nucleoprotamines," J. Mol. Biol., 7:142–163, 1963.

Nebel, B. R., and Coulon, E. M., "The Fine Structure of Chromosomes in Pigeon Spermatocytes," Chromosoma, 13:272–291, 1962.

Peacock, W. J., "Chromosome Duplication and Structure as Determined by Autoradiography," Proc. Nat. Acad. Sci., U.S., 49:793–801, 1963.

Sampson, M., Katoh, A., Hotta, Y., and Stern, H., "Metabolically Labile Deoxyribonucleic Acid," Proc. Nat. Acad. Sci., U.S., 50:459–463, 1963.

Symposium on Macromolecular Aspects of the Cell Cycle, J. Cell. Comp. Physiol., 62 (Suppl. 1), 1963.

QUESTIONS FOR DISCUSSION

40.1. What is the function of a nucleus (such as in the duck erythrocyte) whose DNA seems to be almost completely complexed with histone?

40.2. Discuss the correlation between the melting temperatures of DNA complexed with basic proteins and the inhibition of gene activity.

40.3. What interpretation can you give to the observation of H. Busch that many kinds of tumors show a high synthesis rate of lysine-rich histone?

40.4. How do you explain the observation of P. R. Gross that in unfertilized sea urchin eggs, concentrations of actinomycin D (which apparently completely inhibit messenger RNA production) reduce but do not completely inhibit protein synthesis?

40.5. Discuss the genetic and environmental factors which influence the puffing pattern in the polynemic chromosomes of larval Diptera.

40.6. Discuss the role of "feedback" in the molecular control of genetic activity.

40.7. What can you conclude about gene action from the observation that the histones associated with clumped chromatin show a smaller amount of acetylation per milligram than histones isolated from diffuse chromatin?

40.8. Can you explain why a particular DNase digests clumped but not diffuse chromatin?

40.9. How can you explain that in animal sperm the chromosomes are inactive even when they contain deoxyribonucleoprotamines in place of deoxyribonucleohistones?

40.10. R. S. Chang, P. Goldhaber, and T. H. Dunnebacher (Proc. Nat. Acad. Sci., U.S., 52:709–715, 1964) were able to propagate continuously (for at least two years) cultures of human liver cells that were uninfected or infected with lipovirus. They found, however, that the infected cells contained no more than 10 per cent of the DNA of uninfected parent cells. What, if anything, do these results suggest about:

   (a) genetic content necessary for maintenance of cell integrity and replication?
   (b) chromosomal polynemy?

40.11. Under what conditions might cells use single-stranded DNA as a template for protein synthesis?

Chapter *41

REGULATION OF GENE ACTION—
GROWTH, DIFFERENTIATION,
AND DEVELOPMENT

THE six preceding chapters dealt with the regulation of gene synthesis and action. The aim of this chapter is to show how genetic systems of the types already discussed are or may be involved in the regulation of growth, differentiation, and development.

Phage T4 Morphogenesis [1]

The genome of ϕT4 carries the information for the production of several proteins (noted in Chapter 35). Some mutants of protein-specifying genes can direct the synthesis of an altered protein. Some of these altered proteins function as well, or nearly as well, as the unaltered wild-type proteins in hosts grown at normal temperatures (about 25°C) but become inactive in hosts grown at higher temperatures (about 40°C). Two types of such *temperature-sensitive, ts,* mutants have been found for deoxycytidylate hydroxy-methylase, $d\overline{HMC}$ase (Figure 35–1 and p. 451). Although both show reduced $d\overline{HMC}$ase activity at low temperatures as compared with the wild-type enzyme, their response to a shift (from normal to high) in the temperature at which the infected host is grown is different. In one type of mutant, the altered enzyme is inactivated by heat denaturation at any time during the eclipse

period in which the temperature shift is made; the other type of mutant produces an altered $d\overline{HMC}$ase inactivated only if the temperature shift is made before the first third of the eclipse period and resistant to shifts made later. These results suggest that the former type of enzyme can be denatured by heat after it is synthesized; that the latter type is temperature-sensitive only during its synthesis.

It has been found that the *ts* mutants—really conditional lethals—occur in roughly half of all phage genes. The loci of these genes have been mapped, and their phenotypic effects studied at chemical, physiological, and morphological levels. The results are summarized in Figure 26–4 (p. 343). We see that the circular phage genome is organized into blocks containing genes with common functions. These blocks include the following:

Mutants	*Common Characteristics*
DO	Cannot initiate DNA synthesis (hence, normal alleles initiate DNA synthesis)
DA	Start DNA synthesis, but cease after a short time
DD	Delay DNA synthesis
"tail fiber"	Form (otherwise normal) particles lacking tail fibers
"head"	Form particles with heads missing (free tails are present in lysates)
"tail"	Form particles with tails missing or incomplete

These results strongly suggest that the genes in any block function at the same or nearly the same time, and that the sequence of different blocks of genes may reflect the sequence of events in phage replication and maturation. The thymidylate synthetase (p. 449) locus is apparently an exception to this sequence [2] since it is located well within the tail fiber region rather than in the

---

[1] The following account is based largely upon the work of R. S. Edgar, M. Susman, G. H. Denhardt, L. Boice, and co-workers. See R. H. Epstein, *et al.* (1964).

[2] According to E. H. Simon and I. Tessman (1963).

early region as expected. Because the total number of genes in phage is apparently far greater than the sum of structural proteins in the mature phage plus the enzymes needed to make phage DNA (Chapter 35), it has been suggested that many of the genes that do not specify the manufacture of phage DNA or protein nevertheless play roles in particle morphogenesis.

Developmental Genetics of Amphibia

The zygotic nucleus of a fertilized frog egg can be removed by microsurgery.[3] The enucleated cell cannot normally perform the functions of maintenance, growth, division, and differentiation; lacking the normal chemical reactions to carry on such functions, it eventually undergoes degeneration. That the cell's metabolic failure is attributable to the loss of the nucleus rather than to the operation itself, is proved by the normal behavior zygotes show after undergoing similar operations without being enucleated. More important, however, is the observation that when the same (or a similar) nucleus is replaced in a second operation, normal zygotic activity resumes. Nuclei from blastula, gastrula, and later embryological stages can be transplanted into enucleated zygotes. Such experiments reveal that the later the stage supplying the nucleus, the more abnormal the development, demonstrating that in the course of embryogenesis, nuclei are progressively less able to promote complete, normal development.

Nuclei can be transplanted between different species of frog. *Rana pipiens* nuclei which have multiplied in the cytoplasm of *R. sylvatica* eggs are unable to promote gastrulation when retransferred to eggs of their own species. Since this limitation persists through repeated transfers to enucleated eggs,[4] we can conclude that upon exposure to cytoplasmic factors the chromosomes' ability to function can become permanently fixed (p. 487).

Injection of small amounts of various protein fractions (albumin or histone) from adult frog liver cells into zygotes of the same species stops cell division and arrests development at the late blastula stage.[5] At about the same time, chromosomes become essential for further development. Although new cytoplasmic ribosomes do not appear until the later tail-bud stage and new RNA is first detected at the gastrula stage,[6] protein synthesis—using messenger RNA and ribosomes synthesized before fertilization—begins with fertilization.

Differentiation and Transcription

The similarities and differences among the populations of nucleic acids in various tissues of the mouse can be assessed by the formation of double-stranded structures from single-stranded DNA or RNA complexed with single-stranded DNA entrapped in agar. Competition reactions among radioactively labeled and unlabeled sets of molecules fail to show any differences in DNA polynucleotide sequences, providing additional evidence for the same DNA content in all somatic cells. On the other hand, large differences are found among rapidly labeled RNA molecules isolated from different organs, as expected if differentiation is associated with the production of different populations of mRNA in different kinds of differentiated tissues.[7] Other RNA-DNA hybridization experiments[8] show that the mRNAs from three growth phases of *Bacillus subtilis* are derived from distinctly different groups of loci, supporting the concept that differential transcription of the genome occurs during morphogenesis.

---

[3] Based upon work of R. W. Briggs and J. T. King.
[4] See J. A. Moore (1960).

[5] See C. L. Markert and H. Ursprung (1963).
[6] According to D. D. Brown and J. D. Caston.
[7] See B. J. McCarthy and B. H. Hoyer (1964).
[8] See R. H. Doi and R. T. Igarashi (1964).

Genetic Regulation of Mitosis

The genetic control of the structural and physiological features of nuclear and cell division is exemplified in corn and Drosophila by mutants which modify spindle shape during meiosis (p. 383) and in a snail by alleles which determine the orientation of the spindle during mitosis. (During snail cleavage, if the spindle becomes oriented one way, a shell with a right-handed coil results; when it becomes oriented the other way, a shell with a left-handed coil is produced.) At present, however, our interest is restricted to the biochemical control of mitosis, especially its genetic basis.

The microspore of the lily remains in interphase for several weeks. During this time *thymidine kinase* activity starts at a specific time and lasts no more than 24 hours. This observation and others indicate [9] that thymidine kinase (needed for DNA replication preceding mitosis) is not always present in the cell but is newly formed for this purpose, and destroyed or inactivated after it has completed its function. This cyclical behavior system resembles induced enzyme systems in bacteria (p. 458). Should this system prove representative, it would mean that many of the problems of interphase and mitosis concern cyclically-regulated gene action. Recall (p. 487), however, that during a cell generation not all gene action is cyclical.

Viral Regulation of Growth and Differentiation

Phages regulate the growth and differentiation of their bacterial hosts, at least in part, by the messenger RNA produced using the phage genome. In cells infected by virulent T-even phages, the host materials for DNA and protein synthesis are taken over to synthesize viral DNA and protein. Temperate phages and various episomes also turn on or off certain of the host's genes, resulting in modification of cellular growth and/or differentiation. Two cancer-inducing viruses, polyoma and SV-40, are each capable of permanently altering the properties of mouse fibroblast cells grown in tissue culture. The characteristics acquired by the virus-infected cells appear to involve latent properties of the cell. For example, infected cells can regain their ability to synthesize collagen suppressed in the uninfected state. We may therefore hypothesize that certain genes are functionally turned on in virus-infected cells, and that the cellular transformations observed are functional and not mutational genetic events. [10]

Somatic Cell Mating

In tissue cultures and sometimes *in vivo,* successive cell fusions occur between uninucleated cells infected with viruses (measles, varicella, herpes, and some mxyoviruses) and noninfected cells—in a process called *polykaryocytosis*—to produce giant multinucleated cells which may contain thousands of nuclei. These fusions are postulated to be associated with an alteration of the cell surface by infecting virus. Polykaryocytes are characterized by clumped nuclei. [11]

Several mouse tissue culture lines are unique in that each has some chromosomes with a characteristic morphology. After certain pairs of such cell lines are mixed and grown together, uninucleate hybrid cells are produced whose initial chromosome number is approximately the sum of those of the two parent lines and includes chromosomes morphologically characteristic of each line. [12] Over the course of several months, clones of these hybrid cells show

---

[9] See Y. Hotta and H. Stern (1963), and H. Stern and Y. Hotta (1963).

[10] See N. Sueoka and T. Kano-Sueoka (1964), and G. J. Todaro, H. Green, and B. D. Goldberg (1964).
[11] See B. Roizman (1962).
[12] See B. Ephrussi and S. Sorieul (1962).

some reduction in chromosome number—probably because of nondisjunction. Although the *in vivo* frequency of *somatic cell mating* in mammals is unknown, one possible example of somatic cell mating has been reported in cattle.[13] This case involved a pair of twins, whose members both showed erythrocyte mosaicism due to the presence of genetically different tissues which formed antigenically different blood cells. At three years of age one twin had blood 10 per cent of which represented his own genotype and 90 per cent the genotype of his co-twin. At eight years of age, however, this twin had three blood types: the two "parental" types, each representing two per cent, and a "hybrid" type representing 96 per cent of the cell population.

Somatic cell mating is known to occur in filamentous fungi such as Aspergillus and Penicillium.[14] This *parasexuality* involves the formation of diploid nuclei by rare, probably accidental, nuclear fusions in a multinucleate mycelium containing haploid nuclei. The diploid nuclei formed multiply side by side with haploid nuclei and undergo chromosome loss or "segregation" by means of mitotic crossing over and/or nondisjunction.

Further study of somatic cell mating and subsequent chromosome segregation may provide valuable information with regard to differentiation.

RNA and Antibodies [15]

In the rat, the production of antibodies involves the following stages. Young *plasmablasts,* which divide about every ten hours, have free-floating ribosomes and a poorly developed endoplasmic reticulum. After exposure to antigens these cells begin to synthesize ribosomes and mRNA at a high rate, and the endoplasmic reticulum undergoes extensive development. Each plasmablast undergoes about nine successive divisions—each successive division taking longer—to produce a clone of mature *plasma cells* which do not divide. Whereas the plasmablasts produce a great deal of RNA and protein—mainly structural proteins and enzymes—the mature plasma cell synthesizes mainly protein, 90 to 95 per cent of which is antibody. The plasma cell nucleus is shrunken and dense and the nucleoli seem to disappear.

The first antibody molecules a given cell produces have a molecular weight of about a million (19s); later ones are smaller, with a molecular weight of only 160,000 (7s). The small antibodies are *7s gamma globulins*—tetramers composed of a pair of identical B chains of 20,000 molecular weight and a pair of identical A chains of 50,000 to 60,000 molecular weight. With rare exceptions each cell makes one type of antibody, even when other plasma cells in the lymph nodes are synthesizing other antibodies. It is not known how antibody is released from the cell to neutralize an antigen. Since little or no antigen enters the antibody-producing cell, it is possible that mere surface contact with the antigen is sufficient to start a cell into antibody synthesis. It is still too early to specify the detailed roles of the antigen and the genotype in the production of specific antibodies.

RNA in Differentiation and Learning

Developmental changes can be induced in a growing cell by the introduction of RNA or RNA-containing compounds. Although serum albumin is not produced by mouse ascites tumor cells *in vitro,* such cells acquire the ability to manufacture this protein after exposure to RNA isolated from normal mouse or calf liver. Using RNA, several strains of cancer cells can be induced to synthesize such enzymes as tryptophan pyr-

[13] See W. H. Stone, J. Friedman, and A. Fregin (1964). See also H. Harris and J. F. Watkins (1965).
[14] See G. Pontecorvo (1958).
[15] See G. J. V. Nossal (1964).

rolase and glucose-6-phosphatase.[16] The type of protein synthesized by the recipient cell seems to have some if not all of the specificity produced by the RNA-donor cell. Some of the introduced RNA seems to function as messenger RNA for at least an hour.

When the responses to stimuli do not involve learning, the neurons of rats show an increase in nuclear RNA but no shift in base ratios. However, when rats are placed in a learning situation (involving balance), not only does nuclear RNA increase but also the A/U ratio increases and C decreases. The RNA content and base ratios can be studied in single cortical neurons of right-handed rats forced to use the left hand to obtain food. Neurons serving the learning side not only show an increased RNA content but an increased $\dfrac{A + G}{C + U}$ ratio and a decreased $\dfrac{G + C}{A + U}$ ratio as compared with that of control neurons in the contralateral part of the same cortex. In Parkinson's disease profound changes in RNA base ratios arise in the nervous tissue; interference with RNA synthesis in the brain sometimes impairs learning in rats. These results strongly suggest that the learning process is associated with production of messenger RNA.[17]

Both protein and RNA synthesis can be stimulated by estrogens (in uterine tissue); testosterone (in the prostate gland); and by a flowering hormone, presumably a sterol (in a plant bud). The flowering hormone also reduces the histone to DNA ratio, which suggests that steroids can bring about the removal of histone from chromatin.[18] Low concentrations of thyroxine in a cell-free system prepared from rat liver will stimulate the incorporation of amino acids into protein. This effect is dependent upon the presence of mitochondria and an oxidizable substrate, is independent of DNA-dependent RNA polymerase activity or mRNA synthesis, and seems to involve the transfer of sRNA-bound amino acid to protein synthesizing ribosomes.[19]

Differentiation in Paramecium [20]

Although Paramecium is normally a single animal, or *singlet*, double animals, or *doublets*, occur. Singlets and doublets reproduce true to type through numerous fissions. A doublet can also conjugate with two singlets and each singlet exconjugant regularly produces singlet clones and the doublet exconjugant, a doublet clone. The singlet-doublet difference cannot be due to micronuclear genes since exconjugants are identical in this respect. This same phenotypic result is obtained even when a cytoplasmic bridge lasts long enough to permit an extensive exchange of cytoplasm. Consequently, the difference between doublet and singlet does not have a basis in any cytoplasmic component free to migrate. Other evidence seems to exclude the macronucleus from being involved. The only portion of the cell unaccounted for then is the immobile 0.5 micron-thick outer layer of ectoplasm, the *cortex*.

In one experiment, after cytoplasmic bridge formation between a singlet and doublet, a rare free singlet exconjugant was found bearing a conspicuous extra piece of cortex. The doublet exconjugant, on the other hand, showed a corresponding nick in its cortex. The extra piece in the singlet later flattened out and, after fission, one of the two daughter cells gave rise to a clone phenotypically intermediate between singlets and doublets. This natural grafting of only a small piece of a paramecium's

[16] See M. C. Niu, C. C. Cordova, L. C. Niu, and C. L. Radbill (1962), and A. H. Evans (1964).

[17] See H. Hydén and E. Egyházi (1963, 1964).

[18] See reference to J. Bonner and P. O. P. Ts'o on p. 499. See also T. H. Hamilton (1964).

[19] See L. Sokoloff, C. M. Francis, and P. L. Campbell (1964).

[20] See T. M. Sonneborn (1963, 1964).

oral segment gave rise to a strain having a complete extra oral segment including an extra vestibule, mouth, and gullet. Other studies reveal that various experimental modifications of visible cortical organization are perpepuated during cell reproduction, and that certain visible cortical structures initially absent, do not arise *de novo*.

These and other results establish the importance of the cortex in differentiation. The cortex is not completely autonomous, however, since some nuclear genes are known to determine visible cortical structures or their morphogenesis. As already mentioned, a small additional piece of cortex can give rise to cortical changes of greater degree. Clearly then, the nature and action of the cortex is dependent not only upon its own composition but upon nuclear genes and their products as well as metabolism in general. It should be noted

that double-stranded DNA has been reported in human erythrocyte membranes.[21] This DNA has a molecular weight of about 10^6 and a G + C content of approximately 39–42%. Its homogeneity (and its possible higher $\dfrac{A + T}{C + G}$ ratio) suggest that this is not merely adsorbed DNA. At present, the mode of operation of the cortex can only be described in general, largely speculative, terms. "The much more difficult task for the future is to define and specify in molecular terms the decisive structures, gradients, and inductor-response systems and to reveal how specific absorption, orientation, and activation of migratory molecules leads to visible morphogenesis and genetic stability of cell organization." (T. M. Sonneborn, 1963).

[21] See L. Philipson and Ö. Zetterqvist (1964).

SUMMARY AND CONCLUSIONS

The synthesis of mature ϕT4 progeny is regulated by blocks of parental viral genes which function at the same or nearly the same time and which are arranged in the circular linkage map in a sequence reflecting successive stages of phage morphogenesis.

Nuclear transplantation, somatic cell mating, antibody-antigen, and biochemical embryological investigations are revealing the genetic and molecular bases of differentiation and development.

Studies of thymidine kinase indicate that mitosis involves cyclical gene action. Base-specific RNA plays an intracellular role in learning and an intercellular role in differentiation. Steroids seem to be involved in RNA production and histone distribution.

Although the chemical mechanism is unknown, studies of Paramecium reveal the importance of the cortex in differentiation, and emphasize that morphogenesis depends upon both the nuclear genetic material and the remainder of the protoplasmic and metabolic environment.

REFERENCES

Cytogenetics and Developmental Genetics, Amer. Zool., 3 (No. 1), 1963.

Demerec, M., "Clustering of Functionally Related Genes in *Salmonella typhimurium*," Proc. Nat. Acad. Sci., U.S., 51:1057–1060, 1964.

Differentiation and Development, Boston: Little, Brown, 1964; and J. Exp. Zool., 157, No. 1, 1964.

Doi, R. H., and Igarashi, R. T., "Genetic Transcription during Morphogenesis," Proc. Nat. Acad. Sci., U.S., 52:755–762, 1964.

Ephrussi, B., and Sorieul, S., "Mating of Somatic Cells *In Vitro,*" pp. 81–97, in *Approaches to the Genetic Analysis of Mammalian Cells,* Merchant, D. J., and Neel, J. V. (Eds.), Ann Arbor: Univ. Michigan Press, 1962.

Epstein, R. H., *et al.,* "Physiological Studies of Conditioned Lethal Mutants of Bacteriophage T4D," Cold Spring Harb. Sympos. Quant. Biol., 28:375–394, 1964.

Evans, A. H., "Introduction of Specific Drug Resistance Properties by Purified RNA-Containing Fractions from Pneumococcus," Proc. Nat. Acad. Sci., U.S., 52:1442–1449, 1964.

Hamilton, T. H., "Sequences of RNA and Protein Synthesis During Early Estrogen Action," Proc. Nat. Acad. Sci., U.S., 51:83–89, 1964.

Harris, H., and Watkins, J. F., "Hybrid Cells Derived from Mouse and Man: Artificial Heterocaryons of Mammalian Cells from Different Species," Nature, London, 205:640, 1965.

Hotta, Y., and Stern, H., "Molecular Facets of Mitotic Regulation, II. Factors Underlying the Removal of Thymidine Kinase," Proc. Nat. Acad. Sci., U.S., 49:861–865, 1963.

Hydén, H., and Egyházi, E., "Glial RNA Changes During a Learning Experiment in Rats," Proc. Nat. Acad. Sci., U.S., 49:618–624, 1963.

Hydén, H., and Egyházi, E., "Changes in RNA Content and Base Composition in Cortical Neurons of Rats in a Learning Experiment Involving Transfer of Handedness," Proc. Nat. Acad. Sci., U.S., 52:1030–1035, 1964.

Locke, M. (Ed.), *Cytodifferentiation and Macromolecular Synthesis,* New York: Academic Press, 1963.

Markert, C. L., and Ursprung, H., "Production of Replicable Changes in Zygote Chromosomes of *Rana pipiens* by Injected Proteins from Adult Liver Nuclei," Develop. Biol., 7:560–577, 1963.

McCarthy, B. J., and Hoyer, B. H., "Identity of DNA and Diversity of Messenger RNA Molecules in Normal Mouse Tissues," Proc. Nat. Acad. Sci., U.S., 52:915–922, 1964.

McElroy, W. D., and Glass, B. (Eds.), *A Symposium on the Chemical Basis of Development,* Baltimore: The Johns Hopkins Press, 1958.

Moore, J. A., "Serial Back-Transfers of Nuclei in Experiments Involving Two Species of Frogs," Develop. Biol., 2:535–550, 1960.

Niu, M. C., Cordova, C. C., Niu, L. C., and Radbill, C. L., "RNA-Induced Biosynthesis of Specific Enzymes," Proc. Nat. Acad. Sci., U.S., 48:1964–1969, 1962.

Nossal, G. J. V., "How Cells Make Antibodies," Scient. Amer., 211 (Dec.):106–115, 154, 156, 1964.

Philipson, L., and Zetterqvist, Ö., "The Presence of DNA in Human Erythrocyte Membranes," Biochim. Biophys. Acta, 91:171–173, 1964.

Roizman, B., "Polykaryocytosis Induced by Viruses," Proc. Nat. Acad. Sci., U.S., 48:228–234, 1962.

Sokoloff, L., Francis, C. M., and Campbell, P. L., "Thyroxine Stimulation of Amino Acid Incorporation into Protein Independent of Any Action on Messenger RNA Synthesis," Proc. Nat. Acad. Sci., U.S., 52:728–736, 1964.

Sonneborn, T. M., "Does Preformed Cell Structure Play an Essential Role in Cell Heredity?" Chapter 7, pp. 165–221, in *The Nature of Biological Diversity,* Allen, J. M. (Ed.), New York: McGraw-Hill, 1963.

Sonneborn, T. M., "The Differentiation of Cells," Proc. Nat. Acad. Sci., U.S., 51: 915–929, 1964.

Stern, H., and Hotta, Y., "Regulated Synthesis of RNA and Protein in the Control of Cell Division," Brookhaven Sympos. Biol., 16:59–72, 1963.

Stone, W. H., Friedman, J., and Fregin, A., "Possible Somatic Cell Mating in Twin Cattle with Erythrocyte Mosaicism," Proc. Nat. Acad. Sci., U.S., 51:1036–1044, 1964.

Sueoka, N., and Kano-Sueoka, T., "A Specific Modification of Leucyl-sRNA of *Escherichia coli* after T2 Infection," Proc. Nat. Acad. Sci., U.S., 52:1535–1540, 1964.

Symposium on Macromolecular Aspects of the Cell Cycle, J. Cell. Comp. Physiol., 62 (Suppl. 1), 1963.

Todaro, G. J., Green, H., and Goldberg, B. D., "Transformation of Properties of an Established Cell Line by SV40 and Polyoma Virus," Proc. Nat. Acad. Sci., U.S., 51:66–73, 1964.

Waddington, C. H., *New Patterns in Genetics and Development,* New York: Columbia University Press, 1962.

Weiler, E., "Immunologically Determined and Competent Cells Are Affected Differently by Actinomycin D," Science, 144:846–849, 1964.

QUESTIONS FOR DISCUSSION

41.1. Apply the concept of the operon to the development of ϕT4.

41.2. The work on nuclear transplantation by R. W. Briggs and T. J. King, J. A. Moore, and others has proved that development sometimes involves irreversible changes in the nucleus. Should such changes be termed mutations? Explain.

41.3. In the snail *Limnea peregra,* self-fertilization of pure-line individuals whose shell coils to the right, dextrally, or to the left, sinistrally, produces progeny all of which coil as their parents. A cross of dextral ♀ by sinistral ♂ yields all dextral F_1 which, when self-fertilized, yield all dextral progeny in F_2. After self-fertilization, however, ¾ of the F_2 give rise to dextral F_3 and ¼ of the F_2 to sinistral F_3. The reciprocal cross, dextral ♂ by sinistral ♀, yields all sinistral F_1. The F_1 produces F_2 and F_3 phenotypically the same as the reciprocal cross. Give a genetic explanation for these results. Are cytoplasmic genes involved? Explain.

41.4. T. Yamada has found that isolated prospective ectoderm gives rise only to epidermal cells when cultured *in vitro* in standard medium, but forms mesodermal tissues if a protein fraction from bone marrow is added to the medium. To what can you attribute these results?

41.5. Suggest an explanation for the dedifferentiation which chondrocytes in vertebral cartilage undergo when grown *in vitro*.

41.6. Defend the following statement of J. D. Ebert (1963): "The principal theme, coursing through and underlying research in embryology today, is the impact of genetics on development. More than at any time in the past half-century, molecular embryology is clearly the logical extension of molecular genetics."

41.7. What conclusions can you draw from the following evidence concerning Down's syndrome as found in the Victoria region of Australia: The incidence of the syndrome varies year by year, with peaks occurring about every five years; about 40% of the cases are clustered geographically, more occurring in urban than in rural areas.

Chapter 42

THE ORIGIN AND EVOLUTION
OF GENETIC MATERIAL

IN CONSIDERING the nature and effects of genes, the origin and evolution of genetic material has been neglected. Before taking this up in detail, it would be desirable to reconsider the nature of presently-known genetic materials, DNA and RNA.

The replication of either type of nucleic acid involves the use of a single or double polynucleotide strand as a template for complementary monomers subsequently joined to form complementary polynucleotides. The nucleic acid properties responsible for its ability to serve as a template must include a specific physical configuration of linearly-arranged monomers as well as a specific pattern of net electrical charges. Although the utilization of the nucleic acid template for the formation of a complement is a relatively passive process with regard to the polynucleotide strand, it is an active process if we consider the highly specific action of nucleic acid polymerase or synthetase. Since the nucleic acid fiber which serves as a template is mostly passive, it is not surprising that nucleic acid can be used as a template by different enzymes, provided that the raw materials collected on the template have suitable physical and electrical properties. That nucleic acids are used as templates for the formation of polymers not their complements, is exemplified by DNA used as template by DNA-dependent RNA polymerase to make RNA, and by RNA used *in vitro* and *in vivo* as a template to make DNA. Whether nucleotides other than those in DNA and RNA, or still other substances, make use of the nucleic acid template in a similar manner is yet to be determined. (Note that the basic proteins in nucleoproteins may be associated with nucleic acids through a template mechanism, at least in part.) The simplest and the broadest working hypothesis, therefore, is that all the functional characteristics of genes depend upon the linear sequence of nucleotides and upon the ways this polymer is used as a template by various substances and enzymes; in other words, *the only function of genetic material is to serve as a template.*

Although nucleic acid is self-replicating, the process is apparently not accomplished in one step. In fact, two replications seem to be required before a given strand can be duplicated. The first replication produces a complementary strand; the second replication produces a copy of the first strand. We are probably justified in thinking of self-replication in this way for the following reasons:

1. The self-replication of single-stranded DNA and RNA viruses must be considered a two-step process.
2. Double-stranded nucleic acid may preferentially or exclusively replicate one of the complements.
3. One of the two strands in a double helix may be defective (mutant) and incapable, at least in some places, of both replication and self-replication; however, its normal, complementary chain would be capable of both.

Consequently, we can now define *genetic material as any template whose use eventually results in its self-replication and which either retains this ability after mutation or is a mutant of a template which has this ability.* We can also consider genetic material to be any substance which produces the same phenotypic effects as known genetic material.

Should pure DNA *in vitro* be considered to be genetic material? Originally, the identification of genetic material depended upon its presence in organisms and its production of a phenotypic effect; we can now dispense with these requirements. Pure virus DNA in a test tube should be considered genetic material even though no longer within an organism, recombining, mutating, replicating, or performing any phenotypic function. This statement is valid on the basis that such DNA either is known to or expected to possess genetic properties when introduced into an organism. DNA synthesized *in vitro* is physically and chemically almost identical to chromosomal DNA. It is capable of:

1. Replicating itself and some of its variants
2. Undergoing strand separation and recombination
3. Producing a phenotypic effect by genetic transformation.

We may conclude, therefore, that DNA synthesized *in vitro* also fulfills the requirements of our definition for genetic material.

The simplest biological synthesis of DNA or RNA requires the presence of nucleoside triphosphates; an enzyme (DNA polymerase or RNA synthetase); and water—at the correct pH—containing the ions necessary to activate the enzyme. It seems unlikely that the first gene-like material had these numerous and specific requirements for replication. We may hypothesize that in the course of evolution, the first really successful genetic material resembled RNA rather than DNA; although DNA (by lacking an O at the 2' position) is more stable than RNA as a template, it is the RNA polyribotide which serves as a carrier (as sRNA) for amino acids. This amino-acid carrying ability may have led to the synthesis of the

polymerizing enzymes essential for rapid gene synthesis, and for the synthesis of other proteins (including enzymes) which stabilize and preserve the chemical integrity of the genetic material.

The preceding discussion leads to the question of the origin of genetic material on earth. Were RNA (and/or DNA) and proteins present during the early stages of genetic evolution? Would their presence in early evolution correlate with existing knowledge about the course of chemical evolution on earth?

Eras of Chemical Evolution [1]

Era I. We now understand that at an early prebiotic stage in its history—some 4 billion years ago—the earth had a reducing atmosphere rich in water, hydrogen, methane, and ammonia, but poor in free oxygen and carbon dioxide. Using mixtures of these and similar compounds predicated to have been present in such a reducing atmosphere plus a source of energy (such as electrical discharges, sunlight and ultraviolet light, microwaves, ultrasonic vibrations, heat, high energy electrons, X rays, and proton irradiation), it is possible to produce in the laboratory a large number of simple radicals and organic molecules. Moreover, since a projectile propelled through a gas and into a liquid can cause the formation of a large number of complex chemical compounds, it is very likely that in prebiotic times chemosynthesis was also induced by meteorites.[2] Some of the compounds synthesized experimentally in a "primitive" atmosphere include alanine, glycine, glutamic acid, aspartic acid, acetic acid, formic acid, proprionic acid, lactic acid, succinic acid, some fatty acids, urea, some sugars, phosphoric acid, adenine, and uracil. Although we are not yet able to determine which of

[1] See article by H. Gaffron in M. Kasha and B. Pullman (1962).
[2] See A. R. Hochstim (1963).

the energy sources were primarily responsible, there cannot be any doubt that synthesis and accumulation of a great variety of organic molecules took place in the oceans, making an "organic soup." During this era, whose length has not been established, most of the free hydrogen escaped from the earth's atmosphere.

Era II. Its atmosphere was also a reducing one with only traces of free oxygen. Initially, the same energy sources were available for chemosynthesis in this era as in Era I. As traces of oxygen escaped to the atmosphere, ultraviolet rays from the sun converted the oxygen into ozone. Since ozone absorbs ultraviolet light, the ozone layer in the atmosphere acted as a blanket so that the main chemosynthetic energy from the sun was visible light and heat.

A study of the comparative biochemistry of present higher plants and animals, bacteria, and many viruses, shows that all are intimately associated with the same 20 or so amino acids. Accordingly, protein and nucleic acid are, perhaps, the most durable chemical features of the earth, having existed for more than a billion years. In the presence of excess aspartic acid and glutamic acid, temperatures of 200°C or less can be used [3] in a dry heat synthesis to polymerize amino acids into *proteinoids,* polymers containing, in peptide linkage, all or most of the amino acids common to proteins. Proteinoids are linear polymers with a molecular weight of up to 10,000, show weak catalytic activity, and, for the most part, are indistinguishable from natural proteins or polypeptides of similar size. Although proteinoids are nonantigenic, in hot water they tend to form spheres about two microns in diameter. Since the spheres swell and shrink as the sodium chloride concentration of the medium is changed, we are reminded of osmotic behavior. Sometimes

such microspheres undergo a kind of fission and show a double-layered outer membrane in electron micrographs. Homopolymers and copolymers of certain amino acids can also be produced by dry heat.

On the basis of such evidence and reasoning, it is expected that during Era II complex organic substances were synthesized—polypeptides, nucleotides, carotenes, polyphosphates, pigments, and porphyrins. It is also expected that adsorption and primitive catalysis occurred involving surfaces of clays and/or polypeptides.

Era III. This era is assumed to be mainly anaerobic with only trace amounts of free oxygen and some carbon dioxide. It is suggested that during this period synthetic cycles evolved (as did specific catalysis and photochemistry) on the surfaces of large organic molecules. As the last evolutionary step of this era, primitive enzymes and genes also arose, leading to the first organism.

Some recent research and speculation [4] may throw more light upon the evolution and interdependence of polynucleotides and proteins. As mentioned, it is likely that proteins and mononucleotides were already present at the start of Era III. In the presence of dehydrating agents, water is removed and nucleotides are joined to form polynucleotides with molecular weights of up to fifty thousand. Note that such a polymer is made without the use of an enzyme. The rate of such a nonenzymatic synthesis of polyuridylic acid has been found [5] to increase more than tenfold in the presence of polyadenylic acid, which suggests that the latter homopolymer can serve as a template during the nonenzymatic synthesis of the former homopolymer. A hypothetical scheme has been proposed to form DNA by the re-

[3] See S. W. Fox (1960, 1964).

[4] See article by A. Rich in M. Kasha and B. Pullman (1962).
[5] By G. Schramm, H. Grötsch, and W. Pollmann (1961).

action of glyceraldehyde, acetaldehyde, ammonia, oxaloacetic acid, glycine, and formyl residues.

Molecular evolution leads not only to greater complexity but to greater stability of molecules. Accordingly, separate protein and polynucleotide chains might join to form a more stable complex. (We know that a DNA-histone complex stabilizes DNA; double-strandedness and polynemy could also be nucleic acid stabilizing factors.) The final protein-nucleic acid complex, however, need not have started with a protein or a polynucleotide. Single nucleotide-single amino acid units might have occurred which polymerized to form a polypeptide first and a polynucleotide later or the reverse. Regardless of the manner in which the nucleic acid-protein complex evolved, such a complex must already have entailed *a primitive code by which nucleotides and amino acids code for each other*. Since nucleic acids make better templates for replication than proteins, the nucleic acid portion of a nucleoprotein became genetic material. As chemical evolution proceeded, the number of nucleotides specifying a single amino acid could have increased from one to the three—the size of our present codon.

Even if the evolution of proteins and polynucleotides was independent for some time, it seems clear that the two substances became interdependent in their later evolution. In view of the relative chemical inactivity of nucleic acids, we may hypothesize that one primary result of their evolution was the stabilization of enormous numbers of protein molecules and protein cycles which arose in Era III; a second primary result of nucleic acid evolution led to protein replication by ribonucleic acid. In other words, *chemical evolution seems to have been largely a matter of protein evolution during which nucleic acids came to serve as stabilizers of and templates for protein synthesis*. Such an evolution would be expected if nucleic acids were first formed in an environment whose organic components were largely protein. Since nucleic acids do not include sulfur (and many other elements) in their basic makeup, they lack the proteins' *chemical drive for stability*. The stabilization of proteins was probably further enhanced by retaining the information in DNA, rather than RNA whose use became more and more restricted to the translation process. As the nucleic acid transcription and translation processes evolved, it surely became advantageous to step up the rate of these reactions through the use of nucleic acid polymerizing enzymes. It also became advantageous to protect nucleic acids from peroxides formed in the environment by radiation. Thus, it is likely that the nucleic acids which encoded catalase protected the nucleic acid directly and protein synthesis indirectly. Since prebiotic and biotic chemo-evolution is largely describable in terms of protein structure and function, the present view—that genetic nucleic acids played a lesser role—is already generally accepted and not at all novel. The subservient role of nucleic acids is generally evidenced in present day organisms not only in the requirement of GPP in protein synthesis and of APP for the transport of energy, but also of UPP and CPP for the transport of monomers in the synthesis of carbohydrates and lipids.[6]

Because of the intimate relationship between amino acids and genetic material, we need to learn more about the evolution of all kinds of organic compounds, especially energy-rich compounds (such as ATP), catalysts (such as iron-containing compounds), and energy-capturing compounds (such as chlorophyll).

[6] See R. E. Eakin (1963).

In considering the origin of the first gene, we should keep in mind the possibility that its nongenic predecessor might have been capable of self-replication to some degree, but might not have been able to replicate any of its mutant forms. The search for information about nongenetic systems with some but not all the properties of genetic material is clearly highly necessary and desirable.

Subgenic chemicals may occur in present-day cells. Constituents of the cytoplasm which contain DNA and are able to self-replicate include chloroplasts, mitochondria, the centriole, and the kinetosome. If the DNA in these structures is mutable and still able to self-replicate, it can be classed as cytoplasmic or extranuclear genetic material. Experimental study of these and other organelles is expected to reveal details of their chemistry. We would also like to know a great deal more about the synthesis of RNA genes; how the metagonic RNA of *Paramecium* replicates in *Didinium*; and whether it is still self-replicating after mutation. Answers to such questions would be valuable in enabling us to speculate more fruitfully upon the nature of pregenetic and primitive genetic materials.

Eras IV and V. The early environment in these eras was probably much the same as in Era III, but after an increase followed by a decrease in carbon dioxide, a large increase in the amount of free oxygen took place. Though we do not yet have sufficient information to decide precisely which pathways led to the chemical evolution of the first gene, we do have some evidence concerning the subsequent history of genes in organisms. The only genetic material found exclusively in free-living organisms today is DNA; this substance is found in all such organisms, be they unicellular or multicellular, plant, animal, or microorganismal. Whether or not types of genes other than DNA and RNA have ever existed, DNA genes must have a definite advantage for survival—after all, they have persisted as the main genetic material for about a billion years, approximately the period the evolution of plants and animals have been separate. It is likely that the formation of chromosomes with telomeres, centromeres, and polynemy, as well as the establishment of special methods of separating daughter and homologous chromosomes (by mitosis and meiosis) and of recombining them (fertilization) were innovations involving DNA which occurred some time prior to the divergence of the plant and animal kingdoms.

Evolution must have led to the transcription of only one of the two complementary polynucleotide strands in producing complementary RNA and viruses with single-stranded nucleic acids, and must have occurred in the genetic code and the apparatus for translation. The quantity of DNA per organism and the basic proteins which regulate gene activity as well as the materials which serve to regulate mutability must also have evolved.

We may reasonably suppose that an evolution in gene activity also took place. On primitive earth it is likely that large amounts of different, more or less complex, organic materials accumulated and remained undegraded before the advent of the first gene-containing organisms. As the organisms used up these resources in their metabolism, however, there would have been a selection in favor of those mutants capable of synthesizing such organic materials from simpler organic, or from inorganic, components.[7] This hypothesis means that natural selection acted in favor of those mutant genes which specified the synthesis of a component no longer available in the environ-

[7] See N. H. Horowitz (1945).

ment. Independence of the environment would also have been advanced by the physical association of genes involved in different portions of a given biochemical sequence, this independence leading eventually to the selection of mutant genes whose function, other than self-replication, was to regulate the functioning of other genes. Thus, in addition to genes for structure, evolution might well have produced genes for regulation—operator and regulator genes—and genes for synthesizing specific basic proteins for the regulation of chromosome coiling, replication, and functioning.

Cosmic Chemo-evolution

In our search for information regarding either pregenetic, preorganismal evolution or postgenetic, postorganismal evolution, we do not have to confine ourselves to this planet. The universe is about ten billion years old; the earth is roughly half this age. Because the universe contains an infinite number of stars (suns) with planets, there must be vast numbers of suns the size of our own that have planets about the same size as the earth and at comparable distances from their suns. Some of these planets are surely younger, others surely older than our own. What is the possibility that a chemical and biological evolution similar to ours took place on other planets? The answer to this question depends, of course, upon their chemical composition.

Most of the universe is hydrogen and helium (most of the earth's hydrogen escaped from our atmosphere in Era I, as already mentioned). Of the remaining elements, the universe has abundant oxygen and nitrogen and is, in fact, richer than the earth in carbon—the element essential for organic compounds which have played such an integral role in chemical and biological evolution on earth. It is therefore likely that numerous places in the universe do exist where a chemical evolution of biological interest might have been successfully initiated. Since the relative scarcity of carbon makes the earth a rather poor place for such an evolution (which nevertheless occurred), most surely the universe contains numerous planets in early stages of chemical evolution, early stages of biological evolution, as well as planets older than our own, which very probably have more advanced types of organisms.

Evidence has been obtained for the presence of organic radicals such as CH, CN, CC, and CO in comets, and for organic molecules of an asymmetric type on Mars. Astronomers have also reported variations in the color and texture of Mars with changes of season, which strongly suggest that Mars, with an atmosphere thinner than the earth's, contains appreciable quantities of organic matter, although we are not yet able to determine whether their origin is preorganismal or organismal.

Further information about the chemistry of our sun and its planets will undoubtedly be provided by telescopes orbiting far into and above our atmosphere. Plans for interplanetary research now underway include sending additional instruments to or near various planets in our solar system. Such missions will be designed to record the detailed chemistry of our neighboring planets and, of course, to detect the presence of organic compounds, of organisms, and of DNA and RNA. We have already sent radio signals into space in an attempt to contact other organisms capable of receiving and/or replying.

In any space mission it is of utmost importance to avoid the accidental transplantation of terrestrial genotypes to other planets; if a single bacterium such as *E. coli* were placed on a planet containing a suitable medium, its progeny would occupy a volume the size of the earth in about 48 hours. Such an unscheduled transplantation would doubtless be disastrous to any future plans for studying either the preorganismal evolution of organic compounds or any indigenous organisms. As a safeguard against such contamination, objects sent beyond our atmosphere are sterilized. Recall also that the impact of a missile on a planet may cause the production of organic chemical substances.

Which heavenly objects likely to be investigated in the near future are interesting from the point of view of preorganismal and organismal evolution? We have already mentioned Mars. Consider Venus, whose unknown surface is hidden completely by an opaque, highly reflecting cloud layer containing abundant carbon dioxide and water. Although estimates of Venus' temperature vary widely (its surface is usually considered to be dry and hot), we can assume that organic compounds have evolved there even if biological evolution has been impossible. After studying its chemistry in sufficient detail, perhaps we might wish to colonize Venus, first by placing a chlorophyll-containing microorganism in its outer atmosphere. In a short time, such an organism, by utilizing great quantities of atmospheric components for growth and reproduction, might radically change the climate of Venus.

Our own satellite, the moon, has no atmosphere and probably no water. Therefore, the presence of earthlike life there today is almost out of the question. The moon, however, may be as old as the earth and may have had an organic and even a biological evolution similar to our own before losing its atmosphere. So it will be interesting to analyze samples of the lunar surface and, particularly, its subsurface material. It has been suggested that the moon acts as a gravitational trap for fossil spores drifting between planets. Although improbable, the very possibility of an interplanetary gene flow is too important to ignore in the exploration and exploitation of space. Planetary research has many motivations; but the search for evidence of chemical evolution, DNA and RNA, and organisms—life of any type —would seem to be among the most significant.

SUMMARY AND CONCLUSIONS

The earth has undergone a chemical evolution. This process resulted in the synthesis of most types of compounds and cycles of synthesis found in present-day organisms. It also resulted in the production of proteins, polynucleotides, and nucleoproteins. These latter compounds evolved to a stage where a nucleic acid was able to replicate itself as well as some of its changed forms and so could be identified as genetic material. Chemo-evolutionary drive on earth is based largely upon protein since nucleic acids provide much less chemical diversity; therefore we hypothesize that nucleic acid evolution (which presumably went from RNA to DNA) was subservient to evolution directed primarily toward the stabilization and synthesis of protein.

DNA has been the primary genetic material on earth for about a billion years. During this time DNA and its associated materials have undergone a structural evolution leading to the establishment of chromosomes and mechanisms for genetic recombination and regulation of mutability. Also, genes have probably undergone a functional evolution, which proceeded from genes which serve structurally (specifying the synthesis or organization of nongenetic compounds) to those which serve functionally (regulating gene action).

REFERENCES

Abelson, P. H., "Extra-Terrestrial Life," Proc. Nat. Acad. Sci., U.S., 47:575–581, 1961.

Blum, H. F., "On the Origin and Evolution of Living Machines," Amer. Sci., 49:474–501, 1961.

Calvin, M., "The Origin of Life on Earth and Elsewhere," Ann. Int. Med., 54:954–976, 1961.

Clark, F., and Synge, R. L. M. (Eds.), *The Origin of Life on the Earth,* New York: Pergamon Press, 1959.

Eakin, R. E., "An Approach to the Evolution of Metabolism," Proc. Nat. Acad. Sci., U.S., 49:360–366, 1963.

Fox, S. W., "How Did Life Begin," Science, 132:200–208, 1960.

Fox, S. W., "Experiments in Molecular Evolution and Criteria of Extraterrestrial Life," Bio-Science, 14:13–21, 1964.

Fox, S. W. (Ed.), *The Origins of Prebiological Systems,* New York: Academic Press, 1964.

Green, D. E., and Hechter, O., "Assembly of Membrane Subunits," Proc. Nat. Acad. Sci., U.S., 53:318–325, 1965.

Hochstim, A. R., "Hypersonic Chemosynthesis and Possible Formation of Organic Compounds from Impact of Meteorites on Water," Proc. Nat. Acad. Sci., U.S., 50:200–208, 1963.

Horowitz, N. H., "On the Evolution of Biochemical Syntheses," Proc. Nat. Acad. Sci., U.S., 31:153–157, 1945.

Huang, S.-S., "Life Outside the Solar System," Scient. Amer., 202 (No. 4):55–63, 1960.

Kasha, M., and Pullman, B. (Eds.), *Horizons in Biochemistry,* New York: Academic Press, 1962.

Keosian, J., *The Origin of Life,* New York: Reinhold Publ. Corp., 1964.

Lederberg, J., "Exobiology: Approaches to Life Beyond the Earth," Science, 132:393–400, 1960.

Lederberg, J., and Cowie, D. B., "Moondust," Science, 127:1473–1475, 1958.

Miller, S. L., and Urey, H. C., "Organic Compound Synthesis on the Primitive Earth," Science, 130:245–251, 1959.

Oparin, A. I., *The Origin of Life on Earth,* 3rd Ed., New York: Academic Press, 1957.

Oparin, A. I., *The Chemical Origin of Life,* Springfield, Ill.: Chas. C. Thomas, 1964.

Penrose, L. S., "Self-Reproducing Machines," Scient. Amer., 200 (No. 6):105–114, 1959.

Ponnamperuma, C., Lemmon, R. M., Mariner, R., and Calvin, M., "Formation of Adenine by Electron Irradiation of Methane, Ammonia and Water," Proc. Nat. Acad. Sci., U.S., 49:737–740, 1963.

Sagan, C., "The Planet Venus," Science, 133:849–858, 1961.

Sagan, C., "On the Origin and Planetary Distribution of Life," Rad. Res., 15:174–192, 1961.

Sinton, W. M., "Further Evidence of Vegetation on Mars," Science, 130:1234–1237, 1959.

Tax, S. (Ed.), *The Evolution of Life,* Vol. 1 of *Evolution after Darwin,* Chicago: University of Chicago Press, 1960.

Wolstenholme, G. (Ed.), *Man and His Future,* Boston: Little, Brown & Co., 1963. See Supplement VII.

QUESTIONS FOR DISCUSSION

42.1. Which do you think came first in evolution, the gene or what we now call the "gene product"? Explain.

42.2. Do you believe that the genetic material on earth has undergone a biochemical evolution? A structural evolution? A functional evolution? Why?

42.3. Do you believe there are "superhumans" on other planets? Why?

42.4. Do you suppose that in the future we will need to be as careful in avoiding contaminants from other planets to our own, as we now are in avoiding the reverse? Why?

42.5. In what respects would you expect the environment of Venus to be changed if a photosynthesizing microorganism were introduced into its atmosphere?

42.6. What information would you seek from landing on the moon? Mars? Venus?

42.7. What characteristics would you expect of genes from other planets?

42.8. Is protein genetic material? Justify your answer.

42.9. What is your present opinion of the assumption, stated on p. 10, that genetic material arises only by the replication of pre-existing genetic material?

42.10. What is your definition of a gene? Of genetics?

Appendix

ELEMENTARY BIOMETRICAL INFERENCES

I.   Introduction: Statistics and Parameters
II. Discrete Variables
     A. Range of Statistics Expected from a Parameter Involving One Variable
     B. Range of Parameters Expected from a Statistic Involving One Variable
     C. Specific Probabilities Expected from Parameters Involving One Variable
        1. Rules of probability
           a. The addition rule
           b. The multiplication rule
        2. The binomial expression
     D. Comparing Observed with Expected Statistics
        1. The binomial test of a parameter involving one variable
        2. The confidence interval test of a parameter involving one variable
        3. Chi-square test of a parameter involving one variable
        4. Chi-square test of a parameter involving two or more variables
     E. Comparisons Between Statistics
        1. Involving one variable
           a. Observed difference vs. expected standard deviation
           b. The plus-minus test
           c. Contingency table approach to the chi-square test
        2. Involving two or more variables
           Contingency table approach to the chi-square test
III. Indiscrete Variables
     A. Parameters and the Normal Curve
        The normal curve vs. the binomial distribution
     B. Statistics Expected from a Normal Curve
        1. Distribution of individual statistics
        2. Distribution of the means expected for groups of statistics
        3. Testing hypotheses regarding μ
           a. The τ test
           b. The t test
           c. Confidence intervals for μ
           d. Comparison of $\overline{X}_1$ and $\overline{X}_2$
IV. The Power of the Test

√ I. INTRODUCTION: STATISTICS AND PARAMETERS

There are numerous occasions when one may wish to arrive at some genetic conclusion on the basis of experimental data. Whenever these data are subject to chance variation, it is necessary to make use of biometrical ideas and techniques in order to draw the most precise conclusions. Let us consider, therefore, some of the basic principles and methods which are likely to be valuable in a study of genetics. (The Table of Contents at the beginning of this chapter will make it easier to find the section that describes a particular biometrical technique.)

A *statistic* is a measurement obtained from a sample. A sample can be considered as having been drawn from an ideal population composed of an infinite number of measurements. Whereas the measurements of a sample are statistics, the measurements of the ideal, infinitely large, population are expressed in terms of *parameters*. The difference between a statistic and a parameter can be illustrated with a penny. Let the ideal population be composed of the results of an infinite number of tosses. In this ideal population one would expect the coin to fall heads up 50% of the time, and tails up 50% of the time. The population can be characterized in terms of a parameter, the probability of heads up, expressed as $p = 0.5$. If one actually takes a sample of this infinite population by tossing a penny a finite number of times, one obtains the statistic, the frequency of heads up relative to the total number of tosses.

Given a parameter, one may want to predict the range of statistics expected to comprise a sample (Figure A-1A). Alternatively, one might like to be able to determine from a statistic the range of parameters from which this statistic could have been obtained by sampling (Figure A-1B).

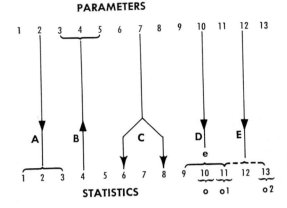

FIGURE A–1. *Biometrical procedures to be discussed with respect to discrete variables (see text for explanation).* o = *observed,* e = *expected. Arrows show direction of prediction.*

One may want to determine the probabilities (i.e., parameters) that different alternatives will occur in samples drawn from an ideal population (Figure A-1C). One may wish to compare the statistics expected (e) in a sample with those actually obtained (o) (Figure A-1D). And finally, using a parameter, one may wish to compare two groups of statistics (o1 and o2) (Figure A-1E). Methods for making these and other comparisons are presented here.

Heads vs. tails, black vs. white, smooth vs. rough, and tall vs. short all involve *discrete variables* which are measured by enumeration, since the outcomes or alternatives fall into discontinuous, easily distinguished and separable, classes. On the other hand, the statistics of weight, height, and intelligence are all quantitative, continuous, or *indiscrete variables*. The difference between the two lies in the number of alternatives possible in each case; there is an infinite variety of alternatives possible in the indiscrete case, but only a limited number of outcomes in the discrete one. This difference disappears, however, once the outcomes are tallied. For example, although the number of different weights possible in the range of weights between fat and skinny people is infinite, weights are scored with a scale whose number of possible readings is limited. In other words, an infinite variety of outcomes must always be scored or measured in a finite number of ways. So far as statistics are concerned, the only difference between indiscrete and discrete outcomes is the possible occurrence of a much larger number of scored outcomes in the former case. In either group of outcomes, scoring a statistic requires the use of some measuring device, be it the eye, ear, finger, etc., very often in combination with a ruler, photoelectric cell, and so forth. We will study first statistics and parameters for discrete outcomes (small number of classes) and then those for indiscrete outcomes (large number of classes).

It should be emphasized at this point that the accuracy of the conclusions reached from the use of biometrical procedures depends upon four major factors: (1) imagination and flexibility, (2) proper sampling methods, (3) accurate recording of statistics, and (4) correct choice and use of biometrical procedures. It is unreasonable to expect that good biometrical technique can overcome poor data; the biometrical analysis becomes more efficient the closer one adheres to the first three factors in carrying out experiments.

II. DISCRETE VARIABLES

A. RANGE OF STATISTICS EXPECTED FROM A PARAMETER INVOLVING ONE VARIABLE (FIGURE A-1A)

One often formulates a hypothesis in terms of the probability that an event will occur. It is also often desirable to know the kind of result one would obtain were this hypothesis tested. For example, common sense suggests that "unbiased" pennies

tossed in an unbiased manner have equal likelihood of falling heads up or tails up. Let heads up be considered a *success*. We can state as a *hypothesis* (Ho) that the parameter p, the *probability of success*, is 50%, or 0.5, of all the times the coin falls flat. Note that there are only two alternatives involved—success and failure. Since 50% of the time we would expect failure, the *probability of failure* is $1 - p$. One need only use a single variable, probability of success, to describe all the outcomes possible. (If one were to toss an unbiased die, there would be 6 different and equally possible outcomes, and 5 variables. But if one considered as a success only when the die falls "one" up, then there would be only one variable and we could state as an hypothesis that $p = \frac{1}{6}$.) What kind of statistics would one expect to obtain from actual tosses of an unbiased penny? Clearly the result will depend upon whether 1, 2, or many trials, i.e., tosses, are made.

Expected range of f values

Let us represent the *number of successes* by X, the total *number of trials* or *size of sample* by N, and the *proportion of success* by f.

$$\text{Therefore, } \frac{X}{N} = f,$$

our statistic. Suppose one collected many relatively large samples. What f values would result? It has been shown that this can be determined by using the expression

$$\sqrt{\frac{p(1-p)}{N}},$$

which is called the *standard deviation* of p, or s_p. If the value of N (p) (1 − p) is equal to or greater than 25, it is found that 95% of the f values obtained lie between $p - 1.96\ s_p$ and $p + 1.96\ s_p$.

If one stated that f can have only the values included in this 95% *confidence interval*, he would be right 95% of the time and

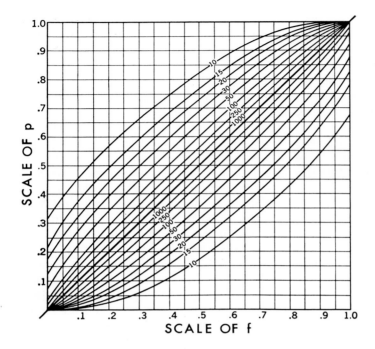

FIGURE A–2. *95% confidence limits (1) for f based on a single-variable parameter, p. To determine confidence intervals, find p on the vertical scale. Move right to the intersections with the two curves indicating the sample size. Finally, read down to determine on the horizontal scale the confidence limits of f. (2) For p based on a single-variable statistic, f. To determine confidence intervals, find f on the horizontal scale. Move upward to the intersections with the two curves indicating the sample size. Finally, read left to determine on the vertical scale the confidence limits of p. (Courtesy of the Biometrika Trustees.)*

wrong 5% of the time. In the penny-tossing example (p = 0.5), if N = 100, s_p is approximately 0.05 and 95% of the time we would expect f to be in the interval 0.4 − 0.6. If many samples of N = 100 are drawn, one can state that 95% of all f's will lie in the interval 0.4 − 0.6. If one draws a single sample of N = 100, it can be stated that f will be in 0.4 − 0.6 and we would have a 95% chance of being right and a 5% chance of being wrong.

Why should one resign himself to the handicap of being wrong 5% (or any per cent) of the time? In order to be right 100% of the time one would have to admit that, 5% of the time, f can lie outside the 95% confidence interval. In the example this would mean that 5% of the time f may lie anywhere between 0 (no successes) and 0.4 and between 0.6 and 1.0 (all successes). To be 100% correct, to have 100% confidence, one would have to predict f to range between 0 and 1. However, electing

to be 100% right also means that all other values of p would also have an expected range of f's from 0 to 1. Accordingly, the 100% range does not provide different expectations of f for different values of p; it provides no power at all to discriminate between different p values. However, by being willing to be wrong 5% of the time, the range of expected f's (when p = 0.5 and N = 100) can be reduced from (0 − 1) to (0.4 − 0.6). And were p = 0.3 and N = 100, f would be roughly between 0.2 and 0.4 95% of the time. Accordingly, accepting a 5% chance of being wrong permits one to have different statistical expectations for different p values. In genetics and biology in general, researchers usually agree to the use of the 95% confidence interval both for statistics and parameters.

Using the expression given on page 521, one can calculate the different values of s_p for numerous combinations of p and N. The 95% range for f can be determined from these calculations. For convenience, the 95% ranges for f for various values of p and N are plotted in Figure A-2. For values of N not shown, one can interpolate between curves. Note that if N were infinitely large, f would equal p and for any given value of p, the range would become wider as N decreased.

B. Range of Parameters Expected from a Statistic Involving One Variable (Figure A-1B)

If one had no notion what the parameter for the chance of a successful toss of a penny should be, one could make an inference about the p value from the statistics obtained. An estimate of the unknown parameter, p, can be obtained from the statistic f. Suppose that 100 tosses of a penny yield 30 successes. The value f = 0.30 is a single statistic. The *single best estimate* of p is f. From the single f value, the best estimate is p = 0.30. However, it should not be surprising if p were really 0.31, 0.29, or some other nearby value. What would also be valuable to know is the range of p values likely when f = 0.3 and N = 100. This range can be determined by calculating

$$\sqrt{\frac{f(1-f)}{N}},$$

which is the *standard deviation* of f, or s_f. The values lying between $f - 1.96\ s_f$ and $f + 1.96\ s_f$ make up the 95% confidence interval of p, because 95% of the time we would expect this particular sample to have a p value in this interval. If we say that p cannot be outside this range, we will be wrong only 5% of the time. In the present case, s_f is about 0.05 and the 95% confidence interval of p is roughly 0.20 to 0.40. If one asserts that p must lie between 0.20 and 0.40 he will be wrong only about 5% of the time. By reading upward and then

to the left, one may use Figure A-2 to determine the 95% confidence intervals of p for different values of f.

PROBLEMS

A. 1. You suspect that the sex ratio of the fruit fly Drosophila is 0.5 ♂♂ and 0.5 ♀♀. Let success be ♂. What range of successes might you expect with 95% confidence from an unbiased count of 100 flies? 250 flies? 1000 flies?

What is happening to your confidence limits as sample size increases? What does this mean?

A. 2. You expect to draw a sample in which N = 100. What is the 95% range for f when the hypothesis is p = 0.5? p = 0.3? p = 0.1? How does the range of f change according to the hypothesized p values?

A. 3. You expect 8 different equally-frequent types of gametes to be produced by a certain trihybrid. Only one of these is of interest to you. If you sample 50 gametes, what range, in numbers of these interesting gametes, are you likely to obtain?

A. 4. Under certain conditions, white-eyed Drosophila males do not mate very readily with red-eyed females. If the chance of mating is 10%, about how many opportunities for mating should you provide to be reasonably sure that 5 matings will occur?

A. 5. A student finds 25 brown-eyed flies among 100. Determine with 95% confidence the true probability of a fly's being brown-eyed.

A. 6. Using Figure A-2, determine the 95% confidence limits of p when f = 0.60, and N = 100, 250, and 1000.

A. 7. After meiosis of the genotype *Aa Bb* in Neurospora you obtain 100 asci. If you assume independent segregation, how many ascospores do you expect to have the following genetic constitution: *AB*? *Ab* plus *aB*?

A. 8. When placed in an iodine solution, one allele causes pollen to stain blue and another allele causes it to stain red. Pollen from the hybrid is obtained and stained.

(a) Sample 1 is 100 grains, of which 30 are blue and 70 red. What do you conclude regarding the expected 1 : 1 ratio?

(b) Sample 2 is 150 grains, of of which 81 are blue and 69 red. What are your conclusions regarding this sample and the 1 : 1 ratio?

(c) Combine the data in samples 1 and 2, and test against a 1 : 1 ratio. What do you conclude? Is this procedure permissible? Is it desirable? Explain.

A. 9. You want to test whether a particular penny is unbiased by tossing it 100 times. How can you tell if the coin is biased?

A.10. In a population of 1000 chickens, only 250 are homozygous for the gene pair (*WW*) producing white feathers. Assuming genetic equilibrium, what do you calculate to be the frequency of *W* in the gene pool? Give (a) your best single estimate, and (b) your estimate with 95% confidence.

✓C. SPECIFIC PROBABILITIES EXPECTED FROM PARAMETERS INVOLVING ONE VARIABLE (FIGURE A-1C)

Without tossing an unbiased penny, one can assign a value p = 0.5. Without recourse to trial, one can propose the hypothesis that p = $\frac{1}{8}$ that a particular side of an unbiased octahedron will fall down. Similarly, the probability that an unbiased die will fall with a given side up is $\frac{1}{6}$. In such cases one has no difficulty in deciding

upon the probability of success. At other times one does not know the probability of success, and this parameter must then be determined.

✓ **1. Rules of Probability**

a. *The addition rule.* Sometimes a success can occur in two or more different ways, each way excluding the others. What is the total probability of success in such cases?

If on a single toss of a die the probability of a "one" is $\frac{1}{6}$ and the probability of a "two" is $\frac{1}{6}$, then the expectation or probability of either a "one" or a "two" is $\frac{1}{6} + \frac{1}{6} = \frac{1}{3}$. In general, the probability that *one* of several mutually exclusive successes will occur is the *sum* of their individual probabilities. If the probability that an event will succeed is p, and the probability that it will fail is q, then the probability of either success or failure is p + q. But if it is certain that the event must either succeed or fail, then p + q = 1, p = 1 − q, and q = 1 − p.

b. *The multiplication rule.* Sometimes over-all success depends upon the occurrence simultaneously or consecutively of two or more successes, and the occurrence (or failure) of one success in no way influences the occurrence (or failure) of the others.

If the probability of "one" in the toss of a die is $\frac{1}{6}$ and if the probability of another "one" in a second toss is also $\frac{1}{6}$, then the probability of "one" on the first and "one" on the second is $\frac{1}{6} \times \frac{1}{6} = \frac{1}{36}$. In general, the probability that *all* of several *independent* successes will occur is the *product* of their separate probabilities.

✓ **2. The Binomial Expression**

Given a parameter involving only one variable, one can determine the exact probabilities of obtaining specific combinations of successes and failures by expanding the binomial expression $(q + p)^N$. If a "one" on a die is a success and the die is tossed 5 times, the probabilities of 0 ones, 1 one, 2 ones, 3 ones, etc., among the 5 tosses are given by successive terms of the expansion of the binomial

$$\left(\frac{5}{6} + \frac{1}{6}\right)^5.$$

In this expression $\frac{5}{6}$ represents the probability of not obtaining a one on a single trial, $\frac{1}{6}$ the probability of obtaining a one, and the exponent 5 the number of trials. The expansion is shown in Table 1, below. Note that each result is possible, each having its own exact probability of occurrence.

PROBLEMS

A.11. If you roll a die three times, what is the probability of obtaining (a) three "fours" in succession? (b) "One," "two," and "three" in that order?

A.12. If you roll two dice at the same time in a single trial, what is the probability of obtaining a total of eleven? Two? Seven?

A.13. What is the chance that a simultaneous toss of a penny, a nickel, a dime, a quarter, and a half-dollar will fall:
    (a) All heads or all tails?
    (b) 3 heads and 2 tails?

A.14. What is the exact probability (using an unbiased penny) of a run of tosses which:
    (a) Starts with 2 heads and ends with 3 tails?
    (b) Has 4 successive heads?
    (c) Has 5 successive tails?

A.15. What is the exact probability of 10 successes, if $p = \frac{1}{3}$ and $N = 15$?

A.16. How often will you expect to obtain less than 3 successes if $p = \frac{1}{4}$ and $N = 5$?

A.17. You have just etherized Drosophila which are the progeny of a cross between $ci^+ ci$ and $ci^+ ci$. What is the probability that there is only 1 $ci\ ci$ fly among the first 3 flies chosen at random? Among the first 5 flies chosen at random?

A.18. Following independent segregation of $Aa\ Bb\ Cc$, an ascus is formed. What is the probability that if two ascospores are chosen at random they will be $A\ B\ C$? $a\ b\ c$? Either $A\ B\ C$ or $a\ b\ c$?

A.19. An albino (aa) man of blood type MN marries a heterozygote for albinism (Aa) also of MN blood type. They plan to have 4 children. If you assume independent segregation, what is the exact probability that they will have:
    (a) No albinos?
    (b) 2 nonalbino children with MN blood type?
    (c) 3 children with M blood type?

TABLE 1

$$\left(\frac{5}{6}\right)^5 + 5\left(\frac{5}{6}\right)^4\left(\frac{1}{6}\right) + 10\left(\frac{5}{6}\right)^3\left(\frac{1}{6}\right)^2 + 10\left(\frac{5}{6}\right)^2\left(\frac{1}{6}\right)^3 + 5\left(\frac{5}{6}\right)\left(\frac{1}{6}\right)^4 + \left(\frac{1}{6}\right)^5$$

Exact p =	0.4019	0.4019	0.1607	0.0321	0.0032	0.0001
Number of "ones" =	0	1	2	3	4	5

√ D. Comparing Observed with Expected Statistics (Figure A-1D)

1. The Binomial Test of a Parameter Involving One Variable

From a certain cross, genetic theory predicts a 1 : 1 ratio (p = 0.50) in F_1. Among 6 individuals one expects, according to the binomial expansion, to observe 3 of one type and 3 of another $\frac{5}{16}$ of the time. This is the outcome most frequently obtained, all others occurring with lower frequency. Suppose, however, that one actually observes that all 6 are of one type. Must one consider this observation of no statistical significance and due only to chance variation? Or, is the difference statistically significant, indicating that expectation and observation do not always agree? This question can be answered by considering the probability of obtaining all 6 alike on the basis of our hypothesis. According to this expectation, the probability that a single individual will be of the first type is $\frac{1}{2}$ and the probability that it will be of the second type is also $\frac{1}{2}$. The probability that all 6 will be of the first type is $(\frac{1}{2})^6$; the probability that all 6 will be of the second type is also $(\frac{1}{2})^6$. And the probability that either all 6 will be of the first type or all of the second is $(\frac{1}{2})^6 + (\frac{1}{2})^6 = 0.03$. But since the probability of this outcome, if the hypothesis holds true, is so low, one must conclude one of two things. Either the hypothesis is correct but a very improbable situation has occurred, or else the hypothesis does not fit the observations. Since an event with a probability of 0.03 is expected to occur only 3 times in a hundred trials, the latter alternative is chosen. It is concluded, therefore, that the hypothesis is probably incorrect.

In general, to test whether an observed result is consistent with a parameter, one tests the *null hypothesis*, that is, the likelihood that the statistic really has the hypothesized parameter. Accordingly, one calculates the total probability with which he would expect to obtain from the parameter a statistic which is as extreme as, or more extreme than, the observed statistic. If this probability is low (by convention, 0.05 or less), it can be concluded that observation and expectation do not agree. One rejects the hypothesis with 95% confidence and at a 5% level of significance (5% chance of rejecting the hypothesis when it is really true). If the probability is greater than 0.05 (5%), one can conclude that the observations provide no evidence against the hypothesis. This is an acceptable hypothesis. If the probability falls well below 0.05 to the 0.01 level or less, the difference is usually considered to be highly significant.

As a further example, consider finding 6 of one type and 2 of another among a group of 8 individuals. Suppose the theoretical ratio is 1 : 1. The probability of obtaining a result this extreme or more extreme according to the null hypothesis is given by computing the sum of the following terms, obtained by expanding $(\frac{1}{2} + \frac{1}{2})^8$.

Probability of 0 of first type		=		$(\frac{1}{2})^8$
"	1	"	=	$8 \times (\frac{1}{2})^8$
"	2	"	=	$28 \times (\frac{1}{2})^8$
"	2 of second type		=	$28 \times (\frac{1}{2})^8$
"	1	"	=	$8 \times (\frac{1}{2})^8$
"	0	"	=	$(\frac{1}{2})^8$

Adding together these separate exact probabilities, one finds that the total probability of 2 or less of same type = 74/256 = 0.29. Since the total probability is greater than 0.05, the statistic is consistent with the hypothesis, which is consequently acceptable.

2. The Confidence Interval Test of a Parameter Involving One Variable

In the examples just discussed the binomial test involved N values less than 10. The binomial test can also be used when N is larger. However, it is less cumbersome to make use of the expected range for f from an expected single-variable parameter as given in Figure A-2.

Suppose f = 0.3 and N = 100. What could one conclude about Ho p = 0.5? If p = 0.5 and N = 100, 95% of f's would lie between 0.4 and 0.6. Since f = 0.3, one may reject Ho p = 0.5. Had f = 0.43 and N = 100, one could accept Ho p = 0.5. Remember that the decisions made from Figure A-2 about a parameter are at the 5% level of significance; and one can only reject or accept parameters, for these represent idealized inferences about statistics. Statistics are observations or facts, and are not subject to rejection.

3. Chi-square Test of a Parameter Involving One Variable

It will be useful to describe another method of testing a single-variable parameter when N is reasonably large, which differs from the expected range test. Suppose one expects a 1:1 ratio and hence, ideally, 50 cases of one type and 50 cases of another out of a sample of 100. But suppose one observes 55 of one type and 45 of the other. In order to judge whether the observations agree with expectation, one must find the probability of obtaining, on a null hypothesis, a result this extreme or more extreme in samples of 100 taken from an ideal population. Although the probability could be determined by summing the appropriate terms of $(\frac{1}{2} + \frac{1}{2})^{100}$, the time required is prohibitive (unless, of course, one has access to a computer). It has been found that an approximate value of the desired probability may be obtained

from a quantity called *chi-square* (χ^2), a comparatively easy computation:

$$\chi^2_{(1)} = \Sigma \frac{[(\text{observed} - \text{expected}) - \frac{1}{2}]^2}{\text{expected}}$$

The term $\frac{1}{2}$ is called Yates' correction. It may be omitted when N and the expected values are large, but it is safer to include it in a routine calculation. The formula requires that for each class (here there are only two, success and failure, and hence the χ^2 is considered to have one degree of freedom—$\chi^2_{(1)}$) one find the absolute difference between the observed and expected numbers, subtract $\frac{1}{2}$ from this remainder (making it closer to 0 by $\frac{1}{2}$), and square the result. This value is divided by the expected number. We do this for each class and sum the terms for all classes. Thus, in our case:

$$\chi^2_{(1)} = \frac{[(45 - 50) - \frac{1}{2}]^2}{50} + \frac{[(55 - 50) - \frac{1}{2}]^2}{50}$$

$$= \frac{(4\frac{1}{2})^2}{50} + \frac{(4\frac{1}{2})^2}{50} = \frac{40.5}{50} = 0.8 .$$

The probability is obtained from a chart of χ^2 (Figure A-3) under one degree of freedom. (The number of degrees of freedom for such a test is one less than the number of classes; that is, it equals the number of variables). Thus, from Figure A-3 one finds that the probability lies between 0.35 and 0.40. The difference between what is observed and what is expected according to the null hypothesis is nonsignificant. Therefore, one may accept the hypothesis.

The chi-square method is an approximation and is valid for relatively large samples only. Its use requires that no class have an expected value of less than 2 and that most of the expected values be at least 5.

4. Chi-square Test of a Parameter Involving Two or More Variables

The χ^2 test is applicable to parameters involving more than 2 alternative outcomes, hence involving two or more variables.

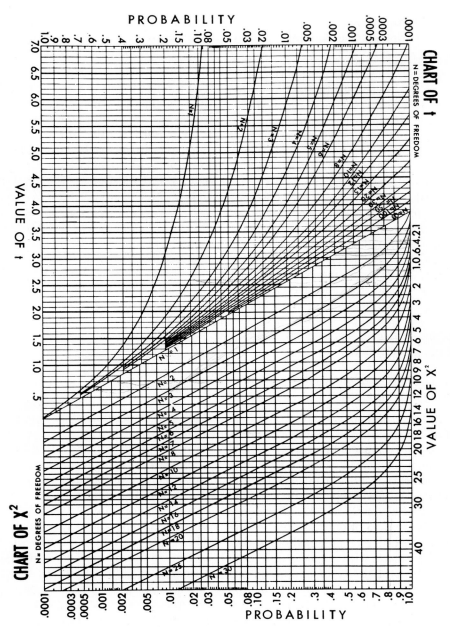

FIGURE A–3. *The χ^2 and t distributions. To read the chart with a χ^2 value of 17 based on 7 degrees of freedom, the vertical line corresponding to a χ^2 value of 17 is followed upward until it intersects the curve corresponding to N = 7. Directly to the left of this point the probability, .017, is read off. With the chart inverted, probabilities for the t distribution are read in exactly the same way. The probability given is the probability of a numerically greater deviation. (Courtesy of J. F. Crow; from Genetics Notes, Burgess Publ. Co.)*

The chi-square test can be used to determine whether a sample is consistent with an hypothesized $9:3:3:1$ ratio, for example. If a $9:3:3:1$ ratio were being tested, the ideally expected numbers in a group of 80 individuals would be 45, 15, 15, and 5, respectively. Since there are four classes, there are three variables or degrees of freedom. If we observed 40, 20, 12, and 8, respectively, we would calculate

$$\chi^2_{(3)} = \frac{(40 - 45)^2}{45} + \frac{(20 - 15)^2}{15}$$
$$+ \frac{(12 - 15)^2}{15} + \frac{(8 - 5)^2}{5} = 4.6 .$$

(The term $\frac{1}{2}$, the Yates' correction, is not applicable if there is more than one degree of freedom.) Since the probability lies between 0.20 and 0.25, the difference is nonsignificant, and one accepts the null hypothesis.

It is interesting to note that the probability of obtaining a χ^2 value equal to or greater than 0.004 for one degree of freedom, 0.1 for two degrees of freedom, etc. is 0.95. It follows the probability of obtaining χ^2 values smaller than these must be 0.05. Such low values in an actual test indicate that the agreement between observation and expectation is suggestively better than expected. The question of whether the data represent authentic random samples may be legitimately raised in such cases.

PROBLEMS

A.20. A person with woolly hair marries a nonwoolly-haired individual; they have 8 children, 7 woolly-haired and 1 nonwoolly-haired. Test the hypothesis that woolly hair is due to a rare, completely dominant gene.

A.21. Given the data in A.20, test the hypothesis that woolly hair is due to a completely recessive mutant.

A.22. A penny is tossed seven times. One time it falls on edge, five times it falls heads, and once it falls tails. Is this an "honest" coin?

A.23. A test cross produces 57 individuals of A phenotype and 43 of A' phenotype. Is one pair of genes involved?

A.24. Given the data in A.23, test the hypothesis that one parent is a dihybrid and that the A phenotype is obtained only when two particular nonalleles are present.

A.25. In a sample of 540, X = 90. What is the value of chi-square if you hypothesize that $p = \frac{1}{4}$? Do you accept this hypothesis?

A.26. Among 60 individuals the phenotypes are 8 A, 12 B, 20 C, and 20 D. Test the hypothesis that:
    (a) A B C D are in the relative proportion $1:3:3:9$.
    (b) All four phenotypes have an equal chance of occurring.
    (c) The ideal ratio is $1A:3B:5C:7D$.

A.27. A random sample from a natural population contains 65 *AA*, 95 *Aa*, and 40 *aa* individuals. Test the hypothesis (after consulting Chapter 15) that:
    (a) The frequency of *a* in the population gene pool is 0.5.
    (b) This sample is consistent with the population being in genetic equilibrium for this locus, if you assume that the observed gene frequency for *a* is also the population frequency.

E. COMPARISONS BETWEEN STATISTICS (FIGURE A-1E)

1. Involving One Variable

a. *Observed difference vs. expected standard deviation.* Suppose that a sample (A) provided 20 males and 30 females, whereas a different sample (B) gave 30 males and 20 females. Is there a significant difference in the frequency of males in the two samples? ($f_A = 0.40$ and $f_B = 0.60$; $N_A = 50$, $N_B = 50$.) We have no expectation as to what p_A or p_B should be. According to the null hypothesis these two samples have the same parameter, p_X. Our best estimate of p_X is f_X, obtained by pooling the results of both samples and obtaining $50/100 = 0.50$. We next calculate how large the difference between the observed f's is, relative to the total standard deviation that one would expect if f_X were obtained in each of the two samples, N_A and N_B. This calculation can be made from the expression:

$$\frac{f_B - f_A}{\sqrt{\dfrac{f_X(1 - f_X)}{N_A} + \dfrac{f_X(1 - f_X)}{N_B}}}$$
$$= \frac{0.20}{\sqrt{\dfrac{0.5 \times 0.5}{50} + \dfrac{0.5 \times 0.5}{50}}} = 2.0 .$$

(The subtraction in the numerator should be made to give a $+$ result, i.e., one should obtain the absolute value of the remainder.) It has been shown that if N_X is greater than 30, values of 2.0 or more will occur by chance only 5% of the time. We conclude, therefore, that the two samples under test are on the borderline of being statistically different at the 5% level of significance.

b. *The plus-minus test.* Suppose a particular treatment is to be tested for its capacity to change a statistic. Suppose, moreover, that one does not care just how much change is being induced as compared with how much is occurring spontaneously. (The treatment might produce only a very small change; under these circumstances, two tremendously large samples, one control and the other treated, would be necessary to obtain a statistically significant difference between their measurements.)

What can be done is to arrange a series of paired observations in which the members of a pair are as similar as possible in order to make the measurement of difference as sensitive as possible.

Imagine, for example, that one wishes to determine whether feeding a salt to the developing Drosophila male has any effect upon the sex ratio of his progeny. Each test consists of scoring the sex of the progeny of two single pair matings, in which one male has and the other has not been treated. Assume that the experiment is performed in an unbiased manner and that the results are as follows:

Paired Obser-vation	Sex Ratio ($\male\male/\female\female$)		$\pm$ Test	
	Un-treated	Treated	Un-treated	Treated
1	0.47	0.46	+	−
2	0.48	0.47	+	−
3	0.49	0.48	+	−
4	0.50	0.50	No Test	
5	0.46	0.44	+	−
6	0.51	0.50	+	−
7	0.48	0.47	+	−

One proceeds to test the null hypothesis that the treatment has no effect upon the F_1 sex ratio. In accordance with this view, there would be an equal chance for the untreated and treated members of a pair of observations to have the higher sex ratio (that is, to be scored $+$); consequently the Ho is $p = \frac{1}{2}$. There are only 6 tests of the Ho, since one test gave the same sex ratio for both untreated and treated. The probability that the relevant 6 untreated shall be all successes or all failures is, according to the null hypothesis, $2(\frac{1}{2})^6$, or $\frac{1}{32}$, or about 3%. (The chance that the remaining 5 tests will be like the first is $(\frac{1}{2})^5$, or also about 3%.) Accordingly, one rejects the null hypothesis at the 5% level of significance. The statistical test indicates that the untreated and treated do not have the same parameter. Upon examining the data, one will conclude that the sex ratio is lower following salt treatment than when such a treatment is omitted. (One cannot determine from these data whether salt raises the number of females or lowers the number of males. One finds only a difference in sex ratio as a function of the presence or absence of salt, the actual mechanism of the effect remaining unknown.)

c. *Contingency table approach to the chi-square test.* Assume that $X_A = 3$ and $N_A = 6$ in sample A, and $X_B = 5$ and $N_B = 18$ in sample B. Are these statistics different at the 5% level of significance? To determine this, one tests the null hypothesis that both samples have the same parameter (p). However, the value of p is completely unknown. If a *contingency table* is constructed, it will give the most likely values of X (and hence $N - X$), a common p for both samples being understood. Having determined these ideally-expected values, one can then proceed as before to calculate chi-square.

The observed data are arranged as shown in Figure A-4A. The best estimates for the values expected according to the unknown p are shown in B. To obtain the value expected in the shaded box in A, for example, multiply together the totals at the end of its column and row and divide by the number $N_A + N_B$. This value ($6 \times 8/24$) is 2.

Since we are dealing with χ^2, recall that it is usually safe to require that no class have an expected frequency less than 2 and that most expected values be at least 5. Note that the other expected values in B can be obtained in a similar manner; this procedure, however, is unnecessary since all the other values are fixed by the mar-

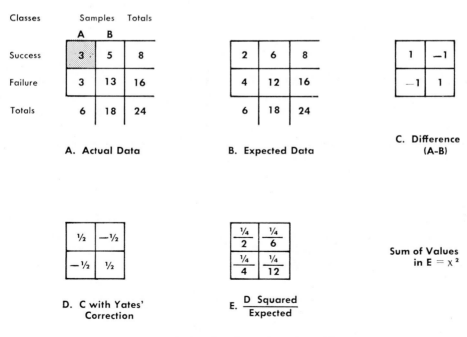

A. Actual Data   B. Expected Data   C. Difference (A-B)

D. C with Yates' Correction   E. $\dfrac{\text{D Squared}}{\text{Expected}}$ Sum of Values in E $= \chi^2$

FIGURE A–4. *2 × 2 contingency table.*

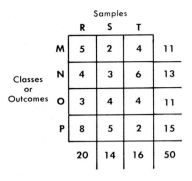

A. Actual Data

B. Expected Data

C. Difference (A-B)

D. $\dfrac{C \text{ Squared}}{\text{Expected}}$

FIGURE A–5. *3 × 4 contingency table.*

ginal totals, which must be the same in B as in A. Accordingly, there is only one degree of freedom (one variable) in the 2×2 contingency table formed. Difference table C is then constructed, the values of which are identical in crisscross position and always total zero. Each of the values in C is made less extreme (closer to zero) by $\frac{1}{2}$, to comply with Yates' correction. This is shown in D. Each of the corrected differences in D is squared and divided by the corresponding expected value shown in B. The sum of the four values obtained $(\frac{1}{4}/2 + \frac{1}{4}/6 + \frac{1}{4}/4 + \frac{1}{4}/12)$ is chi-square. In the present case chi-square is less than 1 (but more than 0.004) and has a probability greater than 10%. The null hy-

pothesis is thus accepted, namely, that the two samples are not statistically different at the 5% level of significance.

2. Involving Two or More Variables

Contingency table approach to the chi-square test. Sometimes the data in a sample fall into more than two classes or outcomes, and more than two such samples are to be compared. This involves "number of classes − 1" variables as well as "number of samples − 1" variables. The total number of variables equals the product of these two sources of variability. The number of degrees of freedom is equal to the total number of variables, which is always (number of rows − 1) times (number of columns − 1) in a contingency table.

Suppose three samples were scored four alternative ways to give the results shown in Figure A-5A. The procedure followed is the same as that already described for the 2 × 2 or four-fold table (note that Yates' correction is not applicable in any larger table). There are 6 degrees of freedom. If one tests at the 5% level, Figure A-3 shows that $\chi^2_{(6)}$ has to be greater than 12.5 if one is to reject the null hypothesis, namely, that all the samples and types can be represented by the same parameters. Moreover, finding that χ^2 is less than 1.6 would mean that the same parameters would produce samples varying this little from the ideally expected values only 5% of the time. In that case one would reject the samples as being random, suspecting that there was some hidden bias in the collection and/or the scoring of the data. The decision that neither obtains can be seen from Figure A-5D. Consequently, one accepts the null hypothesis that these samples are not statistically different at the 5% level of significance.

Assume, however, that chi-square had been 14.1 in the preceding example. One would reject the null hypothesis at the 5% level but could accept it at the 1% level of significance (meaning that these samples have more than 1%, but less than 5%, chance of having the same parameters). Assuming that such a result was obtained in an unbiased manner it might be due to the fact that (a) the null hypothesis is true but one happened to collect data (as will happen by chance one time in 20) which varied at least this much from those expected, or (b) the null hypothesis is incorrect. Even if the hypothesis at the 5% level is rejected, one may wish to test the data further, using smaller contingency tables to determine which samples or outcomes are consistent or inconsistent with each other according to a null hypothesis. Note here that the observed values in a contingency table furnishing the largest contributions to chi-square are those most responsible for the rejection of the hypothesis.

PROBLEMS

A.28. A cross yields 20 offspring of one type and 40 of another. A month later the same cross produces 15 of the first type and 15 of the second. Do these results differ significantly?

A.29. Ten sets of identical twins are selected; only one member (the same one) of each pair is given a particular drug daily for 10 days. All individuals are weighed before and after this period. The changes to the nearest whole pound are as follows:

	Twin	
Pair	*Untreated*	*Treated*
1	+1	+1
2	+2	+1
3	−4	−3
4	+1	+2
5	−3	−2
6	+3	+2
7	−2	+1
8	+4	+3
9	−1	0
10	+5	−4

Analyze the results of this experiment statistically.

A.30. Among the women of population A are 10 blondes, 5 redheads, and 15 of other hair color. In population B there are 7, 7, and 6, respectively; whereas in population C the tally is 8, 4, 8, respectively. Are these populations the same with respect to the relative frequency of these hair color types?

A.31. An experiment is performed four times. X is 5, 7, 10, and 11 when N is 8, 20, 20, 30, respectively. Are all four results mutually consistent?

A.32. Suppose the label on two packages of grass seed states that each package will germinate 40% grass type A, 35% grass type B, 15% grass type C, and 10% weeds D. A sample from package 1 germinates 400A, 400B, 50C, and 150D. A sample from package 2 yields 390A, 410B, 70C, and 130D. Compare the contents of each package with the labelled contents and with each other. What do you conclude?

A.33. A drug manufacturer receives results of using or not using his product. As a check on bias in testing he scores the control and experimental group for eye color and ABO blood type and finds the results tabulated below.

	AB		A	
	Blue	Brown	Blue	Brown
Control	7	6	12	10
Experimental	4	8	13	8

	B		O	
	Blue	Brown	Blue	Brown
Control	4	4	8	9
Experimental	5	2	8	12

What should he conclude about bias?

A.34. Suppose women were classified in two ways: hair color and temperament. Using the results listed below, test the hypothesis that there is no relation between hair color and temperament.

	Blonde	Red	Brown
Pugnacious	23	6	11
Quiet	26	3	31
Normal	41	9	30

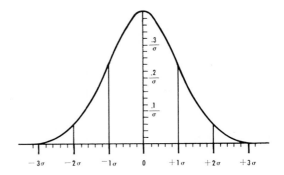

FIGURE A–6. *The normal curve.*

III. INDISCRETE VARIABLES

A. PARAMETERS AND THE NORMAL CURVE

Suppose a particular measurement is the result of the action of a very large number of independent variables, each of which has approximately the same magnitude of effect on the measurement. If, then, an infinitely large number of such measurements are collected, they will be expected to have a range of values which are said to be normally distributed. Figure A-6 shows the *normal distribution* or *curve* formed by plotting these measurements against the frequency with which they would be expected to occur in this infinitely large population. The *population mean*, or *"true" mean*, is denoted by the parameter μ. The *population standard deviation*, or *"true" standard deviation*, is represented by the lower case Greek letter sigma, σ. It is known that about $\frac{2}{3}$ of all the measurements in a normal curve lie within one σ of the mean, and about 95% of all measurements lie within 2σ of the mean (being in the range $\mu \pm 2\sigma$). Strictly speaking, the individual "measurements" or values which comprise the normal curve are also parameters.

The normal curve vs. the binomial distribution. Suppose N = 20 and p = $\frac{1}{2}$. If an infinitely large number of samples each of N = 20 were obtained, the exact probabilities of obtaining different numbers of successes would be expressed in the binomial distribution plotted in histogram form in Figure A-7, where each class of success is represented by a column whose height is proportional to the frequency of the class. Note that there are only 21 ways to score the outcome of a set of 20 of these observations (from 0 to 20 successes), so we are dealing with 20 discrete variables. The smooth curve shown is the normal curve, which has the same mean and standard deviation as the histogram. The larger the sample size, if p = ½, the larger will be the number of outcomes possible per sample, and the closer the plot of the probability of successes will approach the normal curve. Therefore, as N increases without bound, the number of possible outcomes increases to provide us with an example of a continuous variable, whose values are said to be distributed normally.

B. Statistics Expected from a Normal Curve

1. Distribution of Individual Statistics

If one obtains a very large number of statistics having a normal curve as a parameter, they will be distributed in a curve resembling the normal curve. The probability that any given statistic, X, is derived from the hypothetical population with mean μ and standard deviation σ_x, can be determined from the value τ calculated from the following:

$$\tau = \frac{X - \mu}{\sigma_x}.$$

When the absolute value of τ is 1.96, this probability for X is 0.05. Since exactly 5% of the X values in a distribution characterized by the hypothesized μ and

σ_x give absolute τ values of 1.96 or greater we reject the null hypothesis when X gives a τ value that equals or exceeds 1.96.

This equation can be rearranged X = $\mu + \tau\sigma_x$. This expression means that any given statistic is equal to the population mean plus a distance off this mean as measured by $\tau\sigma_x$, where τ is the number of σ_x's that X is away from the population mean. ($[\sigma_x]^2$ is called the *population variance*.)

Suppose one is concerned with height of corn measured to the nearest inch; hypothesize that $\mu = 50$ inches and $\sigma_x = 4$ inches. This information is completely sufficient to describe the properties of a normally distributed population. One plant is 40 inches tall, its height being considered a quantitative trait. Calculation of the value for τ yields

$$\frac{40 - 50}{4} = \frac{10}{4},$$

which is > 1.96. Since p < 0.05 one rejects the null hypothesis and may conclude that the plant measured cannot, at the 5% level of significance, come from a theoretical population where $\mu = 50$ and $\sigma_x = 4$.

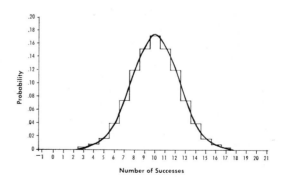

FIGURE A-7. *Histogram of probabilities for different numbers of successes for a binomial distribution (N = 20, p = ½), and a normal curve with the same μ and σ as the histogram.*

2. Distribution of the Means Expected for Groups of Statistics

The *arithmetic sample mean* or *average* of a group of statistics comprising a sample is denoted by $\overline{X}$ (read "X bar") and is the average obtained by adding all the values of X and dividing by N. In more symbolic terms,

$$\overline{X} = \frac{1}{N} \Sigma X .$$

Given a population described by mean μ and standard deviation σ_x, one can predict something about the range of $\overline{X}$'s to be expected from drawing a great many samples of size N from this population. If many samples are drawn, it will be found that the $\overline{X}$ values fall into a distribution which has a theoretical mean equal to μ and which will be normally distributed with a standard deviation $\sigma_{\overline{x}}$. This

$$\sigma_{\overline{x}} = \sqrt{\frac{\sigma_x^2}{N}} = \frac{\sigma_x}{\sqrt{N}} .$$

Since $\sigma_{\overline{x}}$ is smaller than σ_x by a factor of $\sqrt{N}$, it permits greater discrimination in regard to error than does σ_x. When $N \geqq 10$, $\overline{X}$ will be quite nearly normally distributed, if the distribution of X values does not differ too widely from that expected of measurements drawn from a normal curve. Accordingly, the distribution of $\overline{X}$, as measured by $\sigma_{\overline{x}}$, is usually also known by means of calculation whenever μ and σ_x are known.

In scientific papers the *standard error*, $s_{\overline{x}}$ or $\sigma_{\overline{x}}$, is often given in the form $\overline{X} \pm s_{\overline{x}}$ or $\overline{X} \pm \sigma_{\overline{x}}$, and refers to the reliability of the mean of a sample. On the other hand, s_x or σ_x are standard deviations; and when given as $X \pm s_x$ or $X \pm \sigma_x$, they refer to the variability of a single observation X.

3. TESTING HYPOTHESES REGARDING μ

a. *The τ test.* Suppose one finds for N = 100 that $\overline{X} = 68.03$. One may wish next to test the null hypothesis, at the 5% level of significance, that $\sigma_x = 3$ and m = 67.15. In the present case

$$\sigma_{\overline{x}} = \sqrt{\frac{9}{100}} = 0.3; \quad \tau = \frac{\overline{X} - \mu}{\sigma_{\overline{x}}}$$

$$= \frac{68.03 - 67.15}{0.3} = \frac{0.88}{0.3} ,$$

which is > 1.96. Consequently, one rejects the hypothesis.

b. *The t test.* Frequently one may have to test some hypothetical μ when σ_x and $\sigma_{\overline{x}}$ are unknown. In this situation, one utilizes the best available estimate of σ_x; this useful approximation is the *standard deviation of the sample*, s_x. The value for s_x can be determined from the following:

$$s_x = \sqrt{\frac{\Sigma(X - \overline{X})^2}{N - 1}} . \quad \text{Note that } s_{\overline{x}} = \sqrt{\frac{s_x^2}{N}} .$$

With $s_{\overline{x}}$ substituted for $\sigma_{\overline{x}}$, the expression

$$\frac{\overline{X} - \mu}{\sigma_{\overline{x}}} \quad \text{becomes} \quad \frac{\overline{X} - \mu}{\sqrt{\frac{s_x^2}{N}}} = t.$$

(When $\sigma_{\overline{x}}$ is used, the final value is τ; when $s_{\overline{x}}$ is substituted, the final value is called t by convention.) If the value of t is too large, the hypothesis regarding μ will be rejected. The decision to accept or reject the null hypothesis depends upon the number of degrees of freedom, which equals $N - 1$ if one is estimating σ_x from a single sample. Figure A-3 gives the probabilities for various degrees of freedom that t differs from zero in either direction by a value equal to or greater than that observed. If $\overline{X} = 68.03$, the hypothesized $\mu = 67.15$, $s_x = 3.24$, and $N = 9$, then t = 0.81. With 8 degrees of freedom, p > 0.05. The hypothesized μ is accepted.

c. *Confidence intervals for μ.* Suppose one chooses to work at the 5% level of significance. If σ_x is known, the 95% confidence interval for $\mu = X \pm 1.96 \, \sigma_x$, or $\mu = \overline{X} \pm 1.96 \, \sigma_{\overline{x}}$. If only s_x is known, then the 95% confidence interval for μ can be determined as follows. Given, as before, that $\overline{X} = 68.03$, $s_x = 3.24$, and $N = 9$; first find the value of t which has $p = 0.05$ for $N-1$ degrees of freedom. (For $N-1 = 8$, this is about 2.3.) Hence,

$$\frac{\overline{X} - \mu}{\sqrt{\dfrac{s_x{}^2}{N}}} = 2.3 \ .$$

One rejects all values where $\overline{X}$ differs from μ by more than 2.3 $s_{\overline{x}}$, and accepts all values of $\overline{X} - \mu$ with 95% confidence that are less than 2.3 $s_{\overline{x}}$. Substituting, one finds

$$\frac{\overline{X} - \mu}{1.08} = 2.3$$

or, $\overline{X} - \mu = 2.3\ (1.08) = 2.48$. Finally, the 95% confidence level for μ, in the present case, is $\overline{X} \pm 2.48$, or 65.55 to 70.51.

d. *Comparison of $\overline{X}_1$ and $\overline{X}_2$.* Suppose one selects two sample sets of corn plants, and then measures the height of each plant. The statistics obtained are:

Sample 1: $\quad N_1 = 9 \qquad \overline{X}_1 = 72.44$
$\qquad\qquad \Sigma(X_1 - \overline{X}_1)^2 = 65.70$

Sample 2: $\quad N_2 = 10 \qquad \overline{X}_2 = 70.30$
$\qquad\qquad \Sigma(X_2 - \overline{X}_2)^2 = 69.50$

To be tested is the null hypothesis that these two samples have the same μ and the same σ_x. The best estimate of the unknown σ_x is s_x, obtained from the two samples by the following formula:

$$s_x = \sqrt{\frac{\Sigma(X_1 - \overline{X}_1)^2 + \Sigma(X_2 - \overline{X}_2)^2}{(N_1 - 1) + (N_2 - 1)}}$$

$$= \sqrt{\frac{65.70 + 69.50}{8 + 9}} = 2.82 \ .$$

One derives a value of $s_{\overline{x}}$ in the present case equal to 1.29, since it is known that

$$s_{\overline{x}} = s_x \sqrt{\frac{1}{N_1} + \frac{1}{N_2}} \ .$$

The value of t is then found from

$$\frac{\overline{X}_1 - \overline{X}_2}{s_{\overline{x}}} \quad \text{to be} \quad \frac{72.44 - 70.30}{1.29} = 1.66.$$

Since each $\overline{X}$ was obtained from a single sample, the number of degrees of freedom is $(N_1 - 1) + (N_2 - 1)$, or 17. Because $p > 0.1$ one accepts the null hypothesis and may conclude that the two means are not statistically different at the 5% level of significance. If one obtains a value of t inconsistent with the hypothesis, the two samples differ either in their μ's, σ_x's, or both.

IV. THE POWER OF THE TEST

There are two types of error involved in testing a parameter or statistic. One has already been discussed. This type of error is the rejection of the correct hypothesis 5% of the time (when working at the 95% confidence level, or the 5% level of significance) in order to reject incorrect hypotheses. The other type of error is the incorrect acceptance of an hypothesis. Suppose $f = 0.45$ and $N = 100$. The hypothesis that $p = \frac{1}{2}$ is tested and found acceptable at the 5% level. But the real p might lie anywhere between 0.35 and 0.55 (see Figure A-2). If p is not 0.5 but somewhere between 0.35 and 0.55, one may have accepted the wrong hypothesis.

In the present case, the test is only powerful enough to reject incorrect hypotheses where $p < 0.35$ or > 0.55. Had N been 1000 and $f = 0.45$, the discriminatory power of the test would be greater, at the 5% level, causing the rejection of any hypothesis where $p < 0.42$ or > 0.47. Before collecting statistics, it is necessary to determine whether there is adequate power to discriminate against alternative hypotheses.

Suppose, for genetic reasons, one wishes to test whether some statistics obtained by experiment exhibit an expected $3:1$ ratio. One may accept the hypothesis; but if a theoretical $1:1$ or $2:1$ ratio is also accepted, the test is rendered rather weak and is not likely to be useful in describing the nature of the genetic events involved.

One way to increase the meaningfulness of the test is to increase N. Another way is to change the level of confidence. At the 10% level of significance the "power" of the test is greater than at the 5% level; but there is a proportional increase in the chance of rejecting the correct hypothesis. Unless there is some special circumstance, geneticists usually work at the 5% level and increase the power of the test by increasing N. Recall, however, that the size of s or σ decreases as the square root of N increases, so that a fourfold increase in N only reduces the standard deviation by a factor of 2.

PROBLEMS

A.35. Given $\sigma_x = 8$, $N = 265$, $\overline{X} = 12$; test at the 5% level of significance the hypothesis that $\mu = 11$.

A.36. Given $\sigma_x{}^2 = 412$, $N = 53$, $\overline{X} = 142$; test at the 5% level of significance the hypothesis that $\mu = 135$.

A.37. What are the 95% confidence limits for μ when $\sigma_x = 4$, $N = 100$, and $\overline{X} = 35$?

A.38. Given the following statistics: 1, 3, 4, 5, 5, 5, 5, 5, 6, 8; calculate $\overline{X}$, s_x, and $s_{\overline{x}}$.

A.39. A new antibiotic was tested on pneumonia patients with the following results: of those treated, 64 lived and 26 died (28.9% died); of those untreated, 36 lived and 24 died (40% died). Test the hypothesis that the treatment is not effective.

A.40. A random sample of six observations drawn from a certain normal population is as follows: 0, 2, 6, 6, 8, 14. Test the hypothesis that μ, the population mean, equals 10. Use the 5% level of significance.

A.41. Normal barley seeds are treated with X-rays and planted. Of 400 seedlings examined, 55 show sectors with visible mutation. Test the hypothesis that the true mutation frequency at this dosage is 10%.

A.42. Denote the length of an ear of corn by x inches. Explain exactly what is meant when someone says "the probability of x being less than 7 is 0.05."

A.43. A random sample of 25 mice is taken from a certain mutant strain. It is hypothesized that the length of these mice is approximately normally distributed. You find $\overline{X}$ equals 60 mm. and s_x is 10mm. (a) Test the hypothesis that μ equals 61 mm. at the 5% level of significance. (b) Explain what is meant by "5% level of significance" in this experiment.

A.44. Using the data of problem A.43, find confidence limits for $\mu = 61$ mm. with 95% confidence. Explain the practical meaning of your result.

A.45. Given the following data:

Sample 1	Sample 2
N = 10	N = 10
+3.4	+5.5
+0.7	+1.9
−1.6	+1.8
−0.2	+1.1
−1.2	+0.1
−0.1	−0.1
+3.7	+4.4
+0.8	+1.6
0.0	+4.6
+2.0	+3.4

Determine whether these two samples are statistically different.

A.46. Under what circumstances can one use the t table for values of τ?

REFERENCES

Bailey, N. T. J., *Statistical Methods in Biology*, New York: J. Wiley & Sons, 1959.

Falconer, D. S., *Introduction to Quantitative Genetics*, New York: Ronald Press, 1961.

Kempthorne, O., *An Introduction to Genetic Statistics*, New York: J. Wiley & Sons, 1957.

Levene, H., "Statistical Inferences in Genetics," in *Principles of Genetics*, 5th Ed., Sinnott, E. W., Dunn, L. C., and Dobzhansky, Th., New York: McGraw-Hill, 1958, Chap. 29, pp. 388–418.

Mather, W. B., *Principles of Quantitative Genetics*, Minneapolis: Burgess Publishing Co., 1964.

SUPPLEMENTS

I   Part of a Letter (1867) from Gregor Mendel to C. Nägeli *s-9*

II   Nobel Prize Lecture (1934) of Thomas Hunt Morgan *s-15*

III   Nobel Prize Lecture (1946) of Hermann Joseph Muller *s-19*

IV   Nobel Prize Lecture (1962) of Maurice H. F. Wilkins *s-31*

V   Nobel Prize Lecture (1959) of Arthur Kornberg *s-60*

VI   Nobel Prize Lecture (1958) of George Wells Beadle *s-75*

VII   Nobel Prize Lecture (1958) of Edward Lawrie Tatum *s-88*

VIII   Nobel Prize Lecture (1958) of Joshua Lederberg *s-98*

IX   Nobel Prize Lecture (1962) of James Dewey Watson *s-111*

X   Nobel Prize Lecture (1962) of Francis H. C. Crick *s-135*

SUPPLEMENT I

Part of a Letter (1867)
from Gregor Mendel to C. Nägeli

Translated from German by Leonie Kellen Piternick and George Piternick. Reprinted from *The Birth of Genetics*, Supplement to *Genetics*, Vol. 35, No. 5, Part 2 (1950), by permission of Genetics.

GREGOR MENDEL (1822-1884)

SUPPLEMENT II

Nobel Prize Lecture (1934)
of Thomas Hunt Morgan

Reprinted by permission of The Nobel Foundation for *Les Prix Nobel*. The complete lecture is published in *The Scientific Monthly* for July 1935. Only the first portion is reprinted here.

THOMAS HUNT MORGAN (1866-1945)

By permission of The American Genetic Association, *The Journal of Heredity*, frontispiece, Vol. 24, No. 416, 1933.

SUPPLEMENT III

Nobel Prize Lecture (1946)
of Hermann Joseph Muller

Reprinted by permission of The Nobel Foundation for *Les Prix Nobel*. Published in *The Journal of Heredity*, 38:259-270, 1947.

HERMANN JOSEPH MULLER (1890-   )

SUPPLEMENT IV

Nobel Prize Lecture (1962)
of Maurice H. F. Wilkins

Reprinted by permission of The Nobel Foundation for *Les Prix Nobel* and Elsevier Publishing Company. Published in *Science*, 140: 941-950, 1963.

MAURICE H. F. WILKINS (1916-   )

SUPPLEMENT V

Nobel Prize Lecture (1959)
of Arthur Kornberg

Reprinted by permission of The Nobel Foundation
for *Les Prix Nobel*. Published in *Science*, 131:1503-
1508, 1960.

ARTHUR KORNBERG (1918-   )

SUPPLEMENT VI

Nobel Prize Lecture (1958)
of George Wells Beadle

Reprinted by permission of The Nobel Foundation
for *Les Prix Nobel*. Published in *Science*, 129:1715-
1719, 1959.

GEORGE WELLS BEADLE (1903-   )

SUPPLEMENT VII

Nobel Prize Lecture (1958)
of Edward Lawrie Tatum

Reprinted by permission of The Nobel Foundation for *Les Prix Nobel*. Published in *Science*, 129: 1711-1715, 1959.

EDWARD LAWRIE TATUM (1909-   )

SUPPLEMENT VIII

Nobel Prize Lecture (1958)
of Joshua Lederberg

Reprinted by permission of The Nobel Foundation for *Les Prix Nobel*. Published in *Stanford Med. Bull.*, 17:120-132, 1959; and in *Science*, 131:269-276, 1960.

JOSHUA LEDERBERG (1925-   )

SUPPLEMENT IX

Nobel Prize Lecture (1962)
of James Dewey Watson

Reprinted by permission of The Nobel Foundation
for *Les Prix Nobel* and Elsevier Publishing Company. Published in *Science*, 140: 17-26, 1963.

JAMES DEWEY WATSON (1928-   )

SUPPLEMENT X

Nobel Prize Lecture (1962)
of Francis H. C. Crick

Reprinted by permission of The Nobel Foundation
for *Les Prix Nobel* and Elsevier Publishing Company. Published in *Science*, 139: 461-464, 1963.

SUPPLEMENT I

PART OF A LETTER

(1867)

from

GREGOR MENDEL

to

C. NÄGELI

HIGHLY ESTEEMED SIR:

My most cordial thanks for the printed matter you have so kindly sent me! The papers "die Bastardbildung im Pflanzenreiche," "über die abgeleiteten Pflanzenbastarde," "die Theorie der Bastardbildung," "die Zwischenformen zwischen den Pflanzenarten," "die systematische Behandlung der Hieracien rücksichtlich der Mittelformen und des Umfangs der Species," especially capture my attention. This thorough revision of the theory of hybrids according to contemporary science was most welcome. Thank you again!

With respect to the essay which your honor had the kindness to accept, I think I should add the following information: the experiments which are discussed were conducted from 1856 to 1863. I knew that the results I obtained were not easily compatible with our contemporary scientific knowledge, and that under the circumstances publication of one such isolated experiment was doubly dangerous; dangerous for the experimenter and for the cause he represented. Thus I made every effort to verify, with other plants, the results obtained with Pisum. A number of hybridizations undertaken in 1863 and 1864 convinced me of the difficulty of finding plants suitable for an extended series of experiments, and that under unfavorable circumstances years might elapse without my obtaining the desired information. I attempted to inspire some control experiments, and for that reason discussed the Pisum experiments at the meeting of the local society of naturalists. I encountered, as was to be expected, divided opinion; however, as far as I know, no one undertook to repeat the experiments. When, last year, I was asked to publish my lecture in the proceedings of the society, I agreed to do so, after having re-examined my records for the various years of experimentation, and not having been able to find a source of error. The paper which was submitted to you is the unchanged reprint of the draft of the lecture mentioned; thus the brevity of the exposition, as is essential for a public lecture.

I am not surprised to hear your honor speak of my experiments with mistrustful caution; I would not do otherwise in a similar case. Two points in your esteemed letter appear to be too important to be left unanswered. The first deals with the question whether one may conclude that constancy of type has been obtained if the hybrid Aa produces a plant A, and this plant in turn produces only A.

Permit me to state that, as an empirical worker, I must define constancy of type as the retention of a character during the period of observation. My statements that some of the progeny of hybrids breed true to type thus includes only those generations during which observations were made; it does not extend beyond them. For two generations all experiments were conducted with a fairly large number of plants. Starting with the third generation it became necessary to limit the numbers because of lack of space, so that, in each of the seven experiments, only a sample of those plants of the second generation (which either bred true or varied) could be observed further. The observations were extended over four to six generations (p. 13). Of the varieties which bred true (pp. 15–18) some plants were observed for four generations. I must further mention the case of a variety which bred true for six generations, although the parental types differed in four characters. In 1859 I obtained a very fertile descendent with large, tasty, seeds from a first generation hybrid. Since, in the following year, its progeny retained the desirable characteristics and were uniform, the variety was cultivated in our vegetable garden, and many plants were raised every year up to 1865. The parental plants were $bcDg$ and $BCdG$:

B. albumen yellow	b. albumen green
C. seed-coat grayish-brown	c. seed-coat white
D. pod inflated	d. pod constricted
G. axis long	g. axis short

The hybrid just mentioned was $BcDG$.

The color of the albumen could be determined only in the plants saved for seed production, for the other pods were harvested in an immature condition. Never was green albumen observed in these plants, reddish-purple flower color (an indication of brown seed-coat), constriction of the pod, nor short axis.

This is the extent of my experience. I cannot judge whether these findings would permit a decision as to constancy of type; however, I am inclined to regard the separation of parental characteristics in the progeny of hybrids in Pisum as complete, and thus permanent. The progeny of hybrids carries one or the other of the parental characteristics, or the hybrid form of the two; I have never observed gradual transitions between the parental characters or a progressive approach toward one of them. The course of development consists simply in this; that in each generation the two parental characteristics appear, separated and unchanged, and there is nothing to indicate that one of them has either inherited or taken over anything from the other. For an example, permit me to point to the packets, numbers 1035–1088, which I sent you. All the seeds originated in the first generation of a hybrid in which brown and white seed-coats were combined. Out of the brown seed of this hybrid, some plants were obtained with seed-coats of a pure white color, without any admixture of brown. I expect those to retain the same constancy of character as found in the parental plant.

The second point, on which I wish to elaborate briefly, contains the following statement: "You should regard the numerical expressions as being only empirical, because they can not be proved rational."

My experiments with single characters all lead to the same result: that from the seeds of the hybrids, plants are obtained half of which in turn carry the hybrid character (Aa), the other half, however, receive the parental characters A and a in equal amounts. Thus, on the average, among four plants two have the hybrid character Aa, one the parental character A, and the other the parental character a. Therefore $2Aa+A+a$ or $A+2Aa+a$ is the empirical simple, developmental series for two differentiating characters. Likewise it was shown in an empirical manner that, if two or three differentiating characters are combined in the hybrid, the developmental series is a combination of two or three simple series. Up to this point I don't believe I can be accused of having left the realm of experimentation. If then I extend this combination of simple series to any number of differences between the two parental plants, I have indeed entered the rational domain. This seems permissible, however, because I have proved by previous experiments that the development of any two differentiating characteristics proceeds independently of any other differences. Finally, regarding my statements on the differences among the ovules and pollen cells of the hybrids; they also are based on experiments. These and similar experiments on the germ cells appear to be important, for I believe that their results furnish the explanation for the development of hybrids as observed in Pisum. These experiments should be repeated and verified.

I regret very much not being able to send your honor the varieties you desire. As I mentioned above, the experiments were conducted up to and including 1863; at that time they were terminated in order to obtain space and time for the growing of other experimental plants. Therefore seeds from those experiments are no longer available. Only one experiment on differences in the time of flowering was continued; and seeds are available from the 1864 harvest of this experiment. These are the last I collected, since I had to abandon the experiment in the following year because of devastation by the pea beetle, *Bruchus pisi*. In the early years of experimentation this insect was only rarely found on the plants, in 1864 it caused considerable damage, and appeared in such numbers in the following summer that hardly a 4th or 5th of the seeds was spared. In the last few years it has been necessary to discontinue cultivation of peas in the vicinity of Brünn. The seeds remaining can still be useful, among them are some varieties which I expect to remain constant; they are derived from hybrids in which two, three, and four differentiating characters are combined. All the seeds were obtained from members of the first generation, i.e., of such plants as were grown directly from the seeds of the original hybrids.

I should have scruples against complying with your honor's request to send these seeds for experimentation, were it not in such complete agreement with my own wishes. I fear that there has been partial loss of viability. Furthermore the seeds were obtained at a time when *Bruchus pisi* was already rampant, and I cannot acquit this beetle of possibly transferring pollen; also, I must mention again that the plants were destined for a study of differences in flowering time. The other differences were also taken into account at the harvest, but with less care than in the major experiment. The legend which I have added to the packet numbers on a separate sheet is a copy of the notes I made for each individual plant, with pencil, on its envelope at the time of harvest. The dominant characters are designated as A, B, C, D, E, F, G and as concerns their dual meaning please refer to p. 11. The recessive characters are designated $a, b, c, d, e, f, g;$ these should remain constant in the next generation. Therefore, from those seeds which stem from plants with recessive characters only, identical plants are expected (as regards the characters studied).

Please compare the numbers of the seed packets with those in my record, to detect any possible error in the designations—each packet contains the seeds of a single plant only.

Some of the varieties represented are suitable for experiments on the germ cells; their results can be obtained during the current summer. The round yellow seeds of packets 715, 730, 736, 741, 742, 745, 756, 757, and on the other hand, the green angular seeds of packets 712, 719, 734, 737, 749, and 750 can be recommended for this purpose. By repeated experiments it was proved that, if plants with green seeds are fertilized by those with yellow seeds, the albumen of the resulting seeds has lost the green color and has taken up the yellow color. The same is true for the shape of the seed. Plants with angular seeds, if fertilized by those with round or rounded seeds, produce round or rounded seeds. Thus, due to the changes induced in the color and shape of the seeds by fertilization with foreign pollen, it is possible to recognize the constitution of the fertilizing pollen.

Let B designate yellow color; b, green color of the albumen.

Let A designate round shape; a, angular shape of the seeds.

If flowers of such plants as produce green and angular seeds by self-fertilization are fertilized with foreign pollen, and if the seeds remain green and angular, then the pollen of the donor plant was, as regards the two characters
....ab
If the shape of the seeds is changed, the pollen was taken from...........Ab
If the color of the seeds is changed, the pollen was taken from...........aB
If both shape and color is changed, the pollen was taken from..........AB

The packets enumerated above contain round and yellow, round and green, angular and yellow, and angular and green seeds from the hybrids $ab+AB$. The round and yellow seeds would be best suited for the experiment. Among them (see experiment p. 15) the varieties AB, ABb, Aab, and $AaBb$ may occur; thus four cases are possible when plants, grown from green and angular seeds, are fertilized by the pollen of those grown from the above mentioned round and yellow seeds, i.e.

I. $ab+AB$

II. $ab+ABb$

III. $ab+AaB$

IV. $ab+AaBb$

If the hypothesis that hybrids form as many types of pollen cells as there are possible constant combination types is correct, plants of the makeup

AB	produce pollen of the type AB						
ABb	”	”	”	”	”	AB and Ab	
AaB	”	”	”	”	”	AB and aB	
$AaBb$	”	”	”	”	”	AB, Ab, aB, and ab	

Fertilization of ovules occurs:

I. Ovules ab with pollen AB

II.   ” ab ”   ” AB and Ab

III.   ” ab ”   ” AB and aB

IV.   ” ab ”   ” AB, Ab, aB, and ab

The following varieties may be obtained from this fertilization:

I. $AaBb$

II. $AaBb$ and Aab

III. $AaBb$ and aBb

IV. $AaBb$, Aab, aBb, and ab

If the different types of pollen are produced in equal numbers, there should be in

I. All seeds round and yellow

II. one half round and yellow
one half round and green

III. one half round and yellow
one half angular and yellow

IV. one quarter round and yellow
one quarter round and green
one quarter angular and yellow
one quarter angular and green

Furthermore, since the numerical relations between AB, ABb, AaB, $AaBb$ are $1:2:2:4$, among any nine plants grown from round yellow seed there should be found on the average $AaBb$ four times, ABb and AaB twice each, and AB

once; thus the IVth case should occur four times as frequently as the Ist and twice as frequently as the IInd or IIIrd.

If on the other hand, plants grown from the round yellow seeds mentioned are fertilized by pollen from green angular plants, the results should be exactly the same, provided that the ovules are of the same types, and formed in the same proportions, as was reported for the pollen.

I have not performed this experiment myself, but I believe, on the basis of similar experiments, that one can depend on the result indicated.

In the same fashion individual experiments may be performed for each of the two seed characters separately, all those round seeds which occurred together with angular ones, and all the yellow ones which occurred with green seeds on the same plant are suitable. If, for instance, a plant with green seeds was fertilized by one with yellow seeds, the seeds obtained should be either 1) all yellow, or 2) half yellow and half green, since the plants originating from yellow seeds are of the varieties B and Bb. Since, furthermore, B and Bb occur in the ratio of $1:2$, the 2nd fertilization will occur twice as frequently as the 1st.

Regarding the other characters, the experiments may be conducted in the same way; results, however, will not be obtained until next year. . . .

As must be expected, the experiments proceed slowly. At first beginning, some patience is required, but later, when several experiments are progressing concurrently, matters are improved. Every day, from spring to fall, one's interest is refreshed daily, and the care which must be given to one's wards is thus amply repaid. In addition, if I should, by my experiments, succeed in hastening the solution of these problems, I should be doubly happy.

Accept, highly esteemed Sir, the expression of most sincere respect from

> Your devoted,
> G. MENDEL
> (Altbrünn, Monastery of St. Thomas)

Brünn, 18 April, 1867

THE RELATION OF GENETICS TO PHYSIOLOGY AND MEDICINE

NOBEL LECTURE, PRESENTED IN STOCKHOLM ON JUNE 4, 1934

By Dr. THOMAS HUNT MORGAN

DIRECTOR OF THE WM. G. KERCKHOFF LABORATORIES, CALIFORNIA INSTITUTE OF TECHNOLOGY

THE study of heredity, now called genetics, has undergone such an extraordinary development in the present century, both in theory and in practice, that it is not possible in a short address to review even briefly all its outstanding achievements. At most I can do no more than take up a few topics for discussion.

Since the group of men with whom I have worked for twenty years has been interested for the most part in the chromosome-mechanism of heredity, I shall first briefly describe the relation between the facts of heredity and the theory of the gene. Then I should like to discuss one of the physiological problems implied in the theory of the gene; and finally, I hope to say a few words about the applications of genetics to medicine.

The modern theory of genetics dates from the opening years of the present century, with the discovery of Mendel's long-lost paper that had been overlooked for thirty-five years. The data obtained by de Vries in Holland, Correns in Germany and Tschermak in Austria showed that Mendel's laws are not confined to garden peas, but apply to other plants. A year or two later the work of Bateson and Punnett in England and Cuénot in France made it evident that the same laws apply to animals.

In 1902 a young student, William Sutton, working in the laboratory of E. B. Wilson, pointed out clearly and completely that the known behavior of the chromosomes at the time of maturation of the germ-cells furnishes us with a mechanism that accounts for the kind of separation of the hereditary units postulated in Mendel's theory.

The discovery of a mechanism, that suffices to explain both the first and the second law of Mendel, has had far-reaching consequences for genetic theory, especially in relation to the discovery of additional laws; because the recognition of a mechanism that can be seen and followed demands that any extension of Mendel's theories must conform to such a recognized mechanism; and also because the apparent exceptions to Mendel's laws, that came to light before long, might, in the absence of a known mechanism, have called forth purely fictitious modifications of Mendel's laws or even seemed to invalidate their generality. We now know that some of these "exceptions" are due to newly discovered and demonstrable properties of the chromosome mechanism, and others to recognizable irregularities in the machine.

Mendel knew of no processes taking place in the formation of pollen and egg-

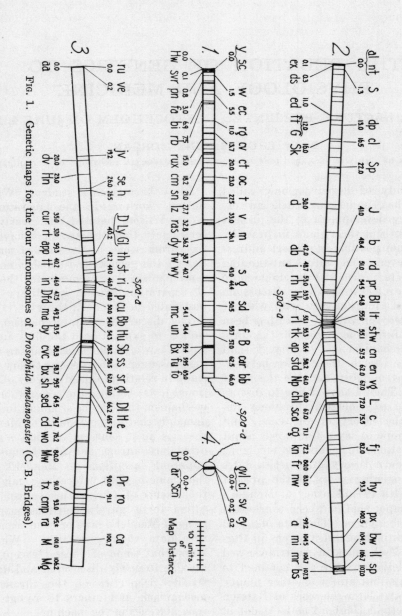

Fig. 1. Genetic maps for the four chromosomes of *Drosophila melanogaster* (C. B. Bridges).

cell that could furnish a basis for his primary assumption that the hereditary elements separate in the germ-cells in such a way that each ripe germ-cell comes to contain only one of each kind of element: but he justified the validity of this assumption by putting it to a crucial test. His analysis was a wonderful feat of reasoning. He verified his reasoning by the recognized experimental procedure of science.

As a matter of fact it would not have been possible in Mendel's time to give an objective demonstration of the basic mechanism involved in the separation of the hereditary elements in the germ-cells. The preparation for this demonstration took all the thirty-five years between Mendel's paper in 1865 and 1900. It is here that the names of the most prominent European cytologists stand out as the discoverers of the rôle of the chromosomes in the maturation of the germ-cells. It is largely a result of their work that it was possible in 1902 to relate the well-known cytological evidence to Mendel's laws. So much in retrospect.

The most significant additions that have been made to Mendel's two laws may be called linkage and crossing over. In 1906 Bateson and Punnett reported a two-factor case in sweet peas that did not give the expected ratio for two pairs of characters entering the cross at the same time.

By 1911 two genes had been found in Drosophila that gave sex-linked inheritance. It had earlier been shown that such genes lie in the X-chromosomes. Ratios were found in the second generation that did not conform to Mendel's second law when these two pairs of characters are present, and the suggestion was made that the ratios in such cases could be explained on the basis of interchange between the two X-chromosomes in the female. It was also pointed out that the further apart the genes for such characters happen to lie in the chromo-

some, the greater the chance for interchange to take place. This would give the approximate location of the genes with respect to other genes. By further extension and clarification of this idea it became possible, as more evidence accumulated, to demonstrate that the genes lie in a single line in each chromosome.

Two years previously (1909) a Belgian investigator, Janssens, had described a phenomenon in the conjugating chromosomes of a salamander, Batracoseps, which he interpreted to mean that interchanges take place between homologous chromosomes. This he called chiasmatypie—a phenomenon that has occupied the attention of cytologists down to the present day. Janssens' observations were destined shortly to supply an objective support to the demonstration of genetic interchange between linked genes carried in the sex chromosomes of the female Drosophila.

To-day we arrange the genes in a chart or map, Fig. 1. The numbers attached express the distance of each gene from some arbitrary point taken as zero. These numbers make it possible to foretell how any new character that may appear will be inherited with respect to all other characters, as soon as its crossing over value with respect to any other two characters is determined. This ability to predict would in itself justify the construction of such maps, even if there were no other facts concerning the location of the genes; but there is to-day direct evidence in support of the view that genes lie in a serial order in the chromosomes.

WHAT ARE THE GENES?

What is the nature of the elements of heredity that Mendel postulated as purely theoretical units? What are genes? Now that we locate them in the chromosomes are we justified in regarding them as material units; as chemical bodies of a higher order than molecules?

Frankly, these are questions with which the working geneticist has not much concern himself, except now and then to speculate as to the nature of the postulated elements. There is no consensus of opinion amongst geneticists as to what the genes are—whether they are real or purely fictitious—because at the level at which the genetic experiments lie it does not make the slightest difference whether the gene is a hypothetical unit or whether the gene is a material particle. In either case the unit is associated with a specific chromosome, and can be localized there by purely genetic analysis. Hence, if the gene is a material unit, it is a piece of a chromosome; if it is a fictitious unit, it must be referred to a definite location in a chromosome—the same place as on the other hypothesis. Therefore, it makes no difference in the actual work in genetics which point of view is taken.

Between the characters that are used by the geneticist and the genes that the theory postulates lies the whole field of embryonic development, where the properties implicit in the genes become explicit in the protoplasm of the cells. Here we appear to approach a physiological problem, but one that is new and strange to the classical physiology of the schools.

We ascribe certain general properties to the genes, in part from genetic evidence and in part from microscopical observations. These properties we may next consider.

Since chromosomes divide in such a way that the line of genes is split (each daughter chromosome receiving exactly half of the original line) we can scarcely avoid the inference that the genes divide into exactly equal parts; but just how this takes place is not known. The analogy of cell-division creates a presumption that the gene divides in the same way, but we should not forget that the relatively gross process involved in cell-division may seem quite inadequate to cover the refined separation of the gene into equal halves. As we do not know of any comparable division phenomena in organic molecules, we must also be careful in ascribing a simple molecular constitution to the gene. On the other hand, the elaborate chains of molecules built up in organic material may give us, some day, a better opportunity to picture the molecular or aggregate structure of the gene and furnish a clue concerning its mode of division....

THE PRODUCTION OF MUTATIONS

IF, as Darwin maintained, the adaptiveness of living things results from natural selection, rather than from a teleological tendency in the process of variation itself, then heritable variations must, under most conditions, occur in numerous directions, so as to give a wide range of choice for the selective process. Such a state of affairs seems, however, in more or less contradiction to the commonly held idea, to which Darwin also gave some credence, that heritable variations of given kinds tend to be produced, in a fairly regular way, by given kinds of external conditions. For then we are again confronted with the difficulty, how is it that the "right kinds" of variations (*i.e.* the adaptive ones) manage to arise in response to the "right kinds" of conditions (*i.e.* those they are adapted to)? Moreover, the de Vriesian notion of mutations does not help us in this connection. On that view, there are sudden jumps, going all the way from one "elementary species" to another, and involving radical changes in numerous characters at once, and there are relatively few different jumps to choose between. This obviously would fail to explain how, through such coarse steps, the body could have come to be so remarkably streamlined in its internal and external organization, or, in other words, so thoroughly adaptive.

The older selectionists, thinking in terms of chemical reactions on a molar scale when they thought in terms of chemistry at all, did not realize sufficiently the ultramicroscopic randomness of the processes causing inherited variations. The earliest mutationists failed, in addition, to appreciate the qualitative and quantitative multiplicity of mutations. It was not long, however, before the results of Baur on *Antirrhinum* and of Morgan on *Drosophila,* supplemented by scattered observations on other forms, gave evidence of the occurrence of numerous Mendelizing mutations, many of them small ones, in varied directions, and they showed no discovererable relation between the type of mutation and the type of environment or condition of living under which it arose. These observations, then, came closer to the statistical requirements for a process of evolution which has its basis in accidents. In what sense, however, could the events be regarded as accidental? Were they perhaps expressions of veiled forces working in a more determinate manner? It was more than ever evident that further investigation of the manner of occurrence of mutations was called for.

If the mutations were really non-teleological, with no relation between type of environment and type of change, and above all no adaptive relation, and if they were of as numerous types as the theory of natural selection would demand, then the great majority of the changes should be harmful in their effects, just as any alterations made blindly in a complicated apparatus are usually detrimental to its proper functioning, and many of the larger changes should even be totally incompatible with the functioning of the whole, or, as we say, lethal. That is, strange as it may seem at first sight, we should expect most mutations to be disadvantageous if the theory of natural selection is correct. We should also expect these mainly disadvantageous changes to be highly diversified in their genetic basis.

Frequency of Mutations

To get exact evidence on these points required the elaboration of special genetic methods, adapted to the recognition of mutations that ordinarily escape detection—(1) lethals, (2) changes with but small visible effects, and (3) changes without any externally visible effects but influencing the viability more or less unfavorably. It would take us too far afield to explain these techniques here. Suffice it to say that they made use of the principle according to which a chromosome is, as we say, "marked," by having had inserted into it to begin with one or more known mutant genes with conspicuous visible effects, to differentiate it from the homologous chromosome. An individual with two such differentiated chromosomes, when appropriately bred, will then be expected to give two groups of visibly different offspring, holding certain expected ratios to one another. If, however, a lethal mutation has occurred in one of the two chromosomes, its existence will be made evident by the absence of the corresponding expected group of offspring. Similarly, a mutated gene with invisible but somewhat detrimental action, though not fully lethal, will be recognized by the fact that the corresponding group of offspring are found in smaller numbers than expected. And a gene with a very small visible effect, that might be overlooked in a single individual, will have a greatly increased chance of being seen because the given group of offspring as a whole will tend to be distinguished in this regard from the corresponding group derived from a non-mutant.

In this way, it was possible in the first tests of this kind, which Altenburg and the writer conducted, partly in collaboration, in 1918-19, to get definite evidence in *Drosophila* that the lethal mutations greatly outnumbered those with visible effects, and that among the latter the types having an obscure manifestation were more numerous than the definite conspicuous ones used in ordinary genetic work. Visible or not, the great majority had lowered viability. Tests of their genetic basis, using the newly found facts of linkage, showed them to be most varied in their locus in the chromosomes, and it could be calculated by a simple extrapolative process that there must be at least hundreds, and probably thousands, of different kinds arising in the course of spontaneous mutation. In work done much later, employing induced mutations, it was also shown (in independent experiments both of the present writer and Kerkis, and of Timoféeff and his co-workers, done in 1934) that "invisible" mutations, which by reason of one or another physiological change lower viability without being fully lethal, form the most abundant group of any detected thus far, being at least two to three times as numerous as the complete lethals. No doubt there are in addition very many, perhaps even more, with effects too small to have been detected at all by our rather crude methods. It is among these that we should be most apt to find those rare accidents which, under given conditions or in given combinations with others, may happen to have some adaptive value. Tests of Timoféeff, however, have shown that even a few of the more conspicuous visible mutations do in certain combinations give an advantage in laboratory breeding.

Because of the nature of the test whereby it is detected—the absence of an entire group of offspring bearing certain conspicuous expected characters—a lethal is surer of being detected, and detected by any observer, than is the inconspicuous or invisible, merely detrimental, mutation. Fortunately, there are relatively few borderline cases, of nearly but not quite completely lethal genes. It was this objectivity of recognition, combined with the fact that they were so much more numerous than conspicuous visible mutations, that made it feasible for lethals to be used as an index of mutation frequency, even though they suffer from the disadvantage of requiring the breeding of an individual, rather than its mere inspection, for the recognition that it carries a lethal. In the earliest published work, we (Altenburg and the author) attempted not only to find a quantitative value for the "normal" mutation frequency, but also to determine whether a certain condition, which we considered of especial interest, affected the mutation frequency. The plan was ultimately to use the method as a general one for studying the effects of various conditions. The condition chosen for the first experiment was temperature, and the results, verified by later work of the writer's, indicated that a rise of temperature, within limits normal to the organism, produced an increase of mutation frequency of about the amount to be expected if mutations were, in essentials, orthodox chemical reactions.

Mutations as Chemical Reactions

On this view, however, single mutations correspond with individual molecular changes, and an extended series of mutations, in a great number of identical genes in a population, spread out over thousands of years, is what corresponds with the course of an ordinary chemical reaction that takes place in a whole collection of molecules in a test tube in the course of a fraction of a second or a few seconds. For the individual gene, in its biological setting, is far more stable than the ordinary chemical molecule is, when the latter is exposed to a reagent in the laboratory. Thus, mutations, when taken collectively, should be subject to the statistical laws applying to mass reactions, but the individual mutation, corresponding to a change in one molecule, should be subject to the vicissitudes of ultramicroscopic or atomic events, and the apparition of a mutant individual represents an enormous amplification of such a phenomenon. This is a principle which gives the clue to the fact, which otherwise seems opposed to a rational, scientific and molarly deterministic point of view, that differences in external conditions or conditions of living do not appear to affect the occurrence of mutations, while on the other hand, even in a normal and sensibly constant environment, mutations of varied kinds do occur. It is also in harmony with our finding, of about the same time, that when a mutation takes place in a given gene, the other gene of identical type present nearby in the same cell usually remains unaffected though it must of course have been subjected to the same macroscopic physico-chemical conditions. On this conception, then, the mutations ordinarily result from submicroscopic accidents, that is, from caprices of thermal agitation, that occur on a molecular and submolecular scale. More recently Delbrück and Timoféeff, in more extended work on temperature, have shown that the amount of increase in mutation frequency with rising temperature is not merely that of an ordinary test-tube chemical reaction, but in fact corresponds closely with that larger rise to be expected of a reaction as slow in absolute time rate (*i.e.* with as small a proportion of molecular changes per unit of time) as the observed mutation frequency shows this reaction to be, and this quantitative correspondence helps to confirm the entire conception.

Now this inference concerning the non-molar nature of the individual mutation process, which sets it in so different a class from most other grossly observable chemical changes in nature, led naturally to the expectation that some of the "point effects" brought about by high-energy radiation like X-rays would also work to produce alternations in the hereditary material. For if even the relatively mild events of thermal agitation can, some of them, have such consequences, surely the energetically far more potent changes caused by powerful radiation should succeed. And, as a matter of fact, our trials of X-rays, carried out with the same kind of genetic methods as previously used for temperature, proved that such radiation is extremely effective, and inordinately more so than a mere temperature rise, since by this method it was possible to obtain, by a half hour's treatment, over a hundred times as many mutations in a group of treated cells as would have occurred in them spontaneously in the course of a whole generation. These mutations, too, were found ordinarily to occur pointwise and randomly, in one gene at a time, without affecting an identical gene that might be present nearby in a homologous chromosome.

Radiation-Effects

In addition to the individual gene changes, radiation also produced rearrangements of parts of chromosomes. As our later work (including that with co-workers, especially Raychaudhuri and Pontecorvo) has shown, these latter were caused in the first place by breakages of the chromosomes, followed afterwards by attachments occurring between the adhesive broken ends, that joined them in a different order than before. The two or more breaks involved in such a rearrangement may be far apart, caused by independent hits, and thus result in what we call a *gross* structural change. Such changes are of various kinds. depending upon just where the breaks are and just which broken ends become attached to which. But, though the effects of the individual "hits" are rather narrowly localized, it is not uncommon for two breaks to be produced at nearby points by what amounts to one local change (or at any rate one localized group of changes) whose influence becomes somewhat spread out. By the rejoining, in a new order, of broken ends resulting from two such nearby breaks, a *minute* change of sequence of the genes is brought about. More usually, the small piece between the two breaks becomes lost (a "deficiency"), but sometimes it becomes inverted, or even becomes transferred into a totally different position, made available by a separate hit.

Both earlier and later work by collaborators (Oliver, Hanson, etc.) showed definitely that the frequency of the gene mutations is directly and simply proportional to the dose of irradiation applied, and this despite the wave length used, whether X- or gamma or even beta rays, and despite the timing of the irradiation. These facts have since been established with great exactitude and detail, more especially by Timoféeff and his co-workers. In our more recent work with Raychaudhuri these principles have been extended to total doses as low as 400r, and rates as low as .01r per minute, with gamma rays. They leave, we believe, no escape from the conclusion that there is no threshold dose, and that the individual mutations result from individual "hits", producing genetic effects in their immediate neighborhood. Whether these so-called "hits" are the individual ionizations, or may even be the activations that occur at lower energy levels, or whether, at the other end of the scale, they require the clustering of ionizations that occurs at the termini of electron tracks and of their side branches (as Lea and Fano point out might be the case), is as yet undecided. But in any case they are, even when microscopically considered, what we have termed "point mutations," as they involve only disturbances on an ultra-microscopically localized scale. And whether or not they are to occur at any particular point is entirely a matter of accident, using this term in the sense in which it is employed in the mathematics of statistics.

Naturally, other agents than photons which produce effects of this kind must also produce mutations, as has been shown by students and collaborators working under Altenburg in Houston for neutrons (Nagai and Locher) and for alpha rays (Ward) and confirmed by Timoféeff and his co-workers (Zimmer, et al). Moreover, as Altenburg showed, even the smaller quantum changes induced by ultraviolet exert this effect on the genes. They cause, however, only a relatively small amount of rearrangement of chromosome parts (Muller and Mackenzie), and, in fact, they also tend to inhibit such rearrangement, as Swanson, followed by Kauffmann and Hollaender. has found. Since the effective ultraviolet hits are in the form of randomly scattered single-atom changes in the purines and pyrimidines of the chromosome, rather than in groups of atom changes, it seems likely that clusters of ionizations are not necessary for the gene mutation effects, at any rate, although we cannot be sure of this until the relation of mutation frequency to dosage is better known for this agent.

Induced and Natural Mutations

Inasmuch as the changes brought about in the genes by radiation must certainly be of an accidental nature, unpremeditated, ateleological, without reference to the value of the end result for the organism or its descendants, it is of interest to compare them with the so-called spontaneous or natural mutations. For in the radiation mutations we have a yardstick of what really random changes should be. Now it is found in *Drosophila* that the radiation-induced mutations of the genes (we exclude here the demonstrable chromosome rearrangements) are in every respect which has been investigated of the same essential nature as those arising naturally in the laboratory or field. They usually occur in one gene without affecting an identical one nearby. They are distributed similarly in the chromosomes. The effects, similarly, may be large or small and there is a similar ratio of fully lethal to so-called visible gene mutations. That is, the radiation mutations of the genes do not give evidence of being more deleterious. And when one concentrates attention upon given genes one finds that a whole series of different forms, or alleles, may be produced, of a similar and in many cases sensibly identical nature in the two cases. In fact, every natural mutation, when searched for long enough, is found to be producible also by radiation. Moreover, under any given condition of living tried, without radiation, the effects appear as scattered as when radiation is applied, even though of much lower frequency. All this surely means then, does it not, that the natural mutations have in truth no innate tendency to be adaptive, nor even to be different, as a whole group, under some natural conditions than under others? In other words, they cannot be determinate in a molar sense, but must themselves be caused by the ultramicroscopic accidents of the molecular and submolecular motions, i.e. by the individual quantum exchanges of thermal agitation, taking this word in a broad sense. The only escape from this would be to suppose that they are caused by the radiation present in nature, resulting from natural radioactive substances and cosmic rays, but a little calculation (by Mott-Smith and the writer, corroborated by others) has shown that this radiation is quite inadequate in amount to account for the majority of mutations occurring in most organisms.

But to say that most natural mutations are the results of the quantum exchanges of thermal agitation, and, further, that a given energy level must be reached to produce them, does not, as some authors have seemed to imply, mean that the physicochemical conditions in and around the organism, other than temperature, have no influence upon their chance of occurrence. That such circumstances may play a decided role was early evident from the studies of spontaneous mutation frequency, when it was found (1921, reported 1928) that the frequency in one experiment, with one genetic stock, might be ten times as high as in another, with another stock. And more recently we have found that, in different portions of the natural life cycle of the same individual, the mutation frequency may be very different. Finally, in the work of Auerbach and Robson, with mustard gas and related substances, it has been proved that these chemicals may induce mutations at as high a frequency as a heavy dose of X-rays. In all these cases, however, the effects are similarly scattered at random, individually uncontrolled, and similarly non-adaptive.

It should also be noted in this connection that the genes are not under all conditions equally vulnerable to the mutating effects of X-rays themselves. Genes in the condensed chromosomes of spermatozoa, for example, appear to be changed more easily than those in the more usual "resting" stages. We have mentioned that, as Swanson has shown, ultraviolet exerts besides its own mutating effect an inhibition on the process of chromosome breakage, or at any rate on that of reunion of the broken parts in a new viable order, while infrared, in Hollaender's and Kaufmann's recent experiments, has a contrary action. And Stadler, in his great work on the production of mutations in cereals, started independently of our own, has obtained evidence that in this material X-radiation in the doses used is unable to produce a sensible rise in the gene mutation frequency, though numerous chromosome breakages do arise, leading to both gross and minute rearrangements of chromosome parts. Either the genes are more resistant in this material to permanent changes by X-rays as compared with their responsiveness to thermal agitation, or a break or loss must usually be produced by X-rays along with the gene change. The milder ultraviolet quanta, on the other hand, do produce gene mutations like the natural ones in these plants.

Such variations in effectiveness are, I believe, to have been expected. They do not shake our conclusion as to the accidental, quantum character of the event which usually initiates a gene mutation. But they give rise to the hope that, through further study of them, more may be learned concerning the nature of the mutation process, as well as of the genetic material that undergoes the changes.

Controlled Mutation?

No one can answer the question whether some special means may not be found whereby, through the application of molar influences, such as specific antibodies, individual genes could be changed to order. Certainly the search for such influences, and for increasing control of things on a microscopic and submicroscopic scale as well, must be carried further. But there is as yet no good evidence that anything of the sort has been done artificially, or that it occurs naturally. Even if possible, there could be no generalized method of control of gene composition without far greater knowledge than we now have of the intimate chemical structure and the mode of working of the most complicated and diverse substances that exist, namely, nucleoproteins, proteins in general, and enzymes. The works of Sumner, North-

rup and Stanley, together with those of other protein chemists, point the way in this direction, but everyone will agree that it is a long and devious system of roads which is beginning here.

It is true that some cases are known of mutable genes which change selectively in response to special conditions. Such cases may be very informative in shedding light on gene structure, but we have as yet no indication that the alterations of these genes, which in the great majority of instances known are abnormal genes, have anything in common with ordinary natural mutations. It is also true that cases are known among bacteria and viruses of the induction of particular kinds of hereditary changes by application of particular substances, but here the substances applied are in each case the same as those whose presence is later found to have been induced, and so there is every reason to infer that they have in fact become implanted in some way, that is, that we do not really have a specifically induced mutation.

So far, then, we have no means, or prospect of means, of inducing given mutations at will in normal material; though the production of mutations in abundance at random may be regarded as a first step along such a path, if there is to be such a path. So long as we cannot direct mutations, then, selection is indispensable, and progressive change in the hereditary constitution of a living thing can be made only with the aid of a most thoroughgoing selection of the mutations that occur since, being non-adaptive except by accident, an overwhelming majority is always harmful. For a sensible advance, usually a considerable number of rare steps must be accumulated in this painful selective process. By far the most of these are individually small steps, but, as species and race crossings have shown, there may be a few large distinctive steps that have been, as Huxley terms it, "buffered", by small changes that readjust the organism to them. Not only is this accumulation of many rare, mainly tiny changes the chief means of artificial animal and plant improvement, but it is, even more, the way in which natural evolution has occurred, under the guidance of natural selection. Thus the Darwinian theory becomes implemented, and freed from the accretions of directed variation and of Lamarckism that once encumbered it.

It is probable that, in a state of nature, most species have a not very much (though somewhat) lower frequency of gene mutation than would be most advantageous for them, in consideration of the degree of rigor of the natural selection that occurs in the given species. A much higher frequency would probably lead to faster genetic degenerative processes than the existing selection could well cope with. But, under conditions of artificial breeding, where selection can be made more effective, a higher mutation frequency can for a time at least be tolerated in some cases, and larger mutations also can be nursed through to the point where they become suitably buffered. Here it may become of practical use to apply X-rays, ultra-violet, or other means of inducing mutations, as Gustafsson especially has demonstrated for X-rays. This will be especially true in species which naturally undergo much inbreeding, or in which there is a well expressed haploid phase, or a considerable haploid portion of the genotype, for under these circumstances many of the spontaneous mutations that might otherwise have accumulated in the population and that could be brought to light by inbreeding, will have become eliminated before they could be found, and the natural mutation rate itself will be lower.

We have above largely confined ourselves to considering the relation of the production of gene mutations to the problems of the general method of evolution, including that of the nature of hereditary variation, because this has been, historically, the main line of approach to the subject of artificial mutations. It was from the first evident, however, that the production of mutations would, as we once stated, provide us with tools of the greatest nicety, wherewith to dissect piece by piece the physiological, embryological, and biochemical structure of the organism and to analyze its workings. Already with natural mutations, such works as those of Bonnevie, Grueneberg, Scott-Moncrief, Ephrussi and Beadle, etc., have shown how the intensive tracing of the effects, and interrelations of effects, of just one or a few mutations, can lead to a deeper understanding of the complex processes whereby the genes operate to produce the organism. But there are thousands of genes, and it is desirable to be able to choose them for study in an orderly fashion as we proceed with our dissection process. For this purpose we have thought that it would often be advantageous to produce mutations artificially in abundance, so as then to take our pick of those more suited for successive steps in our analysis. The work of Beadle and his co-workers on *Neurospora* in recent years, followed by similar work of Malin and Fries and of others, has brilliantly shown the applicability of this method for studies of the paths of bio-chemical synthesis of amino-acids, vitamins, purines and pyrimidines. And yet, in a sense, the surface of the subject as a whole has barely been scratched, and we may look forward with confidence to the combination of this technique with that of tracer substances and with all the other techniques of biochemistry, physiology and experimental embryology, for the increasing unravelling of that surpassingly intricate tangle of processes of which the living organism is constituted. There is no time, however, to go further into this subject here.

Chromosome Analysis

For we cannot neglect here a brief outline of another phase of the artificial mutation work, more specifically of interest to geneticists: that is, the further analysis of the properties of the chromosomes and their parts, gained chiefly from studies in which parts have been removed, added, or rearranged. We have already spoken, in passing, of the studies of the mechanism of such structural change, in which a relatively simple general scheme lying at the basis of all such alterations has emerged: namely, breakage first, followed by adhesion of broken ends. It was early evident that by the use of such rearranged chromosomes additional proof of the physical validity of the linkage maps could be obtained, and this was done (Muller and Painter). Furthermore, it has been possible to throw light on problems of crossing over, as in the demonstration (Muller, Stone, and Offermann) that to whatever position the centromere is moved, it causes a strong inhibition of crossing over, the strenth of which gradually diminishes with distance. Moreover, the same proves to be true of any point of discontinuity in pairing, caused by heterozygosity in regard to a structural change. Such studies on crossing over, and on the pairing forces that affect segregation, are still capable of considerable extension.

We must remember, in speaking of the centromere and other apparently distinctive chromosome parts, that we have no right to infer that they are autonomous, locally determined structures, dependent on the genes of the regions in which they are seen to lie, before observations have been made that show the effects of removing or displacing those regions. Therefore, it has in the main been necessary to wait for the study of induced inversions, deletions and translocations of chromosomes, before the inference could be secure that the centromere is, in most instances, such an autonomous organelle, dependent upon a gene or genes in the immediate neighborhood (but not in all instances in the neighborhood, as Rhoades has recently shown in a special strain of maize). Similarly, it has been possible to show (despite some contrary claims, the validity or invalidity of which cannot be discussed here) that the free end of the chromosome, or telomere, constitutes in much material a locally determined distinctive structure.

By a combined genetic and cytological analysis of various cases of breakage and rearrangement of parts, it was found that there are distinctive, largely locally determined, regions of the chromosomes, usually most markedly developed near the centromeres, which we at first called "inactive" but which are now usually referred to as "heterochromatic." These were also found independently in purely cytological studies by Heitz. It would be fascinating to enter here into a discussion of the remarkable peculiarities which the cytogenetic studies have shown these regions to have—the evidence of repetition of more or less similar parts, of a tendency to conjugation between the differently placed parts, of distinctive cytological appearance correlated with whether or not such conjugation occurs, of inordinately high tendency to structural change, of strong influence of certain of their genes upon segregation, etc.,—and then to go on to discuss hypotheses of their evolutionary origin and their functions. This would unfortunately take us too far afield. We must, however, insist upon one point—as it is not yet generally enough recognized,—namely, that the evidence is very strong that what, in the *Drosophila* chromosome as seen at mitosis, is called "the heterochromatic region," is simply a large temporary body of accessory, non-genic nucleoprotein, produced under the influence of one or two particular genes from among the dozen or more that constitute the whole heterochromatic region, as detected by genetic analysis and by the chromosome as seen at the resting stage (as in the salivary gland). And it is not these conspicuous non-genic blocks which are responsible for the other known peculiarities of the heterochromatin, above mentioned—the function of the blocks is still undetermined. In other words, the so-called "heterochromatin" with which the cytologist deals in studying mitotic chromosomes is a quite different thing from, although in the neighborhood of, the heterochromatin proper having the above described complex of properties. Moreover, it has been possible to show (Sutton-Gersh in collaboration with the author, unpublished) that the conspicuous nucleoli often associated with the heterochromatin are produced under the influence of still other autonomous genes in it, that are separate from those for the mitotically visible blocks.

One of the most interesting findings which has come out of the study of *Drosophila* chromosomes that underwent rearrangement of parts as a result of irradiation has been the generalization of the existence of the phenomenon known as "position effect." This effect was first found by Sturtevant in the case of the spontaneous mutant known as Bar eye, but it was not known to what extent the effect might be a special one until numerous rearrangements could be studied. The term position effect implies that the functioning of a gene is to a certain extent at least dependent upon what other genes lie in its neighborhood. There is now adequate evidence that this is a general principle, applying to very many if not all the genes in *Drosophila,* and that their functioning can be qualitatively as well as quantitatively conditioned by the character of the genes in their vicinity, some of the genes having much more effect than others and different genes working in different ways and to different extents.

It is possible that, as Sturtevant suggested, the position effect is caused by the interaction between gene products in the vicinity of the genes producing them, assuming that such products are more concentrated there and under such circumstances tend to react more with one another than when dispersed. However, the interpretation which we favor is that the functioning of the gene is affected by its shape and that this, in turn, varies with the strength and nature of synaptic forces acting on the region of the chromosome in which it lies. These might consist of forces directly exerted on the gene by other genes, whether allelic or not (Muller), or they might be resultants of the state of spiralization, etc., of the chromosome region, circumstances which in their turn are in part dependent on synaptic forces (Ephrussi and Sutton). This interpretation, in either of its variants, would explain why position effects are so much more general in *Drosophila,* an organism in which the synaptic forces are known to operate strongly even in somatic cells, than in other organisms tested, in which such

forces are much weaker or absent in somatic cells. It would also fit in with the author's findings that the heterochromatic regions tend to have especially strong, extensive, and distinctive kinds of position effects, effects varying in degree with the total amount of heterochromatin present in a cell, as well as with vacillating embryological factors. For these genetic findings are in conformity with the cytological effects of heterochromatin, observed first by Prokofyeva, on the degree of extension, synaptic properties, etc., of euchromatin in its neighborhood, effects which she showed to be subject to similar vacillations, that are correlated with the variations in the phenotypically observed position effects. Recent observations, both by Ephrussi and by Sutton, following suggestions of the author, and by Stern, also seem to point in this direction, for they show an influence, on the position effects exhibited by given parts, of the arrangement of *homologous* chromosome parts. If this interpretation based on gene shape should hold, it would open up a new angle of attack on the structure and method of functioning of the gene, perhaps ultimately relating it to nucleoprotein composition and properties.

Another use to which the process of breakage and rearrangement of chromosome parts by irradiation has been put is for the study of the effects of adding and of subtracting small pieces of chromosomes, in order to determine the relation of gene dosage to gene expression. In this way, it has been found out (1) that most normal genes are, even in single dose, near the upper limit of their effectiveness, and (2) that most mutant genes have a final effect qualitatively similar to but quantitatively less than that of their allelic normal gene. The dominance of normal genes over their mutant alleles, then, turns out in most instances to be a special case of the principle that one dose of a normal gene usually produces nearly though not quite as much effect as two doses. This in turn is best understood as resulting from a long course of selection of the normal gene and its modifiers for stability of expression, when under the influence of environmental and genetic conditions which would affect the gene's operation quantitatively, *i.e.* in a manner similar to that of dosage changes. This does not mean that selection has specifically worked to produce dominance of the normal gene over its alleles, however, because (3) not all mutant genes behave merely like weaker normal genes, and (4) those which the dosage tests show to produce qualitatively different effects from the normal genes seem oftener to escape from the principle of being dominated over by the normals, just as would be expected on our hypothesis.

Among the further results of gene dosage studies carried out by the use of chromosome fragments produced by irradiation, attention should be especially called to the findings coming under the head of "dosage compensation." These have shown (1) that, when the dosage of virtually all genes in the X chromosome except a given one is held constant, the expression of that one is usually so very nearly the same when present in one dose as in two that no difference in the character can ordinarily be seen, and (2) that nevertheless this invisible difference has been so important for the organism that, in the course of the past natural selection, a system of modifying genes, called compensators, has been established, having the function of making the effects of the one and two doses normally present in the two respective sexes much more nearly equal still, when these dosage differences in the given genes are present simultaneously with those in all the other X-chromosomal genes. Each gene seems to have acquired a different system of compensators, the interrelations of all together being extremely complicated. This then gives evidence from a new angle of the meticulousness of natural selection, of the very precise adaptiveness of the characters existing in a species, and of the final grade of a character having ordinarily become established through the accumulation of numerous small mutations having very

complex functional relations with one another. It is in line with our previous thesis of evolution through the selection of multitudinous tiny accidental changes.

When attention is concentrated on a given very circumscribed region of a chromosome, by a comparison of various induced rearrangements all of which have a point of breakage within that region, other facts come to light, bearing on the problems of chromosome and gene divisibility. By means of special genetic methods, which cannot be detailed here, evidence has been obtained that the breaks in any such limited region tend to occur at specific points, giving indication that discrete units or segments lie between these points, and thus arguing against the idea of the chromosome being a continuum and in favor of its genes corresponding to physical entities rather than merely to concepts arbitrarily set up for the convenience of geneticists. We are also enabled in this way to make estimates of the probable number of genes in the chromosome, as well as to get maximally limiting figures for their size. These estimates agree as closely as could have been expected with those based on previous genetic work, using entirely different methods, although not with the estimates based on the "sensitive volume" hypothesis.

Duplications and Evolution

Another finding made in studies of cases having a small fragment of chromosome moved, as a result of irradiation, to another position, was that individuals are frequently able to survive and reproduce even when they have the given chromosome part present in its original position as well as in the new position. In fact, it was in work of this kind that the effect of extra doses of genes was determined. Now, in some of these cases stocks could even be obtained which were homozygous for the duplicated piece as well as for the original piece. This led to the idea that duplications of chromosome material might in this manner have become established in the previous course of evolution. When, in the analysis of a limited region of the

X chromosome, including the locus of the so-called "scute" effect, it was found that there are in fact, within the normal *X* chromosome, two genes of closely related effect ("achaete" and "scute") very close or adjacent to one another, it became evident that this was in all probability an example of the above postulated occurrence. This then showed the way, and apparently the main if not the only way (aside from the far rarer phenomena of polyploidy and "tetrasomy"), by which the number of genes has become increased during the course of evolution. By a curious coincidence, Bridges was at the same time making his studies of salivary chromosomes and finding direct cytological evidence for the existence of such "repeats," as he called them, in the normal chromosome, and he interpreted these in the same manner. In the twelve years since that time, various other clear cases of the same kind have been demonstrated. Thus, increase in gene number, brought about by the duplication of small parts of chromosomes, more usually in positions near their original ones, must be set down as one of the major processes in evolution, in addition to the mutations in the individual genes. By itself, this process would not be of great importance, but it becomes important because, by allowing gene mutations to come afterwards that differentiate the genes in one position from the originally identical ones in the other position. the number of different kinds of genes is increased and so the germ plasm. and with it the processes of development and the organism as a whole, are eventually enabled to grow more complex.

Rearrangements of chromosome parts which do not lead to an increase in gene number can of course also occur in evolution. although it is unlikely that their role is so fundamental. By producing such changes in the laboratory it has been possible to find out a good deal more about what types can arise, and what their properties are. Various inferences can then be drawn concerning the viability and fertility that the different types would have. under varied genetic circumstances, and whether they would tend to become eliminated or to accumulate in a population of a given type. Some of them can be shown to have, under given conditions, an evolutionary survival value, both by aiding in the process of genetic isolation and in other ways, as by affecting heterosis. In this manner, evolutionary inferences have been drawn which have later been confirmed by comparison of the chromosome differences actually existing between related races, sub-species, and species.

Probably of greater ultimate interest will be the results of studies of gene mutations occurring at individual loci. Radiation mutations are frequent enough to lend themselves to comparisons of the potentialities of different loci, although not nearly enough has yet been done along these lines. Similarly, a comparison of the different mutations which can occur at the same locus can lead to very important results, especially since it has been shown that the different alleles may have every complex relationships to one another, so as even, in some cases, to reconstitute the normal type when they are crossed together. The way in which genes may change as a result of successive mutations remains to be gone into at much greater length. So, too, does the question of changes in gene mutability, brought about by gene mutation itself.

Somatic Radiation Effects

The further the analysis of the genetic effects of irradiation has gone, particularly of the breakage and rearrangement of chromosome parts, the more does our conviction grow that a large proportion if not the great majority of the somatic effects of irradiation that have been observed by medical men and by students of embryology. regeneration, and general biology, arise secondarily as consequences of genetic effects produced in the somatic cells The usefulness of this interpretation has been shown in recent studies of Koller, dealing with improved methods of irradiation of mammalian carcinoma. This is too large a subject to digress upon here, but it is to be noted that it has been the analyses based in the first place on genetic and cytogenetic studies of the reproductive cells, as shown by subsequent generations, which are thus helping to clear the way for an understanding of the mechanism by which radiation acts in inhibiting growth, in causing sterilization, in producing necrosis and burns, in causing recession of malignant tissue, and perhaps also, on occasion at least, in inducing the initiation of such tissue.

During the war years, a curious confirmation of the correctness of the above inference regarding the nature of the somatic effects of irradiation has come to light. While working with mustard gas in Edinburgh, J. H. Robson was struck with the remarkable similarity between the somatic effects of this agent and those produced by X-ray and radium irradiation. This led him to wonder whether perhaps mustard gas might produce genetic changes of essentially the same kind as those known to be brought about by irradiation. Comprehensive experiments were thereupon undertaken by C. Auerbach, working in collaboration with Robson, and (as mentioned on p. 263) she succeeded in showing that in fact this substance does produce mutations, both in the individual genes and by breakage and rearrangement of chromosome parts, such as X-rays and radium do, and in similar abundance. Other substances of the same general group were then found to have a similar effect. This constitutes the first decided break in the chemical attack on mutation. The fact that these findings were made as a direct result of the above inference, when so many previous attempts to produce mutations by chemical means had failed, appears to provide strong evidence that these peculiar somatic effects are in truth consequences of the more underlying ones which, when occurring in the germ cells, are analyzed by the geneticist in his breeding tests.

There are, however, some very interesting differences between the nature of the genetic effects of irradiation and of these chemicals, which we cannot go into here, but which give promise of allowing an extension of the genetic and somatic analyses.

We see then that production of mutations by radiation is a method, capable of being turned in various directions, both for the analysis of the germ plasm itself, and of the organism which is in a sense an outgrowth of that germ plasm. It is to be hoped that it may also, in certain fields, prove of increasing practical use in plant and animal improvement, in the service of man. So far as direct practical application in man himself is concerned, however, we are as yet a long way from practicing any intentional selection over our own germ plasm, although like most species we are already encumbered by countless undesirable mutations, from which no individual is immune. In this situation we can, however, draw the practical lesson, from the fact of the great majority of mutations being undesirable, that their further random production in ourselves should so far as possible be rigorously avoided. As we can infer with certainty from experiments on lower organisms that all high-energy radiation must produce such mutations in man, it becomes an obligation for radiologists — though one far too little observed as yet in most countries—to insist that the simple precautions are taken which are necessary for shielding the gonads, whenever people are exposed to such radiation, either in industry or in medical practice. And, with the coming increasing use of atomic energy, even for peacetime purposes, the problem will become very important of insuring that the human germ plasm— the all-important material of which we are the temporary custodians—is effectively protected from this additional and potent source of permanent contamination.

Maurice H. F. Wilkins

The molecular configuration of nucleic acids

Nobel Lecture, December 11, 1962

Nucleic acids are basically simple. They are at the root of very fundamental biological processes, growth and inheritance. The simplicity of nucleic acid molecular structure and of its relation to function expresses the underlying simplicity of the biological phenomena, clarifies their nature, and has given rise to the first extensive interpretation of living processes in terms of macromolecular structure. These matters have only become clear by an unprecedented combination of biological, chemical and physical studies, ranging from genetics to hydrogen-bond stereochemistry. I shall not discuss all this here but concentrate on the field in which I have worked, and show how X-ray diffraction analysis has made its contribution. I shall describe some of the background of my own researches, for I suspect I am not alone in finding such accounts often more interesting than general reviews.

Early Background

I took a physics degree at Cambridge in 1938, with some training in X-ray crystallography. This X-ray background was influenced by J. D. Bernal, then at the Cavendish. I began research at Birmingham, under J. T. Randall, studying luminescence and how electrons move in crystals. My contemporaries at Cambridge had mainly been interested in elementary particles, but the organization of the solid state and the special properties which depended on this organization interested me more. This may have been a forerunner of my interest in biological macromolecules and how their structure related to their highly specific properties which so largely determine the processes of life.

During the war I took part in making the atomic bomb. When the war was ending, I, like many others, cast around for a new field of research. Partly on account of the bomb, I had lost some interest in physics. I was therefore very interested when I read Schrödinger's book « What is Life? » and was struck by the concept of a highly complex molecular structure which controlled living processes. Research on such matters seemed more ambitious than solid-state physics. At that time many leading physicists such as Massey, Oliphant, and Randall (and later I learned that Bohr shared their view) believed that physics would contribute significantly to biology; their advice encouraged me to move into biology.

I went to work in the Physics Department at St. Andrews, Scotland, where Randall had invited me to join a biophysics project he had begun. Stimulated by Muller's experimental modification, by means of X-radiation, of genetic substance, I thought it might be interesting to investigate the effects of ultrasonics; but the results were not very encouraging.

The biophysics work then moved to King's College, London, where Randall took the Wheatstone Chair of Physics and built up, with the help of the Medical Research Council, an unusual laboratory for a Physics Department, where biologists, biochemists and others worked with the physicists. He suggested I might take over some ultraviolet microscope studies of the quantities of nucleic acids in cells. This work followed that of Caspersson, but made use of the achromatism of reflecting microscopes. By this time, the work of Caspersson[1] and Brachet[2] had made the scientific world generally aware that nucleic acids had important biological roles which were connected with protein synthesis. The idea that DNA might itself be the genetic substance was, however, barely hinted at. Its function in chromosomes was supposed to be associated with replication of the protein chromosome thread. The work of Avery, MacLeod, and McCarty[3], showing that bacteria could be genetically transformed by DNA, was published in 1944, but even in 1946 seemed almost unknown, or if known, its significance was often belittled.

It was fascinating to look through microscopes at chromosomes in cells, but I began to feel that as a physicist I might contribute more to biology by studying macromolecules isolated from cells. I was encouraged in this by Gerald Oster who came from Stanley's virus laboratory and interested me in particles of tobacco mosaic virus. As Caspersson had shown, ultraviolet microscopes could be used to find the orientation of ultraviolet absorbing groups in molecules as well as to measure quantities of nucleic acids in cells. Bill Seeds and I studied DNA, proteins, tobacco mosaic virus, vitamin B_{12}, etc. While examining oriented films of DNA prepared for ultraviolet dichroism studies, I saw in the polarizing microscope extremely uniform fibres giving clear extinction between crossed nicols. I found the fibres had been produced unwittingly while I was manipulating DNA gel. Each time

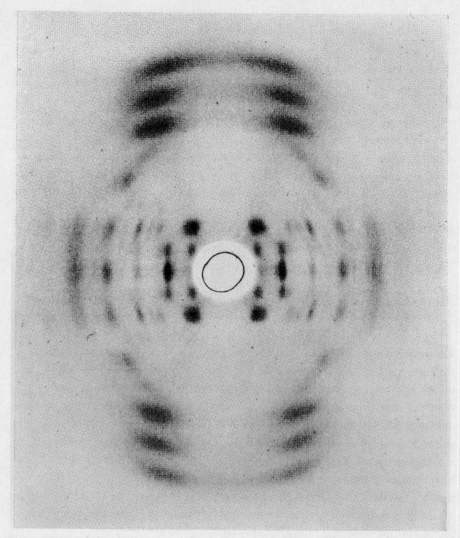

Fig. 1. One of the first X-ray diffraction photographs of DNA taken in our laboratory. This may be compared with the later photograph in Fig. 10. (Photograph with R. Gosling; DNA by R. Signer).

that I touched the gel with a glass rod and removed the rod, a thin and almost invisible fibre of DNA was drawn out like a filament of spider's web. The perfection and uniformity of the fibres suggested that the molecules in them were regularly arranged. I immediately thought the fibres might be excellent objects to study by X-ray diffraction analysis. I took them to Raymond Gosling, who had our only X-ray equipment (made from war-surplus radiography parts) and who was using it to obtain diffraction photographs from heads of ram spermatozoa. This research was directed by Randall, who had been trained under W. L. Bragg and had worked with X-ray diffraction. Almost immediately, Gosling obtained very encouraging diffraction patterns (see Fig. 1). One reason for this success was that we kept the fibres moist. We remembered that, to obtain detailed X-ray patterns from proteins, Bernal had kept protein crystals in their mother liquor. It seemed likely that the configuration of all kinds of water-soluble biological macromolecules would depend on their aqueous environment. We obtained good diffraction patterns with DNA made by Signer and Schwander[4] which Singer brought to London to a Faraday Society meeting on nucleic acids and which he generously distributed so that all workers, using their various techniques, could study it.

Realization that the Genetic Material was a Pure Chemical Substance and Signs that its Molecular Structure was Singularly Simple

Between 1946 and 1950 many lines of evidence were uncovered indicating that the genetic substance was DNA, not protein or nucleoprotein. For instance, it was found that the DNA content of a set of chromosomes was constant, and that DNA from a given species had a constant composition although the nucleotide sequence in DNA molecules was complex. It was suggested that genetic information was carried in the polynucleotide chain in a complicated sequence of the four nucleotides. The great significance of bacterial transformation now became generally recognized, and the demonstration by Hershey and Chase[5] that bacteriophage DNA carried the viral genetic information from parent to progeny helped to complete what was a fairly considerable revolution in thought.

The prospects of elucidating genetic function in terms of molecular structure were greatly improved when it was known that the genetic substance was DNA, which had a well-defined chemical structure, rather than an ill-defined nucleoprotein. There were many indications of simplicity and regularity in DNA structure. The chemists had shown that DNA was a polymer in which the phosphate and deoxyribose parts of the molecule were regularly repeated in a polynucleotide chain with 3'–5' linkages. Chargaff[6] discovered an important regularity: although the sequence of bases along the polynucleotide chains was complex and the base composition of different DNA's varied considerably, the numbers of adenine and thymine groups were always equal, and so were the numbers of guanine and cytosine. In the electron microscope, DNA was seen as a uniform unbranched thread of diameter about 20 Å. Signer, Caspersson, and Hammarsten[7] showed by flow-bire-fringence measurements that the bases in DNA lay with their planes roughly perpendicular to the length of the thread-like molecule. Their ultraviolet dichroism measurements gave the same results and showed marked par-allelism of the bases in the DNA in heads of spermatozoa. Earlier, Schmidt[8] and Pattri[9] had studied optically the remarkable ordering of the genetic material in sperm heads. Astbury[10] made pioneer X-ray diffraction studies of DNA fibres and found evidence of considerable regularity in DNA; he correctly interpreted the strong 3.4 Å reflection as being due to planar bases stacked on each other. The electro-titrometric study by Gulland and Jordan[11] showed that the bases were hydrogen-bonded together, and indeed Gulland[12] suggested that the polynucleotide chains might be linked by these hydrogen bonds to form multi-chain micelles.

Thus the remarkable conclusion that a pure chemical substance was in-vested with a deeply significant biological activity coincided with a consid-erable growth of many-sided knowledge of the nature of the substance. Meanwhile we began to obtain detailed X-ray diffraction data from DNA. This was the only type of data that could provide an adequate description of the 3-dimensional configuration of the molecule.

The Need for Combining X-ray Diffraction Studies of DNA with Molecular Model-Building

As soon as good diffraction patterns were obtained from fibres of DNA, great interest was aroused. In our laboratory, Alex Stokes provided a theory of diffraction from helical DNA. Rosalind Franklin (who died some years later at the peak of her career) made very valuable contributions to the X-ray analysis. In Cambridge, at the Medical Research Council laboratory where structures of biological macromolecules were studied, my friends Francis Crick and Jim Watson were deeply interested in DNA structure. Watson was a biologist who had gone to Cambridge to study molecular structure. He had worked on bacteriophage reproduction and was keenly aware of the great possibilities that might be opened up by finding the molecular structure of DNA. Crick was working on helical protein structure and was interested in what controlled protein synthesis. Pauling and Corey, by their discovery of the protein α-helix, had shown that precise molecular model-building was a powerful analytical tool in its own right. The X-ray data from DNA were not so complete that a detailed picture of DNA structure could be derived without considerable aid from stereochemistry. It was clear that the X-ray studies of DNA needed to be complemented by precise molecular model-building. In our laboratory we concentrated on amplifying the X-ray data. In Cambridge, Watson and Crick built molecular models.

The paradox of the regularity of the DNA molecule

The sharpness of the X-ray diffraction patterns of DNA showed that DNA molecules were highly regular – so regular that DNA could crystallize. The form of the patterns gave clear indications that the molecule was helical, the polynucleotide chains in the molecular thread being regularly twisted. It was known, however, that the purines and pyrimidines of various dimensions were arranged in irregular sequence along the polynucleotide chains. How could such an irregular arrangement give a highly regular structure? This paradox pointed to the solution of the DNA structure problem and was resolved by the structural hypothesis of Watson and Crick.

The Helical Structure of the DNA Molecule

The key to DNA molecular structure was the discovery by Watson and Crick[13] that, if the bases in DNA were joined in pairs by hydrogen-bonding, the overall dimensions of the pairs of adenine and thymine and of guanine and cytosine were identical. This meant that a DNA molecule containing these pairs could be highly regular in spite of the sequence of bases being irregular. Watson and Crick proposed that the DNA molecule consisted of two polynucleotide chains joined together by base-pairs. These pairs are shown in Fig. 2. The distance between the bonds joining the bases to the deoxyribose groups is exactly (within the uncertainty of 0.1 Å or so) the same for both base-pairs, and all those bonds make exactly (within the uncertainty of 1° or so) the same angle with the line joining the C_I atoms of the deoxyribose (see Fig. 2). As a result, if two polynucleotide chains are

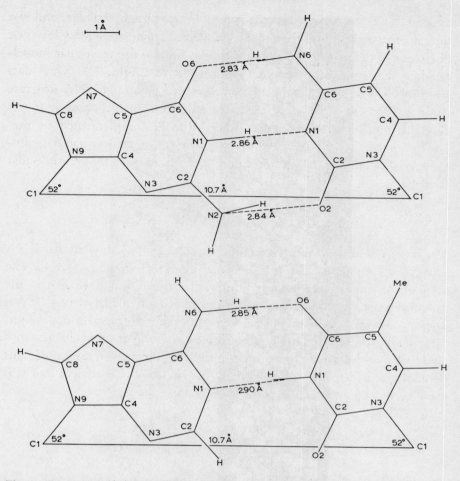

Fig. 2. Watson–Crick base-pairs (revised by S. Arnott). (*Top*): Guanine hydrogen-bonded to cytosine. (*Bottom*): Adenine hydrogen-bonded to thymine. The distances between the ends of the C_1–N_3 and C_1–N_9 bonds are 10.7 Å in both pairs, and all these bonds make an angle of 52° with the C_1–C_1 line.

joined by the base-pairs, the distance between the two chains is the same for both base-pairs and, because the angle between the bonds and the C_1–C_1 line is the same for all bases, the geometry of the deoxyribose and phosphate parts of the molecule can be exactly regular.

Watson and Crick built a two-chain molecular model of this kind, the chains being helical and the main dimensions being as indicated by the X-ray data. In the model, one polynucleotide chain is twisted round the other and

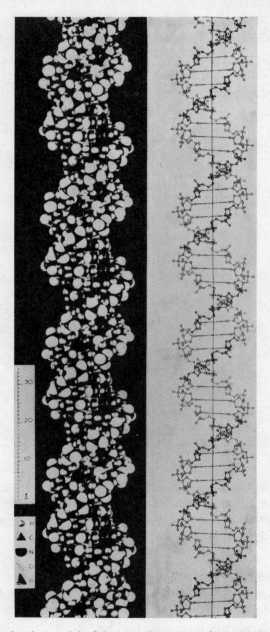

Fig. 3. (*Left*): Molecular model of the *B* configuration of DNA. The sizes of the atoms correspond to Van der Waals diameters. (*Right*): Diagram corresponding to the model. The two polynucleotide chains, joined by hydrogen-bonded bases, may be seen clearly.

the sequence of atoms in one chain runs in opposite direction to that in the other. As a result, one chain is identical with the other if turned upside down, and every nucleotide in the molecule has identical structure and environment. The only irregularities are in the base sequences. The sequence along one chain can vary without restriction, but base-pairing requires that adenine in one chain be linked to thymine in the other, and similarly guanine to cytosine. The sequence in one chain is, therefore, determined by the sequence in the other, and is said to be complementary to it.

The structure of the DNA molecule in the B configuration is shown in Fig. 3. The bases are stacked on each other 3.4 Å apart and their planes are almost perpendicular to the helix axis. The flat sides of the bases cannot bind water molecules; as a result there is attraction between the bases when DNA is in an aqueous medium. This hydrophobic bonding, together with the base-pair hydrogen-bonding, stabilizes the structure.

The Watson-Crick Hypothesis of DNA Replication, and Transfer of Information from one Polynucleotide Chain to Another

It is essential for genetic material to be able to make exact copies of itself; otherwise growth would produce disorder, life could not originate, and favourable forms would not be perpetuated by natural selection. Base-pairing provides the means of self-replication (Watson and Crick[14]). It also appears to be the basis of information transfer during various stages in protein synthesis.

Genetic information is written in a four-letter code in the sequence of the four bases along a polynucleotide chain. This information may be transferred from one polynucleotide chain to another. A polynucleotide chain acts as a template on which nucleotides are arranged to build a new chain. Provided that the two-chain molecule so formed is exactly regular, base-pairing ensures that the sequence in the new chain is exactly complementary to that in the parent chain. If the two chains then separate, the new chain can act as a template, and a further chain is formed; this is identical with the original chain. Most DNA molecules consist of two chains; clearly the copying process can be used to replicate such a molecule. It can also be used to transfer information from a DNA chain to an RNA chain (as is believed to be the case in the formation of messenger RNA).

Base-pairing also enables specific attachments to be made between part of one polynucleotide chain and a complementary sequence in another. Such specific interaction may be the means by which amino acids are attached to the requisite portions of a polynucleotide chain that has encoded in it the sequence of amino acids that specifies a protein. In this case the amino acid is attached to a transfer RNA molecule and part of the polynucleotide chain in this RNA pairs with the coding chain.

Since the base-pairs were first described by Watson and Crick in 1953, many new data on purine and pyrimidine dimensions and hydrogen-bond lengths have become available. The most recent refinement of the pairs (due to S. Arnott) is shown in Fig. 2. We now take the distance between C_I atoms as 10.7 Å instead of the value used recently of 11.0 Å, mainly because new data on N–H...N bonds show that this distance is 0.2 Å shorter between ring nitrogen atoms than between atoms that are not in rings. The linearity of the hydrogen bonds in the base-pairs is excellent and the lengths of the bonds are the same as those found in crystals (these lengths vary by about 0.04 Å).

The remarkable precision of the base-pairs reflects the exactness of DNA replication. One wonders, however, why the precision is so great, for the energy required to distort the base-pairs so that their perfection is appreciably less, is probably no greater than one quantum of thermal energy. The explanation may be that replication is a co-operative phenomenon involving many base-pairs. In any case, it must be emphasized that the specificity of the base-pairing depends on the bonds joining the bases to the deoxyribose groups being correctly placed in relation to each other. This placing is probably determined by the DNA polymerizing enzyme. Whatever the mechanics of the process are, the exact equivalence of geometry and environment of every nucleotide in the double-helix should be conducive to precise replication. Mistakes in the copying process will be produced if there are tautomeric shifts of protons involved in the hydrogen-bonding or chemical alterations of the bases. These mistakes can correspond to mutations.

The Universal Nature and Constancy of the Helical Structure of DNA

After our preliminary X-ray studies had been made, my friend Leonard Hamilton sent me human DNA he and Ralph Barclay had isolated from human leucocytes of a patient with chronic myeloid leukaemia. He was studying nucleic acid metabolism in man in relation to cancer and had pre-

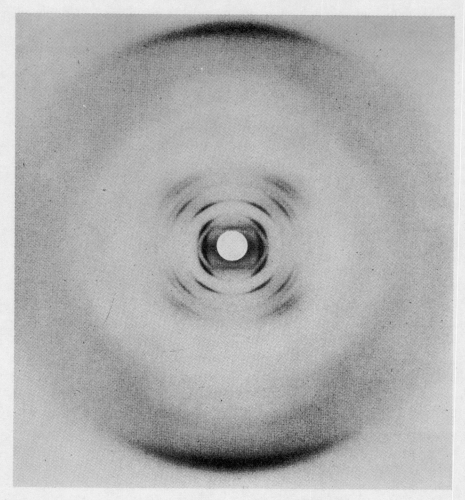

Fig. 4. X-ray diffraction pattern of cephalopod sperm. The DNA molecules in the sperm heads have their axes vertical. The 3.4 Å internucleotide spacing corresponds to the strong diffraction at the top and bottom of the pattern. The sharp reflections in the central part of the pattern show that the molecules are in crystalline array.

pared the DNA in order to compare the DNA of normal and leukaemic leucocytes. The DNA gave a very well-defined X-ray pattern. Thus began a collaboration that has lasted over many years and in which we have used Hamilton's DNA, in the form of many salts, to establish the correctness of the double-helix structure. Hamilton prepared DNA from a very wide range of species and diverse tissues. Thus it has been shown that the DNA double-helix is present in inert genetic material in sperm and bacteriophage, and in cells slowly or rapidly dividing or secreting protein (Hamilton et al.[16]). No difference of structure has been found between DNA from normal and

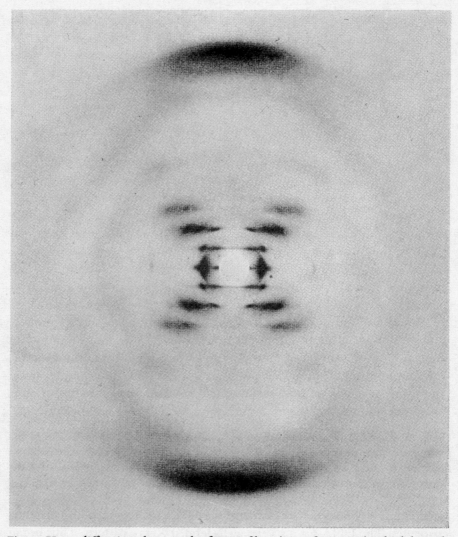

Fig. 5. X-ray diffraction photograph of DNA fibres (B configuration) at high humidity. The fibres are vertical. The 3.4 Å reflection is at the top and bottom. The angle in the pronounced X shape, made by the reflections in the central region, corresponds to the constant angle of ascent of the polynucleotide chains in the helical molecule. (Photograph with H. R. Wilson; DNA by L. D. Hamilton.)

from cancerous tissues, or in calf thymus DNA separated into fractions of different base composition by my colleague Geoffrey Brown.

We also made a study, in collaboration with Harriet Ephrussi–Taylor, of active transforming principle from pneumococci, and observed the same DNA structure. The only exception to double-helical DNA so far found is in some very small bacteriophages where the DNA is single-stranded. We have found, however, that DNA, with an unusually high content of adenine, or with glucose attached to hydroxymethylcytosine, crystallized differently.

DNA Structure is Not an Artefact

It did not seem enough to study X-ray diffraction from DNA alone. Obviously one should try to look at genetic material in intact cells. It was possible that the structure of the isolated DNA might be different from that *in vivo*, where DNA was in most cases combined with protein. The optical studies indicated that there was marked molecular order in sperm heads and that they might therefore be good objects for X-ray study, whereas chromosomes in most types of cells were complicated objects with little sign of ordered structure. Randall had been interested in this matter for some years and had started Gosling studying ram sperm. It seemed that the rod-shaped cephalopod sperm, found by Schmidt to be highly anisotropic optically, would be excellent for X-ray investigation. Rinne[17], while making a study of liquid crystals from many branches of Nature, had already taken diffraction photographs of such sperm; but presumably his technique was inadequate, for he came to the mistaken conclusion that the nucleoprotein was liquid-crystalline. Our X-ray photographs (Wilkins and Randall[18]) showed clearly that the material in the sperm heads had 3-dimensional order, i.e. it was crystalline and not liquid-crystalline. The diffraction pattern (Fig. 4) bore a close resemblance to that of DNA (Fig. 5), thus showing that the structure in fibres of purified DNA was basically not an artefact. Working at the Stazione Zoologica in Naples, I found it possible to orient the sperm heads in fibres. Intact wet spermatophore, being bundles of naturally oriented sperm, gave good diffraction patterns. DNA-like patterns were also obtained from T2 bacteriophage given me by Watson.

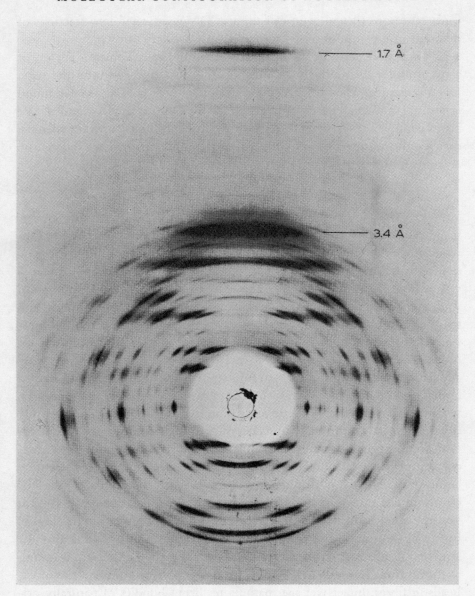

Fig. 6. X-ray pattern of microcrystalline fibres of DNA. The general intensity distribution is similar to that in Fig. 4 but the diffraction is split into sharp reflections owing to the regular arrangement of the molecules in the crystals. Sharp reflections extend to spacings as small as 1.7 Å. (Photograph with N. Chard; DNA by L. D. Hamilton.)

Table 1. Summary of various forms of DNA in fibres

Configuration of molecule	Number of nucleotide pairs per turn of helix	Inclination of base pairs in molecule	Salt	Relative humidity and condition necessary	Crystal class	Crystallinity	Molecular positions	Unit-cell dimensions a (Å)	b (Å)	c (Å)	β
A	11.0	20	Na K Rb	75%	mono-clinic	crystalline	$0, 0, 0$ $\frac{1}{2}, \frac{1}{2}, 0$	22.24	40.62	28.15	97.0
B	10	~0	Li	66% 3% LiCl in fibre	ortho-rhombic	crystalline	$0, 0, \frac{1}{6}$ $\frac{1}{2}, \frac{1}{2}, \frac{1}{6}$	22.5	30.9	33.7	—
			Li	75-90%	ortho-rhombic	semi-crystalline	$0, 0, \frac{1}{8}$ $\frac{1}{2}, \frac{1}{2}, \frac{1}{8}$	24.4	38.5	33.6	—
			Li Na K Rb	92%	hexagonal	semi-crystalline	$0, 0, 0$ $\frac{1}{3}, \frac{2}{3}, \frac{1}{3}$ $\frac{2}{3}, \frac{1}{3}, \frac{1}{6}$	46	—	34.6	—
B₂	9.9	0?	Na	75% under tension	tetragonal	semi-crystalline	$0, 0, 0$ $\frac{1}{2}, \frac{1}{2}, \frac{1}{4}$	27.4	—	33.8	—
C	9.3	~5	Li	44% no LiCl	ortho-rhombic	semi-crystalline	$0, 0, \frac{1}{8}$ $\frac{1}{2}, \frac{1}{2}, \frac{1}{8}$	20.1	31.9	30.9	—
			Li	44% in some specimens only. No LiCl in fibre	hexagonal	semi-crystalline	$0, 0, 0$, or $\frac{1}{2}$ $\frac{1}{3}, \frac{2}{3}, \frac{1}{6}$, or $\frac{1}{3}$ $\frac{2}{3}, \frac{1}{3}, \frac{1}{6}$, or $\frac{1}{3}$	35.0	—	30.9	—

The X-ray Diffraction Patterns of DNA and the Various Configurations of the Molecule

X-ray diffraction analysis is the only technique that can give very detailed information about the configuration of the DNA molecule. Optical techniques, though valuable as being complementary to X-ray analysis, provide much more limited information – mainly about orientation of bonds and groups. X-ray data contributed to the deriving of the structure of DNA at two stages. First, in providing information that helped in building the Watson-Crick model; and second, in showing that the Watson-Crick proposal was correct in its essentials, which involved readjusting and refining the model.

The X-ray studies (e.g. Langridge et al.[19], Wilkins[20]) show that DNA molecules are remarkable in that they adopt a large number of different conformations, most of which can exist in several crystal forms. The main factors determining the molecular conformation and crystal form are the water and salt contents of the fibre and the cation used to neutralize the phosphate groups (see Table 1).

I shall describe briefly the three main configurations of DNA. In all cases the diffraction data are satisfactorily accounted for in terms of the same basic Watson-Crick structure. This is a much more convincing demonstration of the correctness of the structure than if one configuration alone were studied. The basic procedure is to adjust the molecular model until the calculated intensities of diffraction from the model correspond to those observed (Langridge et al.[19]).

As with most X-ray data, only the intensities, and not the phases, of the diffracted beams from DNA are available. Therefore the structure cannot be derived directly. If the resolution of X-ray data is sufficient to separate most of the atoms in a structure, the structure may be derived with no stereochemical assumption except that the structure is assumed to consist of atoms of known average size. With DNA, however, most of the atoms cannot be separately located by the X-rays alone (see Fig. 7). Therefore, more extensive stereochemical assumptions are made: these take the form of molecular model-building. There are no alternatives to most of these assumptions but where there might be an alternative, e.g. in the arrangement of hydrogen bonds in a base-pair, the X-ray data should be used to establish the correctness of the assumption. In other words, it is necessary to establish that the structure proposed is unique. Most of our work in recent years has

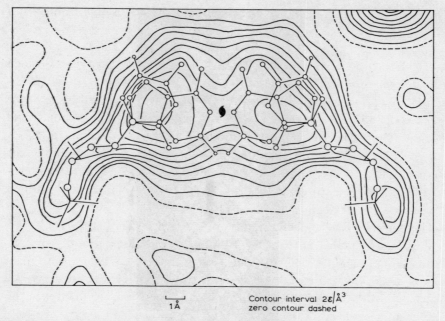

Contour interval $2\varepsilon/\text{Å}^3$
zero contour dashed

1 Å

Fig. 7. Fourier synthesis map (by S. Arnott) showing the distribution of electron density in the plane of a base-pair in the *B* configuration of DNA. The distribution corresponds to an average base-pair. The shape of the base-pair appears in the map, but individual atoms in a base-pair are not resolved. (The Fourier synthesis is being revised and the map is subject to improvement.)

been of this nature. To be reasonably certain that the DNA structure was correct, X-ray data, as extensive as possible, had to be collected.

The B configuration

Fig. 5 shows a diffraction pattern of a fibre of DNA at high humidity when the molecules are separated by water and, to a large extent, behave independently of each other. We have not made intensive study of DNA under these conditions. The patterns could be improved, but they are reasonably well-defined, and the sharpness of many of their features shows that the molecules have a regular structure. The configuration is known as *B* (see also Fig. 3); it is observed *in vivo*, and there is evidence that it exists when DNA is in solution in water. There are 10 nucleotide pairs per helix turn. There is no obvious structural reason why this number should be integral; if it is exactly so, the significance of this is not yet apparent.

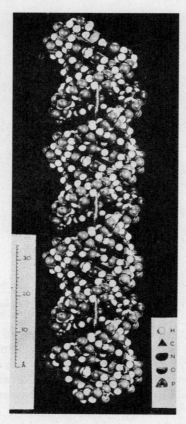

Fig. 8. Molecular model of DNA in the *A* configuration. The base-pairs may be seen inclined 20° to the horizontal.

When DNA crystallizes, the process of crystallization imposes restraints on the molecule and can give it extra regularity. Also, the periodic arrangement of the molecules in the microcrystals in the fibre causes the diffraction pattern to be split into sharp reflections corresponding to the various crystal planes (Fig. 6). Careful measurement of the positions of the reflections and deduction of the crystal lattice enables the directions of the reflections to be identified in three dimensions. Diffraction patterns from most fibrous substances resemble Fig. 5 in that the diffraction data are 2-dimensional. In contrast, the crystalline fibres of DNA give fairly complete 3-dimensional data. These data give information about the appearance of the molecule when viewed from all angles, and are comparable with those from single crystals. Techniques such as 3-dimensional Fourier synthesis (see Fig. 7) can be used and the structure determination made reasonably reliable.

The A configuration

In this conformation, the molecule has 11 nucleotide pairs per helix turn; the helix pitch is 28 Å. The relative positions and orientations of the base, and of the deoxyribose and phosphate parts of the nucleotides differ considerably from those in the B form; in particular the base-pairs are tilted 20° from perpendicular to the helix axis (Fig. 8).

The A form of DNA (Fig. 1) was the first crystalline form to be observed. Although it has not been observed *in vivo*, it is of special interest because helical RNA adopts a very similar configuration. A full account of A DNA will shortly be available. A good photograph of the A pattern is shown in Fig. 9.

The C configuration

This form may be regarded as an artefact formed by partial drying. The helix is non-integral, with about $9\frac{1}{3}$ nucleotide pairs per turn. The helices pack together to form a semi-crystalline structure; there is no special relation between the position of one nucleotide in a molecule and that in another. The conformation of an individual nucleotide is very similar to that in the B form. The differences between the B and C diffraction patterns are accounted for by the different position of the nucleotides in the helix. Comparison of the forms provides further confirmation of the correctness of the structures. In a way, the problem is like trying to deduce the structure of a folding chair by observing its shadow: if the conformation of the chair is altered slightly, its structure becomes more evident.

The Helical Structure of RNA Molecules

In contrast to DNA, RNA gave poor diffraction patterns, in spite of much effort by various workers including ourselves. There were many indications that RNA contained helical regions, e.g. optical properties of RNA solutions strongly suggested (e.g. Doty[21]) that parts of RNA molecules resembled DNA in that the bases were stacked on each other and the structure was helical; and X-ray studies of synthetic polyribonucleotides suggested that

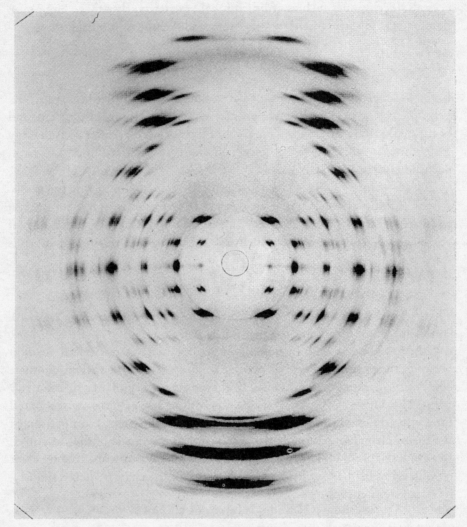

Fig. 9. X-ray diffraction pattern of microcrystalline fibres of DNA in the *A* configuration. (Photograph with H. R. Wilson; DNA by L. D. Hamilton.)

RNA resembled DNA (Rich[22]). The diffraction patterns of RNA (Rich and
Watson[23]) bore a general resemblance to those of DNA, but the nature of
pattern could not be clearly distinguished because of disorientation and
diffuseness. An important difficulty was that there appeared to be strong
meridional reflections at 3.3 Å and 4 Å. It was not possible to interpret these
in terms of one helical structure.

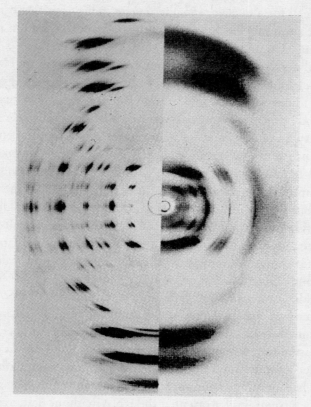

Fig. 10. Comparison of the X-ray diffraction patterns of fibres of DNA in the *A* configuration (*left*) and transfer RNA (*right*). The general distribution of intensity is very similar in both patterns, but the positions of the sharp crystalline reflections differ because the molecular packing in the crystals is different in the two cases. (Photograph with W. Fuller and M. Spencer; RNA by G. L. Brown.)

In early work, many RNA preparations were very heterogeneous. We thought that the much more homogeneous plant virus RNA might give better patterns, but this was not so. However, when preparations of ribo-somal RNA and «soluble» RNA became available, we felt the prospects of structure analysis were improved. We decided to concentrate on «soluble» RNA largely because Geoffrey Brown in our laboratory was preparing large quantities of a highly purified transfer RNA component of soluble RNA for his physical and chemical studies, and because he was fractionating it into various transfer RNA's specific for incorporation of particular amino acids into proteins. This RNA was attractive for other reasons: the molecule was unusually small for a nucleic acid, there were indications that it might have a regular structure, its biochemical role was important, and in many ways its functioning was understood.

We found it very difficult to orient transfer RNA in fibres. However, by carefully stretching RNA gels in a dry atmosphere under a dissecting microscope, I found that fibres with birefringence as high as that of DNA could be made. But these fibres gave patterns no better than those obtained with other types of RNA, and the molecules disoriented when the water content of the fibres was raised. Watson, Fuller, Michael Spencer, and myself worked for many months trying to make better specimens for X-ray study. We made little progress until Spencer found a specimen that gave some faint but sharp diffraction rings in addition to the usual diffuse RNA pattern. This specimen consisted of RNA gel that had been sealed for X-ray study in a small cell, and he found that it had dried slowly owing to a leak. The diffraction rings were so sharp that we were almost certain that they were spurious diffraction due to crystalline impurity – this being common in X-ray studies of biochemical preparations. A specimen of RNA had given very similar rings due to DNA impurity. We were therefore not very hopeful about the rings. However, after several weeks Spencer eliminated all other possibilities: it seemed clear that the rings were due to RNA itself. By controlled slow drying, he produced stronger rings; and, with the refined devices we had developed for stretching RNA and with gels slowly concentrated by Brown, Fuller oriented the RNA without destroying its crystallinity. These fibres gave clearly defined diffraction patterns, and the orientation did not disappear when the fibres were hydrated. It appeared that the methods I had been using earlier, of stretching the fibres as much as possible, destroyed the crystallinity. If instead, the material was first allowed to crystallize slowly, stretching oriented the microcrystals and the RNA molecules in them. Single molecules were too small to be oriented well unless aggregated by crystallization. It was rather unexpected that, of all the different types of RNA we had tried, transfer RNA which had the lowest molecular weight, oriented best.

The diffraction patterns of transfer RNA were clearly defined and well-oriented (Spencer, Fuller, Wilkins, and Brown[24]). These improvements revealed a striking resemblance between the patterns of RNA and A DNA (Fig. 10). The difficulty of the two reflections at 3.3 Å and 4 Å was resolved (Fig. 11): in the RNA pattern the positions of reflections on three layer-lines differed from those in DNA; as a result, when the patterns were poorly

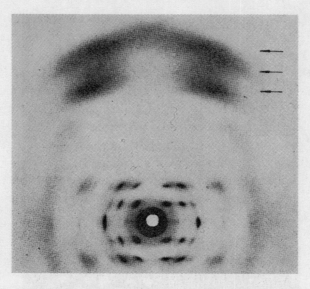

Fig. 11. Diffraction pattern of transfer RNA showing resolution of diffraction, in the regions of 3.3 Å and 4 Å, into three layer-lines indicated by the arrows and corresponding to the *A* DNA pattern. (Photograph with W. Fuller and M. Spencer; RNA by G. L. Brown.)

oriented, the three reflections overlapped and gave the impression of two. There was no doubt that the RNA had a regular helical structure almost identical with that of *A* DNA. The differences between the RNA and DNA patterns could be accounted for in terms of small differences between the two structures.

An important consequence of the close resemblance of the RNA structure to that of DNA is that the RNA must contain base sequences that are largely or entirely complementary. The number of nucleotides in the molecule is about 80. The simplest structure compatible with the X-ray results consists of a single polynucleotide chain folded back on itself, one half of the chain being joined to the other by base-pairing. This structure is shown in Fig. 12. While we are certain the helical structure is correct, it must be emphasized that we do not know whether the two ends of the chain are at the end of the molecule. The chain might be folded at both ends of the molecule with the ends of the chain somewhere along the helix. It is known that the amino acid attaches to the end of the chain terminated by the base sequence cytosine–cytosine–adenine.

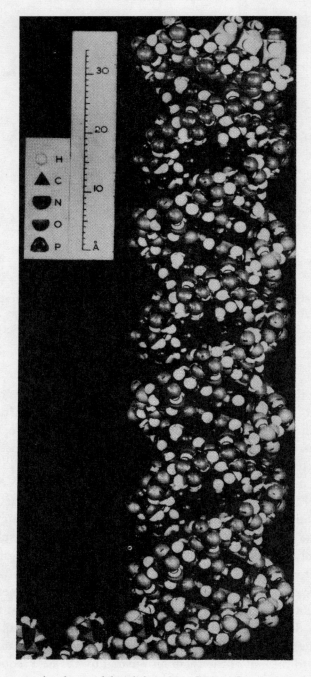

Fig. 12. Molecular model and diagram of a transfer RNA molecule.

Relation of the Molecular Structure of RNA to Function

Molecular model-building shows that the number of nucleotides forming the fold at the end of a transfer RNA molecule must be three or more. In our model, the fold consists of three nucleotides, each with an unpaired base. It might be that this base-triplet is the part of the molecule that attaches to the requisite part of the coding RNA polynucleotide chain that determines the sequence of amino acids in the polypeptide chain of a protein. It is believed that a base-triplet in the coding RNA corresponds to each amino acid. The triplet in the transfer RNA could attach itself specifically to the coding triplet by hydrogen-bonding and formation of base-pairs. It must be emphasized, however, that these ideas are speculative.

We suppose that part of the transfer RNA molecule interacts specifically with the enzyme that is involved in attaching the amino acid to the RNA; but we do not know how this takes place. Similarly, we know little of the way in which the enzyme involved in DNA replication interacts with DNA, or of other aspects of the mechanics of DNA replication. The presence of complementary base sequences in the transfer RNA molecule, suggests that it might be self-replicating like DNA; but there is at present little evidence to support this idea. The diffraction patterns of virus and ribosome RNA show that these molecules also contain helical regions; the function of these are uncertain too.

In the case of DNA, the discovery of its molecular structure led immediately to the replication hypothesis. This was due to the simplicity of the structure of DNA. It seems that molecular structure and function are in most cases less directly related. Derivation of the helical configuration of RNA molecules is a step towards interpreting RNA function; but more complete structural information, e.g. determination of base sequences, and more knowledge about how the various kinds of RNA interact in the ribosome, will probably be required before an adequate picture of RNA function emerges.

The Possibility of Determining the Base Sequence of Transfer RNA by X-ray Diffraction Analysis

Since the biological specificity of nucleic acids appears to be entirely determined by their base sequences in them, determination of these sequences is probably the most fundamental problem in nucleic acid research today. The

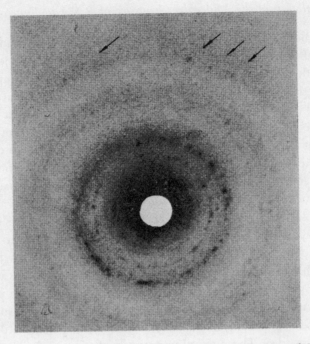

Fig. 13. Diffraction pattern of unoriented transfer RNA, showing diffraction rings with spots corresponding to reflections from single crystals of RNA. The arrows point to reflections from planes ~ 6 Å apart.

number of bases in a DNA molecule is too large for determination of base sequence by X-ray diffraction to be feasible. However, in transfer RNA the number of bases is not too large. The possibility of complete structure analysis of transfer RNA by means of X-rays is indicated by two observations. First, we have observed (Fig. 13), in X-ray patterns of transfer RNA, separate spots each corresponding to a single crystal of RNA. We estimated their size to be about 10μ and have confirmed this estimate by observing, in the polarizing microscope, birefringent regions that probably are the crystals. It should not be too difficult to grow crystals several times larger, which is large enough for single-crystal X-ray analysis.

The second encouraging observation is that the X-ray data from DNA have restricted resolution almost entirely on account of disorientation of the microcrystals in DNA fibres. The DNA intensity data indicate that the temperature factor $(B = 4 \text{ Å})$ is the same for DNA as for simple compounds. It thus appears that DNA crystals have fairly perfect crystallinity and that, if single crystals of DNA could be obtained, the intensity data would be adequate for precise determination of all atomic positions in DNA (apart from the non-periodic base sequence).

We are investigating the possibility of obtaining single crystals of DNA, but the more exciting problem is to obtain single crystals of transfer RNA with crystalline perfection equal to that of DNA, and thereby analyse base sequence. At present, the RNA crystals are much less perfect than those of DNA. However, most of our experiments have been made with RNA that is a mixture of RNA's specific for different amino acids. We have seldom used RNA that is very largely specific for one amino acid only. We hope that good preparations of such RNA may be obtained consisting of one type of molecule only. We might expect such RNA to form crystals as perfect as those of DNA. If so, there should be no obstacle to the direct analysis of the whole structure of the molecule, including the sequence of the bases and the fold at the end of the helix. We may be over-optimistic, but the recent and somewhat unexpected successes of X-ray diffraction analysis in the nucleic acid and protein fields, are cause for optimism.

Acknowledgements

During the past twelve years, while studying molecular structure of nucleic acids, I have had so much help from so many people that all could not be acknowledged properly here. I must, however, thank the following:

Sir John Randall, for his long-standing help and encouragement, and for his vision and energy in creating and directing a unique laboratory;

all my co-workers at various times over the past twelve years; first, Raymond Gosling, Alex Stokes, Bill Seeds, and Herbert Wilson, then Bob Langridge, Clive Hooper, Max Feughelman, Don Marvin, and Geoffrey Zubay; and at present, Michael Spencer, Watson Fuller, and Struther Arnott, who with much ability, skill and persistence (often through the night) carried out the X-ray, molecular model-building, and computing studies;

my late colleague Rosalind Franklin who, with great ability and experience of X-ray diffraction, so much helped the initial investigations on DNA;

Leonard Hamilton for his constant encouragement and friendly cooperation, and for supplying us with high-quality DNA isolated in many forms and from many sources; Geoffrey Brown for giving me moral and intellectual support throughout the work and for preparing RNA for X-ray study; Harriet Ephrussi-Taylor for the privilege of collaborating with her in studying crystallization of transforming principle; the laboratory technicians, mechanics and photographers, including P. J. Cooper, N. Chard, J. Hayward, Mrs. F. Collier, Z. Gabor, and R. Lerner, for having played a valuable part in the work at various stages.

I also wish to thank:

the Medical Research Council for their far-sighted and consistent support of our work; King's College for being our base; I.B.M. United Kingdom Limited and I.B.M. World Trade Corporation and the London University Computer Unit for help with computing; The Rockefeller Foundation and The British Empire Cancer Campaign for financial support; the Sloan-Kettering Institute, New York, and the Stazione Zoologica, Naples, for use of facilities.

More generally, I thank:

Francis Crick and Jim Watson for stimulating discussion; Norman Simmons for having refined techniques of isolating DNA and thereby helping a great many workers including ourselves; many other workers for supplying us with DNA and RNA; and especially, Erwin Chargaff for laying foundations for nucleic acid structural studies by his analytical work and his discovery of the equality of base contents in DNA, and for generously helping us newcomers in the field of nucleic acids.

1. T. Caspersson, *Naturwiss.*, 29 (1941) 33.
2. J. Brachet, *Arch. Biol. Liege*, 53 (1942) 207.
3. O. T. Avery, C. M. MacLeod, and M. McCarty, *J. Exp. Med.*, 79 (1944) 137.
4. R. Signer and H. Schwander, *Helv. Chim. Acta*, 32 (1949) 853.
5. A. D. Hershey and M. Chase, *J. Gen. Physiol.*, 36 (1952) 39.
6. E. Chargaff, *Experientia*, 6 (1950) 201.
7. R. Signer, T. Caspersson, and E. Hammarsten, *Nature*, 141 (1938) 122.
8. W. J. Schmidt, *Die Doppelbrechung von Karyoplasma, Zytoplasma, und Metaplasma*, Borntraeger, Berlin, 1937.
9. H. O. E. Pattri, *Z. Zellforsch. Mikroskop. Anat.*, 16 (1932) 723.
10. W. T. Astbury, *Symp. Soc. Exptl. Biol., I. Nucleic Acid*, Cambridge Univ. Press, 1947, p. 66.
11. J. M. Gulland and D. O. Jordan, *Symp. Soc. Exptl. Biol., I. Nucleic Acid*, Cambridge Univ. Press, 1947.
12. J. M. Gulland, *Cold. Spring Harbor Symp. Quant. Biol.*, 12 (1947) 95.
13. J. D. Watson and F. H. C. Crick, *Nature*, 171 (1953a) 737.

14. J. D. Watson and F. H. C. Crick, *Nature*, 171 (1953b) 964.

15. K. Hoogsteen, *Acta Cryst.*, 12 (1959) 822.

16. L. D. Hamilton, R. K. Barclay, M. H. F. Wilkins, G. L. Brown, H. R. Wilson, D. A. Marvin, H. Ephrussi-Taylor, and N. S. Simmons, *J. Biophys. Biochem. Cytol.*, 5 (1959) 397.

17. F. Rinne, *Trans. Faraday Soc.*, 29 (1933) 1016.

18. M. H. F. Wilkins and J. T. Randall, *Biochim. Biophys. Act.*, 10 (1953) 192.

19. R. Langridge, H. R. Wilson, C. W. Hooper, M. H. F. Wilkins, and L. D. Hamilton, *J. Mol. Biol.*, 2 (1960) 19.

20. M. H. F. Wilkins, *J. Chim. Phys.*, 58 (1961) 891.

21. P. Doty, *Biochem. Soc. Symp.*, No. 21 (1961) 8.

22. A. Rich, in *A Symposium on Molecular Biology* (Ed. Zirkle), Univ. Chicago Press, 1959, p. 47.

23. A. Rich and J. D. Watson, *Nature*, 173 (1954) 995.

24. M. Spencer, W. Fuller, M. H. F. Wilkins, and G. L. Brown, *Nature*, 194 (1962) 1014.

THE BIOLOGIC SYNTHESIS OF DEOXYRIBONUCLEIC ACID

by

ARTHUR KORNBERG.

Nobel Lecture, December 11, 1959.

The knowledge drawn in recent years from studies of bacterial transformation (1) and viral infection of bacterial cells (2, 3) combined with other evidence (3), has just about convinced most of us that deoxyribonucleic acid (DNA) is the genetic substance. We shall assume then that it is DNA which not only directs the synthesis of the proteins and the development of the cell but that it must also be the substance which is copied so as to provide for a similar development of the progeny of that cell for many generations. DNA, like a tape recording, carries a message in which there are specific instructions for a job to be done. Also like a tape recording, exact copies can be made from it so that this information can be used again and elsewhere in time and space.

Are these two functions, the expression of the code (protein synthesis) and the copying of the code (preservation of the race) closely integrated or are they separable? What we have learned from our studies over the past five years and what I shall present is that the replication of DNA can be examined and at least partially understood at the enzymatic level even though the secret of how DNA directs protein synthesis is still locked in the cell.

DNA structure.

First I should like to review very briefly some aspects of DNA structure which are essential for this discussion. Analysis of the composition of samples of DNA from a great variety of sources and by many investigators (4) revealed the remarkable fact that the purine content always equals the pyrimidine content. Among the purines, the adenine content may differ considerably from the guanine, and among the pyrimidines, the thymine from the cytosine.

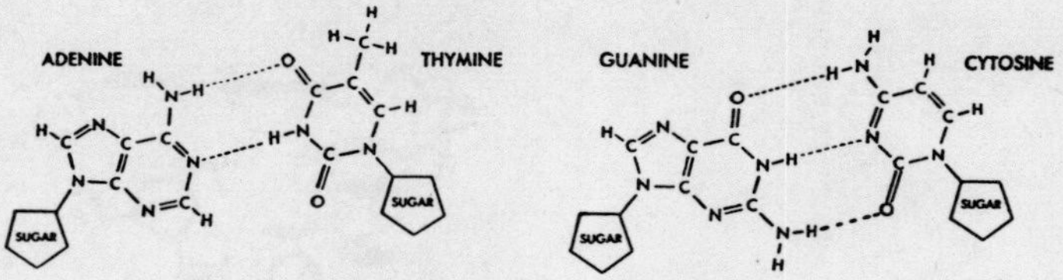

Fig. 1. Hydrogen Bonding of Bases.

However, there is an equivalence of the bases with an amino group in the 6-position of the ring, to the bases with a keto group in the 6-position. These facts were interpreted by WATSON and CRICK (5) in their masterful hypothesis on the structure of DNA. As shown in Fig. 1, they proposed in connection with their double-stranded model for DNA, to be discussed presently, that the 6-amino group of adenine is linked by hydrogen bonds to the 6-keto group of thymine and in a like manner guanine is hydrogen-bonded to cytosine, thus accounting for the equivalence of the purines to the pyrimidines. On the basis of these considerations and the results of X-ray crystallographic measurements by WILKINS and associates (6), WATSON and CRICK proposed a structure for DNA in which two long strands are wound about each other in a helical manner. Fig. 2 is diagrammatic representation of a fragment of a DNA chain about ten nucleotide units long. According to physical measurements, DNA chains are on the average 10 000 units long. We see here the deoxypentose rings linked by phosphate residues to form the backbone of the chain; the purine and pyrimidine rings are the planar structures emerging at right angles from the main axis of the chain. Fig. 3 is a more detailed molecular model (7) and gives a better idea of the packing of the atoms in the structure. The purine and pyrimidine bases of one chain are bonded to the pyrimidine and purine bases of the complementary chain by the hydrogen bonds described in Fig. 1. The X-ray measurements have indicated that the space between the opposing chains in the model agrees with the calculated value for the hydrogen-bond linkage of a purine to a pyrimidine; it is too small for two purines and too large for two pyrimidines. Most rewarding from the biological point of view, the structure provides a useful model to explain how cellular replication of DNA may come about. For, if you imagine that these two chains separate and that a new chain is formed complementary to each of them, the result will be two pairs of strands, each pair identical to the original parent duplex and identical to each other.

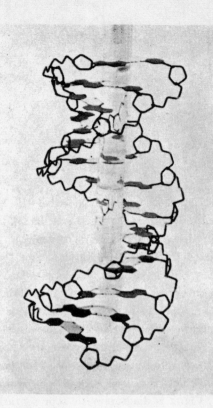

Fig. 2. Double Helical Structure
of DNA (Watson and Crick Model).

Enzymatic approach to the problem of DNA replication.

Although we have in the WATSON and CRICK proposal a mechanical model of replication, we may at this point pose the question: "What is the chemical mechanism by which this super molecule is built up in the cell?" Some sixty years ago the alcoholic fermentation of sugar by a yeast cell was a "vital" process inseparable from the living cell, but through the Buchner discovery of fermentation in extracts and the march of enzymology during the first half of this century we understand fermentation by yeast as a, now familiar, sequence of integrated chemical reactions. Five years ago the synthesis of DNA was also regarded as a "vital" process. Some people considered it useful for biochemists to examine the combustion chambers of the cell, but tampering with the very genetic apparatus itself would surely produce nothing but disorder. These gloomy predictions were not justified then nor are similar pessimistic attitudes justified now with regard to the problems of cellular structure

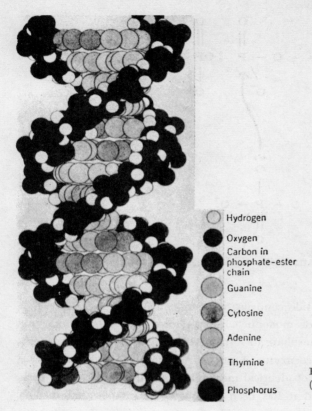

Hydrogen

Oxygen

Carbon in
phosphate-ester
chain

Guanine

Cytosine

Adenine

Thymine

Phosphorus

Fig. 3. Molecular Model of DNA
(After M. FEUGHELMAN, *et al.*
(7)).

and specialized function which face us. High adventures in enzymology lie ahead and many of the explorers will come from the training fields of carbohydrate, fat, amino acid and nucleic acid enzymology.

I feel now, as we did then, that for an effective approach to the problem of nucleic acid biosynthesis it was essential to understand the biosynthesis of the simple nucleotides and the coenzymes and to have these concepts and methodology well in hand. It was from these studies that we developed the conviction that an activated nucleoside 5'-phosphate is the basic biosynthetic building block of the nucleic acids (8). You will recall that the main pathways of purine and pyrimidine biosynthesis all lead to the nucleoside 5'-phosphate (8); they do not, except as salvage mechanisms, usually include the free bases or nucleosides. While the 2' and 3' isomers of the nucleotides are known, they probably arise mainly from certain types of enzymatic degradation of the nucleic acids. You will also recall from the biosynthesis of coenzymes (9),

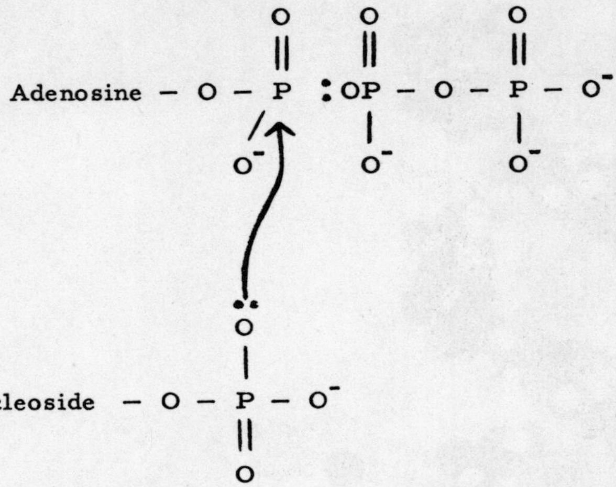

Fig. 4. Nucleophilic Attack of a Nucleoside Monophosphate on ATP.

the simplest of the nucleotide condensation products, that it is ATP which condenses with nicotinamide mononucleotide to form diphosphopyridine nucleotide, with riboflavin phosphate to form FAD, with pantetheine phosphate to form the precursor of coenzyme A and so forth. This pattern has been amplified by the discovery of identical mechanisms for the activation of fatty acids and amino acids and it has been demonstrated further that uridine, cytidine and guanosine coenzymes are likewise formed from the respective triphosphates of these nucleosides.

This mechanism (Fig. 4), in which a nucleophilic attack (10) on the pyrophosphate-activated adenyl group by a nucleoside monophosphate leads to the formation of a coenzyme, was adopted as a working hypothesis for studying the synthesis of a DNA chain. As illustrated in Fig. 5, it was postulated that the basic building block is a deoxynucleoside 5'-triphosphate which is attacked by the 3'-hydroxyl group at the growing end of a polydeoxynucleotide chain; inorganic pyrophosphate is eliminated and the chain is lengthened by one unit. The results of our studies on DNA synthesis, as will be mentioned presently, are in keeping with this type of reaction.

Properties of the DNA-synthesizing enzyme.

First let us consider the enzyme and comment on its discovery (8, 11, 12). Mixing the triphosphates of the four deoxynucleosides which commonly occur in DNA with an extract of thymus or bone-marrow or of *Escherichia coli*

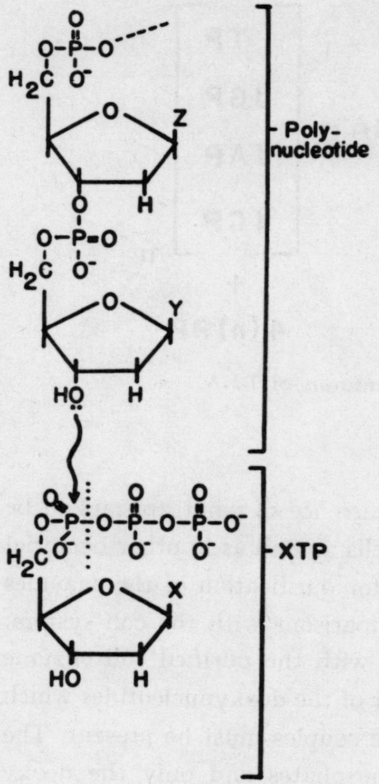

Fig. 5. Postulated Mechanism for Extending a DNA Chain.

would not be expected to lead to the net synthesis of DNA. Instead, as might be expected, the destruction of DNA by the extracts of such cells and tissues was by far the predominant process and one had to resort to the use of more subtle devices for detection of such a biosynthetic reaction. We used a C^{14}-labeled substrate of high specific radioactivity and incubated it with ATP and extracts of *Escherichia coli*, an organism which reproduces itself every 20 minutes. The first positive results represented the conversion of only a very small fraction of the acid-soluble substrate into an acid-insoluble fraction (50 or so counts out of a million added). While this represented only a few $\mu\mu$moles of reaction, it was something. Through this tiny crack we tried to drive a wedge and the hammer was enzyme purification (13). This has been and still is a major preoccupation. Our best preparations are several thousand-fold enriched with respect to protein over the crude extracts, but there are still contaminating quantities of one or more of the many varieties of nuclease

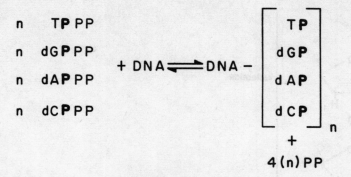

Fig. 6. Equation for Enzymatic Synthesis of DNA.

and diesterase present in the coli cell. The occurrence of what appears to be a similar DNA synthesizing system in animal cells as well as in other bacterial species has been observed (14). We must wait for purification of the enzymes from these sources in order to make valid comparisons with the coli system.

The requirements for net synthesis of DNA with the purified coli enzyme (15) are shown in the equation in Fig. 6. All four of the deoxynucleotides which form the adenine-thymine and guanine-cytosine couples must be present. The substrates must be the tri- and not the diphosphates and only the deoxy sugar compounds are active. DNA which must be present may be obtained from animal, plant, bacterial or viral sources and the best indications are that all these DNA samples serve equally well in DNA synthesis provided their molecular weight is high. The product, which we will discuss in further detail, accumulates until one of the substrates is exhausted and may be 20 or more times greater in amount than the DNA added and thus is composed to the extent of 95 % or more of the substrates added to the reaction mixture. Inorganic pyrophosphate is released in quantities equimolar to the deoxynucleotides converted to DNA.

Should one of these substrates be omitted, the extent of reaction is diminished by a factor of greater than 10^4 and special methods are now required for its detection. It turns out that when one of the deoxynucleotide substrates is lacking, an extremely small but yet significant quantity of nucleotide is linked to the DNA primer. We have described this so-called "limited reaction" (16), and have shown that under these circumstances a few deoxynucleotides are added to the nucleoside ends of some of the DNA chains but

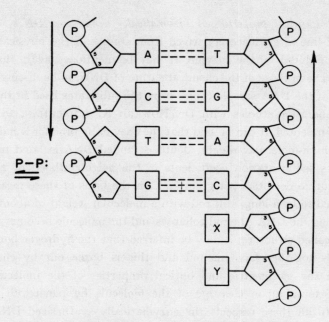

Fig. 7. Mechanism for Enzymatic DNA Replication.

that further synthesis is blocked for lack of the missing nucleotide. Current studies suggest to us that this limited reaction represents the repair of the shorter strand of a double helix in which the strands are of unequal length, and that the reaction is governed by the hydrogen bonding of adenine to thymine and of guanine to cytosine.

When all four triphosphates are present, but when DNA is omitted, no reaction at all takes place. What is the basis for this requirement? Does the DNA function as a primer in the manner of glycogen or does it function as a template in directing the synthesis of exact copies of itself? We have good reason to believe that it is the latter and as the central and restricted theme of this lecture I would like to emphasize that it is the capacity for base pairing by hydrogen bonding between the preexisting DNA and the nucleotides added as substrates that accounts for the requirement for DNA.

The enzyme we are studying is thus unique in present experience in taking directions from a template — it adds the particular purine or pyrimidine substrate which will form a hydrogen-bonded pair with a base on the template (Fig. 7). There are five major lines of evidence that I would like to present to support this thesis.

Physical properties of enzymatically synthesized DNA.

The first line of evidence is derived from studies of the physical nature of the DNA produced by the enzyme. It may be mentioned again that in these descriptions as in those of the chemical nature of DNA, to be discussed shortly, 90—95 % of the DNA sample comes from the substrates used in the reaction. From collaborative studies with Dr. HOWARD K. SCHACHMAN, to whom we are greatly indebted, it can be said that the enzymatic product is indistinguishable from high-molecular weight, double-stranded DNA isolated from nature (17). It has sedimentation coefficients in the neighbourhood of 25, reduced viscosities of 40 deciliters per gram and, on the basis of these measurements, it is believed to be a long, stiff rod with a molecular weight of about 6 million. Upon heating the DNA, the rod collapses and the molecule becomes a compact, randomly coiled structure; it may be inferred that the hydrogen bonds holding the strands together have melted and this is borne out by characteristic changes in the viscometric and optical properties of the molecule. Similar results are found upon cleavage of the molecule by pancreatic deoxyribonuclease. In all these respects the enzymatically synthesized DNA is indistinguishable from the material isolated from nature, and may thus be presumed to have a hydrogen-bonded structure similar to that possessed by natural DNA.

Would one imagine that the collapsed jumbled strands of heated DNA would serve as a primer for DNA synthesis? Very likely one would think not. Guided by intuition derived from everyday experience with a jumbled strand of twine one might regard this as a hopeless template for replication. It turns out that the collapsed DNA is an excellent primer and the nonviscous, randomly coiled, single-stranded DNA leads to the synthesis of highly viscous, double-stranded DNA (18). SINSHEIMER has isolated from the tiny ØX 174 virus a DNA which appears to be single-stranded (19). Like heated DNA it has proved to be an excellent primer (18) and a favorable material in current studies (20) for demonstrating in density gradient sedimentations that it is progressively converted to a double-stranded condition during the course of enzymatic synthesis.

While a detailed discussion of the physical aspects of replication is not feasible in this lecture, it should be mentioned that the DNA in the single-stranded condition is not only a suitable primer but is the only active form when the most purified enzyme preparations are used. With such coli preparations, the native, double-stranded DNA is inert unless it is heated or pretreated very slightly with deoxyribonuclease. BOLLUM has made similar observations with the enzyme that he has purified from calf thymus (21).

Substitution of analogues in DNA synthesis.

The second line of evidence is derived from studies of the activity of the substrates when substitutions are made in the purine and pyrimidine bases. From the many interesting reports on the incorporation of bromouracil (22), azaguanine (23) and other analogues into bacterial and viral DNA, it might be surmised that some latitude in the structure of the bases can be tolerated provided there is no interference with their hydrogen bondings. When experiments were carried out with deoxyuridine triphosphate or 5-bromodeoxy-uridine triphosphate, it was found that they supported DNA synthesis when used in place of thymidine triphosphate but not when substituted for the triphosphates of deoxyadenosine, deoxyguanosine or deoxycytidine. As already described (24), 5-methyl- and 5-bromocytosine specifically replaced cytosine; hypoxanthine substituted only for guanine; and, as just mentioned, uracil and 5-bromouracil specifically replaced thymine. These findings are best interpreted on the basis of hydrogen bonding of the adenine-thymine and guanine-cytosine type.

Along these lines it is relevant to mention the existence of a naturally occurring "analogue" of cytosine, hydroxymethyl cytosine (HMC), which is found in place of cytosine in the DNA of the coli bacteriophages of the T-even series (25). In this case the DNA contains equivalent amounts of HMC and guanine and, as usual, equivalent amounts of adenine and thymine. Of additional interest is the fact that the DNA's of T2, T4 and T6 contain glucose linked to the hydroxymethyl groups of the HMC in characteristic ratios (26, 27, 28) although it is clear that in T2 and T6 some of the HMC groups contain no glucose (27). These characteristics have posed two problems regarding the synthesis of these DNA's which might appear to be incompatible with the simple base-pairing hypothesis. First, what mechanism is there for preventing the inclusion of cytosine in a cell which under normal conditions has deoxy-cytidine triphosphate and incorporates it into its DNA? Secondly, how does one conceive of the origin of the constant ratios of glucose to HMC in DNA if the incorporation were to occur via glucosylated and non-glucosylated HMC nucleotides? Our recent experiments have shown that the polymerase reaction in the virus-infected cell is governed by the usual hydrogen-bonding restrictions but with the auxiliary action of several new enzymes developed specifically in response to infection with a given virus (29, 30). Among the new enzymes is one which splits deoxycytidine triphosphate and thus removes it from the sites of polymerase action (30). Another is a type of glucosylating

DNA		A	T	G	C	$\dfrac{A+G}{T+C}$	$\dfrac{A+T}{G+C}$
M, phle	primer	0.65	0.66	1.35	1.34	1.01	0.49
	product	0.66	0.65	1.34	1.37	0.99	0.48
E, coli	primer	1.00	0.97	0.98	1.05	0.98	0.97
	product	1.04	1.00	0.97	0.98	1.01	1.02
Calf thymus	primer	1.14	1.05	0.90	0.85	1.05	1.25
	product	1.12	1.08	0.85	0.85	1.02	1.29
Becteriophage T2	primer	1.31	1.32	0.67	0.70	0.98	1.92
	product	1.33	1.29	0.69	0.70	1.02	1.90
A-T Copolymer		1.99	1.93	<0.05	<0.05	1.03	>40

Fig. 8. Chemical Composition of Enzymatically Synthesized DNA with Different Primers.

enzyme which transfers glucose from uridine diphosphate glucose directly and specifically to certain HMC residues in the DNA (30).

Chemical composition of enzymatically synthesized DNA.

The third line of evidence is supplied by an analysis of the purine and pyrimidine base composition of the enzymatically synthesized DNA. We may ask two questions. First, will the product have the equivalence of adenine to thymine and of guanine to cytosine that characterize natural DNA? Secondly, will the composition of the natural DNA used as primer influence and determine the composition of the product? In Fig. 8 are the results which answer these two questions (31). The experiments are identical except that in each case a different DNA primer was used: *Mycobacterium phlei, Escherichia coli,* calf thymus and phage T2 DNA. In answer to the first question it is clear that in the enzymatically synthesized DNA, adenine equals thymine and guanine equals cytosine so that the purine content is in every case identical to the pyrimidine. In answer to the second question it is again apparent that the characteristic ratio of adenine-thymine pairs to guanine-cytosine pairs of a given DNA primer is imposed rather faithfully on the product that is synthesized. Whether these measurements are made with isotopic tracers when the net DNA increase is only 1 % or if it is 1 000 % the results are the same. It can be said further that it has not been possible to distort these base ratios by using widely differing molar concentrations of substrates or by any other means. In the last line of Fig. 8 is a rather novel "DNA" which is synthesized under conditions that I will not describe here (18, 32). Suffice it to say that after very long lag periods a copolymer of deoxyadenylate and thymidylate

(A-T) develops which has the physical size and properties of natural DNA and in which the adenine and thymine are in a perfectly alternating sequence. When this rare form of DNA-like polymer is used as a primer, new A-T polymer synthesis starts immediately and even though all four triphosphates be present, no trace of guanine or cytosine can be detected in the product. The conclusion from these several experiments thus seems inescapable that the base composition is replicated in the enzymatic synthesis and that hydrogen-bonding of adenine to thymine and guanine to cytosine is the guiding mechanism.

Enzymatic replication of nucleotide sequences.

The fourth line of evidence which I would like to cite is drawn from current studies of base sequences in DNA and their replication. As I have suggested already, we believe that DNA is the genetic code; the four kinds of nucleotides make up a four-letter alphabet and their sequence spells out the message. At present we do not know the sequence; what SANGER has done for peptide sequence in protein remains to be done for nucleic acids. The problem is more difficult, but not insoluble.

Our present attempts at determining the nucleotide sequences (33) will be described in detail elsewhere and I will only summarize them here. DNA is enzymatically synthesized using P^{32} as label in one of the deoxynucleoside triphosphates; the other three substrates are unlabeled. This radioactive phosphate, attached to the 5-carbon of the deoxyribose, now becomes the bridge between that substrate molecule and the nucleotide at the growing end of the chain with which it has reacted (Fig. 9). At the end of the synthetic reaction (after some 10^{16} diester bonds have been formed), the DNA is isolated and digested enzymatically to yield the 3' deoxynucleotides quantitatively. It is apparent (Fig. 9) that the P atom formerly attached to the 5-carbon of the deoxynucleoside triphosphate substrate is now attached to the 3-carbon of the nucleotide with which it reacted during the course of synthesis of the DNA chains. The P^{32} content of each of the 3' deoxynucleotides, isolated by paper electrophoresis, is a measure of the relative frequency with which a particular substrate reacted with each of the four available nucleotides in the course of synthesis of the DNA chains. This procedure carried out four times, using in turn a different labeled substrate, yields the relative frequencies of all the sixteen possible kinds of dinucleotide (nearest neighbor) sequences.

Such studies have to date been carried out using DNA primer samples from six different natural sources. The conclusions are:

1) All 16 possible dinucleotide sequences are found in each case.

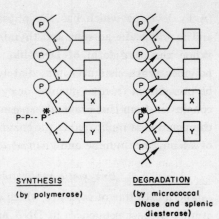

SYNTHESIS
(by polymerase)

DEGRADATION
(by micrococcal
DNase and splenic
diesterase)

Fig. 9. Method for Determining Sequences in
DNA.

2) The pattern of relative frequencies of the sequences is unique and reproducible in each case and is not readily predicted from the base composition of the DNA.

3) Enzymatic replication involves base pairing of adenine to thymine and guanine to cytosine and, most significantly:

4) The frequencies also indicate clearly that the enzymatic replication produces two strands of opposite direction, as predicted by the WATSON and CRICK model.

These studies and anticipated extensions of them should yield the dinucleotide frequencies of any DNA sample which can serve as an effective primer for enzymatic replication and thus provide some clues for deciphering the DNA code. Unfortunately this method does not provide information about trinucleotide frequencies but we are hopeful that with the improvement of enzymatic tools for analysis and chromatographic techniques for isolation some start can be made in this direction.

Requirement for four triphosphates and DNA for DNA synthesis.

Returning to the earlier-stated requirement for all four deoxynucleoside triphosphates and DNA in order to obtain DNA synthesis, we can now regard and understand these requirements as another and final line of evidence for hydrogen bonding. Without added DNA there is no template for hydrogen bonding and without all four triphosphates synthesis stops early and abruptly for lack of a hydrogen bonding mate for one of the bases in the template.

Summary.

The enzymatic approaches to the problem of DNA replication and the properties of the DNA-synthesizing enzyme purified from *Escherichia coli* have been sketched. The unifying and basic generalization about the action of this enzyme is that it catalyzes the synthesis of a new DNA chain in response to directions from a DNA template; these directions are dictated by the hydrogen bonding relationship of adenine to thymine and guanine to cytosine. The experimental basis for this conclusion is derived from the observations of: (1) The double-stranded character of the enzymatically synthesized DNA and its origin from a single stranded molecule, (2) the pattern of substitution of analogues for the naturally-occurring bases, (3) the replication of the chemical composition, (4) the replication of the nucleotide (nearest neighbor) sequences and the antiparallel direction of the strands, and (5) the requirement for all four deoxynucleoside triphosphates (adenine, thymine, guanine and cytosine) and DNA for DNA synthesis.

In closing may I repeat what was said at the banquet last night: Any credit for the work cited here is shared by my colleagues in New York, Bethesda, Saint Louis and Stanford, and by the whole international community of chemists, geneticists and physiologists, which is truly responsible for the progress in nucleic acid biochemistry.

REFERENCES.

1. O. T. AVERY, C. M. MacLEOD and M. McCARTY, J. Exptl. Med. *79*, 137 (1944); R. D. HOTCHKISS, in "The Chemical Basis of Heredity" (W. D. McElroy and B. Glass, editors), p. 321 (1957), Johns Hopkins Press, Baltimore.
2. A. D. HERSHEY, Cold Spring Harbor Symposia Quant. Biol. *18*, 135 (1953).
3. G. W. BEADLE, in "Chemical Basis of Heredity" (W. D. McElroy and B. Glass, editors), p. 3 (1957), Johns Hopkins Press, Baltimore.
4. E. CHARGAFF, in "Nucleic Acids" (E. Chargaff and J. N. Davidson, editors), Vol. I, p. 307—371 (1955), Academic Press, New York.
5. J. D. WATSON and F. H. C. CRICK, Nature *171*, 737 (1953); Cold Spring Harbor Symposia Quant. Biol. *18*, 123 (1953).
6. M. H. F. WILKINS, Biochem. Soc. Symposia (Cambridge, England) *14*, 13 (1957).
7. M. FEUGHELMAN, R. LANGRIDGE, W. E. SEEDS, A. R. STOKES, H. R. WILSON, C. W. HOOPER, M. H. F. WILKINS, R. K. BARCLAY, and L. D. HAMILTON, Nature *175*, 834 (1955).
8. A. KORNBERG, in "The Chemical Basis of Heredity" (W. D. McElroy and B. Glass, editors), p. 579 (1957), Johns Hopkins Press, Baltimore; Rev. Mod. Physics *31*, 200 (1959).

9. A. Kornberg, in "Phosphorus Metabolism" (W. D. McElroy and B. Glass, editor)' p. 392 (1951), Johns Hopkins Press, Baltimore; Advances in Enzymol. *18*, 191 (1957)·

10. D. E. Koshland, Jr., in "The Mechanism of Enzyme Action" (W. D. McElroy and B. Glass, editors), p. 608 (1954), Johns Hopkins Press, Baltimore.

11. A. Kornberg, I. R. Lehman and E. S. Simms, Federation Proc. *15*, 291 (1956).

12. A. Kornberg, Harvey Lectures *53*, 83 (1957—1958).

13. I. R. Lehman, M. J. Bessman, E. S. Simms and A. Kornberg, J. Biol. Chem. *233*, 163 (1958).

14. F. J. Bollum and V. R. Potter, J. Am. Chem. Soc. *79*, 3603 (1957); C. G. Harford and A. Kornberg, Federation Proc. *17*, 515 (1958); F. J. Bollum, Federation Proc. *17*, 193 (1958); *18*, 194 (1959).

15. M. J. Bessman, I. R. Lehman, E. S. Simms and A. Kornberg, J. Biol. Chem. *233*, 171 (1958).

16. J. Adler, I. R. Lehman, M. J. Bessman, E. S. Simms and A. Kornberg, Proc. Nat. Acad. Sci. (U. S. A.) *44*, 641 (1958).

17. H. K. Schachman, I. R. Lehman, M. J. Bessman, J. Adler, E. S. Simms and A. Kornberg, Federation Proc. *17*, 304 (1958).

18. I. R. Lehman, Ann. N. Y. Acad. Sci. *81*, 745 (1959).

19. R. L. Sinsheimer, J. Mol. Biol. *1*, 43 (1959).

20. I. R. Lehman, R. L. Sinsheimer and A. Kornberg (Unpublished observations).

21. F. J. Bollum, J. Biol. Chem. *234*, 2733 (1959).

22. F. Weygand, A. Wacker and Z. Dellweg, Z. Naturforsch. *7 b*, 19 (1952); D. B. Dunn and J. D. Smith, Nature *174*, 305 (1954); S. Zamenhof and G. Griboff, Nature *174*, 306 (1954).

23. M. R. Heinrich, V. C. Dewey, R. E. Parks, Jr., and G. W. Kidder, J. Biol. Chem. *197*, 199 (1952).

24. M. J. Bessman, I. R. Lehman, J. Adler, S. B. Zimmerman, E. S. Simms and A. Kornberg, Proc. Nat. Acad. Sci. (U. S. A.) *44*, 633 (1958).

25. G. R. Wyatt and S. S. Cohen, Biochem. J. *55*, 774 (1953).

26. R. L. Sinsheimer, Science *120*, 551 (1954); E. Volkin, J. Am. Chem. Soc. *76*, 5892 (1954).

27. R. L. Sinsheimer, Proc. Nat. Acad. Sci. (U. S. A.) *42*, 502 (1956); M. A. Jesaitis, J. Exp. Med. *106*, 233 (1957); Federation Proc. *17*, 250 (1958).

28. G. Streisinger and J. Weigle, Proc. Nat. Acad. Sci. (U. S. A.) *42*, 504 (1956).

29. J. G. Flaks and S. S. Cohen, J. Biol. Chem. *234*, 1501 (1959); J. G. Flaks, J. Lichtenstein and S. S. Cohen, J. Biol. Chem. *234*, 1507 (1959).

30. A. Kornberg, S. B. Zimmerman, S. R. Kornberg and J. Josse, Proc. Nat. Acad. Sci. (U. S. A.) *45*, 772 (1959).

31. I. R. Lehman, S. B. Zimmerman, J. Adler, M. J. Bessman, E. S. Simms and A. Kornberg, Proc. Nat. Acad. Sci. (U. S. A.) *44*, 1191 (1958).

32. C. M. Radding, J. Adler and H. K. Schachman, Federation Proc., *19*, 307 (1960).

33. J. Josse and A. Kornberg, Federation Proc., *19*, 305 (1960).

GENES AND CHEMICAL REACTIONS IN NEUROSPORA

by

GEORGE W. BEADLE.

Pasadena, California, California Institute of Technology.

Nobel Lecture, December 11, 1958.

On this occasion of sharing the high honor of a Nobel Award with EDWARD L. TATUM for our ". . . discovery that genes act by regulating chemical events", and with JOSHUA LEDERBERG for his related ". . . discoveries concerning the organization of the genetic material of bacteria", it seems appropriate that I sketch briefly the background events that led to the work on Neurospora thaf TATUM and I initiated in 1940. I shall leave to my co-recipients of the Award the task of describing in detail the developments in Neurospora that followed our first success, and the relation of this to the rise of bacterial genetics, which has depended largely on studies of genetic recombination following conjugation and transduction.

I shall make no attempt to review the entire history of biochemical genetics, for this has been done elsewhere (2, 13, 22, 23).

Anthocyanins and Alcaptonuria.

Soon after DE VRIES, CORRENS and TSCHERMAK "rediscovered" MENDEL's 1865 paper and appreciated its full significance, investigators in the exciting new field, which was to be called genetics, naturally speculated about the physical nature of the "elements" of MENDEL and the manner of their action. Renamed genes, these units of inheritance were soon found to be carried in the chromosomes.

One line of investigation that was destined to reveal much about what genes do was started by WHELDALE (later ONSLOW) in 1903. It began with a genetic study of flower pigmentation in snapdragons. But soon the genetic observations began to be correlated with the chemistry of the anthocyanin and related pigments that were responsible. The material was favorable for both genetic and chemical studies and the work has continued to yield new information ever since and almost without interruption. Many workers and many species of plants have been involved (2, 4, 13, 22, 23).

It became clear very soon that a number of genes were involved and that they acted by somehow controlling the onset of various identifiable and specific chemical reactions. Since an understanding of the genetics helped in interpreting the chemistry and *vice versa*, the anthrocyanin work was well known to both geneticists and biochemists. It significantly influenced the thinking in both fields and thus had great importance in further developments.

A second important line of investigation was begun even earlier by the Oxford physician-biochemist Sir ARCHIBALD E. GARROD. At the turn of the century he was interested in a group of congenital metabolic diseases in man, which he later named, "inborn errors of metabolism". There are now many diseases described as such; in fact, they have come to be recognized as a category of diseases of major medical importance.

One of the first inborn errors to be studied by GARROD was alcaptonuria. Its most striking symptom is blackening of urine on exposure to air. It had been recorded medically long before GARROD became interested in it and important aspects of its biochemistry were understood. The substance responsible for blackening of the urine is alcapton or homogenetisie acid (2,5-dihydroxyphenylacetic acid). GARROD suggested early that alcaptonuria behaved in inheritance as though it were differentiated by a single recessive gene.

By 1908 a considerable body of knowledge about alcaptonuria had accumulated. This was brought together and interpreted by GARROD in his Croonian lectures and in the two editions of his book, *"Inborn Errors of Metabolism"*, which were based on them (11). It was his belief that alcaptonuria was the result of inability of affected individuals to cleave the ring of homogentisic acid as do normal individuals. He believed this to be due to absence or inactivity of the enzyme that normally catalyzes this reaction. This in turn was dependent on the absence of the normal form of a specific gene.

Thus GARROD had clearly in mind the concept of a gene-enzyme-chemical-reaction system in which all three entities were interrelated in a very specific way. In the 1923 edition of "Inborn Errors" (11) he wrote:

"We may further conceive that the splitting of the benzene ring of homogentisic acid in normal metabolism is the work of a special enzyme, that in congenital alcaptonuria this enzyme is wanting . . ."

Failure to metabolize an intermediate compound when its normal pathway is thus blocked by a gene-enzyme defect was a part of the interpretation and accounted for the accumulation and excretion of homogentisic acid. GARROD recognized this as a means of identifying an intermediate compound that might otherwise not appear in sufficient amounts to be detected.

He also clearly appreciated that alcaptonurics would be used experimentally to explore the metabolic pathways by which homogentisic acid was formed. He summarized a large body of evidence indicating that when normal precursors of homogentisic acid are fed to alcaptonurics there is an almost quantitative increase in homogentisic acid excretion. In this way evidence was accumulated that phenylalanine, tyrosine and the keto acid analog of the latter were almost certainly the direct precursors of homogentisic acid.

Despite the simplicity and elegance of GARROD's interpretation of alcaptonuria and other inborn errors of metabolism as gene defects which resulted in inactivity of specific enzymes and thus in blocked reactions, his work had relatively little influence on the thinking of the geneticists of his time. BATESON's "*Mendel's Principles of Heredity*" and a few other books of its time discuss the concept briefly. But up to the 1940's, no widely used later text book of genetics that I have examined even so much as refers to alcaptonuria. It is true that a number of other workers had seriously considered that genes might act in regulating chemical reactions by way of enzymes (2, 13, 17, 21, 23). But there was no other known instance as simple as alcaptonuria. It is interesting — and significant, I think — that it was approximately 50 years after GARROD proposed his hypothesis before it was anything like fully verified through the resolution into six enzymatically catalyzed steps of phenylalanine-tyrosine metabolism via the homogentisic acid pathway, and by the clear demonstration that homogentisate oxidase is indeed lacking in the liver of an alcaptonuric (17). Perhaps it is also well to recall that it was not until 1926 that the first enzyme was isolated in crystalline form and shown in a convincing way to consist solely of protein.

Eye Pigments of Drosophila.

I shall now shift to a consideration of an independent line of investigation that ended up with conclusions very much like those of GARROD and which led directly to the work with Neurospora that TATUM and I subsequently began.

In 1933, BORIS EPHRUSSI came to the California Institute of Technology to work on developmental aspects of genetics. During his stay he and I had many long discussions in which we deplored the lack of information about the manner in which genes act on development. This we ascribed to the fact that the classical organisms of experimental embryology did not lend themselves readily to genetic investigation. Contrariwise, those plants and animals about which most was known genetically had been little used in studies of development.

It would be worth-while, we believed, to attempt to remedy this situation by finding new ways experimentally to study Drosophila melanogaster — which, genetically, was the best understood organism of the time. Tissue culture technics seemed to offer hope. In the spring of 1935 we joined forces in EUPHRUSSI's section of l'Institut de Biologie physio-chimique in Paris, resolved to find ways of culturing tissues of the larvae of Drosophila.

After some discouraging preliminary attempts, we followed EPHRUSSI's suggestion and shifted to a transplantation technic. It was our hope that in this way we could make use of non-autonomous genetic characters as a means of investigating gene action in development.

Drosophila larvae are small. And we were told by a noted Sorbonne authority on the development of diptera that the prospects were not good. In fact, he said, they were terrible.

But we were determined to try, so returned to the laboratory, made micropipettes, dissected larvae and attempted to transfer embryonic buds from one larva to the body cavity of another. The results were discouraging. But we persisted, and finally one day discovered we had produced a fly with three eyes. Although our joy was great with this small success, we immediately began to worry about three points: First, could we do it again? Second, if we could, would we be able to characterize the diffusible substances responsible for interactions between tissues of different genetic types? And, third, how many non-autonomous characters could we find?

We first investigated the sex-linked eye-color mutant vermilion because of the earlier finding of STURTEVANT that in gynandromorphs genetically vermilion eye tissue often fails to follow the general rule of autonomy (20).

Gynandromorphs may result if in an embryo that begins development as a female from an egg with two X chromosomes, one X chromosome is lost during an early cleavage, giving rise to a sector that has one X chromosome and is male. If the original egg is heterozygous for a sex-linked gene, say vermilion, and the lost chromosome carries the normal allele, the male sector will be genetically vermilion, whereas the female parts are normal or wild type. (Other sex-linked characters like yellow body or forked bristles can be used as markers to independently reveal genetic constitution in most parts of the body.)

Yet in STURTEVANT's gynandromorphs in which only a small part of the body including eye tissue was vermilion, the appearance of that tissue was usually not vermilion but wild type — as though some substance had diffused from wild-type tissue to the eye and caused it to become normally pigmented.

It was on the basis of this observation that EPHRUSSI and I transplanted vermilion eyes into wild type larvae. The result was as expected — the transplanted eyes were indeed wild type.

At that time there were some 26 separate eye-color genes known in Drosophila. We obtained stocks of all of them and made a series of transplants of mutant eyes into wild-type hosts. We found only one other clear-cut non-autonomous eye character. This was cinnabar, a bright red eye color, like vermilion but differentiated by a second chromosome recessive gene. We had a third less clear case, claret, but this was never entirely satisfactory from an experimental point of view because it was difficult to distinguish claret from wild-type eyes in transplants.

The vermilion and cinnabar characters are alike in appearance; both lack the brown pigment of the wild-type fly but retain the bright red component. Were the diffusible substances that caused them to develop brown pigment when grown in wild-type hosts the same or different? If the same, reciprocal transplants between the two mutants should give mutant transplanted eyes in both cases. If two separate and independent substances were involved, such reciprocal transplants should give wild-type transplanted eyes in both instances.

We made the experiment and were much puzzled that neither of these results was obtained. A cinnabar eye in a vermilion host remained cinnabar, but a vermilion eye in a cinnabar host became wild type.

To explain this result we formulated the hypothesis that there must be two diffusible substances involved, one formed from the other according to the scheme: $\rightarrow$ Precursor $\rightarrow v^+$ substance $\rightarrow cn^+$ substance $\rightarrow$ Pigment ... where v^+ substance is a diffusible material capable of making a vermilion eye become wild type and cn^+ substance is capable of doing the same to a cinnabar eye (9).

The vermilion (v) mutant gene blocks the first reaction and the cinnabar (cn) mutant gene interrupts the second. A vermilion eye in a cinnabar host makes pigment because it can, in its own tissues, convert the v^+ substance into cn^+ substance and pigment. In it, the second reaction is not blocked.

This scheme involves the following concepts:

a. A sequence of two gene-regulated chemical reactions, one gene identified with each.

b. The accumulation of intermediates prior to blocked reactions.

c. The ability of the mutant blocked in the first reaction to make use of an intermediate accumulated as a result of a genetic interruption of the second reaction. The principle involved is the same as that employed in the cross-feeding technic later so much used in detecting biosynthetic intermediates in microorganisms.

What was later called the one gene-one enzyme concept was clearly in our minds at this time although as I remember, we did not so designate it.

Ours was a scheme closely similar to that proposed by GARROD for alcaptonuria, except that he did not have genes that blocked an adjacent reaction in the sequence. But at the time we were oblivious of GARROD's work, partly because geneticists were not in the habit of referring to it, and partly through failure of ourselves to explore the literature. GARROD's book was available in many libraries.

We continued the eye-color investigations at the California Institute of Technology, EPHRUSSI having returned there to spend part of 1936. Late in the year, EPHRUSSI returned to Paris and I went for a year to Harvard, both continuing to work along similar lines. We identified the source of diffusible substances — fat bodies and malpighian tubercules — and began to devise ways of determining their chemical nature. In this I collaborated to some extent with Professor KENNETH THIMANN.

In the fall of 1937 I moved to Stanford, where TATUM shortly joined me to take charge of the chemical aspects identifying the eye-color substances. Dr. YVONNE KHOUVINE worked in a similar rcle with EPHRUSSI. We made progress slowly. EPHRUSSI and KHOUVINE discovered that under certain conditions feeding tryptophane had an effect on vermilion eye color. Following this lead, TATUM found — through accidental contamination of an asceptic culture containing tryptophane and test flies — an aerobic Bacillus that converted tryptophane into a substance highly active in inducing formation of brown pigment in vermilion flies. He soon isolated and crystallized this, but its final identification was slowed down by what later proved to be a sucrose molecule esterified with the active compound.

Professor BUTENANDT and co-workers (6) in Germany who had been collaborating with Professor KÜHN on an analogous eye-color mutant in the meal moth *Ephestia*, and AMANO *et al.* (1), working at Osaka University, showed that v^+ substance was kynurinine. Later, BUTENANDT and HALLMANN (5), and BUTENANDT *et al.* (7) showed that our original cn^+ substance was 3-hydroxykynurenine.

Thus was established a reaction series of the kind we had originally conceived. Substituting the known chemical, it is as follows:

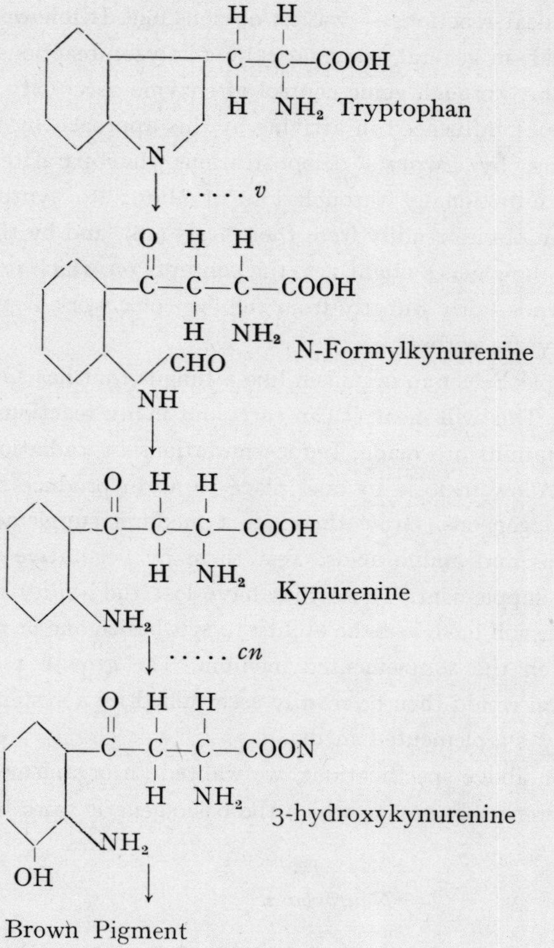

Tryptophan

..... v

N-Formylkynurenine

Kynurenine

..... cn

3-hydroxykynurenine

Brown Pigment

A New Approach.

Isolating the eye-pigment precursors of Drosophila was a slow and discouraging job. TATUM and I realized this was likely to be so in most cases of attempting to identify the chemical disturbances underlying inherited abnormalities; it would be no more than good fortune if any particular example chosen for investigation should prove to be simple chemically. Alcaptonuria was such a happy choice for GARROD, for the chemistry had been largely worked out and the homogentisic acid isolated and identified many years before.

Our idea — to reverse the procedure and look for gene mutations that influence known chemical reactions — was an obvious one. It followed logically from the concept that, in general, enzymatically catalyzed reactions are gene-dependent, presumably through genic control of enzyme specificity. Although we were without doubt influenced in arriving at this approach by the anthocyanin investigations, by Lwoff's demonstrations that parasites tend to become specialized nutritionally through loss of ability to synthesize substances that they can obtain readily from their hosts (18), and by the speculations of others as to how genes might act, the concepts on which it was based developed in our minds fairly directly from the eye-color work Ephrussi and I had started five years earlier.

The idea was simple: Select an organism like a fungus that has simple nutritional requirements. This will mean it can carry out many reactions by which amino acids and vitamins are made. Induce mutations by radiation or other mutagenic agents. Allow meiosis to take place so as to produce spores that are genetically homogeneous. Grow these on a medium supplemented with an array of vitamins and amino acids. Test them by vegetative transfer to a medium with no supplement. Those that have lost the ability to grow on the minimal medium will have lost the ability to synthesize one or more of the substances present in the supplemented medium. The growth requirements of the deficient strain would then be readily ascertained by a systematic series of tests on partially supplemented media.

In addition to the above specifications, we wanted an organism well suited to genetic studies, preferably one on which the basic genetic work had already been done.

Neurospora.

As a graduate student at Cornell, I had heard Dr. B. O. Dodge of the New York Botanical Garden give a seminar on inheritance in the bread mold Neurospora. So-called second division segregation of mating types and of albinism were a puzzle to him. Several of us who had just been reviewing the evidence for 4-strand crossing over in Drosophila suggested that crossing over between the centromere and the segregating gene could well explain the result.

Dodge was an enthusiastic supporter of Neurospora as an organism for genetic work. "It's even better than Drosophila", he insisted to Thomas Hunt Morgan, whose laboratory he often visited. He finally persuaded Morgan to take a collection of Neurospora cultures with him from Columbia to the new Biology Division of the California Institute of Technology, which he established in 1928.

Shortly thereafter when CARL C. LINDEGREN came to MORGAN's laboratory to become a graduate student, it was suggested that he should work on the genetics of Neurospora as a basis for his thesis. This was a fortunate choice, for LINDEGREN had an abundance of imagination, enthusiasm and energy and at the same time had the advice of E. G. ANDERSON, C. B. BRIDGES, S. EMERSON, A. H. STURTEVANT and others at the Institute who at that time were actively interested in problems of crossing over as a part of the mechanism of meiosis. In this favorable setting, LINDEGREN soon worked out much of the basic genetics of Neurospora. New characters were found and a good start was made toward mapping the chromosomes.

Thus, TATUM and I realized that Neurospora was genetically an almost ideal organism for use in our new approach.

There was one important unanswered question. We did not know the mold's nutritional requirements. But we had the monograph of Dr. NILS FRIES, which told us that the nutritional requirements of a number of related filamentous fungi were simple. Thus encouraged, we obtained strains of *Neurospora crassa* from LINDEGREN and from DODGE. TATUM soon discovered that the only growth factor required, other than the usual inorganic salts and sugar, was the recently discovered vitamin, biotin. We could not have used Neurospora for our purposes as much as a year earlier, for biotin would not then have been available in the quantities we required.

It remained only to irradiate asexual spores, cross them with a strain of the opposite mating type, allow sexual spores to be produced, isolate them, grow them on a suitably supplemented medium and test them on the un-supplemented medium. We believed so thoroughly that the gene-enzyme-reaction relation was a general one that there was no doubt in our minds that we would find the mutants we wanted. The only worry we had was that their frequency might be so low that we would get discouraged and give up before finding one.

We were so concerned about the possible discouragement of a long series of negative results that we prepared more than thousand single spore cultures on supplemented medium before we tested them. The 299th spore isolated gave a mutant strain requiring vitamin B6 and the 1 085th one required B1. We made a vow to keep going until we had 10 mutants. We soon had dozens.

Because of the ease of recovery of all the products of a single meiotic process n Neurospora, it was a simple matter to determine whether our newly induced nutritional deficiencies were the result of mutations in single genes. If they were, crosses with the original should yield four mutant and four non-mutant spores in each spore sac. They did (3, 21).

In this long, roundabout way, first in Drosophila and then in Neurospora, we had rediscovered what GARROD had seen so clearly so many years before. By now we knew of his work and were aware that we had added little if anything new in principle. We were working with a more favorable organism and were able to produce, almost at will, inborn errors of metabolism for almost any chemical reaction whose product we could supply through the medium. Thus we were able to demonstrate that what GARROD had shown for a few genes and a few chemical reactions in man was true for many genes and many reactions in Neurospora.

In the fall of 1941 FRANCIS J. RYAN came to Stanford as a National Research Council Fellow and was soon deeply involved in the Neurospora work. A year later DAVID M. BONNER and NORMAN H. HOROWITZ joined the group. Shortly thereafter HERSCHEL K. MITCHELL did likewise. With the collaboration of a number of capable graduate students and a group of enthusiastic and able research assistants the work moved along at a gratifying pace.

A substantial part of the financial support that enabled us thus to expand our efforts was generously made available by the Rockefeller Foundation and the Nutrition Foundation.

The directions of our subsequent investigations and their accomplishments I shall leave to Professor TATUM to summarize.

One Gene—One Enzyme.

It is sometimes thought that the Neurospora work was responsible for the one gene—one enzyme hypothesis — the concept that genes in general have single primary functions, aside from serving an essential role in their own replication, and that in many cases this function is to direct specificities of enzymatically active proteins. The fact is that it was the other way around — the hypothesis was clearly responsible for the new approach.

Although it may not have been stated explicitly, EPHRUSSI and I had some such concept in mind. A more specific form of the hypothesis was suggested by the fact that of all the 26 known eye-color mutants in Drosophila, there was only one that blocked the first of our postulated reactions and one that similarly interrupted the second. Thus it seemed reasonable to assume that the *total* specificity of a particular enzyme might somehow be derived from a single gene. The finding in Neurospora that many nutritionally deficient mutant strains can be repaired by supplying single chemical compounds was a verification of our prediction and as such reinforced our belief in the hypothesis, at least in its more general form.

As I hope Professor TATUM will point out in detail, there are now known a number of instances in which mutations of independent origin, all abolishing or reducing the activity of a specific enzyme, have been shown to involve one small segment of genetic material (8, 12, 24). To me these lend strong support to the more restricted form of the hypothesis.

Regardless of when it was first written down on paper, or in what form, I myself am convinced that the one gene-one enzyme concept was the product of gradual evolution beginning with GARROD and contributed to by many, including MOORE, GOLDSCHMIDT, TROLAND, HALDANE, WRIGHT, GRÜNEBERG and many others (2, 13, 19, 22, 23). HOROWITZ and his co-workers (15, 16) have given it, in both forms referred to above, its clearest and most explicit formulation. They have summarized and critically evaluated the evidence for and against it, with the result that they remain convinced of its continued value.

In additition HOROWITZ has himself made an important application of the concept in arriving at a plausible hypothesis as to how sequences of biosynthetic reactions might originally have evolved (14). He points out that many biologically important compounds are known to be synthesized in a stepwise manner in which the intermediate compounds as such seem not to serve useful purposes. How could such a śynthetic pathway have evolved if it serves no purpose unless complete? Simultaneous appearance of several independent enzymes would of course be exceedingly improbable.

HOROWITZ proposes that the end product of such a series of reactions was at first obtained directly from the environment, it having been produced there in the first place by non-biological reactions such as have been postulated by a number of persons, including DARWIN, HALDANE, OPARIN and UREY and demonstrated by MILLER, FOX and others (10). It is then possible reasonably to assume that the ability to synthesize such a compound biologically could arise by a series of separate single mutations, each adding successive enzymatically catalyzed steps in the synthetic sequence, starting with the one immediately responsible for the end product. In this was each mutational step could confer a selective advantage by making the organism dependent on one less exogenous precursor of a needed end product. Without some such mechanism, by which no more than a single gene mutation is required for the origin of a new enzyme, it is difficult to see how complex synthetic pathways could have evolved. I know of no alternative hypothesis that is equally simple and plausible.

The Place of Genetics in Modern Biology.

In a sense genetics grew up as an orphan. In the beginning botanists and zoologists were often indifferent and sometimes hostile toward it. "Genetics deals only with superficial characters", it was often said. Biochemists likewise paid it little heed in its early days. They, especially medical biochemists, knew of GARROD's inborn errors of metabolism and no doubt appreciated them in the biochemical sense and as diseases; but the biological world was inadequately prepared to appreciate fully the significance of his investigations and his thinking. Geneticists, it should be said, tended to be preoccupied mainly with the mechanisms by which genetic material is transmitted from one generation to the next.

Today, happily, the situation is much changed. Genetics has an established place in modern biology. Biochemists recognize the genetic material as an integral part of the systems with which they work. Our rapidly growing knowledge of the architecture of proteins and nucleic acids is making it possible — for the first time in the history of science — for geneticists, biochemists and biophysicists to discuss basic problems of biology in the common language of molecular structure. To me, this is most encouraging and significant.

REFERENCES.

1. AMANO, T., M. TORII, and H. IRITANI, Med. J. Osaka Univ., 2, 45 (1950).
2. BEADLE, G. W., Chem. Rev. 37, 15 (1945).
3. — and E. L. TATUM, Proc. Nat. Acad. Sci. (U. S. A.), 27, 499 (1941).
4. BEALE, G. H. J. Genetics, 42, 196 (1941).
5. BUTENANDT, A. and G. HALLMANN, Z. Naturforsch., 5 b, 444 (1950).
6. — W. WEIDEL, and E. BECKER, Naturwiss., 28, 63 (1940).
7. — — and H. SCHLOSSBERGER, Z. Naturforsch., 4 b, 242 (1949).
8. DEMEREC, M., Z. HARTMAN, P. E. HARTMAN, T. YURA, J. S. GOTS, H. OZEKI, and S. W. GLOVER, Publication 612, Carnegie Inst. Wash. (1956).
9. EPHRUSSI, B., Quart. Rev. Biol. 17, 327 (1942).
10. FOX, S. W., Amer. Sci. 44, 347 (1956).
11. GARROD, A. E., Inborn Errors of Metabolism, Oxford Univ. Press (1923).
12. GILES, N. H., Proc. X Int. Cong. Genetics (in Press).
13. HALDANE, J. B. S., The Biochemistry of Genetics, London, Allen & Unwin (1954).
14. HOROWITZ, N. H., Proc. Nat. Acad. Sci. (U. S. A.), 31, 153 (1945).
15. HOROWITZ, N. H., and M. FLING, In "Enzymes", p. 139 (Gaebler, O. H., Ed.), New York, Academic Press (1956).

16. HOROWITZ, N. H., and U. LEOPOLD, Cold Spring Harbor Symp. Quant. Biol., 16- 65 (1951).
17. KNOX, W. E., Am. J. Human Genetics, *10*, 95 (1958).
18. LWOFF, A., *L'évolution physiologique*, Paris, Hermann et Cie (1944).
19. MULLER, H. J., Proc. Royal Soc. (London) *B 134*, 1 (1947).
20. STURTEVANT, A. H., Proc. VI Int. Cong. Genetics, *1*, 304 (1932).
21. TATUM, E. L., and BEADLE, G. W., Proc. Nat. Acad. Sci. (U. S. A.), *28*, 234 (1942).
22. WAGNER, R. P. and H. K. MITCHELL, *Genetics and Metabolism*, New York, Wiley (1955).
23. WRIGHT, S., Physiol. Rev., *21*, 487 (1941).
24. YANOFSKY, C., In *"Enzymes"*, p. 147 (Gaebler, O. H., Ed.), New York, Academic Press 1 (1956).

───────────

A CASE HISTORY IN BIOLOGICAL RESEARCH.

By

E. L. TATUM.

Nobel Lecture, December 11, 1958.

In casting around in search of a new approach, an important consideration was that much of biochemical genetics has been and will be covered by Professor BEADLE and Professor LEDERBERG, and in many symposia and reviews, in which many aspects have been and will be considered in greater detail and with greater competence than I can hope to do here. It occurred to me that perhaps it might be instructive, valuable, and interesting to use the approach which I have attempted to define by the title "A Case History in Biological Research". In the development of this case history I hope to point out some of the factors involved in all research, specifically the dependence of scientific progress: on knowledge and concepts provided by investigators of the past and present all over the world; on the free interchange of ideas within the international scientific community; on the hybrid vigor resulting from cross-fertilization between disciplines; and last but not least, also dependent on chance, geographical proximity, and opportunity. I would like finally to complete this case history with a brief discussion of the present status of the field, and a prognosis of its possible development.

Under the circumstances, I hope I will be forgiven if this presentation is given from a personal viewpoint. After graduating from the University of Wisconsin in chemistry, I was fortunate in having the opportunity of doing graduate work in biochemistry and microbiology at this University under the direction and leadership of W. H. PETERSON and E. B. FRED. At that time, in the early 30's, one of the exciting areas being opened concerned the so-called "growth-factors" for microorgaisms, for the most part as yet mysterious and unidentified. I became deeply involved in this field, and was fortunate to have been able, in collaboration with H. G. WOOD, then visiting at Wisconsin, to identify one of the required growth-factors for propionic acid bacteria, as the recently synthesized vitamin B_1 or thiamine (1). This was before the universality of need for the B vitamins, and the enzymatic basis of this requirement, had been clearly defined. The vision of Lwoff and Knight had already indicated a correlation of the need of microorganisms for "growth-factors" with failure of synthesis, and correlated this failure with evolution, particularly in relation to the complex environment of "fastidious" pathogenic microorganisms. However, the tendency at this time was to consider "growth-factors" as highly individual requirements, peculiar to particular strains or species of microorganisms as isolated from nature, and their variation in these respects was not generally considered as related to gene mutation and variation in higher organisms. Actually my ignorance of and naïveté in genetics was probably typical of that of most biochemists and microbiologists of the time, with my only contact with genetic concepts being a course primarily on vertebrate evolution.

After completing graduate work at Wisconsin I was fortunate in being able to spend a year studying at the University of Utrecht with F. Kögl, the discoverer of the growth factor biotin, and to work in the same laboratory with Nils Fries, who already had contributed significantly in the field of nutrition and growth of fungi.

At this time, Professor Beadle was just moving to Stanford University, and invited me as a biochemist to join him in the further study of the eye-color hormones of *Drosophila*, which he and Ephrussi in their work at the California Institute of Technology and at Paris had so brilliantly established as diffusible products of gene-controlled reactions. During this, my first contacts with modern genetic concepts, as a consequence of a number of factors — the observation of Khouvine, Ephrussi and Chevais (2) in Paris that dietary tryptophane was concerned with *Drosophila* eye-color hormone production; our studies on the nutrition of *Drosophila* in aseptic culture (3); and the chance contamination of one of our cultures of *Drosophila* with a particular bacterium — we were able to isolate the v^+ hormone in crystalline state from a bacterial culture supplied with tryptophane (4), and with A. J. Haagen-Smit to identify it as kynurenine (5); originally isolated by Kotake, and later structurally identified correctly by Butenandt. It might be pointed out here that kynurenine has since been recognized to occupy a central position in tryptophane metabolism in many organisms aside from insects, including mammals and fungi.

At about this time, as the result of many discussions and considerations of the general biological applicability of chemical genetic concepts, stimulated by the wealth of potentialities among the microorganisms and their variation in nature with respect to their nutritional requirements, we began our work with the mold *Neurospora crassa*.

I shall not renumerate the factors involved in our selection of this organism for the production of chemical or nutritionally deficient mutants, but must take this opportunity of reiterating our indebtedness to the previous basic findings of a number of investigators. Foremost among these, to B. O. DODGE for his establishment of this Ascomycete as a most suitable organism for genetic studies (6); and to C. C. LINDEGREN (7), who became interested in *Neurospora* through T. H. MORGAN, a close friend of DODGE.

Our use of *Neurospora* for chemical genetic studies would also have been much more difficult, if not impossible, without the availability of synthetic biotin as the result of the work of KÖGL (8) and of DU VIGNEAUD (9). In addition, the investigations of NILS FRIES on the nutrition of *Ascomycetes* (10) were most helpful, as shown by the fact that the synthetic minimal medium used with *Neurospora* for many years was that described by him and supplemented only with biotin, and has ordinarily since been referred to as "Fries medium". It should also be pointed out that the experimental feasibility of producing the desired nutritionally deficient mutant strains depended on the early pioneering work of ROENTGEN, with X-Rays, and on that of H. J. MULLER, on the mutagenic activity of X-Rays and ultraviolet light on *Drosophila*. All that was needed was to put these various facts and findings together to produce in the laboratory with irradiation, nutritionally deficient (auxotrophic) mutant strains of *Neurospora*, and to show that each single deficiency produced was associated with the mutation of a single gene (11).

Having thus successfully tested with *Neurospora* the basic premise that the biochemical processes concerned with the synthesis of essential cell constituents are gene controlled, and alterable as a consequence of gene mutation, it then seemed a desirable and natural step to carry this approach to the bacteria, in which so many and various naturally occurring growth-factor requirements were known, to see if analogous nutritional deficiencies followed their exposure to radiation. As is known to all of you, the first mutants of this type were successfully produced in *Acetobacter* and in *E. coli* (12), and the first step had been taken in bringing the bacteria into the fold of organisms suitable for genetic study.

Now to point out some of the curious coincidences or twists of fate as involved in science: One of the first series of mutants in *Neurospora* which was studied intensily from the biochemical viewpoint was that concerned with the biosynthesis of tryptophan. In connection with the role of indole as a precursor of tryptophan, we wanted also to study the reverse process, the breakdown of tryptophan to indole, a reaction typical of the bacterium *E. coli*. For this purpose we obtained, from the Bacteriology Department at Stanford, a typical *E. coli* culture, designated K-12. Naturally, this strain was later used for the mutation experiments just described so that a variety of biochemically marked mutant strains of *E. coli* K-12 were soon available. It is also of interest that Miss ESTHER ZIMMER, who later became ESTHER LEDERBERG, assisted in the production and isolation of these mutant strains.

Another interesting coincidence is that F. J. RYAN spent some time on leave from Columbia University at Stanford, working with *Neurospora*. Shortly after I moved to Yale University in 1945, RYAN encouraged LEDERBERG, then a medical student at Columbia who had worked some with RYAN on *Neurospora*, to spend some time with me at Yale University. As all of you know, LEDERBERG was successful in showing genetic recombination between mutant strains of *E. coli* K-12 (13) and never returned to medical school, but continued his brilliant work on bacterial recombination at Wisconsin. In any case, the first demonstration of a process analogous to a sexual process in bacteria was successful only because of the clear-cut nature of the genetic markers available which permitted detection of this very rare event, and because of the combination of circumstances which had provided those selective markers in one of the rare strains of *E. coli* capable of recombination. In summing up this portion of this case history, then, I wish only to emphasize again the role of coincidence and chance played in the sequence of developments, but yet more strongly to acknowledge the even greater contributions of my close friends and associates, Professor BEADLE and Professor LEDERBERG, with whom it is a rare privilege and honor to share this award.

Now for a brief and necessarily somewhat superficial mention of some of the problems and areas of biology to which these relatively simple experiments with *Nerospora* have led and contributed. First, however, let us review the basic concepts involved in this work. Essentially these are (1) that all biochemical processes in all organisms are under genic control, (2) that these overall biochemical processes are resolvable into a series of individual stepwise reactions, (3) that each single reaction is controlled in a primary fashion by a single gene, or in other terms, in every case a 1 : 1 correspondence of gene and biochemical reaction exists, such that (4) mutation of a single gene results only in an alteration in the ability of the cell to carry out a single primary chemical reaction. As has repeatedly been stated, the underlying hypothesis, which in a number of cases has been supported by direct experimental evidence, is that each gene controls the production, function and specificity of a particular enzyme. Important experimental implications of these relations are that each and every biochemical reaction in a cell of any organism, from a bacterium to man, is theoretically alterable by gene mutation, and that each such mutant cell strain differs in only one primary way from the non-mutant parental strain. It is probably unnecessary to point out that these experimental expectations have been amply supported by the production and isolation, by many investigators during the last 15 or more years, of biochemical mutant strains of microorganisms in almost every species tried, bacteria, yeasts, algae, and fungi.

It is certainly unnecessary for me to do more than point out that mutant strains such as those produced and isolated first in *Neurospora* and *E. coli* have been of primary utility as genetic markers in detecting and elucidating the details of the often exotic mechanisms of genetic recombination of microorganisms.

Similarly, it seems superfluous even to mention the proven usefulness of mutant strains of microorganisms in unraveling the detailed steps involved in the biosynthesis of vital cellular constituents. I would like to list, however, a few of the biosynthetic sequences and biochemical interrelationships which owe their discovery and elucidation largely to the use of biochemical mutants. These include: the synthesis of the aromatic amino acids via dehydroshikimic and shikimic acids (14, 15), by way of prephenic acid to phenylalanine (16), and by way of anthranilic acid, indole glycerol phosphate (17), and condensation of indole with serine to give tryptophan (18); the conversion of tryptophan via kynurenine and 3-OH anthranilic acid to niacin (19, 20); the biosynthesis of histidine (21); of isoleucine and valine via the analogous di-OH and keto acids (22); the biosynthesis of proline and ornithine from glutamic acid (23); and the synthesis of pyrimidines via orotic acid (24).

If the postulated relationship of gene to enzyme is correct, several consequences can be predicted. First, mutation should result in the production of a changed protein, which might either be enzymatically inactive, of intermediate activity, or have otherwise detectably altered physical properties. The production of such proteins changed in respect to heat stability, enzymatic activity, or other properties such as activation energy, by mutant strains has indeed been demonstrated in a number of instances (25—31). Recognition of the molecular bases of these changes must await detailed comparison of their structures with those of the normal enzyme, using techniques similar to the elegant methods of Professor SANGER. That the primary effect of gene mutation may be as simple as the substitution of a single amino acid by another and may lead to profound secondary changes in protein structure and properties has recently been strongly indicated by the work of INGRAM on hemoglobin (32). It seems inevitable that induced mutant strains of microorganisms will play a most important part in providing material for the further examination of these problems.

A second consequence of the postulated relationship stems from the concept that the genetic constitution defines the potentialities of the cell, the time and degree of expression of which are to a certain extent modifiable by the cellular environment. The analysis of this type of secondary control at the biochemical level is one of the important and exciting new areas of biochemistry. This deals with the regulation and integration of biochemical reactions by means of feed-back mechanisms restricting the synthesis or activities of enzymes (33—36) and through substrate induced biosynthesis of enzymes (37). It seems probable that some gene mutations may affect biochemical activities at this level, (modifiers, and suppressors) and that chemical mutants will prove of great value in the analysis of the details of such control mechanisms.

An equally fascinating newer area of genetics, opened by BENZER (38) with bacteriophage, is that of the detailed correlation of fine structure of the gene in terms of mutation and recombination, with its fine structure in terms of activity. Biochemical mutants of microorganisms have recently opened this area to investigation at two levels of organization of genetic material. The higher level relates to the genetic linkage of non-allelic genes concerned with sequential biosynthetic reactions. This has been shown by DEMEREC and by HARTMANN in the biosynthesis of tryptophan and histidine by SALMONELLA (39).

At a finer level of organization of genetic material, the biological versatility of *Neurospora* in forming heterocaryotic cells has permitted the demonstration (40—42) that genes damaged by mutation in different areas, within the same locus and controlling the same enzyme, complement each other in a heterocaryon in such a way that synthesis of enzymatically active protein is restored, perhaps, in a manner analogous to the reconstitution of ribonuclease from its a and b constituents, by the production in the cytoplasm of an active protein from two gene products defective in different areas. This phenomenon of complementation, which appears also to take place in *Aspergillus* (43), permits the mapping of genetic fine structure in terms of function, and should lead to further information on the mechanism of enzyme production and clarification of the role of the gene in enzyme synthesis.

The concepts of biochemical genetics have already been, and will undoubtedly continue to be, significant in broader areas of biology. Let me cite a few examples in microbiology and medicine.

In microbiology the roles of mutation and selection in evolution are coming to be better understood through the use of bacterial cultures of mutant strains. In more immediately practical ways, mutation has proven of primary importance in the improvement of yields of important antibiotics — such as in the classic example of penicillin, the yield of which has gone up from around 40 units per ml. of culture shortly after its discovery by FLEMING to approximately 4 000, as the result of a long series of successive experimentally produced mutational steps. On the other side of the coin, the mutational origin of antibiotic resistant microorganisms is of definite medical significance. The therapeutic use of massive doses of antibiotics to reduce the numbers of bacteria which by mutation could develop resistance, is a direct consequence of the application of genetic concepts. Similarly, so is the increasing use of combined antibiotic therapy, resistance to both of which would require the simultaneous mutation of two independent characters.

As an important example of the application of these same concepts of microbial genetics to mammalian cells, we may cite the probable mutational origin of resistance to chemotherapeutic agents in leukemic cells (44), and the increasing and effective simultaneous use of two or more chemotherapeutic agents in the treatment of this disease. In this connection it should be pointed out that the most effective cancer chemotherapeutic agents so far found are those which interfere with DNA synthesis, and that more detailed information on the biochemical steps involved in this synthesis is making possible a more rational design of such agents. Parenthetically, I want to emphasize the analogy between the situation in a bacterial culture consisting of two or more cell types, and that involved in the competition and survival of a malignant cell, regardless of its origin, in a population of normal cells. Changes in the cellular environment, such as involved in chemotherapy, would be expected to affect the metabolic efficiency of an altered cell, and hence its growth characteristics. However, as in the operation of selection pressures in bacterial populations, based on the interaction between cell types, it would seem that the effects of chemotherapeutic agents on the efficiency of selective pressures among mammalian cell populations can be examined most effectively only in controlled mixed populations of the cell types concerned.

In other areas in cancer, the concepts of genetics are becoming increasingly important, both theoretically and practically. It seems probable that neoplastic changes are directly correlated with changes in the biochemistry of the cell. The relationships between DNA, RNA, and enzymes which have evolved during the last few decades, lead one to look for the basic neoplastic change in one of these intimately interrelated hierarchies of cellular materials.

In relation to DNA hereditary changes are now known to take place as a consequence of mutation, or of the introduction of new genetic material through virus infection (as in transduction) or directly (as in transformation). Although each of these related hereditary changes may theoretically be involved in cancer, definite evidence is available only for the role of viruses, stemming from the classic investigations of ROUS on fowl sarcoma (45). At the RNA level of genetic determination, any one of these classes of change might take place, as in the RNA containing viruses, and result in an heritable change, perhaps of the cytoplasmic type, semi-autonomous with respect to the gene. At the protein level, regulatory mechanisms determining gene activity and enzyme synthesis as mentioned earlier, likewise provide promising areas for exploration.

Among the many exciting applications of microbial-genetic concepts and techniques to the problems of cancer, may I mention in addition the exploration by KLEIN (46) of the genetic basis of the immunological changes which distinguish the cancer cell from the normal, and the studies on the culture, nutrition, morphology and mutation of isolated normal and malignant mammalian cells of PUCK (47) and of EAGLE (48). Such studies are basic to our exploration and to our eventual understanding of the origin and nature of the change to malignancy.

Regardless of the origin of a cancer cell, however, and of the precise genetic level at which the primary change takes place, it is not too much to hope and expect eventually to be able to correct or alleviate the consequences of the metabolic defect, just as a closer understanding of a heritable metabolic defect in man permits its correction or alleviation. In terms of biochemical genetics, the consequences of a metabolic block may be rectified by dietary limitation of the precursor of an injurious accumulation product, aromatic amino acids in phenylketonuria; or by supplying the essential end-product from without the cell, the specific blood protein in hemophilia, or a specific essential nutrient molecule such as a vitamin.

Time does not permit the continuation of these examples. Perhaps, however, I will be pardoned if I venture briefly on a few more predictions and hopes for the future.

It does not seem unrealistic to expect that as more is learned about control of cell machinery and heredity, we will see the complete conquering of many of man's ills, including hereditary defects in metabolism, and the momentarily more obscure conditions such as cancer and the degenerative diseases, just as disease of bacterial and viral etiology are now being conquered.

With a more complete understandig of the functioning and regulation of gene activity in development and differentiation these processes may be more efficiently controlled and regulated, not only to avoid structural or metabolic errors in the developing organism, but also to produce better organisms.

Perhaps within the lifetime of some of us here, the code of life processes tied up in the molecular structure of proteins and nucleic acids will be broken. This may permit the improvement of all living organisms by processes which we might call biological engineering.

This might proceed in stages from the *in vitro* biosynthesis of better and more efficient enzymes, to the biosynthesis of the corresponding nucleic acid molecules, and to the introduction of these molecules into the genome of organisms, whether via injection, viral introduction into germ cells, or via a process analogous to transformation. Alternatively, it may be possible to reach the same goal by a process involving directed mutation.

As a biologist, and more particularly as a geneticist, I have great faith in the versatility of the gene and of living organisms in providing the material with which to meet the challenges of life at any level. Selection, survival and evolution take place in response to environmental pressures of all kinds, including sociological and intellectual. In the larger view, the dangerous and often poorly understood and controlled forces of modern civilization, including atomic energy and its attendant hazards, are but more complex and sophisticated environmental challenges of life. If man cannot meet those challenges, in a biological sense he is not fit to survive.

However, it may confidently be hoped that with real understanding of the roles of heredity and environment, together with the consequent improvement in man's physical capacities and greater freedom from physical disease, will come an improvement in his approach to, and understanding of, sociological and economic problems. As in any scientific research, a problem clearly seen is already half solved. Hence, a renaissance may be foreseen, in which the major sociological problems will be solved, and mankind will take a big stride towards the state of world brotherhood and mutual trust and well-being envisaged by that great humanitarian and philanthropist Alfred Nobel.

BIBLIOGRAPHY.

1. E. L. TATUM, H. G. WOOD and W. H. PETERSON, Biochem. J., *30*, 1898, 1936.
2. Y. KHOUVINE, B. EPHRUSSI and S. CHEVAIS, Biol. Bull., *75*, 425, 1938.
3. E. L. TATUM, Proc. Nat. Acad. Sci., U. S., *27*, 193, 1941.
4. — and G. W. BEADLE, Science, *91*, 458, 1940.
5. — and A. J. HAAGEN-SMIT, J. Biol. Chem., *140*, 575, 1941.
6. B. O. DODGE, J. Agric. Res., *35*, 289, 1927.
7. C. C. LINDEGREN, Bull. Torrey Bot. Club., *59*, 85, 1932.
8. F. KÖGL, Ber., *68*, 16, 1935.
9. V. DU VIGNEAUD, Science, *96*, 455, 1942.
10. N. FRIES, Symbolae Bot. Upsalienses, *3*, 1—188, 1938.
11. G. W. BEADLE and E. L. TATUM, Proc. Nat. Acad. Sci. U. S., *27*, 499, 1941.
12. E. L. TATUM, Cold Spring Harbor Symposia Quant. Biol., *11*, 278, 1946.
13. J. LEDERBERG and E. L. TATUM, Nature, *158*, 558, 1946.
14. B. D. DAVIS, in Amino Acid Metabolism, Baltimore, *799*, 1955.
15. E. L. TATUM, S. R. GROSS, G. EHRENSVÄRD and L. GARNJOBST, Proc. Nat. Acad. Sci. U. S., *40*, 271, 1954.
16. R. L. METZENBERG and H. K. MITCHELL, Biochem. J., *68*, 168, 1958.
17. C. YANOFSKY, J. Biol. Chem., *224*, 783, 1957.
18. E. L. TATUM and D. M. BONNER, Proc. Nat. Acad. Sci. U. S., *30*, 30, 1944.
19. D. BONNER, Proc. Nat. Acad. Sci. U. S., *34*, 5, 1948.
20. H. K. MITCHELL and J. F. NYE, Proc. Nat. Acad. Sci. U. S., *34*, 1, 1948.
21. B. N. AMES, in Amino Acid Metabolism, Baltimore, 1955.
22. E. A. ADELBERG, J. Bact., *61*, 365, 1951.
23. H. J. VOGEL, in Amino Acid Metabolism, Baltimore, 1955.
24. H. K. MITCHELL, M. B. HONLAHAN and J. F. NYE, J. Biol. Chem., *172*, 525, 1948.
25. W. K. MAAS and B. D. DAVIS, Proc. Nat. Acad. Sci. U. S., *38*, 785, 1952.
26. N. H. HOROWITZ and M. FLING, Genetics, *38*, 360. 1953.
27. T. YURA and H. J. VOGEL, Biochim. Biophys. Acta, *17*, 582, 1955.
28. J. R. S. FINCHAM, Biochem. J., *65*, 721, 1957.
29. D. R. SUSKIND and L. I. KUREK, Science, *126*, 1068, 1957.
30. N. H. GILES, C. W. H. PARTRIDGE, and N. J. NELSON, Proc. Nat. Acad. Sci. U. S., *43*, 305, 1957.
31. T. YURA, Proc. Nat. Acad. Sci., U. S., (In press).
32. V. M. INGRAM, Nature, *180*, 326, 1957.
33. H. J. VOGEL, in Symposium on the Genetic Basis of Heredity, Baltimore, 1957.
34. L. GORINI and W. K. MAAS, Biochim. Biophys. Acta, *25*, 208, 1957.
35. R. A. YATES and A. B. PARDEE, J. Biol. Chem., *221*, 757, 1956.
36. H. E. UMBARGER and B. BROWN, J. Biol. Chem., *233*, 415, 1958.
37. M. COHN and J. MONOD, Symposium Soc. Gen. Microbiol., *3*, 132, 1953.
38. S. BENZER, in Symposium on the Chemical Basis of Heredity, Baltimore, 1957.
39. P. E. HARTMAN, in Symposium on the Chemical Basis of Heredity, Baltimore, 1957.
40. N. H. GILES, C. W. H. PARTRIDGE and N. J. NELSON, Proc. Nat. Acad. Sci., U. S., *43*, 305, 1957.
41. M. E. CASE and N. H. GILES, Proc. Nat. Acad. Sci., U. S., *44*, 378, 1958.
42. J. A. PATEMAN and J. R. S. FINCHAM, Heredity, *12*, 317, 1958.
43. E. CALEF, Heredity, *10*, 83, 1956.
44. L. W. LAW, Nature, *169*, 628, 1952.
45. P. ROUS, J. Exp. Med., *12*, 696, 1910.
46. G. KLEIN, E. KLEIN and L. RÉVÉSZ, Nature, *178*, 1389, 1956.
47. T. T. PUCK, in Symposium on Growth and Development, Princeton, 1957.
48. H. EAGLE, V. I. OYAMA, M. LEVY and A. E. FREIMAN, Science, *123*, 845, 1956.

A VIEW OF GENETICS*

JOSHUA LEDERBERG

Department of Genetics, Stanford University School of Medicine

The Nobel Statutes of 1900 charge each prize-winner to give a public lecture in Stockholm within six months of Commemoration Day. That I have fully used this margin is not altogether ingenuous, since it furnishes a pleasant occasion to revisit my many friends and colleagues in your beautiful city during its best season.

The charge might call for a historical account of past "studies on genetic recombination and organization of the genetic material in bacteria," studies in which I have enjoyed the companionship of many colleagues, above all my wife. However, this subject has been reviewed regularly (36, 37, 38, 41, 42, 45, 49, 54, 55, 58) and I hope you will share my own inclination to assume a more speculative task, to look at the context of contemporary science in which bacterial genetics can be better understood, and to scrutinize the future prospects of experimental genetics.

The dispersion of a Nobel award in the field of genetics symbolizes the convergent efforts of a world-wide community of investigators. That genetics should now be recognized is also timely—for its axial role in the conceptual structure of biology, and for its ripening yield for the theory and practice of medicine. However, experimental genetics is reaching its full powers in coalescence with biochemistry: in principle, each phenotype should eventually be denoted as an exact sequence of amino acids in protein (79) and the genotype as a corresponding sequence of nucleotides in DNA (a, 63). The precise demarcation of genetics from biochemistry is already futile: but when genetics has been fully reduced to its molecular foundations, it may continue to serve in the same relation as thermodynamics to mechanics (69). The coordination of so many adjacent sciences will be a cogent challenge to the intellectual powers of our successors.

That bacteria and their genetics should now be so relevant to general biology is already a fresh cycle in our scientific outlook. When thought of at all, they have often been relegated to some obscure byway of evolution, their complexity and their homology with other organisms grossly underrated. "Since Pasteur's startling discoveries of the important role played by microbes in human affairs, microbiology as a science has always suffered from its eminent practical applications. By far the majority of the microbiological studies were undertaken to answer questions connected with the well-being of mankind" (30). The pedagogic cleavage of academic biology from medical education has helped sustain this distortion. Happily, the repatriation of bacteria and viruses is only the first measure of the repayment of medicine's debt to biology (6, 7, 8).

Comparative biochemistry has consummated the unification of biology revitalized by Darwin one hundred years ago. Throughout the living world we see a common set of structural units—amino acids, coenzymes, nucleins, carbohydrates and so forth—from which every organism builds itself. The same holds for the fundamental process of biosynthesis and of energy metabolism. The exceptions to this rule thus command special interest as meaningful tokens of biological individuality, e.g., the replacement of cytosine by hydroxymethyl cytosine in the DNA of T2 phage (12).

Nutrition has been a special triumph. Bacteria which required no vitamins had seemed simpler than man. But deeper insights (32, 61) interpret nutritional simplicity as a greater power of synthesis. The requirements of more exacting organisms comprise just those metabolites they cannot synthesize with their own enzymatic machinery.

Species differ in their nutrition: if species are delimited by their genes, then genes must control the biosynthetic steps which are reflected

* Received for publication May 14, 1959. Nobel Prize lecture given at the Royal Caroline Medico-Surgical Institute, Stockholm, May 29, 1959. The Nobel Prize in Physiology or Medicine was awarded December 10, 1958, jointly to G. W. Beadle, E. L. Tatum, and J. Lederberg.

in nutritional patterns. This syllogism, so evident once told, has been amplified by Beadle and Tatum from this podium. Its implications for experimental biology and medicine are well known: among these, the methodology of bacterial genetics. Tatum has related how his early experience with bacterial nutrition reinforced the foundations of the biochemical genetics of Neurospora. Then, disregarding the common knowledge that bacteria were too simple to have genes, Tatum took courage to look for the genes that would indeed control bacterial nutrition. This conjunction marked the start of my own happy association with him, and with the fascinating challenges of bacterial genetics.

Contemporary genetic research is predicated on the role of DNA as the genetic material, of enzyme proteins as the cell's working tools, and of RNA as the communication channel between them (63). Three lines of evidence substantiate the genetic function of DNA. Two are related to bacterial genetics; the third and most general is the cytochemical observation of DNA in the chromosomes, which are undeniably strings of genes. But chromosomes also contain other constituents besides DNA: we want a technique to isolate a chromosome or a fragment of one, to analyze it, and to retransplant it to verify its functional capacity. The impressive achievements of nuclear transplantation (29) should encourage the audacity needed to try such experiments. The constructive equivalent to chromosome transplantation was discovered by a bacteriologist thirty years ago (20). The genetic implications of the "pneumococcus transformation" in the minds of some of Griffith's successors were clouded by its involvement with the gummy outer capsule of the bacteria. However, by 1943, Avery and his colleagues had shown that this inherited trait was transmitted from one pneumococcal strain to another by DNA. The general transmission of other traits by the same mechanism (25) can only mean that DNA comprises the genes (b).

To reinforce this conclusion, Hershey and Chase (23) proved that the genetic element of a bacterial virus is also DNA. Infection of a host cell requires the injection of just the DNA content of the adsorbed particle. This DNA controls not only its own replication in the production of new phage but also the specificity of the protein coat, which governs the serological and host range specificity of the intact phage.

At least in some small viruses, RNA also displays genetic functions. However, the hereditary autonomy of gene-initiated RNA of the cytoplasm is now very doubtful—at least some of the plasmagenes that have been proposed as fulfilling this function are now better understood as feedback-regulated systems of substrate-transport (81, 65, 72).

The work of the past decade thus strongly supports the simple doctrine that genetic information is nucleic, i.e., is coded in a linear sequence of nucleotides. This simplification of life may appear too facile, and has furnished a tempting target for agnostic criticism (37, 41, 44, 74). But, while no scientific theory would decry continual refinement and amplification, such criticism has little value if it detracts from the evident fruitfulness of the doctrine in experimental design.

The cell may, of course, carry information other than nucleic either in the cytoplasm or, accessory to the polynucleotide sequence, in the chromosomes. Epinucleic information has been invoked, without being more precisely defined, in many recent speculations on cyto-differentiation and on such models of this as antigenic phase variation in *Salmonella* (71, 52, 56, 47). Alternative schemes have so much less information capacity than the nucleic cycle that they are more likely to concern the regulation of genic functions than to mimic their specificities.

DNA AS A SUBSTANCE

The chemistry of DNA deserves to be exposed by apter craftsmen (86, 31, 13) and I shall merely recapitulate before addressing its biological implications. A segment of DNA is illustrated in Fig. 1. This shows a linear polymer whose backbone contains the repeating unit:

$$-O-PO_2^- -O-CH_2-CH-CH-$$

diester phosphate $\quad C_5' \quad C_4' \quad C_3'$

The carbon atoms are conventionally numbered according to their position in the furan-

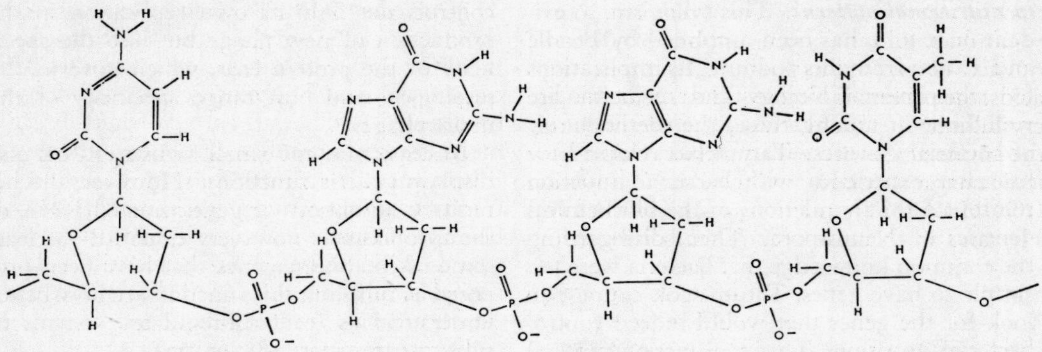

FIG. 1.—Primary structure of DNA—a segment of a polynucleotide sequence CGGT. From (13).

ose ring of deoxyribose, which is coupled as an N-glycoside to one of the nuclein bases: adenine, guanine, cytosine, or thymine, symbolized A, G, C, or T, the now well-known alphabet in which genetic instructions are composed. With a chain length of about 10,000 residues, one molecule of DNA contains 20,000 "bits of information," comparable to the text of this article, or in a page of newsprint.

Pyrophosphate-activated monomer units (e.g., thymidine triphosphate) have been identified as the metabolic precursors of DNA (31). For genetic replication, the monomer units must be assembled in a sequence that reflects that of the parent molecule. A plausible mechanism has been forwarded by Watson and Crick (87) as a corollary to their structural model whereby DNA occurs as a two-stranded helix, the bases being centrally oriented. When their relative positions are fixed by the deoxyribose-phosphate backbones, just two pairs of bases are able to form hydrogen bonds between their respective NH and CO groups; these are A : T and G : C. This pairing of bases would tie the two strands together for the length of the helix. In conformity with this model, extensive analytical evidence shows a remarkable equality of A with T and of G with C in DNA from various sources. The two strands of any DNA are then mutually complementary, the A, T, G, and C of one strand being represented by T, A, C, and G, respectively, of the other. The information of one strand is therefore equivalent to, because fully determined by, the other. The determination occurs at the replication of one parent

strand by the controlled stepwise accretion of monomers to form a complementary strand. At each step, only the monomer which is complementary to the template would fit for a chain-lengthening esterification with the adjacent nucleotide. The model requires the unraveling of the intertwined helices to allow each of them to serve as a template. This might, however, occur gradually, with the growth of the daughter chain—a concept embedded in Fig. 2 which symbolizes the new Cabala. The discovery of a single-stranded configuration of DNA (85) makes complete unraveling more tenable as an alternative model.

For the vehicle of life's continuity, DNA may seem a remarkably undistinguished molecule. Its over-all shape is controlled by the uniform deoxyribose-phosphate backbone whose monotony then gives X-ray diffraction patterns of high crystallinity. The nucleins themselves are relatively unreactive, hardly different from one to the other, and in DNA introverted and mutually saturated. Nor are any of the hydroxyls of deoxyribose left unsubstituted in the polymer. The structure of DNA befits the solipsism of its function.

The most plausible function of DNA is ultimately to specify the amino acid sequence in proteins. However, as there are twenty amino acids to choose among, there cannot be a one:one correspondence of nucleotide to amino acid. Taking account of the code duplication in complementary structures and the need to indicate spacing of the words in the code sequence, from three to four nucleins may be needed to spell one amino acid (19).

While a protein is also defined by the sequence of its monomeric units, the amino acids, the protein molecule lacks the "aperiodic crystallinity" (80) of DNA. The *differentiae* of the amino acids vary widely in size, shape, and ionic charge (e.g., $H_2N \cdot CH_2 \cdot CH_2 \cdot CH_2 \cdot CH_2 \cdot$; $COOH \cdot CH_2 \cdot CH_2 \cdot$; $HO \cdot C_6H_4 \cdot CH_2 \cdot$; $CH_3 \cdot$; $H \cdot$) and in the case of proline, bond angles.

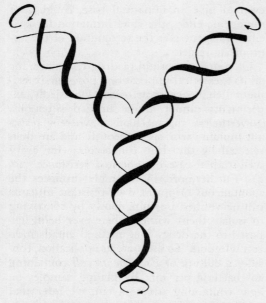

FIG. 2.—The scheme of Watson and Crick for DNA replication. "Unwinding and replication proceed *pari passu*. All three arms of the Y rotate as indicated" (14).

The biological action of a protein is, therefore, attributable to the shape of the critical surface into which the polypeptide chain folds (73). The one-dimensional specificity of the DNA must therefore be translated into the three-dimensional specificity of an enzyme or antibody surface. The simplest assumption would be that the amino acid sequence of the extended polypeptide, as it is released from the protein-building template in the cytoplasm, fully determines the folding pattern of the complete protein, which may, of course, be stabilized by nonpeptide linkages. If not, we should have to interpose some accessory mechanism to govern the folding of the protein.

This issue has reached a climax in speculations about the mechanism of antibody formation. If antibody globulins have a common sequence on which specificity is superimposed by directed folding, an antigen could directly mold the corresponding antibody. However, if sequence determines folding, it should in turn obey nucleic information. As this should be independent of antigenic instruction, we may look instead to a purely selective role of antigens to choose among nucleic alternatives which arise by spontaneous mutation (8, 50).

The correspondence between amino acids and clusters of nucleotides has no evident basis in their inherent chemical make-up and it now appears more probable that this *code* has evolved secondarily and arbitrarily to be translated by some biological intermediary. The coding relationship would then be analogous to, say, Morse-English (binary linear) to Chinese (pictographic). Encouragingly, several workers have reported the enzymatic reaction of amino acids with RNA fragments (22, 75). Apparently each amino acid has a different RNA receptor and an enzyme whose twofold specificity thus obviates any direct recognition of amino acid by polynucleotides. The alignment of amino-acyl residues for protein synthesis could then follow controlled assembly of their nucleotidates on an RNA template, by analogy with the model for DNA replication. We then visualize the following modes of information transfer:

(1) DNA replication — assembly of complementary deoxyribonucleotides on a DNA template.

(2) Transfer to RNA by some comparable mechanism of assembling ribonucleotides. Our understanding of this is limited by uncertainties of the structure of RNA (16).

(3) Protein synthesis:

    (*a*) Aminoacylation of polynucleotide fragments;

    (*b*) Assembly of the nucleotidates on an RNA template by analogy with step (1);

    (*c*) Peptide condensation of the amino acid residues.

Some workers have suggested that RNA is

replicated in step (3) concurrently with protein synthesis, in addition to its initiation from DNA.

The chief difference in primary structure between DNA and RNA is the hydroxylation of C_2' in the ribose, so that a reactive sugar hydroxyl is available in RNA. This may prove to be important in the less ordered secondary structure of RNA, and in its function as an intermediary to protein. It remains to be determined whether the aminoacyl nucleotidates are esterified at C_2' or at C_3' which is also available in the terminal residue. From this résumé we may observe that the DNA backbone constitutes an inert but rigid framework on which the differential nucleins are strung. Their spatial constraint lends specificity to the pattern of hydrogen bonding exposed at each level. This extended pattern is a plausible basis for replication; it is difficult to visualize any reagents besides other nucleotides to which this pattern would be relevant. These conditions are quite apt for a memory device—rubber and guncotton are poor choices for a computing tape.

DNA AND BACTERIAL MUTATION

The *ignis fatuus* of genetics has been the specific mutagen, the reagent that would penetrate to a given gene, recognize and modify it in a specific way. Directed mutation has long been discredited for higher organisms and the "molar indeterminacy" of mutation established both for its spontaneous occurrence and for its enhancement by X-rays (68). However, the development of resistance apparently induced by drugs revived illusions that bacterial genes might be alterable, an inference that would inevitably undermine the conception of "gene" for these organisms. No wonder that the mechanism of drug resistance has excited so much controversy (89)!

What sort of molecule could function as a specific mutagen, a reagent for a particular one of the bacterium's complement of genes, which can hardly number less than a thousand targets? On the nucleic hypothesis, the smallest segment capable of this variety would be a *hexa*nucleotide, all possible configurations of which must be discriminated by the specific mutagen. How could this be generally accomplished except by another molecule of conforming length and periodicity, that is, an analogous polynucleotide? Certainly there is nothing in the chemistry of penicillin or streptomycin to support their direct intervention in nucleic instructions.

In addition, we recognize no chemical reagent capable of substituting one nuclein for another in the structure of existent DNA. However, as the modification of a nuclein, even to give an unnatural base, could have mutagenic effect, the chief limitation for specific mutagenesis is the recognition of the appropriate target.

Of course the origin of drug resistance, for all its theoretical implications, poses an experimental challenge of its own. Concededly, experiments cannot decide untried situations. Nevertheless, the mechanism whereby resistant mutants arise spontaneously and are then selected by the drug can account for every well-studied case of inherited resistance (10, 5). Furthermore, in favorable instances the spontaneous origin of drug-resistant mutants can be verified unambiguously by contriving to isolate them without their ever being exposed to the drug. One method entails indirect selection. To illustrate its application, consider a culture of *Escherichia coli* containing 10^9 bacteria per ml. By plating samples on agar containing streptomycin, we infer that one bacterium per million or 10^3 per ml produce resistant clones. But to count these clones they were selected in the presence of streptomycin which hypothetically might have induced the resistance. We may however dilute the original bacteria in plain broth to give samples containing 10^5 per ml. Since 10^{-6} of the bacteria are resistant, each sample has a mathematical expectation of 0.1 of including a resistant bacterium. The individual bacterium being indivisible by dilution, nine samples in ten will include no resistants; the tenth will have one, but now augmented to 10^{-5}. Which one this is can be readily determined by retrospective assay on the incubated samples. The procedure can be reiterated to enrich for the resistant organisms until they are obtained in pure culture (11). The same result is reached more conveniently if we spread the original culture out on a nutrient agar plate rather than distribute samples into separate test tubes. Replica plating, transposing a pattern of surface growth from plate to plate with a sheet of velvet, takes the place of assaying inocula distributed in tubes (53). Dilution sampling and replica plating are, then, alternative methods of indirect selection whereby the test line is spared direct contact with the drug. Selection is accomplished by saving sublines whose *sibling* clones show the resistant reaction. This proof merely reinforces the incisive arguments that had already been forwarded by many other authors.

If mutations are not specific responses to the cellular environment, how do they arise? We still have very little information on the proximate causes of spontaneous, even of radiation and chemically induced, mutation. Most mutagenic chemicals are potent alkylating agents, e.g., formaldehyde or nitrogen mustard, which attack a variety of reactive groups in the cell. Similar compounds may occur in normal metabolism and account for part of the spontaneous mutation rate; they may also play a role as chemical intermediates in radiation effects. For the most part, then, studies on mutagenesis, especially by the more vigorous reagents, have told us little about the chemistry of the gene. Probably any agent that can penetrate to the chromosomes and have a localized chemical effect is capable of introducing random errors into the genetic information. If the cell were not first killed by other mechanisms most toxic agents would then probably be mutagenic.

Another class of mutagenic chemicals promises more information: analogues of the natural nucleins which are incorporated into DNA. For example, bromouracil specifically replaces thymine in phage DNA when furnished as bromodeoxyuridine to infected bacteria. Freese has shown, by genetic analyses of the utmost refinement, that the loci of resulting mutations in T4 phage are distributed differently from the mutants of spontaneous origin or those induced by other chemicals (18). This method presumably maps the locations of thymine in the original DNA. In order to account for wide variations in mutation rate for different loci, further interactions among the nucleotides must be supposed. So far, these studies represent the closest approach to a rational basis for chemical mutagenesis. However, every gene must present many targets to any nuclein analogue and the specificity of their mutagenesis can be detected only in systems where the resolution of genetic loci approximates the spacing of single nucleotides (4). At present this is feasible only in microorganisms; similar studies with bacteria and fungi would be of the greatest interest.

More specific effects might result from the insertion of oligo- and polynucleotides, a program which, however, faces a number of technical difficulties: even if the requisite polymers were to be synthesized, there are obstacles to their penetration into cells. The use of DNA extracted from mutant bacteria to transfer the corresponding genetic qualities is discussed as "genetic transduction."

RNA is the one other reagent that may be expected to recognize particular genes. As yet we have no direct evidence that the transfer of information from DNA to RNA is reversible. However, the anti-mutagenic effect of nuclein ribosides (21, 71) may implicate RNA in mutation. The reversibility of DNA $\rightleftarrows$ RNA information is also implicit in Stent's closely reasoned scheme for DNA replication (82). The needed experiment is the transfer of DNA information by some isolated RNA. Although not reported, this has probably not been fairly tried.

One motivation for this approach is the difficult problem of finding sources of homogeneous nucleic acids. DNA occurs biologically as sets of different molecules presumably in equimolar proportions. (A useful exception may be a remarkably small phage which seems to be unimolecular [85]). The species of RNA, however, may vary with the predominant metabolic activity of the cells. If so, some molecular species may be sufficiently exaggerated in specialized cells to facilitate their isolation. A purified RNA would have many potential applications, among others as a vehicle for the recognition of the corresponding DNA implied by our theory of information transfer. Pending such advances, *specific* mutagenesis is an implausible expectation.

Adaptive mutations, of which drug resistance is a familiar example, are crucial to the methodology of microbial genetics. Once having connected adaptive variation with gene mutation (78), we could proceed to exploit these systems for the detection of specific genotypes in very large test populations. The genotypes of interest may arise, as in the previous examples, by mutation: the most extensive studies of the physiology of mutation now use these methods for precise assay. For, in order to count the number of mutants of a given kind, it suffices to place large numbers of bacteria into selective media and count the surviving colonies which appear after incubation. In this way, mutation rates as low as one per 10^9 divisions can be treated in routine fashion.

GENETIC RECOMBINATION IN BACTERIA

The selective isolation of designed genotypes is also the most efficient way to detect genetic recombination. For example, the sexual mechanism of *Escherichia coli* was first exposed when prototrophic (nutritionally self-sufficient) recombinants arose in mixed cultures of two auxotrophic (nutritionally dependent) mutants (35, 57, 84). At first only one recombinant appeared per million parental bacteria and the selective procedure was quite obligatory. Later, more fertile strains were discovered which have been most helpful to further analysis (45, 51). This has shown that typical multinucleate vegetative bacteria unite by a conjugation bridge through which part or all of a male genome migrates into the female cell (43). The gametic cells then separate. The exconjugant male forms an unaltered clone, surviving by virtue of its remaining nuclei. The exconjugant female generates a mixed clone including recombinants (46, 1). Wollman, Jacob, and Hayes (88) have since demonstrated that the paternal chromosome migrates during fertilization in an orderly, progressive way. When fertilization is prematurely interrupted, the chromosome may be broken so that only anterior markers appear among the recombinants. All of the genetic markers are arranged in a single linkage group and their order can be established either by timing their passage during fertilization or by their statistical association with one another among the recombinants. Finally, the transfer of genetic markers can be correlated with the transfer of

DNA as inferred from the lethal effect of the radioactive decay of incorporated P^{32} (27).

Sexual recombination is one of the methods for analyzing the gene-enzyme relationship. The studies so far are fragmentary but they support the conception that the gene is a string of nucleotides which must function as a coherent unit in order to produce an active enzyme (4, 33, 67, 15, 90). However, metabolic blocks may originate through interference with accessory regulatory mechanisms instead of the fundamental capacity to produce the enzyme. For example, many "lactase-negative" mutants have an altered pattern of enzyme induction or a defective permease system for substrate transport (55, 65). Several laboratories are now working to correlate the relative sequence of genetic defects with the sequence of corresponding alterations in enzyme proteins; this may be the next best approach to the coding problem short of a system where a pure DNA can be matched with its protein phenotype.

At first these recombination experiments were confined to a single strain of *E. coli,* K-12. For many purposes this is a favorable choice of material—perhaps the main advantage is the accumulation of a library of many thousands of substrains carrying the various markers called for by the design of genetic tests. However, strain K-12 is rather unsuitable for serological studies, having lost the characteristic surface antigens which are the basis of serological typing. In any event it would be important to know the breeding structure of the group of enteric bacteria. Systematic studies have therefore been made of the interfertility of different strains of bacteria, principally with a convenient tester of the K-12 strain (39, 93). About one-fourth of the serotype strains of *E. coli* are fertile with strain K-12, and in at least some instances with one another. Whether the remaining three-fourths of strains are completely sterile, or whether they include different, closed, breeding groups (i.e., different genetic species) has not been systematically tested, partly because of the preliminary work needed to establish suitable strains.

E. coli K-12 is also interfertile with a number of strains of *Shigella* spp. (59). Finally although attempted crosses of *E. coli* with many

Salmonella types and of *Salmonellas* with one another have usually failed, Baron has demonstrated crosses of *E. coli* with a unique strain of *Salmonella typhimurium* (3). This may be especially useful as a means of developing hybrids which can be used to bridge the studies of sexuality in *E. coli* and transduction in *Salmonella*.

GENES AND VIRUSES

Bacteria furnish a unique opportunity to study the genetic relationships with their host cells. Another treasure of strain K-12 was for a time hidden: it carries the temperate bacteriophage, λ, which is technically quite favorable for genetic work. In accord with Burnet's early predictions, we had anticipated that the provirus for λ would behave as a genetic unit, but Dr. Esther Lederberg's first crosses were quite startling in their implication that the prophage segregated as a typical chromosomal marker (34). This was shown quite unambiguously by the segregation of lysogenicity versus sensitivity from persistent heterozygous cells, a test that bypassed the then controversial details of fertilization. The viability of such heterozygous cells supports the hypothesis that lysogenicity depends in part on the development of a cytoplasmic immunity to the cytopathic effects of infecting phage as a secondary result of the establishment of the prophage in a bacterial chromosome. This picture is also brought out by *zygotic induction* (26) whereby the fertilization of a sensitive cell by a prophage-bearing chromosome may provoke the maturation and progressive growth of the phage and the lysis of the complex. On the other hand, the introduction of a sensitive chromosome into a lysogenic bacterium does not result in this induction. The mode of attachment of prophage to its chromosomal site is as unsettled as the general picture of the higher organization of DNA, but most students favor a lateral rather than an axial relationship for the prophage. The isolation of intact chromosomes of bacteria would give a new approach to this question but has so far been inconclusive.

Another infectious particle that has jumped out of our Pandora's box determines the very capacity of *E. coli* to function as a male partner in fertilization (51). For lack of a better inspiration, we call this particle "F." Two kinds of male strains are now recognized according to whether the F particle has a chromosomal or a cytoplasmic location. F+ strains, like the original K-12, are highly contagious for F and will rapidly convert populations of female, F— strains in which they are introduced. Hfr males, on the other hand, have a chromosomal localization of the F factor resulting from occasional transpositions in F+ strains. The different localization of the F particle in the two cases is diagnosed primarily by the behavior of the particle in crosses. In addition, Hirota and Iijima (24) found that the F particle could be eliminated from F+ strains by treatment with acridine dyes. Hfr clones are unaffected by acridine orange, but when they revert to the F+ state, as occasionally happens, the F particle again becomes vulnerable to the dye. The accessibility of extrachromosomal F is paralleled by several other examples of plasmid disinfection (reviewed in 40); perhaps the most notable is the bleaching of green plant cells by streptomycin (17, 76). No reagent is known to inactivate F or prophage while bound to the chromosome.

The virus λ and the plasmagene F are analogous in many features (28, 48). Their main differences are:

(1) Cytopathogenicity. A bacterium cannot long tolerate λ in its cytoplasmic state and remain viable. The vegetative λ must promptly reduce itself to a chromosomal state or multiply aggressively and lyse the host bacterium. F has no known cytopathic effect.

(2) Maturation. Vegetative λ organizes a protein coat and matures into an infective phage particle. F is known only as an intracellular vegetative element; however, the coat of the F+ cell may be analogous to that of the phage.

(3) Transmission. λ is infective, i.e., forms a free particle which can penetrate susceptible cells. F is transmitted only by cell-to-cell conjugation.

(4) Fixation. λ has a foreordained site of fixation on the bacterial chromosome; F has been identified at a variety of sites. How-

ever, this difference may be illusory. In special situations, F does have preferential sites of fixation (77), and generally, translocations of F to different sites are more readily discovered than those of λ would be.

(5) Induction. Exposure of lysogenic bacteria to small doses of ultraviolet light causes the prophage to initiate a lytic cycle with the appearance first of vegetative, then of mature phage (62). Hfr bacteria make no analogous response. However, the kinetics of the reversion, Hfr → F+, has not been carefully studied.

The genetic function of bacteriophages is further exemplified by *transduction* whereby genes are transferred from cell to cell by the intervention of phage particles (42, 91). In our first studies we concluded that the bacterial genes were adventitiously carried in normal phage particles (92, 66, 83). Further studies favor the view that the transducing particle has a normal phage coat but a defective phage nucleus. This correlation has suggested that a gene becomes transducible when a prophage segment is translocated to its vicinity (2, 9, 60).

Transduction focuses special attention on the phenomenon of specific pairing of homologous chromosome segments. Howsoever a transduced gene is finally integrated into the bacterial genome, at some stage it must locate the homologous gene in the recipient chromosome. For in transduction, as in sexual recombination, new information is not merely added to the complement; it must also replace the old. This must involve the confrontation of the two homologues prior to the decision which one is to be retained. Synapsis is even more puzzling as between chromosomes whose DNA is in the stabilized double helix and then further contracted by supercoiling. Conceivably gene products rather than DNA are the agency of synaptic pairing.

The integration of a transduced fragment raises further issues (41). The competing hypotheses are the physical incorporation of the fragment in the recipient chromosome, or the use of its information when new DNA is replicated. The same issues still confound models of crossing over at meiosis in higher forms; once again the fundamentals of chromosome structure are needed for a resolution.

VIRUS VERSUS GENE

The homology of gene and virus in their fundamental aspects makes their overt differences even more puzzling. According to the simplest nucleic doctrine, DNA plays no active role in its own replication other than furnishing a useful pattern. Various nucleotide sequences should then be equally replicable. What then distinguishes virus DNA, which replicates itself at the expense of the other pathways of cellular anabolism? For the T-even phages, the presence of the unique glucosylated hydroxymethylcytosine furnishes a partial answer (12). However, other viruses such as λ display no unique constituents; furthermore, as prophage they replicate coordinately with bacterial DNA. Does the virus have a unique element of structure, either chemical or physical, so far undetected? Or does it instruct its own preferential synthesis by a code for supporting enzymes?

THE CREATION OF LIFE

The mutualism of DNA, RNA, and proteins as just reviewed is fundamental to all contemporary life. Viruses are simpler as infective particles but must, of course, parasitize the metabolic machinery of the host cell. What would be the least requirements of a primeval organism, the simplest starting point for progressive replication of DNA in terms of presently known or conjectured mechanisms? They include at least:

(1) DNA.

(2) The four deoxyribotide pyrophosphates in abundance.

(3) One molecule of the protein, DNA polymerase.

(4) Ribotide phosphates as precursors for RNA.

(5) One molecule of the protein RNA polymerase.

(6) A supply of the twenty amino acyl nucleotidates.

   (*a*) Failing these, each of the twenty enzymes which catalyze the condensation of an amino acid and corresponding RNA fragments together with sources of these components.

(7) One molecule of the protein aminoacyl-RNA polymerase.

In principle, this formidable list might be reduced to a single polynucleotide polymerized by a single enzyme. However, any scheme for the enzymatic synthesis of nucleic acid calls for the coincidence of a particular nucleic acid and of a particular protein. This is a far more stringent improbability than the sudden emergence of an isolated DNA such as many authors have suggested, so much more so that we must look for alternative solutions to the problem of the origin of life. These are of two kinds. The primeval organism could still be a nucleic cycle if nucleic replication occurs, however imperfectly, without the intervention of protein. The polymerase enzyme, and the transfer of information from nucleic acid to protein, would then be evolved refinements. Alternatively, DNA has evolved from a simpler, spontaneously condensing polymer. The exquisite perfection of DNA makes the second suggestion all the more plausible.

The nucleoprotein cycle is the climax of biochemical evolution. Its antiquity is shown by its adoption by all phyla. Having persisted for $\sim 10^9$ years, nucleoprotein may be the most durable feature of the geochemistry of this planet.

At the present time, no other self-replicating polymers are known or understood. Nevertheless, the nucleic system illustrates the basic requirements for such a polymer. It must have a rigid periodic structure in which two or more alternative units can be readily substituted. It must allow for the reversible sorption of specific monomers to the units in its own sequence. Adjacent, sorbed monomers must then condense to form the replica polymer, which must be able to desorb from the template. Primitively, the condensation must be spontaneous but reliable. In DNA, the sorption depends on the hydrogen bonding of nuclein molecules constrained on a rigid helical backbone. This highly specific but subtle design would be difficult to imitate. For the more primitive stages, both of biological evolution and of our own experimental insight, we may prefer to invoke somewhat cruder techniques of complementary attachment. The simplest of these is perhaps the attraction between ionic groups of opposite charge, for example, NH_3^+ and COO^- which are so prevalent in simple organic compounds. If the ingenuity and craftsmanship so successfully directed at the fabrication of organic polymers for the practical needs of mankind were to be concentrated on the problem of constructing a self-replicating assembly along these lines I predict that the construction of an artificial molecule having the essential function of primitive life would fall within the grasp of our current knowledge of organic chemistry.

CONCLUSIONS

The experimental control of cellular genotype is one of the measures of the scope of genetic science. However, nucleic genes will not be readily approached for experimental manipulation except by reagents that mimic them in periodic structure. Specifically induced mutation, if ever accomplished, will then consist of an act of genetic recombination between the target DNA and the controlled information specified by the reagent. Methods for the step-wise analysis and reassembly of nucleic acids are likely to be perfected in the near future in pace with the accessibility of nucleic acid preparations which are homogeneous enough to make their use worth while. For the immediate future, it is likely that the greatest success will attend the use of biological reagents to furnish the selectivity needed to discriminate one among innumerable classes of polynucleotides. Synthetic chemistry is, however, challenged to produce model polymers that can emulate the essential features of genetic systems.

REFERENCES

1. Anderson, T. F., "Recombination and Segregation in *Escherichia coli*," *Cold Spring Harbor Symposia Quant. Biol.*, **23** : 47, 1958.

2. Arber, W., "Transduction des caractères Gal par le bactériophage Lambda," *Archives des Sciences, Soc. Phys. Hist. Nat. Genève*, **11** : 259, 1958.

3. Baron, L. S., Carey, W. F., and Spilman, W. M., "Hybridization of *Salmonella* Species by Mating with *Escherichia coli*," *Abst. 7th Int.*

Cong. Microbiol. (Stockholm), pp. 50–51, 1958.

4. Benzer, S., "The Elementary Units of Heredity," in *The Chemical Basis of Heredity*, W. D. McElroy and B. Glass (eds.), Baltimore: The Johns Hopkins Press, 1957, pp. 70–93.

5. Bryson, V., and Szybalski, W., "Microbial Drug Resistance," *Adv. Genetics*, **7** : 1, 1955.

6. Burnet, F. M., *Biological Aspects of Infectious Disease*, Cambridge: Cambridge University Press, 1940.

7. Burnet, F. M., *Virus as Organism*, Cambridge, Mass.: Harvard University Press, 1945.

8. Burnet, Sir MacFarlane, *The Clonal Selection Theory of Immunity* (Abraham Flexner Lectures, 1958), Nashville: Vanderbilt University Press, 1959.

9. Campbell, A., "Transduction and Segregation in *Escherichia coli* K-12," *Virology*, **4** : 366, 1957.

10. Cavalli-Sforza, L. L., and Lederberg, J., "Genetics of Resistance to Bacterial Inhibitors," in *Symposium on Growth Inhibition and Chemotherapy*, Int. Cong. Microbiol. (Rome), 1953, pp. 108–42.

11. ———, "Isolation of Preadaptive Mutants in Bacteria by Sib Selection," *Genetics*, **41** : 367, 1956.

12. Cohen, S. S., "Molecular Bases of Parasitism of Some Bacterial Viruses," *Science*, **123** : 653, 1956.

13. Crick, F. H. C., "The Structure of the Hereditary Material," *Scient. Am.*, **151** : 54, 1954.

14. Delbrück, M., and Stent, G. S., "On the Mechanism of DNA Replication," in *The Chemical Basis of Heredity*, W. D. McElroy and B. Glass (eds.), Baltimore: The Johns Hopkins Press, 1957, pp. 699–736.

15. Demerec, M., Hartman, Z., Hartman, P. E., Yura, T., Gots, J. S., Ozeki, H., and Glover, S. W., *Genetic Studies with Bacteria*, Washington, D.C.: Carnegie Inst. Publ. 612, 1956.

16. Doty, P., Boedtker, H., Fresco, J. R., Haselkorn, R., and Litt, M., "Secondary Structure in Ribonucleic Acids," *Proc. Nat. Acad. Sc.*, **45** : 482, 1959.

17. von Euler, H., "Einfluss des Streptomycins auf die Chlorophyllbildung," *Kem. Arb.*, **9** : 1, 1947.

18. Freese, E., "The Difference Between Spontaneous and Base-Analogue Induced Mutations of Phage T4," *Pros. Nat. Acad. Sc.*, **45** : 622, 1959.

19. Golomb, S. W., Welch, L. R., and Delbrück, M., "Construction and Properties of Comma-Free Codes," *Biol. Medd. Can. Vid. Selsk.*, **23** : 1, 1958.

20. Griffith, F., "The Significance of Pneumococcal Types," *J. Hyg.*, **27** : 113, 1928.

21. Haas, F. L., and Doudney, C. O., "A Relation of Nucleic Acid Synthesis to Radiation-Induced Mutation Frequency in Bacteria," *Proc. Nat. Acad. Sc.*, **43** : 871, 1957.

22. Hecht, L. I., Stephenson, M. L., and Zamecnik, P. C., "Binding of Amino Acids to the End Group of a Soluble Ribonucleic Acid," *Proc. Nat. Acad. Sc.*, **45** : 505, 1959.

23. Hershey, A. D., and Chase, M., "Independent Function of Viral Protein and Nucleic Acid in Growth of Bacteriophage," *J. Gen. Physiol.*, **36** : 39, 1951.

24. Hirota, Y., and Iijima, T., "Acriflavine as an Effective Agent for Eliminating F-Factor in *Escherichia coli* K-12," *Nature*, **180** : 655, 1957.

25. Hotchkiss, R. D., "The Genetic Chemistry of the Pneumococcal Transformations," *Harvey Lect.*, **49** : 124, 1955.

26. Jacob, F., and Wollman, E. L., "Sur les processus de conjugaison et de recombinaison chez *Escherichia coli*: I. L'induction par conjugaison ou induction zygotique," *Ann Inst. Pasteur*, **91** : 486, 1956.

27. ———, "Genetic and Physical Determination of Chromosomal Segments in *Escherichia coli*," *Symp. Soc. Exper. Biol.*, **7** : 75, 1958.

28. ———, "Les épisomes, éléments génétiques ajoutés," *C. R. Acad. Sc., Paris*, **247** : 154, 1958.

29. King, T. J., and Briggs, R., "Serial Transplantation of Embryonic Nuclei," *Cold Spring Harbor Symposia Quant. Biol.*, **21** : 271, 1956.

30. Kluyver, A. J., and van Niel, C. B., *The Microbe's Contribution to Biology*, Cambridge, Mass.: Harvard University Press, 1956.

31. Kornberg, A., "Enzymatic Synthesis of Deoxyribonucleic Acid," *Harvey Lect.*, **53** : 83, 1959.

32. Knight, B. C. J. G., "Bacterial Nutrition," *Med. Res. Council* (Brit.), Spec. Rep. Ser. No. 210, 1936.

33. Lederberg, E. M., "Allelic Relationships and Reverse Mutation in *Escherichia coli*," *Genetics*, **37** : 469, 1952.

34. Lederberg, E. M., and Lederberg, J., "Genetic Studies of Lysogenicity in *Escherichia coli*," *Genetics*, **38** : 51, 1953.

35. Lederberg, J., "Gene Recombination and Linked Segregations in *Escherichia coli*," *Genetics*, **32** : 505, 1947.

36. ———, "Problems in Microbial Genetics," *Heredity*, **2** : 145, 1948.

37. ———, "Bacterial Variation," *Ann. Rev. Microbiol.,* **3** : 1, 1949.

38. ———, "Genetic Studies with Bacteria," in *Genetics in the 20th Century,* L. C. Dunn (ed.), New York: The Macmillan Company, 1951, pp. 263–89.

39. ———, "Prevalence of *Escherichia coli* Strains Exhibiting Genetic Recombination," *Science,* **114** : 68, 1951.

40. ———, "Cell Genetics and Hereditary Symbiosis," *Physiol. Rev.,* **32** : 403, 1952.

41. ———, "Recombination Mechanisms in Bacteria," *J. Cell & Comp. Physiol.,* **45** (Suppl. 2): 75, 1955.

42. ———, "Genetic Transduction," *Am. Scientist,* **44** : 264, 1956.

43. ———, "Conjugal Pairing in *Escherichia coli,*" *J. Bact.,* **71** : 497, 1956.

44. ———, "Comments on Gene-Enzyme Relationship," in *Enzymes: Units of Biological Structure and Function,* O. H. Gaebler (ed.), New York: Academic Press Inc., 1956, pp. 161–69.

45. ———, "Viruses, Genes and Cells," *Bact. Rev.,* **21** : 133, 1957.

46. ———, "Sibling Recombinants in Zygote Pedigrees of Escherichia coli," *Proc. Nat. Acad. Sc.,* **43** : 1060, 1957.

47. ———, "Genetic Approaches to Somatic Cell Variation: Summary Comment," *J. Cell. & Comp. Physiol.,* **52** (Suppl. 1): 383, 1958.

48. ———, "Extranuclear Transmission of the F Compatibility Factor in *Escherichia coli,*" *Abstr. 7th Int. Cong. Microbiol.* (Stockholm), pp. 58–60, 1958.

49. ———, "Bacterial Reproduction," *Harvey Lect.,* **53** : 69, 1959.

50. ———, "Genes and Antibodies," *Science,* **129** : 1649, 1959.

51. Lederberg, J., Cavalli, L. L., and Lederberg, E. M., "Sex Compatibility in *Escherichia coli,*" *Genetics,* **37** : 720, 1952.

52. Lederberg, J., and Edwards, P. R., "Serotypic Recombination in *Salmonella,*" *J. Immunol.,* **71** : 232, 1953.

53. Lederberg, J., and Lederberg, E. M., "Replica Plating and Indirect Selection of Bacterial Mutants," *J. Bact.,* **63** : 399, 1952.

54. ———, "Infection and Heredity," *Symp. Soc. Growth and Develop.,* **14** : 101, 1956.

55. Lederberg, J., Lederberg, E. M., Zinder, N.D., and Lively, E. R., "Recombination Analysis of Bacterial Heredity," *Cold Spring Harbor Symposia Quant. Biol.,* **16** : 413, 1951.

56. Lederberg, J., and Iino, T., "Phase Variation in *Salmonella,*" *Genetics,* **41** : 743, 1956.

57. Lederberg, J., and Tatum, E. L., "Gene Recombination in *Escherichia coli,*" *Nature,* **158** : 558, 1946.

58. ———, "Sex in Bacteria: Genetic Studies, 1945–1952," *Science,* **118** : 169, 1954.

59. Luria, S. E., and Burrous, J. W., "Hybridization Between *Escherichia coli* and *Shigella,*" *J. Bact.,* **74** : 461, 1957.

60. Luria, S. E., Fraser, D. K., Adams, J. N., and Burrous, J. W., "Lysogenization, Transduction, and Genetic Recombination in Bacteria," *Cold Spring Harbor Symposia Quant. Biol.,* **23** : 71, 1958.

61. Lwoff, A., "Les facteurs de croissance pour les microorganismes," *Ann. Inst. Pasteur,* **61** : 580, 1938.

62. Lwoff, A., Siminovitch, L., and Kjeldgaard, N., "Induction de la production de bactériophages chez une bactérie lysogène," *Ann. Inst. Pasteur,* **79** : 815, 1950.

63. McElroy, W. D., and Glass, B. (eds.), *The Chemical Basis of Heredity,* Baltimore: The Johns Hopkins Press, 1957.

64. Meselson, M., and Stahl, F. W., "The Replication of DNA in *Escherichia coli,*" *Proc. Nat. Acad. Sc.,* **44** : 671, 1958.

65. Monod, J., "Remarks on the Mechanism of Enzyme Induction," in *Enzymes: Units of Biological Structure and Function,* O. H. Gaebler (ed.), New York: Academic Press Inc., 1956, pp. 7–28.

66. Morse, M. L., Lederberg, E. M., and Lederberg, J., "Transduction in *Escherichia coli* K-12," *Genetics,* **41** : 142, 1956.

67. ———, "Transductional Heterogenotes in *Escherichia coli,*" *Genetics,* **41** : 758, 1956.

68. Muller, H. J., "The Production of Mutations," *Les Prix Nobel en 1946,* Stockholm, 1948, pp. 257–74.

69. Nagel, E., "The Meaning of Reduction in the Natural Sciences," in *Science and Civilization,* R. C. Stauffer (ed.), Madison: University of Wisconsin Press, 1949, pp. 99–138.

70. Nanney, D. L., "Epigenetic Control Systems," *Proc. Nat. Acad. Sc.,* **44** : 712, 1958.

71. Novick, A., "Mutagens and Antimutagens," *Brookhaven Symposia in Biology,* **8** (Mutation): 201–15, Washington, D.C.: Office of Tech. Serv., U.S. Dept. Commerce, 1956.

72. Novick, A., and McCoy, A., "Quasi-Genetic Regulation of Enzyme Level," in *Physiological Adaptation,* Washington, D.C.: Amer. Physiol. Soc., 1958, pp. 140–50.

73. Pauling, L., "Molecular Structure and Intermolecular Forces," in *The Specificity of Serological Reactions,* K. Landsteiner, Cambridge,

Mass.: Harvard University Press, 1945, pp. 275–93.

74. Pirie, N. W., "Some Aspects of the Origins of Life Considered in the Light of the Moscow International Symposium," *ICSU Rev.,* 1 : 40, 1959.

75. Preiss, J., Berg, P., Ofengand, E. J., Bergmann, F. H., and Dieckmann, M., "The Chemical Nature of the RNA–Amino Acid Compound Formed by Amino Acid-Activating Enzymes," *Proc. Nat. Acad. Sc.,* 45 : 319, 1959.

76. Provasoli, L., Hutner, S. H., and Pintner, I. J., "Destruction of Chloroplasts by Streptomycin," *Cold Spring Harbor Symposia Quant. Biol.,* 16 : 113, 1951.

77. Richter, A. A., "Determinants of Mating Type in Escherichia coli," Ph.D. Dissertation, University of Wisconsin (University Microfilm, Ann Arbor, Mich.), 1959.

78. Ryan, F. J., and Lederberg, J., "Reverse-Mutation in Leucineless *Neurospora*," *Proc. Nat. Acad. Sc.,* 32 : 163, 1946.

79. Sanger, F., *Les Prix Nobel en 1958,* Stockholm, 1959.

80. Schrödinger, E., *What Is Life?* Cambridge: Cambridge University Press, 1944.

81. Spiegelman, S., Lindegren, C. C., and Lindegren, G., "Maintenance and Increase of a Genetic Character by a Substrate-Cytoplasmic Interaction in the Absence of the Specific Gene," *Proc. Nat. Acad. Sc.,* 31 : 95, 1945.

82. Stent, G. S., "Mating in the Reproduction of Bacterial Viruses," *Adv. Virus Research,* 5 : 95, 1958.

83. Stocker, B. A. D. S., Zinder, N. D., and Lederberg, J., "Transduction of Flagellar Characters in *Salmonella*," *J. Gen. Micróbiol.,* 9 : 410, 1593.

84. Tatum, E. L., and Lederberg, J., "Gene Recombination in the Bacterium *Escherichia coli*," *J. Bact.,* 53 : 673, 1947.

85. Tessman, I., "Some Unusual Properties of the Nucleic Acid in Bacteriophages S13 and ΦX174," *Virology,* 7 : 263, 1959.

86. Todd, Sir Alexander, "Synthesis in the Study of Nucleotides," *Les Prix Nobel en 1957,* Stockholm, pp. 119–33, 1958.

87. Watson, J. D., and Crick, F. H. C., "The Structure of DNA," *Cold Spring Harbor Symposia Quant. Biol.,* 23 : 123, 1953.

88. Wollman, E. L., Jacob, F., and Hayes, W., "Conjugation and Genetic Recombination in *Escherichia coli* K-12," *Cold Spring Harbor Symposia Quant. Biol.,* 21 : 141, 1956.

89. Wolstenholme, G. E. W., and O'Connor, C. M. (eds.), *Ciba Foundation Symposium on Drug Resistance in Microorganisms,* London: J. and A. Churchill, Ltd., 1957.

90. Yanofsky, C., and Crawford, I. P., "Effects of Deletions, Point Mutations, Suppressor Mutations and Reversions on the Two Components of Tryptophane Synthetase of *Escherichia coli*," *Proc. Nat. Acad. Sc.,* 45 (in press), 1959.

91. Zinder, N. D., "Bacterial Transduction," *J. Cell. & Comp. Physiol.,* 45 (Suppl. 2): 23, 1955.

92. Zinder, N. D., and Lederberg, J., "Genetic Exchange in *Salmonella*," *J. Bact.,* 64 : 679, 1952.

93. Ørskov, F., and Ørskov, I., unpublished observations.

NOTES

a. No reader who recognizes *deoxyribonucleic acid* will need to be reminded what DNA stands for.

b. One might be tempted to write: "One DNA molecule = one gene." However, the quanta of factorial genetics, based on mutation, recombination, and enzymatic function are all smaller than the DNA unit of molecular weight $\sim 6 \times 10^6$ (4). There is increasing evidence that such a molecule is a natural unit rather than an artefact of fragmentation.

c. The experimental work from my laboratory summarized in this paper has been generously supported by research grants from the National Institutes of Health, U.S. Public Health Service, the National Science Foundation, the Rockefeller Foundation, the Wisconsin Alumni Research Foundation, the University of Wisconsin, and, most recently, Stanford University. It is also a pleasure to record my thanks to the Jane Coffin Childs Fund for Medical Research for a research fellowship which supported my first association with Professor E. L. Tatum.

JAMES D. WATSON

The involvement of RNA in the synthesis of proteins

Nobel Lecture, December 11, 1962

Prologue

I arrived in Cambridge in the fall of 1951. Though my previous interests were largely genetic, Luria had arranged for me to work with John Kendrew. I was becoming frustrated with phage experiments and wanted to learn more about the actual structures of the molecules which the geneticists talked about so passionately. At the same time John needed a student and hoped that I should help him with his X-ray studies on myoglobin. I thus became a research student of Clare College with John as my supervisor.

But almost as soon as I set foot in the Cavendish, I inwardly knew I would never be of much help to John. For I had already started talking with Francis. Perhaps even without Francis, I would have quickly bored of myoglobin. But with Francis to talk to, my fate was sealed. For we quickly discovered that we thought the same way about biology. The center of biology was the gene and its control of cellular metabolism. The main challenge in biology was to understand gene replication and the way in which genes control protein synthesis. It was obvious that these problems could be logically attacked only when the structure of the gene became known. This meant solving the structure of DNA. Then this objective seemed out of reach to the interested geneticists. But in our cold, dark Cavendish lab, we thought the job could be done, quite possibly within a few months. Our optimism was partly based on Linus Pauling's feat[1] in deducing the α-helix, largely by following the rules of theoretical chemistry so persuasively explained in his classical *The Nature of the Chemical Bond*. We also knew that Maurice Wilkins had crystalline X-ray diffraction photographs from DNA and so it must have a well-defined structure. There was thus an answer for somebody to get.

During the next eighteen months, until the double-helical structure became elucidated, we frequently discussed the necessity that the correct structure have the capacity for self-replication. And in pessimistic moods, we often worried that the correct structure might be dull. That is, it would suggest absolutely nothing and excite us no more than something inert like collagen.

The finding of the double helix[2] thus brought us not only joy but great relief. It was unbelievably interesting and immediately allowed us to make a serious proposal[3] for the mechanism of gene duplication. Furthermore, this replication scheme involved thoroughly understood conventional chemical forces. Previously, some theoretical physicists, among them Pascual Jordan[4], had proposed that many biological phenomena, particularly gene replication, might be based on still undiscovered long-range forces arising from quantum mechanical resonance interactions. Pauling[5] thoroughly disliked this conjecture and firmly insisted that known short-range forces between complementary surfaces would be the basis of biological replication.

The establishment of the DNA structure reinforced our belief that Pauling's arguments were sound and that long-range forces, or for that matter any form of mysticism, would not be involved in protein synthesis. But for the protein replication problem mere inspection of the DNA structure then gave no immediate bonus. This, however, did not worry us since there was much speculation that RNA, not DNA, was involved in protein synthesis.

Introduction

The notion that RNA is involved in protein synthesis goes back over twenty years to the pioneering experiments of Brachet and Caspersson[6] who showed that cells actively synthesizing protein are rich in RNA. Later when radioactive amino acids became available, this conjecture was strengthened by the observation[7] that the cellular site of protein synthesis is the microsomal component, composed in large part of spherical particles rich in RNA. Still later experiments[8] revealed that these ribonucleoprotein particles (now conveniently called ribosomes), not the lipoprotein membranes to which they are often attached, are the sites where polypeptide bonds are made. Most ribosomes are found in the cytoplasm and correspondingly most cellular protein synthesis occurs without the direct intervention of the nuclear-located DNA. The possibility was thus raised that the genetic specificity present in DNA is first transferred to RNA intermediates which then function as templates controlling assembly of specific amino acids into proteins.

We became able to state this hypothesis in more precise form when the structure of DNA became known in 1953. We then realized that DNA's genetic specificity resides in the complementary base sequences along its two intertwined chains. One or both of these complementary chains must serve as templates for specific RNA molecules whose genetic information again must reside in specific base sequences. These RNA molecules would then assume 3-dimensional configurations containing surfaces complementary to the side groups of the 20 specific amino acids.

X-ray Studies on RNA and RNA-containing Viruses

The direct way to test this hypothesis was to solve the RNA structure. Already in 1952, I had taken some preliminary X-ray diffraction pictures of RNA. These, however, were very diffuse, and it was not until I returned to the United States in the fall of 1953 that serious X-ray studies on RNA began. Alexander Rich and I, then both at the California Institute of Technology, obtained RNA samples from various cellular sources. We[9] were first very encouraged that all the RNA samples, no matter their cellular origin, give similar X-ray diffraction pattern. A general RNA structure thus existed. This gave us hope that the structure, when solved, would be interesting. Our first pictures already showed large systematic absence of reflections on the meridian, suggesting a helical structure. But despite much effort to obtain native undegraded high molecular weight samples, no satisfactory X-ray diffraction pattern was obtained. The reflections were always diffuse, no evidence of crystallinity was seen. Though there were marked similarities to the DNA pattern, we had no solid grounds for believing that these arose from a similar helical molecule. The problem whether RNA was a one- or several-chained structure remained unanswered.

We then considered the possibility that RNA might have a regular structure only when combined with protein. At that time (1955) there was no good evidence for RNA existing free from protein. All RNA was thought to exist either as a viral component or to be combined with protein in ribonucleoprotein particles. It thus seemed logical to turn attention to a study of ribonucleoprotein particles (ribosomes) since upon their surfaces protein was synthesized. Our hope again was that the establishment of their structure would reveal the long-sought-after cavities specific for the amino acids.

Then we were struck by the morphological similarity between ribosomes and small RNA-containing viruses like Turnip Yellow Mosaic Virus or Poliomyelitis Virus. By then (1955–1956) I was back in Cambridge with

Crick to finish formulating some general principles on viral structure[10]. Our main idea was that the finite nucleic acid content of viruses severely restricted the number of amino acids they could code for. As a consequence, the protein coat could not be constructed from a very large number of different protein molecules. Instead it must be constructed from a number of identical small sub-units arranged in a regular manner. These ideas already held for Tobacco Mosaic Virus, a rod-shaped virus, and we were very pleased when D. L. D. Caspar[11], then working with us at the Cavendish, took some elegant diffraction pictures of Bushy Stunt Virus crystals and extended experimental support to the spherical viruses.

Structural Studies on Ribosomes

At that time almost no structural studies had been done with ribosomes. They were chiefly characterized by their sedimentation constants; those from higher organisms[12] in the 70s–80s range, while those from bacteria[13] appeared smaller and to be of two sizes (30s and 50s). Because the bacterial particles seemed smaller, they seemed preferable for structural studies. Thus when Alfred Tissières and I came to Harvard's Biological Laboratories in 1956, we initiated research on the ribosomes of the commonly studied bacteria *Escherichia coli*. We hoped that their structure would show similarities with the small spherical RNA viruses. Then we might have a good chance to crystallize them and to eventually use X-ray diffraction techniques to establish their 3-dimensional structure.

Ribosome sub-units

But from the beginning of our Harvard experiments, it was obvious that ribosome structure would be more complicated than RNA virus structure. Depending upon the concentration of divalent cations (in all our experiments Mg^{++}), 4 classes of *E. coli* ribosomes were found, characterized by sedimentation constants of 30s, 50s, 70s, and 100s. Our first experiments in $10^{-4} M Mg^{++}$ revealed 30s and 50s ribosomes. At the same time Bolton[14], at the Carnegie Institute of Washington employing higher Mg^{++} levels, saw faster sedimenting ribosomes and suggested that they were observing aggregates of the smaller particles. Soon after, our experiments[15] revealed that, as the Mg^{++} concentration is raised, one 30s particle and one 50s particle

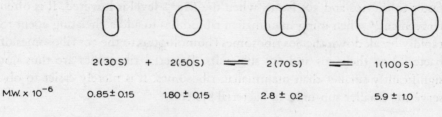

M.W. x 10⁻⁶	2(30S) + 2(50S) ⇌ 2(70S) ⇌ 1(100S)

M.W. x 10^{-6}

2(30 S)	2(50 S)	2(70 S)	1(100 S)
0.85 ± 0.15	1.80 ± 0.15	2.8 ± 0.2	5.9 ± 1.0

All particles are composed of 64% RNA and 36% protein

Fig. 1. Diagrammatic representation of *E. coli* ribosome sub-units and their aggregation products. (The molecular weight data are from Tissières *et al.*[15])

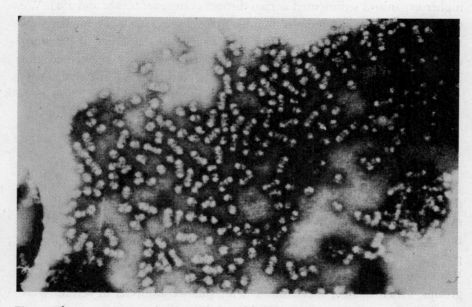

Fig. 2. Electron micrograph of negatively stained *E. coli* ribosomes (Huxley and Zubay[15]). Two particle types are predominant: (1) 70s containing two sub-units of unequal size, and (2) 100s consisting of two 70s ribosomes joined together at their smaller (30s) sub-units.

combine to form a 70s ribosome. At still higher Mg⁺⁺ concentrations, two 70s ribosomes dimerize to form a 100s ribosome. (Figs. 1 and 2).

Ribosomes from every cellular source have a similar sub-unit construction. As with *E. coli* ribosomes, the level of divalent cations determines which ribosomes exist. Bacterial ribosomes seem to require higher Mg⁺⁺ levels in order to aggregate into the larger sizes. Conversely they break down much faster to the 30s and 50s forms when the Mg++ level is lowered. It is often convenient[16] when using mammalian ribosomes to add a chelating agent to rapidly break down the 80s ribosomes (homologous to the 70s ribosomes of bacteria) to their 40s and 60s sub-units. Bacterial ribosomes are thus not significantly smaller than mammalian ribosomes. It is merely easier to observe the smaller sub-units in bacterial systems.

Ribosomal RNA

Already in 1958 there were several reports[17] that ribosomal RNA from higher organisms sedimented as two distinct components (18s and 28s). We thought that the smaller molecules most likely arose from the smaller sub-unit while the faster sedimenting RNA came from the larger of the ribosomal sub-units. Experiments of Mr. Kurland[18] quickly confirmed this hunch. The *E. coli* 30s ribosome was found to contain one RNA chain (16s) with a molecular weight of 5.5×10^5. Correspondingly a larger RNA molecule (23s) of mol. wt. 1.1×10^6 was found in most 50s ribosomes (Fig. 3).

Ribosome proteins

Analysis of the protein component revealed a much more complicated picture. In contrast to the small RNA viruses, where the protein coat is constructed from the regular arrangement of a large number of identical protein molecules, each ribosome most likely contains a large number of different polypeptide chains. At first, our results suggested a simple answer when Drs. Waller and J. I. Harris analysed *E. coli* ribosomes for their amino terminal groups. Only alanine, methionine, with smaller amounts of serine, were present in significant amounts. This hinted that only several classes of protein molecules were used for ribosomal construction. Further experiments of Dr. Waller[19], however, suggested the contrary. When ribosomal protein fractions were analysed in starch-gel electrophoresis, more than 20 distinct bands were seen. Almost all these proteins migrated towards the anode at pH 7 confirming the net basic charge of ribosomal protein[20]. A variety of control experiments suggested that these bands represent distinct polypeptide chains, not merely aggregated states of several fundamental sub-units. Moreover, the band pattern from 30s ribosomes was radically different from that of 50s proteins.

As yet we have no solid proof that each 70s ribosome contains all the various protein components found in the total population. But so far, all attempts by Dr. Waller to separate chromatographically intact ribosomes into fractions with different starch-gel patterns have failed. The total protein component of a 70s ribosome amounts to about 9×10^5 daltons. Since the end group analysis suggests an average mol. wt. of about 30,000, approximately 20 polypeptide chains are used in 50s construction and 10 for the 30s ribosome. It is possible that all the polypeptide chains in a 30s particle are different. Waller already has evidence for 10 distinct components in 30s ribosomes and the present failure to observe more in the 50s protein fraction may merely mean that the same electrophoretic mobility is shared by several polypeptide chains.

We believe that all these proteins have primarily a structural role. That is, they are not enzymes but largely function to hold the ribosomal RNA and necessary intermediates in the correct position for peptide bond formation. In addition a number of enzymes are bound tightly to ribosomes. As yet their function is unclear. One such is a bacterial ribonuclease, found by Elson[21] to be specifically attached to 30s ribosomes in a latent form. No ribonuclease activity is present until ribosome breakdown. Dr. Spahr[22] in our laboratories has purified this enzyme, shown its specificity and from specific activity measurements, concludes that it is present on less than one in twenty

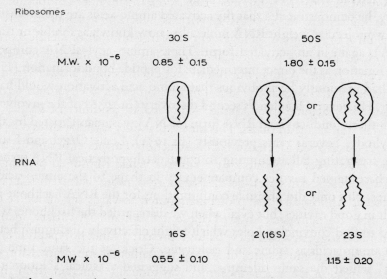

Fig. 3. Molecular weights of RNA isolated from *E. coli* ribosomes. (This picture is diagrammatic and does not represent the true conformation of ribosomal RNA.)

30s particles. It is clear that this enzyme if present in a free active form, would be rapidly lethal to its host cell. Thus its presence in latent form is expected. But why it is stuck to ribosomes is still a complete mystery.

Chemical Intermediates in Protein Synthesis

Our early experiments with ribosomes were almost unrelated to the efforts of biochemists. At that time our research objects seemed very different. The enzymologically oriented biochemists hoped to find the intermediates and enzymes necessary for peptide bond formation. On the contrary, those of us with a genetic orientation wanted to see the template and discover how it picked out the correct amino acid. Very soon, however, these separate paths came together, partly because of a breakthrough in the nature of the amino acid intermediates, and partly from an incisive thought by Crick.

The biochemical advances arose from work in Paul Zamecnik's laboratory at the Massachusetts General Hospital. There was developed a reproducible *in vitro* system[23] containing ribosomes, supernatant factors, and ATP which incorporated amino acids into protein. Using these systems Hoagland made two important discoveries. Firstly, he[24] showed that amino acids are initially activated by ATP to form high-energy AA–AMP complexes. Secondly, he demonstrated[25] that the activated amino acids are then transferred to low molecular weight RNA molecules (now known as soluble or transfer RNA), again in an activated form. These amino–acyl–sRNA compounds then function as the direct intermediate for peptide bond formation (Fig. 4).

It had previously been obvious that amino acid activation would have to occur. However, Hoagland's second discovery (in 1956) of the involvement of a hitherto undiscovered RNA form (sRNA) was unanticipated by almost everybody. Several years previously (in 1954), Leslie Orgel and I spent a quite frustrating fall attempting to construct hypothetical RNA structures which contained cavities complementary in shape to the amino acid side groups. Not only did plausible configurations for the RNA backbone fail to result in good cavities, but even when we disregarded the backbone, we also failed to find convincing holes which might effectively distinguish between such amino acids as valine and isoleucine. Crick, at the same time (early 1955) sensed the same dilemma, and suggested a radical solution to the paradox. He proposed[26] that the amino acids do not combine with the template. Instead each should first combine with a specific adaptor molecule,

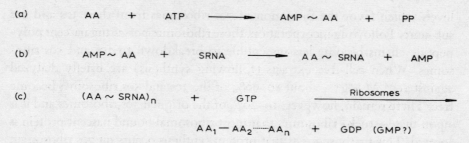

Fig. 4. Enzymatic steps in protein peptide bond formation. Steps (a) and (b) are catalyzed by single enzymes. The number of enzymes required in (c) is unknown.

capable of selectively interacting with the hydrogen bonding surfaces provided by RNA's purine and pyrimidine bases. This scheme requires at least twenty different adaptors, each specific for a given amino acid. These are very neatly provided by the specific sRNA molecules. Soon after Hoagland's discovery of sRNA, many experiments, particularly by Hoagland and Paul Berg[27], established that the sRNA molecules are in fact specific for a given amino acid. It thus became possible to imagine, following Crick's reasoning, that the ribosomal template for protein synthesis combined not with the amino acid side groups, but instead with a specific group of bases on the soluble RNA portion of the amino–acyl–sRNA precursors.

Participation of Active Ribosomes in Protein Synthesis

Very little protein synthesis occurred in the cell-free system developed by the Massachusetts General Hospital Group. Only by using radioactive amino acids could they convincingly demonstrate amino acid incorporation into proteins. This fact, initially seemed trivial and there was much hope that when better experimental conditions were found, significant net synthesis would occur. But despite optimistic claims from several laboratories, no real improvement in the efficiency of cell-free synthesis resulted. Some experiments (1959) of Dr. Tissières and Mr. Schlessinger[28] with *E. coli* extracts illustrate well this point. At 30°C, cell-free synthesis occurs linearly for 5–10 minutes and then gradually stops. During this interval the newly synthesized protein amounts to 1–3 γ of protein per mg of ribosomes. Of this about one third was released from the ribosomes, the remainder being ribosomal bound.

Cell-free synthesis in *E. coli* extracts requires the high ($\sim 10^{-2} M$) Mg++

levels which favor the formation of 70s ribosomes from their 30s and 50s sub-units. Following incorporation, those ribosomes possessing nascent poly-peptide chains become less susceptible to breakdown to 30s and 50s ribo-somes. When cell-free extracts (following synthesis) are briefly dialyzed against 10^{-4} M Mg^{++}, about 80–90% of the 30s and 50s ribosomes become free. There remain, however, 10–20% of the original 70s ribosomes and it is upon these « stuck » ribosomes that most ribosomal bound nascent protein is located. This firstly suggests that protein synthesis occurs on 70s ribosomes, not upon free 30s or 50s ribosomes. Secondly, in the commonly studied *E. coli* extract, only a small ribosome fraction is functional. Tissières and Schles-singer named these particles « active ribosomes » and suggested, they con-tained a functional component lacking in other ribosomes.

Each active ribosome synthesizes on the average between 15,000 and 50,000 daltons of protein. This is in the size range of naturally occurring polypeptide chains. Thus while we remained unsatisfied by the small net synthesis, sufficient synthesis occurs to open the possibility that some com-plete protein molecules are made. This encouraged us to look for synthesis of β-galactosidase. None, however, was then found[29] despite much effort.

Another important point emerged from these early (1959) incorporation studies with *E. coli* extracts. Addition of small amounts of purified deoxy-ribonuclease decreased protein synthesis to values 20–40% that found in untreated extracts[28]. This was completely unanticipated, for it suggested that high molecular weight DNA functions in the commonly studied bacte-rial extracts. But since a basal synthetic level occurs after DNA is destroyed by deoxyribonuclease, the DNA itself must not be directly involved in peptide bond formation. Instead, this suggested synthesis of new template RNA upon DNA in untreated extracts. If true, this would raise the possibil-ity, previously not seriously considered by biochemists that the RNA tem-plates themselves might be unstable, and hence a limiting factor in cell-free protein synthesis.

Metabolic Stability of Ribosomal RNA

All our early ribosome experiments had assumed that the ribosomal RNA was the template. Abundant evidence existed that proteins were synthesized on ribosomes and since the template must be RNA, it was natural to assume that it was ribosomal RNA. Under this hypothesis ribosomal RNA was a collection of molecules of different base sequences, synthesized on the functioning regions of chromosomal DNA. Following their synthesis, they combined with the basic ribosomal proteins to form ribosomes. We thus visualized that the seemingly morphological identical ribosomes were, in fact, a collection of a very large number of genetically distinct particles masked by the similarity of their protein component.

Then there existed much suggestive evidence that ribosomal RNA molecules were stable in growing bacteria. As early as 1949, experiments showed that RNA precursors, once incorporated into RNA, remained in RNA. Then the distinction between ribosomal and soluble RNA was not known, but later experiments by the ribosome group of the Carnegie Institute of Washington and at Harvard indicated similar stabilities of both fractions. These experiments, however, did not follow the fate of single molecules, and the possibility remained that a special trick allowed ribosomal RNA chains to be broken down to fragments that were preferentially re-used to make new ribosomal RNA molecules. Davern and Meselson[30], however, ruled out this possibility by growing ribosomal RNA in heavy (^{13}C,^{15}N) medium, followed by several generations of growth in light (^{12}C, ^{14}N) medium. They then separated light from heavy ribosomal RNA in cesium formate density gradients and showed that the heavy molecules remained completely intact for at least two generations. This result predicts, assuming ribosomes to be genetically specific, that the protein templates should persist indefinitely in growing bacteria.

Experiments Suggesting Unstable Protein Templates

But already by the time of the Davern & Meselson experiment (1959), evidence began to accumulate, chiefly at the Institut Pasteur, that some, if not all, bacterial templates were unstable with lives only several per cent of a generation time. None of these experiments, by themselves, were convincing. Each could be interpreted in other ways which retained the concept of stable templates. But taken together, they argued a strong case.

These experiments were of several types. One studied the effect of suddenly adding or destroying specific DNA molecules. Sudden introduction was achieved by having a male donor introduce a specific chromosomal region absent in the recipient female. Simultaneously the ability of the male gene to function (produce an enzymatically active protein) in the female cell was measured. Riley, Pardee, Jacob, and Monod[31] obtained the striking finding that β-galactosidase, genetically determined by a specific male gene, began to be synthesized at its maximum rate within several minutes after gene transfer. Thus the steady state number of β-galactosidase templates was achieved almost immediately. Conversely when the E. coli chromosome was inactivated by decay of ^{32}P atoms incorporated into DNA, they observed that active enzyme formation stops within several minutes. It thus appeared that the ribosomal templates could not function without concomitant DNA function.

At the same time, François Gros discovered[32] that bacteria grown in 5-fluorouracil produced abnormal proteins, most likely altered in amino acid sequences. 5-Fluorouracil is readily incorporated into bacterial RNA and its presence in RNA templates may drastically raise the mistake level. More unexpected was the observation that following 5-fluorouracil addition the production of all normal proteins ceases within several minutes. Again this argues against the persistance of *any* stable templates.

Unstable RNA Molecules in Phage Infected Cells

At first it was thought that no RNA synthesis occurred in T2 infected cells. But in 1952 Hershey[33] observed that new RNA molecules are synthesized at a rapid rate. But no net accumulation occurs since there is a correspondingly fast breakdown. Surprisingly almost everybody ignored this discovery. This oversight was partly due to the tendency, still then prevalent, to suspect that the metabolism of virus infected cells might be qualitatively different from that of uninfected cells.

Volkin and Astrachan[34] were the first (1956) to treat Hershey's unstable fraction seriously. They measured its base composition and found it different from that of uninfected E. coli cells. It bore a great resemblance to the infecting viral DNA which suggested that it was synthesized on T2 DNA templates. Moreover, and *most importantly*, this RNA fraction must be the template for phage specific proteins. Unless we assume that RNA is not involved in phage protein synthesis, it necessarily follows that the Volkin-Astrachan DNA-like RNA provides the information for determining amino acid sequences in phage specific proteins.

Not till the late summer of 1959 was its physical form investigated. Then Nomura, Hall, and Spiegelman[35] examined its relationship to the already characterized soluble and ribosomal RNA's. Immediately they observed that none of the T2 RNA was incorporated into stable ribosomes. Instead, in low Mg^{++} (10^{-4} M) it existed free while in 10^{-2} M Mg^{++} they thought it became part of 30s ribosomal like particles. At the same time, Mr. Risebrough in our laboratories began studying T2 RNA, also using sucrose gradient centrifugation. He also found that T2 RNA was not typical ribosomal RNA. In addition, he was the first to notice (in early spring 1960) that in 10^{-2} M Mg^{++}, most T2 RNA sedimented not with 30s particles but with the larger 70s and 100s ribosomes.

His result leads naturally to the hypothesis that phage protein synthesis takes place on genetically non-specific ribosomes to which are attached metabolically unstable template RNA molecules. Independently of our work, Brenner and Jacob motivated by the above-mentioned metabolic and genetic experiments from the Institut Pasteur, were equally convinced that conditions were ripe for the direct demonstration of metabolically unstable RNA templates to which Jacob and Monod[36] gave the name *messenger RNA*. In June of 1960, they travelled to Pasadena for a crucial experiment in Meselson's laboratory. They argued that all the T2 messenger RNA should be attached to old ribosomes synthesized before infection. This they elegantly demonstrated[37] by T2 infecting heavy (^{13}C and ^{15}N) labeled bacteria in light (^{12}C and ^{14}N) medium. Subsequent CsCl equilibrium centrifugation revealed that most of the T2 messenger RNA was indeed attached to « old » ribosomes, as was all the ribosomal bound nascent protein, labeled by pulse exposure to radioactive amino acids.

Demonstration of Messenger RNA Molecules in Uninfected Bacteria

We were equally convinced that similar messenger RNA would be found in uninfected bacteria. Its demonstration then presented greater problems, because of the simultaneous synthesis of ribosomal and soluble RNA. François Gros had then (May 1960) just arrived for a visit to our laboratory. Together with Mr. Kurland and Dr. Gilbert, we decided to look for labeled messenger molecules in cells briefly exposed to a radioactive RNA precursor. Experiments with T2 infected cells suggested that the T2 messenger comprised about 2–4% of the total RNA and that most of its molecules had lives less than several minutes. If a similar situation, held for uninfected cells, then during any short interval, most RNA synthesis would be messenger. There would be no significant accumulation since it would be broken down almost as fast as it was made.

Again the messenger hypothesis was confirmed[38]. The RNA labeled during pulse exposures was largely attached to 70s and 100s ribosomes in 10^{-2} M Mg^{++}. In low Mg^{++} (10^{-4} M), it came off the ribosomes and sedimented free with an average sedimentation constant of 14s. Base ratio analysis revealed DNA like RNA molecules in agreement with the expectation that it was produced on very many DNA templates along the bacterial chromosome. Soon afterwards, Hall and Spiegelman[39] formed artificial T2 DNA; T2 messenger RNA hybrid molecules and in several laboratories[40], hybrid molecules were subsequently formed between *E. coli* DNA and *E. coli* pulse RNA. The DNA template origin for messenger RNA was thus established beyond doubt.

The Role of Messenger RNA in Cell-Free Protein Synthesis

It was then possible to suggest why deoxyribonuclease partially inhibits amino acid incorporation in *E. coli* extracts. The messenger hypothesis prompts the idea that DNA in the extract is a template for messenger RNA. This newly made messenger then attaches to ribosomes where it serves as additional protein templates. Since deoxyribonuclease only destroys the capacity to make messenger, it has no effect upon the messenger present at the time of extract formation. Hence, no matter how high the deoxyribonuclease concentration employed, a residual fraction of synthesis will always occur. Experiments by Tissières and Hopkins[41] in our laboratories and by Berg, Chamberlain, and Wood[42] at Stanford confirmed these ideas. First it was shown that addition of DNA to extracts previously denuded of DNA significantly increased amino acid incorporation. Secondly, RNA synthesis occurs simultaneously with *in vitro* protein synthesis. This RNA has a DNA like composition, attaches to ribosomes in 10^{-2} M Mg^{++}, and physically resembles *in vivo* synthesized messenger RNA.

Furthermore, Tissières showed that addition of fractions rich in messenger RNA stimulated *in vitro* protein synthesis 2–5 fold. More striking results came from Nirenberg and Matthaei[43]. They reasoned that *in vitro* messenger destruction might be the principal cause why cell-free systems stopped synthesizing protein. If so, *preincubated extracts* deficient in natural messenger should respond more to new messenger addition. This way they became able to demonstrate a 20-fold increase in protein synthesis following addition of phenol-purified *E. coli* RNA. Like Tissières' active fraction, their stimulating fraction sedimented heterogeneously arguing against an effect due to either ribosomal or soluble RNA. More convincing support came when they next added TMV RNA to preincubated *E. coli* extracts. Again a 10–20 fold stimulation occurred. Here there could be no confusion with possible ribosomal RNA templates. Even more dramatic[44] was the effect of polyuridylic acid (like TMV RNA single stranded) addition. This specifically directed the incorporation of phenylalanine into polyphenylalanine. With this experiment (June 1961) the messenger concept became a fact. Direct proof then existed that single stranded messenger was the protein template.

Presence of Messenger RNA in Active Ribosomes

In *in vitro* systems ordinarily only 10–20% of *E. coli* ribosomes contain attached messenger RNA. This first was shown in experiments of Risebrough[45] who centrifuged extracts of T2 infected cells through a sucrose gradient. Ribosomes containing labeled messenger were found to centrifuge faster than ordinary ribosomes. Similarly, Gilbert[46] showed that these faster sedimenting ribosomes are « active », that is, able to incorporate amino acids into proteins. A fresh cell-free extract was centrifuged through a sucrose gradient. Samples along the gradient were collected and then tested for their ability to make protein. A complete parallel was found between « activity » and the presence of messenger.

Furthermore, if an extract is centrifuged *after* it has incorporated amino acids, the nascent protein chains also sediment attached to a small fraction of fast sedimenting ribosomes[45]. These ribosomes still contain messenger RNA. For when the messenger molecules are destroyed by ribonuclease (ribosomes remain intact in the presence of γ amounts of ribonuclease), the ribosomal bound nascent protein sediments as 70s ribosomes. The nascent protein is thus not attached to messenger RNA but must be directly bound to ribosomes.

Binding of sRNA to Ribosomes

Experiments by Schweet[47] and Dintzes[48] show that proteins grow by stepwise addition of individual amino acids beginning at the amino terminal end.

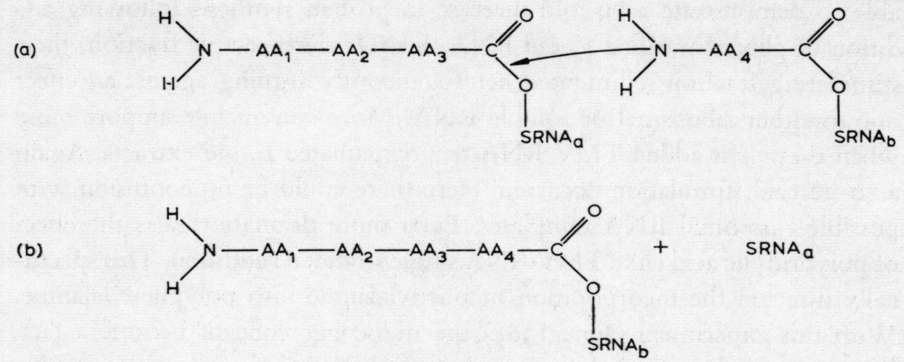

Fig. 5. Stepwise growth of a polypeptide chain. Initiation begins at the free NH$_2$ end with the growing point terminated by a sRNA molecule.

Since the immediate precursors are amino–acyl–sRNA molecules, their result predicts that the polypeptide chain is terminated at its carboxyl growing end by an sRNA molecule (Fig. 5). To test this scheme, we began some studies to see whether sRNA bound specifically to ribosomes. Cannon and Krug[49] first examined binding in the absence of protein synthesis. They showed that in 10^{-2} M Mg^{++} each 50s sub-unit of the 70s ribosome reversibly bound one sRNA molecule. The same amount of reversible binding occurs with amino–acyl–sRNA or with free sRNA and in the presence or absence of protein synthesis.

Protein synthesis, however, effects the binding observed in 10^{-4} M Mg^{++}. In the absence of protein synthesis no sRNA remains ribosomal bound when the Mg^{++} level is lowered from 10^{-2} M to 10^{-4} M. On the contrary, following amino acid incorporation, sRNA molecules become tightly fixed to the «stuck» 70s ribosomes, whose nascent polypeptide chains prevent easy dissociation to 30s and 50s ribosomes. One sRNA molecule appears to be attached to each stuck ribosome. Prolonged dialysis against 10^{-4} M Mg^{++} eventually breaks apart the stuck ribosomes. Then all the bound sRNA as well as almost all the nascent protein is seen attached to the 50s component supporting the hypothesis that these bound sRNA molecules are directly attached to nascent chains (Fig. 6). Direct proof comes from recent experiments in which Gilbert[50] used the detergent duponol to further dissociate the 50s ribosomes to their protein and RNA components. Then the nascent protein and bound sRNA remained together during both sucrose gradient centrifugation and separation on G200 Sephadex columns. Following exposure, however, to either weak alkali or to hydroxylamine, treatments known to break amino–acyl–bonds, the sRNA and nascent proteins move separately.

The significance of the reversible binding by non–active (no messenger) ribosomes is not known. Conceivably inside growing cells, all ribosomes have attached messenger and synthesize protein. Under these conditions, only those sRNA molecules corresponding to the specific messenger sequence can slip into the ribosomal cavities. But when most ribosomes lack messenger templates, as in our *in vitro* extracts, then any sRNA molecule, charged or uncharged, may fill the empty site.

All evidence suggests that covalent bonds are not involved in holding nascent chains to ribosome. Instead it seems probable that the point of firm attachment involves the terminal sRNA residue, bound by Mg^{++} dependent

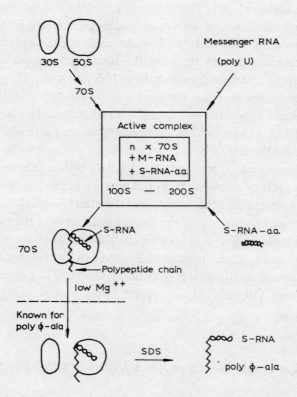

Fig. 6. Diagrammatic summary of ribosome participation in protein synthesis. (The active complex is pictured in Fig. 7.)

secondary forces to a cavity in the 50s ribosome. Extensive dialysis against 5×10^{-5} M Mg^{++} (which leaves intact 30s and 50s ribosomes) strips the nascent chains off the 50s ribosomes[50,51]. The released polypeptides sediment about 4s and if the latent ribonuclease is not activated, most likely still have terminally bound sRNA. When the Mg^{++} level is again brought to 10^{-2} M many released chains again stick to ribosomes.

Movement of the Messenger Template over the Ribosomal Surface

At any given time, each functioning ribosome thus contains only one nascent chain. As elongation proceeds, the NH$_3$-terminal end moves away from the point of peptide bond formation and conceivably may assume much of its final three-dimensional configuration before the terminal amino acids are added to the carboxyl end. The messenger RNA must be so attached that only the correct amino–acyl–sRNA molecules are inserted into position for possible peptide bond formation. This demands formation of specific hydrogen bonds (base-pairs?) between the messenger template and several (most likely three) nucleotides along the sRNA molecule. Then, in the presence of the necessary enzymes, the amino-acyl linkage to the then terminal sRNA breaks and a peptide bond forms with the correctly placed incoming amino-acyl-RNA (Fig. 5). This must create an energetically unfavorable environment for the now free sRNA molecule, causing it to be ejected from the sRNA binding site. The new terminal sRNA then moves into this site completing a cycle of synthesis. It is not known whether the messenger template remains attached to the newly inserted amino-acyl-sRNA. But if so, the messenger necessarily moves the correct distance over the ribosomal surface to place its next group of specific nucleotides in position to correctly select the next amino acid. No matter, however, what the mechanism is, the messenger tape necessarily moves over the ribosome. They cannot remain in static orientation if there is only one specific ribosomal site for peptide bond formation.

Attachment of Single Messenger RNA Molecules to Several Ribosomes

Addition of the synthetic messenger poly U to extracts containing predominantly 70s ribosomes creates new active ribosomes which sediment in

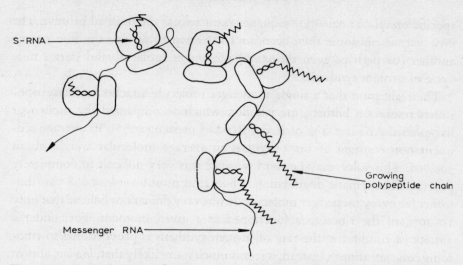

S-RNA

Growing
polypeptide chain

Messenger RNA

Fig. 7. Messenger RNA attachment to several ribosomes. (This illustration is schematic since the site of messenger attachment to ribosomes is not known.)

the 150–200s region[52]. Fixation of a single poly U molecule (mol. wt. = 100,000) to a 70s ribosome (mol. wt. = 3×10^6) should not significantly increase ribosomal sedimentation. Nor is it likely that a very large number of poly U molecules have combined with individual ribosomes. In these experiments, the molar ratio of fixed poly U to 70s ribosomes was less than $\frac{1}{5}$. Instead, the only plausible explanation involves formation of ribosomal aggregates attached to single poly U molecules. The 300 nucleotides in a poly U molecule of mol. wt. ~ 10^5 will have a contour length of about 1000 Å if the average internucleotide distance is 3.4 Å. Simultaneous attachment is thus possible to groups of 4–8 ribosomes (diameter ~ 200 Å) depending upon the way the messenger passes over (through) the ribosomal surface. This estimate agrees well with the average aggregate size suggested by the sedimentation rate of the « active » complexes. Sedimentation of extracts *after* incorporation reveals most polyphenylalanine attached to the rapidly sedimenting « active » ribosomes.

Single messenger molecules thus most likely move simultaneously over the surfaces of several ribosomes, functioning on each as protein templates (Fig. 7). A progression of increasingly long polypeptide chains should be attached to successive ribosomes depending upon the fraction of the messenger tape to which they were exposed. When all the messenger has moved across the site of synthesis, some mechanism, perhaps itself triggered by a specific template nucleotide sequence must release the finished protein. The now vacant ribosome then becomes competent to receive the free end of another (or perhaps even the same) messenger molecule and start a new cycle of protein synthesis.

The realization that a single messenger molecule attaches to many ribosomes resolves a bothersome paradox which accompanied the messenger hypothesis. About 2–4% of *E. coli* RNA is messenger[40,53]. Its average sedimentation constant of 14s[54] suggests an average molecular weight about 500,000. This value may be too low since it is very difficult to completely prevent all enzymatic degradation. There thus must be *at least* 6–8 70s ribosomes for every messenger molecule. It was very difficult to believe that only 10–20% of the ribosomes functioned at a given moment. For, under a variety of conditions, the rate of protein synthesis is proportional to ribosome concentration[55]. Instead, it seems much more likely that, *in vivo*, almost all ribosomes are active. During the preparation of cell extracts, however, many ribosomes may lose their messenger and become inactive. If true, we may expect that use of more gentle techniques to break open *E. coli* cells will reveal larger fractions of fast-sedimenting active material. Already there are reports[56] that over 50% of mammalian reticulocyte ribosomes exist as aggregates of 5–6 80s particles. Furthermore, it is these aggregated ribosomes which make protein, both *in vivo* and *in vitro*.

Template Lifetime

Under the above scheme a messenger molecule might function indefinitely. On the contrary, however, the unstable bacterial templates function on the average only 10–20 times. This fact comes from experiments done in Levinthal's laboratory[57] where new messenger synthesis was blocked by addition of the antibiotic antinomycin D. Preexisting messenger (*Bacillus subtilus* growing with a 60 minute generation time) then broke down with a half-life of 2 minutes. Correspondingly, protein synthesis ceased at the expected rate. A mechanism(s) must thus exist to specifically degrade messenger molecules. Several enzymes (polynucleotide phosphorylase and a K^+ dependent diesterase) which rapidly degrade free messenger are active in bacterial cell extracts[58]. They function, however, much less efficiently when the messenger is attached to ribosomes[59]. Conceivably, a random choice exists whether the free forward-moving end of a messenger tape attaches to a vacant ribosome, or is enzymatically degraded. If so, this important decision is settled by a chance event unrelated to the biological need for specific messengers.

Conclusion

We can now have considerable confidence that the broad features of protein synthesis are understood. RNA's involvement is very much more complicated than imagined in 1953. There is not one functional RNA. Instead, protein synthesis demands the ordered interaction of three classes of RNA – ribosomal, soluble, and messenger. Many important aspects, however, remain unanswered. For instance, there is no theoretical framework for the ribosomal sub-units nor, for that matter, do we understand the functional significance of ribosomal RNA. Most satisfying is the realization that all the steps in protein replication will be shown to involve well-understood chemical forces. As yet we do not know all the details. For example, are the DNA base-pairs involved in messenger RNA selection of the corresponding aminoacyl-sRNA? With luck, this will soon be known. We should thus have every expectation that future progress in understanding selective protein synthesis (and its consequences for embryology) will have a similar well-defined and, when understood, easy-to-comprehend chemical basis.

Acknowledgment

I have been very fortunate in having the collaboration of many able students and colleagues. The Ph.D. thesis work of Dr. C. G. Kurland, Dr. David Schlessinger and Dr. Robert Risebrough established many ideas reported here. Equally significant have been experiments by Drs. Kimiko Asano, Michael Cannon, Walter Gilbert, François Gros, Françoise Gros, Johns Hopkins, Masayasu Nomura, Pierre François Spahr, Alfred Tissières, and Jean-Pierre Waller. The visit of François Gros in the spring of 1960 was crucial in focusing attention on messenger RNA. Most importantly, I wish to mention my lengthy and still continuing successful collaboration with Alfred Tissières. Since 1960, I have the good fortune to also work closely with Walter Gilbert.

1. L. Pauling and R. B. Corey, *Proc. Natl. Acad. Sci. U.S.*, 37 (1951) 235.
2. J. D. Watson and F. H. C. Crick, *Nature*, 171 (1953) 737.
3. J. D. Watson and F. H. C. Crick, *Nature*, 171 (1953) 964.
4. P. Jordan, *Physik. Z.*, 39 (1938) 711.
   The reader is also referred to the discussion of possible implications of long-range forces in biology, by H. J. Muller in his 1946 Pilgrim Trust Lecture, *Proc. Roy. Soc. London*, B (1947).
5. A sample of Pauling's views is found in his note with M. Delbrück, *Science*, 92 (1940) 77.
6. J. Brachet, *Arch. Biol. Liege*, 53 (1942) 207; T. Caspersson, *Naturwiss.*, 29 (1941) 33.
7. H. Borsook, C. L. Deasy, A. J. Haagen-Smit, G. Keighley, and P. H. Lowy, *J. Biol. Chem.*, 187 (1950) 839; and T. Hultin, *Exp. Cell Res.*, 1 (1950) 376.
8. J. W. Littlefield, E. B. Keller, J. Gross, and P. C. Zamecnik, *J. Biol. Chem.*, 217 (1955) 111; V. G. Allfrey, M. M. Daly, and A. E. Mirsky, *J. Gen. Physiol.*, 37 (1953) 157.
9. A. Rich and J. D. Watson, *Nature*, 173 (1954) 995; A. Rich and J. D. Watson, *Proc. Natl. Acad. Sci. U.S.*, 40 (1954) 759.
10. F. H. C. Crick and J. D. Watson, *Nature*, 177 (1956) 473; F. H. C. Crick and J. D. Watson, *Ciba Foundation Symposium*, «*The Nature of Viruses*», 1957.
11. D. L. D. Caspar, *Nature*, 177 (1956) 475.
12. M. L. Peterman and M. G. Hamilton, *J. Biol. Chem.*, 224 (1957) 725; P. O. Tso, J. Bonner, and J. Vinograd, *J. Biophys. Biochem. Cytol.*, 2 (1956) 725.
13. H. K. Schachman, A. B. Pardee, and R. Y. Stanier, *Arch. Biochem. Biophys.*, 38 (1952) 245.
14. E. T. Bolton, B. H. Hoyer, and D. B. Ritter, *Microsomal Particles and Protein Synthesis*, Pergamon Press, New York, 1958, p. 18.
15. A. Tissières and J. D. Watson, *Nature*, 182 (1958) 778; A. Tissières, J. D. Watson, D. Schlessinger, and B. R. Hollingworth, *J. Mol. Biol.*, 1 (1959) 221; C. E. Hall and H. S. Slayeter, *J. Mol. Biol.*, 1 (1959) 329; H. E. Huxley and G. Zubay, *J. Mol. Biol.*, 2 (1960) 10.
16. H. Lamfrom and E. R. Glowacki, *J. Mol. Biol.*, 5 (1962) 97; P. O. Tso and J. Vinograd, *Biochim. Biophys. Acta*, 49 (1961) 113.
17. B. Hall and P. Doty, *J. Mol. Biol.*, 1 (1959) 111, U.Z. Littauer and H. Eisenberger, *Biochim. Biophys. Acta*, 32 (1959) 320; S. M. Timasheff, A. Brown, J. S. Colter, and M. Davies, *Biochim. Biophys. Acta*, 27 (1958) 662.
18. C. G. Kurland, *J. Mol. Biol.*, 2 (1960) 83.
19. J. P. Waller and J. I. Harris, *Proc. Natl. Acad. Sci. U.S.*, 47 (1961) 18.
20. P. F. Spahr, *J. Mol. Biol.*, 4 (1962) 395.
21. D. Elson, *Biochim. Biophys. Acta*, 27 (1958) 216 and 36 (1959) 372.
22. P. F. Spahr and B. R. Hollingworth, *J. Biol. Chem.*, 236 (1961) 823.
23. J. W. Littlefield, E. B. Keller, J. Gross, P. C. Zamecnik, *J. Biol. Chem.*, 217 (1955) 111; J. W. Littlefield and E. B. Keller, *J. Biol. Chem.*, 224 (1957) 13; P. C. Zamecnik and E. B. Keller, *J. Biol. Chem.*, 209 (1954) 337; E. B. Keller and P. C. Zamecnik, *J. Biol. Chem.*, 221 (1956) 45.

24. M. B. Hoagland, P. C. Zamecnik, and M. L. Stephenson, *Biochim. Biophys. Acta*, 24 (1957) 215.

25. M. B. Hoagland, M. L. Stephenson, J. F. Scott, L. I. Hecht, and P. C. Zamecnik, *J. Biol. Chem.*, 231 (1958) 241.

26. F. H. C. Crick, *Symp. Soc. Exptl. Biol.*, 12 (1958) 138.

27. P. Berg and E. J. Ofengand, *Proc. Natl. Acad. Sci. U.S.*, 44 (1958) 78.

28. A. Tissières, D. Schlessinger, and F. Gros, *Proc. Natl. Acad. Sci. U.S.*, 46 (1960) 1450.

29. F. Gros and D. Schlessinger, unpublished experiments.

30. C. I. Davern and M. Meselson, *J. Mol. Biol.*, 2 (1960) 153.

31. M. Riley, A. Pardee, F. Jacob, and J. Monod, *J. Mol. Biol.*, 2 (1960) 216.

32. S. Naono and F. Gros, *Compt. Rend.*, 250 (1960) 3889.

33. A. D. Hershey, J. Dixon, and M. Chase, *J. Gen. Physiol.*, 36 (1953) 777.

34. E. Volkin and L. Astrachan, *Virology*, 2 (1956) 149.

35. M. Nomura, B. D. Hall, and S. Spiegelman, *J. Mol. Biol.*, 2 (1960) 306.

36. F. Jacob and J. Monod, *J. Mol. Biol.*, 3 (1961) 318.

37. S. Brenner, F. Jacob, and M. Meselson, *Nature*, 190 (1961) 576.

38. F. Gros, H. Hiatt, W. Gilbert, C. G. Kurland, R. W. Risebrough, and J. D. Watson, *Nature*, 190 (1961) 581.

39. B. D. Hall and S. Spiegelman, *Proc. Natl. Acad. Sci. U.S.*, 47 (1961) 137.

40. M. Hayashi and S. Spiegelman, *Proc. Natl. Acad. Sci. U.S.*, 47 (1961) 1564; F. Gros, W. Gilbert, H. Hiatt, G. Attardi, P. F. Spahr, and J. D. Watson, *Cold Spring Harbor Symp. Quant. Biol.*, 26 (1961).

41. A. Tissières and J. W. Hopkins, *Proc. Natl. Acad. Sci. U.S.*, 47 (1961) 2015.

42. M. Chamberlin and P. Berg, *Proc. Natl. Acad. Sci. U.S.*, 48 (1962) 81 and W. B. Wood and P. Berg, *Proc. Natl. Acad. Sci. U.S.*, 48 (1962) 94.

43. M. W. Nirenberg and J. H. Matthaei, *Biochem. Biophys. Res. Commun.*, 4 (1961) 404.

44. M. W. Nirenberg and J. H. Matthaei, *Proc. Natl. Acad. Sci. U.S.*, 47 (1961) 1588.

45. R. W. Risebrough, A. Tissières, and J. D. Watson, *Proc. Natl. Acad. Sci. U.S.*, 48 (1962) 430.

46. W. Gilbert, *J. Mol. Biol.*, 6 (1963) 374.

47. J. Bishop, J. Leahy, and R. Schweet, *Proc. Natl. Acad. Sci. U.S.*, 46 (1960) 1030.

48. H. Dintzes, *Proc. Natl. Acad. Sci. U.S.*, 47 (1961) 247.

49. M. Cannon, R. Krug, and W. Gilbert, *J. Mol. Biol.*, 7 (1963) 360.

50. W. Gilbert, *J. Mol. Biol.*, 6 (1963) 389.

51. D. Schlessinger and Françoise Gros, *J. Mol. Biol.*, 7 (1963) 350.

52. S. H. Barondes, M. W. Nirenberg, *Science*, 138 (1962) 813; G. J. Spyrides and F. Lipmann, *Proc. Natl. Acad. Sci. U.S.*, 48 (1962) 1977; W. Gilbert, *J. Mol. Biol.*, 6 (1963) 374.

53. S. S. Cohen, H. D. Barner, and J. Lichtenstein, *J. Biol. Chem.*, 236 (1961) 1448.

54. R. Monier, S. Naono, D. Hayes, F. Hayes, and F. Gros, *J. Mol. Biol.*, 5 (1962) 311; K. Asano, unpublished experiments (1962).

55. O. Maaløe, *Cold Spring Harbor Symp. Quant. Biol.*, 26 (1961) 45; F. C. Neihardt and D. Fraenkel, *Cold Spring Harbor Symp. Quant. Biol.*, 26 (1961) 63.

56. A. Gierer, *J. Mol. Biol.*, 6 (1963) 148; J. R. Warner, P. M. Knopf, and A. Rich, *Proc. Natl. Acad. Sci. U.S.*, 49 (1963) 122.

57. C. Levinthal, A. Keynan, and A. Higa, *Proc. Natl. Acad. Sci. U.S.*, 48 (1962) 1631.

58. H. Sekiguchi and S. S. Cohen, *J. Biol. Chem.*, 238 (1963) 349; D. Schlessinger and P. F. Spahr, *J. Biol. Chem.*, 238 (1963) 6.

59. R. Gesteland and J. D. Watson, (will be published, 1963).

SUPPLEMENT X

FRANCIS H. C. CRICK

On the genetic code

Nobel Lecture, December 11, 1962

Part of the work covered by the Nobel citation, that on the structure and replication of DNA, has been described by Wilkins in his Nobel Lecture this year. The ideas put forward by Watson and myself on the replication of DNA have also been mentioned by Kornberg in his Nobel Lecture in 1959, covering his brilliant researches on the enzymatic synthesis of DNA in the test tube. I shall discuss here the present state of a related problem in information transfer in living material – that of the genetic code – which has long interested me, and on which my colleagues and I, among many others, have recently been doing some experimental work.

It now seems certain that the amino acid sequence of any protein is determined by the sequence of bases in some region of a particular nucleic acid molecule. Twenty different kinds of amino acid are commonly found in protein, and four main kinds of base occur in nucleic acid. The genetic code describes the way in which a sequence of twenty or more things is determined by a sequence of four things of a different type.

It is hardly necessary to stress the biological importance of the problem. It seems likely that most if not all the genetic information in any organism is carried by nucleic acid – usually by DNA, although certain small viruses use RNA as their genetic material. It is probable that much of this information is used to determine the amino acid sequence of the proteins of that organism. (Whether the genetic information has any other major function we do not yet know.) This idea is expressed by the classic slogan of Beadle: « one gene –one enzyme », or in the more sophisticated but cumbersome terminology of today: « one cistron–one polypeptide chain ».

It is one of the more striking generalizations of biochemistry – which surprisingly is hardly ever mentioned in the biochemical text-books – that the twenty amino acids and the four bases, are, with minor reservations, the same throughout Nature. As far as I am aware the presently accepted set of twenty amino acids was first drawn up by Watson and myself in the summer of 1953 in response to a letter of Gamow's.

In this lecture I shall not deal with the intimate technical details of the problem, if only for the reason that I have recently written such a review[1] which will appear shortly. Nor shall I deal with the biochemical details of messenger RNA and protein synthesis, as Watson has already spoken about these. Rather I shall ask certain general questions about the genetic code and ask how far we can now answer them.

Let us assume that the genetic code is a simple one and ask how many bases code for one amino acid? This can hardly be done by a pair of bases, as from four different things we can only form $4 \times 4 = 16$ different pairs, whereas we need at least twenty and probably one or two more to act as spaces or for other purposes. However, triplets of bases would give us 64 possibilities. It is convenient to have a word for a set of bases which codes one amino acid and I shall use the word « codon » for this.

This brings us to our first question. Do codons overlap? In other words, as we read along the genetic message do we find a base which is a member of two or more codons? It now seems fairly certain that codons do *not* overlap. If they did, the change of a single base, due to mutation, should alter two or more (adjacent) amino acids, whereas the typical change is to a single amino acid, both in the case of the « spontaneous » mutations, such as occur in the abnormal human haemoglobin or in chemically induced mutations, such as those produced by the action of nitrous acid and other chemicals on tobacco mosaic virus[2]. In all probability, therefore, codons do not overlap.

This leads us to the next problem. How is the base sequence, divided into codons? There is nothing in the backbone of the nucleic acid, which is perfectly regular, to show us how to group the bases into codons. If, for example, all the codons are triplets, then in addition to the correct reading of the message, there are two *in*correct readings which we shall obtain if we do not start the grouping into sets of three at the right place. My colleagues and I[3] have recently obtained experimental evidence that each section of the genetic message is indeed read from a fixed point, probably from one end. This fits in very well with the experimental evidence, most clearly shown in the work of Dintzis[4] that the amino acids are assembled into the polypeptide chain in a linear order, starting at the amino end of the chain.

This leads us to the next general question: the size of the codon. How many bases are there in any one codon? The same experiments to which I have just referred[3] strongly suggest that all (or almost all) codons consist of a triplet of bases, though a small multiple of three, such as six or nine, is not completely ruled out by our data. We were led to this conclusion by the study of mutations in the A and B cistrons of the r_{II} locus of bacteriophage

T4. These mutations are believed to be due to the addition or subtraction of one or more bases from the genetic message. They are typically produced by acridines, and cannot be reversed by mutagens which merely change one base into another. Moreover these mutations almost always render the gene completely inactive, rather than partly so.

By testing such mutants in pairs we can assign them all without exception to one of two classes which we call + and −. For simplicity one can think of the + class as having one extra base at some point or other in the genetic message and the − class as having one too few. The crucial experiment is to put together, by genetic recombination, three mutants of the same type into one gene. That is, either (+ with + with +) or (− with − with −). Whereas a single + or a pair of them (+ with +) makes the gene completely inactive, a set of three, suitably chosen, has some activity. Detailed examination of these results show that they are exactly what we should expect if the message were read in triplets starting from one end.

We are sometimes asked what the result would be if we put four +'s in one gene. To answer this my colleagues have recently put together not merely four but six +'s. Such a combination is active as expected on our theory, although sets of four or five of them are not. We have also gone a long way to explaining the production of « minutes » as they are called. That is, combinations in which the gene is working at very low efficiency. Our detailed results fit the hypothesis that in some cases when the mechanism comes to a triplet which does not stand for an amino acid (called a « nonsense » triplet) it very occasionally makes a slip and reads, say, only two bases instead of the usual three. These results also enable us to tie down the direction of reading of the genetic message, which in this case is from left to right, as the r_{II} region is conventionally drawn. We plan to write up a detailed technical account of all this work shortly. A final proof of our ideas can only be obtained by detailed studies on the alterations produced in the amino acid sequence of a protein by mutations of the type discussed here.

One further conclusion of a general nature is suggested by our results. It would appear that the number of nonsense triplets is rather low, since we only occasionally come across them. However this conclusion is less secure than our other deductions about the general nature of the genetic code.

It has not yet been shown directly that the genetic message is co-linear with its product. That is, that one end of the gene codes for the amino end of the polypeptide chain and the other for the carboxyl end, and that as one proceeds along the gene one comes in turn to the codons in between in the linear order in which the amino acids are found in the polypeptide chain. This seems highly likely, especially as it has been shown that in several systems mutations affecting the same amino acid are extremely near together on the genetic map. The experimental proof of the co-linearity of a gene and the polypeptide chain it produces may be confidently expected within the next year or so.

There is one further general question about the genetic code which we can ask at this point. Is the code universal, that is, the same in all organisms? Preliminary evidence suggests that it may well be. For example something very like rabbit haemoglobin can be synthesized using a cell-free system, part of which comes from rabbit reticulocytes and part from *Escherichia coli*[5]. This would not be very probable if the code were very different in these two organisms. However as we shall see it is now possible to test the universality of the code by more direct experiments.

In a cell in which DNA is the genetic material it is not believed that DNA itself controls protein synthesis directly. As Watson has described, it is believed that the base sequence of the DNA – probably of only one of its chains – is copied onto RNA, and that this special RNA then acts as the genetic messenger and directs the actual process of joining up the amino acids into polypeptide chains. The breakthrough in the coding problem has come from the discovery, made by Nirenberg and Matthaei[6], that one can use synthetic RNA for this purpose. In particular they found that polyuridylic acid – an RNA in which every base is uracil – will promote the synthesis of polyphenylalanine when added to a cell-free system which was already known to synthesize polypeptide chains. Thus one codon for phenylalanine appears to be the sequence UUU (where U stands for uracil: in the same way we shall use A, G, and C for adenine, guanine, and cytosine respectively). This discovery has opened the way to a rapid although somewhat confused attack on the genetic code.

It would not be appropriate to review this work in detail here. I have discussed critically the earlier work in the review mentioned previously[1] but such is the pace of work in this field that more recent experiments have already made it out of date to some extent. However, some general conclusions can safely be drawn.

The technique mainly used so far, both by Nirenberg and his colleagues[6] and by Ochoa and his group[7], has been to synthesize enzymatically «random» polymers of two or three of the four bases. For example, a polynucleotide, which I shall call poly (U,C), having about equal amounts of uracil and cytosine in (presumably) random order will increase the incorporation of the amino acids phenylalanine, serine, leucine, and proline, and possibly threonine. By using polymers of different composition and assuming a triplet code one can deduce limited information about the composition of certain triplets.

From such work it appears that, with minor reservations, each polynucleotide incorporates a characteristic set of amino acids. Moreover the four bases appear quite distinct in their effects. A comparison between the triplets tentatively deduced by these methods with the *changes* in amino acid sequence produced by mutation shows a fair measure of agreement. Moreover the incorporation requires the same components needed for protein synthesis, and is inhibited by the same inhibitors. Thus the system is most unlikely to be a complete artefact and is very probably closely related to genuine protein synthesis.

As to the actual triplets so far proposed it was first thought that possibly every triplet had to include uracil, but this was neither plausible on theoretical grounds nor supported by the actual experimental evidence. The first direct evidence that this was not so was obtained by my colleagues Bretscher and Grunberg-Manago[8], who showed that a poly (C,A) would stimulate the incorporation of several amino acids. Recently other workers[9,10] have reported further evidence of this sort for other polynucleotides not containing uracil. It now seems very likely that many of the 64 triplets, possibly most of them, may code one amino acid or another, and that in general several distinct triplets may code one amino acid. In particular a very elegant experiment[11] suggests that both (UUC) and (UUG) code leucine (the brackets imply that the order within the triplets is not yet known). This general idea is supported by several indirect lines of evidence which cannot be detailed here. Unfortunately it makes the unambiguous determination of triplets by these methods much more difficult than would be the case if there were only one triplet for each amino acid. Moreover, it is not possible by using polynucleotides of « random » sequence to determine the *order* of bases in a triplet. A start has been made to construct polynucleotides whose exact sequence is known at one end, but the results obtained so far are suggestive rather than conclusive[12]. It seems likely however from this and other unpublished evidence that the amino end of the polypeptide chain corresponds to the « right-hand » end of the polynucleotide chain – that is, the one with the 2', 3' hydroxyls on the sugar.

It seems virtually certain that a single chain of RNA can act as messenger

RNA, since poly U is a single chain without secondary structure. If poly A is added to poly U, to form a double or triple helix, the combination is inactive. Moreover there is preliminary evidence[9] which suggests that secondary structure within a polynucleotide inhibits the power to stimulate protein synthesis.

It has yet to be shown by direct biochemical methods, as opposed to the indirect genetic evidence mentioned earlier, that the code is indeed a triplet code.

Attempts have been made from a study of the changes produced by mutation to obtain the relative order of the bases within various triplets, but my own view is that these are premature until there is more extensive and more reliable data on the composition of the triplets.

Evidence presented by several groups[8,9,11] suggest that poly U stimulates both the incorporation of phenylalanine and also a lesser amount of leucine. The meaning of this observation is unclear, but it raises the unfortunate possibility of ambiguous triplets; that is, triplets which may code more than one amino acid. However one would certainly expect such triplets to be in a minority.

It would seem likely, then, that most of the sixty-four possible triplets will be grouped into twenty groups. The balance of evidence both from the cell-free system and from the study of mutation, suggests that this does not occur at random, and that triplets coding the same amino acid may well be rather similar. This raises the main theoretical problem now outstanding. Can this grouping be deduced from theoretical postulates? Unfortunately, it is not difficult to see how it might have arisen at an extremely early stage in evolution by random mutations, so that the particular code we have may perhaps be the result of a series of historical accidents. This point is of more than abstract interest. If the code does indeed have some logical foundation then it is legitimate to consider all the evidence, both good and bad, in any attempt to deduce it. The same is not true if the codons have no simple logical connection. In that case, it makes little sense to guess a codon. The important thing is to provide enough evidence to prove each codon independently. It is not yet clear what evidence can safely be accepted as establishing a codon. What is clear is that most of the experimental evidence so far presented falls short of proof in almost all cases.

In spite of the uncertainty of much of the experimental data there are certain codes which have been suggested in the past which we can now reject with some degree of confidence.

Comma-less triplet codes

All such codes are unlikely, not only because of the genetic evidence but also because of the detailed results from the cell-free system.

Two-letter or three-letter codes

For example a code in which A is equivalent to O, and G to U. As already stated, the results from the cell-free system rule out all such codes.

The combination triplet code

In this code all permutations of a given combination code the same amino acid. The experimental results can only be made to fit such a code by very special pleading.

Complementary codes

There are several classes of these. Consider a certain triplet in relation to the triplet which is complementary to it on the other chain of the double helix. The second triplet may be considered either as being read in the same direction as the first, or in the opposite direction. Thus if the first triplet is UCC, we consider it in relation to either AGG or (reading in the opposite direction) GGA.

It has been suggested that if a triplet stands for an amino acid its complement necessarily stands for the same amino acids, or, alternatively in another class of codes, that its complement will stand for no amino acid, i.e. be nonsense.

It has recently been shown by Ochoa's group that poly A stimulates the incorporation of lysine[10]. Thus presumably AAA codes lysine. However since UUU codes phenylalanine these facts rule out all the above codes. It is also found that poly (U,G) incorporates quite different amino acids from poly (A,C). Similarly poly (U,C) differs from poly (A,G)[9,10]. Thus there is little chance that any of this class of theories will prove correct. Moreover they are all, in my opinion, unlikely for general theoretical reasons.

A start has already been made, using the same polynucleotides in cell-free systems from different species, to see if the code is the same in all organisms. Eventually it should be relatively easy to discover in this way if the code is universal, and, if not, how it differs from organism to organism. The preliminary results presented so far disclose no clear difference between *E. coli* and mammals, which is encouraging[10,13].

At the present time, therefore, the genetic code appears to have the following general properties:

(1) Most if not all codons consist of three (adjacent) bases.
(2) Adjacent codons do not overlap.
(3) The message is read in the correct groups of three by starting at some fixed point.
(4) The code sequence in the gene is co-linear with the amino acid sequence, the polypeptide chain being synthesized sequentially from the amino end.
(5) In general more than one triplet codes each amino acid.
(6) It is not certain that some triplets may not code more than one amino acid, i.e. they may be ambiguous.
(7) Triplets which code for the same amino acid are probably rather similar.
(8) It is not known whether there is any general rule which groups such codons together, or whether the grouping is mainly the result of historical accident.
(9) The number of triplets which do not code an amino acid is probably small.
(10) Certain codes proposed earlier, such as comma-less codes, two- or three-letter codes, the combination code, and various transposible codes are all unlikely to be correct.
(11) The code in different organisms is probably similar. It may be the same in all organisms but this is not yet known.

Finally one should add that in spite of the great complexity of protein synthesis and in spite of the considerable technical difficulties in synthesizing polynucleotides with defined sequences it is not unreasonable to hope that all these points will be clarified in the near future, and that the genetic code will be completely established on a sound experimental basis within a few years.

The references have been kept to a minimum. A more complete set will be found in the first reference.

1. F. H. C. Crick in *Progress in Nucleic Acid Research*, J. N. Davidson and Waldo E. Cohn (Eds.), Academic Press Inc., New York (in the press).

2. H. G. Wittmann, *Z. Vererbungslehre*, 93 (1962) 491.
   A. Tsugita, *J. Mol. Biol.*, 5 (1962) 284, 293.

3. F. H. C. Crick, L. Barnett, S. Brenner, and R. J. Watts-Tobin, *Nature*, 192 (1961) 1227.

4. M. A. Naughton and Howard M. Dintzis, *Proc. Natl. Acad. Sci. U.S.*, 48 (1962) 1822.

5. G. von Ehrenstein and F. Lipmann, *Proc. Natl. Acad. Sci. U.S.*, 47 (1961) 941.

6. J. H. Matthaei and M. W. Nirenberg, *Proc. Natl. Acad. Sci. U.S.*, 47 (1961) 1580.
   M. W. Nirenberg and J. H. Matthaei, *Proc. Natl. Acad. Sci. U.S.*, 47 (1961) 1588.
   M. W. Nirenberg, J. H. Matthaei, and O. W. Jones, *Proc. Natl. Acad. Sci. U.S.*, 48 (1962) 104.
   J. H. Matthaei, O. W. Jones, R. G. Martin, and M. W. Nirenberg, *Proc. Natl. Acad. Sci. U.S.*, 48 (1962) 666.

7. P. Lengyel, J. F. Speyer, and S. Ochoa, *Proc. Natl. Acad. Sci. U.S.*, 47 (1961) 1936.
   J. F. Speyer, P. Lengyel, C. Basilio, and S. Ochoa, *Proc. Natl. Acad. Sci. U.S.*, 48 (1962) 63.
   P. Lengyel, J. F. Speyer, C. Basilio, and S. Ochoa, *Proc. Natl. Acad. Sci. U.S.*, 48 (1962) 282.
   J. F. Speyer, P. Lengyel, C. Basilio, and S. Ochoa, *Proc. Natl. Acad. Sci. U.S.*, 48 (1962) 441.
   C. Basilio, A. J. Wahba, P. Lengyel, J. F. Speyer, and S. Ochoa, *Proc. Natl. Acad. Sci. U.S.*, 48 (1962) 613.

8. M. S. Bretscher and M. Grunberg-Manago, *Nature*, 195 (1962) 283.

9. O. W. Jones and M. W. Nirenberg, *Proc. Natl. Acad. Sci. U.S.*, 48 (1962) 2115.

10. R. S. Gardner, A. J. Wahba, C. Basilio, R. S. Miller, P. Lengyel, and J. F. Speyer, *Proc. Natl. Acad. Sci. U.S.*, 48 (1962) 2087.

11. B. Weisblum, S. Benzer, and R. W. Holley, *Proc. Natl. Acad. Sci. U.S.*, 48 (1962) 1449.

12. A. J. Wahba, C. Basilio, J. F. Speyer, P. Lengyel, R. S. Miller, and S. Ochoa, *Proc. Natl. Acad. Sci. U.S.*, 48 (1962) 1683.

13. H. R. V. Arnstein, R. A. Cox, and J. A. Hunt, *Nature*, 194 (1962) 1042.
    E. S. Maxwell, *Proc. Natl. Acad. Sci. U.S.*, 48 (1962) 1639.
    I. B. Weinstein and A. N. Schechter, *Proc. Natl. Acad. Sci. U.S.*, 48 (1962) 1686.

AUTHOR INDEX

Supplements not indexed; page numbers in bold face refer to photographs.

Abelson, P. H., 516
Adams, J. N., 378
Adelberg, E. A., 277, 303, 304, 315, 320, 321, 327, 328, 329, 337, 338, 355, 358, 361, 402, 420, 463
Akinrimisi, E. O., 303
Alexander, P., 186, 199
Allen, J. M., 462
Allen, M. K., 300, 304
Allfrey, V. G., 431, 432, 493, 494, 497, 498, 499
Allison, A. C., 212
Ames, B. N., 461, **462**
Anderson, T. F., 318
Anfinsen, C. B., 418, 420
Arber, W., 336, 337
Auerbach, C., 162, 226
August, J. T., 433
Avery, O. T., 295, 303

Bachmann, B., 29
Bacq, Z. M., 186
Baglioni, C., 413, 416, 420, 435
Bailey, W. T., 344, 539
Balboni, E. R., 24
Balis, M. E., 458, 462
Baltimore, D., 366, 367
Bangham, A. D., 113
Barigozzi, C., 370, 380
Barnett, L., 351, 436
Barr, M. L., 486, 489
Barratt, R. W., 145
Basilio, C., 446
Bateson, W., 49, **53**
Bauer, H., 162
Baumiller, R. C., 219
Bautz, E. K. F., 432
Beadle, G. W., **127**, 145, 408, 420
Beale, G. H., 380, 454, 455
Bearn, A. G., 176, 420
Becker, H. J., 492, 498
Becker, Y., 426, 432
Beermann, W., 492, 496, 498
Beers, R. F., Jr., 264
Belling, J., 151, 157, 162, 228
Bender, M. A., 186

Bendich, A., 276, 277
Bennett, D., 83
Bennett, T. P., 445, 446
Benzer, S., 344, 346, 351, **352**, 392, 401, 439, 440, 446, 447
Berg, P., 289, 290, 394, 428, 429, 434
Bernfield, M. R., 443
Bertsch, L. L., 290
Bessman, M. J., 290, 450, 455
Beutler, E., 485, 489
Billeter, M. A., 368
Binnington, J. P., 186
Birnstiel, M. L., 427, 432
Bladen, H. A., 431, 432
Blakeslee, A. F., 151, 157, 162, 228
Bloch, D. P., 499
Blum, H. F., 516
Boehner, L., 344, 352
Boice, L., 501
Bollum, F. J., 288, 290, 397
Bolton, E. T., 304
Bonner, D. M., 420, 434
Bonner, J., 425, 496, 497, 499, 505
Borek, E., 429
Borst, P., 368
Boveri, T., 14
Boyce, R. P., 397, 401
Boyer, S. H., IV, 420
Brachet, J., 12, 28
Bradshaw, A. D., 28
Brehme, K. S., 29, 162
Brenner, S., 339, 351, 432, 436, 445
Brewen, J. G., 182, 186
Bridges, C. B., 29, 95, **98**, 99, 105, 113, 154, 162, 474, 482
Briggs, R., 502, 508
Brink, R. A., 465, 466, 467, 470, **471**
Brown, D. D., 427, 432, 502
Brown, D. F., 470, 471
Bryson, V., 290, 446
Bunker, M. C., 162
Burdette, W. J., 162
Burdon, R. H., 368
Burnet, F. M., 363, 367
Burnham, C. R., **127**
Burns, S. N., 327, 328, 355, 361
Burton, K., 290
Busch, H., 500
Byrne, R., 431, 432, 461

Cairns, J., 327, 328, 453, 455
Calvin, M., 516
Callan, H. G., 494, 499
Campbell, A., 336, 337, 350, 358, 361, 376, 380, 446
Campbell, P. L., 505, 507
Canellakis, E. S., 289, 290

Carlson, E., 398, 402
Carlson, J. G., 181
Carlton, B. C., 445, 447
Carothers, E. E., 19, 28
Carrier, W. L., 397, 402
Caston, J. D., 502
Cavalieri, L. F., 289, 290
Ceppellini, R., 416
Cerhova, M., 290
Chamberlin, M., 289, 290
Champe, S. P., 346, 351, 439, 440, 446
Chandler, B., 426, 432
Chandler, B. L., 275, 277
Chang, R. S., 500
Chargaff, E., 264, 286, 291
Chase, M., 340, 344, 352, 353
Chesley, P., 83
Chèvremont, M., 378, 380
Childs, B., 485, 489
Chipchase, M. I. H., 427, 432
Chovnick, A., 481, 482
Chu, E. H. Y., 186, 226
Clark, A. J., 328, 358, 361
Clark, F., 516
Clark, J. O. D., 374, 381
Claus, W. D., 186
Cleland, R. E., 9, 16, 228, 231, **232**, 239
Clever, U., 492, 498
Clowes, R. C., 367
Cobb, V., 4
Cock, A. G., 489
Coe, E. H., Jr., 142
Cohen, S. S., 431, 453, 455
Cohn, W. E., 264, 432
Cooper, K. W., 185, 186
Cordova, C. C., 505, 507
Coulon, E. M., 496, 499
Cowan, C. A., 373, 381
Cowie, D. B., 336, 516
Cox, E. C., 434
Craig, L. C., 412, 420, 445, 446
Crawford, L. P., 420
Creighton, H. S., 126, 128
Crick, F. H. C., 267, 268, 271, 277, 395, 432, 436, 446, 447
Crow, J. F., 66, 199, **210,** 212, 217, 218, 219, 226, 387, 528

Dais, D., 444, 446
Darlington, C. D., 12, 28, 379
Davidson, D. R., 485, 489
Davidson, E. H., 499
Davidson, J. N., 264, 432
Davidson, P. F., 352
Davies, D. R., 304
Davis, J. E., 363, 367, 368
Dawson, M. H., 295
Day, P. R., 29, 144
Deering, R. A., 401
DeGeorge, F. V., 86

Delbrück, M., 344
De Mars, R., 487, 489
Demerec, M., 29, 173, 326, 332, 388, 389, 394, 506
Denhardt, G. H., 344, 353, 501
DeRobertis, E. D. P., 28
DeVries, H., 228, **239**
Dintzes, H., 429
Dobzhansky, Th., 39, 70, 86, 162, 212, **213**, 216, 217, 218, 221, 226, 243, 246, 250, 539
Dodson, E. O., 39
Doermann, A. H., 344, 352
Doi, A. H., 425
Doi, R. H., 502, 506
Doty, P., 250, 301, 304
Dunn, L. C., 39, 79, 80, 81, 83, 84, 250, 539
Duryee, W. R., 494
Dunnebacher, T. H., 500

Eakin, R. E., 512, 516
Ebert, J. D., 508
Edelman, M., 373, 381
Edgar, R. S., 343, 344, 353, 501
Edwards, J. H., 64, 66
Egyházi, E., 505, 507
Ehrlich, P. R., 250
Ehrman, L., 246, 250
Eigner, J., 301, 304
Elder, A., 458, 462
Ellis, D. B., 454, 455
Elson, D., 431, 434
Emerson, R. A., **127**, 145
Emerson, S., 228
Engelberg, J., 447
Engelhardt, D. E., 365, 367
Enger, M. D., 363, 367
Ephrussi, B., **421**, 503, 507
Ephrussi-Taylor, H., 296, 304, 381, **421**
Epling, C., 243
Epstein, H. T., 373, 381
Epstein, R. H., 501, 507
Evans, A. H., 505, 507

Fairbanks, V. F., 485, 489
Falconer, D. S., 66, 539
Falkow, S., 304
Fancher, H., 289, 290
Faulkner, R., 497, 498
Ferguson-Smith, M. A., 160
Felsenfeld, S., 496, 499
Fiala, J., 431, 434
Finch, J. T., 367
Fincham, J. R. S., 29, 144
Flax, J. G., 434
Flemming, W., 12
Fogel, S., 12, 28, 127, 199, 212, 264
Fong, P., 453, 455
Fowler, W. M., 485, 490

Fox, M. S., 299, 300, 304
Fox, S. W., 511, 516
Fraenkel-Conrat, H., 365, 366, 367, 368, 446
Francis, C. M., 505, 507
Francis, T., 83
Fraser, A. C., 145
Fredericq, P., 359, 361
Freese, E., 392, 398, 399, 401
Freese, E. B., 399, 401
Fregin, A., 504, 508
Freifelder, D., 352
Freire-Maia, N., 226
Frenster, J. H., 498, 499
Friedman, J., 504, 508
Furth, J. J., 432, 433

Gabriel, M. L., 12, 28, 127, 199, 212, 264
Gaffron, H., 510
Gahan, P. B., 494, 499
Gall, J. G., 494, 495, 499
Gallant, J., 462
Gardner, R. S., 446
Garen, A., 440, 458, 462
Garnjobst, L., 145
Garrod, A. E., 404
Gartner, T. K., 461, 463
Gates, R. R., 39
Gay, H., 432
Geiduschek, E. P., 432, 433
Gellert, M., 304
German, J. L., III, 176
Giacomoni, D., 428, 433, 445
Gibson, I., 454, 455
Gierer, A., 365, 367
Gilbert, W., 429, 433
Gilden, R. V., 497, 499
Giles, N. H., 186, 226
Gish, D. T., 365, 368
Glass, B., 337, 351, 353, 507
Glucksohn-Waelsch, S., 86
Godoy, G. A., 374, 381
Goebel, W. F., 359, 361
Gold, M., 429
Goldberg, B. D., 503, 508
Goldhaber, P., 500
Goldman, M., 432
Goldschmidt, R. B., 86, **87**, 113
Goldstein, J., 445, 446
Gomatos, P. J., 366, 367
Gonano, F., 447
Gooch, P. C., 186
Goodman, H. M., 445, 446
Gordon, J. A., 304
Gorini, L., 463
Gowen, J. W., 212
Green, D. E., 378, 381, 516
Green, H., 503, 508
Green, M., 278
Green, M. C., 140
Green, M. H., 336, 426, 433

Green, M. M., 488
Greer, S., 402
Grell, E. H., 29
Griffen, A. B., 162
Griffith, F., 295
Groman, N. B., 452, 456
Gross, F., 433
Gross, P. R., 500
Grossman, L., 448
Grötsch, H., 511
Grumbach, M. M., 485, 489
Grunberg-Manago, M., 446
Grüneberg, H., 86
Guest, J. R., 445, 447
Guidotti, G., 412, 420
Gunsalus, I. C., 337
Gurdon, J. B., 427, 432
Guthrie, G. D., 340, 352

Habermann, U., 290
Habermannova, S., 290
Hadorn, E., 70, 71, 86
Haldane, J. B. S., 101
Hall, B., 389, 390
Hall, B. D., 432, 433
Hamburger, V., 79
Hamilton, T. H., 505, 507
Hanafusa, H., 352
Hanafusa, T., 352
Hannah-Alava, A., 113
Hardy, G. H., 212
Harm, W., 350, 352
Harnden, D. G., 484
Harrington, H., 394, 401
Harris, H., 420, 504, 507
Harris, W., 212, 213
Hart, R. G., 364
Hartman, P. E., 332, 333, 334, 461, 462
Haruna, I., 366
Harvald, B., 89
Haselkorn, R., 367
Haskell, G., 29
Haslbrunner, E., 378, 381
Hauge, M., 89
Hayashi, M., 425, 426, 432, 433
Hayashi, M. N., 426, 432, 433
Hayes, W., 317, 319, 328, 329, 352, 358, 359, 361, 367
Hechter, O., 516
Hede, R., 352
Heitz, E., 162
Helinski, D. R., 349, 352, 445, 447
Henning, U., 445, 447
Herriot, R. M., 304
Hershey, A. D., 340, 342, 344, **352**, 353
Herskowitz, I., **76**
Herskowitz, I. H., 9, 16, 29, 80, 81, 84, 183, 219, 226, 393, 401, 465, 466, 467, 480

Herskowitz, J., **76**
Hess, O., 496, 498
Hiatt, H., 433
Hinegardner, R. T., 447
Hiraizumi, Y., 387, 388, 390
Hirst, G. K., 363, 367
Hoagland, M. B., 433
Hochstim, A. R., 510, 516
Hogness, D. S., 336, 338
Holland, J. J., 453, 455, 494, 499
Hollaender, A., 176
Holm, R. W., 250
Holtz, A. M., 70, 86
Hopkins, J. W., 427, 434
Horn, E. C., 499
Horne, R. W., 351, 367
Horowitz, N. H., 513, 516
Hotchkiss, R. D., 304
Hotta, Y., 493, 499, 503, 507, 508
Howard-Flanders, P., 397, 401
Hoyer, B. H., 304, 502, 507
Hsia, D. Y.-Y., 420
Hsu, T. C., 159
Huang, R. C. C., 425, 497, 499
Huang, S.-S., 516
Hurwitz, J., 426, 429, 432, 433
Hydén, H., 505, 507
Hymer, W. C., 431, 434
Hudson, W. R., 367

Igarashi, R. T., 502, 506
Ingerman, M. L., 277
Ingram, V. M., 412, 413, 414, 417, 418, 420
Inhorn, S. L., 162
Isaacson, R. G., 148
Ishida, M. R., 373, 381
Itano, H. A., 412, 416, 420
Izawa, M., 493, 494, 499

Jackson, J. F., 290
Jacob, F., 319, 321, 323, 327, **328**, 329, 335, 337, 338, 350, 353, 355, 361, 432, 460, 463
Janaki-Ammal, E. K., 12
Jehle, H., 16, 28, 277
Jenks, W. P., 304
Jinks, J. L., 381
Johannsen, W. L., 1, 12, **13**
John, B., 28, 146
Johnston, A. W., 160
Joklik, W. K., 426, 432
Jones, O. W., 441, 446, 462, 463
Jukes, T. H., 442, 446

Kaesberg, P., 363, 367
Kaiser, A. D., 336, 338, 350, 353
Kallman, F. J., 86
Kammen, H. O., 289, 290
Kaplan, W. D., 487, 490
Karpechenko, G. D., 248
Kasha, M., 510, 511, 516

Katoh, A., 493, 499
Kano-Sueoka, T., 503, 508
Kaufmann, B. P., 29, 154, 174, 175
Keeler, C. E., 4
Kellenberger, E., 293, 336, 337, 340, 351, 353
Kempthorne, O., 539
Kendrew, J. C., 420
Keosian, J., 516
Kermickle, J. L., 470, 471
Kernaghan, R. P., 481, 482
Kessinger, M. A., 212, 213
Khorana, H. G., 290
Kiesselbach, T. A., 29
Kihara, H., 251
Kilkson, R., 339, 353
Kim, Y. T., 367
King, T. J., 502, 508
Kinosita, R., 487, 490
Knight, C. A., 365, 368
Konetzka, W. A., 327, 329
Konigsberg, W., 412, 420
Kornberg, A., 280, 290, 291, 402, 456
Kossikov, K. V., 482
Kostyanovskii, R. G., 276, 277
Krakow, J. S., 289, 290, 426, 434
Krauss, M., 481, 482
Krieg, D. R., 401
Krieger, H., 226
Kubitschek, H. E., 401
Kuff, E. L., 431, 434
Kurland, C. G., 433, 434

Lampen, J. O., 290, 446
Landauer, W., 79, 86
Landsteiner, K., 57, 58
Lane, D., 301, 304
Larsson, A., 449, 456
Laughlin, J. S., 183
Laughnan, J. R., 477, 482
Leboy, P. S., 434
Leder, P., 444, 446, 461
Lederberg, E. M., 307, 309, **315**, 335, 338
Lederberg, J., 307, 309, 310, 313, 314, **315**, 330, 334, 335, 338, 516
Lee-Huang, S., 289, 290
Lehrmann, H., 412
Lemmon, R. M., 516
Lengyel, P., 446
Lennox, E., 332
Lerman, L. S., 296, 302, 304, 394, 402
Levan, A., 389, 390
Levene, H., 539
Levin, J. G., 431, 432
Levine, L., 304
Levine, P., 57
Levinthal, C., 352

Lewis, E. B., 478, 479, 480, 482
Lewis, K. R., 28, 146
L'Héritier, P., 370, 381
Li, C. C., 212
Lima de Faria, A., 379, 493, 499
Lindsley, D. L., 29
Lipmann, F., 434, **447**
Lipsett, M. N., 304
Litman, R. M., 303, 304
Littau, V. C., 497, 498
Littauer, U. Z., 429
Locke, M., 507
Lockhart, R. Z., Jr., 454, 456
Loeb, T., 318, 363, 367
Luck, D. J. L., 378, 381
Lunt, M. R., 290
Luria, S. E., 334
Luzzati, V., 277, 496, 499
Lyon, M. F., 485, 487, 489

Maas, R., 361
MacDowell, E. C., 83
MacLeod, C. M., 295, **297**, 303
Maestre, M. F., 339, 353
Magni, G. E., 383, 389, 448
Maheshwari, N., 425
Mahler, I., 463
Makino, S., 12
Mandel, M., 304
Margolin, P., 460, 463
Mariner, R., 516
Markert, C. L., 502, 507
Marmur, J., 301, 304, 361, 452, 456, 463
Mather, W. B., 539
Matthaei, J. H., 440, 446
Mayer, E., 250
Mazia, D., 12
McCarthy, B. J., 304, 336, 494, 499, 502, 507
McCarty, M., 295, 303
McClintock, B., 126, **127**, 128, 384, 386, 389, 390, 469, 470, 471
McConkey, E. H., 427, 434
McElroy, W. D., 337, 351, 353, 507
McKusick, V. A., 113, 139, 490
McLeisch, J., 28
Mead, C. G., 394, 402
Melechen, N. E., 294, 308
Mendel, G., 31, 39, 42, 53, 138
Merchant, D. J., 507
Merrill, D. J., 250
Meselson, M., 271, 274, 277, 351, 353, 432
Metz, C. W., 236
Meyer, G. F., 496, 498
Miescher, F., 253, 264
Miller, R. S., 446
Miller, S. L., 516
Mills, S. E., 420

Mirsky, A. E., 12, 28, 431, 432, 493, 494, 497, 498, 499
Mitchell, H. K., 29, 378, 381, 420
Mitchell, M. B., 378, 381
Mitra, S., 363, 367
Mohr, O. L., 40
Monod, J., 350, 460, **463**
Montagu, A., 86
Moohr, J. W., 432
Moore, J. A., 503, 507, 508
Moorhead, P. S., 389, 390
Morgan, D. T., Jr., 173
Morgan, T. H., 91, 99, 128
Morishima, A., 485, 489
Morse, M. L., 335, 338
Morton, N. E., 217, 219, 226
Mosig, G., 353
Muench, K., 429
Mukai, F. H., 460, 463
Muller, H. J., *ix*, 29, 176, 183, 186, 194, 195, 198, **199**, 200, 217, 218, 219, 226, 398, 402, 474, 482, 489, 490
Müntzing, A., 226

Nagata, T., 328
Nakamoto, T., 433
Nance, W. E., 420
Nathans, D., 440, 446
Nebel, B. R., 496, 499
Neel, J. V., 40, 412, 507
Neumann, J., 463
Newman, H. H., 86
Newmeyer, D., 145
Nichols, W. W., 389, 390
Nicolaïeff, A., 496, 499
Nirenberg, M. W., 431, 432, 440, 441, 443, 444, 446, **447**, 461, 462, 463
Niu, L. C., 505, 507
Niu, M. C., 505, 507
Nitowsky, H. M., 485, 489
Noll, H., 442
Nordqvist, T., 493, 499
Norris, A. T., 428, 434
Nossal, G. J. V., 504, 507
Notani, G., 440, 446
Novick, A., 391, 402
Novitski, E., 29
Nowinski, W. W., 28
Nozu, K., 366

Ochoa, S., 366, 368, 426, 434, 441, **447**
Oehlkers, F., 228
Ohno, S., 487, 490
Ohtaka, Y., 366, 461, 463
Olson, M. E., 424
Oparin, A. I., 516
Orias, E., 461, 463
Osborn, F., 86
Osborn, R. H., 86

Oster, I. I., 200
Östergren, G., 389, 390
Otsuji, N., 458, 462
Ottolenghi, E., 297
Oura, H., 442
Ozeki, H., 334, 338

Painter, T. S., 162
Paranchych, W., 454, 455
Pardee, A. B., 463
Parke, W. C., 277
Parsons, D. F., 378, 381
Passano, K., 186, 226
Patau, K., 162, 176
Patterson, J. T., 239
Pauling, L., 412
Pavlovsky, O., 246, 250
Peacock, W. J., 275, 277, **492**, 499
Pearson, C. M., 485, 490
Penrose, L. S., 516
Perkins, D. D., 145
Perrin, D., 460, 463
Perutz, M. F., 412
Peters, J. A., 12, 28, 39, 99, 113, 128, 146, 162, 199, 212, 277, 303, 315, 367, 389, 420, 482
Petersen, G. B., 290
Peterson, H. M., 477, 482
Peterson, P. A., 390
Philipson, L., 506, 507
Piña, M., 278
Plus, N., 370, 381
Pollister, A. W., 379, 381
Pollister, P. F., 379, 381
Pollmann, W., 511
Pond, V., 186
Ponnamperuma, C., 516
Pontecorvo, G., 504
Potter, V. R., 264
Prokofyeva-Belgovskaya, A. A., 482
Puck, T. T., 180, 186
Pullman, B., 510, 511, 516

Raacke, I. D., 431, 434
Rabinovits, M., 424
Race, R. R., 66
Radbill, C. L., 505, 507
Ragni, G., 297
Ramachandran, L. K., 367
Rapoport, I. A., 276, 277
Rasmuson, M., 213
Ravin, A. W., 304
Reddi, K. K., 367, 453, 456
Rees, M. W., 351
Reich, E., 378, 381, 426, 434
Reichmann, M. E., 445, 446
Renner, O., 228
Rhoades, M. M., 21, 28, 29, **127**, 142, 175, 370, **371**, 381
Rich, A., 429, 434, 445, 446, 511

Richardson, C. C., 291
Richter, A., 367
Riley, M., 463
Ris, H., 275, 277
Risebrough, R. W., 433
Robinson, E. A., 416, 420
Roeser, J., 327, 329
Roger, M., 304
Roizman, B., 503, 507
Roscoe, D. H., 452, 456
Rosencranz, H. S., 276, 277
Rotman, R., 344
Rownd, R., 304
Rubenstein, I., 353
Rubin, H., 352
Ruddle, F. H., 12
Rudkin, G., 493
Rudnick, D., 79
Ruhland, W., 381
Rupert, C. S., 350, 352
Russell, L. B., 162, 176, 486, 490
Russell, W. L., 88
Ryan, F. J., 29

Saez, F. A., 28
Sagan, C., 516
Sager, R., 373, 378, 381
Saksella, E., 389, 390
Salser, J. S., 458, 462
Salyers, A. A., 277
Sampson, M., 493, 499
Sanchez, C., 460, 463
Sandeen, G., 496, 499
Sander, C., 303
Sandler, L., 388, 390
Sang, J. H., 86, 88
Sanger, R., 66
Sarabhai, A. S., 445
Sarkissian, I. V., 212, 213
Schalet, A., 200, 398, 402, 481, 482
Schatz, G., 378, 381
Schiff, J. A., 373, 381
Schildkraut, C. L., 291, 301, 304
Schrader, F., 12, 379
Schramm, G., 365, 511
Schreil, W. H. G., 293
Schull, W. J., 40
Schulman, H. M., 434
Schultz, J., 253
Schwartz, D., 487
Schwartz, J. H., 440, 446
Schweet, R., 429
Seaman, E., 361
Seecof, R. L., 381
Sekiguchi, M., 431
Setlow, J. K., 397, 402
Setlow, R. B., 397
Shettles, L. B., 109, 113
Shipp, W., 367
Shirven, R. M., 277
Sia, R. H. P., 295

Siddiqi, O. H., 300, 304, 440
Siebke, J. C., 290
Simon, E. H., 501
Simon, L., 366
Singer, B., 366, 367
Singer, M. F., 441, 446, 462, 463
Sinnott, E. W., 39, 539
Sinsheimer, R. L., 291, 340, 352, 363, 367, 368
Sinton, W. M., 516
Slatis, H., 218
Smellie, R. M. S., 434
Smith, D. W., 162
Smith, M., 449, 456
Smith, P. E., 83
Smith, R. A., 367
Snell, G. D., 83
Snoad, B., 28
Sonneborn, T. M., 373, 374, **380**, 381, 454, 455, 505, 507, 508
Spahr, P. F., 429
Sparrow, A. H., 186
Spencer, J. H., 286, 291
Speyer, J. F., 446
Spiegelman, S., 366, 424, 425, 426, 427, 428, 432, **433**
Spirin, A. S., 367, 434
Spottswood, T., 462
Sobels, F. H., 186
Sokoloff, L., 505, 507
Sorieul, S., 503, 507
Spassky, B., 246, 250
Spector, W. S., 13
Spiess, E. B., 213
Sprague, G. F., 29, 213
Stadler, L. J., *ix*, **187**
Staehlin, T., 442
Stahl, F. W., 271, 274, 277, 343, 353, 402
Stanier, R. Y., 337
Stanley, W. M., 365, 367, 368
Stebbins, G. L., 250
Steffenson, D. M., 155, 162, 276
Steinberg, J., 353
Steiner, R. F., 264
Stent, G. W., 277, 337, 338, 351, 352, 353, 463
Stern, C., 40, 60, 79, **128**, 194, 213, 219, 490
Stern, H., 493, 499, 503, 507, 508
Stevens, A., 426, 434
Stevens, J. G., 452, 456
Stocker, B. A. D., 334
Stoeckenius, W., 377
Stone, W. H., 504, 508
Stone, W. S., 239
Strauss, N., 463

Streisinger, G., 344, 351, 353, 402
Stretton, A. O. W., 445
Strickberger, M. W., 29
Strickland, W. N., 29
Sturtevant, A. H., 103, 113, **145**, 146, 228, 474, 482
Sueoka, N., 277, 288, 327, 329, 503, 508
Sugiyama, T., 366
Suomalainen, E., 162
Susman, M., 501
Sutton, W. S., 28
Swanson, C. P., 13, 28
Swartz, M. N., 402
Synge, R. L. M., 516
Sypherd, P. S., 463
Szilard, L., 391, 402, **421**
Szybalska, E. H., 297, 304
Szybalski, W., 297, 302, 304

Takahashi, I., 452, 456
Tal, M., 431, 434
Tamm, I., 366, 367
Tarmy, E., 361
Tatum, E. L., 310, 315, 408, 420
Tax, S., 516
Taylor, A. L., 320, 321, 324, 329, 388, 390
Taylor, J. H., 290, 401, 420, 455, 485, 489
Teissier, G., 370
Temin, H. M., 455, 456
Temin, R. G., 199, 218, 226
Tergazhi, B. E., 402
Tessman, I., 402, 501
Therman, E., 162
Thoman, M. S., 324, 329
Thomas, C. A., Jr., 353
Thurline, H. C., 115
Todaro, G. J., 503, 508
Tolmach, L. J., 296, 302, 304
Trautner, T. A., 402
Ts'o, P. O. P., 303, 496, 499, 505
Tsugita, A., 365, 368
Tucker, R. G., 452, 456
Tuppy, H., 378, 381

Urey, H. C., 516
Ursprung, H., 502, 507

Van Beneden, E., 28
van Schaik, N. W., 471
van Wagtendonk, W. J., 374, 381
Vogel, H. J., 290, 446
von Ehrenstein, G., 444, 446, 447
Von Halle, E. S., 481, 482
von Hippel, P. H., 496, 499

Wacker, A., 402
Waddington, C. H., 86, 508
Wagner, H. P., 162
Wagner, R. P., 29, 420
Wahba, A. J., 443, 446
Wallace, B., 218, 227
Wallace, E. M., 23, 50, 103, 106, 151, 156
Warner, J. R., 429, 434, 435
Watanabe, T., 359, 361
Watkins, J. F., 504, 507
Watson, J. D., 267, 268, 271, 277, 395, 433, 434
Watts-Tobin, R. J., 436
Weigle, J. J., 336, 337, 351, 353
Weijer, J., 29
Weiler, E., 508
Weinberg, W., 213
Weisblum, B., 447
Weiss, S. B., 426, 432, 433
Weissmann, A., 14
Weissmann, C., 366, 368
Welshons, W. J., 481, 482, 490
Wettstein, F. O., 442
Wexler, I. B., 66
White, M. J. D., 162, 239
Whiting, P. W., 111, 113
Wiener, A. S., 66
Wildman, S. G., 367
Wilkins, M. H. F., 268, 434
Williams, R. C., 365, 367
Wilson, E. B., **28**
Woese, C. R., 447
Wollman, E. L., 319, 321, 323, 327, **328**, 329, 335, 337, 338, 350, 353, 361
Wolstenholme, G. E. W., 516
Wright, S., 86, **213**
Wright, S. W., 485, 490

Yamada, T., 508
Yankovsky, S. A., 424, 427, 434
Yanofsky, C., 349, 352, 410, 420, 445, 447
Yeh, M., 485, 489
Yoshikawa, H., 327, 329
Young, J., 365, 368

Zamecnik, P. C., 424, 434
Zamenhof, S., 402
Zelle, M., 313
Zetterqvist, Ö., 506, 507
Zichichi, M. L., 351, 353
Zinder, N. D., 318, 330, 334, **337**, 338, 363, 365, 367, 440, 446
Zubay, G., 427, 434

SUBJECT INDEX

Supplements not indexed; page numbers in bold face refer to figures.

acetylation, histone, 497–498
acridines, 317, **393**, 394, 437
actinomycetes, 452
actinomycin D, 363, 426, 431, 494
activation, 179
Activator, 384–386, **386**, 457
adapter RNA (*see* RNA)
adaptive value (*see* fitness, biological)
adenine, 255, **256**, 391, 394, 395
  2-methyl, **256**
adenosine, and analogs, 391–392, 453
  triphosphate (ATP), **279**, 428, **450**
adenylosuccinase, 410
Aerobacter, 452
albinism, **37**, 38, 406
alcaptonuria, 404, **405**, 406
aleurone, **25**, 26, 470
alkylation and mutation, 402
alleles, 33
  iso-, 59–60, 384
  multiple, 57–62, 478–479
  pseudo-, 479–480
allopatric, 243
allopolyploidy (amphiploidy), 155, 247–249
amino acids, coded by nucleic acids, 436–445
  in DNA, 276
  sequences, 365, **414**, **417**
  types, **411**
amorphs, 194
amphibian development, 502
anaphase, 8, 9, **17**, 18, **20**, **21**
anemia, 39, 71–72, **71**, 209, 413–416, **413**
anlage (imaginal disc), 82
anthocyanin, 470
anthropology, 241–242
antibiotics, 221
antibodies, 57, 504
antigens, 57, 359, 360, 504
Antirrhinum (snapdragon), 54, 69

anucleolate, 427
antipodal nuclei, **25**, 26
apples, 247
apurinic acid, 396
arabinose in DNA, 394
Artemia (water shrimp), 152
Ascaris, 14, 152, 383, 384, 494
ascospores and ascus, 26, **27**
Aspergillus, 479, 504
asynapsis, 168, 190, 383
ataxia, 41
atmosphere, "primitive," 510
attached-Xs, 122, **123**, 478, **479**
auxotroph, 295
autopolyploidy, 152, 246
autosome, 90

Bacillus, 297, 329, 426, 435, 445, 452, 502
backbone, nucleic acid, **260**, 271, 397
backcross, 46
bacterial mutation, 306–309
bacteriophage (phage, ϕ), 330
  BF-23, 360
  development in host, 340, **341**
  f2, 363, 365, 440, 445, 453
  ghosts, 360
  helper, 336
  host range, 343
  immature, 340, **341**
  lambda, 334–336
  MS2, 363, 365, 366, 425
  P2, 362
  PBSI, 452
  plaque type, 342–343, **342**
  pro-, 331, 362
  R or R17, 340, 365, 454
  recombination mechanism, 350–351
  RNA, 363
  S13, 271, 395
  T, **266**, 339–349, **339**
  T1, 360, 403
  T2, 360, 395, 396, 402, 450
  T4, 396, 436, 440, 445, 481
    deletion 1589, 438–439
    morphogenesis, 501–502
  T5, 360, 391–392
  T6, 360, 391–392
  tail, 339, 360
  temperate (nonvirulent), 331, 336, 349–351
  virulent (intemperate), **342**, 348
  X174, 271, 286, 340, 395, 397, 402, 426
balancers (halteres), **480**
Bar and *Ultrabar,* 474–477, **476**
Barr body, 484, 486
Basc method, 195, **196**, 197

base, changes and mutation, 394
  changes in new genes, 398–399
  changes in old genes, 395–398
  methylation, 429
  pairs, **269**, **395**
  ratios, 265, **266**
  variation in DNA, 452–453
binomial expression, 524, 535
biometrics, 519–539
biotin, 408
birds, 93–95 (*see also* poultry)
bithorax and postbithorax, **480**
bronze variegation, 469–470
balanced lethals, 229
balanced polymorphism, 218
baldness, 88
beans, 1, **2**
benzene, 253, **254**
bivalent, 16
blood types, 57, **58**, **59**, 77, 241–242
bobbed bristles, 119, 194, 195, 487
Bonellia, 111–112
Brachyury (Brachy), 83, **84**
bread mold (*see* Neurospora)
bridge-breakage-fusion-bridge cycle, 165, 166
broad bean (*Vicia faba*), 453
butterflies, 95

cabbage, **248**
cancer, 89, 504
carbamates, 192
carbon-14, 224–225
carbon dioxide sensitivity, 369–370
carriers, 205
cartilage, 80
catnip (Nepeta), 373
cats, **4**, 115, 490
cattle, 55, 68, 504
cell, 5, **7**
  competence, 297
  mating, somatic, 503–504
  membrane, **7**, 506
  organization, 506
  plasma, 504
centriole, 378–379, 513
centromere (kinetochore), 6, 185, **379**
centrosome, **7**, 378–379
cesium-137, 224–225
cesium chloride, 273, 323
chemical evolution, 510–514
chemical stability, 512
chemorecovery, 191, 397
chiasma interference, 136
chiasmata, 16, 18, **19**, 22, **124**, **125**, 133, 135 (*see also* crossing over)
chicken (*see* poultry)

chi-square, 527, **528**, 529, 532–533

Chironomus, 492

Chlamydomonas, 275, 376–378

chloramphenicol, 308

chloroplasts, 370–373, 378, 423, 513

chromatid, 6, **19**, 22, **134**, 135, 166

chromatin, 8, 484, 496
  sex, 484–486

chromatophoric groups, 396

chromocenter, **154**, 155

chromomere, **495**

chromosome, 6, 9
  acentric, 164
  aneucentric, 168
  aneuploidy, 155
  aneusomy, 155–161
  arm, 10
  attached-X, 122, **123**, 478, **479**
  B, in maize, 369
  bacterial, 323–324, 453
  balance, 105, 155–161, 484
  break, 164, **165**, 166, 180, 384–386, 388–389
  bridge, **165**, 166
  changes and radiation, 179–185
  circles, 231–236, **231, 232, 234, 235**
  coils or gyres, 153, 182, 184, 484, 486, 492, 494, 496
  complexes, 229–231
  cross-bands in, 153, **154**, 492
  deficiency or deletion, **167**, 175, **237, 238**, 345, 393, 438–439
  dicentric, 164, **180**, 384
  donation in bacteria, 319
  doublet in, 481
  eucentric, 168
  fibrils, DNA content of, 275
  as genetic material, 10, 11, 97–98
  heteromorphic, 94, **95**
  homologous, 10
  human, 10, **159, 160**, 178, **180**
  intra-, exchange, 477
  iso-, 164
  lampbrush, 494, **495**, 496
  loops, **169, 173**, 494, **495**
  loss, 160, **183** (see also non-disjunction)
  movement, 6, 231–233
  number, 10, 108, 110, 159, 237
  polycentric, 189, 383
  polynemic (polytenic), 153, **154**, 155, **173, 174, 175**, 481, 492, **493**
  puffs, 492, **493**, 494, 495
  pycnosis, 155, 388, 484, 487

rearrangements, 228–238, 338–389
recombination, 19
replication, 8–10, 449
ring, **167**, 180
rod, 167, **237, 238**
salivary gland, 153, **154**, 155, **173, 174, 175**, 481, 487, 492, **493**
segregation, 18–23
sex, 90–98
shape, 10, 236, **237, 238**
shift, **174**
structural changes, 164–175
unbroken, and changes, 149–161

Chrysanthemum, 246

chymotrypsin, 412

cinquefoil (Potentilla), 243

cis, **349**, 459, 477, **478**

cistron, **346**, 349, 410–411, 481

clear mutants, 349, **350**

clearing (plaque), 342

climate and mutability, 384

clone, 292, **293, 294**, 295, 374
  sampling methods, 306–309, **308, 309**

clover, sweet, 366

clubfoot, 77

code, genetic, 425, 437
  ambiguous, 436, 440, 444
  colinearity, 445
  degenerate, 436
  inter-, transcription, 454–455
  nonoverlapping, 438
  primitive, 512
  triplet, 438, **443**
  universality of, 445

codon, 436–445, **443**
  identified, 440–445
  missense, 439
  no sense or nonsense, 439

coincidence, coefficient of, 136

colchicine and colcemide, 152, 247

cold and autopolyploidy, 152

colicinogenic factors, 359–361

collagen, 503

collochores, 185, 383

color-blindness, 95, 119, **139**

comb types, 55

competence, 82

complementation, **345**

concordance and discordance, 76–78

conditional distortion, 388

confidence interval, 521–522

congenital malformations, 158, 208, 405

conidia, 26

conjugation, in *E. coli,* 309–314
  intergeneric, 314

in Paramecium, **374, 375**, 376, 505–506
contingency tables, **531, 532**
copolymer, 287, 288, 399
copy-choice, 299, **300**
core of phage, **339**
corn, Indian (maize, *Zea mays*), 10, **20, 21, 25**, 26, 470, 479
  Ac and *Ds* in, 384, 385, **386**
  bibliography, 29
  crossover map, **142–143**
  extranuclear genes, 370, **371**, 372, 373
  gene control systems, 465
  heterosis in, 210–212, **211**
  pericarp variegation, 465–469
cortex, 107, 505–506
cosmic chemo-evolution, 514–515
cotton, 56, 247, 251, 479
coupling and repulsion, 118
cousin marriage, 207, 217–218
crab, 288, 449
Creeper, 79–81, **80**
Crepis, 251
cristae, **377**, 378
crossing over (*see also* chiasmata), 136, 169, 185
  and linkage, 116–126
  within cistron, 480–481
crossover, 117, 131
cubitus interruptus, 59, **60**
culture medium, complete, 310
cyprus, 251
cytochemistry, 260
cytogenetics, 23, 126, 174–175, 231–236, 319, 492
cytoplasm, 6, **7**
cytoplasmic mixing, **375**
cytosine, 254, **255**
  5-bromo, 284
  5-hydroxymethyl, **255**, 392, **450**, 451
  5-methyl, 254, **255**, 284, 452
cytosome, 6

daisy, 56
Datura (Jimson weed), **151**, 152, 157, **158**
DDT, 221
deamination, 396
death, genetic, 219–220
  infant, 208
degeneracy in code, 436, **443**, 444
deintegration, 329
deletion (*see* chromosome)
Delphinium (larkspur), **248**, 249
denaturation and renaturation, 301–302, 435
density gradients, 273
deoxyadenosine, 257, **258**
deoxyadenylic acid, **259**

deoxycytidine, 257, **258**
deoxycytidylic acid, **259**
deoxyguanosine, 257, **258**
deoxyguanylic acid, 259
DNase (deoxyribonuclease), 261, 281–282, 285
DNA (deoxyribonucleic acid), 253
  amino acids in, 276, 453
  backbone, **260**, 271, 276, 397
  of Bacillus, 287
  base composition, 266, 452–453
  biological replication, 288–289
  breakage and exchange, 299, **300**
  5-bromo uracil in, 452
  calf thymus, 286
  in cell membrane, 506
  in chloroplasts, 372
  coiling, 268
  conserved or not, 423, 492–494
  copolymers, 287–288, 301, 399, 449
  containing ribotides, 289
  content of col factors, 360
  content of F, 323
  crab, 288
  denaturation and renaturation, 275, 301–302, 496–497
  de novo synthesis, 287–288
  dinucleotide sequences, 285–288
  double helix, **267**
  enzymatic degradation, **281, 282**
  enzymes for precursors, **450,** 451
  evolution of, 511–514
  as genetic material, 261–262, 296, 340
  per genome, **265,** 287, 323, 360
  glucose in, **450,** 452
  with heavy nitrogen, 272–274
  H-bonding in, **269, 284**
  homologous, 298
  homopolymers, 287–288, 301
  major and minor grooves, 269, 426
  melting, 275, 301, 496–497
  as messenger, 494
  methylation of, 429
  in mitochondria, **377,** 378
  molecular weight, 301, 348
  of Mycobacterium, 286
  native, 275
  nucleoside and nucleotide ends, 280–281
  organization *in vivo,* 265–271, 275–276
  parallel synthesis, 453

  penetration, 297
  polymerases, 280, 288, **450, 451**
  and polynemy, 275
  primary structure, 259–260, 265
  as primer-template, 271, 283–285, 509
  quantity measured, 260–261
  replication and strand separation, 272
  replication *in vitro,* 279–289
  replication *in vivo,* 271–274, 484
  reversible synthesis, 285
  satellite, 323
  scission, 302
  secondary structure, 266, 267–271, **267**
  strand growth, **281, 282,** 286, 453
  strand recombination, 271–275
  swivel in replicating, 453
  and synapsis, 298
  synthesis, extended and limited, 281–283
    regulation, 449–453
    from RNA, 289, 455
  terminology, 262
  and transduction, 331
  and transformation, 296, 396
  ultraviolet absorption, 275
  uracil in, 452
  Watson-Crick model, **267**
  X ray diffraction pattern, **267,** 268
deoxyribonucleoprotein, 253
deoxyribosidase (reductase), 449
deoxyriboside, 257, **258**
deoxyribotide, 257, **258, 259**
depurination, 396
derepression, 458
detecting chromosomal changes, 174–175
detrimental equivalents, 218
development, and gene action, 79–85, 501–506
  human, 107–110, 417, 486
diabetes, 4, 220
diakinesis, **17,** 18, **20**
Didinium, 454, 513
differentiation and gene action, 501–506
diffuse (growth) stage, 18
dihybrid, 45
dimers, in hemoglobin, 412
  thymine, **396,** 397
  uracil, 397
Diplococcus (*see* Pneumococcus)
diploid, 11
diplonema, 16, **17,** 18, **19**
discrete variables, 520, 521–534

disomic, 156
Dissociation, 384–386, **386,** 400
dogs, 55
dominance, 35, 49, 195, 202, 242
donors, intermediate, 357
dosage compensation, 484–489
"double cross" breeding, **211,** 212
double recessive, 45
doublets, shared, **443,** 444
doubling dose, 223
Down's syndrome (mongolism), 158–160, **160,** 172
drift, random genetic, 203, 219, 242
Drosophila, bibliographies, 29
  chromosomes in nature, **236,** 237, **238**
  dosage compensation, 487–489
  and extranuclear genes, 369–370
  eye anlage, 422
  larval salivary gland, **253**
  melanogaster, **23, 24, 480**
    chromosome, 95
    chromosome map, **185**
    crossover map of X, **132**
    monosomic and trisomic, **156**
    mutant detection in, 195–198
    salivary gland chromosomes, 153, **154,** 155
    sex determination, 102–107
    and sex-linkage, 90–98
    triploid, **152**
  persimilis, 245–246
  position effects, 473–481
  pseudoobscura, 209, **216, 217,** 242, **243,** 245–246, 488–489
  segregation distortion in, 386–388
  wing, **50, 60,** 480
duplication, **170,** 474, 477
dwarfism, 79, 83, 204
dyad, 16

earthworm, 111
ecdysone and puffing, 492
Echinus (sea urchin), 152
eclipse period, 340, **341,** 501
ecological barriers, 244
egg, 5, **24, 25,** 26
electrons, fast, and mutation, 182, **183**
embryo, **25,** 26
embryology, 79–81, **81,** 417, 486, 502
encephalitis, 363
endolysin, 342
endoplasmic reticulum, **7,** 504
endoreplication, 153–155
endosperm, **25,** 26, 384, 487

endosymbiotes, 374, 454
enol form, 395
environment, 3, 74, 132
enzymes, and genes, 408–410, 501
    constitutive, 458
    induced, 458
episomes, 317–327, 470
    bacterial, 355–361
    and temperate phages, 336
    as mutagens, 388–389
epistasis, 51, 74, 103, 242
epoxide, 192
equator, spindle, 6
eras of chemical evolution, 510–514
erythrocyte, duck, 497
    membrane DNA, 506
Escherichia coli, 292–295, **293,** 297
    DNA base content, 266
    Lac segment, 457–459
    linkage map, 314, **324–325**
estrogen, 505
ethology, 245
euchromatin, 155, 388, 474, 481, 486
Euglena gracilis, 445
euploid, 151
evening primrose (*see* Oenothera)
evolution, 161, 238, 241–249, 488, 509–515
    biological, 203
    and duplications, 418–419
    and genetic material, 509–515
    and mutation, 220–221
exchanges, 164
exogenote, 334
exonuclease, 366
expressivity and penetrance, 72–74
eye, anlage transplanted, 422
    color in Drosophila, 60, 442, 478–479, 487–488

F$_1$, F$_2$, 32
F$^-$ and F$^+$, 317
F particle, 317–327, 336, 356, 379
F-mediated transduction (F-duction, sexduction), 358
F-merogenote transfer, 358
facets, eye, 474, **476**
fallout, 224
family method, 37, 58–59
feedback systems, 458, 461
female sterile, 216, **217**
fertilization, 5, 44
    double, **25,** 26
    self- or cross-, 31, 206
Feulgen, 8, 261, 484
fibroblast, **180**
"fingerprints," 412, **413**

fingers, 72–74, **73**
fish, 252, 265, 266
fission of Paramecium, 374
fitness, biological, 193, 202, 221, 236, 243
flagellum, 376, 379
frog (Rana), 502
fruiting bodies, 26
fungus gnat (*see* Sciara)

gamete, 5
gametophyte, 26
gene (*see also* mutant), 33
    action, cyclical, 503
        phenotypic effect of, 69–85
        and polypeptides, 404–419
        regulation, 492–498, 501–506
    arrangement, 131–139
    chemical nature, 252–264, 296, 363–366
    complexes, 229
    controlling, 469–470
    distribution, 501–502
    dosage, **194,** 488
    dosage compensator, 488–489
    duplication, 418–419, 481
    extrachromosomal, 318–327
    extranuclear, 369–379
    for function, 460
    functional forms of, 487
    interaction, 50–52, 457–462, 465–470, 473–481, 484–489
    inter-, spacer, 276, 439, 453
    intra-, recombination, 345–348, 481
    lethal, 69, **70,** 195, **196,** 197, 216, **217**
    mutator, 384
    nonchromosomal, 377–378
    number, increasing, 173–174, 418–419, 481
    operator, 459, 514
    pairs, 43
    phenotypic effects, 69–85, 193–195, 404
    polarity, 189
    pool, 201–203, 220–221
    recombinational, 149
    regulator, 385, 457–460, **460,** 489
    for structure, 460
    suppressor, 460–461, 488
    synthesis, regulation, 449–455
        in vitro, 302–303
    untainted, 33
genetic, code, 437–445 (*see also* code)
    control of mutation, 383–389
    death, 219–220
    equilibrium, 201–212, 222, **223**
    factor, 1
    fine structure, 344–349, **346**

load, 216–225
material, 1–5
    and chromosomes, 97–98
    defined, 509
    and DNA, 261–262
    origin and evolution, 509–515
    of phage, 340
    and RNA, 263, 363–366
    recombination, 35, 149
        in bacteria, 355–361
        and conjugation, 309–314
        and nonalleles, 42–53
        in phages, 339–351
        of RNA, 363–365
        smallest unit, 349
        by transduction, 330–336
        by transformation, 297
    reconstitution, 36
    symbols, 32, **36,** 116
    variation, 4 (*see also* mutation)
genetics, biochemical, 404
    human (*see* human)
    population, 201–212, 216–225
genome, 18, **265** (*see also* maps)
genotype, 1
    and sex determination, 111–112
geographical barriers, 244
germ line, 121, 222–225
gland, larval salivary, **253**
globulins, 497, 504
glucose-6-phosphatase, 505
glucose-6-phosphate dehydrogenase (G6PD), **139,** 485
glucosyl transferases, **450,** 451–452
Glyptotendipes, 492
goat grass, 251
goatsbeard, 247
Golgi body, **7**
gonad, 19, 107
grasshopper, 1$\mathbf{8}$1
growth and gene action, 501–506
growth stage, 18
guanidine, 453
guanine, 255, **256**
    1-methyl, **256**
    derivatives, **256**
guanosine, as antimutagen, 391–392
    triphosphate, 431
guinea pig, 40, 73
gynandromorph, **106,** 107

Habrobracon juglandis, 110–111
half-sib matings, 207
halteres (balancers), **480**
haploid (monoploid), 11, 106, 152
haplosomic, 157
Hardy-Weinberg principle, 202n
head membrane, **339**

heat and mutation, 179
Hela cells, 427
Helix (snail), 111, 494
hemizygosis, 93
hemoglobin, 424, 431, 435, 440, 442, 445
  A, 412–416
  A_2, 416–417
  biochemical genetics of, 412–418
  chains, **414, 417**
  F, 417
  molecular evolution of, 418–419
hemophilia, **95, 119, 139**
Hemophilus, 297, 350, 397
hermaphroditism, 111
heterocaryon, 27
heterochromatin, 156, 384, 388, 474, 481, 484, 486
heterocytosome, 378
heterogamety, 95
heterogenote, 332
heteroploidy, 151–155
heterosis (hybrid vigor), 208–212, 236
heterozygosity, enforced, 229
  and inbreeding, 206–208
heterozygote (hybrid), 35
hexagonal plate, **339**
hexaploid, 151
Hexaptera, 149, **150**
hexasomic, **158**
Hfr, **318, 319, 320, 321, 322, 323**
histidine, genetics of, **333**
histogram, 535
histones, 252, 379, 496–498
histochemistry, 260
Holmes rib grass, 365
homogenote, 338
homogentisic acid, 404, **405**
homopolymer, 288, 426
homozygote, 34
hormones, 83, 107, 492, 505
horse, 412
host range of phage, 343
"hot spots" of mutation, 392
human, cell line transformed, 297
  chromosomes, 10, **159, 160**
  DNA base content, 266
  genetics, 37–39, 107–110, 217–225
    aneusomy, 158, **159, 160**
    map of X, **139**
    and radiation, 180, 222–226, **222**
  twins, 36, 38, 74–79, **76**
hybrid, interspecific, 246–249, 251
  inviability and sterility, 245
  vigor (heterosis), 208–212, 236
hydrogen bond, **269, 284**

hydroxymethylase, 451, 501
Hymenoptera, 110–111
hyperploidy, 168
hyphae, 26, **27**
hypomorph, 194, 487, 488
hypoploid, 167
hypostasis, 52, 74, 103
hypoxanthine, **284**, 396

imaginal disc (anlage), 82
imago, 24
imidazole ring, 253
imino form, 395
immunity, bacterial, 331, **350**, 360
inborn errors of metabolism, 405
inbreeding, 206–208
incipient species, 244
indiscrete variables, 534–537
inducer, lactose as, 458
induction, embryonic, 84
infection and sex, 317
inhibition, end product, 457
inosinic acid pyrophosphorylase, 297
insulin, 4, 220
integration, 298–300, **300**, 322, 355
intelligence, 79
interference, 136
interferon, 454
interphase, 8, **9, 17**, 18
intersex, 103–105, **103**
introgression, 249
inversion, 168, **169**, 170, **173**, 237
  in natural populations, 242–243, **243**
  X, 196
iodine-131, 227
iojap, 373
ionization, 179
isoalleles, 59–60, 384
isogenic strains, 70
isolation, reproductive, 243–249

Jimson weed (*see* Datura)
juvenile amaurotic idiocy, 204–205, **205**, 219

kappa, **373**, 374–376
karyosomes (chromatin knots), 484
karyotype, Drosophila, **95, 216, 236**
  human, **160, 161**
kernel, **25**, 26, **386**
keto form, 254
killers, 374–375
kinetoplast and kinetosome, 379, 513
Klinefelter's syndrome, 108

Lac segment, 457–459
lactic dehydrogenase, 362
lambda particle in Paramecium, 374
larkspur (Delphinium), **248,** 249
larva, **24**
law of parsimony (Occam's rule), 33
lawn, bacterial, 308
lysozyme, 339
learning and RNA, 504
leprosy, 227
lethal equivalents, 218
lethals, 69, **70,** 80, **183,** 195–197, 216, **217**
  balanced, **229, 230**
  conditional, 501–502
leptonema, 16, **20**
leucoplasts, 370
life cycles, 23–27
life on other planets, 514
lily, **16, 17,** 19, 503
Limnea (snail), 503, 508
linkage, and crossing over, 116–126
  groups, limitation in, 136
  map (*see* maps), 131
liver cells in tissue culture, 500
loads, balanced vs. mutational, 218–219
locus, 122
locust DNA base ratio, 266
lysis and lysogen, 331
lysosome, **7**
lytic cycle, 341

macronucleus (meganucleus), 374
maize (Zea; *see* corn)
malaria, 209
male sterile, 216, **217**
manganese, 394
manifold effects (*see* pleiotropism)
maps, chromosome, **185**
  crossover (or linkage), **132, 139, 140, 141, 142, 143, 144**
  genetic, of E. coli, 314, 324–326, 351
    of lambda, **350**
    of T4, **343, 346–347**
Mars, 514, 515
master plate, 307, **308, 309**
mate-killer, 374, 454
mating, assortive, 206
  nonrandom, 205–208
  reaction, 375
  reciprocal, 32
  sib-, 207
Maxy technique, 198
mean, arithmetic, 63

measles, 78, 389
medulla, 107
megasporocyte and megaspores, 25, 26
meiosis, 15–23, 156, 157
 and gene pairs, **47, 48**
 in Neurospora, **124, 125,** 126
meiotic drive, 388
Melandrium, 115
Melanoplus, 493
melanotic tumors and episomes, 370
merogenote, 320
meromixis and merozygote, 320
messenger RNA (mRNA), 425–431, **430** (*see also* RNA)
metagon, 454, 513
metamorphosis, 24
metaphase, 8, **9, 17,** 18, **20, 21**
methyl green stain, 261
methylation, DNA and RNA, 429
micronucleus, 374
microspectrophotometry, 261
microspores and microsporocytes, 25
migration, 203, 242
mistakes, incorporation and replication, 398
mitochondria, **7,** 377, 378, 505, 513
mitomycin C, 396
mitosis, 5, 6, 8, **9,** 10
 radiation effect on, 184–185
 regulation of, 503
mitotic rate and mutations, 222, 383
Modulator, 466–469
molecular evolution of hemoglobin, 418–419
mollusc chromosome, 496
monad, 16
monoecious, 25
monohybrid, 45
monomers, 280
monosomic, 107–108, **156**
moon, 515
morphological barriers, 245
mosaicism, 106–108, **106,** 161, 370–373, **371,** 474
 erythrocyte, 504
 functional, 485
mosquito, 246
mosses, 111
moths, 95, 107
mottled vs. sectored plaques, 344
mouse, **69,** 83, 84, 88, 107–110, 114, 479, 502
 aneusomy, 160
 crossover map, **140–141**
 heart mitochondria, **377**

position effect in, 486–487
tissue culture, 503
multigenic (polygenic) traits, 62–65
muscular dystrophy, 485
mutagens and antimutagens, 192, 225, 391–392
mutant, 5 (*see also* gene; mutation)
 bacterial, isolation of, 294
 constitutive, 459
 detection of, 149–151, 195–198
 detrimental nature, 193–194
 lethal (*see* lethals)
 in natural populations, 216, **217**
 pre- or postadaptive, 306–309
 sub- and supervital, 216, **217**
 suppressor, 437–440
 temperature sensitive, 501
 visible, 198
mutation (*see also* mutant), 5
 in bacteria, 306–309
 defined operationally, 399–400
 and evolution, 220–221
 frequency, 192, 204
 gene, 190
 genetic control of, 383–389
 germinal, 222–225
 intergenic, 191
 molecular basis of, 391–400
 point, 189–198, 345, 392–399
 and populations, 202
 repair from, 397
 rate, 192, 193, 224–225, 309, 392
 reverse, 393, 468
 somatic, 221–222
 at specific loci, 192
 spontaneous, 179, 192, 224
 sub-nucleotide, 394–399
 time of, 193
 and ultraviolet, 396–397
 whole nucleotide, 393–394
mutational damage, 221–225
mutational "hot spots," 392
mutational spectra, 192, 392–393
mycelium, 26
Mycobacterium, 452
myoglobin, 418–419

natural selection, 202–205, 245, 513
nearest-neighbor analysis, 286–288, 397
Neisseria, 297
neomorph, 194
neurons and RNA, 505
Neurospora (bread mold), 26, **27, 124, 125,** 126, 408–410
 bibliography, 29
 crossover map, **144**
 mitochondria, **377,** 378

newt, 493, **495**
Nicotiana (tobacco), 60–62
nitrous acid as mutagen, 396
nondisjunction, 95–98, 159, 384, 475–476
nonlysogenic (sensitive) strain, 331
normal curve, 534
nuclear body in *E. coli,* **293**
nuclear membrane, **6, 7**
nuclear transplantation, 502
nucleic acid, 253
 as genetic material (*see* genetic material; DNA; RNA)
 hybrid, 425
 methylated, 429
 subservient role of, 512
nucleolus, 6, **7,** 427, 493, **495,** 496
 organizer, 11, 427
nucleoplasm, 6
nucleoprotein, 263, 496–498
nucleoside, 257, **258,** 263
 phosphate kinases, 450
nucleotide, 257, 263
 sequence in TMV, 366
nucleus, 6, **7, 9, 25, 26**
null hypothesis, 526
nullosomic, 159
nurse cells, 24, 492, 494

octoploid, 151
ocular albinism, 490
Oenothera (evening primrose), 151, 228–236, **228,** 481
oligonucleotide, 287
ommatidia, 474, **476**
one gene one enzyme, 408–410
one gene one polypeptide, 410–418
one gene one primary effect, 407–408
onion, 9, 496
oocyte, 24, 160, 223, 493–496
oogenesis, 24
oogonia, 24
operons, 457–462, 469–470, 489, 514
Ophryotrocha, 111
organic bases, 253–256
origin (O), point of, 320
ovaries and ovarioles, 24
oxidase, homogentisic, 406
oxygen and mutation, 182
ozone, 511

P_1, P_2, 32
pachynema, 16, **17, 19, 173**
panmixis, 205
paracentric, 166, **167**
parahydroxylase, 407

Paramecium, **373, 374, 375,** 376, 454, 505–506
parameter, 520
paramutation, 470
paranemic and plectonemic, 268, 496
parasexuality, 504
Parkinson's disease, 505
parthenogenesis, 152
pea, garden, 10, 31, 42, 116–118
 gene action in, 497
 sweet, 119
pedigree, **73, 95**
 of causes, 72
 method, 37
 symbols, **36**
penetrance and expressivity, 72–74
Penicillium, 504
pentasomic, **158**
pentose, **257**
pericarp, **25,** 26
 variegation, 465–469
pericentric, **167,** 237
perifertilization stages, 193
peroxide, 192, 360, 512
persistence, 219
perspiration, 491
petites, segregational or vegetative, 378
phage (*see* bacteriophage)
phagocytosis, 298
phenocopy, 4, 317, 358, 439–440
phenogenetics, 79
phenol, 364
phenotype, 3, 52
phenotypic ratios, 49–52, **49**
phenylketonuria, 205, 206, 406–407
phenylpyruvic acid, **407**
phenyl thiocarbamide (PTC), 214
phocomelia, 4, 80
phosphate, pyro- and ortho-, 279, 450, 451
phosphodiesterase, splenic, 281–282, 285
phosphorous-32 as mutagen, 395
photoproduct, ultraviolet, 396
photorecovery, 191, 397
pigeon chromosome, 496
pine, 251
pinocytosis, **7,** 298
pistil, 26, **61**
planetary research, 515
plaque (clearing), 342–344, **342**
plasmablast, 504
plastids, 370–373
pleiotropism, 70–72, **70,** 404, 406
ploidy, 151
plus-minus test, 530
poky in Neurospora, 378

Pneumococcus (Diplococcus), 295, 452
point mutants and phenotype, 193–195
polar nuclei, 24, **25,** 26
polarity, strand, 260, **270,** 271
poliomyelitis, **77,** 78, 363, 453
pollen, **25,** 26, 60–62
poly (A + U), 289
poly (dA + T), 289
polyamines, 339
polydactyly, 72, **73**
polydeoxyribotide, 259, **260**
polykaryocytosis, 503
polymer, 260
polymorphism, 218, 241
polynemy (polyteny), 153, **154,** 155, 383, 481
polynucleotide, 263
 phosphorylase, 431, 441, 442
polypeptide, amino (N-) end, 429
 carboxyl (C-) end, 429
 and gene action, 404–419
 synthesis and RNA, 423–431
polyploidy, 151, 383
polyribotide, 263
 homo-, 443
 mixed, 441
polysaccharide, 295, 296
polysomes (polyribosomes, ergosomes), **430,** 431, 435
polysomic, 157, **158**
population genetics, 201–212, 216–225
population mean, 534
population method, 37
position effect, 385, 468
 in Drosophila, 473–481
potato, 246–247
Potentilla (cinquefoil), 243
poultry, **55,** 56, 68, 79–81, **80,** **81,** 93, **94,** 266
power of the test, 537–538
precursors determined, **405,** 406, **407**
presence-absence view, 57
probability, 134, 136, 524
proboscis, 111, 112
proflavin, **393**
promotor, 358
prophage, 331
prophase, 6, 9, 16, **17,** 18, **19, 20,** **21**
protamine, 252, 497
protein, 410, 496–498
protein evolution, 512
protein of TMV, 364, **365**
proteinoids, 511
Proteus, 336
protoplast, 340
prototroph, 295
provirus, 338

Pseudomonas, 336, 435
pupa, **24**
pure line, 1, 150
purine, 253, **254, 256**
 2-amino-, 399
 dimethylamino-, **256**
 6-methylamino-, 255, **256**
 ribosides as antimutagens, 391–392
puromycin, 424
putrescine, 339
pyrimidine, 253, **254, 255**

quadrivalent, 248
quail, Japanese, 88
quantum, 192
Queen Victoria, **101**

rII region, 344–349, **344,** 392–393, 436–440, 481
rabbit, 4, 57, 67, 71
races, 241–249
rad, 181
radiation, and genetic load, 223–225
 and mutation, 179–185
radish, **248**
Rana (frog), 502
Raney Nickel, 448
rats, 487, 504, 505
ravelase (unravelase), 302
recessive, 35
reciprocal translocation, 170, **183, 234,** 237–238
recombination, unit of, 302
reconstitution experiments, 365
red blood corpuscles, 57, **71,** 413, 485
redundancy, 344
regression, 64, **65**
regulatory, super-, mechanisms, 470
replica plating, 307–311, **308,** **309, 310, 311**
replication, 8, 10, 449 (*see also* DNA; RNA)
replicative form (RF), 366, 426
repressor substance, 457
reproduction, 5
 vegetative, 292, **293**
reproductive barriers, 244–245
reproductive isolate, 206
reproductive potential (*see* fitness, biological)
repulsion and coupling, 118
resistance to colicins, 360
resistance transfer factors (RTF), 359
restitution, 164–166
reticulocyte, 425, 435, 440, 445
retinoblastoma, 204, 219
Rhesus (Rh) factor, 58

Rhyncosciara, 492, **493**
RNase (ribonuclease), 263, 364, 425, 431, 435
  denatured and renatured, 435
RNA (ribonucleic acid), 262–263
  and antibodies, 504
  coding for amino acids, 436–445
  and differentiation, 504
  double-stranded, 366
  as genetic material, 263, 363–366
  and genetic recombination, 363
  and learning, 504
  messenger (mRNA), 438, 481, 489, 502, 503, 504, 505
  methylation of, 429
  polymerase, DNA-dependent, 426
    RNA dependent, 366, 426
  and polypeptide synthesis, 423–431
  in puffs, 492
  replicase, 366
  ribosomal, 426–427, 496
  secondary structure, **428**, 462
  soluble (sRNA) (transfer or adapter), 427–428, **428**, 429, **430**, 444
  synthesis regulation, 453–454
  synthetase, 366
  as template for DNA, 289
  terminology, 262
ribonucleoprotein, 262
ribonucleotides in DNA, 289
ribose, D-, **257**, 262
  2'-deoxy-D-, **257**
riboside, 263
ribosomes, 423–425, **424**, 429–431, 496
  poly-, **430**, 431
ribotide, 262
  oligo-, 442–444
rickettsia, 376
roentgen (r) unit, 180
rotational substitution, 398
roundworm (*see* Ascaris)
rye, 246

salmon DNA bases, 266
Salmonella, 297, 330-334, **333**, **334**, 358, 360, 388, 460–461
schizophrenia, 79
Sciara (fungus gnat), 492, 494
scission of DNA, 302
sea urchin, 152, 266, 500
seasonal barriers, 245
sedimentation unit (s), 423
seedlings, corn, 371–372, **372**
segregants, bacterial, 313
segregation, 156
  of alleles, 31–39

alternate, 231–233, **232**
  independent, 42–49
  distortion, 386–388, 470
selection, 65, 202–205, 513
  coefficient, 204
selective markers, 313–314
selfers, 388
self-sterility, 60–62, **61**
semilethals, 216, **217**
Serratia, 323
sex, 5
  in bacteria, 312, 317–327
  in Chlamydomonas, 376
  chromatin, 484–486
  chromosomes, 90–98
  determination, 102–112
  factor, 357–358
  index, **105**
  -linked genes, 90–98
  mosaics, **106**, 107
  ratio, human, 109–110
  types, abnormal, **103**, 104, **105**
sexduction, 358
sexual barriers, 245
sexuality, importance of, 112
  para-, 504
sheath, **339**
Shigella, 358
sib matings, 207
sibling, 75
  species, 245
sickle-cell anemia, **71**, 72, 209, 413–416, **413**
sigma in Drosophila, 370, 376
sigma (population standard deviation), 534
silks, 26
silkworm, 10
singlet or doublet Paramecium, 505
sister strands, 122
skin color, 51, 56
snail, 111, 494, 503, 508
snake venom diesterase, 282, 366
snapdragon (Antirrhinum), 54, 69
Solanum, 246–247
Solenobia, 152
soluble RNA (sRNA) (*see* RNA)
somatic cell mating, 503–504
somatic line, 15, 221–222
somites, 83
sonication, 273, 280, 299
Sordaria fimicola, **148**
Spartina, 247–248
speciation, 203, 241–249
sperm, 5, 24, 180, 184
  human, **109**
  nuclei, 26
spermadine, **339**
spermatheca, 24

spermatid and spermatocyte, 24
spermatogenesis, 24
spermatogonia, 24
spermiogenesis, 109
spindle, 6, 9
  achromatic, 155
  divergent, 383
  orientation, 503
spirochaete, 110, 370, 376
sporophyte, 25
spreading effect, 473
standard deviation, 521–523
standard error, 536
Staphylococcus, 336
statistic, 520
sterility, 245
  mutants, 216, **217**
stillbirths, 208
strand recombination *in vitro*, 301–303
strand synthesis, direction of, 286
streaking method, **294**
streptomycin, 299, 306, **307**, **309**, 376, 440
strontium-90, 224–225
style, 26
subvitals, 216, **217**
suicide experiment, 327, 395
sulfanilamide, 393
superfemale and -male, 103–105, **103**
superposition, 51
superrepressor, 458
surface-volume relations, 153
symbols, **116**
sympatric, 243
synapsis, 16, 153, 298, 481
  oblique, 474, **475**
synergid nuclei, **25**, 26

t test, **528**, 536
tasters and nontasters, 214
tarweeds, 246
τ(tau) test, 536
tautomerism, **394**, **395**
taxonomy, and DNA hybrids, 302, 305
telomere, 164
telophase, 8, 9, **17**, 18, **21**
temperature and mutation, 192, 402
tempo preference, 78, **79**
teosinte, 251
test cross, 46
testosterone, 505
tetrad, 16
tetrad analysis, 147–148
tetramers, 412, 504
tetraploid, 105, 151, **158**, 484
tetrasomic, 157
thalassemia, 39
theophylline as mutagen, 391

thiamin (vitamin B$_1$), 408–409
thymidine, 257, **258**
  kinase, 503
thymidylate synthetase, 449, 501
thymidylic acid, 259
thymine, 254, **255**
  dimers, **396**, 397
  as mutagen, 392
thyroxine, 505
tiny yeast colonies, 378
Tipula, 493
tissue culture, 84, 180, 427
toad (Xenopus), 427, 491
tobacco (Nicotiana), 60–62
TMV (tobacco mosaic virus), 340, 363–365, **364**, **365**, 442, 453
toes, 72, **73**, 74
tomatoes, 129
traits, qualitative vs. quantitative, 62–65
trans position, **349**, 477, **478**
transcription, 425, 454–455, 461, 512
  differential, 502
  and differentiation, 502–503
  one-complement, 426
  unit, 460
transduction, genetic, 330–336, **333**, **334**, 388
transfer RNA (see RNA)
transformation, genetic, 295–300, 303, 336
transformer, **102**, 103, 488
transition, **398**
translation, 425, 461, 481, 512
translocation, 237–238
  half-, 172, 237
  reciprocal, **170**, **171**, **175**, **183**, 234–236, **234**, 486
transplantation of eye anlage, 422
transposition, 174, 466, 469
transversion, **398**
triplet, 462
triploid, 104, 151
trisomic, **156**
Triturus, **495**

trivalent, 156, 248
tropical vs. temperate, 384
Trypanosoma, 379
trypsin, 289, 412–413
tryptophan, synthetase, 410–411, 442, 504
  pyrrolase, 504
tuberculosis, **77**, 78, 266
tulips, 247
Turner's syndrome, 107
twin method, 37
twin patches of kernels, 467
twins, **36**, 38, 74–79, **76**
  in cattle, 504
typhoid, mouse, 330

ultracentrifugation, 273, **274**
ultraviolet light (UV), 179, 360
  -induction, 335, 350
  and mutation, 192–193, 396–397
  on polyuridylic acid, 448
univalent, 16
unselected markers, **313**, 314
uracil, **255**, 262, **284**
  5-bromo, **284**, 392–393, 453
  in DNA, 452, 453
  dimers, 397
  5-fluoro, 431
  tautomers, **394**

variables, discrete, 520, 521–534
  indiscrete, 534–537
variance, 63, 535
variegated (V-type) position effect, 474, 486
vegetative nucleus, 26
ventral receptacle, 24
Venus, 514, 515
viability, 69, **70** (see also mutant)
Vibrio, 336
Vicia faba (broad bean), 453
virus (see also bacteriophage)
  herpes, 388, 503
  infectious bovine rhinotracheitus, 452

influenza, 363
  lipo-, 500
  measles, 389, 503
  morphology, **339**, 340
  as mutagens, 388–389
  polio-, 363, 453
  polyoma, 445, 503
  pox-, rabbit, 369
  pro-, 455
  regulatory effects, 503
  reo-, 366
  Rous sarcoma, 388, 455
  simian, SV$_{40}$, 389, 503
  tobacco mosaic (see TMV)
  turnip yellow mosaic, 340, 363
  vaccinia, 266, 426, 445
  wound, 366
visible light, 179
visibles, 198
vitamin B$_1$ (thiamin), 408–409

war, nuclear, 225
water shrimp (Artemia), 152
watermelon, 251
Watson-Crick model of DNA, **267** (see also DNA)
wheat, 155, 251, 493
white region, 478, **479**
wild type, 23
woolly hair, 38

X-linked muscular dystrophy, 485
xanthine, 396
Xanthomonas, 297
Xenopus (toad), 427, 491
Xg locus, **139**
X ray diffraction pattern, **267**
X rays and mutation, 180–185, **180**, **181**

yak, 245
yeast, 266, 378, 396, 452

zygonema, 16
zygote, 5
zygotic induction, 335